HIGH SCHOOL
SUBJECTS
SELF TAUGHT

HIGH SCHOOL SUBJECTS SELF TAUGHT

Edited by
LEWIS COPELAND
and a Staff of Teachers and Editors

Introduction and Suggestions for Studying
By **WILLIAM L. SCHAAF**, Ph.D.
Professor of Education, Brooklyn College

NEW REVISED
AND ENLARGED EDITION

GARDEN CITY BOOKS
Garden City, New York

Introduction

MODERN life and contemporary events make a heavy demand upon the education and resourcefulness of the individual. In dealing successfully with personal, social, and vocational problems, a basic education is an unquestionable asset.

The primary value of an education is not simply to amass knowledge, but rather, through ideas as well as information and skills, to develop the power of thinking and to cultivate understanding and appreciation that will serve many purposes. These purposes may concern self-improvement and advancement in your business or vocation; efficient conduct of your household and personal affairs; intelligent consumer activities; adequate participation in civic and community life; helpful guidance where your children are concerned; effective and enjoyable use of your leisure time, devoted to recreation, hobbies, or other avocational pursuits.

Possibly you never had an opportunity to attend High School; or, having begun your studies, you were, for one reason or another, unable to complete them. Perhaps you finished your High School course some years ago, but since graduation you have forgotten a good deal of what you once learned, and have come to appreciate its significance somewhat more fully than you did when you were in school. In any event, you now wish to refresh yourself on many of these matters, and perhaps may even want to strike out in one or two new directions.

One is never too old to learn if one has the desire to do so. It is an accepted fact that, under ordinary circumstances, you can learn just as well at 25 or 30 as you could at 15 years of age; indeed, there are good reasons why you may learn even more effectively as an adult than as an adolescent. To be sure, it isn't always easy to stick to it. There are pressing demands and inevitable distractions—the business of earning a living, the fatigue at the end of the day, the need for relaxation, the desire for recreation. But that is just where your determination comes in; if you *want* to badly enough, you will be amazed at how much you *can* learn, even at 40 or more!

The contributing authors and editors of this book are your teachers. In a simple, narrative style, and by skillful organization and exposition, they have presented clearly the salient features and fundamental principles of their respective subjects. They are all teachers and writers of wide experience. Here they are:

THEODORE D. BENJAMIN, Head of Physical Science Department, De Witt Clinton High School, New York City, and Instructor in Teaching of Science, Teacher's College, Columbia University.

HENRY BERKMAN, Instructor in History, William Howard Taft High School, New York City.

GAYLORD DU BOIS, Instructor in Foreign Languages in public and private schools.

RALPH L. FALLIG, Instructor in Mathematics, Abraham Lincoln High School, New York City.

DAVID J. GLATZER, Head of the Clerical Department, Central High School, New York City.

MEYER L. GOTTLIEB, Instructor in Science, De Witt Clinton High School, New York City.

LAURENCE J. LAFLEUR, Lecturer at Brooklyn College.

JEROME S. MEYER, Formerly Instructor in Mathematics and author of books on mathematics and science.

HENRIETTA RAHTZ, Formerly Instructor in Art in New York City High Schools.

ROBERT RAHTZ, Formerly on the faculty of the College of the City of New York and Instructor in English in New York City High Schools.

LLOYD EDWIN SMITH, Formerly Instructor at Trinity College, Hartford, Conn.

LEO TANENBAUM, Instructor in Mathematics, Bronx High School of Science, New York City.

ARLENE STADD, Editor.

RICHARD L. SASSOON, Editor.

LAWRENCE W. LAMM, Editor of High School and College textbooks and adult education books.

LEWIS COPELAND, well-known editor of books in the field of self-education.

WILLIAM L. SCHAAF, Professor of Education, Brooklyn College.

A moment's reflection will reveal that there are, in all, but a half dozen or so large fields of human learning and achievement into one or another of which virtually all subjects fall. These fields include: (1) *social studies, including history, geography, and the social sciences;* (2) *language and literature;* (3) *fine arts;* (4) *foreign languages;* (5) *mathematics;* (6) *physical and natural sciences;* (7) *philosophy and logic;* and (8) *practical arts.* All but the last two fields are represented by the twenty-eight subjects discussed in this volume. Philosophy and logic are not ordinarily thought of as subjects suitable for a general High School education, while the practical arts hardly lend themselves to home study without a teacher and the necessary equipment and facilities.

The study of *history* enables one to understand the present-day world in terms of the past—the heritage of other cultures of by-gone days. It enlarges our perspective, affects our sense of values, and helps us to understand how people and nations live, their motives and desires. Thorough familiarity with the basic concepts of *civics* and *sociology* and the fundamental principles of *economics* together constitute an imperative need; more, perhaps, today than ever, in a rapidly changing, complex world. Social adjustment, economic understanding, efficient consumer habits, and intelligent citizenship—these and many other values are to be derived from a study of the social sciences. Today, an understanding of *psychology* is of particular interest, both in its practical areas and in its essential contribution to a fuller grasp of many aspects of the social sciences.

The effective use of *English* and a familiarity with *good literature* are of inestimable value. The importance of facility in one's native language, both written and spoken, can scarcely be overestimated. Skill in expressing one's own ideas and in comprehending and interpreting the ideas of others is an indispensable achievement, for this is the basis for all forms of communication, whether for business or social purposes. Furthermore, successful learning in nearly all other subjects depends to a large extent upon one's mastery of English.

Some acquaintance with classic and modern *painting, architecture, sculpture,* and *music* is necessary to appreciate the art of living. There is far more to life than earning a living. Art is a style or mode of living, which expresses many things beyond mere utility.

A working knowledge of a *modern foreign language* such as French or Spanish can be of service in two ways: it may stand one in good stead in practical business or professional activities, or it may be useful in pursuing other studies by making accessible the writings of foreign scholars and scientists. The study of Latin is of interest in view of the fact that it is one of the parent languages of English and is the source of many English words.

Some acquaintance with *mathematics* is of paramount value, not only for the obvious utility of arithmetical computation in our daily affairs, but for other powers that are cultivated. Thus through *algebra* we gain facility with the use of symbols, skill in the solution of problems, and insight into the nature of quantitative relationships. Through both *plane* and *solid geometry,* we develop our ability to reason logically, and to recognize the strategic roles played by assumption and definitions in all careful thinking. *Trigonometry,* as the branch of mathematics fundamental to solving problems in numerous practical fields, is of great interest.

An understanding of the *physical* and *natural sciences,* in addition to giving us insight into the workings of nature, the constitution of matter and its relation to energy, and the fundamentals of life, makes us appreciative of man's age-long struggle with natural forces, the marvel of his control over many of these forces, the significance of the achievements of technology and engineering in our everyday lives and in the entire social scene. Today the great advances which are being made in many of the sciences are profoundly affecting our lives, and an acquaintance with such newly developed fields as electronics and nuclear physics is basic to a full understanding of our times. An insight into science should deeply affect many of our attitudes and produce new ones—a firmer grasp on the principles of cause and effect, a clearer view of mysticism and superstition, a more solid faith in experimentalism and in the scientific method of thinking.

If you reflect upon the foregoing observations, and if you follow the suggestions for studying which are presented in the succeeding pages, you can profit immeasurably from this book. No one pretends that the treatment given here is more than an introduction to these subjects. But it is an excellent beginning and will lay the foundations. Should you wish to continue your studies further in any subjects, the references to other books given at the end of each section will serve as a useful guide. You can get them at your local library or bookstore; many of them are available in inexpensive editions and are worthy of purchase. No matter how great the sacrifice or how considerable the effort in mastering these subjects you will be amply rewarded. No one can ever take your education away from you.

W. L. S.

Acknowledgments

THE EDITOR wishes to acknowledge his thanks to Dr. William L. Schaaf, Professor of Education at Brooklyn College, for his many valuable suggestions; to Robert Rahtz for his able assistance in managing to the last detail the exacting task of revision and to the staff of teachers and editors who collaborated in this work; to Charles Todd for his excellent illustrations and maps; and to Richard C. MacKenzie and Paul Doring for the painstaking work required in the proofreading and indexing of this book.

L. C.

Editor's Note to the New
and Enlarged Edition

In order to increase still further the usefulness of this book, this new edition includes three entirely new subjects: Introduction to General Science, Solid Geometry, and Trigonometry. At the same time, all of the sections have been brought up to date by the inclusion of important recent developments. This will be noted especially, of course, in the sections on history, geography, physics, chemistry, literature, and the arts, all of which present much completely new material. The names of the authors and editors who have contributed so valuably to this revision have been added to the earlier names in the list of teachers and writers in the Introduction.

L. W. L.

Suggestions for Studying this Book

By WILLIAM L. SCHAAF, Ph.D.
Professor of Education, Brooklyn College

WHAT IT MEANS TO LEARN

MERELY READING A BOOK may no more result in learning than listening to a lecture. To learn something requires active effort on your part. You must have a goal. You must know how you are progressing. And above all, you must *want* to learn.

Your learning may result in any one or more of several kinds of things. You may, for example, acquire new *skills,* or improve and extend old ones. Thus you may improve your skill in computation when studying arithmetic, or you may extend it to using algebra, or you may learn to read a foreign language. Of course, doing these things requires some *understanding* as well. Another kind of learning results in acquiring *information and facts*. Such descriptive material is learned by associating and relating items as they are encountered. For example, much of history and science represents such learning. A third outcome of learning involves getting hold of *ideas and concepts*. This means understanding general principles and relationships. It means gaining insight. In many ways it is perhaps the most important kind of learning one can do. Ideas permeate all the subjects included in this book. Still another result of learning is the cultivation of *attitudes and appreciation*. Most of our learning influences our tastes, our preferences, our standards, our values, and our ideals. In fact, we can scarcely learn anything without at the same time influencing our feeling about what we learn or what we do. This is just as true of science and mathematics as it is of literature and art. Finally, a good part of what we learn can help us in *critical and reflective thinking*. If we are attentive to methods of thinking, of analyzing situations, and of solving problems, we may learn to think more effectively. In this connection, the study of science and mathematics can again be very helpful. The study of English can also contribute to this end, since the precise use of language is essential to sound, logical thinking.

Your Purpose in Studying

An important consideration which will determine the way in which you pursue your studies is the particular purpose you have in mind. This in turn will depend largely upon your previous experience and background.

Some of the subjects you are about to undertake you will doubtless be studying for the first time. In this case, your progress will probably be slow, and you may at times become discouraged. Don't let this deter you. Remember that it is a common tendency among mature learners and adults to be impatient, and to expect to succeed in a fraction of the time that a high school boy or girl requires.

Or you may undertake to study some subjects with which you are already slightly familiar. Your chief purpose will then be to refresh your memory, or to make quite sure that you understand the material thoroughly. Your progress will in this case be appreciably more rapid; there will be fewer difficulties; and the readiness with which your earlier knowledge will come back to you may well prove to be an agreeable surprise.

Perhaps you know a subject fairly well to begin with, and wish to go over it with a view to more thorough mastery. It may even be your ultimate intention to pursue the subject still further, making use of additional reference books such as suggested at the end of each section. In this case your studying will of course be more intensive; you will give close attention to the details as well as to the fundamental principles; and you will have to concern yourself more than ever with "practice" and "self-testing."

How to Study

The suggestions made here, if carefully followed, should help you considerably in your studying. To begin with, never read or study when you are tired or worried about something; instead, relax for a little while before you begin. Always study in a quiet place, with no conversation or radio to disturb you. Be sure you have a good light; work at a table or a desk, rather than just in a chair. Get the habit of studying in a regular place and at a regular time.

Here are some additional hints on how to study effectively:

1. Try to understand the *general scheme* of what you are trying to learn. If it is fairly complicated, *make an outline* of the main items.

2. *Several short periods* on successive days are usually better than one lengthy period of study.

3. Use *various ways* of making yourself think over what you are studying.

4. Try to associate new facts or ideas *with something you already know*.

5. Form the habit of *reviewing* mentally every paragraph or section *before you go on* to the next one. See how much of it you can recall; this will help you to remember it.

6. Sometimes *reading aloud* helps one to remember material; it is better to read rapidly rather than slowly.

7. When you have to stop studying, interrupt yourself at a *logical point,* but make note of some cue which will enable you to pick up the thread when you begin again.

8. When you have learned something new, try to *make use* of it as soon as you can; the oftener the better.

9. When you have completed a reasonable amount of material, take time out to *summarize* what you have covered. You may want to write out your summary.

10. Always have a *good dictionary* handy. Make frequent use of it. When you have discovered the meaning of a new word, try to use the word yourself.

PLANNING YOUR WORK

The above suggestions concerning study habits should be helpful if you cultivate them, as you should. But effective methods of studying, of themselves, will not suffice. Careful planning is also essential. Studying on the run, or at odd moments, or at irregular intervals is not likely to prove satisfactory. You must lay out your work systematically before you begin. It must be deliberately planned, like a budget. Only in this way can you be assured of success.

There is, of course, no perfect or even a best plan; each individual's time, facilities, and preferences are personal matters. Two suggested plans are given below as workable for most people. You may wish to follow whichever one suits your purpose better. Or you may wish to modify either plan a bit to suit your own taste. The main consideration is to adopt *some* plan, and then, as with your budget, stick to it as conscientiously as you can.

It should be noted that most of the subjects fall into "natural" groups.

Thus English, Public Speaking, Literature, and the Arts constitute a group of related subjects, since each deals, in one way or another, with a form of self-expression and interpretation. Or again, History, Civics and United States Government, Geography, and Economics form another group of related subjects, each of which deals with some aspect of mankind's social problems, past and present. General Science and the sciences of Biology, Physiology, Psychology, Sociology, Physics, Chemistry, Astronomy, and Geology likewise form a closely knit group of subjects, dealing with the nature of the physical world and with man's reactions to his environment. The last group really consists of two groups of studies, Mathematics and Foreign Languages, both of which, however, have much to do with the understanding and use of new symbols.

CLASSIFICATION OF SUBJECTS FOR STUDY PURPOSES

GROUP I	GROUP II	GROUP III	GROUP IV
English	Ancient History	General Science	Mathematics
Public Speaking	Medieval History	Biology	Algebra
Literature	Modern History	Physiology	Plane Geometry
Arts	American History	Psychology	Solid Geometry
	Civics and Government	Sociology	Trigonometry
		Physics	French
	Geography	Chemistry	Spanish
	Economics	Astronomy	Latin
		Geology	

In general, it is better to study the various subjects within each group *successively,* rather than simultaneously. The order suggested in the table (reading down) is perhaps preferable, although you may wish to alter it somewhat to suit your taste.

If you plan to study more than one subject at a time (for example, the same evening, or on successive days), it is desirable to select subjects from *different* groups. This is especially important if the subjects are quite new to you, or if your main purpose is to make a preliminary survey of the subject. On the other hand, should you wish to review a subject to refresh your memory, you may arrange your work so as to pursue more intensive study. If you wish to extend your study of any subject beyond the scope of this book, you should use the suggested readings given at the end of the section after you have studied it here.

PLAN A

(For the beginner, to whom most of the subjects are new; time required, 6 hours per week.)

FIRST FEW MONTHS:	MONDAY	WEDNESDAY	FRIDAY
Any subject from GROUP I	1 hour	1 hour	1 hour
Any subject from GROUP III	1 hour	1 hour	1 hour
NEXT FEW MONTHS:			
Any subject from GROUP II	1 hour	1 hour	1 hour
Any subject from GROUP IV	1 hour	1 hour	1 hour
NEXT FEW MONTHS:			
Another subject from GROUP I	1 hour	1 hour	1 hour
Another subject from GROUP III	1 hour	1 hour	1 hour
Alternate as before until you have studied all the subjects.			

PLAN B

(For the reader who is merely reviewing the subjects to refresh his mind; time required, 7½ hours per week.)

FIRST FEW WEEKS:	MONDAY	TUESDAY	THURSDAY
Any subject from GROUP IV	1 hour	1 hour	1 hour
Any subject from GROUPS I, II, or III	¾ hour	¾ hour	¾ hour
Another subject from GROUPS I, II, or III	¾ hour	¾ hour	¾ hour
NEXT FEW WEEKS:			
A second subject from GROUP IV	1 hour	1 hour	1 hour
A new subject from GROUPS I, II, or III	¾ hour	¾ hour	¾ hour
Another new subject from GROUPS I, II, or III	¾ hour	¾ hour	¾ hour
Alternate as before until you have studied all the subjects.			

As stated before, these plans may be varied to suit your own needs and convenience. The important thing is to adopt a plan and then *carry it out regularly and faithfully;* success is never achieved by good intentions and casual activities.

USING THE EXAMINATION QUESTIONS

You should also make some allowance in your plan for testing yourself by means of the Examination Questions following or in each section. These questions test your understanding of specific aspects of each subject. Except for the three mathematics sections, you should attempt to answer the questions only when you have completed your study of a particular subject; in mathematics do the exercises and problems as you reach them in the text. Sit down quietly with pencil and paper; read each question carefully and write your answer to it as fully and as correctly as you can. If you wish to pass a question by for the time being, leave room on your paper and return to it later.

When you have answered the questions to your satisfaction, turn to the Answers, beginning on page 1363. Compare your answers with those given there. Generally your answer need not be word for word the same as the printed answer, but it should convey the same meaning and information. Check those of your answers which are correct. In grading yourself, credit yourself with 2 points for each correct answer. Then add up the number of points for the subject. As there are 50 questions in each subject, perfect grade is 100. Any score from 90 to 100 is "A" or "Excellent"; from 80 to 89, "B" or "Good"; 70 to 79, "C" or "Fair"; 60 to 69, "D" or "Poor"; grades below 60 are failing. The three exceptions to this grading system are: Literature (with 100 questions), where you should credit yourself with 1 point for each correct answer; and United States Government and General Science (each with 35 questions), where you should credit yourself with 3 points for each correct answer, which will give a perfect score of 105.

You will note that in the printed Answers, pages are given which refer to the place in the text where the subject of the question is discussed. If you have made an error on a question, refer back to the text to refresh your memory and to fix the answer in your mind.

You may, if you choose, keep a record of the questions you have answered incorrectly and then try to answer them again at some later time. This will provide drill material on your weak points and will help you towards full mastery of the subject matter.

Contents

IV. A SHORT HISTORY OF THE UNITED STATES

IX. EFFECTIVE SPEAKING

X. A GUIDE TO LITERATURE

XI. A GUIDE TO THE ARTS

XII. FRENCH SELF TAUGHT

XIII. SPANISH SELF TAUGHT

XIV. AN INTRODUCTION TO LATIN

XVIII. SOLID GEOMETRY

XIX. TRIGONOMETRY

XX. INTRODUCTION TO GENERAL SCIENCE

XXI. ASTRONOMY FOR EVERYBODY

XXII. GEOLOGY FOR BEGINNERS

XXIII. PHYSICS SELF TAUGHT

XXIV. CHEMISTRY SELF TAUGHT

XXV. BIOLOGY FOR BEGINNERS

XXVI. PHYSIOLOGY SIMPLIFIED

XXVII. PSYCHOLOGY FOR BEGINNERS

List of Maps

List of Maps

HIGH SCHOOL
SUBJECTS
SELF TAUGHT

I

An Outline of Ancient History

THE DAWN OF HISTORY

HISTORY BEGINS when the written record starts—which was all of seven thousand years ago. Man was *prehistoric* until he began to record—on stone, in clay, on papyrus—the story of his own activities.

The generally accepted theory of evolution explains the origin and development of mankind from lowly forms of animal life into the savage, and from the primitive savage into the more highly civilized being who inhabited the earth at the dawn of history.

The very long period of man's development before he learned to speak, and especially to write, would remain a complete mystery to us if archaeologists had not found so many markings and leftovers of prehistoric men—among these, tools, pottery, cave dwellings and drawings. Geologists studying the earth's history have discovered that major changes in climate and massive glacial movements occurred at intervals in prehistoric times; these evidently brought about migrations and other events in the development of primitive groups. Through combined studies we have arrived at a rather clear picture of certain stages of mankind before the time of recorded history.

The earliest representatives of the human race evidently roamed with the wild herds, on which they largely depended for food. Later, men learned to domesticate animals as a permanent supply of meat and milk, and were thus able to found homes and establish the beginnings of societal structure. Farming became highly developed, especially as methods of irrigation were learned. Tools were at first chipped out of stone and later shaped by grinding and polishing. The long period in world history before men learned to work metals has thus been called the Stone Age. There are indications that early men in Europe, Asia, and Africa lived in Stone Age conditions, probably with little if any contact between widely separated groups. In any event, this period drew to a close at different times as men in different regions began to discover ways of using copper, and then other metals, in fashioning their tools, implements, and weapons. Before the end of the Stone Age, men had left their cave dwellings; they were building huts, which grew into villages. And from early pictorial representations, which for magic purposes had been drawn on cave walls, there developed the all-important art of writing.

During the time when primitive man was still wholly at the mercy of climate and other physical elements, struggle for survival was decided often by physical characteristics. In different regions different physical traits predominated among those who survived. This explains the early division of mankind into races, which were later to be further distinguished by striking differences in language.

In easy communication with other peoples has lain the secret of the world's progress. The tremendous advance of civilization in modern times is due to the facility of communication and transportation, encouraging exchange of goods (commerce) and ideas (literature, scientific discovery), and to the ability to profit by the past from recorded history. In ancient times travel was slow and laborious; communication was by messenger only. When early peoples were conquered, their civilizations were at least partly lost. Progress was consequently slow, tending to confine itself to the favorite localities.

Egypt, in the valley of the Nile River, and Mesopotamia, lying between the Euphrates and the Tigris rivers, were scenes of early progress, which was to come into conflict with the later civilizations of Greece and Rome. Warm climate and the fertility of valley soil attracted settlements in these two regions at about the same time. Geographical barriers, however, at first kept the rival civilizations from communicating with one another. As migrations from Mesopotamia, northward along the rivers, extended and spread to the west, Syria—a strip of habitable land on the Mediterranean Sea—became the common ground for a clash of cultures, for Egyptians traveled north along the Nile and crossed the sea to the near shores of Syria. At the meeting place of these two ancient civilizations, new centers developed which were to increase in importance.

In both of these civilizations, religion played a dominant part; mighty temples were erected to fierce gods, and from a powerful priesthood great kings often strode into politics to rule over the people.

THE STORY OF EGYPT

In the valley of the Nile River, early tribes found that they could live pleasantly the year around; hence settlements arose. These people were not nomadic, for the quest of the things they desired did not take them afar. The annual floods from the river, although inconvenient in some ways, insured a perpetual re-fertilization of the land, and the climate was favorable to raising food. Later, the Egyptians found that irrigation and a system of reservoirs added to the natural bounty of the Nile. The need for keeping these canals, and also for maintaining the dikes which kept the annual torrent from sweeping away their huts and appliances, united the early tribes into some sort of government. Kings early controlled the water supply and land cultivation.

Meanwhile, nomadic peoples were foraging from the neighboring, less-favored regions, and the long, long story of the looting or the conquest of settled peoples by roving tribes or by stronger civilizations began. First the roving tribes looted their more settled neighbors; later they conquered them, making the subdued people continue their agriculture for the benefit of those who held the upper hand. The conquerors became the rulers; the conquered became the laboring classes.

Egyptian history began about five thousand years before Christ. The first available records have been identified as of that period. The date is written "5000 B.C.," as our calendar reckons time backward and forward from the birth of Christ; the years after the birth of Christ are distinguished by the letters A.D. (*Anno Domini,* meaning "In the year of the Lord").

In Egypt writing was done on papyrus (whence our word, paper), made from reeds of the Nile. For many years these early symbols, called *hieroglyphics,* could not be deciphered; but the finding of the Rosetta stone (about 1800 A.D.), which contained parallel inscriptions in hieroglyphic writing and in Greek, provided the key which unlocked the written secrets of the Egyptians. Champollion, a soldier in Napoleon's army, successfully deciphered the hieroglyphics on the Rosetta stone.

The civilization of Egypt extended southward from the mouth of the Nile to the First Cataract of the Nile, where early transportation along the river had to stop. Thebes and Memphis were the ancient cities of Egypt. A long line of rulers, called Pharaohs, governed the people. They conquered, and were conquered.

Because the Egyptians believed strongly in a life after death, and filled the tombs of their dead with tools and implements to aid the soul or shadow, many objects associated with early Egyptian life survive, recovered in modern times by extensive excavations. Most of these relics were found in the pyramids, which, with the Sphinx, are even today the symbolic landmarks of Egypt. The pyramids were tombs which the self-centered Pharaohs built for themselves, driving their laborers with the sting of whips into muscular endeavor which has perhaps never been equaled elsewhere in history. The great pyramid of Cheops was numbered in ancient times as one of the Seven Wonders of the World.

To restore the lines of their fields after the annual inundation, the Egyptians devised the beginnings of geometry. To learn the times of flood, they watched the stars, and began the science of astronomy. To build the pyramids, the Egyptians also had to have considerable knowledge of principles which are the basis of modern engineering. From their observation of the stars, they computed the length of the solar year, based on the earth's revolution around the sun, to be about 365¼ days, which is exactly right.

For a period known as the Old Kingdom, the capital of Egypt was the city of Memphis (from 3400 to about 2400 B.C.). At the end of this period arose the splendid fourth dynasty of Egyptian rulers, during which the great pyramids were built by forceful Pharaohs. About 2400 B.C. the power of the Old Kingdom Pharaohs declined. Thebes, farther up the Nile, became the leading city. Long internal conflict marks the centuries from the fourth to the fifteenth dynasty—wars between rival communities, and wars resulting from religious differences. There was some spreading southward into Ethiopian Africa, and some foreign conquest in Syria. But Egypt for the most part was cut off from the developing civilizations of Asia until the Nile region was conquered about 1800 B.C. by roving tribes from the North, probably Semitic. Their chiefs, called the Hyksos or "Shepherd Kings," apparently dominated the fifteenth and sixteenth dynasties in Egypt.

In this period, from Arabia, the horse first came into Egypt, and chariots appeared. Since the leaders of armies could now travel faster and farther, a new era of conquest opened. Egypt wrested freedom from her Hyksos conquerors around 1600 B.C., at which time a powerful new dynasty of Theban princes came into power and established the New Empire. For a period of two hundred years or more Egyptian armies battled across the isthmus which is now cut by the Suez Canal. Conquering Syria, they pushed on as far as the Euphrates valley. Here, meanwhile, another independent civilization had been growing outside of Egyptian influence. Contact through military operations was the introduction to trade between Egypt and the peoples to the eastward, and through these connections the first great oriental empire was launched. At its height it included Syria, Phoenicia, Palestine, and part of Nubia; Cyprus and the Cretan cities were obliged to enter into alliance with the Egyptian rulers. Pharaohs Thutmose III and Rameses II (19th dynasty) were the illustrious kings of this period. Despite a brief intervening revolt by Syria, these reigns mark a glorious phase of Egyptian history. The many fine monuments and great buildings, particularly the temple of Karnak, testify to the splendor and prosperity of the age.

In the years following, Egyptian power suffered a marked decline. Egypt in Syria was overthrown by Hittites from the north, and the Egyptians gradually withdrew to the Nile. About 670 B.C. they fell under the sway of Assyria, which country was ruled successively by Tiglath-pileser III, Sargon II, and Sennacherib. Now Egypt's glory began a continuous decline. A brief revival of prosperity under Psammetichus (26th dynasty) led to halfhearted and unsuccessful attempts to recover the empire. Even when, under Necho II, the Egyptian empire extended again to the Euphrates, splendid Nineveh fell to the Medes and Chaldeans, and Egypt was conquered by the Chaldeans under Nebuchadnezzar II, of Biblical fame.

Then Persia conquered Chaldea, and in the fifth century B.C., Egypt as well. There was another short period of independence, which was lost when Alexander the Great added Egypt to his conquests. Egypt was ruled, after the death of Alexander, by the Greek Ptolemies, descendants of one of Alexander's generals. Cleopatra (31 B.C.) was the last of their line. The Romans then came, other conquerors followed, and for more than twenty centuries Egypt did not regain her independence.

THE PEOPLES OF MESOPOTAMIA

In the fertile valley area known as Mesopotamia, between and surrounding the Tigris and Euphrates rivers, civilized communities grew up about the same time as in the Nile valley. Mesopotamia was the scene of continual rivalry and amalgamations between the various peoples that established themselves in close proximity. Following the early Sumerians, there were the Babylonians, the Assyrians, and the Chaldeans—all of whom settled in the general region. And in turn each of these would extend its territories, and then give way or be absorbed by the next growing power.

So far as we know, the people of Sumer, who settled in southeastern Mesopotamia, probably established the first city-states in the region. By about 2000 B.C., the Sumerians were largely united and began to expand. Because the area has no stone quarries, they built their homes of sun-dried bricks. Like the Egyptians, they irrigated the fields in which their crops were planted. Instead of writing on papyrus as the Egyptians did, they pressed their records on clay tiles. Their writing is known as *cuneiform,* because of the wedge shape of the symbols.

From the territory somewhat to the west in Mesopotamia, Sargon I (270 B.C.), commanding a Semitic people known as the Akkadians, invaded Sumer and, extending his power to the north and further west, established the Sumerian-Akkadian empire. Contrary to what one would expect, the language and culture of the conquered were adopted by the conquerors, and thus Sumerian pioneering in civilization had a marked influence on the whole subsequent history of the region. The Sumerian-Akkadians, having become contented and peaceful, were attacked from the east and west and finally conquered by the Babylonians, another Semitic people whose chief city, Babylon, was situated on the Euphrates River. The Babylonians achieved pre-eminence in Mesopotamia under the powerful Hammurabi (2100 B.C.), who was king of the first Babylonian empire. Hammurabi codified the laws and had them engraved on stone. They were set up in the temple in Babylon and are the oldest preserved code of laws.

Simultaneously, the warlike Assyrians to the north were achieving a position of power. From their capital at Nineveh on the Tigris River, they set out to expand their domain. Under Tiglath-pileser I (1100 B.C.), they conquered Babylon. Tiglath-pileser III (745 B.C.) conquered Syria and Palestine. Sargon II, a very ambitious ruler, laid the foundations of the empire by his conquests; and his son, Sennacherib, headed the Assyrian march into Egypt. Following these mighty rulers, Assurbanipal completed the conquest of Egypt. This ruler also founded at Nineveh the first great library of the Ancient World.

The armies of the Chaldeans, another Mesopotamian people from the south, aided by the Medes and Persians from the east, overcame the Assyrian empire, and Nineveh bowed to their might in 606 B.C. The great Nebuchadnezzar ruled over the Chaldean or second Babylonian empire, restoring the architectural glories of Babylon and enclosing the city with great walls; but the empire was to fall in the reign of his successor.

It was at this time that Persia began to grow in importance. The Persians were an Indo-European, Aryan people in the area east of Mesopotamia. They set out for conquest under the great Cyrus, whose hosts of invaders captured all of Babylonia in 539 B.C. At the end of the sixth century B.C. the Persian empire extended westward to include all of Asia Minor. This conquest was only one of a cycle, for the Persians would later be subjugated by Alexander the Great.

From the Mesopotamian region the world has a heritage of great value. The Mosaic Code of the Bible owes some of its principles to the great code of laws formulated by Hammurabi, who was called "the lawgiver." From the Babylonian's arithmetical system, in which they used the unit of 60 (originating perhaps from a use of the multiple 12 as well as our familiar 10), we derive our 60 minutes to the hour and 360 degrees to the circle. The Assyrians invented the sundial, and the modern apothecary symbols and the signs of the zodiac originated with the Babylonians.

Nearby Arabia gave us our numerals, which are still called Arabic to distinguish them from the Roman system of notation.

EASTERN MEDITERRANEAN PEOPLES

In the region bordering the coast at the eastern end of the Mediterranean Sea and extending northwest into Asia Minor were three early civilizations, whose histories were closely related to each other and to those of Egypt and Mesopotamia. The Hittites, of whom we know very little, dominated much of Syria and Asia Minor, and around 1500 B.C. were probably the most important military and cultural power in all western Asia. The Phoenicians, earliest important shipbuilders and navigators, sailed to all the coasts of the Mediterranean and founded a number of important colonies; however, they never achieved great political power and were successively dominated by Egyptians, Assyrians, and Persians. The Hebrews, originally wandering tribes from Mesopotamia, began around 2000 B.C. to settle in Canaan. Although they early developed a culture of their own, rivalry among themselves and with neighboring powers prevented their becoming a nation until the times of King David and King Solomon.

THE HITTITES

The Hittites were a warlike people of Indo-European origin, who at various times in their history vigorously challenged the power of Egypt and Mesopotamia. They organized themselves into a rigid militaristic society, and from 2000 B.C. expanded their influence through conquests and alliances. Archaeological excavations in Asia Minor have revealed that at their height the Hittites dominated a formidable empire. Egypt was for a brief period ruled by Hittite kings; and the Hittites were constantly threatening the successive states of Mesopotamia, as well as their closer neighbors in Asia Minor. By 1200 B.C. the Hittite nation had broken into a number of petty states, and their civilization rapidly disappeared. Modern scholars have shown that the language used by the ruling classes of the Hittites is related to the European languages of today.

THE HEBREWS

The story of the Hebrews reflects the turbulent times in which they lived. They began as desert tribes of wandering shepherds. Abraham, who is believed to have established their race, began the rule of the patriarchs or fathers. His descendants were Isaac and Jacob. According to the Old

Testament, Jacob and his sons were driven into Egypt by famine. Moses, who was born in Egypt, headed the flight of his enslaved followers from Egypt. Joshua, who succeeded Moses, led the Hebrews (about 1250 B.C.) to the conquest of the region known as Canaan, where they contended for a long time with hostile neighbors. The first Hebrew king was Saul, during whose reign there were many conflicts with the neighboring Philistines. It was David, Saul's successor, who really united the Hebrews into a nation. Under David's son, Solomon, the Hebrews controlled a considerable empire. Then, possibly on account of the heavy taxes demanded by the ruler, the twelve tribes divided again. Ten of them formed the Kingdom of Israel, which lasted 250 years; the two remaining tribes comprised the country of Judah.

Israel then fell to the Assyrians, and the ten tribes were exiled by Tiglath-pileser III and lost forever to history. Judah, whose capital was Jerusalem, endured four centuries. The people often paid tribute to Assyria or Babylonia, and when they revolted, Nebuchadnezzar quelled them and took them into captivity in Babylonia.

Although this is the end, until the present century, of the political history of the Jews as a state, as a racial nation they have always survived. When the Persians conquered Babylonia, they allowed the Jews to return to Judea, but kept them ever subject to the nearest state in power—in turn the Persian, Greek, and Roman empires—except when, after the successful revolt of Judas Maccabaeus, the Jews were an independent kingdom from 145 to 63 B.C. After that they were a province of Rome or paid tribute.

Jewish rebellion in 70 A.D. brought a quick and terrific punishment. Roman legions bore down on them, razed the city of Jerusalem, and sold the inhabitants into slavery. As a result of this dispersal, they were scattered throughout the world. We owe to the ancient Hebrews the Old Testament of the Bible and the foundation for our present-day code of morality.

THE PHOENICIANS

Phoenicia was north of Palestine (Canaan). It was a narrow strip of seacoast, and its people were navigators. In their early ships they roved the waters of the Mediterranean, and established colonies. Thus their culture became widespread. Their cities, Tyre and Sidon, are still synonyms of greatness.

The Phoenicians were not conquerors. On the contrary, they were frequently conquered, and their conquerors used them to good advantage in building cities and extending their maritime affairs. The Phoenicians were traders, however, and their seagoing vessels were kept active by commerce.

The fact that trading men must keep records led to the development of the Phoenician alphabet, from which is derived the English alphabet that we use today. Moreover, a basis of exchange became necessary, and cattle became the first standard. (It is interesting to note that the Latin *pecunia,* meaning *money,* comes from *pecus,* cattle, and gave us the English word *pecuniary.* It was in nearby Lydia in western Asia Minor under Croesus, whose wealth is proverbial, that metal coins were first used and stamped with a picture of the ruler to guarantee their value.)

THE STORY OF GREECE

The mainland of Greece, the surrounding islands of the Aegean Sea, and the adjacent parts of Asia Minor comprised the territory included in Greek history from the earliest times. Early Greek history involves a number of peoples who at various times invaded and occupied the islands and the mainland areas, in each instance absorbing the existing civilization. Racial fusion and cultural interchanges through trade and rivalry produced the civilization which we call Ancient Greek. The early inhabitants, the Aegeans, were slowly absorbed by two great Indo-European migrations into this area; first to come were the Achaeans, and the Dorians followed afterward. Two important groups who somewhat later dominated certain areas of the mainland and migrated to the islands and Asia Minor were the Ionians and the Aeolians, both descended from the Achaeans. These early Indo-European invasions and later migrations, in addition to bringing about local cultural and political changes, often resulted in shifting the cultural leadership and centers of military power from one of the regions to another.

THE AEGEANS

The earliest civilization in the Greek world sprang up in the Aegean islands. This Aegean civilization was fully as ancient as Egypt. Occupying the coasts as well as islands, these people were trading with the Egyptians as early as 3000 B.C. Their use of cuneiform writing indicates they had intercourse with Mesopotamia. The island of Crete, with its magnificent city of Cnossus, was the first flourishing center of Aegean civilization. Like the Phoenicians, the Cretans were seagoing traders. Cretan clay tablets dating from 1600 B.C., whose inscriptions had long puzzled archaeologists, were recently deciphered. They proved to be records and computations of business transactions, and the language was found to be related to Akkadian or Babylonian.

The Aegean New Stone Age came to its height when the peoples of the

Nile and Euphrates were going through the Bronze Age and Egypt was passing through the Old Kingdom, in which the Great Pyramid was built by Cheops. By the time bronze had reached Crete and the nearby Aegean Islands (2500 B.C.), Sargon's Babylonian empire was past its height and Egypt was in the Middle Kingdom.

This phase of Aegean history dominated by Crete is referred to as Minoan, after the fabulous King Minos who may have been a real Cretan king. Cretan culture spread over the other islands and to Asia Minor where the city of Troy was located. Originally Aegean, and later influenced by nearby civilizations in Asia Minor, this city was destroyed, rebuilt, and destroyed again many times throughout its history. It was probably the seventh city built on the site that the Achaean Greeks from Mycenae destroyed in the famous Trojan War.

THE EARLY GREEKS

These Achaeans were an Indo-European people who migrated from the north into the Aegean area around 1900 B.C. A barbarian people at the time, they slowly integrated with the Aegeans, assimilating much of their culture and establishing important settlements on the mainland. Unlike the dark Mediterranean peoples of early Aegean history, these intruders were probably fair-haired. The Achaeans are considered the first Greeks. The later Ionians and Aeolians were their descendants.

Although the Achaean influence was felt throughout the Aegean world, this new race settled most heavily on the mainland of Greece, where Mycenae grew up as the most important city. In the fourteenth century B.C. Mycenae assumed political and cultural pre-eminence over all the Aegean world, the Cretans declining in importance. Numerous shifts in population were caused by political antagonism between the leading cities, and internal strife in the Achaean-Aegean area culminated around 1200 B.C. in the Trojan War, so brilliantly described by Homer in the *Iliad*. Also about this time the Dorian invasion occurred. The Dorians, another Indo-European group related to the Achaeans and likewise coming from the north, overran the Aegean Islands and Greece in a relatively short time, forcing many natives to flee. Some of those who fled found refuge in Egypt and Syria; others in Palestine, where they became known as Philistines. The speed of the Dorians' conquest was due in considerable part to their possession of iron weapons. Spreading over Asia Minor and the Greek mainland as well as the islands, the Dorians inherited the Minoan (Cretan) and Mycenaean (Achaean) cultures of the Aegean world, and thus they were a strong unifying factor in the new Greek world. They concentrated, however, in the Peloponnesus, where they later founded the

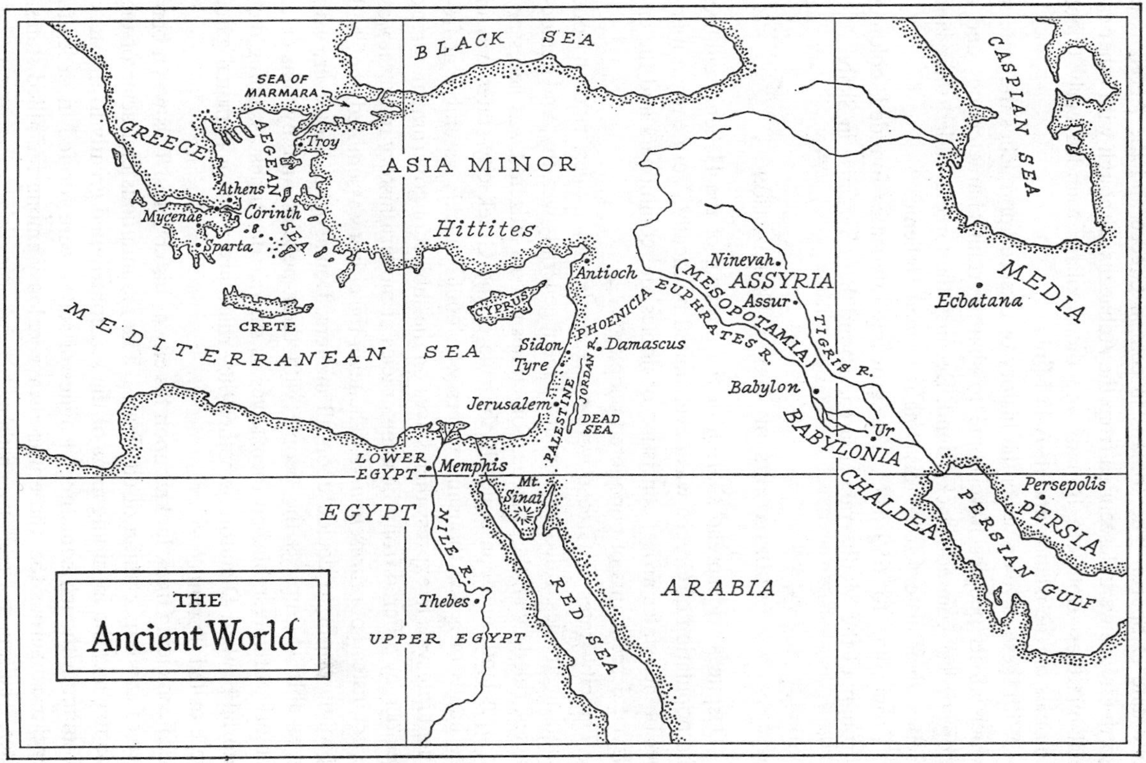
THE
Ancient World
BLACK SEA
CASPIAN SEA
SEA OF MARMARA
GREECE
AEGEAN SEA
Troy
ASIA MINOR
Athens
Corinth
Mycenae
Sparta
Hittites
Antioch
Ninevah
ASSYRIA
MEDIA
Ecbatana
Assur
(MESOPOTAMIA)
EUPHRATES R.
TIGRIS R.
CYPRUS
CRETE
MEDITERRANEAN SEA
PHOENICIA
Sidon
Damascus
Tyre
JORDAN R.
Jerusalem
PALESTINE
DEAD SEA
Babylon
BABYLONIA
Ur
CHALDEA
LOWER EGYPT
Memphis
Mt. Sinai
Persepolis
PERSIA
PERSIAN GULF
EGYPT
NILE R.
Thebes
UPPER EGYPT
RED SEA
ARABIA

city-state of Sparta. The Ionians in central Greece and the Aeolians in north Greece were descended from the Achaeans, although with other racial mixtures. Both the Ionians and the Aeolians founded early Greek colonies on the islands and in Asia Minor.

With these developments the history of Greece approaches the state in which all its peoples have come to share certain characteristics and a more or less common background. Because the Greeks called their land Hellas, their history from this time is termed Hellenic.

From 800 to 650 B.C. the growing city-states founded colonies throughout the Mediterranean area, among them Syracuse in Sicily.

FOUNDATIONS OF GREEK CIVILIZATION

Despite a widespread sharing of the growing of the Hellenic culture, the population of Greece was never united politically. Very early a number of city-states arose, consisting of nobles and commoners and the enslaved descendants of conquered peoples.

The city-states of Greece were successively monarchies, ruled by one man; oligarchies, ruled by a group of men, generally wealthy; and democracies, ruled by all the citizens. Sometimes to be a citizen it was necessary to own land, and consequently the rule of the Greek city-states was in the hands of a few thousand voters who could quickly assemble at frequent intervals to express themselves on the subject of government. Greek democracy differed from the democracies of modern history in that it was *direct* instead of *representative:* whenever the citizens assembled, they had absolute power to decide upon all matters. Demagogues, however, who were able to impress the people with their policies and by masterful rhetoric, often established themselves as rulers, sometimes assuming dictatorial powers. Dictators, whether they ruled justly or for personal gain, were called "tyrants."

The ancient Greek looked upon his city as his country. This was a barrier to any larger union of city-states. The mountainous character of the country and the intruding arms of the sea contributed greatly to this lack of unity. Although sometimes leagues of states were formed in order to repel a dangerous foe, there was always jealousy among the allied states, often resulting in war between them.

Culturally, however, the Greeks all drew upon a common background. They had, of course, the same language and the same literary heritage. Homer, the great bard of the eighth century B.C., sang of the earlier heroic days and the traditional legends in the *Iliad* and the *Odyssey,* epics of the times of the Trojan War which are among the world's masterpieces.

They are used by historians as a source of knowledge of Greece during the period up to 800 B.C.

Greek religion originated in a worship of nature-divinities; gods and goddesses were associated with the sun, the moon, the stars, streams, trees, and with crops and fertility. Gradually the religion became somewhat formalized and twelve major deities were recognized as governing human affairs from the top of Mount Olympus, whence they were called the Olympians. They were conceived of as supernatural beings who shared, nonetheless, the passions, ambitions, and often the weaknesses of human nature. Many fanciful legends grew up about their activities. Their father and chief was Zeus. Temples were built to the deities, sacrifices offered to them, and feasts held in their honor. There were a number of famous oracles, such as the one at Delphi (dedicated to the god Apollo), to whom the Greeks turned for "divine guidance." These oracles were supported by several states together, and the priest or priestess of the god would give counsel to those who sought it, often in vague ambiguous statements that could be interpreted in several ways.

Another aspect of Greek life which has continued to interest us were the Greek athletic meets in which the pick of the Greek youths gathered to show their prowess and strength. Most famous of these meets were the Olympic games, in which competitors from all the Greek states took part. Held every four years at Olympia, these games furnished the term Olympiad, the unit of four years in the Greek calendar. And it is from the first Olympic games, known definitely to have been held in 776 B.C., that we have the first exact date in Greek history.

ATHENS AND SPARTA

There were two Greek cities of exceptional importance. Sparta arose in 900 B.C. in the Peloponnesus, in the region of Laconia (Lacedaemon). Athens grew up about the same time in the area of the Greek mainland to the northeast, the region known as Attica.

Sparta was ruled jointly by two kings, whose individual power was consequently so small that the Spartans did not try to overthrow them. Hardy soldiers were developed at Sparta, for the harsh Spartan custom ruled that babies who were weak should be left outside to die, and that from the age of seven to manhood the youth should be trained by the state. Physical pain or punishment must be borne unflinchingly. The Spartans also had an enslaved class of farmers and soldiers known as helots, who were descended from the conquered Achaeans.

Besides being cultivated, Spartan hardihood was inherited from the rude Dorian tribes who overran and dominated this part of Greece.

Sparta conquered Laconia and made allies of other tribes of the Peloponnesus. The speech of the Spartans (Laconians) was clipped and pithy, and our word *laconic* comes from this fact.

Spartan government became democratic in the restricted ancient sense. The citizens—comprising only the original members of the conquering tribe or their descendants living in the country—elected senators and had a popular assembly. In 725 B.C. they had chief rulers called Ephors. Instead of delegating political power to individuals, however, the people as a rule retained the right to revoke any power that was abused, and through the Ephors they could even "arrest" the king.

If they deemed it necessary, the Spartan citizens frequently killed off the more powerful of the farmer-soldiers (helots). This was for the purpose of keeping them in subjection, and the action was regarded as a proper privilege of the state. The best weapons were in the hands of the Spartans themselves, and consequently they were the best armed soldiers. There was another class composed of the residents of surrounding towns. They were neither citizens nor slaves, but freemen, and although they ran the government of their own cities, they were subject to Spartan domination.

Greece thus had an army. It was a Spartan army, but in later warfare with the Persians it was to be a *Greek* army, while Athens, the other leading city, supplied the navy. For centuries there was no political connection between the two cities, and their only point of contact was through their meeting at the Olympic games every four years, at the oracles, or in friendly conclave.

The district of Attica was a region dominated by the Ionians, who were a milder people than the Dorians of Sparta, and its great city was Athens. The geographical position of Attica rendered it almost impregnable, as it could be approached by land only through narrow mountain passes.

In the Ionian people were seeds of greatness and glory. Little by little, between 1000 and 500 B.C., they evolved what has since been regarded a priceless legacy of art, philosophy, and government. The nobles were the chiefs of the various clans in Attica. In the beginning the land was under their control, and the peasantry were forced to pay them the lion's share of what they could produce. Sometimes the crops failed, and if the peasants could not pay, they were sold into slavery. Naturally these tenants were discontented and gradually the power of the nobles in war declined. Four classes of soldiers came into being. Their standing was determined by the manner in which they were armed. Since the higher classes were those who produced the most from their land, agricultural wealth secured the upper hand over inherited nobility. Both military position and political power found their basis in wealth.

At first the nobility in Athens also ruled with an iron hand, interpreting unwritten customs in their favor and at the expense of the common people. By popular demand, these customs were written down in 621 B.C. by Draco, so that everyone might know them as laws. As a result their injustices became more grossly apparent. It was Solon, one of the great reformers of ancient times (died 559 B.C.), who initiated drastic reforms and drew up a more just and systematic code of laws. The tenants were given ownership of lands they cultivated, all Athenian slaves in Attica were freed, and the amount of land that might be owned by one man was limited.

Because political power was based on wealth, whether of property or otherwise, the new tenant-landowners became a force in the government. The members were chosen by lot. The procedure was supposed to be under divine guidance. All the problems of government, however, were not solved. Solon's reforms did not prevent jealousy among the landowners, merchants, and small farmers, and anarchy threatened. In 560 B.C. Pisistratus forcibly took over the government and assumed the political power of a king. He became a "tyrant." There were some tyrants of old who were beneficent rulers, but so many of them were cruel and stern that the word has now come to have that meaning only.

Pisistratus was a mild tyrant. He followed in the traditions of Solon, and fostered commerce, art, and public works. His sons, who came into power later, were not so successful in holding it. The line was overthrown in 510 B.C., and Clisthenes, espousing the people's cause, came into power. Under him Athens became a true democracy. Clisthenes marked off Attica into political divisions, and allowed the foreigners then living in the district to vote. He devised a system called *ostracism,* which decreed that any citizen who was considered dangerous to the state could be exiled for a certain length of time by popular vote. An interesting feature of ostracism was that it carried no stigma when the victim returned at the expiration of the required time.

Athenian art rose to magnificent heights. The temples of the city were of surpassing beauty with their tall columns and the friezes (sculptured decorations) around the supporting stones just under the roof. It was a golden age of literature, not only in Athens but in other parts of Greece. Long before this time, the epics sung by Homer, the *Iliad* and the *Odyssey,* had been set down for the delight of succeeding ages. Poets of the seventh and sixth centuries were busy composing odes and songs. This was the time of Sappho, poetess of the island of Lesbos, whom some consider the greatest of women poets. There was Pindar, who sang of athletic achievement. Like Hesiod (800 B.C.), he came from Boeotia, northwest of Attica.

Philosophy had its beginnings with Thales of Miletus and his pupils. A number of famous early philosophers followed, including Pythagoras, Parmenides, Heraclitus, Empedocles, and Democritus. These men were beginning to ponder about the nature of things in general—life, the composition and regulation of the earth and the universe. They were what might be termed speculative scientists, for they thought about what might be true instead of experimenting to prove it true.

In spite of not being a political unity, the Greeks around 500 B.C. considered themselves one people, with Athens and Sparta the leading city-states. Greece needed the products of other regions, and mainly for the purposes of trade had established colonies along the shores of the Mediterranean and the Black seas. Sparta became a military power, and democracy prevailed.

THE WAR WITH THE PERSIANS

The Medes, east of the region of the Euphrates and Tigris rivers, had become fierce warriors around 850 B.C. They were conquered by Assyria at first, but, having borrowed their neighbors' civilization, they made improvements in their methods of fighting and overthrew Assyria in 606 B.C. In the century between 600 and 500 B.C. the known world was divided between Babylonia, Egypt, Lydia, and Media (where the Medes lived). They were all on fairly friendly terms.

Cyrus established a Persian monarchy. He went to war with his neighbors, the Medes, of whom he had been a tributary prince, and overcame them. Then he and his Persian armies conquered Lydia and Babylonia, which were allied with the Medes. The son of Cyrus, Cambyses, obtained control of Egypt. In 490 B.C. the Persian empire extended from the Indus River (adjacent to India), westward south of the Caspian Sea, and embraced the whole of Mesopotamia, all of Asia Minor, Syria, Arabia, and Egypt. The population of this empire was 75,000,000.

It was inevitable that Persia would attempt to conquer the Greeks, whose colonies in Asia Minor had come under the control of Croesus, ruler of Lydia. When Lydia was overcome, these colonies were absorbed by the Persian empire. The Ionians, who were the Greeks in Asia Minor living east of Athens, were conquered by Cyrus, who put Persian tyrants in charge of their cities.

In the meantime the Phoenician colony of Carthage on the Mediterranean coast of Africa attacked the Grecian colonies in southern Italy and Sicily, sending out ships from the stronghold on the coast of northern

Africa. This operation kept the western Greeks from helping the Greek natives, who had taken a warning from the fate of the Ionians. Sparta alone, with her loosely knit Peloponnesian league, was prepared for war. But in the face of a common foe, the Greeks would combine their forces as a matter of self-preservation.

Darius I launched his first expedition against Hellas (the ancient name of Greece) in 492 B.C., but a tremendous storm wrecked his ships. The rejection by the Greeks of Darius's terms for surrender, added to the cold reception accorded his ambassadors, determined Darius upon a final conquest of the Greeks. In 490 B.C. the Persians again sailed across the Aegean and landed on the plain of Marathon, not very far from Athens.

Miltiades, one of the generals of Athens, persuaded the Athenians to give battle to the Persian invaders, with the result that 10,000 hoplites (heavily armed infantry) faced them at Marathon. Phidippides, the famous messenger, ran to Sparta, a distance of 150 miles, to get reinforcements, and covered the distance in about forty-eight hours. Sparta was slow in sending aid, but from Boeotia came 1,000 hoplites. Thus Greek soldiers totaling only 11,000 were victorious over an army which, according to possibly unreliable ancient figures, was ten times as large.

It was the strategy of Miltiades plus the superiority of Greek weapons and armor that decided the victory. After the battle of Marathon, the spent soldiers marched to Athens, toward which the Persian fleet was proceeding. Phidippides, worn out from his efforts, ran ahead twenty-two miles to announce the victory. He reached Athens, and, just enough breath left to shout the news, fell dead. (Modern Marathon races are named after this second historic run.) The Greek soldiers arrived in advance of the ships of the Persians, who, loath to encounter them in combat again, sailed back from whence they came. Thus the Greek people and their civilization were saved from eastern oppression.

Egypt revolted from Persia, and through this fact Athens had ten years in which to get ready for another attack. Aristides, called "the Just," fought for leadership in Athens with Themistocles with the result that Aristides was ostracized. Themistocles showed the Athenians the necessity for building a navy, and this was ready for the third Persian attack in 480–479 B.C. Threatened from without, the Greeks were not insensible to the value of concerted action, but Sparta was in the habit of dallying. Now Xerxes, heading his Persian troops, invaded Attica. Attempting to defend the narrow mountain pass of Thermopylae, 300 brave Spartans under Leonidas met their death. The Boeotians of Central Greece joined the victorious Persians, and Athens was invaded and destroyed. Most of the Athenians, however, had reached safety in the ships of Themistocles.

It was at the great naval battle in the bay of Salamis that Themistocles gained the victory. The Persian fleet could not prevail against the maneuvering of the Greek ships. After that, the Persians tried to buy the Athenians, promising to rebuild Athens at Persian expense. Victory, however, had tasted good to the Greeks. Their native pride came to the surface, and they refused to be bribed. Sparta rallied. The Persian army was defeated again at Plataea in 479 B.C., with great slaughter. Thus closed the first period of the Persian wars. The Greeks were taking the offensive, and the Persian soldiery never again set hostile foot on Greek soil.

THE ATHENIAN EMPIRE

After the rout of the Persians and their expulsion from Greece, Athens began reconstruction by building walls around the city. The ruined homes and temples could wait until the walls were built. This plan did not appeal to the other Greek cities, particularly Sparta, which had been the leader of the loosely knit union that had fought the Persians. Athens, however, had done most and sacrificed most to defeat the enemy. It was under the inspiration of Themistocles that almost impregnable walls were built around Athens; and the port of Piraeus, four miles away, was fortified.

Athens now continued to increase her sea power, adding twenty new ships every year to her fleet. A league to embrace the whole of Greece was proposed by Athens, but instead two rival leagues were formed—the Athenian and Peloponnesian, the latter being under Spartan leadership. Sparta's military strength had made her take the lead during the Persian wars, but for popularity Athens was now the leading city.

The Athenian fleet was commanded by Aristides the Just, and the Greek colonies in Ionia were being gradually freed from Persian domination. Cimon, son of Miltiades (of Marathon fame), was the chief leader in this movement. When the Persian menace was no longer dangerous, some of the allies of Athens wished to secede from the league, but Athens would not allow such withdrawal, and when necessary subdued the offending city by force and made it a dependent state. Athens was in the position of a "tyrant city," and had an "empire" which covered the land around the shores and all the islands of the Aegean Sea; but she fulfilled her duties with judgment and fairness, and, moreover, furthered the progress of her own civilization.

Pericles attained to leadership in Athens at about 450 B.C., and began to consolidate the empire by making it equally powerful on land and sea. There were petty wars with other Greek cities, resulting, in the beginning, in victories for Athens. Alliances were formed with Thessaly, Boeotia, and others. Between Athens and the port of Piraeus, Pericles built defensive walls. He sent Athenian ships to help the Egyptians in a revolt against Persia. These ships were propelled by oarsmen because sails were not reliable in the generally calm waters of the Mediterranean.

The military activities of the Athenians were amazingly diverse and far-reaching, but, splendidly directed as they were, the situation was to change. Two hundred and fifty ships and thousands of men were lost on the expedition to Egypt, thus affording an opportunity for the allied states to revolt. Sparta invaded Attica. Pericles maneuvered to keep Attica intact, which was fortunate for Athens, and in 445 B.C. made a thirty-year truce with Sparta. This was destined to last for only fifteen years, but during this time of peace, Athens gained much.

Most of the Athenian land empire was lost, but her sea empire she kept whole. The taxes that she levied were fair, and, compared with the heavy taxes of the Persians, not excessive. Out of her own treasury Athens built ships for the defense of the empire from attack by foreign foes and the raids of pirates.

THE AGE OF PERICLES

Pericles was elected to the office of general fifteen times, and with his great power of oratory he was able to defend his leadership. The office of general was under the control of the popular assembly and had come to have the highest importance. At this period Athenian citizens played a large part in the government of the state. As one historian points out, Athens ruled her own people and her empire much as though the citizens of Boston were to rule not only Boston but all the United States as well, by popular vote and by the active participation of every citizen.

Any surplus revenues of the empire were used during the age of Pericles for the beautification of Athens. On the commanding rocky eminence of the Acropolis, which was originally a citadel but after the city walls were built no longer needed for defensive purposes, the Athenians then built the architectural and sculptural masterpieces whose beautiful ruins today inspire the reverent homage of the world. Among these ancient buildings was the Parthenon, which was dedicated to the virgin goddess Athene. The sculptures of this temple were either done or directed by Phidias, who was the leading artist of this period—the fifth century B.C.—in which the art was at its height. This period is called the classical period. Under Phidias the earlier rigid, geometric stylization of the archaic period (sixth century B.C.) had given way to a greater freedom. Gracefully flowing drapery often adorned the human body, which the sculptors traditionally portrayed as an idealized form rather than as the portrait of any one model. Proportion and balance of design were primary aims. The artists of the fourth century B.C. felt less bound by established form and, still respecting the classical trend, produced works of great beauty, the best of these being by Praxiteles. It was not until much later, when Greek art was declining, that artists strove for highly realistic representations.

In order to fully appreciate the classical period, it is important to realize that, in decorating the temples, the artists never lost sight of the architectural design for the sake of ornament, but always made their sculptures fit into it as an integral part. The Elgin Marbles in the British Museum, which Lord Elgin brought to England in 1800 A.D., were a part of the frieze of the Parthenon.

Athenian literature of the fifth century B.C. (and carried over somewhat into the fourth century) rose to unexampled heights. The theater was popularly attended. It was at this period that the famous tragedies of Aeschylus, Sophocles, and Euripides and the comedies of Aristophanes were written.

The great historians, Herodotus and Thucydides, were also of this period. Oratory came into its own, largely as a political instrument.

At this time, the philosopher Socrates was discoursing with groups of young men gathered at homes or at market places in the streets of Athens, inquiring with them into the nature of the good life. His technique of asking them pertinent questions which would lead them to discover for themselves the truth of the matter under discussion is known as the "Socratic method." It was Plato, who had been a pupil of Socrates, who recorded Socrates' philosophy in magnificent prose. Famous among the dialogues which Plato set down is one in which Socrates, condemned to death on the false charge of corrupting Athenian youth, refuses the offer of his friends to help him escape, explaining to them that the laws of the state, even when wrongly applied, must be honored. Plato in his own right was one of the greatest philosophers of all time, and many of the dramatically conceived dialogues present his own thought rather than solely that of Socrates, who is nonetheless the main speaker in all the dialogues. Ranking in greatness with Plato was Aristotle, who had been one of Plato's pupils, but who initiated a distinctly separate trend in philosophy. The large difference between these two great thinkers was that Plato turned his attention chiefly to ideas as an understanding of the ideal life, and Aristotle was more interested in realistic and scientific knowledge.

CONFLICT BETWEEN ATHENS AND SPARTA

Sparta, unlike Athens, never developed a significant culture. She remained throughout the fifth century a disciplined militaristic society and in the Peloponnesian War brought about the downfall of Athens. Into this conflict Sparta drew Athens when but half of the thirty-year truce had elapsed. Sparta and her allies harassed Athens, her colonies, and her dependent states from 431 to 404 B.C. During this time there were battles on sea and land, ravaging of homes and farms, and massacres. Some 4,000 citizens of Athens were taken prisoner and put to death. Corinth, whose naval power rivaled that of Athens, was in Sparta's league and urged her into the war with the slogan that they would set Greece free from the "tyrannical" Athenians.

Peasants and their families had taken refuge within the walls of Athens where a plague was raging with weakening and devastating effect. The wise Pericles was one of its victims, and the control of the city fell into less able and experienced hands. These leaders were Cleon and Hyperbolus, men of the people, and Nicias and Alcibiades, who were aristocrats. Brasidas and Lysander were famous Spartan commanders.

An ill-advised Athenian expedition against Syracuse (in Sicily) was a dismal failure and resulted in the destruction of hundreds of ships and the death of many thousand soldiers. A group called the Four Hundred took over control of the Athenian government in 411 B.C. but after a few months of this oligarchy, democracy was restored. Then Sparta made a bargain with Persia. Sparta, in exchange for ships built at Persian expense, promised to give them the Greek colonies in Asia if Sparta won the war. Against such heavy odds, the Athenians were forced to surrender in 404 B.C.

The glory of Greece for seventy years, Athens bowed to the military triumphs of Sparta. Sparta's rule was cruel and vicious. She doubled taxes, sent garrisons into the city, and was tyrannically arrogant. Under Lysander, she sent thirty men to govern Athens. These were the Thirty Tyrants. Their disgraceful rule did not last, however, for in 403 B.C. Athens freed herself and democracy was restored for a little while. Moreover, Sparta, in turn, was to fall. War had killed many of her citizens, and she was doomed by internal weakness.

With the treacherous help of Sparta, Cyrus the Younger at this time tried to usurp the Persian throne in Asia Minor. Cyrus failed, although ten thousand Greeks marched in his army. It is described in Xenophon's *Anabasis* how the Greeks, under Xenophon's leadership, escaped in the well-remembered retreat of the Ten Thousand. Expecting to gain new power, Sparta went to war with Persia, but the Spartan invasion also failed. The Greek cities of Thebes, Corinth, Athens, and Argos united against Sparta, wiping out her naval power. She remained for some time the dominant city-state—until Thebes under Epaminondas achieved a brief supremacy, when the Spartan military leadership was overthrown by his military genius. This victory served only to further disrupt Greek unity. The city-states were weakened by war between themselves; and groups of states, even when they were temporarily allied, were no longer secure from those who sought to invade them. A new world-conquering power north of Greece was to arise—Macedonia.

PHILIP AND THE MACEDONIANS

Philip II of Macedon was ambitious, unscrupulous, and scheming, but he was a wise judge of men, and he led the Macedonians to a position of power. Macedonia needed an outlet to the sea, and she secured it by fighting southward into Chalcidice and subsequently into Thessaly. Philip paid the costs of empire with the revenue from gold mines that he captured, and he had secret agents in many of the Grecian cities paving the way for his conquests.

The Greeks, however, were not without their suspicions of the Macedonians. Orators in Athens begged the people to save Greece from the threatening foe. Demosthenes, the greatest orator in Greek history, spoke against Philip and inveighed against his character (from which his orations came to be called *Philippics*), but with all his persuasive skill, his words had little effect.

As a youth, Philip had been held a hostage in Thebes, and he made good use later of what he had seen. He copied the massed phalanx of armed soldiers, which was a Theban military invention, and developed it in the Macedonian armies. It was this fighting phalanx, vastly superior to other contemporary military tactics, that made it possible for Philip's son Alexander to conquer the world.

Philip and his Macedonian army invaded Greece in 338 B.C. Athens and Thebes made in their desperation a united effort to retard his advance, but without success. Out of this came a congress of states at Corinth. Here the Greeks agreed to recognize Philip as the head of their country, in foreign affairs at least, although it was stipulated that the Greek states could retain their home governments. And Philip made himself commander-in-chief of the combined Greek and Macedonian armies.

Through the conquests of Alexander's armies, Greek civilization was to make its influence felt throughout the world. The Macedonians had much in common with the Greeks, and they carried on the civilization the Greeks had developed.

ALEXANDER THE GREAT

Philip II of Macedon was assassinated in 336 B.C. when his son Alexander was only twenty years old. It was not expected that so youthful a man could keep up control of his father's empire, and without delay there were revolts. Everyone knows how wrong these ideas were. Alexander quickly showed himself a commander. He was forceful, energetic, and he had inherited military genius. He put down rebellions, and in only a few years he became a world conqueror.

It was in 334 B.C. that Alexander made up his mind to avenge Greece against Persia. The series of marches that he began when he crossed the Hellespont causes military men to marvel even to this day. On several occasions his army of perhaps 35,000 trained soldiers met and vanquished armies of ten times that number. As his own veterans fell, he replaced them with new men whom he enlisted and trained.

With the defeat of the Persians at the battle of Issus (333 B.C.), the northern part of Asia Minor succumbed to Alexander. After the conquest of the Persian naval base at Tyre, Alexander led his victorious troops through Palestine into Egypt.

As conqueror, Alexander received a welcome from Egypt. He founded the city of Alexandria (named after himself) on the delta of the Nile, where the Greek dynasties of the Ptolemies would one day rule. There were other cities also called Alexandria which Alexander's cohorts would build throughout what had formerly been the Persian empire, and they would be controlling strongholds, both from the military and cultural standpoints. The seas of the eastern Mediterranean region were under Alexander's control by 332 B.C.

Alexander marched across the connecting isthmus and went up through Syria. He met Darius III and his army at Arbela, and in the third decisive battle the Persians were routed completely. Darius was assassinated, and Babylon, Susa, Ecbatana, and Persepolis surrendered. The Persian empire was now under the rule of Alexander the Great.

It seemed as though Alexander would never stop. He pushed his way eastward far into the Punjab region of northern India, to a point farther than had ever been penetrated by western armies. In this unaccustomed part of the world, however, the soldiers in Alexander's army became disheartened, and wanted to turn back homeward. So, after having extended his empire beyond the Indus River, Alexander proceeded northward and westward.

Babylon became the capital of his empire. The reign of Alexander was now nearly over. In 323 B.C., while planning expeditions against the Arabs, Carthage, and the Italian states, he suddenly sickened and died. He had crowded all this amazing activity into but thirty-three years.

THE HELLENISTIC AGE

The immediate result of Alexander's conquests was the fusion of the Greek civilization with that of the oriental world. In the wake of Alexander's armies followed Greek philosophers, scientists, architects, artists, colonists, merchants, and artisans. With Alexander the Great the history of Greece joins with the history of the oriental world. The Hellenic culture of classic Greece had declined, and when Greek influence spread widely throughout Alexander's empire, Greek culture entered a new and less characteristic phase, to which we give the name Hellenistic. The years 320 B.C. to 150 B.C. are generally referred to as the Hellenistic period.

As soon as Alexander died, his generals vied with one another for the privilege of succeeding him. He died at too early an age to have left an heir old enough to take his place. A self-centered man, he does not appear to have concerned himself with the thought of who was to be his successor.

From 323 to 280 B.C. were fought what are known as the Wars of the Succession. They were marked by blood and assassination. The various states and leagues into which, by about 280 B.C., the East was split up fought with one another, formed alliances, and engaged in commerce. The underlying culture of them all was that of ancient Greece. The Gauls, barbarians from northern Europe who a hundred years before had invaded and despoiled Rome, now in 278 B.C. swept down through Greece and across the Hellespont into Asia Minor. The barbarian hordes were resisted by monarchs everywhere until at last the Gauls decided to live in peace.

Both east and west, the world under Greek influence was in decline. By 220 B.C. Seleucus (whose ancestor Seleucus I had founded the city of Antioch) had made Syria an independent monarchy of importance. He spread Greek culture in the Alexandrian tradition, but rising princes of India checked Syria's eastern domination about 250 B.C., and there was a further check by the Parthians from the northeast.

Syria continued to be mighty until she was vanquished by Rome in 190 B.C. When Alexander died, Ptolemy, one of his generals, had seized the rule of Egypt and founded the dynasty of his name, and the power of Egypt, which extended over Cyprus and the Syrian coast, became great. The city of Alexandria grew to be a center of commerce and culture. Egypt declined in the later Ptolemaic dynasties and came finally under the domination of Rome. Like Greece, Macedonia had not been of much importance after Alexander settled in Babylon, but it retained military leadership until Rome conquered it in 146 B.C.

A federation of Greek states was formed between 280 and 222 B.C., all the members of which took equal part in the central government. This was called the Achaean League, and was a model for the federation of the United States of America. It was this federation that freed Athens from Macedonian control. Later the League became Macedonia's vassal, to punish Sparta. The war that ensued brought Sparta under Macedonian control, and for the first time in the history of that proud city, a foreign army invaded its precincts.

Hellenistic Athens and the splendid new cities of Alexandria, Antioch, Rhodes, and Pergamum (all in parts of the Mediterranean area away from Greece) were the intellectual centers of this period. There was considerable development in prose romance and pastoral poetry. Painting came into its own. In general, however, the Hellenistic period experienced a slow decline in the arts. The Greek genius for sculpture persisted in these times, and the famous Venus de Milo is thought by most critics, despite its perfection and classic proportions, to be Hellenistic. Other famous works more typical of this period were the Dying Gaul and Apollo Belvedere (both of which commemorated events in the Gallic invasion of 278 B.C.), and the Laocoön. For the most part, the artists of this period displayed a less imaginative and sometimes decadent naturalism that marked the decline of Greek art.

The philosophers of this age, though minor as compared with Plato and Aristotle, made important contributions. In Athens, Epicurus taught that happiness was the goal of life, but a happiness that was to be secured by temperance rather than sensual indulgence. Zeno, who taught from a *stoa* (porch), founded Stoicism, which emphasized virtue as the aim of life and looked upon happiness as incidental. Philosophy exerted a strong influence on the democratic politics of the whole Greek world.

The first universities were founded, and they were called museums, as they were pledged to the worship of the nine Muses, the goddesses who symbolized the arts. Rapid strides were made in the sciences. Euclid made great progress with the science of geometry. Archimedes of Syracuse invented the lever and discovered the facts of specific gravity. The knowledge of astronomy was developed by Eratosthenes, Aristarchus, and Hipparchus. That early wonder of the world, the lighthouse in the harbor of Alexandria, was constructed by Pharos.

This great activity of the Hellenistic world, especially in the sciences, may well be credited in considerable part to the tradition of imaginative and intellectual inquiry that had typified the Greeks from earliest times. They had accumulated in their brief history a vast fund of knowledge in all fields. For instance, it was Aristotle who nearly two thousand years before Columbus was born had affirmed that the earth was round and that one could reach the Orient by sailing westward.

THE STORY OF ROME

While great activity was astir in the eastern Mediterranean regions, a new power was arising in the area which we now know as Italy, the long boot-shaped peninsula which stretches southward into the Mediterranean to the west of Greece (separated from it by the Adriatic Sea). At the tip of the Italian peninsula and on the adjacent island of Sicily, roving Greeks had founded colonies, among them Syracuse and Tarentum. Greek colonies were also on the southern coast of what is now France, in Sardinia, and in Corsica. To the southwest of Italy, on the jutting coast of Africa, the Phoenicians had established Carthage, which was to become strong enough to war with rising Rome; and the Carthaginians had settled farther to the west on what is the southern coast of Spain.

The early history of the Italian peninsula is shrouded in obscurity. Before 1200 B.C. the inhabitants were dark-skinned tribes (perhaps Iberians), probably barbaric. Then, as happened in Greece and Asia Minor, Indo-European, Aryan-speaking tribes migrated from the north, and by 1000 B.C. had spread over Italy more than halfway to the tip. Their language formed the basis of several tongues, chief among them Latin, which was to be the speech of the later Romans. Then along came a dark race called Etruscans, whose origins are a mystery; perhaps they came from the eastern Aegean, having been driven out by invading tribes there.

For a time the Etruscans held the upper hand in northern and central Italy. They left many traces of their civilization—stone fortresses, metals, pottery. The Latins, on the southern bank of the Tiber, lived in comparative barbarism at this time. But they traded with the Etruscans at a point where Rome was to spread over its seven hills.

Later the Etruscans conquered the Latins, and their tyrants ruled Rome, by then a growing Latin city. The Tarquins were Etruscan monarchs. The Latins expelled the tyrants—probably about the sixth century B.C.—and Latin speech survived. The ensuing struggle between the Latins (Romans) and Etruscans provided Lord Macaulay with the episodes he narrates in *The Lays of Ancient Rome*. The Etruscans might have soundly whipped the presumptuous Romans, but the Greeks of Syracuse (in Sicily) wiped out the Etruscan fleet in 474 B.C. The weakened Etruscans suffered a significant defeat in 392 B.C. Meanwhile the barbaric Gauls from the north had invaded Italy, and they sacked Rome in 390 B.C.

The Romans paid a ransom for their city, and the Gauls, suffering from the Italian fever (malaria), departed northward. The Romans then rebuilt their city and set about conquering Italy, and by 290 B.C. Rome dominated central Italy from the Arno River to just south of Naples.

The Spartan city of Tarentum allied with Pyrrhus, king of Epirus, now decided to check Roman expansion. The Romans met the invading armies of Pyrrhus (equipped with elephants, new to the Romans), and were defeated at Heraclea in 280 B.C., and again at Ausculum a year later. Pyrrhus' losses, however, were so great that the term "Pyrrhic victory" has ever since denoted a victory at too high a cost, actually an "empty" victory. Making a truce with the Romans, Pyrrhus advanced toward Sicily across Greek territory in southern Italy. Carthage now became alarmed, and united herself with Rome to keep Pyrrhus out of Sicily. The alliance was successful; in 275 B.C. Pyrrhus retired to Epirus.

EARLY ROMAN DEVELOPMENT

Italy and Greece, geographically, stood back to back: Rome was on the western side of Italy, separated from the eastern shore by a north-and-south range of mountains. Thus, at first, Rome and Greece were out of touch with one another. (According to the famous *Aeneid* of the Roman poet Virgil, Rome was supposed to have been founded by the descendants of the vanquished Trojans, who were aided by the goddess Aphrodite.) Within Italy, around Rome, the land was congenial to settlement and to unified development, instead of being split up by geographical barriers as was Greece.

The seven hills about which Rome was built were at first the armed fortresses of rival tribes. As the tribes met in trade of friendly intercourse, on the lowlands between the hills, the most famous of which were the Palatine, Capitoline, and Quirinal, they developed common interests and gradually united. Etruscans drained the marshes and built some of the structures and the defensive wall of early Rome.

Roman citizens early became divided into an upper (aristocratic) and lower (common) class: the patricians at the top and the plebeians below. Both classes had citizenship, but foreigners did not. Early government included a king, a senate nominated from among the patricians, and the assembly of all patricians. At first the plebeians had no rights; early Roman history is a tale of their struggles for privileges. Because they were needed in war, the plebeians gained a voice in the government, but the upper class still dominated.

After the establishment of the republic in 509 B.C., the king's place was taken by two magistrates called consuls. They enjoyed equal prestige and authority. Unless both agreed, nothing could be done. They thus served as a check upon each other, as we have seen was the case with the two Spartan kings.

When the state was in grave danger and unity of action was needed, a dictator was appointed. The consuls gave up their authority to him and the people put their property and lives completely at his disposal. The dictator's term of office did not exceed six months, but during this time he had all the power formerly wielded by the kings.

Patrician land monopoly with its heavy taxes on plebeian farms impoverished the "plebs." This was perhaps the chief cause of the ensuing class struggle which raged internally in Rome from 510 to 367 B.C. The first triumph of the plebeians was their right to appoint tribunes, who were their representatives. A tribune, in person, could halt a magistrate in any official act by calling out, "Veto! (I forbid!),", whence came our word *veto*. This power of veto increased until the tribunes could bring the patrician government to a standstill at any time.

As the Greeks had done, the people now clamored for revision of the laws. Before 451 B.C. the Romans did not have written laws. They had simply unwritten laws, which, as in Athens before the time of Draco, were interpreted by patrician judges. The plebeians demanded that the customs be set down in writing—be made laws—so that everyone might know them and secure justice in the courts. The laws, which came to be known as the Twelve Tables, were engraved on twelve bronze tablets and set up in the Forum. They mark the beginning of Rome's legal system. About 445 B.C. the plebeians began to demand the right to be consuls; it took them almost ninety years to achieve this desire. Patricians tried to retain some privileges, but they finally accepted plebeian equality.

Meanwhile the Roman religion, inherited largely from the Etruscans, included a group of gods and goddesses who were later identified and fused with those of Greece. Thus, the chief deity of the Romans was called Jupiter, and inherited all the characteristics of the Greek Zeus. The other eleven Greek Olympians also became Roman deities with no change except in their names. Far less imaginative than the Greeks, the Romans developed no mythology of their own but merely took over the Greek legends. The pontiffs, augurs, and soothsayers were the "priests" of Roman religion. There were no oracles, but the will of the gods was sought in omens such as the flight of birds or the quivering entrails of freshly butchered animals.

Not only in religion but in the arts, and to a lesser extent in literature, the Romans followed Greek models, often imitating or copying them. Although there were exceptions, Rome's cultural and intellectual life was to an extraordinary degree borrowed from that of classical Greece.

After the expulsion of the Gauls, Rome set about unifying Italy under her leadership. There were minor wars with other tribes, and a Latin revolt, but Rome triumphed and, with a capacity to assimilate which Athens had lacked, Rome now developed the beginnings of empire and its rule. To consolidate Italy, Rome built magnificent roads which have survived to this day, the most famous being the Appian Way, named after the Appius Claudius who built it. He also built a twelve-mile aqueduct to bring pure water to Rome.

Between about 360 and 200 B.C., Roman life was at its finest. Greek influence had entered as a result of the conflict with Pyrrhus and relations with the Greek colonies of southern Italy. Rome adopted much of Greek culture; Greek teachers educated Roman youths. The Roman toga, a robe flung gracefully about the body, was the common masculine costume. Life was simple and stern, without many material comforts. The Roman ideal was to subordinate one's individuality to the welfare of the state.

This is well illustrated by the story of Curius, the conqueror of the Samnites. When approached by the envoys of the Samnites, offering rich bribes, he answered, "Go tell the Samnites that Curius counts it glory, not to possess wealth, but to rule those who do." Such men as these, despite their many faults, soon made the little city-state by the Tiber great among the nations. The history of Roman development is principally the history of a people, rather than of a few great men. Roman soldiers became a great fighting machine; the discipline of the legions hardened Roman men in the service of their country. Chariot races entertained the people; later, spectacles of the amphitheater contrasted brutally with the milder and more intellectual Greek theater.

Meanwhile, though the distinctions between patrician and plebeian were decreasing, the government was kept aristocratic by inherited powers and privileges. A newer common class arose, whose murmurs of discontent were to increase with the years. Great wealth was accumulated by the few, in contrast with an increasingly impoverished many. Government of the elite tended to be replaced by a senatorial oligarchy. All the while Rome flung herself afar in a world empire, but she was to decline and fall in her turn.

THE PUNIC WARS

Roman Italy was a republican country, and much in the same way Carthage was a republican city—in form. Carthaginian government was really in the hands of a few; it was an oligarchy.

It was almost fifty years after Alexander's death, when Rome had unified Italy and rivalry rose to the pitch of war between Rome and Carthage. Enmity arose first in Sicily, which had been divided for a long period between the Greeks and the Carthaginians. Carthage ruled northern Africa, collecting tribute and forcing the tribesmen to serve in her armies as mercenaries. Neither Carthage nor Rome wished to see the other dominate Sicily.

The First Punic War (the word *Punic* came from the Latin for "Phoenician"; Carthage was originally a Phoenician colony) lasted twenty-three years (264–241 B.C.). Carthage controlled about as many people as did Rome (roughly 5,000,000), but did not have the national unity of Roman Italy. Moreover, her allies did not especially like her. The early triumph of Carthage was due to her navy, for Rome had no navy until this war forced her to construct one and learn to use it. Rome then invaded Africa (256 B.C.) and laid unsuccessful siege to Carthage.

The famous Carthaginian general Hamilcar established himself in Sicily (247 B.C.), and with a small force held Roman armies back for six years. Rome lost her fleets, but patriotic citizens supplied funds to rebuild them. Thus Rome's loyal patriots risked even their personal fortunes for the good of the state. Finally they won a complete victory over the enemy. According to the terms of the treaty Carthage was forced to give up all claims to Sicily, and that island became a Roman province. Rome now became queen of the western Mediterranean, and Carthage had to retire from the war, suing for peace and paying a heavy indemnity to Rome.

The peace was no more than an armed truce. Twenty-three years elapsed before the Second Punic War. Meanwhile Carthage had troubles at home. Her mercenaries revolted, and African (Berber) tribes followed suit. The Carthaginian islands of Sardinia and Corsica, to the west of Italy, rebelled and offered allegiance to Rome, which was accepted. Rome extended her dominions by provincial government northeast of Rome into Cisalpine Gaul, which extended south and west of the Alps into northern Italy. (*Cisalpine* Gaul means Gaul *this side of the Alps.*) Self-government was no longer accorded to conquered peoples.

At the beginning of the Second Punic War (218 B.C.), Rome controlled all Italy from the foothills of the Alps southward, all Sicily, Sardinia, and Corsica. Carthage ruled southern Spain and northern Africa. Hamilcar had put down the revolts, and Carthage, resenting Rome's acquisition of Sardinia and Corsica, began to seek revenge by conquering Spanish (Iberian) tribes. In 220 B.C. the death of Hamilcar left the command in the capable hands of his son Hannibal, a youth of twenty-six, whom his father had trained much as Philip of Macedon trained Alexander. Hannibal had sworn eternal enmity to Rome. The genius of this young commander colors the Second Punic War.

When Hannibal laid siege to Saguntum, an old Greek colony in Spain, Rome declared war on Carthage (218 B.C.). Rome set out to take the offensive, but Hannibal accomplished one of the most amazing feats of military history. He led his army northeastward, just inside the coast, fought through Gallic tribes, braved the hardships of crossing the Alps, and appeared in Cisalpine Gaul with the remnant of his forces, a fourth of the number who had begun the march—about 26,000 brave shadows of soldiers. Nevertheless, wasted and worn though they were, these men under Hannibal quickly shattered two Roman armies, and annihilated a

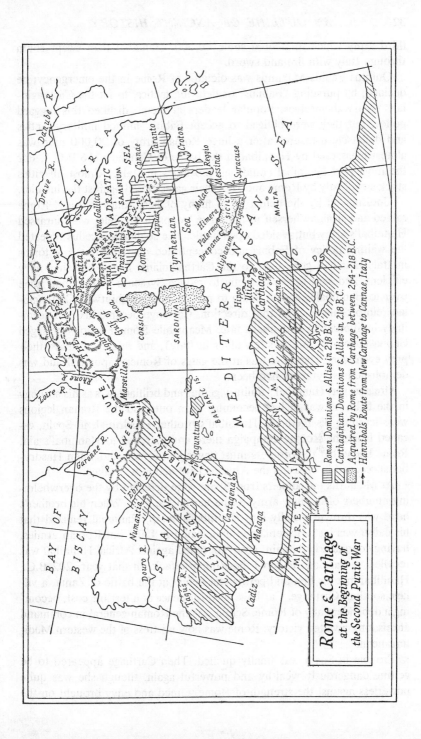

Rome & Carthage
at the Beginning of
the Second Punic War

||||| Roman Dominions & Allies in 218 B.C.
//// Carthaginian Dominions & Allies in 218 B.C.
Acquired by Rome from Carthage between 264-218 B.C.
· · · Hannibal's Route from New Carthage to Cannae, Italy

third army which numbered some 40,000. Hannibal then swept south through Italy with fire and sword.

Quintus Fabius Maximus was dictator of Rome in the emergency; he decided, by pursuing "Fabian" or delaying tactics, to let the Carthaginians weary themselves. Popular leaders at Rome disliked this laggard policy, but they were obliged to accept Fabius' limited military tactics and defensive measures after a huge Roman army of 90,000 men was almost massacred by Hannibal in the battle of Cannae (216 B.C.). For the most part Hannibal could gain no allies in Italy. Almost all cities stuck steadfastly by Rome and kept their gates closed against the invader.

Undismayed by the defeat of so many of her armies in Italy, Rome rallied and strained herself to put more troops in the field, who harassed Hannibal's army but avoided open battle. The soldier Marcellus repeated the waiting policy of Fabius and concentrated on punishing any towns in Italy that had gone over to the Carthaginians. Rome kept her navy efficient, and sent forces to Sicily to reduce Syracuse (which had gone over to Hannibal), and to Spain to prevent the possibility of Carthaginian reinforcements from that direction. Carthage became lax and seemingly indifferent to Hannibal's fate. Meanwhile Roman legions besieged Capua (one of Hannibal's few allies in Italy), and refused to leave their prey even when Hannibal was at the gates of Rome. Capua fell and was demolished as Syracuse had been.

Great as was Hannibal's military genius and brilliant as was his strategy in the field, he was at last becoming worn out—and the Roman legions were learning his methods. Hannibal's brother Hasdrubal, in Spain, escaped from the Roman campaign there and marched to Hannibal's aid. Rome knew that the brothers must never join forces, and when Hasdrubal succeeded in crossing the Alps decisive action was taken.

At Metaurus the soldiers from Spain were defeated by the overwhelming numbers of the new army Rome had in the field. When his brother's head was thrown brutally into Hannibal's camp, Hannibal realized that his cause was lost. He remained undefeated in Italy, but Roman armies, having conquered all Spain, now proceeded against Africa. Hannibal was recalled to Carthage to repel the Roman attack. In that year, 202 B.C., Hannibal met his first and permanent defeat at the battle of Zama, a village south of Carthage. Carthage sued for peace at a terrible cost, becoming a dependent ally of Rome. Scipio was the Roman general in command at this long-awaited victory. Rome was now mistress of the western Mediterranean.

Trouble in Spain was finally quelled. Then Carthage appeared to be getting dangerously wealthy and powerful again, though she was quite powerless against the strength of Rome. Greed and envy brought on the

Third Punic War. Cato the Elder summarized the purpose of the Third Punic War when he included in numerous speeches before the Senate his famous phrase, *"Delenda est Carthago!"* Carthage must be destroyed!

Rome's excuse for war was that Carthage had taken up arms in defense of an encroaching African prince; it was self-defense, and Rome had encouraged the African prince, but according to her treaty Carthage might not make war without Rome's consent. So Rome attacked, first treacherously disarming Carthage with the apparent purpose of punishing her without war. When the Carthaginians saw that the Roman legions were going to raze their city, they flew into a feverish activity of defense, and Carthage withstood a Roman siege for four years! But Rome triumphed and Carthage vanished from history (146 B.C.).

At the beginning of the Punic Wars, in 264 B.C., Rome had shared world power with the successors of Alexander's empire; by 146 B.C., at the razing of Carthage, Rome was the *only power* (imperial or military) in the Mediterranean world. While the Punic Wars were raging, Roman legions and Roman representatives had been busy in the East. Reluctant to invade Greece, Rome had nevertheless been drawn into Macedonian wars. At first Rome established protectorates, merely offering beneficent protection to Greece and adjacent states. But Roman greed grew; nobles became lustful for power, and merchants wanted wider and richer trade. Abandoning protectorates, Rome put provinces under direct administration. The Roman *empire* was materializing, so that by 146 B.C. Roman dominions included all Spain, northern Africa, Italy and adjacent islands, Macedonia, and Greece. Western Asia, including Syria, was a Roman dependency. The onward sweep of Roman power was ruthless: the ancient Greek city of Corinth was laid waste with such thoroughness that few of her art treasures have survived.

INTERNAL STRIFE

From 146 to 49 B.C. Roman history is a welter of class wars and conflicts within the republic: a chaos of oppression, wealthy aristocracy run to seed, attempts at reform, street brawls, impoverished farmers, slavery, abuses of governors of provinces, revolts, barbarian invasions, and the gradual rise of individuals to dictatorial military power, culminating in the colossal Roman empire of Julius Caesar and his successors.

Rome's senatorial oligarchy had waged successful wars, but it never learned how to govern the new peoples and territories embraced within the arms of the republic. It forgot or made light of the danger of barbarian invasion on the frontiers. Pirates roamed unmolested on the seas. At home, untold wealth in the hands of nobles, politicians, and merchants resulted in sensual splendor: fine houses had marvelous fountains and baths, and were adorned with art treasures pillaged from conquered Greek cities, while the poor lived in squalor and filth. Mammon ran riot in Rome. The government was exploited by "millionaires" who "profiteered." Trade monopolies and trusts developed. In this period the gladiatorial games in the arena became popular—fights to the death between armed men and fights with savage beasts. Such spectacles were often given by rich usurpers of power to bribe the people.

The lack of representative government hampered politics. Assembly and senate weakened in their ability to administer the needs of the unwieldy republic. Subjects, natives of conquered states, outnumbered Roman citizens, who insolently held their "inferiors" with their noses to many sorts of grindstones. The practice of "tax farming" was characteristic of the period—Rome sold the right to collect taxes (from dependencies) to the highest bidder, who made what profit he could for himself in the transaction. Corrupt governors were seldom called to account for gross misdeeds. Slavery became a crying evil. Captive and conquered peoples were sold into harsh labor and made to sweat in shackles. A slave could have only two activities: working and sleeping, with no more than necessary of the latter. Slavery and cheap foreign grain had completed the ruin of Italian farmers, whose holdings had been laid waste by the ravages of war—such as Hannibal's raids in the peninsula—and later confiscated by the wealthy.

The warrior Marius and his lieutenant Sulla appeared momentarily (106–78 B.C.) to dominate the scene with military rule. A group of Italian cities, discontented with their share of the imperial prosperity, allied to form a republic of their own and revolted against Rome. From 91 to 88 B.C. the revolt was suppressed, largely by the efforts of Sulla. Sulla now commanded a large army and was appointed by the Senate to put down a revolt in the East. However, the plebeians and equestrians (a new class of wealthy businessmen) opposed the Senate and appointed Marius to the same post. Sulla marched his army against Rome, Marius fled, and the city fell to Sulla's military control in 88 B.C. Then he had to rush to the East, where the Roman dominions were crumbling before the onslaught of Mithridates, king of Pontus, who appeared to the inhabitants of Greece as their savior from Roman tyranny. When Sulla came back, having restored Roman authority in the East, he was made dictator of Rome in 81 B.C. The democratic party was massacred and the oligarchic senate was restored. Sulla soon abdicated and died in debauchery.

Who should now become master of Italy? Pompey, one of Sulla's officers, got himself sent to Spain to subdue Sertorius, a democratic governor whom Sulla's officers had not been able to conquer. This gave Pompey an indefinite term as commander of the army, and almost unlimited powers. He reduced Spain, and returned to Italy in triumph in 71 B.C. The democrats had regained power in 83 B.C., and now saw fit to appoint as consuls Pompey and Crassus, a rival general—for their armies were encamped at the gates of Rome!

After conquering Sicilian pirates, and again subduing Mithridates and other rebellious peoples, by 62 B.C. Pompey was the greatest man in the Roman world. He dragged hundreds of abject princes, whom he had conquered, behind his chariot as he paraded in Rome. Meanwhile, Cato, a young aristocrat, supported the oligarchic republic, and Cicero, the famous orator, shifted from radical democrat to conservative aristocrat. Cicero, as consul in 63 B.C., crushed the conspiracy of Catiline, a profligate democrat, who planned to murder the rulers and seize the property of the rich. This temporarily nipped in the bud the rising championship of the democrats by Julius Caesar, whose career was eclipsed for a time by Pompey's return.

The senate now turned somewhat against Pompey. Caesar, meanwhile governor of Spain, united with Pompey and Crassus in a triple dictatorship or *triumvirate*. Caesar, elected consul in 59 B.C., quickly became the first man of Rome. For the next ten years he carried on his famous campaigns in Gaul, extending the Roman dominion to the Rhine and even into Britain. Pompey was ruling Spain, but lived (illegally) in Rome; Crassus went to Asia (where he was killed in the war), but soon Pompey was sole consul, and the fight between Pompey and Caesar for supremacy was at hand. Caesar, waiting with his victorious soldiers outside Rome, wished to be re-elected consul; instead, the senate ordered him to disband his army. One result was inevitable: civil war.

THE FOUNDING OF THE ROMAN EMPIRE

Great numbers of Roman citizens were corrupt. Barbarians threatened the frontiers. Only a monarchy, it seemed, could save the Roman dominions, provided that the monarch was the right man. Monarchy would result if this one man could be both consul in the field and tribune at Rome. Caesar was destined to fill that office: he crossed the Rubicon, the stream which separated his Gallic province from Italy, with one legion of devoted soldiery. As he crossed the Rubicon, Caesar in an order of the day to his troops made his famous statement, "The die is cast."

Pompey, slow-minded, failed to meet Caesar successfully, and in two months Caesar was master of Italy. In three months, now with military power enough, Caesar routed Pompey's lieutenants from Spain. He followed Pompey into Greece, and in the decisive battle of Pharsalus, in Thessaly, became master of the Roman world. Then followed further consolidating campaigns in Egypt and in Asia; Caesar summed up his victory in the historic words: "I came, I saw, I conquered." Caesar crushed Cato at Thapsus in Africa. Wherever opposition arose, he quelled it.

The end of the civil war resulted in the death of Pompey and the overthrow of the senatorial party, and the complete supremacy of Caesar. He returned to Rome to receive from the servile senate the title of "Father of his country" (*Pater Patriae*) and to enjoy the power his military genius had won.

Italy soon became reconciled to the imperial government of Caesar—for it was imperial though the old republican forms remained. He was a generous-minded ruler, bent on giving all provinces equal rights and all peoples Roman citizenship. His good deeds were many: he rebuilt many a wasted land; he fed the poor; he made reforms in law, reduced taxes, started a census, founded a library, reformed the calendar. Caesar was granted the title of Imperator (meaning "commander" and origin of the title Emperor); and his rule was essentially a dictatorship.

Conspiracy dogged Caesar's footsteps. Cassius and Brutus, the one envious and the other a democratic enthusiast lacking in imagination, planned Caesar's death, and consummated it in the notorious assassination in the senate house, in March, 44 B.C. The assassins, of whom Cassius and Brutus were the ringleaders, expected to be hailed as liberators. But the populace was suspicious, and the funeral oration of Marcus Antonius (Mark Antony) over Caesar's body roused the people to such fury that the assassins had to flee from Rome. Mark Antony and Octavius Caesar (grandnephew and adopted son of Caesar) united their forces, and took in with them Lepidus, governor of Spain and Gaul, forming the second triumvirate, in 43 B.C. The merciful policy of Julius Caesar was abandoned and Rome again was torn by civil war.

Brutus and Cassius rallied the former forces of Pompey in the East, recruiting troops from distant Parthia, Armenia, Media, Pontus, and Thrace. Octavius and Antony met and crushed them at the battle of Philippi in Macedonia (42 B.C.). The two generals now ousted Lepidus and divided the Roman world between them. Antony got the East, and fell an easy victim to the wiles of Cleopatra in Egypt, where he dallied. Octavius championed the Roman cause and met and defeated Antony in the naval battle of Actium, off the coast of Greece, in 31 B.C.

Octavius returned triumphant to Rome, in 29 B.C., where he ruled as sole dictator. Although he declared the republic restored, Rome was now really an empire with Octavius at its head. He was Imperator, received the name Augustus, and inaugurated a useful reign. Augustus, as he was thenceforth known, scorned the pomp of monarchy and lived simply. Internal organization resembled that of a modern state. Augustus established a happy tradition his successors were to follow—for a while. Architecture reached new heights. His age was a golden or "Augustan Age" in Roman history. He ruled until his death in 14 A.D. (From this point, dates on our calendar change to A.D.—after the birth of Christ.)

THE ROMAN EMPIRE

A great emphasis is placed on this period by historians, because so much of what characterized the empire influenced later European history. (Notice how the name *Caesar,* as an imperial title, runs through later history in such related words as *kaiser, tsar, czar.*)

In this period a system of hereditary succession was established, although the power of the army could always win the support of the senate and the succession be diverted, or an Imperator challenged. Tiberius, stepson of Augustus, succeeded as Imperator, and reigned from 14 to 37 A.D. The grandnephew of Tiberius, Caligula, succeeded him, reigning from 37 to 41 A.D.; Caligula was mad, extravagant, foolish, and tyrannical. Officers of his guard slew him. The praetorians (city magistrates) set up Claudius, uncle of Caligula, whose power lasted from 41 to 54 A.D. He extended citizenship, protected slaves, and conquered southern Britain for Rome. Nero, emperor from 54 to 68 A.D., was stepson to Claudius. He was an egotistical devotee of art and music, restrained at first by his mentor, the philosopher Seneca. In later years of his reign, when Rome was laid in ashes by a great fire, he watched—dancing and reciting poetry.

Flavius Vespasianus (Vespasian), who ruled from 70 to 79 A.D., rectified much of the confusion Nero had caused. He constructed many public works, including the famed Colosseum. His reign inaugurated an era of peace.

When Vespasian was called to the throne, he was in Judea putting down a rebellion. The region had been made tributary to Rome by Pompey in 63 B.C., and was ruled by Herod the Great from 40 B.C. to 4 A.D. Vespasian left his son, Titus, in command of the Roman forces. It was Titus who in 70 A.D. entered Jerusalem, razed the city, and dispersed the Jews. At about this time the Romans began to look upon the new religious sect known as Christians as politically suspect. The first persecution of Christians occurred near the end of Nero's reign.

During the reign of Titus (79–81 A.D.) Pompeii and Herculaneum were buried by an eruption of the volcano Vesuvius. Domitian, a younger brother of Titus and last of the Flavian emperors, ruled from 81 to 96 A.D. During this time the conquest of Britain was completed by Agricola, Domitian's general, who governed the province ably for seven years and was then recalled by the jealous emperor. Domitian had assumed new monarchial powers at Rome, and had the senate under his thumb. He ruled harshly and was assassinated. In his reign was the second persecution of the growing group of Christians.

The senate chose the next emperor from among themselves, establishing the line of Antonine Caesars. Of these, Trajan (98–117) extended the boundaries of the Roman Empire beyond the Euphrates and to the north of the Danube. Magnificent Roman roads were constructed through Britain, central Europe, the Mediterranean basin, and Asia. The Roman Empire now included practically all the known western world: it extended from the Persian Gulf to the North Sea (including Britain), taking in all the shores and the islands of the Mediterranean Sea, all Spain, all Gaul, all Italy, all Greece, all western Asia, and all Egypt. Hadrian (117–138) ruled wisely and well. Marcus Aurelius Antoninus (161–180) was both emperor and the philosopher-author of the famous *Meditations*. Barbarian uprisings became more violent; a plague swept through the Roman world. The Christians, unpopular because they would not honor the Roman gods, were again persecuted.

ROMAN LIFE AND THOUGHT

The first two hundred years of the empire were characterized by general peace. Travel became popular *within* the empire (there was almost no exploration beyond the frontiers), partly because one language could be heard from Britain to Babylonia. Commerce extended to few regions beyond the empire.

In architecture, famous structures were the Pantheon, Colosseum, and Trajan's column at Rome. Roman architecture was largely imitative of Greek models, though often more grandiose and lacking the Greek balance and refinement of adornment. However, it is important to note that the barrel vault, a highly significant engineering achievement, which permitted the construction of arched edifices, was invented by the Romans. In sculpture, the Romans were good realistic portraitists.

Famous names in Roman literature included: among the poets, Virgil, Horace, Ovid, Catullus, Lucretius, Lucan, and Martial; the dramatists, Plautus, Terence, and Seneca; the historians, Caesar, Livy, Tacitus, Plutarch (who, though he belongs to this period, and probably lived at Rome, was a Greek and wrote in Greek); philosophers and orators, Cicero, Marcus Aurelius, Epictetus, and Pliny the Younger; the natural-

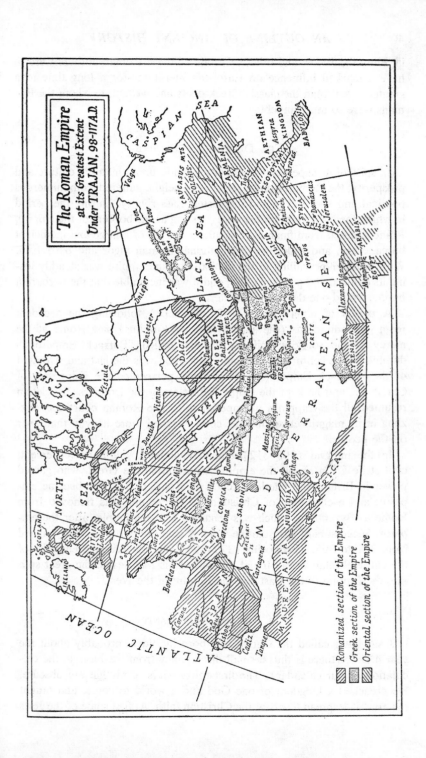

The Roman Empire at its Greatest Extent Under TRAJAN, 98-117 A.D.

CASPIAN SEA

Volga
Don
SEA OF AZOV
CAUCASUS MTS
COLCHIS
ARMENIA
Tigris
MESOPOTAMIA
ASSYRIA
PARTHIAN KINGDOM
BABYLONIA
Euphrates
SYRIA
Damascus
Antioch
PALESTINE
Jerusalem
ARABIA
CILICIA
CYPRUS
EGYPT
Memphis
Alexandria
CYRENAICA

BLACK SEA
Constantinople
THRACE
Smyrna
Rhodes
CRETE
Athens
Sparta
GREECE
Corinth
MEDITERRANEAN SEA

Dnieper
Dniester
Vistula
BALTIC SEA
DACIA
Danube
MOESIA
Balkan Mts
ILLYRIA
Vienna
Danube

NORTH SEA
Elbe
Weser
Mains
Cologne
Reims
ROMAN
Paris
Tours
GAUL
Lyons
Geneva
Marseilles
CORSICA
SARDINIA
ITALY
Rome
Naples
Brindisi
Messina
SICILY
Syracuse
Belgium
Carthage
NUMIDIA
MAURETANIA
AFRICA

ATLANTIC OCEAN
SCOTLAND
IRELAND
BRITAIN
York
London
SPAIN
Bordeaux
Coronne
PYRENEES MTS
Barcelona
Cartagena
BALEARIC IS
Lisbon
Cadiz
Tangier
Douro
Tagus

Romanized section of the Empire
Greek section of the Empire
Oriental section of the Empire

ist Pliny the Elder; and others. Certain of these Roman authors were to have a marked influence on European literature—for a long time to a greater extent than the classic Greek poets and writers, to whom the Romans were so much indebted.

THE DECLINE OF EMPIRE

In spite of its superficial splendor and widespread material culture and prosperity, the Roman Empire, even at its height, suffered from numerous political and social evils and increasing class rivalry. During the period in which the barbarian hordes were pressing at the borders of the empire, Rome suffered from financial difficulties, the ills of a large and inefficient bureaucracy, and a decline of traditional Roman vigor and patriotism. With disorder prevailing in the capital city, the empire was steadily losing its cultural and political unity; and it was inevitable that the barbarian hordes would one day bring disaster.

A period of ninety years (193–284 A.D.) following the decadent reign of Commodius (the son of Marcus Aurelius) saw Rome at the mercy of the soldiery; military leaders, called "Barrack Emperors," dominated the century. Diocletian (284–305) was the last and strongest of the "Barrack Emperors." He severely persecuted the rising sect of Christians, and he kept the empire intact along the frontiers. Diocletian resumed all the trappings of imperial rule. The Roman court was dazzling in its magnificence, and the costs weighed more heavily than ever on the people.

In the interval (305–312) after Diocletian's voluntary retirement, civil strife again shook the empire. Constantine the Great, who gained power in Britain and Gaul, marched on Rome in 312. He became emperor, and a champion of Christianity. The capital was removed from Rome to Byzantium, which was renamed Constantinople, after the emperor. Successors of Constantine were of small importance; they reigned from 337 to 395. Theodosius (379–395) was the last sole emperor of the entire Roman world, for at the end of his reign came the great split into the Empire of the East and the Empire of the West.

THE RISE OF CHRISTIANITY

Jesus, later called the Christ, was born in Judea, probably about the year 4 B.C. (there is thus a small discrepancy from the basis in the calculation of our calendar). The first thirty years of his life are obscure. He preached a kingdom of one God and a world to come, and taught the now widespread tenets of the Christian faith. At first some of the Jews followed him, hoping that he might be a Messiah who would free them from the tyranny of Rome. In Judea there were many factions which were frequently in conflict with one another because of their different points of view, yet all of them agreed in their opposition to Roman domination. It was in this complex setting that Jesus was accused of plotting against Rome, was declared guilty, and was crucified.

Paul of Tarsus became a convert to Christianity and traveled about the empire preaching its gospel. At first Christianity spread chiefly among slaves and the lower oppressed classes, who found in it a release from their burdens. The Christians, opposing the established religions as they did, aroused suspicion everywhere. Their secret meetings were annoying to the Romans. They were often persecuted, but under Constantine they were tolerated. Christianity gained new converts slowly but surely, founding one of the greatest religions in the history of the world.

THE TEUTONS AND THE FALL OF ROME

The Roman Empire was in decline. Many Germanic tribes, partly by conquest and partly by tolerated and peaceful invasion, filtered into the Roman world and settled on the outer borders of the empire. They adopted and assimilated much that was Roman, while retaining to a great extent their Germanic heritage. The Germanic tribes (Goths, Franks, Alemanni, Vandals, Angles, Jutes, Saxons, Lombards, etc.) and other nomadic tribes farther to the west were astir. Although the name Teuton originally referred to a particular Germanic tribe, it has come to be applied to all the Germanic peoples.

Alaric, first important chieftain of the Goths, invaded Greece while the grave of the emperor Theodosius was still fresh. Alaric, temporarily recognized by Rome, watched his chance for further gains. In 402 A.D. he began his advance toward the city which had so long been the head of the empire; and in 410 he and his Gothic hosts sacked Rome. The Vandals, who had seized Spain, were widely destructive—hence our word *vandalism*. In 455, after ravaging the Mediterranean region, they invaded and sacked Rome. The great city that had withstood even the mighty army of Carthage had finally fallen. The Franks, who were to give their name to France, invaded northern Gaul. The Angles, who were to give their name to England, invaded Britain, together with the Jutes and Saxons. Farther to the south and east, eastern Slavic tribes were pushed westward by Huns, Tatars, Finns and Avars—as perhaps the Teutons were to some extent.

The Huns, under the notorious Attila, came from the steppes of Asia, menacing Roman and Teuton alike with destruction. All southwestern

Europe rallied in common defense; Theodoric, king of the Visigoths (West Goths) in Spain, united with Aetius, one of the last Roman generals (himself of barbaric descent). The Huns were stopped in 451 A.D. at the terrible battle of Châlons in northern France. Attila turned southeast and pounced on Rome, but Pope Leo, it is said, persuaded him to spare the city.

Now all the Empire of the West was abandoned to Teutons except Italy. At the new capital of Ravenna, the last line of the western emperors came to an end when Romulus Augustulus was deposed in 476 A.D.

Italy became a province of the Empire of the East, where, after Constantine, the last semblance of the Roman Empire struggled along with its capital at Constantinople. But in the East it was Hellenistic and not Roman culture that survived.

DEVELOPMENTS IN ASIA

Although there was so very little contact between Europe and the Far East during these early centuries, it is important for the reader to realize that, almost simultaneously with the rise of civilization along the Tigris and Euphrates and along the Nile, great and distinctive civilizations were developing in India and China.

In the valley of the Ganges in India, Dravidian peoples were settled, and their communities were not advanced far when Aryan-speaking tribes from the north conquered them—at about the time that Hammurabi was ruling Babylonia. The history of India was for some time largely a succession of wars and jealous kings.

About the middle of the sixth century B.C. the great thinker and religious teacher, Siddhartha Gautama, was born in India. His followers called him the Buddha (the enlightened one); and after his death (in 483 B.C.) he was worshiped as divine. He established Buddhism as one of the great and influential religions of Asiatic civilization.

In 321 B.C. an adventurer by the name of Chandragupta conquered the Ganges region, and in 303 B.C. he waged successful war against Seleucus I of Syria who had conquered Persia. Chandragupta advanced the spread of Buddhism. His grandson was the great Asoka, "king of kings," who ruled India from 264 to 227 B.C. Asoka established Buddhist monasteries and encouraged extensive missionary work. Asoka's contributions to the civilization of India were outstanding, and his name is revered by millions.

In China the earliest civilization grew up along the Hwang-ho and the Yangtze Kiang, two great rivers flowing through the eastern bulge of

Asia. The origin of the Chinese people has not been determined, but doubtless several stocks amalgamated during their early history. The use of iron came quite late into China, probably not before 500 B.C.

Not much is known about the early history of China, during which the country was ruled by a succession of dynasties of varying duration. Among these were the Shang dynasty, which lasted approximately from 1750 to 1125 B.C., and the Chou dynasty, which lasted approximately from 1125 to 250 B.C. During these dynasties China remained divided into many petty city-states with their own hereditary princes. Warfare between the city-states was frequent, and a period of general anarchy preceded the downfall of the Chou dynasty. At this time, the Ts'in dynasty was established; and during the reign of Shi Hwang-ti, China was to a large extent united under an effective central government. Shi Hwang-ti greatly expanded his empire, and divided it into provinces with separate governors responsible to himself. This ruler also built the historic Great Wall of China, as a protection against barbarians, who particularly from the north and west had been raiding the Chinese from earliest times. (These barbarians were of the same racial group as the Tatars, Huns, and Avars.) Civil war again broke out in China, and brought the Ts'in dynasty to an end. The victor in the new strife was able to reunite the country; the Han dynasty was established and ruled China, with one interruption, into the era in which Christianity was spreading through the Roman world. During this period the Chinese empire grew, the barbarians were completely stopped, and westward expansion brought the first contacts with peoples of other lands. By around 100 B.C. caravan trade was being carried on with Persia.

In the sixth century B.C., during the long Chou dynasty, the Chinese philosopher Lao-tse wrote and taught about "Tao" (the way), which gives the name of his philosophy, Taoism, which had many followers in ancient China. It was also in the sixth century B.C. that the renowned Confucius lived and taught. During his life he attracted numerous disciples and his fame as a teacher spread widely. His personality and his moral teachings had a profound and lasting influence on the development of Chinese character. He founded no formal religion, but his ethical thought permeated the great mass of Chinese people and has survived to the present age. The Buddhist religion, which was introduced from India, gained a very large following in China.

In southeastern Asia and other parts of the Far East, a number of independent civilizations developed, and remained more or less distinct from those of China and India; yet we have little to indicate whether in ancient times any of these achieved great importance culturally or politically. It is interesting to note that once upon a time there was a fertile river bed of the Tarim River in the region west of the Gobi Desert. Archaeological remains indicate that a small civilization grew up in this area and later disappeared. Remains of several other very early settlements have been found in the region of the Gobi, and there may be some grounds for asserting that the very earliest culture was here.

EXAMINATION QUESTIONS

1. When was man prehistoric?
2. What is the Stone Age?
3. What was the sole means of communication in ancient times?
4. What was the approximate date of the beginning of Egyptian history?
5. Who built the pyramids of Egypt and for what use?
6. Who was Cleopatra?
7. How did the written records of the Sumerians differ from those of the Egyptians?
8. What Assyrian was called the "law giver"?
9. Where did our most frequently used numerals originate?
10. For what were the Phoenicians chiefly famed?
11. What three forms of government were successively used in ancient Greece?
12. What is the first exact date in Greek history?
13. What were the Olympiads?
14. Over what empire did Tiglath-pileser I rule?
15. Who were helots?
16. What great ruler reformed the Athenian government by devising new and juster laws?
17. Where did the poetess Sappho live?
18. What were the Athenian hoplites?
19. Who was Phidippides?
20. In attempting to defend what narrow pass did 300 Spartans die?
21. For what was Pericles noted?
22. Who wrought or directed the sculptures on the Parthenon at Athens?
23. Who was the originator of the "Socratic method" and what was it?
24. What conflict brought about the downfall of Athens?
25. What great monarch conquered Greece in 338 B.C.?
26. What was the name of the son of Philip II of Macedon?
27. What city in Egypt did Alexander the Great found?
28. How far eastward did Alexander and his armies go?
29. Who founded the dynasty of the Ptolemies in Egypt?
30. From what earlier civilization did Rome derive its religion and a large part of its culture?
31. How long did the First Punic War last?
32. What was Rome's status at the time of the razing of Carthage?
33. What did Roman dominions include by 146 B.C.?
34. What was "tax farming" as practiced by the Romans?
35. Who, during the first century B.C., dragged hundreds of princes, whom he had conquered, behind his chariot as he paraded in Rome?

36. When did Julius Caesar become consul?

37. At what decisive battle did Caesar become master of the Roman world?

38. How did Caesar meet his death?

39. How did the emperor Caligula come to an end?

40. What Roman emperor danced and recited poetry while Rome was burning?

41. In the reign of what Roman emperor was Jerusalem destroyed?

42. When were Pompeii and Herculaneum destroyed by an eruption of Mount Vesuvius?

43. Why were the Christians unpopular in Rome?

44. What highly significant engineering achievement did the Romans contribute to architecture?

45. Who was the last Roman emperor of the entire Roman world?

46. What Roman emperor supported the Christians?

47. Who sacked Rome in 410 A.D.?

48. Where did Attila and the Huns come from?

49. Who established Buddhism?

50. Who was the builder of the Great Wall of China?

FOR FURTHER STUDY

ANCIENT TIMES, by James Henry Breasted. (Ginn & Co., Boston, Mass.)

DAILY LIFE IN ANCIENT ROME, by Jerome Carcopino. (Yale University Press, New York.)

EVERYDAY LIFE IN THE OLD STONE AGE, by Marjorie and Charles Quennell. (G. P. Putnam's Sons, New York.)

HELLENIC HISTORY, by George Willis Botsford and Charles Alexander Robinson, Jr. (The Macmillan Co., New York.)

HISTORY OF THE ANCIENT WORLD, by M. I. Rostovtsev. (Oxford University Press, New York.)

HISTORY OF EGYPT, by James Henry Breasted. (Charles Scribner's Sons, New York.)

HISTORY OF GREECE, by George Grote. (Everyman's Library, E. P. Dutton & Co., New York.)

HISTORY OF ROME TO 565 A.D., by Arthur Boak. (The Macmillan Co., New York.)

WORLD HISTORY AT A GLANCE, by Joseph Reither. (Barnes & Noble, New York.)

II

An Outline of Medieval History

THE MIDDLE AGES

ANCIENT HISTORY "ended" in 476 A.D. with the deposition of Romulus Augustulus, the last of the Roman emperors (a boy king who was exiled to Naples and there disappeared from history). Although we look upon this date as marking a major transition in European history, it is only when the past is seen in the perspective of centuries that changes seem sharp and sudden. Life no doubt went on in much the same manner as before: farmers plowed their land; slaves sweated at their labor; people of wealth ate, drank, and made merry much as usual.

The Middle Ages is the name generally given to the period commencing in the fifth century (fall of Rome) and ending in the fifteenth century, or somewhat earlier in some parts of Europe. The history of these centuries is called *medieval* (from Latin words meaning "middle age"). With the conquests of the barbarians, the Roman Empire was reduced to the Empire of the East, under the sway of the emperors in Constantinople, and western Europe passed into an intellectual decline known as the Dark Ages. The Germanic tribes, though they were semi-civilized, did not carry on the Roman civilization as the Romans had the Greek. They allowed many Roman public works, such as aqueducts, bridges, and baths, to fall into disrepair and ruin. Trade and commerce lapsed. Schools, universities, and libraries, and with them most forms of education, disappeared for a time. The barbarian kingdoms were without any previous civilization of their own to cherish and maintain. Yet they were vigorous. Also it must be realized that inevitably during the many years of conflict with and exposure to the Romans, the Germanic tribes—especially those who settled in southern Europe—adopted many features of Roman life; several aspects of Roman law, the Latin language, and other Latin traditions strongly influenced later European cultures. The barbarians adopted

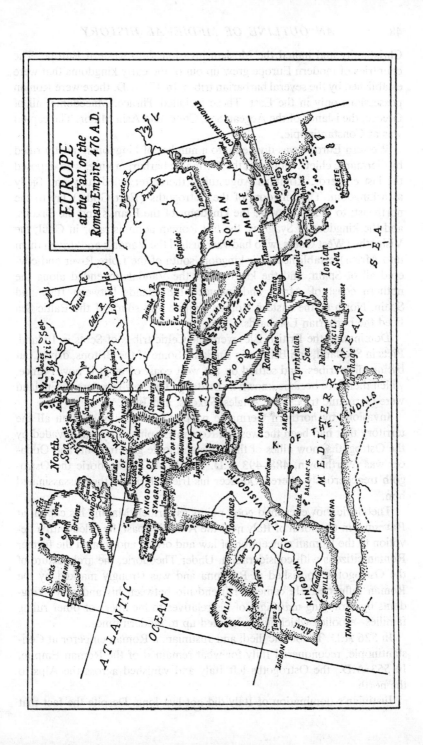

EUROPE
at the Fall of the
Roman Empire 476 A.D.

Christianity and halted the Moslem invasions into western Europe. The countries of modern Europe grew up out of the early kingdoms that were established by the several barbarian tribes. In 476 A.D. there were Roman possessions only in the East. These included Thrace, Macedonia, all of Greece, the islands of the Aegean Sea, Crete, and Asia Minor. The capital was at Constantinople.

Western Europe was divided into a number of kingdoms, mostly ruled by Germanic chiefs. Odoacer, the Germanic barbarian king, who deposed the last emperor, Romulus Augustulus, thereafter ruled Italy and Sicily as a kingdom. The kingdom of the Ostrogoths (East Goths) lay to the northeast; to the north were the kingdoms of the Franks and the Saxons, and the kingdom of Syagrius, the last Roman administrator in Gaul; the Visigoths (West Goths, who had vanquished the Vandals and driven them into Africa) established their kingdom south of the Loire River and covered all of Spain; and the kingdom of the Vandals extended along the nothern coast of Africa and included the islands between Italy and Spain. North of the eastern Roman Empire and south of the Baltic Sea lived the barbarian Lombards.

Dominating the British Isles were the Celtic tribes of Scots in Ireland, Picts in Scotland, and Britons in England. Some of the Britons, driven out by invading tribes, had settled on the west coast of what is now France, which therefore became known as Brittany. The new invaders of England were Germanic tribes—the Angles, Saxons, and Jutes.

Invasions by northern Germanic peoples successfully overran all the territory that had been the western Roman Empire. Italy was invaded by the Ostrogoths, now allies of the Constantinople government, and Odoacer was overthrown, 488–493 A.D. In 493 A.D. Theodoric the Ostrogoth treacherously offered Odoacer his friendship and then assassinated him.

Theodoric, however, had good points as a ruler. Making his capital at Ravenna, in the north of Italy near the Adriatic coast, he ruled with a devotion to the Roman conception of law and order, and treated the former Roman citizens with consideration. Under Theodoric, the architecture of the Ostrogoths flourished at Ravenna and was strongly marked by the Roman influence. He cemented friendship between his and other kingdoms by arranging marriages of his relatives to members of other ruling families—a policy which has continued up to modern times.

In 526 A.D. Theodoric died, and Justinian, a Roman emperor at Constantinople, reconquered Italy for what remained of the Roman Empire. In 553 A.D., the Ostrogoths left Italy and vanished across the Alps to the north.

Justinian's domination of Italy did not last long. Despite the fact that the empire of Justinian was to follow the fate of its predecessors, his reign was noteworthy for the contribution it made to the field of law. During the reign of Justinian (527–565 A.D.) all the sources of Roman law were collected and put into scientific form. The result was the famous code called the "Body of Civil Law," which was destined to become the foundation of the legal systems of most of western Europe.

WESTERN EUROPE

The region north of the Po was conquered by the Lombards, the last of the barbaric German hordes who came southward from the forests of the north, and the region has since been known as Lombardy. They made scattered settlements throughout the peninsula, but the Lombards did not succeed in uniting Italy. The country was to remain divided and in political chaos until the nineteenth century. Cavour and Garibaldi brought eventual order out of chaos. Like the Franks, and the Visigoths in Spain, the Lombards adopted Latin, and today Italian, French, and Spanish, known as Romance languages—"romance" being derived from *Roman*—have much in common with classical Latin. The Lombard kingdom lasted from 568 to 774 A.D., and then two centuries later it was conquered by Charlemagne and the Franks.

THE FRANKS

From the region of the lower Rhine there had been an early invasion westward into Roman territory by the Germanic tribes known as the Franks. Clovis, whose name is outstanding in history, became the first Frankish king in 481 A.D., when he united all the Frankish tribes by conquest. As Clovis was a Salian Frank, this particular group greatly influenced the future of the kingdom. The code of laws of the Salian Franks became known as Salic Law, and elements of it later prevailed in several European countries, particularly the Salic law which prohibited succession of the throne through a female line. Clovis led the Franks through Roman Gaul, and with his conquering army was able to extend the Frankish kingdom as far as the river Loire. He likewise vanquished the Alemanni, Germanic tribes to the eastward (it is after them that the French still call Germany *Allemagne*), in 496 A.D. Later Clovis extended the rule of the Franks from the Loire southward to the Pyrenees and pushed the Visigoths back into Spain. He conquered his southeastern neighbors, the Burgundians, and exacted tribute from them. For these achievements, Clovis may rightfully be called the founder of France, which took its name from the Franks.

Clovis ruled as king of the Franks until 511 A.D. He was baptized with many of his followers in 496, and thereafter was considered the great champion of Christianity in barbaric Europe. His descendants, called the Merovingians, ruled over the Franks for 250 years after Clovis' death— a period characterized by useless wars, assassinations, and treacheries. (The word Merovingian is derived from Meroveus, the name of Clovis' grandfather.) The dominions of the Franks covered what are now France, Belgium, Holland, and a part of Germany.

In the years following 650 A.D. the Frankish kings suffered the loss of most of their power, and the government was in the hands of ministers called "mayors of the palace." Of these unofficial rulers, the most important was Charles Martel. He was known as Charles the Hammer because when the Mohammedans were invading western Europe, he "hammered" them into defeat near Tours. His virtual reign came to a close in 741 A.D., and his place was filled by his son Pepin (or Pippin) the Short.

First having obtained the consent of the bishop of Rome, Pepin removed the last of the "do-nothing" kings from the throne, and made himself king of the Franks in 751 A.D. It was he who established the Carolingian dynasty of France. Pope Stephen II came to the court of Pepin in 754 A.D. and anointed him king. In exchange for the co-operation of the church, Pepin gave his own by helping to keep the Lombards out of Rome. Moreover, he forced them to cede much territory lying between Rome and Ravenna to the papal dominions which were centered around Rome. This was known as the Donation of Pepin (756 A.D.). Pepin's rule came to an end in 768, when he was succeeded by his two sons, one of whom, Charlemagne (Charles the Great), soon became the sole ruler and reigned for nearly fifty years.

CHARLEMAGNE'S REIGN

At this point the history of the world becomes broken up into separate stories covering various regions and kingdoms. While there was activity among the Franks and other people of western Europe, it must be remembered that civilizations parallel and overlap each other. During this period, the eastern Roman or Byzantine Empire was asserting itself in the East. The followers of Islam had spread their dominion from North Africa into Spain, and in the Far East, India and China were still powerful.

Charlemagne (Charles the Great) ruled the Franks from 768 to 814 A.D. His political and cultural vision was far greater than that of his predecessors. His name shines against the dark shadow that hovers over European civilization of this period. Although he had his faults and shortcomings in many ways, within his limited opportunities and powers, he was a progressive ruler.

Northward over the Saxons, southward into Italy, including Rome, and eastward over the wild Avar tribes who had come from the region of the Caspian Sea—Charlemagne pushed his influence and extended the Frankish kingdom. He was a Christian, and as champion of this growing religious faith he spread the Gospel throughout the territory he conquered.

Following a summons from the pope, Charlemagne conquered the Lombards of Italy, and in reward for this service was crowned emperor (Charles Augustus) of the Romans by Pope Leo III in 800 A.D. This did not mean much to Charlemagne, for he already was emperor over his dominions. Yet it signified to some a definite break with the Roman Empire of the East and a revival of the Roman Empire of the West.

Charlemagne was the first of the Germanic successors to the old Roman Empire to attempt to revive civilization in western Europe. He founded schools in the monasteries and cathedrals, where not only the clergy but also the common people might receive some training. He collected the manuscripts of Latin authors and had them copied so that the knowledge of the past should not be forgotten. All this work, together with the peace and order he maintained throughout his wide dominions, made his reign the most brilliant of the early Middle Ages.

Charlemagne died in 814 A.D. His successors lacked the strength to keep his power and realms intact, and from 814 to 870 A.D. his empire disintegrated. After the death of Louis the Pious, his three sons, who had been quarrelsome, adjusted their differences in the Treaty of Verdun in 843 A.D. From Rome upward through Lombardy, a portion of Burgundy, and certain adjacent parts of the Rhine and Rhone, Lothair ruled as king. To the west of Lothair's kingdom, Charles ruled. Upon the death of Lothair, Louis, whose kingdom lay to the north of Lothair's, and Charles made the Treaty of Mersen (Holland) in 870 A.D., by which they divided all of Lothair's lands to the north of the Alps, leaving only a portion of Italy to Lothair's son.

Thus it is possible to envisage the beginnings of modern Europe. Out of the East Frankish kingdom, under Louis, Germany grew. Its people were mostly Teutonic. The West Frankish kingdom, under Charles, would eventually become France. Its peoples were largely Romanized Gauls. The northern portion of Lothair's kingdom was to become Belgium, Holland, Switzerland, Alsace, and Lorraine.

From various directions during this period, the Franks were being harassed by other peoples ambitious to conquer them. Included among these warriors were Mohammedans in southern France, who came from Spain, and in Italy, who came from Africa. There were Northmen from

Denmark and Norway appearing along the French coast and up the Rhine, and they destroyed Cologne and Charlemagne's capital, Aix-la-Chapelle. There were Slavs in eastern Germany, and Magyars and Huns from western Asia.

There were many different peoples in Europe at the beginning of the tenth century. The Irish, Picts, Jutes, Welsh, Danes, and English (descended chiefly from Angles and Saxons) were in the British Isles. The Northmen, Swedes, and Danes, also Jutes and Angles, were in Scandinavia. On the continent proper, the Germanic peoples included Saxons, Bavarians, Franks, Alemanni, Burgundians, and Lombards. Farther south there were the Romanic French of Roman origin, the Italians, a small group of Basques, and in Spain the Spanish and Portuguese. In eastern Europe were the Bulgarians and the Avars, and to the northeast the Magyars (Hungarians). To the north, in what is now eastern Germany, Poland, and the Baltic States, there were Slavic peoples—Bohemians, Moravians, and Poles; and Lettic peoples—Lithuanians and Latvians; and still farther north, Estonians and Finns.

THE GERMAN STATES

The dynasty of the descendants of Charlemagne expired early in the tenth century. What had been the eastern Frankish kingdom was divided into five territorial states or stem-duchies, of which the most important was Saxony. This was the stage for quarreling between Saxon kings and nobles. There were Slavic tribes east of the river Elbe. At this time some of the duke-kings were virtually independent, even after the Treaty of Verdun, when they recognized a single sovereign. Subsequent to the passing of the Carolingian dynasty (of Charlemagne) the nobles elected their own kings.

The first important king who was thus elected was Henry I, a duke of Saxony, who was called Henry the Fowler because he found great enjoyment in hunting birds. He reigned from 919 to 936 A.D., and devoted much of his energy to warring against the Magyars, Slavs, and other enemies. Brandenburg, which was eventually to come under the rule of the Hohenzollerns, was taken from the Slavs.

The son of Henry I was Otto I, who later was called Otto the Great. He was outstanding in stature and personality, and ruled for thirty-seven years (936 to 973 A.D.). Not only did he defend Germany from many petty enemies, but he swept downward into Italy and became king of the Lombards. He was crowned Holy Roman Emperor by Pope John XII in 962 A.D. This was in the nature of a reward for saving the pope from his enemies at a time when even the church was having its troubles. At a later date German kings had their difficulties with the papacy, for they also claimed mastery of Italy. The empire of Charlemagne, which was thus restored by Otto the Great, constituted the Holy Roman Empire—signifying a world government under a lay ruler, united with a universal (Catholic) church under a pope. But it was seldom, however, that the popes and lay rulers agreed. Nevertheless, Otto the Great and his successors, by claiming to be the heirs of Charlemagne, Constantine, and Augustus Caesar, kept alive the imperial idea for more than eight hundred years. It did not disappear from European politics until the opening of the nineteenth century.

Hungary (named after the Huns, of whom the Magyars were kin) was formed when, after Otto held back the Magyars in battle on the river Lech in 955 A.D., these tribes settled down. Otto established the East Mark, which was a division ruled by a margrave or marquis, to prevent further Magyar attacks, and this later became Austria (Oesterreich).

THE BRITISH ISLES

The Angles and Saxons, who later formed the group called the Anglo-Saxons, came into England (as the Jutes did a little later) in the fifth century A.D., but it took them 150 years to subdue the native tribes. At that, they did not win much more than the fertile country of southeastern Britain. In their invasion they destroyed many of the evidences of the Roman settlement, and killed the warriors. They married the native women, and brought the farmers into a state of slavery. Some of the natives, whose traditions and language were Celtic, took refuge in the western and northern hills, which became known as Wales. There the Welsh developed a distinct culture of their own.

These Anglo-Saxons, who warred among themselves, established the kingdoms of Kent, Sussex (South Saxony), Essex (East Saxony), East Anglia, Northumbria, Mercia, Wessex (West Saxony). Under King Egbert, ancestor of the English line of kings, Wessex maintained leadership from 802 to 839 A.D.

The Anglo-Saxons had a very marked effect on English tradition, customs, and language. It is for this reason that present-day English has less relationship with Latin than have French, Italian, and Spanish. The Latin influence was lost when the island was invaded by the barbarians, but it was to have a revival with the coming of the Normans in 1066 A.D.

St. Augustine came to England as a Christian missionary. A slow exchange of ideas was developing with the Continent, for communication had been established. The pope in Rome at this period was Gregory the Great. The inhabitants of Kent were the first converts in England, for their king, Ethelbert, became a Christian after his marriage to Bertha, who was a Frankish princess. Monks made Canterbury their residence, and the town became to a large extent the religious center of England.

In the second century, missionaries from Rome had tried to convert the early Britons to Christianity, but their efforts had been nullified by the "heathen" Germanic tribes, or they had driven the Celtic Christians to the west. Many of these went to Ireland, in which island St. Patrick was a missionary in the fifth century.

Differences of religious procedure, notably the method by which the date of Easter was decided, were adjusted at the Synod of Whitby in 664 A.D. Whitby was significant in that it put Britain, and at a later date Ireland and Scotland, under the control of the pope at Rome in matters of religion. This continued until the time of King Henry VIII.

THE ADVANCE OF CHRISTIANITY

Christianity had been placed by the Roman emperor Constantine on an equal basis with the religions of the pagans. After making Christianity the state religion, Theodosius started persecuting those who were not Christians. At the head of the Christians, every large city had a bishop, who was assisted by priests and deacons. The elaborate system of the Roman Catholic Church was an outgrowth of this early ecclesiastical government. The spread of Christianity was effected by association, by conquest, and by missionary activity; it extended its influence throughout Europe, both western and eastern, and penetrated southeastward into the eastern Roman Empire.

The bishop of Rome, particularly after the decline of the Roman Empire in the West, became the pope, or head, of the Catholic Church in all western Europe. In this manner the *Roman* Catholic Church, ruled by the pope, or chief bishop, at Rome, was eventually distinguished from the eastern branch which divided from it and was afterward known as the Greek Church (Holy Orthodox Church). Until 1054, the two churches remained in formal unity. Disputes on points of nominal doctrine led to their final rupture. They have never reunited.

EASTERN EUROPE

During the early Middle Ages, while western Europe was submerged in conflicts among the uncivilized Germanic tribes in eastern Europe and western Asia, the great civilization of the Roman Empire endured. Further to the east, the magnificent civilization of Moslem Arabia was developing. The Moslems were followers of Islam, the religion founded by Mohammed.

THE BYZANTINE EMPIRE

The Roman Empire in the East had its capital at Constantinople, built on the site of the earlier Greek city Byzantium—hence the name of the Byzantine empire to distinguish it from the earlier empire founded in the West by Rome. The Byzantine empire still kept the name of Rome, but its civilization was essentially Hellenistic in its character and culture. This eastern empire survived, largely because of its vast wealth, until the year 1453 when the Turks captured Constantinople. The armies of the eastern empire were powerful, and its capital city on the Bosporus between Asia Minor and Europe occupied a nearly impregnable position.

Following Constantine and Theodosius, Justinian was the next emperor of importance. Rome had not yet fallen, and Justinian, who reigned from 527 to 565 A.D., won back from the barbarians considerable territory for the empire. He was distinguished by his brilliancy and his progressive ideas, for which considerable credit must be given to his wife, Theodora, who strongly influenced his policies.

Justinian's armies, under the leadership of the general Belisarius, cleaned out the Vandals from northern Africa, vanquished the Ostrogoths in Sicily and southern Italy, and wrested southern Spain from the Visigoths. Roman law was codified by Justinian, and the record that he wrote down became the basis of modern law in Italy, Spain, France, Germany, and elsewhere.

Shortly after, however, Justinian's empire came to an end, and the power of Constantinople in the West again declined, this time never to be revived. Northeastern Italy was seized by the Lombards; and the Persians, under Chosroes II, made battlegrounds of many of the Asiatic parts of the empire. The Roman emperor Heraclius, who reigned from 610 to 641 A.D., revenged himself on the Persians for the capture of Jerusalem and the stealing of the "true cross"; but so great was the cost in men and money that the provinces which were recovered soon were recaptured by the advancing Arab army—composed of Moslems who were the fighting followers of Mohammed.

The power of the eastern empire continued to diminish until the eleventh century, when the ravagings of the Seljuk Turks brought about the First Crusade. On the appeal of the Holy Roman Emperor in the West, Europe sent armies to fight the heathens, who were threatening the existence of Christianity in the East. The Byzantine empire was Christian, and its church remained associated with the Roman Church until 1054.

Meanwhile, the Slavic hordes from the north, who had penetrated the eastern empire shortly after the death of Justinian, were roaming southward into the Greek Peninsula; and today their descendants occupy the Balkans. Bulgars, related to the Huns, also harassed the land, but later they adopted much of the Slavic mode of living. Barbaric hordes from Russia also came down the Dnieper and Dniester rivers to attack Constantinople. They were led by Northmen.

The Byzantine empire was in its glory between the ninth and eleventh centuries. Its civilized splendor and intellectual activity were prodigious. Constantinople, which was its metropolis, was a great trading center where goods of every sort from far-off lands were bartered. The dome was one of the developments of Byzantine architecture, and the interiors of the churches were distinguished by their magnificent decorations. The Byzantine influence extended into Italy, and throughout modern Russia its characteristics can still be seen, especially in the older churches of Leningrad and Moscow. Byzantine influence can also be seen in the Mohammedan mosques.

Constantinople did not provide much in original learning, yet its libraries and museums preserved classical learning. Byzantine scholars did not make new discoveries, preferring to compile huge encyclopedias from the books which antiquity had handed down to them. Eastern Europe thus cherished classical learning until the time came when western Europe was ready to receive it and profit by it. In common with the greater Roman empire that preceded it, the eastern wing was static, for it went neither forward nor backward. But while the civilization of Byzantium was standing still and western (Christian) Europe was mired in the Dark Ages, the Arabians and the Moors were making rapid strides in every branch of science and art.

THE RISE OF ISLAM

Islam came out of Arabia. From that great land of nomadic desert tribes lying between the Persian Gulf, the Indian Ocean, and the Red Sea came the religion founded by Mohammed (also written Muhammad and Mahomet) and his disciples. Its fundamental assertion is "There is no god but Allah, and Mohammed is his prophet." This religion is called Islam, which means resignation or surrender, and a believer is a Moslem, or one who surrenders himself to the belief. The Christian Crusaders later called their Moslem enemies Saracens.

Syria and Palestine fell to the Mohammedan Arabs early, and with them went the cities of Damascus, Antioch, and Jerusalem. Mesopotamia was wrested from the Persians: the Persian power was overthrown. Egypt fell before the onslaught of the soldiers of Islam. Islam, or Mohammedanism, became the dominant religion throughout Syria, Persia, Egypt. Eastward, the Moslems penetrated to India and central Asia.

Sweeping through northern Africa, the Moslems converted the Berber tribes; the mixed Arabs and Berbers came to be known as Moors—later, any Mohammedan in northern Africa or Spain was called a "Moor." The Moslems soon crossed into Spain by way of Gibraltar (which received its name from "Gibal al Tarik," meaning the mountain of Tarik, who was the Moslem leader of the invasion) in 711 A.D., and proceeded to build cities. The Moslems even crossed the Pyrenees and invaded Gaul, but they were stopped, near Tours, by the armies of Charles Martel the Frank, in 732.

Arabian civilization has contributed much to the modern world. Having conquered a people, the Arabians would quickly absorb their culture and improve on it. They developed farming into an agricultural science, and it is due to their efforts that we have cotton, buckwheat, rice, coffee, asparagus, artichokes, oranges, and apricots. They excelled in manufacturing. At Damascus, brocades, tapestries, and tempered steel of wonderful quality were made. Cordova, Spain, was famous for its leather; Toledo, Spain, for its armor; and Granada for its silks. Other Arabian contributions to the arts were dyeing, and the making of crystal and plate glass.

Many English words that we use today are from the Arabian. Some of these are: *damask* from Damascus, *cordovan* from Cordova, and *muslin* from Mosul. Also note the Arabic words, *alchemy, alcohol, alembic, algebra, alkali,* and *almanac,* all of which begin with the Arabic definite article *al,* meaning *the.*

Even at the height of their empire, the Romans neglected exploration, but the Arabs were active in their efforts to gain knowledge of the distant regions of the world. In commerce the Arabs were outstanding. They traded with India, China, the East Indies, the interior of Africa, Russia, and even the Baltic lands. Their trade, their wide conquests, and their religious pilgrimages vastly increased the knowledge of the world. There is some reason to believe that the mariner's compass was first introduced into Europe by the Arabs. While schools were virtually unknown in western Europe during the Middle Ages, they were common among the Arabs, who excelled in the sciences of chemistry, mathematics, and medicine. Their mathematical genius is responsible for our system of numerals, and for most of algebra. Of Arabian literature, the *Thousand and One Nights* (The Arabian Nights' Entertainments) is famous. At Granada, Spain, the Alhambra, with its magnificent citadel and palace buildings built by Moorish kings, is a world-famous example of the splendid architecture of the Arabs. From the fanciful and complicated ornamental designs in Arabian architecture, the word "arabesque" has come into use to denote a complex design of interweaving curves.

DEVELOPMENTS IN NORTHERN LANDS

THE VIKINGS

Away to the north, in the lands now designated as Norway, Sweden, and Denmark, the Northmen, or Norsemen, were making their entrance into the historic scene. This Scandinavian historic period began about 800 A.D. The opening of the so-called Viking Age was contemporary with the crowning of Charlemagne as emperor of Rome, and a long time after Mohammed's founding of Islam.

The Vikings were warrior-seamen. The coastline of their lands was deeply indented with inlets from the ocean, so that these sturdy people were bred to the sea. Their ships were hardy and fast. The Vikings decorated them with black markings and sometimes with gilt. They explored their own coasts, and as the population of their country increased they ranged farther afield in search of new lands. As sailors, the Vikings were efficient, and as fighters they were rough.

Teutonic in origin, at the time of their first invasions they were barbarians, similar to the other tribes of the same origin who had swept over western Europe in the early Middle Ages. Odin, Thor (god of thunder), and Balder were their chief deities. Their mythology was characterized by harshness, gloom, and war-like spirit. Later the Northmen were converted to Christianity. It was under King Olaf that Norway was converted in the early eleventh century; by 1100 A.D. most of Scandinavia had turned Christian.

Along the coasts of England, France, and Germany the early Norsemen raided. With their shallow Viking boats they were able to sail up the rivers into the interior. At first they traded peacefully, but presently they found plundering a more profitable occupation, and the Viking raiders became a menace and a terror to western Europe. They pushed their way across the Atlantic Ocean, invading Scotland, Ireland, Iceland (colonized 874 A.D.), and the smaller groups of islands. They went to Greenland, and, under Leif Ericson (about 1000 A.D.), voyaged as far as the coasts of Labrador and Newfoundland, and probably as far as Nova Scotia. Thus, for the first time, the continent of North America came into European history, though only momentarily. Its next entrance was to be 500 years later, when Christopher Columbus would sail westward in his three tiny caravels.

It was chiefly the Norwegian Vikings who roved westward. The Swedes went eastward and invaded Finland, whose inhabitants were related to Asiatic peoples, and for several centuries they ruled over that land. The Northmen also invaded Russia and went southward along its rivers. Norse chiefs led the Russians in their attack on Constantinople in the tenth century. The Norseman, Rurik, is credited with founding the Russian empire. During the reign of his descendant, Vladimir, Christianity made its appearance in Russia. Vladimir was converted in 988 A.D. to the Greek Orthodox Church, which then became the official Russian church. The influence of Byzantine civilization in Russia from this time is very strong.

The Northmen were merciless in their plundering of France. In 911 A.D., Rollo, the Viking chief, embraced Christianity and was granted a duchy in Normandy, the region of the lower Seine. The Scandinavian invaders became French in character. (The name Norman is a clipped form of Norseman or Northman.) The Normans, always absorbing from the people they conquered, eventually disappeared from history, but they left definite evidences of their influence. Hugh Capet, whose descendants were to rule France for eight hundred years, was assisted into power by Norman dukes in 987 A.D. He succeeded the Carolingian line of rulers, which was established by the father of Charlemagne.

In the ninth century, England was overrun by the Danes, who pushed back Egbert of Wessex. Egbert's grandson, King Alfred the Great, became the ruler in 871 A.D., and he served England by preventing the Danish Vikings from completely conquering the country. After effecting a truce with the Danes, Alfred was active in the reconstruction of England's dawning civilization and in fostering early English literature. When Alfred died, the Danes renewed their attacks. From 1016 to 1035, Canute the Dane occupied the throne. With the accession of Edward the Confessor, the Saxon line returned; but as Edward had been raised in Normandy, he brought with him a Norman court.

THE CONQUEST OF ENGLAND BY THE NORMANS

When the throne of England fell vacant, Duke William of Normandy, who was a cousin of Edward the Confessor, laid claim to it. With a large fleet bearing thousands of fighting men, he crossed the Channel and landed in England. William of Normandy was opposed by King Harold at the decisive battle of Hastings in 1066 A.D. This battle settled the fate of England. The victorious Duke of Normandy was crowned King of England on Christmas Day, 1066.

Normans of the merchant and noble classes settled extensively in southeastern England. With much early French and a large admixture of Latin, they gave to the English tongue the language of the court and the upper classes. When it was united with Normandy, England became powerful in European affairs. Religion in England came under the power of the pope, who had given encouragement to William the Conqueror. By degrees the Normans in England amalgamated with the Anglo-Saxons, and the marriage of these two elements produced what is now the English people.

NORMANS IN SOUTHERN ITALY

Taking advantage of a disunited Italy, the Normans invaded and conquered the toe of the boot and the nearby island of Sicily. The Normans were led in this venture by Robert Guiscard. Most of southern Italy had previously been separated from the eastern Roman Empire by 1085 A.D., and Sicily had been wrested from the Moslems. After the Norman invasion a single state was evolved, known as the Kingdom of the Two Sicilies, which the Normans controlled for a century and a half. The kingdom, under other rulers, retained its identity until the unification of Italy in the nineteenth century.

THE FEUDAL SYSTEM

In western Europe, the feudal system was the dominant form of political organization in the later Middle Ages, from the ninth to the fourteenth centuries. The nobles, who held the land, gained great power after the power of the kings declined following the disruption of Charlemagne's empire. And following the break-up of cities when trade disappeared after the decline of the western Roman Empire, land property remained the only form of wealth. Thus, under feudalism local lords had the powers that we customarily think of as belonging only to the king. This was especially the case in France, Italy, and Germany, and for a somewhat briefer period in England.

The feudal system was based on land. This was held by a noble or lord, theoretically from the king, who was the owner of all land. Actually, since the king's power in the early Middle Ages was only nominal, his leadership amounted to little. The tenants, under the noble, controlled the peasants, who were at first serfs and later freemen, and the lord received his share of the produce. The tenants, in vassalage, held the land in fealty to the lord, to whom they owed allegiance and military service in his battles. The land held by a tenant was known as a fief. Such control was either inherited or granted by a noble.

In its essence feudalism was a form of government. It naturally affected many aspects of life, just as a republic or monarchy does: (1) Feudalism provided for the ownership and inheritance of land—or what is known as land tenure. (2) It provided a system of local government. (3) It provided for carrying on the economic activities necessary for sustaining life. (4) It provided a military organization. (5) Most important of all, it determined the development of social classes. The lord had his obligations, for in return for their homage, he was bound to protect his vassals and their property against invaders and robbers. There were many practical objections to feudalism, and it did not always function smoothly, but it doubtless served to keep western Europe of the ninth century from a state of anarchy.

Local justice of a sort was administered in an assembly of the lord and his vassals. Ordeals by fire or water were a popular method for trying the accused, as it was assumed that the innocent would be favored by God. There were also trials by combat, in which the accused and accuser fought with each other and the winner was presumed to be innocent. Throughout later history such combats were common as tests of personal honor.

The mounted knight in armor was an important feature in the feudal hierarchy. Armor was improved and built up until the knight was encased in a fortress-like housing of metal so heavy that the warrior had often to be lifted onto his horse by means of a pulley. These knights fought the private battles of their lords up to the time when the power of the kings increased sufficiently to control the nobles. Gradually warfare was associated with the policies of the king, and the lords contributed their knights, on request, to the royal army.

From great castles, virtual fortresses, made first of wood and then of stone, the feudal lords exerted their power in the twelfth and thirteenth centuries. Heavily constructed and built on high rocks or hills, these castles were almost impregnable before the longbow and the musket were invented. Prison-like, such castles often had in their cellars dank, gloomy dungeons, in which captured foes or other prisoners were left to rot.

Life inside the castle offered few amusements for the occupants. Large banquets were held, minstrels recited or chanted tales of love and heroism, and the game of chess, learned from the Arabians, was played. Outside the castle walls, the lords and their vassals hunted.

The declining importance of cities favored the establishment of feudalism, which was especially suited to an agricultural society concentrated in settlements in the rural districts forming great estates or manors. These manors were of various sizes, but generally they were self-sufficient and did not depend much on trade with other communities and countries. During the five or six hundred years in which feudalism prevailed, farming methods did not develop from their crude state. There was little fun for the peasants, working hard under lords who were frequently harsh. Peasants were classed as serfs, and they belonged to their land. Instead of being bought and sold themselves, as slaves were, they were bought and sold with the land they cultivated. They could look forward to nothing but continued servitude to the lord and the land. Peasant rebellions were not uncommon in the Middle Ages, but they achieved no great reforms in the feudal system.

The decline of feudalism began in the fourteenth century. Royal rulers were becoming more powerful. They began to abolish private warfare between the nobles, administer justice, and maintain order within their kingdoms. Another contribution to the decline of feudalism was the revival of trade and manufacturing, which began to centralize population again in the cities.

EMPERORS VERSUS POPES

The part played by the Roman Catholic Church in the Middle Ages was an important one. Education was confined almost wholly to the clergy. The popular imagination was captured by the elaborate ritual of the Catholic service, and there was a ready response to religious ceremony. Therefore the church and its sacraments, such as baptism, confirmation, matrimony, and extreme unction, had a tremendous influence on the life of the time. Fearing the wrath of God, the people felt that the requirements of the church were necessary to secure heavenly salvation.

The church courts functioned not only in trying offending clerics, but also laymen whose offenses came within the province of the church. Moreover, the holy church could provide a fleeing criminal with temporary sanctuary from harm. A custom of the time was the privilege of clergymen to be tried in an ecclesiastical court. An evil aspect of this judicial feature, called "benefit of clergy," was that a man could become a monk or priest so that he might carry on criminal practices and, if discovered, receive the normally lighter sentence of a church court. And, as it was assumed that only a clergyman could read, the ability to read a single line of writing would often secure this benefit. However, the civil courts at this time administered barbarous and cruel punishments, so that when the benefit of clergy was later extended legally to the educated and the well-born, it was a way of securing for the upper classes, at least, a more humane justice.

In the development of monasticism the early monks were self-sacrificing and tried to secure salvation by living as hermits, fasting, and fore-going bodily comforts. But later they gained control of property, either by gift or by feudal tenure, and they became more worldly and occasion-ally corrupt. New orders arose in the tenth and eleventh centuries—the Cluny order, and the Cistercian order, made famous by St. Bernard (1090–1153). Beginning with St. Francis of Assisi and St. Dominic, in the thirteenth century, came the orders of friars, or holy brothers, who lived among their fellow men, devoting themselves to their salvation. These religious men were directly responsible to the pope, whose power was greatly extended by these orders.

Monasticism played an influential role in the evolution of civilization during the Middle Ages. The monks, by careful cultivation of their lands, set an example of good farming wherever they settled. They performed many works of charity, feeding the hungry and healing the sick who were brought to their doors. They trained in their schools boys who intended to enter the ranks of the clergy. The monks, too, were the scholars of the age. By copying the manuscripts of classical authors, they preserved valuable books that would otherwise have been lost. By keeping records of the important events of their time, they acted as the chroniclers of medieval history.

At about the beginning of the tenth century the popes and the em-perors started to disagree concerning their own fields of jurisdiction. Charlemagne and, later, Otto the Great, of Germany, had been crowned Holy Roman Emperor by the pope. But though the Holy Roman Em-peror was supposed to have the power over men's bodies, the pope was to control the destiny of their souls. In theory the division of duty might be clear, but in practice claims to authority inevitably overlapped.

Otto the Great exacted a promise from the Italian nobles that they would not recognize any man as pope of whom he, the emperor, did not approve; and he stirred up strong opposition by deposing a pope who went contrary to his wishes. Among Otto's imperial successors who fol-lowed his precedent was Henry III, who gained the name of Pope-Maker because he appointed four different popes during his reign. Owing to the fact that Henry III's successor was weak, the papacy regained some of the spiritual independence that it had lost. In 1059 it was decided by a council of legates in the Lateran Palace that thereafter the supreme pon-tiff (pope) should be elected by the college of cardinals, high officials in the Catholic hierarchy.

Investiture was also a cause of dissension between the secular and the ecclesiastical authorities. Investiture was the granting of land and author-ity by a feudal overlord. A man pledged homage to a liege lord, the head of a feudal manor, in return for the fief or fee of land (feudal tenure). Such fiefs were held by bishops and abbots, in return for which they owed dues and allegiance to their laymen lords. The inner organization of the Roman church showed a tendency to be disrupted by this lay investiture, for, owing to their power of granting land tenure, lords held control of the appointing of abbots and bishops, which should have been accomplished within the church.

Between spiritual and lay investiture, the Concordat of Worms—named after the German city of Worms—made a careful distinction in 1122. Frederick I, who was called Barbarossa because he had a red beard, was second of the Hohenstaufen dynasty, and ascended to the German throne in 1152. Frederick desired to bring the Italian states under German rule, and he also wished to dominate the papacy. His ambition, however, was opposed by certain large cities in northern Italy as well as the papacy. Frederick was beaten at the battle of Legnano in 1176, and had to humble himself before Pope Alexander III.

Innocent III (1198–1216) was a powerful pope. He forbade the divorce and second marriage of King Philip Augustus of France, and when Philip tried to ignore the order, placed France under an interdict, whereby the entire country was deprived of religious sacrament. All worship ceased and the people, temporarily excommunicated, were cut off from what were considered the means of salvation. As a result of this, Philip's retainers deserted him, and Philip finally capitulated to the pope. Another ruler who had to bow before the papacy was King John of England, who even paid tribute from England and Ireland over a period of years. It was through the influence of Innocent III that Frederick II (1212–1250) was raised to the German throne. From the death of this ruler, the Holy Roman Empire declined in importance until it was, as the eighteenth-century wit, Voltaire, commented, "neither holy, nor Roman, nor an empire."

Frederick II's son died in 1254, and for almost two decades afterward Germany was without a king. This period, from 1254 to 1273, is called the Interregnum. The pope threatened to choose a ruler if the German states failed to do so, and the electors chose Rudolf of Hapsburg. Rudolf resigned all his claims to Italy, but squared matters by conquering Austria and establishing the dynasty of the Hapsburgs on the Austrian throne. The title of Holy Roman Emperor from this time became in practice an attachment to the ruling family of Austria.

Like Italy, Germany was now a group of small states. These were duchies, archbishoprics (an archbishop was head bishop of a sizable district or of a single country), free cities, and the like. It was in the nineteenth century that Germany became a unified nation.

The HOLY ROMAN EMPIRE

ABOUT 1100 A.D.

Holy Roman Empire Moslem Territory

Byzantine Territory

THE CRUSADES

It was perhaps inevitable that western Europe should come into conflict with the East. During the twelfth and thirteenth centuries, Europe, with its growing cities, a developing taste for commerce, and its new consciousness of political unities, began to encroach upon the Moslems of western Asia and northern Africa. Inspired by a fervent zeal to retake Jerusalem and the Holy Land for the followers of Christ, Christian armies were organized into Crusades, and they warred with the Moslems at intervals from 1095 to 1291. There were seven or eight such Crusades —so called because they were fought in the name of the Christian cross (*crux* in Latin).

With the spread of Christianity throughout Europe, many people were eager to make pilgrimages to Jerusalem and other places connected with the life of Christ. Pilgrimages of lesser importance were frequently made to various shrines and to Rome, the home of the popes. In the turbulence of the day, when people went on these journeys, it was merely good sense to go armed. The voyages were made in groups of soldiers or knights, and if they were attacked or obstructed, they naturally fought. Thus did the Crusades have their beginning.

These Christian pilgrimages to the Holy Land were not opposed by the early Arabian caliphs, but from the steppes east of the Caspian Sea came savage nomads who had been converted to Mohammedanism. They swept down into Asia Minor, and laid it waste. These fierce nomads were called the Seljuk Turks, after Seljuk, their first chieftain. Their abuse of the Christians aroused the strong antagonism of all Christendom.

There were behind the Crusades other reasons than religious zeal. Rewards were promised by the pope, so that in addition to the lure of adventure, the soldier of the cross had hopes of material benefit and special favors. In these rough and ready days, fighting was one of the recognized forms of adventure. And though they offered many hardships, the Crusades offered release from the monotony of daily life.

After brief Christian triumph in Asia Minor, there appeared the great Saladin, strong Moslem monarch, a devout Mohammedan and a brilliant general. First sultan of Egypt, Saladin conquered the cities of Syria, and united its rulers under him. He then captured Jerusalem in 1187. Again Christian possessions in the East were lost.

The third Crusade (1189–1192) was spurred on in the hope of regaining Jerusalem. Although they failed, Philip of France, Richard I of England, and Frederick Barbarossa of Germany all co-operated under the sign of the cross. One reason for their failure was the weakening effect of the long overland trip. When they arrived, they were much below their usual fighting strength. Richard of England finally was left to encounter the Moslems alone, and so bravely did he maneuver over a period of fourteen months that he earned for himself his sobriquet of Richard the Lion-Hearted, or, in French, Richard Cœur de Lion. But although Jerusalem could not be wrested from Saladin, a treaty was made whereby Christians could visit the holy city without paying tribute.

To such a point did the religious zeal of the time extend, that, in 1212, there was a so-called Children's Crusade. French children assembled and started on the march, but they were stayed by hunger. One German boy, Nicholas, succeeded in leading a children's crusade over the Alps, with the intention of going to the East by ship. The children were lost, some of them dying and others being sold into slavery.

The Crusades, judged by their aims, must be accounted a failure. After two centuries of conflict (1095–1250), the Holy Land remained in Moslem hands. The indirect results of the Crusades were, nevertheless, important. For instance, they helped to undermine feudalism. Thousands of nobles either mortgaged or sold their lands or failed to return. The Crusades created a constant demand for shipping and thus extended the exchange of goods between the East and Europe. The Crusades also contributed to intellectual and social progress. The intercourse between Christians and Moslems stimulated the development of civilization in Europe. This was due to the fact that the East at this time surpassed the West in civilization.

THE RISE OF EUROPEAN NATIONS

The development of western Europe was progressing simultaneously with the Crusades. Gradually monarchs were increasing their strength, and nations were gaining in political unity and power. By the end of the thirteenth century, the system of feudalism was declining. Nationalism, however, was slow in developing. Feudal lords struggled hard to retain their ancient powers, and the Catholic Church claimed to be a centralized power with authority above that of the kings. National cultures were slow to develop, and Latin was still used as the common language of Europeans. Except in England, a country isolated from the Continent, a sense of patriotic devotion, as such, did not come until the fifteenth century.

ENGLAND

William the Conqueror was crowned King of England in 1066, after the Norman conquest. His was a despotic rule. He suppressed native rebellions and took over all the land. He demanded first allegiance from all feudal vassals. Loyalty to the overlords came afterward. It was in his reign that the Tower of London was built, and he also garrisoned other towers and built fortified castles. It was difficult for the nobles to revolt against this king, as the estates in England were scattered. William was also a sponsor of English customs, and he was as fair as he could be in administering justice.

The royal house of Plantagenet began with King Henry II, who was the son of Matilda, daughter of William the Conqueror. Henry's father was Geoffrey, Count of Anjou. The derivation of the name Plantagenet is from the Latin, meaning "a sprig of broom plant," and the name was given to Geoffrey because he wore such a sprig in his hat. Although Henry II was frequently away overseeing the Norman-English possessions on the Continent, he saw to it that the English government was well founded in the courts, the jury system, and in English common law, on which modern English law is founded.

The king's court of justice was composed of circuit judges who were sent among the counties to try civil cases, and juries of twelve knights whose duty it was to investigate crimes and bring in a verdict, or "true statement." The jurors were thus named from the Latin expression which means "to take an oath." A grand jury made accusation in public of great crimes, or brought powerful offenders to justice. These proceedings had the effect of supplanting the former ordeals and feudal courts that had been the custom. Thus "common law," which was nothing more than the customs or laws "common" among the English people through tradition, gained an impetus that has never ceased.

Richard I (the Lion-Hearted), the famous crusader, succeeded his father, Henry II. Richard's reign was not long, and he spent little of it at home. His brother, the harsh and cruel John, succeeded him, and ruled from 1199 to 1216. Through war with the French king, Philip Augustus, the Norman possessions on the Continent were lost.

In 1215 the united nobles and commons revolted against King John on account of his tyrannical rule, and took London. They compelled the king to affix his seal to the Magna Carta (Great Charter), which was a document guaranteeing to them rights that King John had sought to take away. The serfs were ignored in these rights, which applied only to the nobles, but the fundamental privileges involved have survived and been extended in modern times to all citizens. These included three principles: no taxation except with the consent of the council of nobles and lords, immediate justice without the payment of fees, and prompt trial by one's peers (equals).

Henry III (1216–1272) was John's son. Through his encouragement the English Great Council of nobles developed. Under the Magna Carta of 1215, the Great Council's consent was required before the king might levy feudal dues or taxes. The next king, Edward I, called a representative Parliament. The word *parliament* is from the French, meaning "to speak," referring to the discussion of problems. The division of Parliament into two chambers occurred in the fourteenth century. There was the House of Lords, which was composed of nobles and higher clergy, and the House of Commons, which was made up of representatives of the common people of the cities and counties. In the beginning, Parliament had only the power to grant funds to the king. Later developments were its election of members and its legislative powers. Out of the power to control the funds of the king, however, all the other powers would inevitably develop.

It was the wish of Edward I (1272–1307) to combine the British Isles under one government. He succeeded in conquering Wales, whither the Welsh (Britons) had fled before the invading Anglo-Saxons hundreds of years before. To the Welsh demand for their own ruler, Edward countered by making his first son, who had just been born, the "Prince of Wales." This title has since been regularly bestowed on the British heir apparent.

Edward I of England captured and put to death William Wallace, the Scottish champion. Scotland had been settled in the fifth century by tribes of Scots from Ireland. Temporarily it came under English rule, but under Robert Bruce the Scots won back their independence. Bruce defeated Edward II in 1314 at Bannockburn, and Scotland remained an independent nation until 1603 when James VI of Scotland ascended the throne of England as James I.

FRANCE

It will be remembered that Hugh Capet, aided by the Norman dukes, became King of France in 987. At this time the French were of mixed blood; they were Romanized Gauls, Burgundians, Franks, Normans (Norsemen). In spite of their various origins, the French were becoming a unified people. This evolution of France's unity was helped along by the geographical position of the Frankish dominions. The northeast border, however, was not well defined. France had only fourteen kings in the 341 years between 987 and 1328, and sons succeeded their fathers in an unbroken line following Hugh Capet. Many of them were strong and worthy monarchs. With the increase in royal power, feudal subdivisions ceased to carry any authority. Paris became the capital of France.

The Estates-General, including the three Estates—nobles, clergy, and

commons (the commons being the "third estate")—were assembled by
Philip IV (1285–1314) for the purpose of voting sums of money to the
government. But this assembly did not progress as the English Parliament
had done, and France continued to be an almost absolute monarchy until
the revolution which took place in the eighteenth century.

Before the French kings could rule undisputed in their own land, however, they had to expel the English. The struggles which followed are
known as the Hundred Years' War (1337–1453). The cause was a dispute regarding the succession to the French throne. In 1328 the direct
line from Hugh Capet was broken. It was the feeling of Edward of England, son of the daughter of Philip IV of France, that he should inherit
the French throne. But the French nobles had other ideas. As king, they
appointed Philip's nephew, backing up their choice by maintaining that
a Salian Frankish law, known as the Salic law, made it impossible for
royal power to be inherited through the mother.

The French knights were defeated at Crécy in 1346 by Edward III,
who, having constantly made himself troublesome to the French, crossed
the Channel with an armed force. Ten years later, in 1356, armed with
longbows from which they were adept in shooting arrows, the English
again prevailed over the French at Poitiers.

The battles of Crécy and Poitiers mark the decline of the feudal type
of warfare, for they were won by English foot-soldiers armed with the
longbow. Ordinary iron mail could not resist the heavy, long arrows
which fell with murderous effect upon men and horses alike. Henceforth
infantry was to prove itself more than a match for feudal cavalry.

Edward III's son, called the Black Prince because he wore black
armor, distinguished himself at Crécy. Ten years later he captured the
French king, John, at Poitiers, and accorded him the gracious treatment
which was prescribed by chivalry. But a prince could be chivalrous to
another prince without being endowed with the feelings of humanity; at
the same time it was possible for the victor to put to death thousands
of captured men, women, and children.

Avoiding any further battles, the French retired into their castles and
fortified towns. For some years there was a cessation of war. The fighting was renewed, however, early in the fifteenth century, and the English
captured much of France north of the river Loire. They did not take
Orléans, which was saved by Joan of Arc, the "Maid of Orléans."
Strongly imaginative, pious almost to the point of madness, Joan believed that she was endowed with a divine mission to save her country.
She was only seventeen years old when she prevailed on the French king
to allow her to lead the army to the relief of Orléans, which was being
besieged by the English. The imagination of the people was caught by

the Maid's piety and apparent holiness. She put on a suit of armor and, carrying a white banner, rode horseback at the head of her troops. She was the inspiration of the French knights who dispelled the English from Orléans in 1429. Two years afterward, Joan of Arc was captured by the English, and at Rouen she was burned at the stake as a witch. To the French people, her death was a heroic martyrdom.

The French now completely repulsed the English, who abandoned fighting in 1453. Already weakened by the war in France, England soon after was engaged in the domestic struggle known as the War of the Roses. The royal power in France was much strengthened by the expulsion of the English, and both nobles and commons were reduced to subjugation under the king.

In the reign of King Louis XI (1461–1483), Anjou, Provence, and Burgundy were added to France. In the reign of King Charles VIII (1483–1498), Brittany was added, which nearly completed the unification of France.

SPAIN AND PORTUGAL

The settlement and conquest of Spain (called Hispania by the Romans) had been accomplished in turn by Iberians, Celts, Carthaginians, Romans, Vandals, Visigoths, and Moors (African Moslems). When the Moors first entered Spain in 711 A.D., they rapidly conquered the whole country and moved northward into France. After the battle of Tours, the Moors were pushed back into the Spanish peninsula and far enough south to leave unoccupied a northern region bordering the Pyrenees. The small Christian states that arose here included Leon, Castile, Navarre, and Aragon, two of which would later unite and conquer Spain.

Between these Christian states and the Moors, who occupied the greater part of Spain, there was a long struggle, which gradually unified the northern states. Rodrigo Diaz, whom the Moors called the Cid, which means Lord, won heroic fame by his military exploits. Castile was joined with Aragon in 1479 by the marriage of King Ferdinand of Aragon to Queen Isabella of Castile. In 1230 Leon had combined with Castile, and the Castilian language became the language of modern Spain. Now the greater part of Spain was under the control of Ferdinand and Isabella, and the Moors were confined to the region of Granada, a little section in the southeast. In the meantime, the Ottoman Turks had captured Constantinople, but in spite of the fact that the Turks were Moslems, they did not try to come to the aid of the Spanish Moors. Granada, at last overwhelmed by superior numbers, capitulated to Ferdinand and Isabella in 1492. This year was to be a celebrated one in history, for it marked the achievement of a young man named Christopher Columbus, who, bent on reaching India, made the important westward voyage across the Atlantic under the sponsorship of Ferdinand and Isabella, that resulted in the discovery of the New World.

These sovereigns were contemporary with Henry VII of England (first of the Tudor line) and Louis XI of France. Ferdinand and Isabella, who at that time were among the principal European rulers, established an absolute monarchy in Spain. When, somewhat later, their daughter was married to the heir to the Austrian throne, a Hapsburg, their influence on European affairs was to expand.

Portugal, on the west coast of the Spanish peninsula, was a Christian state. Little in size and importance for a long time, it kept its independence when the rest of the peninsula was unified.

AUSTRIA AND SWITZERLAND

Austria is called *Oesterreich* in German, meaning East Kingdom. It had its beginning in the valley region of the Danube River to the east of Bavaria, and Vienna became its capital. The region had been established by Otto the Great, of Germany, as a buffer state against the Magyar tribes of Hungary. As a German state its borders were extended, and Frederick Barbarossa made Austria a duchy. In 1273, Rudolph of Hapsburg was made emperor, and thus the Hapsburg dynasty was established.

Hapsburg Austria, by the end of the fourteenth century, grew to include much of eastern Germany, extending south to the Adriatic Sea. Slavic Bohemia was added in the sixteenth century, and so was a part of Magyar Hungary. Thus it can be seen how Austria became a union of several nationalities. The Hapsburg rulers controlled the title of Holy Roman Emperor.

There was a close relationship between Austria and the mountain communities or cantons of Schwyz (which gave Switzerland its name), Uri, and Unterwalden adjoining Lake Lucerne. These German-speaking cantons, together with French-speaking and Italian-speaking communities in neighboring mountain areas, united to win independence in 1499, although it was not until 1648 that Switzerland was recognized as a nation. The Swiss in the three parts of their country still speak their three original languages.

GERMANY AND PRUSSIA

Germany was a group of principalities and municipalities until the nineteenth century. These were loosely united, and the boundaries were not marked by any prominent geographical features. Deserting their own northern regions when they swept south to invade the Roman Empire, the Teutonic tribes in subsequent centuries were forced to win these areas from the Slavs. There were two reasons for Germany's expansion eastward—one their Christian crusading venture, and the other economic necessity. Henry the Fowler took Brandenburg and territory between the Oder and Vistula rivers. Included in the expansion was Pomerania.

On the Baltic Sea, between the Vistula and the Niemen rivers, lay Prussia, populated by natives who were related to the Slavs. Although the Germans conquered them and completely absorbed the original Prussians, the name of Prussia remained.

DEVELOPMENTS IN THE EAST

THE MONGOLS IN ASIA

From the steppes of central and northern Asia, like their kin before them (Huns, Bulgars, Magyars), came the nomadic, yellow-skinned Mongols and Ottoman Turks, roving westward, conquering as they came, in the thirteenth and fourteenth centuries. Mongols today range with their cattle in east-central Asia in the region just south of Siberia. When they invaded Europe they were semi-barbarous warriors.

The scattered Mongol tribes were united under the chieftain known to history as Genghis (or Jenghiz) Khan, a name meaning "Mighty King." Under his command, Mongol soldiers, with Turkish allies, swarmed over the Great Wall of China, and soon built a Mongol empire that extended from the China Sea to the Dnieper River of Russia (including Turkestan and Persia). Between 1206 and 1227, such civilized Moslem cities as Samarkand, Bokhara, Herat, and Merv were destroyed and their inhabitants killed by the Mongols.

Later additions to the Mongol domains were Korea, southern China, and Mesopotamia, and also most of Asia Minor and modern Russia. When Baghdad fell to the yellow hordes and was sacked, the famous Arabian caliphate ended. The Japanese, more secure in their islands off the east coast of Asia, were able to repulse the Mongols.

For a century and a half the Mongols ruled China, absorbing all they could of Chinese culture. Kublai, grandson of Genghis Khan, reigned from 1259 to 1294; his capital later became the city of Peking (Peiping). It was during Kublai's reign that the famous Venetian traveler, Marco Polo, visited the Mongol realms, which he described in his *Travels,* a classic of literature. When the Mongol dynasty fell in 1368, China remained closed to Europe until rediscovered, so to speak, by the Portuguese in the sixteenth century.

The vast empire of Genghis Khan disintegrated into small states in the fourteenth century. Then arose Timur the Lame (Tamerlane), descended from Genghis Khan, but a Turk and a Mohammedan. Tamerlane swept ferociously and cruelly throughout Armenia, Syria, India, Asia Minor, and Russia, leaving behind him the smoking ruins of cities and towering monuments of human heads. His empire fell apart at his death. Neither Genghis Khan nor Tamerlane was a statesman, or their empires might have surpassed those of Alexander the Great and of imperial Rome. Tamerlane died in 1405, at the age of seventy.

Following the example of Tamerlane, who had invaded India and sacked the city of Delhi, a later Turkish chieftain named Baber conquered India anew in 1525, and established there the so-called Mogul (Arabic for Mongol) empire in the northern part of the region. The Mogul power waned in the eighteenth century, and soon afterward India was conquered by Great Britain.

THE MONGOLS IN RUSSIA

Between 1237 and 1240 the Mongols had conquered most of Russia, sacking the cities of Moscow and Kiev and massacring the people. The Golden Horde, as these Mongols were called from the fabulous tent of their ruler, Batu Khan, reached as far westward as Hungary, which was laid waste. Poland was invaded and devastated. According to one account, the Mongols who defeated the German knights in Silesia in 1241 packed the right ears of their slaughtered foes into nine huge sacks.

No decisive battle turned back the Mongols from western Europe. They returned eastward of their own accord, probably owing to troubles at home. Until 1486, however, the Mongols or Tatars (also called Tartars) continued to rule Russia as the Kipchak Empire. While they forced the Russians to pay heavy tribute into the Mongol treasury, they interfered very little with the domestic life of the people. The Mongol domination, though it cut Russia off from western Europe at first, finally forced the native Russians to unite as a nation in order to expel the foreigners.

Muscovy (the state which included Moscow) gained control of its neighbor states, added the city of Novgorod to its domain, and grew in power until it could drive the Mongols out of Russia. Ivan III, called the Great, was the Russian monarch who rose from his authority as duke under the Mongols and at last evicted the Mongols (in 1480); he ruled from 1462 to 1505. Ivan was an absolute monarch, as were the later emperors, called czars (tsars).

THE OTTOMAN TURKS

A Turkish chieftain by the name of Othman, whence his people came to be called the Ottoman Turks, secured independence in 1300 for those Turks who had settled in Asia Minor at the death of Genghis Khan (1227). At first they had been under the protection of the Seljuk Turks, to whom they were related, and they adopted Islam from them, but the Ottomans finally gained control. By 1400 the Ottoman Turks had conquered all that had been the eastern Roman Empire, including Gallipoli and Adrianople and excepting only Constantinople and its vicinity.

The Turks had a specially trained body of troops, called Janizaries, an excellent fighting machine. In 1453 the sultan, Mohammed II, led them against Constantinople. The gallant Christians within the walls held out for two months; Constantinople fell and was sacked.

The Ottoman Turks included in their expanding empire modern Bulgaria, Rumania, Serbia, Albania, and Greece. Montenegro was the only Balkan state to maintain its independence: it was shielded by mountains. The Turks remained an Asiatic people, occupying parts of southeastern Europe by force of arms.

THE RISE OF THE CITIES

City life had almost disappeared in western Europe in the early Middle Ages. The formation of the feudal system came about partly through the lack of money or a monetary system. Ownership of land was the basis of wealth. The manors, with their tenants and peasants, ruled over by a lord, were obviously in rural districts. Commerce, however, gave city life a new impetus toward the end of the Middle Ages. Trade developed slowly but surely when the invading Northmen, the clash of peoples in the Crusades, and other contacts forced on the populace an awareness of other countries. Several well-known trade routes had been established between the Orient and western Europe by the end of the Middle Ages.

The sites of some of the old Roman cities provided foundations for other cities. On convenient harbors and navigable rivers—with trading in mind—other cities were founded in new locations. In the beginning the cities were units in the feudal system, and owed allegiance and dues to an overlord, but in time they achieved their freedom, and received charters which guaranteed them certain rights. Many of the cities had their own government, similar to the ancient Greek city-states. Eventually, only freemen lived in cities, and any serf who resided in a city for a year and a day was given his freedom. As the cities came to be directly responsible to the king, they were an important factor in reducing the regional powers of nobles and strengthening monarchy.

Between the nobility and clergy, who formed the upper class of society, and the peasants, who formed the lower class, was the new middle class, fostered by the growth of the cities. The shopkeepers and other merchants formed this middle class. The French called them the *bourgeoisie,* from the word for "town."

Picturesque though they were, with their protecting walls, their watchtowers, and their narrow streets, these medieval cities were congested, dirty, and unhealthful. In that early day, sanitation as we know it did not exist. There were no sewers, and the water was not pure. They did not segregate the sick, and, owing to the restrictions of space within the walls, there were no decent burial grounds. There was a high rate of mortality as a natural consequence, but a high birth rate enabled the cities to hold their own in population. There were criminals, too, in these medieval cities, and, with little or no police protection for the inhabitants, it was dangerous to go out at night.

The urban dwellers, however, made progress. They erected fine buildings, which included churches and abbeys, markets and guilds. A council of merchants governed the city. At their head was the burgomaster, or mayor, and his chief assistants, or aldermen—or elders.

Guilds, or early trade unions, came into being among the local industries concentrated in the cities. The merchants organized themselves for the protection of their privileges and rights, and frequently adopted aggressive measures to protect their territory against invasion by outsiders. Similar guilds were formed by the crafts. All the candlemakers, for instance, were members of one organization. The officials of the guild supervised and regulated the hours of labor, the price of goods, and the quality of the work.

Full membership in a guild was reached only by degrees. A boy started as an apprentice, that is, a learner. He paid a sum of money to his master and agreed to serve him for a fixed period, usually seven years. The master, in turn, promised to provide the apprentice with food, lodging, and clothing, and to teach him all the secrets of the craft. The apprentice had to pass an examination by the guild at the end of his term. If he was found fit, he then became a journeyman and worked for daily wages. In the event he made enough money to set up his own shop, he became a master.

The city market places were the center of trade. Yearly fairs were also held in many of the towns, and these lasted a month or more at a time. Here traders came together to barter goods of all kinds. The fairs held at Cambridge, Winchester, and St. Ives, England, were famous. Money came back into circulation again with the revival of trade in the later Middle Ages. Christians were forbidden to lend money at interest, or practice usury, as it was called. Financial matters in medieval Europe became centered in Italian cities.

In the thirteenth and fourteenth centuries, the leading Italian cities were Milan, Genoa, Venice, Florence, and Pisa. With the exception of Venice, which formed a maritime empire of its own, all of these cities fell into the clutches of despotic nobles. Venice acquired vast possessions in the East by prevailing on the soldiers of the fourth Crusade to attack Constantinople. The whole Mediterranean region looked upon the Venetian ships, with their sailors and traders, as leaders, and Venice gave herself the proud name of "Queen of the Adriatic." Reminders of the medieval splendor and power of the city are St. Mark's Cathedral, the Doge's Palace, and the Rialto Bridge.

In the north, many prominent German cities joined to form the Hanseatic League, a trade protectorate, which reached the height of its power in the fourteenth and fifteenth centuries. The first cities to unite were Hamburg and Lübeck. By the year 1400 the alliance consisted of about eighty cities. They were in the League for the mutual protection of their trade rights from robbers, invaders, and non-members. Other outstanding German cities of the period (not members of the League) were Augsburg, Nuremberg, Ulm, Cologne, and Strassburg.

In France, the famous cities were Paris, Lyons, and Marseilles; in England, London, Oxford, Cambridge, and York. The early factories were trading posts, where "factors," or trading agents, transacted business. Such factories included Bergen, Norway; Novgorod, Russia; and Bruges, Flanders.

During the later Middle Ages the region called Flanders became prominent. This part of Europe in time became Holland and Belgium. The Teutonic inhabitants were known as Flemings, and the French were called Walloons. The Flemings were notable for their trade in wool and their weaving. The important cities of Flanders were Bruges, Ghent, and Ypres. In Ghent there were about 40,000 workshops, while in Ypres 200,000 workmen were at one time employed. It was later that Antwerp became a trading center.

THE CULTURE OF MEDIEVAL TIMES

It was natural that medieval cities should become centers not only of the trades and crafts but of artistic and intellectual achievement, as in literature, art, and architecture. This tendency was strengthened when the accumulation of wealth allowed a greater leisure among the upper classes.

Latin was used in the church as an international ecclesiastical language, and the Latin hymns, such as *Dies Irae* and *Stabat Mater,* were a product of the later Middle Ages. Educational facilities were developed through schools and universities, and Latin was the language of scholarship. Students entertained themselves on their long travels between the intellectual centers with songs of feasting, drinking, and love. In southern France the troubadours sang of love and gallant deeds, and in the north of France epics were recited by minstrels and in later years set down on parchment. Chiefly legendary, the *Song of Roland* is an epic of the return of Charlemagne from Spain after he had beaten the Moslems. Of Celtic origin, the romantic tales of King Arthur and his Knights of the Round Table came out of medieval England. The *Nibelungenlied,* an epic of Siegfried, came from Germany. And in the time of Richard the Lion-Hearted appeared the medieval English legend of Robin Hood and his band of merry men in Sherwood Forest.

Medieval creative genius reached its highest expression in architecture. Modeled after the structures built by the Romans, Romanesque architecture appeared in northern Italy and southern France between 800 and 1100 A.D. and spread somewhat to the rest of Europe. Gothic architecture, which was to predominate for four centuries, originated around 1100. Some fine examples of Gothic cathedrals are Notre Dame at Paris, the Chartres Cathedral, the Reims Cathedral, and the Amiens Cathedral.

In the later part of the Middle Ages there was a revival in education, but the courses of instruction in the schools were meager. Between 1150 and 1500 about eighty universities were founded in western Europe. The universities of Paris and Bologna attained a leading position. The degrees of Bachelor of Arts and Master of Arts had their origin in the later Middle Ages. An eminent scholastic teacher of this period was Pierre Abélard (1079–1142), whose tragic romance with Héloïse is one of the celebrated love affairs of history.

Antagonism grew up between townspeople and students, for the latter considered that they were a class apart, with special privileges, and there were many sanguinary encounters between them. New universities were occasionally formed by migrations of dissatisfied students. In this period the universities of Oxford, Cambridge, and Salamanca, and a little later Leipzig, were established. In certain universities special courses were evolved for students with particular interests. There were schools of law at Orléans and Bologna; of medicine at Padua, Salerno, and Montpellier; and of theology at Paris. Thomas Aquinas, the famous scholastic, lived from 1227 to 1274. Scholasticism, a combination of philosophy and theology, was the basic approach in medieval learning.

The later Middle Ages were brightened by the work of two of the world's greatest writers, Dante and Chaucer. Famous for their writings, they greatly influenced the formation of new national languages because of their use of native tongues. The first of these great writers was the Italian poet Dante (1265–1321). Dante's *Divine Comedy* describes an imaginary visit to hell, purgatory, and paradise. It was the first important literary work in western Europe after the fall of Rome. It established the Florentine vernacular as the national language of Italy. The other great writer was the English poet Geoffrey Chaucer (1340–1400). His best-known work is the *Canterbury Tales,* a long poem composed of stories told by a group of pilgrims as they make their way along the roads from London to the cathedral town of Canterbury.

Roger Bacon, a thirteenth-century scientist (1214–1294), was doing his part toward the progress of scientific learning; but the general intellectual level in the Middle Ages was slow, and enlightenment was very gradual due to a widespread adherence to superstitious belief. Alchemy was the predecessor of chemistry, and its students sought the "philosopher's stone" by which they believed they could transmute the baser metals into gold. The "elixir of life" was another object of their research, for they believed it would ensure eternal youth. Progress in the science of astronomy was slow on account of the hampering influence of astrology, which supposed that the future could be scientifically foretold in the stars.

In the Middle Ages there was a general belief in dragons, unicorns, and other mythical monsters, as well as magic charms, incantations, fairies, gnomes, goblins, giants, werewolves, and such. The power of the "evil eye" inspired terror; there were cults of witchcraft and "black magic," and their adherents were often persecuted. The people believed in unlucky days, and it was in these times that Friday received its unsavory reputation.

There was little variety of amusements in medieval times. There was much hunting, feasting, and the like; and from the Orient came playing cards, which were introduced mainly to tell fortunes. Ball games—the forerunners of polo, football, tennis, hockey, golf, and others—had their beginnings then. Some of the sports of these people were crude or cruel, or both. There was cockfighting, and there was the baiting or tormenting of animals with dogs.

On special days of religious or seasonal import there were festivals which were attended by rich and poor alike. Associated with May Day was the morris dance, which was also performed in pageants and processions. (The word morris is derived from Moorish.) There were also mummers, dressed as animals, who serenaded the people or acted in plays. And the religious miracle plays, or morality plays, which depicted scenes from the Bible, were the precursors of modern drama.

The earlier castles were displaced by rough stone manor houses, miserably cold in winter and far from comfortable in the heat of summer. There were few carpets, and the floor coverings of the poor were straw and rushes. Window glass was a comparatively late innovation. Among the well-to-do the costumes worn were extremely elaborate, while those of the working classes were cruder and at the same time more sensible. Most of the men shaved their faces until after the Crusades, when it became the fashion to wear beards like those seen among Eastern peoples. There was much variety in the food, and, among the rich at least, it was as a rule plentiful; but as there was no refrigeration, food often spoiled and was unhealthful. People still ate with their fingers, as forks did not appear until about the fourteenth century.

Although it had its origin in China centuries before, gunpowder came into use in Europe about the fourteenth century. It changed the whole face of warfare and rendered obsolete the feudal castles and armored knights, as well as the weapons and defenses they employed. In considerable part the changes in methods of warfare greatly hastened the end of the feudal system and encouraged the consolidation of individual nations under the strong central governments of the kings.

EXAMINATION QUESTIONS

1. The period known as ancient history "ended" in what year and with what event?
2. What period is comprised by the Middle Ages?
3. In the reign of what eastern Roman emperor was the famous code called the "Body of Civil Law" collected?
4. Who were the Franks?
5. Who united all the Frankish tribes and to what Frankish tribe did he belong?
6. How long did Charlemagne reign over the Franks?
7. What was Charlemagne's religious belief?
8. When was the Eastern Roman Empire at its height?
9. When did the Angles and Saxons invade England?
10. Who was St. Augustine?
11. How long did the Roman Empire survive?
12. What Roman emperor placed Christianity on an equal footing with the pagan religions?
13. Where does Byzantine civilization get its name?
14. From what country did the Mohammedan religion come?
15. Name three Arabian contributions to civilization.
16. Where did the Northmen (or Norsemen) come from?
17. Who were the Vikings?
18. What part of France was settled by the Vikings?
19. What Danish king sat on the throne of England in the eleventh century?
20. In what year did William of Normandy conquer England?
21. What state evolved in southern

Italy and Sicily after the Normans conquered that region?

22. During what period was the feudal system the dominant form of political organization in western Europe?

23. On what was the feudal system based?

24. What was "trial by combat"?

25. What was "benefit of clergy"?

26. Who were the leading scholars during the period of the Middle Ages?

27. What pope placed France under an interdict when the French king ignored his order?

28. What was the Interregnum in Germany?

29. What was the period of the Crusades?

30. Who was Saladin?

31. From whose reign does the Tower of London date?

32. What guarantee of fundamental privileges was King John forced to grant?

33. The English Parliament was divided into what two chambers in the fourteenth century?

34. What was the first power of the English Parliament?

35. What were the three Estates in the French Estates-General?

36. The English won the battles of Crécy and Poitiers with the use of what new weapon?

37. What countries fought in the Hundred Years' War?

38. How old was Joan of Arc when she persuaded the French king to let her lead the army to the relief of Orléans?

39. What popular Spanish hero was known as the Cid?

40. What ruling family came to control the title of Holy Roman Emperor?

41. To what people were the original natives of Prussia related?

42. Who was Genghis Khan?

43. Who was Marco Polo?

44. What was the Kipchak Empire?

45. Who were the Janizaries?

46. What were the three ranks in a guild?

47. What was the Hanseatic League?

48. Who were the two great writers of the later Middle Ages who wrote in their native tongues?

49. In what art did medieval genius reach its highest expression?

50. What effect did the use of gunpowder have on medieval warfare?

FOR FURTHER STUDY

CRUSADES, by Harold Lamb. (Doubleday & Co., New York.)

INTRODUCTION TO MEDIEVAL EUROPE, by J. W. Thompson and E. N. Johnson. (W. W. Norton, New York.)

LIFE IN THE MIDDLE AGES, by George Gordon Coulton. (The Macmillan Co., New York.)

LIFE ON A MEDIEVAL BARONY, by William Stearns Davis. (Harper & Bros., New York.)

MEDIEVAL CITIES, by Henri Pirenne. (Princeton University Press, Princeton.)

MIDDLE AGES, by Edward M. Hulme. (Henry Holt, New York.)

WORLD HISTORY AT A GLANCE, by Joseph Reither. (Barnes & Noble, New York.)

III

An Outline of Modern History

THE DAWN OF MODERN HISTORY

THERE WAS no sharp line of demarcation to terminate the Middle Ages, and "modern" history begins at different times in the various countries of Europe. However, in the fifteenth century, a great number of events indicate that in many fields of activity the characteristic life of medieval times was coming to a close. The great period of exploration leading up to the discovery of America began in this century. Vigorous new styles of art and architecture developed in Italy and spread throughout Europe. This was the period when national literatures began to take root, and the Latin language gave way to modern tongues in writing. In the field of economics, new trade and prosperity outmoded the old guild systems and the beginnings of labor and capital as separate groups were noticeable. Also at this time there was the great religious Reformation, which more than any of the other developments of this period affected the political scene in Europe.

EXPLORATION AND DISCOVERY

In western Europe medieval geography was based on legends, Biblical lore, and plain supposition, although the Arabs and Moors had more accurate notions of the earth. Common belief held that the earth was surrounded by oceans populated by enormous sea serpents, and that at the equator the water boiled.

The Crusades were a factor in helping to correct some of these fantastic ideas. Those who went on the Crusades learned something of the extent of the world. The existence of China and India was revealed through trade, and through the Mongols something was learned about remote eastern countries. The *Travels* of Marco Polo was widely read throughout western Europe; and, stimulated by these accounts of the Far East, the people made voyages of exploration and discovery. These were an expression of the inquiring tendency in European minds, which was to characterize the transition to the "modern" period.

Nautical instruments, invented or borrowed from the Moors, made possible voyages away from the seacoast, and they made them relatively safe. Navigation was tremendously advanced by the mariner's compass, which possibly came from the Chinese through the Arabs. Fears of the unknown were gradually overcome through the chartering of coasts and by the possibilities of profit through trade. When by their conquests the Ottoman Turks closed the usual routes to the East, it was necessary to find a new route, and preferably by water.

Great advances in the art of navigation were made by Prince Henry of Portugal (1394–1460), called "the Navigator." He was responsible for numerous voyages of exploration. Sails had now supplanted oarsmen. In 1471, the equator was crossed by Portuguese sailors, who found to their surprise that the sea did not boil. In 1497, Vasco da Gama set sail from Lisbon, the capital of Portugal, voyaged around Africa and across the Indian Ocean, reaching the great Indian trading city of Calicut. When he returned home he had with him a cargo that he sold for a tremendous profit over the expenses of his expedition.

Portugal formed an ambitious colonial empire in India, the East Indies, and a little later Brazil, which was discovered in 1500. For some time Portugal was enriched by these new trade routes, and was able to keep them and all the lands her explorers discovered for her own exclusive use. In the seventeenth century, however, her colonies were broken up by the French, English, and Dutch, as she was not powerful enough to maintain her monopoly.

THE DISCOVERY OF AMERICA

Christopher Columbus, a splendid sailor and a man of foresight, had read widely and knew that the earth was probably a sphere. This conclusion had been reached by some thinkers in the Middle Ages; and it was suspected, even if not proved, in ancient Greece and Egypt. Columbus, therefore, believed that he could reach the Indies by sailing westward across the Atlantic Ocean.

Because the maritime power of the Italian cities after the Turkish wars was on the wane, Columbus applied to Portugal for aid. When Portugal turned him down, he went to the Spanish monarchs and enlisted the interest of Queen Isabella. It was at the expense of Spain that Columbus undertook his first voyage in 1492. This resulted in the discovery of the Bahama Islands, believed by Columbus to be a part of the East Indies. These, with the other islands, are today called the West Indies because of that error.

On three other voyages Columbus explored the Caribbean Sea and the coasts of Central and South America. In 1519, Magellan, a Portuguese, set out to circumnavigate the globe. He died on this voyage, but his sailors completed it and reached Europe safely. It was proved beyond a doubt that America and Asia were separate continents. Men began to have more definite ideas of the earth's size and of its spherical shape.

In the meantime the English were active on the sea. John Cabot, the Italian navigator, was employed by Henry VII, the first Tudor king of England, and he made a voyage to the North American coast between Labrador and Nova Scotia in 1497. He landed, perhaps, at about the same spot where Leif Ericson's Northmen had touched some centuries before. The following year Cabot pushed his explorations southward to what is now Florida. He thought he had reached India, but he found no indications of wealth, and consequently his discoveries were forgotten for the time being.

The American natives were called Indians because those who found them believed they had reached India. European explorers and invaders regarded the Indians as subjects for plunder and ruthlessly took their gold and silver ornaments, gems, and other valuable belongings back to Europe. From American mines the European countries were enriched. The "New World" also furnished Europe with new crops developed by the American Indians, including maize (Indian corn), the potato, tobacco, and other products native to America such as chocolate, quinine (Peruvian bark), and mahogany.

Europe looked westward to the New World, and began to colonize it. There would be wars for supremacy between the Spaniards, French, and English, and, of course, with the Indians. Western discoveries changed trade routes, and new cities of Europe became important as trading centers, among them Lisbon, Cádiz, Bordeaux, Cherbourg, Antwerp, and Amsterdam. Wealth was increased by the new sources of gold and silver, and there was a corresponding increase in prosperity. Businesses developed and increased in size, wages went up, and the standard of living rose.

The horizon of the known world spread out, and the progress of exploration and development was added to the already great stimulation resulting from the revival of classic learning which occurred at this same time.

Economic Changes

The economic situation was also changing radically at the close of the Middle Ages. With the growth of cities and commerce and the increased circulation of money, the manorial tenant was going out of existence. There was a marked decline in serfdom, and farmers began to pay rent instead of feudal dues. The lords became rich, and antagonism began to develop between capital and labor.

In 1349 the Black Death, or bubonic plague, had devastated England, and through many years of the fourteenth century it swept through Europe with a death toll of millions of people. Thus was labor made scarce and the demand for hired laborers increased.

Parliament in England made an attempt in 1351 to limit the wages that workmen could legally receive, and repeated the effort thirteen different times during the next hundred years; but in spite of these efforts, wages kept going up, with consequent encouragement for the laboring class to stand up for their rights.

The condition of serfdom was coming to an end, and the struggle between labor and capital was beginning. By the end of the fifteenth century, serfdom was a thing of the past in the greater part of France, Italy, and England, whereas in sections of central Europe it prevailed as late as the nineteenth century. The peasants' condition was very slowly ameliorated.

THE RENAISSANCE

"Renaissance" means *rebirth*. The Renaissance is the name given to the period of transition between medieval and modern times, and is also the term used to describe the intellectual spirit that brought the Middle Ages to a close. The events we have been discussing are associated with the outburst of curiosity and energy in almost all fields of thought and activity which typifies the Renaissance.

In the fourteenth century there was a reappearance of classicism in arts and letters, initiated by the poet Petrarch and the Italian humanists. In this period both the language and literature of the Greeks were being rediscovered in Italy. The study of ancient literature and man's cultural past was central to the new spirit called *humanism;* and these studies were termed the "humanities" to distinguish them from the less realistic scholasticism of the medieval period. The leading figures in the new literature of Italy were Dante, Petrarch, and Boccaccio.

The invention of printing and the use of paper furnished the chief impetus to the spread of knowledge. Paper was made in China at some much earlier period, and its manufacture was known to the Moors. It was introduced to Italy through the Arabian occupation of Sicily. From Italy it was sold to northwestern Europe.

About 1450, in Germany, Gutenberg first printed from movable types; and the Gutenberg Bible still stands as a monument of civilization. After Gutenberg came such oustanding printers as Aldus Manutius in Venice and William Caxton in London. No more would manuscripts have to be laboriously copied by hand. Books could now be reproduced with comparative speed and ease, and the spread of knowledge was destined to receive an unprecedented impetus.

Painting and sculpture renewed their vigor in Italy during the Renaissance, and there appeared such masters as Leonardo da Vinci, Michelangelo, and Titian. Music also developed notably, and in the sixteenth century the violin was first used, and also the harpsichord (the ancestor of the modern piano). Palestrina, a church organist, was the first great composer of the Renaissance. His church music laid the foundation for modern composition.

The Renaissance had spread northward from Italy by the middle of the fifteenth century. Erasmus (died in 1536) was a famous Dutch humanist whose works in Latin were read throughout western Europe. During the Middle Ages literature had always been written in Latin, but authors now began to write in the native tongues or vernaculars of the different countries.

When the Renaissance of the arts had gotten fully under way, modern science began its rapid rise. Up to this time superstition and religious taboos (such as those which prevented the dissection of the human body) had stood in the way of scientific progress, but with the new increase in enlightenment the way to tremendous progress was opened.

CHURCH AND STATE

The attempt made by the Roman Catholic Church to bring the world together under one government, in the manner of the Roman Empire, had failed. Because the church developed controversial customs, it became divided into monkish clans and involved itself in petty quarrels with the emperors and kings. Even within the papacy there were quarrels for the elections. The church had lost its temporal power by the end of the Middle Ages, and its religious influence was shaken by opposition on the grounds of theology and spiritual matters.

In the year 1453, Constantinople fell to the advancing Ottoman Turks from the East. This date has often been chosen to signal the beginning of modern history. The Ottoman or Turkish Empire continued its advance into Europe until in the sixteenth century the Turks held the whole of Greece, Thessaly, Macedonia, Bosnia, Serbia, and parts of Hungary, Bulgaria, Transylvania, and Moldavia. The Turks, however, met a crushing defeat before the walls of Vienna in 1529; and in the naval battle of Lepanto, in 1571, their fleet was destroyed. Little by little, Turkey was pushed back into Asia, except for the small European area around Constantinople, which the Turks called Istanbul. Thus Christendom had triumphed throughout Europe, although the various countries were growing more distinct, nationalistic, and ambitious for themselves.

The popes had made considerable progress in their attempt to reestablish the Roman Empire as a vassal of the church, but the Holy Roman Empire was an empire in name only. Insisting on papal supremacy, Pope Boniface VIII (1294–1303) had issued a papal bull, or edict, forbidding the collection of taxes from church property by laymen. He was opposed by Philip of France, who refused to allow any gold or silver to leave his country, thus cutting off revenue to Rome. The pope came to an agreement, but the quarrel was not ended. Philip arrested one of the papal legates, and the pope objected, whereupon Philip gathered French patriots around him, and they declared that their king was responsible to God alone. At Anagni, in 1303, Pope Boniface VIII was captured by French soldiers, but he was freed by the populace. He died soon after. Philip influenced the selection of the next pope, who made Avignon, within the southeastern boundary of France, the new seat of the papacy.

The papal government remained at Avignon for about seventy years (1309–1377), and during this time the papacy was virtually a fief of the French crown. This period in church history is known as the "Babylonian Captivity." Under this arrangement the power of the popes declined rapidly.

When Rome again became the residence of the popes, an Italian, Urban VI, was elected, whereas the French-controlled cardinals named Clement VII. Thus Clement became pope at Avignon, while Urban became pope at Rome. This was the Great Schism (1378–1417). It was corrected at the Council of Constance (1414–1418) when Martin V in Rome was made the only pope, but the power of the papacy was weakened beyond recovery.

THE REFORMATION

In the fifteenth century the worldliness of the popes, bishops, and priests subjected them to severe criticism and open opposition. This was heresy, of course, and heretics were not tolerated by the church. They were punished as criminals—sometimes with torture and frequently with death. The Catholic Church was officially the state religion everywhere in Europe, and therefore heresy was considered a crime not only against God but, under firmly Catholic rulers, a crime against the state.

From time to time the popes promoted persecutions of the more powerful heretics. In 1209–1229, Pope Innocent III waged a crusade against the Albigenses, who were a heretical sect in southern France. Thousands of them—men, women, and children—were killed. Another group, the Waldensians, or followers of Peter Waldo, did not fare as badly, and some of their survivors still live in Italy today as a Protestant sect.

John Wycliffe, the English reformer, to whom other reformers on the Continent owed much, preached that a belief in the truth of the Bible was the only source of grace, and that interpretation by the church was unnecessary. During his life (1320–1384) he escaped persecution, but after his death the Council of Constance declared him a heretic and ordered his remains to be dug up and burned. Wycliffe's beliefs were spread throughout England by his followers, who were known as Lollards and who preached to the common people in English instead of the more orthodox Latin of the church.

Anne of Bohemia, who was the wife of King Richard II of England, was in sympathy with Wycliffe's teachings. Through her, his views spread to Bohemia on the Continent, where John Huss championed them at the University of Prague. As a result, in 1413 the Council of Constance summoned Huss before them, promising him safe conduct—stating that, whatever the judgment passed on him, he should be allowed to return freely to Bohemia to be punished by the king. But the assembled churchmen sentenced him to death and had him burned at the stake. This aroused Bohemians in rebellion against the Holy Roman Empire, and the Hussite wars followed.

By the sixteenth century the church had drifted far toward disunity, and the ground was prepared for the religious upheaval known as the Reformation. The Reformation began with an attempt to *reform* the church, which was accused of worldliness and ecclesiastical tyranny. The Reformation started in the religious unrest of the late Middle Ages, but it was given impetus by the revival of learning during the Renaissance, when men's minds were stimulated toward independent thinking.

MARTIN LUTHER

The leading spirit of the Reformation was Martin Luther (1483–1546), although he was not personally aware of it at the time. So that all might become acquainted with his views, he posted them on the door of the Castle Church in Wittenberg in 1517 and offered to debate them with anyone. The sensational effect of Luther's ideas was to start a movement of public protest against church abuses—a movement which was to sweep over central and northern Europe. Luther was denounced as a heretic by the church, and the Diet of Worms, which Charles V, the Holy Roman Emperor and Hapsburg ruler of Austria, called in 1521, tried in vain to check the Reformation.

For the next few years Charles V was kept occupied by wars with France, Turkey, and the Mohammedans of North Africa. He was victorious over France in 1529. Subsequently, at the Diet of Spires, a definite decree was issued against the teachings of Luther. The German princes who endorsed Luther's attitude thereupon entered a protest, and since that time the dissenters from the Roman Catholic Church have therefore been known as Protestants.

The present creed of Lutheran churches was drawn up at the Diet of Augsburg by the Protestants in 1539. (What were called *diets* were imperial councils which were summoned by the Holy Roman Emperor. Their purpose was to consider methods of effecting certain results in the administration of church or empire. Each diet was named after the city in which it was held—such as Worms or Augsburg.) Before Luther's death in 1546, there had been no serious fight against his doctrines.

Charles V engaged in religious wars with the Protestants (most of whom were then Lutherans) beginning in 1547. These wars ended in 1555 in the Peace of Augsburg, which allowed each German prince to select either Catholicism or Lutheranism for his people. After that, peace among the German states lasted for sixty years. When Charles V abdicated (1555–1556) he left his dominions to his son Philip II and his brother Ferdinand I. The latter, as ruler of Austria, Bohemia, and Hungary, became Holy Roman Emperor.

OTHER LEADERS OF THE REFORMATION

While the influence of Luther's Protestantism was spreading in Europe, other reformers made their appearance. Ulrich Zwingli (1484–1531) led the reform movement in Switzerland. John Calvin (1509–1564), a Frenchman, was active in the Reformation at Geneva (Switzerland), and founded Calvinism (since broken up into various sects), which had an influence on the Thirty-nine Articles of the Episcopal Church of England. John Knox, a Scotsman, met Calvin at Geneva, after which he returned to Scotland to preach the Reformation. He died in 1572. It was in Scotland that the Presbyterian Church developed. In Denmark, Norway, Sweden, Finland, and Estonia, the tenets of Luther were also widely adopted; and today Scandinavia remains predominantly Lutheran.

THE ENGLAND OF HENRY VIII

The Tudors came to power in England as a result of the War of the Roses. This domestic struggle for the English throne took place between the house of York, with a white rose for its emblem, and the house of Lancaster, whose emblem was a red rose. The house of Lancaster was victorious in 1485, and Henry Tudor became King Henry VII of England. This was the beginning of more than a hundred years of absolute monarchy.

Henry VIII succeeded to the throne in 1509. His reign was to be one of the most colorful and critical in the history of England. Cardinal Wolsey, who became the British Chancellor, was the king's right-hand man and to a degree the power behind the throne. When Henry's brother died, Henry secured a dispensation from the pope to marry his brother's widow, Catherine. This royal marriage was thought politically advisable because Catherine was a daughter of Ferdinand and Isabella of Spain. All the children of this union died with the exception of a daughter, Mary. The king had meantime become enamored of a court lady, one Anne Boleyn, and wished to marry her in the hope that she would bear him a male successor to the throne. Henry therefore asked Cardinal Wolsey to obtain for him a papal divorce from Catherine.

Catherine's nephew, Charles V, was opposed to the divorce, being unwilling to have his aunt humiliated. Charles, as Holy Roman Emperor, exerted pressure on the pope, and consequently Wolsey failed in his mission. In a rage at the cardinal, Henry degraded him and confiscated his property.

Wolsey's post was given to Thomas Cromwell; and Thomas Cranmer became Archbishop of Canterbury, and virtually religious chief of England. *The Book of Common Prayer,* prepared under Cranmer's direction, became a part of the Church of England ritual. Finally, through Cranmer's encouragement, Henry made his decision to ignore the pope, and accepted a divorce from Catherine, pronounced by a church court with Cranmer at its head. Henry then married Anne Boleyn, who became the mother of Elizabeth, who was to be one of England's greatest sovereigns. All relations with the Church of Rome were severed in 1534 by the English Parliament when it passed the Act of Supremacy. Henry confiscated much of the wealth of the Catholic monasteries.

Henry VIII had six wives in all. His son, Edward VI—the child of Jane Seymour, whom he married after he had sent the hapless Anne Boleyn to the block—came to the throne in 1547 at the age of nine. The Duke of Somerset ruled in Edward's stead, and helped to spread Protestantism throughout England. *The Book of Common Prayer,* revised in

1552 in the reign of Edward VI, under the direction of Cranmer, confirmed Protestant reforms in the English Church. Under Henry's successors, despite abrupt reversals—especially the persecution of Protestants by the Catholic "Bloody Mary"—the Reformation became established among the English people.

In the early part of Elizabeth's reign, the Thirty-nine Articles of faith—originally forty-two in 1552—were drafted by a group of bishops. They defined clearly the Calvinistic slant in Anglican theology, and firmly declared the supremacy of the Crown. Under Elizabeth, who came to the throne in 1558 and ruled until 1603, the Church of England became distinct from any other, and England became the leading Protestant power in Europe.

THE COUNTER-REFORMATION

Combating the Protestant Reformation, the Roman Church brought forces to bear in a Counter-Reformation. There had been no appreciable effect from decrees against Protestantism. While popes of a worldly tendency had been among the underlying causes of the Reformation, subsequent popes who were less open to criticism assisted the church in regaining some of its lost ground; but the Roman Catholic Church was destined never again to dominate the western world politically.

The religious order called the Society of Jesus, founded in 1534 by a Spanish soldier-monk named Ignatius Loyola, was the most important agency of the Counter-Reformation. The members are still called Jesuits. Loyola and his adherents, by methods which have been criticized at times, were the means of bringing back into the Catholic fold many princes and their peoples. Jesuit missionaries, among whom was the illustrious Marquette, went to America to convert the Indians, and achieved considerable fame in the field of exploration.

An arbitrary action taken by the Catholics was the establishment of the drastic Spanish Inquisition, which was a revival of the earlier courts of investigation organized for the trial and punishment of heretics from Catholicism. This was chiefly held in Spain and Portugal in the thirteenth, fifteenth, and sixteenth centuries. Its investigations were carried on with the help of torture. It issued a condemnation of all Protestant tenets, and effected some reforms within the church. It also established the Index, or list of heretical books forbidden for Catholic reading.

The Reformation was completed before the close of the sixteenth century. By 1600 nearly half of the subjects of the Roman Catholic Church had renounced their allegiance. The unity of western Christendom, which had been preserved throughout the Middle Ages, thus disappeared and has not since been restored.

ENGLAND'S RISE TO POWER

When he was fifteen years old, Edward VI died. The Duke of Northumberland, who had succeeded the Duke of Somerset as regent, placed his daughter-in-law, Lady Jane Grey, on the throne in an effort to retain regal power. She ruled nine days. The rightful queen, Mary Tudor, who was the daughter of Catherine, had the support of the people and ascended the throne in 1553. So sternly and cruelly did she rule that she gained the sobriquet "Bloody Mary." She was a devout Catholic, and condemned many heretics to death. She also executed the usurpers, Northumberland and Lady Grey, who was a pretty young girl of sixteen years. Among her other victims was Archbishop Cranmer, who was burned at the stake. Mary was wedded to Philip II, who was the son of Charles of Austria and became the King of Spain. Mary, against the will of the English people, joined Philip in Spain's war against France. When Mary died, England pursued a policy of opposition to Spain.

Mary was succeeded, in 1558, by Queen Elizabeth, who had a remarkable reign of forty-five years. During her reign there was a great revival of English learning and a flowering of literature, especially the drama. This was the time of William Shakespeare. This period is commonly known as the Elizabethan Age. As she never married, Elizabeth was called the Virgin Queen; and the American colony of Virginia was named in her honor. She had the advice of a number of competent men, including Lord Burghley; and she was for the most part an exceptionally wise ruler.

Elizabeth's mother, Anne Boleyn, was a Protestant, and Elizabeth sponsored the Episcopal Church of England. As she saw it, however, religious matters were subservient to the political destiny of England. At first she was not opposed to celebrating mass herself when a state visit to her court made it an advantageous courtesy. It was not until several years after her coronation that the pope was absolutely sure he had no place in the Church of England. She kept British Catholics from showing opposition to her rule by appearing to favor them. During the later years of her reign, Catholics were executed for refusing to join the English church. In reducing the Irish to a state of subjugation, Elizabeth's treatment of them was such that they remained Catholic in spite of her attempts to bring them into the English church.

Mary, Queen of Scots, enters English history as the Catholic party's candidate for the throne at this time. Mary was descended from Henry

VII. Scotland was a Protestant country, but Mary, having been brought up in France, was a Catholic. Mary bore a son to her second husband, Henry Stuart (Lord Darnley); this son was later to sit on the throne of England as James I, first of the Stuart line. Suspected of plotting her husband's death, Mary fled from Scotland to England, where she was imprisoned by Queen Elizabeth for nineteen years. Being accused of complicity in a plot to secure the British throne, she was beheaded in 1587.

One of the outstanding events in Elizabeth's reign was the defeat of the Spanish Armada in 1588. It was the intention of Philip II of Spain, who was a champion of the Catholic Church, to conquer England and put his own heir on the throne. The threat united English Protestants and Catholics to defend their country against invasion. Under the command of Lord Howard, Sir Martin Frobisher, and Sir Francis Drake, three of England's greatest sea fighters, the British met and wiped out the Armada, which was then the greatest fleet of the greatest power in Europe. The power of Spain on the seas was forever broken, and England assumed the place of Spain in the New World.

RELIGIOUS WARS ON THE CONTINENT

On the Continent there was sanguinary conflict between Catholic and Protestant, while in comparative religious peace Elizabeth and her successors were ruling England. The Inquisition had quelled Protestantism in Spain and Italy, whereas in Scandinavia Protestantism had prevailed without fighting. The story, however, was different in France, the Netherlands, and Germany.

Under Francis I and his successors, French Protestants—called Huguenots—were vigorously persecuted. In their battles with the French Catholics, the Huguenots were led by Prince de Condé and Admiral Coligny. The Catholics were under the leadership of the Duke de Guise and Catherine de Medici. What is known as the Massacre of St. Bartholomew's Day occurred on August 24, 1572, when the French Catholics swept through Paris, slaughtering the Huguenots, and a few days later through other French territory.

Henry IV, a Bourbon king known as Henry of Navarre, was a Protestant. Inheriting the French throne in 1589, he won possession of it only after a long fight. Henry embraced the Catholic faith as a move toward national peace, because most Frenchmen of his time were Catholics. In 1598, however, by the Edict of Nantes, he gave freedom of worship and full political rights to the Protestants.

Henry was assassinated in 1610. At this time Cardinal Richelieu appeared on the scene. He lived from 1585 to 1642, and was one of the wiliest statesmen in all history. He was the adviser to that weak-kneed monarch, King Louis XIII, and from 1624 to 1642 he was master of France. Depriving the Huguenots of their power, he still left them freedom of worship and civil rights. He subordinated the French nobility to the Crown after squelching their growing mutiny against the king. During Germany's Thirty Years' War, Richelieu used his diplomatic offices to curb the increasing power of the Hapsburg ruler of the Holy Roman Empire.

Owing to intermarriage between royal families, the Netherlands, in the sixteenth century, was under the domination of the sovereign of Spain. Most of the Dutch people had become Protestants, and Charles V and later Philip II of Spain wished to bring them back to the Catholic Church. There was, therefore, a severe and ruthless persecution of these people under a local revival of the Inquisition. Sent to put down local uprisings, the Duke of Alva arrived in Brussels with a Spanish army in 1567 and set up a terrible "Council of Blood."

William the Silent, called Prince of Orange, had sought refuge in Germany from the persecutions of Alva, and now he returned to lead an army against the oppressor. In 1574, the natives broke the dikes at Leyden and made the sea their ally, so that the Spaniards were driven away or drowned. The Dutch Republic was formed in 1579, and was called Holland. The first governor was William, and when in later years the country became a monarchy, his descendants sat on the throne. The country that is now Belgium bowed to Spain and later to Austria, but at last gained its independence. As a result of rewards offered by Philip II of Spain, William was assassinated in 1584.

The end of religious strife through force of arms came with the Thirty Years' War, which lasted from 1618 to 1648. It was a bloody conclusion, for of all the religious wars between Catholics and Protestants, it was the worst. The chief battleground was in the duchies and kingdoms that one day would be united into Prussian Germany.

The Thirty Years' War originated in 1618 with a revolt of the Protestant nobles of Bohemia against the imperial authority of the Hapsburgs, who also controlled the Crown of Bohemia. Fearing the accession of the Catholic Ferdinand, they elected Frederick, the leader of the Protestant League of German states, as their king. A year later, Ferdinand succeeded to the throne of the Holy Roman Empire and was able to defeat Frederick. Christian IV of Denmark entered the war against the Hapsburgs and suffered severe defeat. Meanwhile, the Austrian general Wallenstein had entered the conflict, apparently as a defender of the empire; he laid Germany waste, paying his soldiers in plunder, and retired to live luxuriously at Prague. In 1630, Gustavus Adolphus, king of Sweden, invaded Germany. He had a Protestant army, and his purpose was to save Protestantism, which had become the official religion of most northern states. The Protestant religion was gravely threatened after the losses it suffered during the early years of the war. The Swedes were victors by 1632, and the power of the Hapsburg house over Germany came to an end.

Cardinal Richelieu went into the Thirty Years' War during its last period, for though he was a Catholic, he wanted to humble the Hapsburgs. So he dispatched his armies, which, united with the victorious Swedes, were successful. The war had cost Germany possibly half her population and the loss of inestimable wealth in property. It took a century for the country to recover from its ravages.

The Thirty Years' War was ended with the Treaty of Westphalia in 1648. By its terms Sweden received territory on the Baltic and North seas; the independence of Holland and of Switzerland was recognized; and France was given the territory called Alsace. The jurisdiction of the Holy Roman Emperor, who had nominally controlled the German states, was reduced to Austria. Although they were too weak as yet to be of much political importance, the German states became independent. Although the situation was not sanctioned by the pope, Lutheran and Calvinist were placed on a basis of equality with Catholic. As had been planned by the astute Richelieu, France was now the greatest power in Europe.

The bloody and ruthless character of the Thirty Years' War impressed thinking men with the necessity of formulating rules to protect noncombatants, to care for prisoners, and to do away with pillage and massacre. In 1625, Hugo Grotius, a Dutch jurist, published in Paris a work called *On the Laws of War and Peace*. This book of Grotius founded international law. Gustavus Adolphus of Sweden carried a copy with him on his campaigns. Its important doctrines were recognized in the Peace of Westphalia. Grotius, in his book, gave up the concept of a temporal and spiritual head of Christendom. All nations were regarded as equal in the sight of international law.

SEVENTEENTH-CENTURY ENGLAND

THE FIRST STUARTS

When Queen Elizabeth died without direct heirs, the throne passed to her nearest male relative, who proved to be a weak monarch. He was James I (King James VI of Scotland), who took the English throne in 1603. The son of Mary, Queen of Scots, he was a Stuart. And now, although their parliaments were separate and distinct, England and Scotland were joined under the same sovereign.

In England, religious reformers came to be called Nonconformists and Separatists. These dissenters opposed the similarities of the Church of England ritual to that of the Roman Catholic Church, and were therefore known as Puritans, the word being used at first with a sense of reproach. Owing to King James's persecution of the Puritans, many of them went to Holland and America. The Pilgrim Fathers, who were Puritans, landed near Plymouth, Massachusetts, in 1620. Under James, in 1611, a new translation of the Bible into English was made, and it has since been known as the King James Version.

James's mother was a Catholic, and at first he was more tolerant of Catholics, but before long he enforced the Elizabethan laws against them. This led to the Gunpowder Plot, with one Guy Fawkes at its head, although the real leader was Robert Catesby. In this plot certain Catholics made a conspiracy to blow up the king and the Houses of Parliament in 1605. Before the plot was carried out, Fawkes was captured, and for about two hundred years after, November 5 was celebrated in England as Guy Fawkes Day, on which effigies of the plotter, called "guys," were burned. For many years afterward, the Catholics were unpopular and oppressed in England.

Under the Tudors, England had been virtually an absolute monarchy. James and the Stuarts who came after him tried to keep it so. But the Stuarts were not so strong as the Tudors, and besides, the English people had become more conscious of liberty. Civil war came as a result of the strife between the Stuart kings and Parliament. Although Parliament had as yet no legislative powers, the principle of "no taxation without representation" was traditional. A king who wished to raise money from taxation was obliged to call Parliament. The Tudors had enjoyed several sources of income over which the Crown alone had control. An outstanding example of strictly royal income is the money Henry VIII realized from the confiscation of church property after the Act of Supremacy made him head of the English church. This monarch also debased the intrinsic (actual metal) value of government-minted coin money, thus making a profit. Elizabeth amassed wealth from the pillaging and the ultimate ransack of the Spanish fleet, as well as by astute management of her subjects. The Stuarts, however, unpopular for many reasons, found themselves dependent on Parliament for funds.

In 1625, James I died. This occurred nine years after the death of Shakespeare, and eighteen years after the founding of the Virginia colony named for him—Jamestown. James's son, Charles I, succeeded him.

Charles and his badly chosen ministers were not popular. For lack of the co-operation he demanded, Parliament after Parliament was dissolved, and for eleven years he ruled, not without success, with no Parliament at all. In 1628, he signed the Petition of Right, which followed the tradition of the Magna Carta in establishing fundamental English liberties. King Charles endeavored in many ways to raise money without Parliament's help, but many of his powers were curtailed by the famous Long Parliament (1640–1653), which had among its leaders Oliver Cromwell and John Pym.

OLIVER CROMWELL AND THE COMMONWEALTH

Oliver Cromwell became the leader of the Puritans, who were called Roundheads because they shaved their heads as a part of their rigidly plain costume. They were bitterly opposed to the king. The king's supporters were known as Cavaliers. In 1642 these two factions became engaged in civil war, and, through the death of other leaders, Cromwell became the most important figure in the country. Under him, the Roundheads defeated the royalists at Marston Moor in 1644, and they were subsequently victorious in all England. Those members of the Long Parliament who were favorable to the king were expelled in 1648 by Pride's Purge, led by Thomas Pride; and the remaining members were called the Rump Parliament. The opposition and uncompromising attitude of King Charles toward the dissenters resulted in his being tried for treason and executed in 1649.

Then England became a Commonwealth with Cromwell at its head, with the title of Lord Protector of England, Scotland, and Ireland. Leading his armies, Cromwell swept through Ireland, which was in a state of rebellion, forced back the Scots, who were resentful, and in 1653 dissolved the Rump Parliament. Abroad, Cromwell carried on successful wars with the Spaniards and Dutch. However, there were discontented rumblings among the people in England. Weary, harassed, and in fear of assassination, Cromwell died in 1658. His power had been great, and he had proved that the people need never tolerate a tyrannical king. However, Cromwell's rule in his later years was unpopular with the majority of Englishmen.

THE RESTORATION IN ENGLAND

Amidst almost unparalleled rejoicing by the populace, the Stuart Charles II—son of Charles I—entered London in 1660. The Commonwealth had disintegrated following Cromwell's death, and the restoration of the Stuart line of kings was a welcome change to the English people. No more did the monarch have absolute power. From this date onward, Parliament's control over the king would increase.

Charles II is usually labeled "the merry monarch." Gay, licentious, easily led into primrose ways, but as often the leader, he set the pace for an equally merry England. Literature and the theater reflected the immorality of the day. During the stern rule of the Puritans of the Commonwealth, the pendulum had reached one limit. With the Restoration, it swung to the other. It was thus perhaps natural that the new Parliament should treat Puritans and other dissenters with scant consideration.

Among the outstanding events in Charles II's reign was the enactment by Parliament in 1679 of the Habeas Corpus Act, which made it impossible for anyone to be imprisoned without a hearing or trial. In wars with the Dutch, England took the American colony of New Netherlands, which was renamed New York, after the king's brother, the Duke of York. The reign of Charles marked the beginning of two famous British political parties: the Whigs and the Tories. The Whigs favored a powerful Parliament and popular government, while the Tories wished more power for the king and less for the people.

THE "GLORIOUS REVOLUTION"

Charles II died in 1685, and his brother, James II, succeeded him. He was a Catholic, and new persecutions under him brought on the revolution of 1688. The English invited the Dutch Protestant William of Orange and his wife Mary, who was King James's eldest daughter, to rescue them from tyranny. William came with an army and, meeting no resistance, he took the English throne at the request of Parliament.

William of Orange and his wife ruled jointly as King William III and Queen Mary II. Mary died five years later, leaving William as sole ruler.

This bloodless dethronement of James II became known as the "Glorious Revolution." Such a peaceful change was possible because the English had in their earlier history made great strides toward representative government and personal liberties. The idea of the divine right of kings, which the Stuarts had attempted to impose on Parliament, was accepted only theoretically by the English. According to this theory, a king ruled by election of God and was responsible to no man for his actions. During the Glorious Revolution, the nobles and commons of Parliament virtually assumed power without attacking the king. Fearful of imprisonment, James II fled the land. Parliament then declared that by departure he had, in effect, abdicated. The Glorious Revolution, moreover, established that the Common Law of the land was superior to the king's will and pleasure.

Ireland showed opposition to the new king, and James, in exile, tried to get a foothold there. He was defeated, however, at the battle of the

Boyne in 1690. This victory was a great source of satisfaction to the Orangemen—the name given to Protestant Irishmen, who accepted William of Orange as their king. The French tried to support James's fight to regain the British throne in 1692, but the French fleet was defeated.

With the accession of William and Mary to the throne, Parliament took care to continue its own authority and the Protestant religion by enacting the Bill of Rights, which has an equal place with the Magna Carta and the Petition of Right among the great documents of English constitutional history. The Bill of Rights included these provisions: (1) it required the sovereign henceforth to be a member of the Anglican Church; (2) it forbade him to "suspend" the operation of the laws, or to levy money, or to maintain a standing army without the consent of Parliament; (3) it guaranteed free election of members of Parliament and freedom of speech and action within the two Houses; (4) it forbade excessive bail or the imposition of cruel and unusual punishments; (5) it affirmed the right of subjects to petition the king and ordered the holding of frequent Parliaments.

Although these were not new principles of political liberty, the English people were now able to give them the binding form of laws. They reappear in the first ten amendments to the Constitution of the United States. The Revolution of 1688–1689 was a great step forward in limiting the power of the king, and it set England on the road to a greater democracy.

CONTINENTAL POWERS

European powers in the seventeenth and eighteenth centuries were beginning to develop strongly nationalistic ambitions. There were continual wars for political supremacy, of conquest for more territory, for seaports or other commercial outlets. The people began to assert themselves and to demand their rights in spite of kings and leaders from the aristocracy.

THE ERA OF LOUIS XIV OF FRANCE

France became an absolute monarchy at an early date. Henry IV, crowned in 1589, was the first of the Bourbon kings, and under the scheming hand of Cardinal Richelieu, minister for Louis XIII, who humbled the powerful Hapsburgs of Austria, France came to be a leading power. In 1643, Louis XIV, five years old, became king, and his reign was destined to last from 1643 to 1715—72 years. It was a long story of royal indulgence, palatial magnificence, and the crushing of the people by heavy taxation. It was a golden age for the upper classes alone.

The young king's mother, Anne of Austria, ruled during the king's childhood. After Richelieu's death, she was assisted by his less astute pupil, Mazarin. The nobles were kept in subjection, and their military uprising was squelched in the War of the Fronde. Mazarin died in 1661, and Louis XIV took over the reins of government, which he held until his death. He believed that kings were divinely ordained to rule and were responsible only to God. Although he balked at any help, more good was done for the economic development of the government by the financial minister, Colbert, than the king was capable of. Under Colbert the French government became solvent, as he made the royal revenues exceed the tremendous expenditures. He fostered manufacturing by placing heavy duties on imports of foreign goods. Colbert was also successful in establishing a great French colonial empire, where raw materials could be obtained for manufacturing. Roads were built and improved within France in order to encourage trade and commerce. Vauban, Louis's war minister, built the great fortifications on the French-German frontier and supervised the organization and equipment of the French armies that were to wage the wars which mark practically the whole of the reign of Louis XIV.

The battles in the Netherlands (1667–1668) were included in the French wars, the French being opposed by the Dutch under William of Orange. A hundred years or more of intermittent war between England and France now began, for when, in 1689, William became king of England, that country entered the coalition to resist France's ambition to dominate Europe. King William's War extended as far as the American colonies.

Then the War of the Spanish Succession followed (1702–1713). The American phase of this conflict was called Queen Anne's War. In Europe the war was precipitated by the attempt of Louis XIV to unite the French and Spanish thrones under one Bourbon ruler. The war was ended with the Treaty of Utrecht in 1713, whereby the Spanish throne was given to a French prince, with the proviso that the two countries remain separate. In America, Acadia (now called Nova Scotia), Newfoundland, and Hudson Bay territory became English, and France lost her colonial power in the New World. England also secured Gibraltar, and Austria gained southern Italy and the Spanish Netherlands. Louis XIV died two years later, having exhausted his country with war.

The Edict of Nantes, by which toleration was granted to the French Huguenots, having been revoked by Louis XIV, the Huguenots left the country by the thousands, some to go to Germany, others to England, and still others to America. France was to feel the loss of the Huguenots keenly as time went on, for they were an important industrial class, and the loss of their labor and activity was a serious blow.

Prussia and Frederick the Great

The northern German state of Brandenburg was ruled by a margrave, who was one of the electors of the Holy Roman Empire. In 1415, Frederick I founded the famous Hohenzollern dynasty when he became the Elector of Brandenburg. (The Hohenzollerns in the nineteenth century were to become the rulers of all Germany.) By the early years of the seventeenth century Brandenburg had gained possession of a territory separated from it and well to the east, known as Prussia. Frederick William, who was called the Great Elector (1640–1688), set out to get control of the regions lying between, and his work did a great deal toward rehabilitating the lands which were devastated during the Thirty Years' War. He encouraged immigrants, held out a welcoming hand to French Huguenots, and, although a Protestant himself, welcomed those of the Catholic faith. He fostered large public improvements.

Frederick William's son was a much weaker man. Although he assumed the title of king in 1701, he accomplished little else. From about this time, the name of Brandenburg declined in importance. The united territories were called Prussia. The king following was Frederick William I (1713–1740). His son, Frederick the Great (1740–1786), was intelligent and despotic, and in a short time he advanced Prussia to a powerful position in Europe. This period was marked by the encouragement of industry and manufacturing, as it was fast becoming obvious that in modern times supremacy could not be maintained by force of arms alone.

Russia and Peter the Great

In the fifteenth century, Ivan the Great, by conquest and reform, established Russia as a nation. Peter the Great, who ruled from 1696 to 1725, distinguished himself by extending the boundaries northward and southward; it was Peter who made Russia a powerful empire. Without the advantages of an education at home, Peter traveled abroad in his youth and to good advantage learned the ways of other peoples. Urged on by the nobility, the military leaders known as the Streltsi rebelled, and Peter returned to Russia to quell the rebellion. Following the disciplinary procedure customary in the country at this time, he cut off the heads of hundreds of his enemies. He was cruel and treacherous, but he governed constructively and progressively. He gained control of the church, made reforms in dress, and was a force toward the modernization of Russia. He engaged in a war with Sweden, which was then ruled over by the young Charles XII. Although they were at first defeated, the Russian armies were finally victorious. The capital of Russia was founded in 1703 and named St. Petersburg after Peter the Great. (In 1914 it was renamed Petrograd, and later changed to Leningrad, after Lenin.)

Catherine the Great (1762–1796) was the next of the great Russian monarchs. Her cruelties and amorous intrigues were notorious. Peter and Catherine (by marriage) were of the house of Romanoff, which continued to rule Russia until the revolution of 1917.

THE PARTITION OF POLAND

Up to the eighteenth century Poland maintained her national independence and territorial extent, which she had won with great difficulty. She then fell prey to greater European powers; and between the years 1772 and 1795 the country was divided between Russia, Prussia, and Austria. Rebellions and uprisings had been fostered by these larger powers so that the country would be weakened and thus more easily split up among them. The largest portions of Poland were secured by Catherine the Great, of Russia, and Frederick the Great, of Prussia. Maria Theresa, empress of Austria, accepted a share because she knew that if she did not, the others would have divided that part between them also. And so, as a separate state, Poland lost its identity until the peace treaty that followed the World War of 1914–1918.

COLONIZATION

In the seventeenth and eighteenth centuries, colonies had been established in various parts of the newly discovered lands. Most active in the movement of colonization were England, France, Spain (at an earlier date), Portugal, and Holland. By the Treaty of Utrecht, most of North America was controlled by Great Britain.

It was in this period that the British gained their supremacy over India, which they held until the twentieth century with varying success. Great trading companies were organized, such as the British East India Company, which was chartered in 1600, and the French East India Company, which was chartered in 1664. They had the full power to make war locally with one another and to maintain their authority by any expedient means; and they exploited India and the East Indies.

Robert Clive, British statesman and general who founded the empire of British India, destroyed the power of Joseph Dupleix, governor-general of the French establishment in India in the eighteenth century, leaving only a small French foothold in India. During these battles among the British and French and the Indian rajahs occurred the tragedy of the Black Hole of Calcutta, when a Bengalese nabob imprisoned 146 Britishers in a small room of the old fort. This was in the stifling heat of the sultriest part of the year, and only twenty-three of the group survived the night.

Many wars were caused by colonial expansion. During the eighteenth-century period of British colonization, the English Prime Minister, Sir Robert Walpole, achieved historical eminence. Meanwhile George I, first of the house of Hanover, had ascended the British throne in 1714. He was German by birth, and could not speak English. George I and George II both ruled under the guidance of Walpole.

The French and Indian War in America was the counterpart of the Seven Years' War in Europe (1756–1763), the fight between France and Austria on the one hand and England and Prussia on the other. The victory was won by Frederick the Great of Prussia on the Continent, and in America by the English, under the Prime Minister William Pitt, the elder. The battle of Quebec, in 1759, decided the issue between the English and French in America. English rule in North America was challenged, however, a little over fifteen years later by her own colonies, which were to achieve independence by revolution and to become the United States in 1776.

In the midst of all these events, in widely separated parts of the globe, the leaven of the Renaissance had been working. Science and industry were forging ahead, and machinery was beginning to be developed. There were James Watt's steam engine (about 1770), Hargreaves' spinning jenny (about 1765), and Cartwright's power loom (about 1785). Weaving became a very important industry.

THE AGE OF THE FRENCH REVOLUTION

The splendor of the absolute monarchy in France, with its colorful grandeur, its courtly pageantry, the excesses of the ruling class, and the oppression of the people resulted in the French Revolution. This social and political upheaval, lasting from 1789 to 1799, covered a decade of battling, uncertainty, popular uprisings, bloody massacres, and turmoil. Royal extravagance and luxury made hunger and oppression intolerable, and the common people rebelled. They followed various leaders, some of them strong and others weak.

There were other privileged classes in France besides the king and his court. In addition to the king, all the nobles and clergy were engaged in the exploitation of the lower classes, who were hard put to it to get a slim livelihood from their labor after they had paid the high taxes necessary to finance the luxurious living of the nobles and worldly clerics. Another cause for the resentment of the common people was the fact that nobles and clergy were exempt from taxation.

Reforms were urged by progressive writers before the outbreak of the Revolution. There were contributions from Montesquieu (1689–1755), Voltaire (1694–1778), Diderot (1713–1784), and Rousseau (1712–1778). Montesquieu, in his *Spirit of Laws,* advocated a system of government based upon a separation of powers among the legislative, executive, and judicial departments. The Constitution of the United States shows the influence of Montesquieu's ideas.

Voltaire was the dominant intellectual figure of the eighteenth century. In his *Letters on the English* and in *Candide,* he championed freedom of speech and press, and attacked sham and superstition. He criticized the prevailing system of government and society because it was not based on reason. Although he was no atheist, he leveled his sharpest criticism at the Roman Catholic Church because he believed that the church, by reliance on dogma, blocked scientific progress.

Diderot, editor of the *Encyclopedia,* aimed to revise all human knowledge in accordance with the new discoveries in science and the new philosophy in politics and economics.

Rousseau was perhaps the most popular as well as the most radical of the French reformers. In the *Social Contract,* he stressed the idea that governments should be based on the consent of the governed rather than on divine right.

Adam Smith, John Locke, and Beccaria were other important writers outside France who by their writings influenced people against the society of the Old Regime. Adam Smith, in his *Wealth of Nations,* attacked mercantilism, or the system of government interference in industry, and urged a policy of laissez-faire (let things alone). John Locke was a strong advocate of individual liberty and democracy. Beccaria, in his *Essay on Crimes and Punishments,* attacked the barbaric criminal codes of the eighteenth century.

It was, however, the gnawings of physical hunger that really aroused the French people. The writers had a more pronounced influence on the "benevolent despots" of eastern Europe: Frederick the Great of Prussia, Catherine the Great of Russia, and Joseph II of Austria, absolute though they were, introduced into their governments many constructive and humanitarian reforms.

In the meantime the British colonies in America had begun the Revolution, but they were better off than the French revolutionists, for they did not have their internal difficulties. They were a long distance from the central government they were opposing, and they were more homogeneous in their sense of liberty. In order to weaken England, France, which was yet a monarchy in 1776, helped the American colonies. A large deficit in the French treasury was caused by France's aid to America, which hastened the French Revolution. But the success of the American Revolution in 1776 and the spectacle of the sturdy growth of the young republic of the United States inspired and encouraged the French revolutionary leaders.

Following the death of the Grand Monarch of France, Louis XIV, in 1715, the debauched Louis XV tried to match his grandeur. He was not only selfishly extravagant, but through his attitude of contempt toward the suffering peasantry he paved the road to revolution. Louis XVI ascended the throne in 1774, but though he was not a rake and libertine like his grandfather, he was not a ruler of strength. His queen was the hapless Marie Antoinette, sister of Joseph II of Austria and daughter of Maria Theresa. Indiscreet as many of her actions doubtless were, it is probable that much of the scandalous gossip about her was not founded on fact, but it served to fan popular excitement to a white heat.

It was the deficit in the French treasury that made immediate action necessary. In May, 1789, the Estates-General was called for the first time since 1610. It was made up of the three estates—the nobles, or First Estate; the clergy, or Second Estate; and the common people, or Third Estate. To get a hearing in the proceedings, the Third Estate insisted that all three meet as one assembly and that voting be by head rather than by Estate. When this was denied them, they declared themselves a representative assembly of the whole nation and, inviting members of the other two Estates to join them, made an agreement to remain together until France had a constitution. Here independence of the lower classes threatened, and the kings and nobles were alarmed. The Third Estate were spurred on by Count de Mirabeau, who was the first strong voice of the Revolution.

The conflict between the king and the Third Estate excited the people of Paris. They began to realize their importance, and to express themselves in the open on the subject of unjust taxation. Rebellion might be the means of getting something to eat.

THE OUTBREAK OF THE REVOLUTION

It was in July, 1789, when the mobs of Paris, storming the weakened fortress of the Bastille, overcame it and released its few prisoners. This marked the first military action, and the beginning of the French Revolution is given this date. July 14 has been celebrated in France ever since in much the same manner as the Fourth of July is celebrated in the United States. The frenzied condition of Paris was extended to the provinces, and the châteaux were stormed and looted. The people made a particular point of finding and tearing up the deeds which held their lands in feudal tenure to the nobles.

Now controlled by the Third Estate, the National Assembly ruled France until 1791. Sieyès was prominent in framing the constitution. Mirabeau was a powerful influence in the assembly. The nobles saw the handwriting on the wall, and on August 4, 1789, they renounced their ancient privileges. All the different classes thereafter were to be taxed alike. It was the achievement of the "equality of man" that was the real victory of the French Revolution. And although France would again be a monarchy, this fundamental conception of human equality would remain.

Spurred on by hunger and discontent, in October, 1789, the people marched to Versailles in the hope of getting food. Lafayette, who had previously gone to America to help General Washington, commanded the volunteer National Guards, and tried to keep the mob in order. Impending assassination for the king and queen was averted, and the royal family was removed to the Tuileries in Paris. Under the National Assembly and the new constitution, the king was retained as the nominal governmental head. Mirabeau did not succeed in his attempt to effect a truce between the royalists and the Third Estate, and he died in 1791 leaving France at the mercy of the rival factions.

This lack of unity among the revolutionary groups is one of the most significant factors of the French Revolution. It should be noted that prior to the first violence in 1789, the nobles themselves were in opposition to the absolute monarchy. Some of them continued to be. Although they were living very luxurious lives at the state's expense, the king had succeeded in removing from them the last vestiges of power. When the matter of taxation to support the royal government necessitated a calling of the Estates-General, there were many nobles who wished to exert their ancient powers. They wished to participate in government. Unfortunately, they were not able to ally their interests with those of the country at large. The bourgeoisie, or middle class, were ultimately the victors of the Revolution. They demanded constitutional rights. They were, however, very far from wishing legislative powers to be extended equally to all classes. They were wealthy people, mostly dependent on business, and they envisioned a prosperous France governed by themselves. The common people—hungry, with nothing to lose, and everything to gain, violent—were a great force in the Revolution. Among them were many parties, ranging from those allied with the bourgeoisie, in the endeavor to establish equity before the law and other constitutional privileges, to those more radical ones who wished to tackle the problem of poverty directly. These more "socialistic" groups added energy to the Revolution but ultimately accomplished very little. Other groups to be reckoned with were the church and the peasantry. The latter, oddly enough, were rarely allied with the poor mobs of Paris. They had different goals again.

According to the first constitution—while the king still reigned nominally—the Legislative Assembly was to be elected in 1791 to take the place of the National Assembly. Dissension within tore it apart, and the leading factions were Girondists and Jacobins. The Jacobins were the chief opponents of the government under the constitution; they wished to set up a republic and abolish monarchy entirely. Also republicans, the Girondists were more moderate than the Jacobins. At this point the revolutionary leaders, Robespierre, Marat, and Danton, came into prominence.

The influence of French nobles was exerted toward securing foreign intervention, and Austria and Prussia felt that it was their duty to put a quietus on republicanism in France. Their presumption enraged the newly aroused French patriots, and the Assembly declared war on Austria in 1792. The Duke of Brunswick led the invading armies and in effect spoke the doom of the French king by proclaiming that he had come to restore the power of the French monarchy.

The French populace replied to this threat by dethroning Louis XVI; and from Marseilles marched an army of Frenchmen demanding the abolition of monarchy to the stirring strains of the celebrated *Marseillaise* war hymn. An insurrection was stirred up by the Jacobins. The Tuileries were stormed on August 10, 1792; the king's Swiss Guards were assassinated; and the monarchy had fallen.

Meanwhile the French were urged by Danton to defend their country against invasion by foreigners. The French turned back their enemies under Dumouriez, and gained what they had not had before, a military prestige. Ostensibly conducted to terrify the First and Second Estates, the first massacres under the Commune were held in Paris in September. They served as a warning to the nobles and clergy, lest they should try to seize the government while the army was absent repelling invaders on the northwestern frontier.

THE FIRST FRENCH REPUBLIC

The Legislative Assembly was followed by the National Convention. The king was deposed. France was proclaimed a republic. The republic lasted the twelve years from 1792 to 1804. Louis XVI was decapitated on the guillotine January 21, 1793, and in October of the same year Marie Antoinette came to the same end.

The Reign of Terror extended from March, 1793, to August, 1794, although the principal beheadings covered a much shorter period—from September to the following July. During this time the Jacobins used their suddenly acquired power to decapitate anyone whom they suspected of royalist sympathies, or indeed anyone whom they did not approve of. It is estimated that about 3,000 met their death on the guillotine.

A coalition was formed against France by European powers to punish the revolutionists for the crime of regicide—putting to death their king, Louis XVI. But new generals led French armies to new successes, and by the end of 1793 the danger had passed.

Following the seething conflict between Girondists and Jacobins in the National Convention, there were revolts throughout France. In quelling the Toulon revolt came the first appearance of a man who was to determine the fate of France and leave his mark on the history of Europe—a young artillery officer named Napoleon Bonaparte.

The end of the Jacobins' Reign of Terror came almost at the same time as the death of their leader Robespierre, who was guillotined July 28, 1794. Charlotte Corday, who believed that she was doing a service to France, assassinated the French radical leader Marat; and Danton, who had opposed the unrestrained use of the guillotine, also came to his end by its "sharp tongue."

There was a new constitution formed in 1795 by the National Convention, and for four years France was governed under the Directory. Five Directors held the reins of government. During the Consulate (1799–1802), France was under the nominal head of consuls, and one of them was Napoleon Bonaparte.

Despite the violence of the Reign of Terror, the permanent achievements of the National Convention must not be overlooked. The metric system of weights and measures, based on decimals, was adopted. Negro slavery was declared illegal in the colonies. A state system of education was established and a beginning was made in codifying the laws. Napoleon established an equality of inheritance and the eldest son was no longer favored.

NAPOLEON'S CAREER

Corsica was a French dependency when, in 1769, Napoleon Bonaparte was born on this island. The future leader received his military education in France, and grew up to be a commander in the French artillery. He figured at Toulon and later at Paris. Faced with an Austrian war, the Directory sent the best French generals to the north, but Napoleon was put in command of a smaller army to attack by way of Italy. He seized this opportunity and promised his men loot and booty in Italy. Then by a series of brilliant attacks he won Italy for France. The French government was dazzled by this surprising success because the other expeditions had failed. Napoleon's successes in Italy, with his plans to make an early march on Vienna, caused Austria to sue for peace.

Napoleon then persuaded the Directory to allow him to lead an expedition into Egypt, but this was an abysmal failure. Returning to France, Napoleon was able to minimize his mistakes in Egypt. Meanwhile the people were weary of an unstable, vacillating government, and were ready to give their allegiance to a strong man.

Imitating Cromwell, Napoleon dispersed the French Council of Five Hundred. He made the Directory resign, and formed a consular government which was an imitation of Caesar's government of Rome; and made himself First Consul in 1799. He became First Consul for life in 1802, and had the privilege of naming his successor. Now he was indeed master of the whole of France.

France had lost Italy while Napoleon was away in Egypt, but he won it back at the battle of Marengo (1800). The Austrians were beaten by General Moreau at the battle of Hohenlinden. Napoleon brought about peace with Great Britain in 1802 by the peace of Amiens, but to remain at peace did not suit him. What he contributed to government at this time was primarily with the object of solidifying his own power. He restored the Catholic Church to its former position in France by negotiating the Concordat with Pius VII in 1801. Under him the educational system was reconstructed, and experts were appointed to codify the laws of France, the result being the Napoleonic Code.

His imagination inspired by his prototype Julius Caesar, Napoleon's aspirations toward an emperor's crown grew until, on December 2, 1804, he was made emperor as Napoleon I at Paris in the presence of Pope Pius VII. He placed the crown upon his own head. He retained his power by petty tyrannies at home and costly military victories abroad.

Russia, Austria, and Great Britain now formed the Third Coalition against France. The second had been just preceding the formation of the consular government, and the first during the Revolution. In 1805, Napoleon won a tremendous victory over the Austrians and Russians at Austerlitz. This was possibly the greatest battle of his ill-starred career. French territory and French dependencies were now extended into central Europe, and the following year saw the formal abolishment of the Holy Roman Empire.

Britain's naval supremacy must inevitably have kept Napoleon from invading England, although he would not admit it. But in 1805, Nelson, at the celebrated battle of Trafalgar, nearly annihilated the combined French and Spanish fleets.

Napoleon goaded Prussia into war, and defeated her at the battle of Jena. This was in 1806. In 1807 he overcame the Russians at Friedland. The Treaty of Tilsit was effected with young Czar Alexander I on a raft in the Niemen River, where the two rulers, flattering each other's vanity, made roseate plans to conquer the world and divide it between them.

Napoleon's career was now at its height. He placed his brothers and other relatives on several petty thrones under him. Louis Bonaparte was made king of Holland; Joseph Bonaparte, king of Naples; Jerome Bonaparte, king of Westphalia, Napoleon's brother-in-law, Murat, was made king of Naples when Joseph became king of Spain; and Bernadotte, one of Napoleon's marshals, was chosen by Sweden to occupy its throne.

In an attempt to humble England, Napoleon tried to shut her off from Europe. In November, 1806, he issued the Berlin and Milan Decrees, which declared the British Isles in a state of blockade and prohibited all commerce or correspondence with them. The plan was not successful, however, for it impoverished the merchants of France and the public was antagonistic to it. England retaliated by issuing the Orders in Council, which required neutral powers to observe a counter-blockade of the Continent. This blockade was one of the causes of the War of 1812 between Great Britain and the United States.

In the meantime there was dissatisfaction in Spain under Napoleonic rule. The country had not been treated fairly, and the Spaniards were not pleased by Napoleon's dethroning of Charles IV and the substitution of Joseph Bonaparte as king. With all his efforts, Napoleon could not subdue Spain more than temporarily. England saw an opportunity to send an army into Europe by way of Spain. This was commanded by Sir Arthur Wellesley, who was later to become the celebrated Duke of Wellington. The French were driven out of Spain in the Peninsular War, and Napoleon's star was on the wane.

Trouble developed in Austria following Napoleon's misfortunes in Spain. He was defeated at Aspern in 1809, and even his victory at Wagram the same year could not stay the doom that was impending. He was angry at Russia's failure to co-operate with him in blockading England, so in 1812 Napoleon started out with over half a million men and led them across Germany and Poland into Russia. But Napoleon did not give the czar enough credit for cleverness. If the invaders had been met in a pitched battle, the result might have been different, but the Russians retreated instead, and lured Napoleon farther and farther away from his source of supplies. They made it impossible for him to live on the land by laying waste the surrounding country so that it could not support Napoleon's army. The Russians burned Moscow so that he could not winter there; and in the face of Russian snow and cold he had to retreat to the west. It was a disorderly, straggling army of hungry, frozen men who turned homeward. Their leader entered Warsaw with hardly 20,000 of the Grand Army of 500,000.

The European countries decided that they had had enough of Napoleon, and they joined in the War of the Liberation. In haste the emperor went to Paris and raised another army, composed chiefly of raw recruits, and invaded Germany in 1813. The tide could not be stemmed by a few victories, but Napoleon would not listen to any offers of compromise. Napoleon's forces were overpowered at Leipzig in the "Battle of the Nations." He fled, and from all sides his enemies came at him like a pack of hungry wolves. Paris fell in 1814, and Napoleon abdicated at Fontainebleau. He was permitted, as a courtesy, to keep his title of emperor, and was granted the little island of Elba (south of France, off the Italian coast) as his domain.

The political boundaries of Europe were reorganized by the council of nations at Vienna. The Bourbons were reinstated on the French throne, and a brother of Louis XVI became Louis XVIII. (Louis XVI's son never reigned, as he died in childhood, but he was called Louis XVII.) After a year of this rule, the French were ready to welcome Napoleon back.

Meanwhile, with plenty of time to think in Elba, Napoleon believed that he could return in triumph. Escaping past the British ships whose duty it was to keep him prisoner, on March 1, 1815, he landed on the French coast with a few hundred faithful followers, and marched toward Paris. His glamor still persisted, and the French armies that were sent to stop his progress one by one capitulated to his personality and joined his forces. Louis XVIII fled, and for a hundred days Napoleon was once again the ruler of France.

It was, however, far from expedient for the European powers to permit such a triumph, and they assembled armies to bring it to an end. And at Waterloo, the Belgian battlefield whose name has become a synonym for "defeat," Napoleon was decisively beaten in June 1815. His opponents were the British, Dutch, Belgians, and Germans, under the Duke of Wellington. This time he was not trusted. He was exiled to the island of St. Helena, in the southern Atlantic many hundred miles west of Africa, where he died in 1821.

Napoleon is famous not only for his military prowess, but for his constructive statesmanship in France, and for the effect of his career on Europe. The series of reforms which Napoleon instituted in France while First Consul are a far more worthy monument to his genius and to his skill as a ruler. Napoleon, in his reforms, completed and consolidated the work of the Revolution.

In 1800, Napoleon founded the Bank of France to serve as the central financial institution of the country. The Concordat of 1801, or treaty with the pope, united church and state in France. The Concordat lasted until 1905, when it was terminated by the Separation Act. The laws of France were revised and arranged into the orderly system known as the Napoleonic Code. The government of France was stabilized and centralized into a number of departments, under-prefects, and sub-prefects. A plan for a state system of schools was adopted. A central body, the University of France, was created to supervise all educational activities. (The New York State Board of Regents is modeled after Napoleon's centralized system.) Paris was beautified and an extensive system of roads and bridges was built in order to facilitate commerce. To reward distinguished service to the state, Napoleon created the Legion of Honor.

Napoleon left his mark on all of Europe. Serfdom and other feudal practices were abolished, and the principles of the Napoleonic Code were widely adopted. The seeds of equality were scattered throughout Europe. The emphasis on fraternity gave a new meaning to nationalism, which is illustrated by the fact that the freed serfs in Germany fought vigorously in the War of Liberation against Napoleon. With the increase in nationalistic spirit, however, warfare became vaster and more far-reaching in both its causes and its effects. Modern militarism and total wars were a part of Napoleon's legacy to Europe.

EUROPE IN THE NINETEENTH CENTURY

The French Revolution and Napoleon's career had great consequences on the course of history. Germany had been a collection of many little independent states, and central Europe had been divided into a large group of principalities and petty kingdoms. Through Napoleon's campaigns some 300 independent governments were reduced to less than 40.

THE CONGRESS OF VIENNA AND AFTER

Various European kings and diplomats met at Vienna to ponder the map of Europe. They included the celebrated Metternich, an Austrian prince with a great genius for statesmanship, and Talleyrand of France. Everything that France had won since the French Revolution had been lost, but through Talleyrand's efforts France was saved from being divided up as Poland had been not very long before.

Under the house of Orange, Holland and Belgium were united as the Kingdom of the Netherlands. Thirty-eight German states which formerly had been members of the Holy Roman Empire became the German Confederation. Prussia took half of Saxony and Rhine territory, and Venice and Lombardy went to Austria. The majority of the Italian states were restored to their respective rulers.

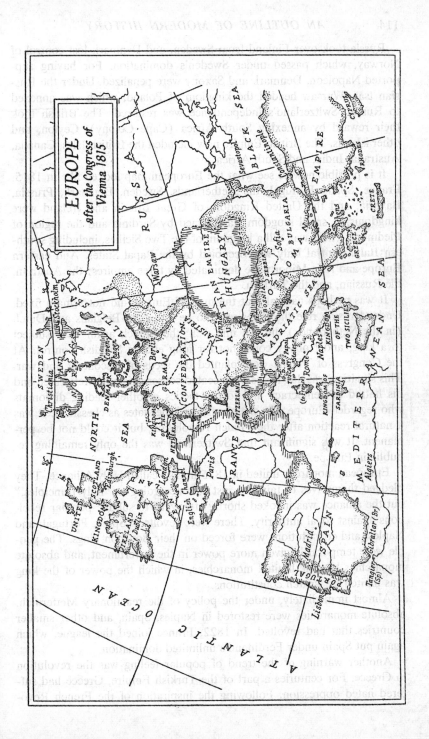

Russia took over Finland from Sweden, and Denmark lost control of Norway, which passed under Sweden's domination. For having supported Napoleon, Denmark and Saxony were penalized. Under the Russian tsar, Warsaw headed the kingdom of Poland, which was annexed to Russia. Switzerland's independence was restored. The British took their reward by annexing South Africa (Cape Colony), Ceylon, and other islands. The British Empire now included the British Isles, Canada, Australia, India, and South Africa.

It is possible now to see what the European map looked like in 1815. France, Spain, Portugal, the Netherlands, Sweden, Denmark, Prussia, Bavaria, and the United Kingdom of Great Britain and Ireland were kingdoms. A small kingdom was formed by Sardinia and the region of Piedmont. There was still a kingdom of the Two Sicilies, including southern Italy. Central Italy was occupied by the Papal States. And eastern Europe and Asia Minor were dominated by three empires: the Austrian, the Russian, and the Turkish.

It was perhaps natural that the map of Europe did not remain fixed. Under Russian rule the Poles were to be unhappy; Belgians and Dutch (in the Netherlands) did not mix well; the French again were subject to a king; and Norway could not for long endure Swedish control. At the Congress of Vienna were planted the seeds of discontent and war. This situation was due to the deep-seated conservatism of Metternich and his hatred of democracy and to the tactics of other leading diplomats who regarded Europe as a chessboard and the states as chessmen. It was a natural reaction after the French Revolution, but it could not be permanent. It was significant that Switzerland was the only remaining republic in Europe.

European monarchs united in 1815 in a so-called Holy Alliance. They pledged themselves to fair and just rule according to "holy principles," but the alliance was invoked shortly afterward to subdue popular rebellions against royal authority. There were revolts in Spain, Portugal, and Naples, and constitutions were forced on their Bourbon kings. The people were temporarily given more power in the government, and absolute monarchies became limited monarchies, in which the power of the king was limited by written constitutions.

Almost immediately, under the policy of the reactionary Metternich, absolute monarchies were restored in Naples, Spain, and other smaller countries that had revolted. In 1822, France joined the league, which again put Spain under Ferdinand's unlimited domination.

Another warning of the trend of popular feeling was the revolution in Greece. For centuries a part of the Turkish Empire, Greece had suffered hated oppression. Following the inspiration of the French Revolution, the native Greeks revolted in 1821, and in 1829 won their independence.

The people of France were not enthusiastic when Louis XVIII returned to the throne after Napoleon's second exile. They made the best of it, however, and Louis made a compromise by a liberal constitution establishing a legislature of two houses. French nobles returning home conspired to win their privileges again.

Louis's younger brother, Charles X, became king in 1824, and he was to be the last of the Bourbon line. As a reactionary, Charles probably was more extreme than the Austrian Metternich. He revived the idea of kingship by divine right. In the beginning he was successful in his effort to restore absolute monarchy in France, but he had failed to apply the lesson of 1789. His methods brought on the revolution of 1830, at which time he was exiled.

It was a different story in South America. Having revolted before during Napoleon's ascendancy, these former Spanish and Portuguese colonies—from Mexico to Argentina—were now befriended by Great Britain and the United States. Thereafter these countries remained republics.

THE INDUSTRIAL REVOLUTION

Revolution does not necessarily involve fighting. Another, more peaceful kind of revolution was going on in Europe at this time. A sudden impetus had been given to inventive genius, and the world was at the beginning of a mechanical age. Up to around the year 1750 there had been little change in the methods of transportation and travel since the days of early Egypt. The fastest means known were provided by the horse and the vehicles that he drew. The weaving of cloth was accomplished by hand, and agriculture was carried on with very primitive tools.

There was to be a rapid change in all these matters. The development of James Watt's steam engine was carried forward; threshing machines were invented; the iron plow came in 1800; the steamboat of Robert Fulton in 1807, and Stephenson's locomotive in 1814. Better roads were built, and a new understanding of metallurgy and smelting was attained. This was a mechanical revolution, a scientific step forward in knowledge. It was the precursor of the machine age, during which the economic upheaval known as the industrial revolution was to occur.

The industrial revolution may be viewed as a series of changes—technological, economic, social, and political. It began with the invention of complicated power-driven machines. Two resources, coal and iron, became the foundation for industrialization. Iron was needed for the construction of machinery, buildings, and equipment of all kinds.

Coal was employed to smelt the iron ore, to convert iron into steel, and to generate the steam which drove the machinery. Factories were erected to house the machines and the workers who tended them. The growth of the factory system led to a sharp distinction between the capitalists and the workers.

Both industry and agriculture were benefited by the practical application of scientific principles and discoveries. New methods of transportation and communication revolutionized business and made possible large-scale production and distribution of agricultural and industrial products.

The industrial story of the nineteenth century does not make pleasant reading. Capital and labor often engaged in violent disputes—a conflict which was to be carried on until our own time. Little by little, in the latter part of the nineteenth century, trade unions developed. They were protective organizations of workers and did a great deal toward lessening the evils from which industrial workers suffered.

People were drawn from the rural districts by the factory system, and the effect was to concentrate large numbers of people in cities and towns. Thus a by-product of low wages and high living costs was the development of tenement districts and slums.

The advance of science through the nineteenth century to the present day has swiftly brought railroads, steamships, telegraph, postal systems, telephone, wireless, radio, television, and aviation. Gradually the standard of living rose, for with the greater facilities of manufacture and trade national wealth increased with great rapidity.

THE AGRICULTURAL REVOLUTION

While great transformations were going on in industry, similar changes were taking place in agriculture. The agricultural revolution was important, for without it, the industrial revolution could not have proceeded very far. It was agriculture that supplied the increased quantities of cotton, wool, flax, and other raw materials which the factories required. And it was agriculture that supplied the food for the workers in the factories. Finally, it was agriculture that furnished industry with an extensive market for almost every kind of manufactured product.

In the eighteenth century a small group of "gentlemen farmers," men with money, intelligence, and a love for the land, initiated a series of improvements which made farming a science and a business. Jethro Tull introduced in 1701 a seed drill which automatically planted seeds in straight rows. Lord Townshend, who came to be known as "Turnip" Townshend, introduced crop rotation in order to conserve the fertility of the soil. Robert Bakewell introduced selective breeding of cattle. His breeding methods were copied far and wide. Knowledge of these progressive methods was spread rapidly, especially through the writings of Arthur Young, whose *Annals of Agriculture* had a wide circulation.

The pioneering efforts of these men were later supplemented by the invention of machines adapted to farming, such as the invention of the reaper by Cyrus McCormick in 1834. Later, the invention of the gasoline engine, the development of the tractor, and the use of electric power made possible the employment of power-driven machinery on the farm.

In the nineteenth century, agriculture made rapid progress by applying scientific principles to the solution of farm problems. Agricultural societies, schools, and experiment stations in Europe and America studied practically every phase of farm life. The results of these researches proved of incalculable value to millions of farmers.

The agricultural revolution wrought a transformation in rural life. Farming became a business. In many instances small landowners, finding themselves unable to compete with those who had more land and more capital, sold their holdings and either shifted to the cities or remained on the land as farm laborers. In England this process was speeded by the "enclosure movement," whereby powerful landlords partitioned and fenced pasture lands to exploit them for profit. Small farmers who had enjoyed the privilege of using these "commons" were obliged to seek a living as hired workers, usually in the cities. As interdependence between the farm and the city became more pronounced, the rural communities lost their isolation. Improved methods resulted in large-scale production for a world market, with the resultant problems of surpluses, low prices, and overproduction.

THE LABOR MOVEMENT AND POLITICAL DEMOCRACY

The growth of the factory system created a wide gulf between the worker, who toiled for wages, and the factory owner, who supplied the capital. With the development and spread of the factory system, the worker became more and more dependent on his employer for a job. It was the job that provided him with the means for a living. Long hours of labor at extremely low wages, harsh treatment, and the fear of unemployment aroused in the worker an intense desire for better conditions. The aims of the workers were higher wages, shorter hours, decent working conditions, and greater economic security. The campaign to attain these aims is known as the labor movement. It was waged along three fronts—trade-unionism, socialism, and political democracy.

Labor organizations were at first forbidden in England as well as on the Continent. The law held that combinations were dangerous conspiracies. Trade unions were legalized in England by the Act of 1824, although with many restrictions. The unions, by dint of constant agitation, gained the legal right to collective bargaining.

DEMOCRACY AND REFORM IN GREAT BRITAIN

Having reigned for sixty years, King George III of England died in 1820. It was he whom the American colonies opposed in their war for independence (1775–1783). The most famous premier of his reign was William Pitt, whose father had been called the "Great Commoner." It was under the younger Pitt that the War of 1812 was fought between England and the United States, resulting in the acceptance of the principle of the freedom of the seas. It was in 1800 that the Irish secured representation in Parliament and the United Kingdom of Great Britain and Ireland was formed.

England by the nineteenth century had achieved limited monarchy but not democracy. The chief undemocratic elements in the British government may be summarized as follows: (1) the restriction of the right to vote largely to property holders; (2) religious discrimination, which barred large numbers of Catholics, Jews, and Protestant dissenters from the right to hold office; (3) the open ballot, which led to bribery and corruption; (4) unfair representation in the House of Commons. There had been no reapportionment of seats since 1664; as a result "rotten boroughs" (districts whose population had declined or disappeared) continued to send representatives to Parliament. New industrial cities like Manchester, Leeds, and Birmingham remained practically unrepresented; (5) the hereditary and conservative House of Lords, which was the dominant branch of Parliament.

Under the stimulus of the rising industrial class, the House of Commons passed the first great reform bill—the Act of 1832. The Reform Bill of 1832 eliminated many of the "rotten boroughs" and reapportioned seats to provide representation for the new industrial cities. Property qualifications were reduced to a level which made it possible for a much greater number of the middle class to vote. Control of the government thus passed from the landed aristocracy to the industrial middle class. By the Lords Veto Act of 1911, the House of Commons achieved supremacy over the House of Lords. England is now a democracy, although monarchical in name and form.

However, the Act of 1832 conferred no rights whatsoever on the factory workers. The organization of the Chartist movement attempted to achieve reforms for the workers. Despite the fact that the Chartists failed to achieve their immediate objectives, many of their demands were ultimately adopted. By the Acts of 1867 and 1884, the workers achieved the right to vote.

Long hours of labor had been the result of the factory system. In 1883 factory laws were beginning to be passed, and slowly but surely they did away with child labor, reduced the hours of labor, and improved working conditions.

The later history of English government shows an increasingly liberal attitude toward labor. David Lloyd George was made chancellor of the exchequer and subsequently, as head of the Liberal party, became prime minister. After a short period of power, the House of Lords declined into a mere debating body; and at the present time England's government is almost entirely in the hands of the House of Commons, from which Britain's ministers come. The Labor party, with James Ramsay MacDonald as prime minister, ruled Great Britain for a few years after the First World War. Labor obtained a majority in the House of Commons in the general election of 1945.

By the early nineteenth century, a profitable trade in slaves had developed. Ships were taken to Africa, filled with black people, and brought back with their cargoes of human freight. The slaves were sold in Europe, the West Indies, and the United States. England and continental Europe never had as many slaves as America, but gradually public conscience, or other considerations, put an end to the trade and set the slaves free. All the slaves in British dominions were freed by an act passed in 1833, but as early as 1807 England had prohibited British ships from taking part in the slave trade in British colonies. In the United States the slaves were emancipated as a result of the Civil War (1861–1865).

In 1841 Sir Robert Peel became prime minister. He advocated the repeal of the Corn Laws. These were so named because they put heavy tariffs on imported grains and thereby kept up the price of wheat so that landowners became very wealthy and the poor were further impoverished. The question was brought to a crisis by a famine in Ireland (1845), and the Corn Laws were repealed in 1846. Great Britain finally established the principle of free trade through this beginning.

SOCIALISM

Despite the reforms accomplished by the advances in trade-unionism and the achievements in political democracy, the workers felt that more fundamental changes were needed. Groups of workers turned to the principles of socialism.

The socialist movement was founded not by workers, but by members of the middle class. Robert Owen was one of the earliest socialists. Two other pioneers were Saint-Simon and Fourier. These men were known as *utopians* because they dreamed of a perfect world in which employers and employees would co-operate with one another. Unfortunately, the co-operative communities established by the utopian socialists failed. The ideal systems which they worked out on paper failed in practice.

The founder of modern, scientific socialism was the German writer, Karl Marx (1818–1883). Together with Friedrich Engels, Marx, in 1848, issued the *Communist Manifesto,* a pamphlet which contained the chief principles of the new socialism. During his exile in England, Marx wrote *Das Kapital,* a work which became the bible of the socialist movement. Marx argued that history should be viewed as a struggle between masters and workers; that the industrial revolution had intensified this struggle by creating a sharper cleavage between the two classes; and that conflict between the workers, or proletariat, and the capitalists, or bourgeoisie, was inevitable. Maintaining that labor was the source of all wealth, Marx called upon the workers to unite, to gain the ballot, and to elect socialists to office. Once in control of the government the socialist leaders could carry through an economic and social revolution. Private capitalism would be abolished, the state taking over the ownership and management of factories, railroads, mines, lands, and other means of production and distribution.

In 1864, the First International was organized. A Second International organized in 1884 was disrupted by the First World War. After the war the Second International was revived. At the same time the Bolshevists organized the Third, or Communist International. In the midst of the Second World War, the Communist International was disbanded.

Offshoots of the Marxian socialists in the late nineteenth century, such as the French syndicalists, sought to organize all the workers in an industry into one big union, which could then engage in a general strike to oust the capitalists from control. In the United States, the Industrial Workers of the World (I.W.W.) were organized along the same lines as the syndicalists. They were especially active during and immediately after the First World War, particularly among the lumbermen of the Pacific Northwest.

REVOLUTIONS OF 1830

Exiled by a revolution in 1830, Charles X, absolute monarch of France, fled to England, where he died. The leaders of the middle class, who had directed the Revolution of 1830, selected Louis Philippe, head of the house of Orléans, as king. Having received his crown directly from the people, Louis Philippe at first did not usurp much power.

In other parts of Europe, meanwhile, revolts were inspired by the example of the French Revolution of 1830. Belgium, having won its independence, was recognized as a separate kingdom in 1831 under Leopold, a prince of the small German state of Saxe-Coburg-Gotha. In Switzerland, a more liberal constitution was inaugurated.

Prodded by Metternich, the Austrians put down an Italian revolt; and, due to Metternich's disapproval, German revolts had little effect. The Poles under Russian control failed in an attempt to revolt, and Russia took from them what little self-government they had. Their territory was definitely incorporated into the Russian Empire.

THE REVOLUTION OF 1848 IN FRANCE

King Louis Philippe tried hard to be a popular monarch, but in vain. France was in varying degrees of turmoil for eighteen years. A revolution in 1848 was the cause of Louis Philippe's abdicating in favor of his grandson; but the people did not want a king, and in February, 1848, the second French Republic was proclaimed. There was a popular election in which was offered the name of Louis Napoleon Bonaparte. He was the son of Louis Bonaparte, a brother of the Emperor Napoleon. Napoleon's own son had died in 1832.

The magic of the name appealed to the people, among whom were many of Napoleon's former soldiers, and Louis Napoleon was elected president by a tremendous majority. The new Napoleon's support of the republic was not sincere, however, and in 1851 he forcibly seized the government, dispersed the Assembly, and suppressed the radicals. A new constitution was proclaimed, and he became president for ten years, with kingly powers. Twelve months later, December 2, 1852, Louis Napoleon was crowned Emperor Napoleon III of France. (The son of Napoleon I was called Napoleon II out of courtesy, but he never reigned.) Such was the popular approval of this action that it was ratified by a plebiscite.

OTHER REVOLUTIONS OF 1848

There were many uprisings in Europe in 1848. Other peoples were set aflame with liberal aspirations by the example of the French, and throughout the Continent the idea of reform had taken on definite shape. Central Europe was dominated by the empire of Austria, under the Hapsburgs, guided by Metternich's crafty hand. Many of the revolts that occurred in 1848 were caused by Austrian oppression. The real necessity was for establishing "natural boundaries" in Europe—kingdoms or states composed of people speaking one language and having common national traditions.

During the uprisings in Vienna, Metternich had to flee from Austria, and the emperor was prevailed upon to promise a constitution to the people. Meanwhile rebellions in Bohemia and Hungary were suppressed. The writings of Mazzini, an Italian journalist, induced revolts in Italy. They were unsuccessful at the time, but they were to have an influence later. There were German revolts which resulted in a constitution which united the German states. Frederick William IV of Prussia, a Hohenzollern, was offered the German crown, but he refused as he was afraid of Austria. The good that had been done was demolished by reaction, and the revolutionists were driven into exile.

THE DEVELOPMENT OF MODERN EUROPEAN COUNTRIES

In the later half of the nineteenth century, nationalism in Europe resulted in the unification of two countries of considerable power—Italy and Germany. This was the period also of British colonization and the height of the British Empire. Russia meanwhile was becoming increasingly restless under the absolute rule of the czars, and in 1917 the Bolshevist Revolution was to inaugurate the Communist regime in this country.

THE UNIFICATION OF ITALY

The idea of the unification of Italy under one ruler came out of the revolutions of 1848. The sovereign who succeeded in accomplishing this was Victor Emmanuel II, king of Sardinia-Piedmont. Italian unity was helped most by the enlightened statesmanship of Cavour (1810–1861), who was King Victor Emmanuel's prime minister. He followed in the footsteps of Mazzini, the philosopher-idealist. Among the young Italians many patriotic societies were formed, but Cavour's ideas were more practical. He believed that unity could be accomplished more definitely by building roads and encouraging industry and agriculture, thus obtaining the support of the middle class. A prominent part was played by Giuseppe Garibaldi (1807–1882), the patriot and liberator. By 1860, except for Rome and Venice, Italy was ruled by one sovereign. Before the unification was completed, Cavour died, in 1861.

In the year 1866 Prussia opposed Austria in the Seven Weeks' War, whereupon Italy seized the opportunity to join Prussia, and while Austria was warring on two fronts, Italy took Venice. Since 1849 French soldiers had been quartered in Rome, but in 1870, during the Franco-Prussian War, they were withdrawn. The city was invaded by Italians, and the populace voted to join united Italy. Rome was made the capital.

It was as a protest against this usurpation of his temporal dominions that the pope became a voluntary prisoner in the Vatican. This tradition was maintained by every succeeding pope until 1929, when the Fascist dictator, Benito Mussolini, made a treaty with the pope recognizing the small independent papal state called Vatican City.

THE UNIFICATION OF GERMANY

Although the German people formed a distinct national group and could look back to more than a thousand years of growth, they were not able, until 1871, to achieve political unity. The nationalist movement in Germany was hampered by the existence of numerous petty states, by the selfishness of the hereditary rulers of these areas, by the rivalries between large states and small states, and by the opposition to unification on the part of both Austria and France.

Three important steps toward unity were taken during the Napoleonic Era. Napoleon's abolition of the Holy Roman Empire rid Germany of a cumbersome medieval organization which no longer exercised any control over the hundreds of practically independent principalities. Napoleon's reorganization of Germany consolidated many of the smaller states into larger countries. It reduced the number of kingdoms, duchies, principalities, and free cities from more than 300 to less than 100. The wars to free Germany from Napoleon's domination resulted in a spirit of national patriotism.

Further partial steps toward unification came about with the organization of the *German Confederation* by the Congress of Vienna in 1815, and the organization, under the leadership of Prussia in 1834, of the *Zollverein,* or tariff union, which established free trade among the German states. The *Zollverein* taught the Germans the value of co-operation. By adding a strong economic bond to the racial and cultural bonds already in existence, it prepared the way for political unity. The revolutionary uprisings of 1848, which swept Metternich into exile, at first gave promise of creating a united Germany. The National Assembly which met at Frankfort for the purpose of organizing a national government ended in failure.

The Revolution of 1848 had two important results. First, the failure to achieve unity by democratic methods enabled the militarists to take command of the situation. Second, the king of Prussia kept his promise and in 1850 granted a Constitution.

William, the brother of Frederick William IV, became king of Prussia in 1861. His chief minister was Otto von Bismarck, who was later made Prince Bismarck. He was known as the "Iron Chancellor." In 1866, in the Seven Weeks' War with Austria, the Prussians, who were led by Count Moltke, won the battle of Sadowa (Bohemia). The terms of peace were dictated by Bismarck. Hanover was annexed to Prussia. The emperor of Austria also became king of Hungary in 1867, and thereafter until the end of the First World War there was the dual monarchy known as Austria-Hungary.

The Franco-Prussian War in 1870 was brought about by the political ambitions of Prussia and by economic rivalry and growing jealousy between Prussia and France. The French were not prepared for war, and Moltke surprised their country with a strong army. Bismarck's alliance of southern German states had been made, and their fighting side by side in this war was the first step in the unification of Germany. The French were badly beaten, and the Germans finally captured the whole French army, including the Emperor Napoleon III. The siege of Paris resulted in its capitulation in 1871.

Through their sweeping victory the Prussians gained Alsace and part of Lorraine, and an indemnity of a billion dollars was exacted from France. The Franco-Prussian War had another result besides helping to unify the German states: it sowed seeds of hate and fear that were to grow into some of the causes of the Great War of 1914–1918, in which practically the whole world became involved.

The German Empire, born in 1871, lived forty-seven years, and came to an end in 1918. The king of Prussia became emperor of Germany, and assumed the title of kaiser. With full control of war and peace, his power was almost absolute. The sovereigns of the states appointed delegates to a legislative body—the Bundesrat, or Federal Council. The lower house was the Reichstag, and its members were elected by manhood suffrage. With the exception of Russia and Turkey, Germany had a government which was more autocratic than any other in Europe.

THE THIRD FRENCH REPUBLIC

Prussian victory spelled the end of the French Empire. In 1871 French radicals set up a Commune and the streets of Paris ran with the blood of civil war. The Third French Republic was declared, and the first president was Thiers, who had been a leading figure as a statesman in the revolution of 1848. There was for a time conflict among several parties: the Imperialists who desired the restoration of Louis Napoleon; the Orléanists, whose idea it was to have the grandson of Louis Philippe on the throne; the Legitimists, who tried to restore the Bourbon line; and the Republicans, who achieved success.

With the president at its head, a centralized government was formed. The government ruled not only in national affairs but took an interest in local matters as well. The Chamber of Deputies and the Senate made up the National Assembly in France. The former was elected by manhood suffrage and the latter chosen by electoral colleges. The French president was elected by the Assembly, and the president appointed his ministers, who were responsible to the Chamber of Deputies. After 1871 France made rapid progress in education, industry, and matters of state.

The bitter defeat by Prussia and the humiliating Treaty of Frankfort (1871) fostered a spirit of revenge. France did not forget its harsh terms. The army was enlarged, conscription was adopted, and a huge system of fortifications was constructed on the Franco-German frontier. While the militarists were strengthening France at home, the diplomats were strengthening her position abroad. In the end, alliances with Russia and with England were concluded. At the same time, France sought to compensate for her loss of Alsace-Lorraine by acquiring colonies in Africa.

The history of the Third French Republic prior to 1914 was marked by two crises which threatened the security of the government. In 1889, an adventurer, General Boulanger, attempted unsuccessfully to establish a military dictatorship. A more serious attempt to undermine the Republic culminated in the famous Dreyfus Affair, which for more than a decade was the leading political issue in France. The case concerned itself with the unsuccessful attempt of the clericals and monarchists to denounce the Republic by accusing Captain Dreyfus, a Jew, of treason. Liberals and republicans, convinced that Dreyfus was innocent, rallied to his aid. Writers like Émile Zola and Anatole France kept the issue before the public. It was proved that Dreyfus had been "framed" and that the conspiracy against Dreyfus had been in reality a conspiracy to overthrow the Republic.

The Dreyfus Affair resulted in a concerted drive to curtail the power of the church. In 1901, an Associations Act declared that no religious order could exist in France without a permit from the government and that only authorized orders could maintain schools. Finally, the Separation Act of 1905 revoked the Concordat of 1801, and ended the favored position which the Catholic Church in France had enjoyed for more than a century. The government ceased to participate in the appointment of bishops and stopped paying the salaries of the clergy. The Catholic Church in France assumed the status of a religious organization supported by the contributions of its members.

THE PROGRESS OF GERMANY

Prussia became strongly military. The most important citizen was the soldier, and under the rigid rule of Bismarck and his successors the activities of private citizens were sternly curtailed. With the intention of rendering France powerless against Prussia, in 1879 Bismarck completed an alliance between the German Empire and Austria-Hungary, which was joined by Italy in 1882. This formed the Triple Alliance, on which Germany counted when war broke out in 1914. But Italy joined the Allies on this occasion.

Frederick III succeeded his father William I as emperor in 1888. In three months he died and was succeeded by his son William II, who was the Kaiser Wilhelm, Germany's ruler in the First World War.

From 1871 until 1890, Bismarck served as Chancellor of the German Empire while retaining the post of Prime Minister of Prussia. Shortly after the accession of William II, Bismarck resigned his positions and retired. The new kaiser was anxious to direct the government personally, but in general he followed the policies of Bismarck. Industry and trade continued to forge ahead. The value of Germany's exports in 1913 was three times that of 1890; she had become England's chief industrial and commercial rival. This economic development, coupled with the emperor's desire to play a leading role in international politics, gave rise to a more aggressive foreign policy. Germany backed her ally, Austria, in the Balkans. The promise of economic concessions in Asia Minor, especially the right to build the Berlin-Baghdad Railway, caused her to become more friendly with Turkey. Germany participated in the partition of China, securing control over the province of Shantung. She also became involved in a series of disputes with France over Morocco. Militarism was exalted. A navy, second only to Great Britain's, was built. The army was steadily enlarged and the weapons of war were perfected until Germany possessed the most efficient military machine in the world.

THE BALKAN STATES

Gradually the Ottoman Turkish Empire was pushed back into Asia. It was felt that the Turks did not belong in Europe, and their problem came to be regarded as the Eastern Question. The oppression of the Christians in the Balkan States caused the Turks to be hated. In 1829 Greece won her independence, but other rebellions in the Balkan States were not as successful, and there were Turkish reprisals.

In 1877, Russia set out to free the Balkan States, but the Treaty of San Stefano came under the scrutiny of the Congress of Berlin, and the European powers allowed the Turks to keep control of the Balkans. Only Serbia and Rumania were recognized as independent kingdoms, while Bosnia and Herzegovina were given to Austria-Hungary, to become a part of that empire in 1908. The Balkan States in 1913 included Rumania, Serbia, Bulgaria, Montenegro, Albania, and Greece.

Balkan wars occurred in 1912–1913, when the allied states of Serbia, Bulgaria, Greece, and Montenegro struck vigorous blows at the Turkish Empire. The Balkans were victorious; and except for the city of Constantinople and the adjacent region, the Turks were forced to evacuate Europe.

THE BRITISH EMPIRE

Great Britain took part in the Crimean War (1854–1856), in which it was allied with France and Sardinia-Piedmont to put an end to Russian aggression in Turkey. The war was fought principally in the Crimea north of the Black Sea.

Outstanding British political leaders were Lord John Russell, Lord Derby, and Lord Aberdeen.

In 1833 William Gladstone entered the House of Commons. He became prime minister in 1868, and in his policies he was liberal and progressive. His reforms went contrary to the ideas of so many classes of voters that in 1874 his ministry was defeated.

Queen Victoria ascended the British throne in 1837, after the death of her uncle, William IV, who ruled from 1830 to 1837. She was eighteen years old. Her reign covered sixty-four years, and she was probably the best-loved ruler in English history.

For a brief time in 1868, Benjamin Disraeli became her prime minister. From 1874–1880 he was again prime minister, during which time he was made Lord Beaconsfield. In the meantime, Parliament continued to reform its own membership, and little by little the franchise was extended to include all adult British men. Eventually women were to be given the vote in England. They were destined to take part in the government by the end of the first quarter of the twentieth century.

There had been sporadic attempts to place Ireland in complete subjection, but they had failed. However, the Irish peasants' land was parceled out among English landlords, and there were resulting abuses which had to be corrected sooner or later. Ireland became a part of the United Kingdom in 1800, and was given representation in Parliament. Championed by Charles Parnell and agitators of a later date, Home Rule for Ireland became a recurring factor in English politics. In 1905, the Sinn Feiners made their appearance and continued over a period of years to agitate for Home Rule. Following the First World War, Ireland was divided into two parts—the self-governing Irish Free State, of which the Gaelic name was Saorstat Eireann, and Northern Ireland, which was made up of six counties of Ulster, which had never wanted Home Rule. Great Britain became the United Kingdom of Great Britain and Northern Ireland.

Queen Victoria's long and popular reign ended in 1901. She was succeeded by her eldest son Edward VII, who reigned from 1901 to 1910. Then George V ascended the throne. He died in 1936, and was succeeded by Edward VIII, who abdicated in 1937 in favor of his brother, George VI. Elizabeth II came to the throne in 1952.

During the nineteenth century the British Empire was broadened to include about 12,000,000 square miles of territory throughout the globe. The empire included Canada (self-governing), Australia and South Africa, India, Newfoundland, New Zealand, British Guiana, widespread African possessions, Ceylon, Trinidad, Jamaica, Bermuda, and other possessions. In recent years there have been significant changes. India was given complete independence in 1947. She remained a member of the Commonwealth of Nations. The British Empire came to be known as the British Commonwealth of Nations, the larger units recognized as independent nations, their tie to the mother country being primarily financial and economic, with loosely defined co-operation in foreign policy.

THE RUSSIAN EMPIRE AND THE BOLSHEVIST REVOLUTION

Russia, occupying almost half of Europe, rose to a powerful position under Peter the Great. The Russian people were chiefly of Slavic origin. Russia's share in the partition of Poland was secured by Catherine the Great. Additional regions were added by conquest in war, and these included the great frigid expanse of Siberia, which was won from the Tatars. The Russian Empire became nearly as big as the British Empire, and it was consolidated in one area. But, on the other hand, Russia was under the rule of despotic tsars. A bureaucracy, composed of large numbers of government officials, mostly nobles, carried on the imperial commands. The peasants lived in great poverty, ignorance, and servitude.

Tsar Nicholas I, stern and severe, ruled between 1825 and 1855, but his successor, Alexander II (1855–1881), was more humane and enlightened, and instituted many reforms. The Nihilists, a radical party, assassinated him just as he was about to give a constitution to the people. In the reign of Alexander III there was a reversion to absolute government. Then came Nicholas II in 1894. He was the last of the tsars, for he was deposed and murdered in the revolution of 1917.

In the war with Japan (1904–1905), Russia lost. Russian affairs were not moving smoothly at home, and a revolution in 1905 was an indication that the despotic government was far from popular. For their cruelty in suppressing popular revolt, the Cossacks became notorious. The people were promised a Duma, or national assembly, by Tsar Nicholas, but inasmuch as, when it was elected, it included landowners for the most part, whose sympathies were with the tsar, it accomplished very little.

The result of the final uprising was to be the revolution of 1917 and the establishment of today's Communist government, known as the Union of Soviet Socialist Republics, including Soviet Russia, the Ukraine, White Russia, the Transcaucasian Federation, and other constituent republics. Under communism Russia became a powerful, industrialized nation.

The Communist regime was destined to opposition with the Western world. Although Russia fought with the Western Allies in the two World Wars, her political ideology and practices were violently opposed to the democratic system. From 1918 to 1921 the Communists employed terrorist practices to establish their control of the country. Subsequent history contains lurid accounts of "purges" by the Communist party (or the strongest element within it) of political opponents. Mass liquidations or exportations to Siberia were accepted political practice. Lenin's political doctrines, based on Marxist ideology, called for a government of the proletariat alone. In theory and practice, one party was to rule the country. Democratic institutions, as free election, a balance of power between legislative, executive, and judicial bodies, and the rights of citizens, were nonexistent in the early Leninist constitution. At the death of Lenin (Russia's first revolutionary leader), Trotsky and Stalin engaged in a duel for supreme power. With no firm basis for the choice of leaders, struggle for the control of Russia's one party was always cutthroat. It involved invariably the extinction of all opponents.

The Stalin constitution of 1936 confirmed totalitarian government. Every activity within the state was co-ordinated and controlled by the party leadership. Published or voiced opposition to the government was punishable by death. It was necessary to the system that knowledge of Western democracy within Russia be strictly limited. A "cold war" between Russia and the West began after the Second World War. In the words of the British Prime Minister, Winston Churchill, there was between the two sides an "Iron Curtain."

Russia greatly extended her world power through state-controlled industrial and agricultural economy, and through infiltration into the governments of states surrounding her. These states, whose puppet governments received orders from Moscow, came to be referred to as the satellites. This expansion was an expression of the Marxist theory of world revolution, which Lenin had made a primary part of Russian political aims. Under Stalin, the doctrine of "peaceful co-existence" between communism and capitalism was put forward. The Russians maintain that Western capitalistic imperialism was the cause of hostility in the world. In the 1950s constant attempts to work out differences and to bring about mutual disarmament between the Western Powers and Russia were made. None was successful.

MAJOR CHANGES IN ASIA

THE FAR EAST

The Far East embraces China, Korea, Indo-China, Thailand (Siam), the Malay Peninsula, and Burma on the Asian continent, and the islands of Japan, Formosa, the Philippines, and the East Indies. This area comprises slightly more than 6,000,000 square miles, one-eighth of the world's land area, and contains more than 750,000,000 people, nearly one-third of the world's population.

Western peoples knew little of eastern Asia until the beginning of modern times. The period of extensive exploration of Asia and the Pacific coincided with the beginning of modern nation-states in western Europe. These new nations set the patterns for our modern world of nations, and their destinies were vitally affected by the exploration of the Far East. Their later conquest of much of Asia and of the islands of the Pacific affected their political relations, caused some of their wars, and made possible the growth of their economic and political power.

Portuguese and Spanish explorers during the sixteenth century were the first to make permanent contacts in the Far East. Portuguese and Spaniards, sailing east and west, met in the western Pacific. The Spaniards took and held the Philippines while the Portuguese were establishing posts on India's shores and in the East Indies. Little friction occurred between Spain and Portugal in the Orient. By the end of the sixteenth century, however, Portugal's power was on the wane. By 1580, Portugal, which had come under the Spanish crown, found its possessions fair game for the English and Dutch, who were at war with Spain. The real conquerors of Asia were henceforth to be England, the Netherlands, and France.

The Dutch drove the Portuguese from Ceylon and the English from Amboina, seized Malacca, and established themselves in Batavia. By 1641, they had ousted the English from the Indies and forced them to fall back on control of ports in India. For a century and a half the Dutch remained in control of the Indies, which were then retaken by the English. By the settlement of the Congress of Vienna, after the Napoleonic Wars, the Dutch were given back the Indies. In 1819, Singapore became a British settlement. Although European rivalries caused the trading ports of the East to change hands in the course of the seventeenth and eighteenth centuries, the basis for territorial conquest had already been established.

The opening of the nineteenth century, therefore, saw the gradual dissolution of the trading companies which had formerly been active in the Orient. The British, Netherlands, and French governments began to take over their interests and to open the trade to all home merchants. These governments now assumed the task of protecting their trade and defending the lives and property of their citizens in Asia. In the nineteenth century and early twentieth century, conquest continued, accompanied by increasing exploitation of the resources of eastern Asia. This process changed the lives of peoples, upset their native economies, and began to transform their political ideas.

At the very end of the nineteenth century, southeast Asia was almost completely under European control. By 1895 the British had extended their rule over the Malay States. In 1886, Burma was made a province of British India. By 1907 the Dutch had extended their hold over the East Indies. In 1873 the French in Indo-China established a protectorate over Cambodia; between this date and 1907, Cochin-China was made a French colony, and protectorates were established over Annam, Tonkin, and Laos to complete the French conquest. The Philippines, under Spanish rule for 300 years, were ceded to the United States in 1898. Siam (Thailand), alone of all southeast Asia, escaped subjugation.

In each colony foreign rule was both direct and indirect. Whether the rule was direct or indirect, colonial policy in general has been marked by the efforts of the colonial governments to establish conditions favorable to profitable exploitation of the colony's resources by Westerners. Prior to 1914, few fundamental reforms had been undertaken, and almost everywhere both officials and private interests were far more concerned with maintaining their prestige and their profits than with the advancement of the people whom they governed and exploited. Except in the case of administration of the Philippines, the idea that a colony should be administered in trust for the benefit of its native inhabitants was slow in developing; it began to gain general currency after the First World War, and received its sharpest stimulus during and after the Second World War.

The development of the industrial revolution among the Western Powers led to more intensive exploitation of southeast and eastern Asia and laid the groundwork for the rivalries that broke out in the First and Second World Wars. The emergence of Japan on the scene as a highly industrialized nation and a world power intensified the rivalry. On the eve of the First World War, colonial imperialism was on the defensive, challenged by the slow awakening of the colonial peoples to a sense of national identity distinct from their common subjection to the white man's rule, though often stimulated by the white man's teachings. The movement for colonial independence burst forth again after the Second World War, with the outbreak of a revolt in the East Indies against Dutch rule and the stirrings of revolt in Siam, China, and Korea.

CHINA AND THE WEST

The civilization of China had been highly developed for many centuries before the earliest contacts with Europeans. Only limited success attended the efforts of the traders and missionaries who came to China in the seventeenth and eighteenth centuries. By the middle of the nineteenth century, however, the Manchu government was forced to sign a treaty with Great Britain regulating trade conditions and opening Shanghai, Amoy, Foochow, and Ningpo, in addition to Canton, to British trade. In 1844, these privileges were extended to the United States and France. By these and subsequent treaties, China was forced to open additional ports and to grant special rights to foreign powers that were to restrict her sovereignty. Until the First World War, twenty-eight nations, including all of the Western nations and Japan, possessed these special treaty rights.

These unequal treaties provided for extraterritoriality—the right of foreigners to live and do business in China under their own laws exempt from Chinese law and taxation. This privilege later became a burden to the Chinese. In addition, separate residential areas, known as settlements and concessions, were established in the ports which were opened to trade. Furthermore, each foreign nation established its own postal system, and maintained its own troops and naval forces for protection of the lives and property of its citizens. These treaties provided the medium for Western domination of China.

By 1899, Russia, Germany, Japan, Great Britain, and France had succeeded in dividing Chinese control among themselves. The acquisition of the Philippines gave the United States an Asiatic possession. It then proceeded to take steps toward preventing the further division of China.

In a series of notes, formulated in 1899 by John Hay, American Secretary of State, and accepted by the other great powers, the United States attempted to keep the door open to the trade of all nations in the special spheres and leased territories of other powers. In 1900, the United States announced a policy of striving to maintain the independence of China against further aggression.

In the Boxer Rebellion, which occurred in 1900, Prince Tuan's many followers (known as Boxers) besieged the foreigners at Peking (now Peiping). Troops were sent from the United States and other countries to quell the rebellion, and China was forced to pay $320,000,000 as an indemnity.

The spread of Western ideas, the steady decline of the Manchu government, and its evident inability to prevent the penetration of the foreign powers were in large part responsible for a revolutionary movement under the leadership of Sun Yat-sen that had begun at Canton before the turn of the century. By 1911, the revolutionaries had gained considerable support and openly defied Manchu authority, with the result that the Manchus were driven from power, and a Chinese Republic was established in 1912. This action was hailed as China's attempt to become modernized and to adopt the ways of Western civilization.

The first attempt at modernization was not entirely successful. The government soon became the prey of greedy politicians with little interest in reform. Local governors and generals set up their own governments in many provinces. The foreign powers still competed for influence and concessions. Despite these handicaps, Western ideas spread still more rapidly throughout the country and more Chinese went abroad to study and learn. Chinese students were in the forefront as advocates of reform and nationalism. The First World War saw China in a ferment of changing ideas and a growing nationalist feeling as expressed in resentment against the special treaty rights of the foreign powers, and in a desire for unqualified independence as a nation.

THE RISE OF JAPAN

In the sixteenth century, Portuguese, Spanish and, later, Dutch and English traders and missionaries were admitted to Japan. Christianity gained many converts and, for a while, commerce flourished. But the Japanese soon became suspicious of the West as both missionary and trader competed for ultimate conquest of their islands. The Japanese then adopted a policy of isolation. By 1641, all foreigners had been excluded from the country and soon only one Dutch ship a year was allowed to trade. The ruling Tokugawa family enforced this isolation for two hundred years. While other parts of eastern Asia were being slowly opened to Western trade and Christianity, Japan remained outside of and aloof from the currents of Western penetration.

Japan's inhospitable and often brutal treatment of shipwrecked sailors, the need for coaling stations, the hope of trade, and the general rivalry for any unexploited Asiatic territory, led the United States to send Commodore Perry and his "black ships" to Japan in 1853. In 1858, Townsend Harris, first American representative to Japan, was able to negotiate a trade treaty with Japan similar to the treaty with China.

Like the Chinese, the Japanese resented Western penetration, but, unlike the Chinese, decided that resistance to the West was useless. The Japanese decided to adopt Western instruments of power, modernize their country, and free themselves from foreign restrictions. The old ruling class of Shoguns was overthrown, and a constitution became operative with the Emperor "restored" to power. By 1900, the Japanese had persuaded the foreign powers, beginning with the United States, to give up their special treaty rights, thus achieving full independence—the first country in Asia to achieve this position and this recognition from the West.

The Japanese were quick to adopt the industrial methods of the West. By 1914, Japanese industrialization had reached a point where the label "Made in Japan" was becoming a familiar sight in the markets of the world. The Japanese concentrated, as well, on the creation of a modern army through employment of German military advisers and adoption of universal military conscription, and on the creation of a modern navy and merchant marine. Japan's new armed forces were successful against China in 1895, and, most surprising to the world, against Russia in 1905. Within sixty years after Perry's visit, Japan had become a conquering nation. Formosa was acquired in 1895, a foothold in southern Manchuria and southern Sakhalin in 1905, and Korea was annexed in 1910.

Japan's modernism was a façade. In reality a veneer of material progress had been overlaid on a civilization based upon medieval customs and traditions. The Japanese were taught that their civilization was unique and, therefore, superior to all other cultures. This belief was woven into their daily life and into their religious ceremonies and rituals. To them, their emperor was the only divinely descended monarch on earth, representative of an imperial line unbroken for 2,000 years. Under a divinely appointed Emperor, ruling over a land selected by the gods for a "master" race, Japan's leaders easily persuaded themselves that Japan was destined to rule other nations. They had no trouble in convincing their people that the world could progress best if the Japanese spread their language, their culture, and their ideas everywhere, that other nations ought to recognize Japanese superiority and accept Japanese leadership. It was just as easy to spread the belief that if other peoples would not "co-operate" then Japan must force them to, for "nothing must alter Japan's divine mission." Her early victories after 1895 strengthened the Japanese belief in their "divine mission"—a fact that was to bode trouble for the world.

INDIA

India (including Pakistan) was for nearly two hundred years largely under British control. It is a vast peninsula with more than 400 million people. Britain's control over India was first established by the officials and soldiers of the British East India Company, a trading company chartered by Parliament. During the Seven Years' War (1756–1763), England and France fought for control of India. Clive's victory over the French at Plassey (1757) assured the supremacy of the English. In a series of later wars, the British extended their power over all of India.

The English were successful in conquering this vast empire because of the following conditions: (1) India was divided into hundreds of practically independent states and the English were thus able to play off one native ruler against another; (2) the existence of religious hatreds between Hindus and Moslems, of racial differences, and of rigid caste distinctions, prevented united action against the invaders; (3) the English possessed modern weapons and a military organization.

In 1857, an uprising took place, however, which threatened the existence of British authority. This revolt is known as the Sepoy Mutiny, because it began with a revolt of the Sepoys, or native soldiers, in the British army. Following the suppression of the revolt, Parliament deprived the East India Company of its military and political powers and assumed direct control of the government. The administration of Indian affairs was vested in a member of the British Cabinet, the Secretary of State for India. The viceroy, as representative of the king, was made the chief executive officer in India. Parliament enacted all necessary laws. Queen Victoria was crowned Empress of India in 1877.

Despite the British conquest and whatever benefits to India may have ensued therefrom, the desire for self-government remained strong. The First World War, with its emphasis on the principles of nationalism and democracy, spread this desire throughout India. In 1919, Parliament passed the Government of India Act, which created a legislature of two houses with authority over local matters. This did not satisfy the Nationalists, who found a leader in Mohandas Gandhi, known as the Mahatma. Gandhi organized a campaign of passive resistance, hoping to bring the British to terms by boycotting British goods and by refusing to co-operate with British officials. In 1927, the British government appointed a commission, headed by Lord Simon, to investigate the situation. The Simon Commission, in 1930, recommended a gradual increase of self-government but emphasized the need for continued British control. The Nationalists now increased their agitation for dominion status.

A series of Round Table Conferences were held in London in 1931 and 1932, between Moslems and Hindus and between high-caste Brahmins and the lowest social group, the "untouchables." These conferences broke up without any definite agreements. In March, 1933, after the failure of a third Round Table Conference, the British government, under Prime Minister MacDonald, made public a proposed new constitution for India. In 1935, Parliament adopted a revised draft of the proposed constitution as the Government of India Act of 1935. This basic law which went into effect early in 1937 provided for: (1) the organization of the British provinces and the native states into an All-India Federation; (2) the establishment of a bicameral legislature; (3) an increase in local self-government for the British provinces; (4) the protection of British interests, granting considerable power to the viceroy. This constitution did not give the people of India the opportunity to gain practical experience in representative government or to demonstrate that they were capable of ruling themselves.

The outbreak of the Second World War gave renewed impetus to the Indian Nationalists' demands not only for dominion status but for complete independence. The leadership of the movement was carried forward by Gandhi and an able leader of the more radical groups among the Hindus, Jawaharlal Nehru. Nehru and Gandhi were both interned during most of the war. The British attempted to appease the Nationalists' demands in 1941, when they sent Sir Stafford Cripps to India to work out some arrangement which would grant dominion status to India after the end of the war. The situation was further complicated by the demands of the Moslem Nationalists, led by Ali Jinnah, for the creation of an independent Moslem state within India, to be known as Pakistan. The Cripps mission was doomed to failure. The end of the war, however, made the problem more serious than ever. The Attlee government dispatched a Parliamentary Committee to India in 1945 to make a renewed study of the problem.

In 1947, British rule ended, and King George VI surrendered the title of Emperor of India. Two separate dominions—India and Pakistan—were created out of the old Indian Empire. Between the Dominion of India, mainly Hindu, with a population of 360 million, and the Dominion of Pakistan, whose 75 million were mostly Moslem, warfare broke out. The situation was aggravated by the fact that Pakistan was established in two disconnected parts with about a thousand miles of Indian territory separating them. The status of Kashmir, a northern region which India moved to annex, caused further hostility.

Shortly after achieving independence, India rejected dominion status and became a republic. She chose, however, to remain within the Commonwealth of Nations. The nations of the British Commonwealth consult together and act jointly in matters of common interest and especially foreign policy. In the 1950s, India, as a growing power who found herself lodged between Communist Russia and the West with whom her traditional sympathies lay, adopted a policy of maximum neutrality. She acted, almost invariably, quite independently of Great Britain. India's dual situation—economic interdependence with the West and proximity to Russia—influenced Nehru in his attempt to play the role of peacemaker between the opposing powers; and diplomatic experts found it difficult to determine India's position in the international balance of power.

PALESTINE

At the close of the First World War, under the mandate system of the League of Nations, Great Britain acquired Palestine (which also included Trans-Jordan) and Iraq (Mesopotamia). In 1932 the British government voluntarily gave up its mandate over Iraq, which became an independent nation. At the time, the chief problem confronting Britain in the Middle East was the hostility of the Arabs and Jews in Palestine.

In the Balfour Declaration of 1917, Great Britain announced her intention to establish a national home for the Jewish people in Palestine. Zionist (Jewish nationalist) activities resulted in an influx of Jewish immigrants into the Holy Land. The Arabs, who outnumbered the Jews ten to one, had been enraged by the Balfour Declaration. They protested vigorously against the increasing flood of Jewish immigration and against the steady acquisition of land by the Jews. The hostility of the two groups was intensified after 1933, when Nazi persecution drove thousands of German Jews to seek entry into Palestine. In 1939 the British government turned its back on the Balfour Declaration and, in a White Paper, announced the following as its new policy: (1) termination of the mandate and establishment of an "independent Palestine State" at the end of ten years; (2) limitation of Jewish immigrants to a total of 75,000 for the next five years; (3) a complete cessation of Jewish immigration thereafter. Jewish leaders at once denounced the new plan as a betrayal. Outbursts of violence were common.

The extension of Nazi conquests in Europe during the Second World War and the hopeless condition of the remaining Jewish minority in Europe sharpened the problem of Palestine. The British government considered the Zionist agitation for an independent Jewish state in Palestine as a threat to her imperial position and remained adamant in her policy of restricting Jewish immigration into Palestine. The Arabs, under the leadership of King Ibn Saud of Arabia and the Arab League, placed pressure on the British government to continue the policy of the White Paper.

Such pressure was strengthened by threats to terminate valuable oil concessions in the Middle East desired by both the British and Americans. In 1946 an Anglo-American Committee was set up to study the condition of the Jews in Europe and recommend relaxing immigration quotas to Palestine.

When in 1948 the British mandate terminated, the separate state of Israel was proclaimed under the auspices of the United Nations. The neighboring Arab states in the Middle East—Egypt, Trans-Jordan (Jordan), Syria, Lebanon, Iraq, and Saudi Arabia—refused to accept the sovereignty of Israel, and they sent armed forces into the territory of the new state. For eighteen months, war raged. The Israelis were successful in expelling the invaders. Armistice agreements were signed between Israel and the Arab countries, while the United Nations continued to study the problem. Although Israel maintained control over the territory granted her, intermittent border attacks and reprisals continued between the new state and her Arab neighbors. Wholly unresolved was the question of the future of approximately one million Arabs who had fled from Israel when warfare first broke out and who were temporarily in camps in Arab territory near the Israeli border. The United Nations was unable to find a permanent basis for peace in the Middle East.

CULTURAL DEVELOPMENTS AND THE ADVANCE OF SCIENCE

The end of the nineteenth century and the early twentieth century witnessed a remarkable advance in technology and scientific discovery, and at the same time great advances were made in social reform in Europe and the United States. The cultural interests of the majority of people were considerably enlarged through increased facilities of education and the several modern media of widespread communication, beginning with the newspapers.

Public education became an increasingly widely accepted principle. State-supported and state-controlled school systems have largely replaced private and church schools in many countries. State-subsidized universities, scholarships, technical and scientific schools have multiplied to an amazing extent. The spread of knowledge has been greatly facilitated by the growth of libraries. The level of illiteracy has continually decreased in almost all countries. The steady reduction in the length of the working day as a result of the adoption of labor-saving machinery has provided greater leisure. The rapid development of motion pictures, the radio, and more recently television, the wide circulation of newspapers, magazines, and books, all have exerted a tremendous influence in the spread of culture.

Increased education contributed greatly to the fervor for reform which the latter half of the nineteenth century witnessed. In this period occurred such notable events as the abolition of slavery, reform of penal codes, and improved care for the needy, aged, orphaned, physically handicapped, and mentally defective. More effective humanitarian work was made possible by the formation of many welfare organizations. The efforts of the Swiss, Henri Dunant, resulted in the organization of the International Red Cross. In 1878 the Englishman, William Booth, founded the Salvation Army. Owners of great fortunes contributed generously to social agencies. Outstanding examples in America are the Rockefeller, the Carnegie, and the Nobel foundations.

Woman suffrage also received its greatest impetus during the nineteenth and twentieth centuries. In the middle of the nineteenth century, the feminist movement found a champion in the noted English philosopher, John Stuart Mill. Two British Dominions, Australia and New Zealand, were the pioneers in the adoption of woman suffrage. In England, the suffragists were led by Emmeline Pankhurst. In the United States, the movement was led by Susan B. Anthony. It was the First World War which finally brought the ballot not only to the women of England (Reform Bills of 1918 and 1928), and the women of the United States (Nineteenth Amendment, 1920), but also to women throughout a greater part of Europe. Women have also been accepted more and more in business and the professions.

The scientific progress of the twentieth century had its beginnings in the nineteenth when steamboats and railroads came into widespread use and the telegraph, telephone, electric light, and the Atlantic cable were developed. Transportation facilities greatly stimulated commerce. Improved means and heightened speed of communication brought the entire world closer together. Then came the automobile in the twentieth century —cheap and rapid transportation for everyone—and on its heels followed the airplane, the radio, the world-girdling telephone, the motion pictures and the talking pictures, television and radar.

There have been other scientific marvels in the twentieth century—advances in methods of hygiene and medicine, more light on the value of foods (including vitamins and calories), the production of rayon and nylon fabrics, quick-drying paints, new methods of canning and preserving foods, mechanical refrigeration for the home, air conditioning, and so on.

Mankind thus came to an unprecedented understanding of the universe it inhabits. Man has been enabled to explore the skies through his great telescopes and to realize something of the magnitude of the universe; with microscopes he has looked into the minutiae of the universe, and he has discovered the composition of the atom. Further scientific developments have resulted in the discovery of the secret of atomic energy, used in making the atomic bomb and in powering numerous peacetime projects.

THE FIRST WORLD WAR

The latter part of the nineteenth century seemed to promise much for the perpetuation of peace. There were powerful forces, however, tending toward war. Chief among these were the excesses of nationalism, imperialism, militarism, and the system of secret alliances. In a world where power was measured by industrial development at home and control over colonies abroad, Germany, which lagged behind her Western neighbors in these respects, speeded her development to catch up with and surpass other powers. The result was the First World War.

Since the year 1871, the education of German youth tended to exalt Prussian superiority, Prussian military glory, and Prussian industrial prosperity. The young Germans were taught to believe in the ultimate Prussianization of the world.

There was an understanding between France, Russia, and Great Britain, known as the Triple Entente. Balancing this was the Triple Alliance of Germany, Austria-Hungary, and Italy. When the Archduke Francis Ferdinand of Austria-Hungary was assassinated in the little Balkan town of Serajevo in 1914, Europe was ready to be involved in conflict. From the nervous apprehension that had existed, the impact of the assassination led the European countries only a few weeks later into a conflagration that spread destruction through the world.

There was a chaotic exchange of international messages—ultimatums and their replies. On July 28, 1914, Austria declared war on Serbia. On the August 1 following, Germany declared war on Russia, which was mobilizing troops to prevent Austrian aggression in the Balkans. As France was allied with Russia, she began to mobilize her troops. Germany, on August 3, 1914, declared war on France.

Expediency is the law of war, and because the Belgian-French frontier was weak, Germany violated the neutrality of Belgium and of Luxembourg. Germany sent its armies across these countries in an offensive movement against France. Although the Belgians bravely resisted the advancing Germans, they halted them but briefly, and in the face of heavy artillery Liége, Brussels, and Mons fell. Determined to terrify the people into submission, the Prussians conducted a "reign of terror" in Belgium.

In order to defend the neutrality of Belgium, Great Britain declared war on Germany August 4, 1914. In the meantime the French armies were retreating toward Paris, and it appeared as if the Germans would reach the French capital. They were stopped, however, at the battle of the Marne River, and had to fall back. Modern warfare now began to come into its own. The Germans entrenched themselves, as did the Allies, and the battle line soon extended across northeastern France from Flanders to Switzerland.

Neither side gained much in the early years of the war. The British held the Germans back at the first battle of Ypres. In spite of the fact that the Germans, for the first time, used poison gas at the second battle of Ypres, the Allied troops held. The gas mask, as a defense against poison gas, was devised, for as an instrument of modern warfare, poison gas had arrived.

Except for its tremendous number of casualties, the offensive of the Crown Prince in the Argonne in 1915 had no definite effect. A deadlock had been reached in trench warfare. There was incessant firing, but the battle line changed little. A terrific offensive against Verdun took place in February, 1916, but the French held the Germans.

In the meantime Germany's submarines, another new war weapon, began to show activity. A naval engagement took place off the coast of Chile, and there was the battle of the Falkland Islands. Great Britain gained control of the sea, a position which the naval battle of Jutland in May, 1916, did not change.

The *Lusitania* was torpedoed and sunk by the Germans on May 7, 1915, with a loss of 1,195 lives. This was followed by other ruthless sinking of Allied and neutral ships. The United States was drawn into war in 1917 by Germany's announcement of unrestricted submarine warfare.

The war extended from the earth to under the sea to the air. German zeppelins dropped bombs on London. Powerful anti-aircraft guns were developed, and airplanes were armed with machine guns. The Allies began the great Somme offensive in July, 1916, but it failed. The armored, motor-driven car known as the tank then first appeared as a weapon of war. In the month of March, 1917, the Germans retired to the "Hindenburg line," where they were able to remain until the American troops participated in the Allied offensive of 1918. Having counted on Italy's aid, it was a blow to the Central Powers when Italy declared war on Austria in May, 1915. Italy, however, did little except to establish a line of trenches that occupied the attention of Austrian troops, which might have been used to advantage elsewhere.

The United States declared war in 1917, and as soon as was practicable thereafter, American troops arrived in France. This acted as a stimulus to the war-tired Allies. Russia having suffered internal collapse, the Germans were receiving reinforcements from the Eastern front, and they made many gains early in 1918. In June the tide began to turn. In July the battle of Château-Thierry resulted in pushing the Germans back. There was a new Somme offensive in August, and in October there was a general German retreat.

Soon after the middle of 1918 the Central Powers began to surrender. They were weakened by a tremendous casualty list, outnumbered, discouraged, and were suffering from confusion among their leaders. Bulgaria capitulated in September, Turkey in October, Austria on November 4; and the general Armistice came on November 11. The peoples of Central Europe were in revolt and setting up independent states, and the empire of Austria-Hungary was torn with internal dissension. There were rebellions in Germany that showed how the tide had turned, and two days before the Armistice, Kaiser Wilhelm and the Crown Prince fled from Germany and took refuge in Holland.

The repercussions of the war were not to be settled in a day. In spite of Woodrow Wilson's idealistic plans, which included a League of Nations, a shortsighted peace was concluded at Versailles. The great war premier of France, Georges Clemenceau, nicknamed "the tiger," had not forgotten the Franco-Prussian War (1870–1871) which occurred when he was a young man; and he spoke for a vengeful France. Lloyd George was for maintaining British imperialism. Orlando of Italy also spoke up for the special interests of his countrymen. All negotiators except Wilson claimed their share of the spoils.

It was a modern war, but the peace was settled in an old-fashioned manner. It was a peace treaty of indemnities and the victors' "give and take" by governments and rulers who showed little concern for the future. They failed to realize that dissatisfaction among large sections of people could be, in itself, cause for war.

Most of the civilized world had been drawn into the war, and the only neutral countries in Europe were Switzerland, Holland, Spain, Denmark, Norway, and Sweden. The remainder of Europe was engaged in combat; and almost all of Africa, most of Asia, and virtually all of North America were implicated. Brazil, China, and Japan also joined in the conflict.

In all the opposing armies engaged in the war the staggering total of mobilized forces was more than sixty-five millions of men. Of these, eight and one-half million were killed, and twenty million were wounded. In addition to the aggregate sum of money spent for the war, the loss of property, materials, and income was incalculable. The war left the nations of the world heavily saddled with debt, and was probably the main cause of the economic depression that began a decade later.

The war broke up the empires of Germany, Austria-Hungary, and Russia; and the map of Europe then showed many new independent countries, established in accordance with the principle of self-determination which Wilson had so strongly urged. Among these new countries—most of them republics—were: Poland (independent again at last), Czechoslovakia (which includes Bohemia), Yugoslavia (including the smaller Balkan states of Serbia and Montenegro and the Austrian states of Bosnia and Herzegovina), Austria, Hungary, Finland, and the Balkan states of Estonia, Latvia, and Lithuania. The Union of Soviet Socialist Republics was the new name for most of the territories included in the former Russian Empire.

THE PEACE OF 1919–1939

When the First World War ended, and especially after the peace treaties were signed at Versailles in 1919, it was hoped that the world was entering on a period of true peace. The League of Nations was to be a means of reviewing and adjusting any problems which arose from the peace treaties or from other conflicts in the aims of nations.

After the war, Germany—following the intentions of the peacemakers at Versailles—became a republic. A new German constitution was adopted at Weimar; and Friedrich Ebert, a socialist, was elected the first president. In the elections of 1925, evidently marked by a conservative trend, General von Hindenburg, military leader in the war, was chosen as the second president. By the time of his death in 1934, autocracy was already being revived in Germany by the newly instated Chancellor, Adolf Hitler.

Tsar Nicholas of Russia had been forced to abdicate in 1917, and soon afterward a Communist dictatorship was established under Lenin and Trotsky, and later under Stalin. Southward of the former Russian Empire arose the independent republics of Georgia and Azerbaijan in Caucasia. Later they joined the Soviet Union.

Turkey had to abandon much of its European and Asiatic territory, and recognize the independence of Armenia, Iraq (a British mandate), Syria (a French mandate), and Hedjaz, a part of Arabia.

In the twenty years following the First World War, colonial governments were faced with demands by groups in each colony for economic and social reforms and for a larger share in the colonial government. In various attempts to meet native demands and changing conditions colonial policies were altered, and between 1919 and 1939 the colonies of southeast Asia were in a period of gradual transition.

Independence had been officially promised the Filipinos in 1916, and there was increasing agitation in the twenties for fulfillment of this promise. By 1933, the continued demand of the Filipinos, supported by a combination of special interests in the United States, resulted in the passage of the Hare-Hawes-Cutting Act. This was turned down by the Philippine Legislature and was succeeded by a somewhat similar measure, the Tydings-McDuffie Act. By its terms, a Philippine Commonwealth was established with full independence scheduled for July 4, 1946. Prior to this date the United States remained responsible for the defense and the foreign affairs of the Commonwealth.

Burma was given greater self-government in 1918 by means of the Montagu-Chelmsford reforms. Burma continued to remain a province of India until the passage of the Government of India Act of 1935. Under this Act, Burma was separated from India and was given a new status as a "self-governing unit within the British Commonwealth." The Act became effective on April 1, 1937. Although the new government was not permitted a free hand in defense, foreign affairs, or monetary policy, it did have freedom in tariff matters.

In Burma and the Philippines, the farthest advance in self-government was made, while in the Netherlands Indies, Indo-China, and in Malaya, political progress was slow and concessions to native demands for a greater share in government were small. In 1916, the Dutch created a legislative body—the Volksraad—for Indonesia, which opened its first session in 1918. This body tended to supersede the once powerful Council of the Netherlands Indies, but it possessed few real powers. Until 1927, its functions were wholly advisory, but as a result of growing nationalist expressions and a few severe outbreaks, it was given limited legislative powers. Because of its limited powers, the Volksraad was only a short, tentative step toward self-government. Local government remained either in the hands of various councils controlled by the Dutch, or in the hands of petty sultans under the direction of Dutch administrators or residents.

The League of Nations, established in 1919 to further the interests of world peace, was a new approach to international relations, with only a small precedent in the traditions of the Hague Conferences in Holland. (These were begun in 1899 for the purpose of settling international disputes by arbitration.) The United States did not join the League of Nations. The Central Powers were barred, and at first some of the neutral nations were left out. The League showed its limitations in its failure to prevent Japanese aggression in China in 1931–1932, and later in failing to enforce sanctions against Italy for its attack on Ethiopia during 1935 and 1936. After freedom for many centuries, Ethiopia was subdued by the Italians under the dictator Benito Mussolini in 1936, and the Emperor Haile Selassie was forced to flee from Addis Ababa to England.

In 1935, Adolf Hitler, Nazi dictator of Germany, instituted military

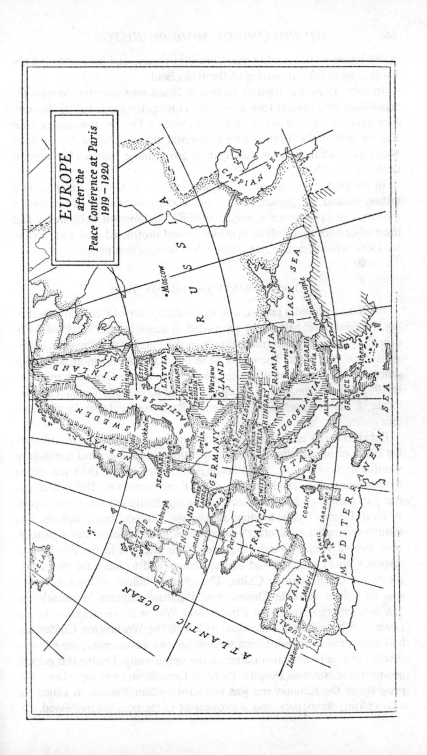

EUROPE
after the
Peace Conference at Paris
1919–1920

conscription in defiance of the Versailles treaty, and in continuing defiance, began the militarizing of the Rhineland.

In July, 1936, the Rightist faction in Spain took up arms to oust the republican government then in power. This uprising was led by the military under the command of General Francisco Franco. Because of their Fascist beliefs, the Franco forces received the support of the German Nazis and Italian Fascists; the Spanish government received the support of the Soviet Union.

In the light of later events, it is apparent that Spain was being used as a testing ground for planes, tanks, and modern techniques of warfare, a rehearsal of fascism for a world conflict. The Spanish belligerents and their allies became involved in a bloody and protracted civil war, ending by 1939, when Franco established a firm dictatorship in Spain.

DEVELOPMENTS IN THE FAR EAST

Japan had played a passive role as a military ally of Great Britain during the First World War, but succeeded in acquiring the spoils of "conquest" by seizing the German islands in the Pacific—the Carolines, Marshalls, and Marianas. These acts were but a prelude to more ambitious schemes. Japan presented the notorious Twenty-one Demands to China in 1915. These demands, if accepted, would have made China a protectorate of Japan. Protests by the United States forced Japan to withdraw them.

Between 1919 and 1921, American-Japanese tension increased over the issues of immigration, naval competition, and the general question of stability in the Far East. The Washington Conference of 1921 was called by Secretary of State Hughes to settle these questions. The conference was part success and part failure. Some naval limitation was agreed upon. A Four Power Treaty binding Japan, the United States, Britain, and France to respect each other's possessions in the Pacific was signed. A Nine Power Treaty bound the powers with interests in the Far East to respect China's integrity and independence, and to maintain the principle of the Open Door in China. The greatest failure of the conference was its failure to settle Chinese and Japanese disputes in Manchuria.

China emerged from the First World War with membership in the League of Nations and little else. Although the Washington Conference had attempted to permit China to stabilize her government, the Chinese seemed unable to avail themselves of the opportunity. During this period, however, the National Peoples' Party or Kuomintang was organized. The program of the Kuomintang was provided by Sun Yat-sen. It called for nationalism, democracy, and improvement of the people's livelihood. Dr.

Sun, however, died in 1925, and the leadership of the Kuomintang passed to Chiang Kai-shek. Chiang launched a campaign to unify China, but in the course of the campaign a serious split developed between the Communists in the Kuomintang and the more conservative groups.

China's attempts to unify herself were destined to be short-lived. On September 18, 1931, an explosion on the South Manchuria Railway near Mukden touched off a well-planned Japanese invasion of Manchuria, and became the first in a chain of violent reactions in many parts of the world leading to the Second World War. Between 1934 and 1937, the Japanese did their best to exploit China's lack of unity for their own purposes. By 1937, Chiang succeeded in achieving temporary unity with the Chinese Communists. The Japanese were now confronted with a China united against them to a greater degree than ever before. Japan invaded China in 1937. The Chinese armies lost battles and territory but did not lose heart. The Chinese, after losing more than one-third of their country, including the most productive of their territories, established their capital at Chungking and continued their resistance.

THE AXIS POWERS

The Fascist governments of Italy, Germany, and Japan formed an alliance in 1937, ostensibly to fight communism. This alliance became known as the Rome-Berlin-Tokyo Axis.

In 1938, Europe was divided into armed camps. The atmosphere of suspicion and political tension resembled that which preceded the First World War. Taking advantage of the military weakness and pacifist leanings of the democratic nations, Nazi Germany, under Hitler, "absorbed" Austria in 1938 and made it a part of Germany.

In September, 1938, Hitler mobilized the German army on the borders of Czechoslovakia, demanding the immediate cession of the Sudeten areas to Germany. A European war was averted at the eleventh hour by a conference of Chamberlain, Daladier, Hitler, and Mussolini at Munich, but at the eventual cost of the independence of Czechoslovakia. The policy pursued by Great Britain and France at this time was known as "appeasement."

THE SECOND WORLD WAR

The aggressions of Germany and Italy were clearly leading to war. Danzig and the Polish Corridor became Nazi objectives in 1939. Here the democracies took a stand. Great Britain and France declared war on Germany in September when that country invaded Poland. Just before this war began, Hitler and Stalin surprised the world with the signing of German-Russian non-aggression and trade treaties. Russia, not sure of the attitude of the Western Powers toward her, was able to gain almost two years of grace by this move.

THE MILITARY PHASES OF THE WAR

Poland, whose cities were mercilessly bombarded from the air, was no match for Nazi Germany with its millions of soldiers and tens of thousands of tanks and dive bombers. Poland soon collapsed.

By the spring of 1940 the Second World War was on in full swing. The Nazi legions occupied Denmark and invaded Norway, Holland, Belgium, and France. As France was reeling from the German attack it was invaded by the Italians under Mussolini, who also declared war on England.

In August the Nazis began a ruthless air attack on Great Britain, causing much destruction and great loss of life. Britain rallied under Winston Churchill, the new Prime Minister, and its defense was successful. Hitler's invasion plans of Britain were thwarted.

Meanwhile the United States was preparing to come to the aid of the beleaguered democracies. It was arming and sending munitions and food to Britain.

Germany and Italy then attacked and invaded Greece and Yugoslavia, and extended their control over Hungary, Rumania, and Bulgaria. In June, 1941, Hitler broke his pact with Stalin and invaded Russia, meeting heroic resistance.

As the Japanese became involved in an increasingly larger offensive in China, they announced their intention of establishing a "New Order in East Asia." Originally this new order was to be imposed on China only to bring that country into a "co-prosperity sphere" with Manchukuo and Japan. But after the fall of France in June, 1940, the Japanese saw new opportunities for expansion. In September, 1940, Japan entered into a full military alliance with Hitler and began to push into northern Indo-China. The "New Order in East Asia" became the "New Order in Greater East Asia" and the Japanese frankly stated that they intended to include China, Indo-China, the Philippines, Siam, Malaya, Burma, India, and the islands of the South Pacific within its scope. On December 7, 1941, Japan made her bid—an attempt that was to have disastrous consequences for her.

Japan's treacherous attack on Pearl Harbor on December 7, 1941, brought the United States into the Second World War. Before the Allied Nations could stop Japan it had invaded the Philippines, Burma, and the

British and Dutch East Indies. Japan achieved brilliant successes in the early stages of the Second World War, bringing Indo-China, Siam, and Malaya also under her control. It was only at the battles of Midway and the Coral Sea that the tide began to turn against her.

The year 1943 saw the war turning in favor of the Allies. Russia was rolling the Nazis back. The British and Americans expelled the Nazis and Italians from North Africa. Mussolini was overthrown. The Allies were poised in Sicily for an invasion of Europe. In October, 1943, the Allies called for Japan's unconditional surrender and the reduction of Japan to her status of 1894. This meant the complete stripping of Japan's gains, leaving her only the home islands of Japan. At the time of this declaration, ultimate victory over Japan seemed in the far-distant future, yet within four months after the collapse of Germany in May, 1945— Japan would be suing for surrender to the Allied Powers.

The final phase of the Second World War found the Allies definitely on the offensive both on the European front and in the Pacific theater. On June 6, 1944, the Allies launched the invasion of the European continent under the leadership of General Dwight D. Eisenhower, while in the Pacific theater the armies of General Douglas MacArthur and naval forces under Admirals Chester Nimitz and William Halsey were softening up Japan for an invasion of the Philippines and the ultimate invasion of the Japanese islands.

The campaigns met with unprecedented success. By August of 1944, Paris was liberated and the Allied armies plunged headlong to the German frontier. A temporary and almost disastrous setback was suffered about Christmas, 1944, when the German armies launched a counteroffensive through the weakly defended Ardennes forest in a drive to capture Liége and Antwerp. The Allies suffered tremendous losses, but finally succeeded in slowing down and finally checking the German offensive in the heroic "Battle of the Bulge." By the early part of the spring of 1945, the Allies were prepared to launch the final drive into the heart of the Third Reich. By dint of slow but stubborn fighting, the Allied armies drove through the "Siegfried Line" and were poised for a crossing of the Rhine. By one of those pieces of fortune that dot the past history of the world's wars, the Nazis neglected to entirely destroy one bridge across the Rhine at Remagen. The crossing of the Rhine was the final seal of doom for the Wehrmacht. The Russians by this time were hammering at the gates of Berlin and were fighting in the streets of Berlin itself. On May 12, 1945, the German general staff surrendered at Reims, France, to General Eisenhower and to the Russian forces. The "second" or final surrender took place in Berlin several days later.

The factors responsible for the speedy defeat of Japan were the achievements of the United States armed forces—the Army, Navy, and Marine Corps; the entrance of Russia into the war against Japan in August, 1945; and the tremendous effects of the atomic bombing of Hiroshima and Nagasaki.

THE POLITICAL PHASES OF THE WAR

The Second World War was unique in the number of personal meetings that occurred between Allied political and military leaders. Even before Pearl Harbor, President Roosevelt and Prime Minister Churchill had met in the North Atlantic aboard the cruiser *Augusta,* a meeting which resulted in the Atlantic Charter, an important document outlining the joint Anglo-American objectives for maintaining world peace in the future. Immediately after Pearl Harbor, the Prime Minister was at the White House for conferences. In June, 1942, Churchill was again in this country to consult with the President and his aides and to plan for a method of assisting in the North African campaign. The Casablanca meeting in January, 1943, lasting ten days and including top-ranking military personnel, planned the invasions of Sicily and Italy, helped to engender better feelings between the French generals, De Gaulle and Giraud, and laid down the blanket terms of "unconditional surrender" for the Axis powers. In August, 1943, this time at Quebec, Churchill and Roosevelt met and, among other matters dealing with the prosecution of the war, laid plans for the Moscow Conference of Foreign Ministers for October, 1943. The Moscow Conference resulted in a pronouncement of agreement among the United States, the Soviet Union, China, and Britain regarding their war aims and their plans for the postwar years. The Moscow Pact shattered any hope the Axis might have had for lack of unity among the United Nations. The pact provided for: (1) united action against their respective enemies; (2) joint prosecution of the war; (3) joint enforcement of peace terms; (4) an international organization which would recognize both large and small states and recognize the principle of sovereign equality; (5) joint action to maintain peace and security pending the establishment of a system of general security.

In November and December, 1943, two significant conferences were held. At Cairo, Roosevelt, Churchill, and Chiang Kai-shek (leader of the Nationalist Chinese forces) met and, with their military leaders, mapped the plans for the unconditional surrender of Japan. In the postwar world Japan would be stripped of her conquests of the last fifty years and China would become the dominant power in the Far East. At the Teheran Conference, Roosevelt, Churchill, and Stalin reaffirmed, in this first personal meeting of the three leaders, the principles of the Moscow Pact of 1943 and settled plans for military operations against Germany.

In August, 1944, at Dumbarton Oaks, Washington, D.C., statesmen representing the United States, England, the Soviet Union, and China drafted tentative proposals for a world security organization to maintain peace.

The final conference between the "big three" leaders of the Allies— Roosevelt, Churchill, and Stalin—was held at Yalta, in the Crimea, in February, 1945. The declaration published at the conclusion of the Yalta Conference indicated that the "Big Three" had reached agreement on several points: (1) military plans for the defeat of Germany; (2) common policies for enforcing unconditional surrender terms, which were not revealed but, it was indicated, would include disarmament, break-up for all time of the German general staff, the elimination or destruction of all German industry that could be used for military production, payment of reparations in kind to be determined by an Allied commission meeting in Moscow, the occupation of Germany by Great Britain, the United States, and Russia, and possibly France; (3) a conference of the United Nations, to be held at San Francisco starting on April 25, 1945, to prepare the charter for a world security organization; (4) the question of voting procedure for the Security Council of the world security organization, which had been left unsettled at the preliminary conference held at Dumbarton Oaks; (5) a reaffirmation of the principles of the Atlantic Charter; (6) a promise that the Big Three would jointly assist the liberated peoples to form governments "broadly representative of all democratic elements"; (7) the creation of a new Polish Provisional Government of National Unity, which would take the place of the Lublin Committee recognized by the Soviet Union and the London Polish government recognized by Great Britain and the United States; (8) the settlement of the eastern boundary of Poland, which, it was stated, would follow with minor exceptions the Curzon line proposed after the First World War; (9) establishment of a provisional government for Yugoslavia, which at the time was under the leadership of the Partisan, pro-Soviet leader, Marshal Tito (Josip Broz); (10) consultation every three or four months by the foreign secretaries of the United States, England, and the Soviet Union.

The immediate effect of the conference was to demonstrate to the world that, in spite of disagreements, the three nations were united and were determined to achieve a "continuing and growing co-operation" among themselves and all peace-loving nations to the end of establishing a secure and lasting peace.

Besides the concrete steps taken at these conferences among the Allied leaders, the foundations for international co-operation had been laid down at meetings of the representatives of the United Nations on problems that needed solution for a more lasting peace. At a conference of forty-four nations convened at Hot Springs, Virginia, the nations agreed to pool their efforts for postwar rehabilitation and recovery by contributing financial support to the UNRRA—the United Nations Relief and Rehabilitation Administration. At Bretton Woods, New Hampshire, in July, 1944, a conference of the United Nations formulated plans to stabilize international currencies and to establish a world bank to finance foreign trade and economic reconstruction.

The period between the Teheran Conference (December, 1943) and the Yalta Conference (February, 1945) was troubled by problems that arose over Poland and Greece. These problems almost threatened the unity of the Big Three.

During the closing months of 1944 the so-called Polish question came to the surface. The Soviet Union was determined to retain the eastern portion of Poland, which she had acquired after the defeat of Poland in September, 1939. The Soviet Union argued that the Poles in that area were outnumbered by White Russians and Ukrainians. The Soviet government suggested that as compensation Poland should receive portions of East Prussia. The Polish government-in-exile at London rejected this proposal, but a government for Poland established on Polish soil at Lublin accepted it. Churchill urged the London Polish government to accept Moscow's proposals, hinting that an agreement to this effect had been reached at the Teheran Conference. The question was again discussed and settled at the Yalta Conference, as we have seen. The Polish National Government in Warsaw was ultimately recognized by Great Britain and the United States.

While the Polish question was being debated during the closing months of 1944, a crisis developed concerning the liberated government of Greece. Revolutionary forces, known as the E.L.A.S., desired control of the government. These forces, who claimed to be the real representatives of the Greek people, refused to surrender their arms. After several weeks of sporadic outbursts of violence, which were finally suppressed by the British, a government was organized with Archbishop Damaskinos acting as regent for King George II of Greece.

THE UNITED NATIONS ORGANIZATION

While specific issues were causing no end of trouble, the Allies were asked to discuss the plans for the world security organization that had been drafted during August of 1944, at Dumbarton Oaks, Washington,

D.C. On a suggestion of President Roosevelt, the Allies had called themselves the United Nations during the war. Tentative proposals were drawn up for a permanent United Nations organization for peacetime and were discussed at the United Nations Conference which opened in San Francisco on April 25, 1945. The plans that were formulated at this conference were based upon the experience of the League of Nations. In brief, the United Nations would function through a General Assembly, a Security Council, a World Court, an Economic and Social Council, a Secretariat, and several subsidiary agencies entrusted with special duties. The proposed General Assembly would be made up of delegates of all nations which were members of the organization. This General Assembly, however, according to the original plan, was to have little power; its functions would be largely exploratory and advisory. It could make recommendations, but all matters requiring action would be handled by the Security Council.

Most of the power of the new organization was to be exercised by the Security Council. By the agreements concluded at the conference, the Council would consist of eleven members, with the United States, Great Britain, Russia, China, and France (the "Big Five") as permanent members, and six others to be chosen by the Assembly to serve for two-year periods. The main task of the Security Council would be to check aggression and to prevent war. To accomplish this purpose, it would decide upon measures to be used, and it could call upon members of the United Nations to put them into effect. If the Security Council should decide that such measures as diplomatic pressure and economic sanctions were inadequate, it could order naval, air, and land operations against the aggressor.

The Economic and Social Council, composed of delegates from eighteen nations chosen for three-year terms by the General Assembly, would handle "international economic, social, and other humanitarian problems and promote respect for human rights and fundamental freedom."

In the years following the war, the United Nations discussed and decided upon measures of great international importance. However, its power was limited by its structure. It remained to be seen if it could actually "maintain international peace and security," as prepared in the charter.

THE FINAL PHASE OF THE WAR

Many world-shaking developments occurred in the year 1945. The war in Europe was won by May 12. President Roosevelt had died a month earlier. The Churchill government in England was overwhelmingly defeated in a general election during the summer of 1945 by the Labor Party, which selected Clement Attlee as Prime Minister. The Big Three, now consisting of President Truman, Prime Minister Attlee, and Marshal Stalin, met at Potsdam to lay down the terms for the treatment of Germany and Japan. On August 6, 1945, the dropping of an atomic bomb over Hiroshima heralded not only the rapid end of the war in the Pacific but also the opening of the Atomic Age.

At the Potsdam Conference, which was concluded on August 2, 1945, the Allied Powers, including the United States, Britain, and China (Russia was not yet at war with Japan), set down the concrete, unalterable terms upon which Japan could end the war. The phrase "unconditional surrender" was still used. But it applied only to the armies in the field. In substance, the terms were as follows: (1) defeated Japan could have industries, but not a war industry; (2) she could have a government, but not a government of militarists; (3) Japanese territory was to be restricted to her four home islands; (4) Japan would be occupied by Allied troops.

The Japanese government at first rejected the terms of the Potsdam Declaration, but the combination of the atomic bombs dropped on Hiroshima and Nagasaki and the entrance of Russia into the war against Japan on August 10, 1945, acted as convincing arguments. The Japanese sued for peace on August 12, 1945, and after protracted negotiations which revolved about the position of the Emperor in Japan, the Japanese accepted the terms of the Potsdam Declaration. General MacArthur was appointed Supreme Commander in Japan; and the Emperor was permitted to retain his throne, but merely as a figurehead.

In September, 1945, in accordance with agreements reached at Potsdam, the Big Five Council of Ministers met at London to draft the peace treaties for the former satellites of the Axis, particularly Italy, Hungary, Rumania, and Bulgaria. This Conference of Ministers was a complete failure, but a later conference, held in Moscow, was more successful.

THE FAR EAST AND THE WAR

Japan's rapid conquests after Pearl Harbor cut short the gradual change to greater autonomy in government. This was particularly true in the Philippines, and in the Netherlands East Indies, in Burma, in Indo-China, and Malaya.

Japanese aggression was accompanied by a further growth of nationalistic feeling throughout eastern Asia. The Chinese were stunned and embittered by the inability of the United States and Britain to hold the line in the Pacific and the Far East. For four and a half years Chinese regular and guerrilla armies had fought the Japanese, hoping for the day when Tokyo would be at war with the great powers. The day came in December, 1941; but the rapid loss by the Western Powers of their Eastern outposts resulted in a transformation of Chinese feeling and a decline of respect for the West.

Chinese nationalism after Pearl Harbor—like the nationalism of most countries—had many conflicting features. The Chinese realized with pride that China had been one of the few countries to withstand the Axis successfully. Chinese nationalism was still in a formative state and was complicated by open conflict, verging on civil war, between the Chinese Nationalists led by Chiang Kai-shek and the Chinese Communists. Chinese Communists were, it should be noted, also nationalists. During the Second World War the Communists established themselves in the northwest provinces where they waged effective guerrilla warfare against the Japanese. Although the major avowed objective of the Chinese Communists was agrarian reform and economic democracy, their struggle with the Nationalists was primarily a battle for complete political control of the country. Moves toward unity were undertaken by the opposing factions in 1946, with the United States serving as mediator.

The end of the Second World War saw a revived and stronger nationalism also in southeast Asia and the East Indies, with the Indonesians demanding complete independence from the Netherlands. Armed revolt broke out in November, 1945; the Dutch were willing to concede dominion status to the Indonesians, but such concession was rejected. However, Indonesia achieved full independence a few years later.

The war left the Philippines with tremendous problems of reconstruction; they were to gain independence shortly.

POSTWAR PROBLEMS

The problems of the world were by no means solved by the ending of the Second World War. As a matter of fact, almost as soon as peace was established, the questions which had lain dormant during the war and those which arose because of the war sprang into public view and demanded attention. Among them were: the control of the atomic bomb; the relations between Communist Russia and the powers of the West; the demand for independence of the colonial peoples; the rule of conquered Germany and Japan; the establishment of order and democracy in the liberated countries of Europe; the conditions resulting from fascism in such countries as Spain, Portugal, and Argentina; the maintenance of a healthy world economy; elimination of racial and religious prejudice in the world.

Two years after the end of the war, the Allied Powers still had a great number of troops stationed in Europe and the Far East. Russian troops in Germany, Finland, Austria, Hungary, Poland, Rumania, Yugoslavia, Korea, and Manchuria numbered over two million. About 750,000 British troops were located in some of these countries and in Italy, Greece, Palestine, Iraq, Suez Canal Zone, Egypt, Trans-Jordan, Libya, Eritrea, Italian Somaliland, and in the Dutch Indies. The United States had about 650,000 troops stationed in Germany, Austria, Italy, China, Korea, Japan, the Philippines, Pacific islands, and scattered air bases.

THE COLD WAR

Aware of the growing power of Russia's Communist bloc of European satellites and Eastern allies, and in order to counterbalance it, the United States, Canada, Britain, France, the Netherlands, Belgium, Luxembourg, Italy, Denmark, Norway, Iceland, and Portugal in 1949 signed the North Atlantic Defense Pact. The members proclaimed that an armed attack upon any one of them would be considered an act of aggression against all. The North Atlantic Treaty Organization (NATO), with Greece and Turkey admitted in 1952 and West Germany in 1955, undertook to raise and maintain an army capable of defense against Russia and her satellites. The purposes stated in the charter were emphatically declared to be within the context of the goals of the United Nations, which expressly recognizes regional defensive associations. The greatest military and financial contributions to NATO came, of course, from the United States; and General Dwight D. Eisenhower served as its chief until 1952. The Western world made in these years increasing demands upon the United States to assume leadership and responsibility for the maintenance of freedom and peace in the world. With the Soviet Union armed to the extent of an estimated force of 175 ready-for-action divisions in Russia alone, the United States was practically obliged to contribute to the defensive strength of western Europe.

The Truman Doctrine of 1947 declared that the United States would support smaller countries threatened by the active danger of subjugation: economic and military aid would be extended to peoples who might otherwise come under Soviet domination. Greece and Turkey were the first countries to benefit. This policy of the United States under President Truman was supplemented by the Marshall Plan (European Recovery Program), sanctioned by the United States Congress the next year, whereby this country made available economic and technological assistance to those nations of western Europe which joined the program.

In the 1950s development of atomic bombs and weapons had reached such an advanced stage that scientists declared the possibility of well over half the population of a country as large as America being destroyed by a two-hour planned atomic attack. The United States, Great Britain, and Russia were all known to possess highly developed atomic weapons. Defensive weapons were also being developed, and the most powerful hydrogen bombs were known to be so vastly lethal that no country would be likely to risk initiating their use in warfare. The international situation was, however, so tense that several attempts were made to negotiate disarmament and to limit or outlaw tests and production of nuclear weapons. In 1947 the United States made overtures looking toward the destruction of atomic stockpiles and an international control of their manufacture and use in all countries. The United States made it a condition that an efficient system of inspection be set up by the United Nations. This condition, Russia in the United Nations rejected. Proposals and counter-proposals were made in the following years, but no agreements were reached. In 1957, Harold Stassen, President Eisenhower's disarmament adviser, was abroad discussing with Western Powers and Russia such conditions of disarmament as might be agreeable to all.

By this time, despite some openings in the "Iron Curtain"—in 1955 Western tourists were permitted to enter Russia for the first time since the war—the division of almost all countries of the world into two power camps was firmly established. Discussions between the two were fruitless. The "cold war" was still on. Russian satellites, countries virtually under direct control from Moscow, included: Poland, Czechoslovakia, Hungary, Rumania, Bulgaria, Albania, and East Germany. These countries were occupied by Soviet troops after the war. They came under Russian domination through military pressure, severe political measures involving mass executions and exportations, and highly organized propaganda. Greece, Turkey, and Finland were also subjected to pressure, but they remained outside the Soviet orbit. Yugoslavia, which came under the Communist dictatorship of Marshall Tito after the war, broke away from Moscow's leadership when Tito quarreled with Stalin. Although Yugoslavia remained Communist and a dictatorship, the West found it expedient to grant aid to its people to insure the country's policy of independence from Moscow, which was continued from 1948.

DISTURBANCES WITHIN THE SOVIET ORBIT

In 1953, Stalin died and there ensued another domestic struggle in Russia for supreme power. Malenkov was the apparent victor, but in 1955 the premiership was assumed by Bulganin. Khrushchev and Molotov were other high-ranking members of the Soviet hierarchy. In 1957 another reversal gave Khrushchev, as head of the Party, supreme power; Molotov was removed from the government, and Malenkov lost all influence. With shifts in power, Soviet policy gave the appearance of promising radical changes. These changes later seemed more to serve Russian propaganda than world peace.

A more liberal attitude toward the satellite countries may have been one cause of the October 1957 rebellions in Poland and Hungary. In these two countries a confused succession of open rebellion, concessions from Moscow, and renewed Russian repression led to different results. Poland's revolt, more organized and milder in its aspirations, was relatively successful. The Polish government became more representative of the people; Russia terminated its military activity in Poland and accepted the more liberal Gomulka as the new Polish premier.

At first the Hungarian revolt, a spontaneous uprising of the people aimed at establishing a democracy, seemed successful. Russia promised to recognize the popular government of Premier Nagy and accepted its demands for evacuation of Russian troops and total independence. Only a few days later, Russian troops marched back into Budapest with their tanks, massacring men, women, and children; military government prevailed. A new premier, a Russian puppet, was placed in power; there were mass deportations, and all the former Russian concessions were retracted. Thousands of Hungarians fled across the border into Austria and were granted refuge in many of the free countries.

The question of Russia's treatment of Hungary came before the United Nations. The potentially powerful Security Council was prevented from taking action by the Russian veto. The General Assembly strongly censured Russia; and in June of 1957, when the United Nations commission authorized to investigate the degree and extent of Russian aggression in Hungary reported cruelties and a gross injury to the people, the United States called for further action in the United Nations on the part of the 29 countries that voted to create the investigating committee. Russia maintained that the matter was an internal Hungarian one and hence not under United Nations jurisdiction.

GERMANY

After the war, Germany was divided into American, British, and Russian sectors, occupied by the troops of these countries. The Russians continued to occupy East Germany, and molded it to the status of a satellite country. In 1955, West Germany (which had been occupied by the Americans and British) became a sovereign independent state; and in the same year Austria became independent by agreement of all four allies of the war. West Germany elected Konrad Adenauer as its first Chancellor and pursued a pro-Western policy. All attempts on his part and with the co-operation of the Western Powers failed to elicit any response from Russia favorable to the re-unification of Germany.

CONFLICT IN THE FAR EAST

COMMUNISM IN CHINA

China, the greatest power in the Far East after the Second World War, was involved in civil war from 1946 to 1949. The Nationalists under Chiang Kai-shek and the Kuomintang had the open support of the United States. The Communists, under Mao Tse-tung and supported by Russia, were offered a place in the Kuomintang but refused. They fought instead, and in 1949 they were in control of the vast mainland. Chiang and the Nationalist forces retreated to the island of Formosa (Taiwan), where they maintained sovereignty with the help of the American navy. America continued to recognize Chiang's government as the government of China. Red China, recognized by most of the rest of the world, was not admitted to the United Nations. Chiang's avowed hope remained the "liberation" of China, while Mao's government pressed claims for control of Formosa. Mao, the Party leader, set up the new Communist regime in close co-operation with Moscow. In 1957, however, at approximately the time of the Russian concessions toward greater independence of action in Poland (which Tito of Yugoslavia applauded), Chou En-lai, Chinese premier and foreign minister, indicated that China's position was not necessarily one of subservience to Moscow.

JAPAN'S PEACE TREATY

At the end of the Second World War, all Chinese territories taken by Japan were returned to China, then governed by Chiang Kai-shek. Japan was occupied by a United Nations force under General Douglas MacArthur. Measures were taken to end Japan's ancient militaristic society.

In 1951, a Treaty of Reconciliation between Japan and 49 nations was signed in San Francisco. Japan's policy in the years following tended to be pro-Western; and the United States contributed extensively to Japanese economic rehabilitation.

THE KOREAN WAR

Korea had been an independent country through the centuries until 1910, when it was forcibly annexed by the Japanese Empire. After the Second World War it was agreed that the occupation of Korea would be in two zones: north of the 38 degree line of latitude was the zone occupied by Russian troops; below that line the country was occupied by the United States forces. This arrangement was agreed upon at the Potsdam Conference as a temporary measure, and it was decided that Korea was ultimately to have complete independence. Because the two occupying countries could reach no agreement, in 1948 two separate states were created. A democratic Republic of Korea was established in the south, and in the north a Communist Korean People's Republic was formed.

On June 25, 1950, the North Korean army made a sudden attack on South Korea. The matter was instantly brought to the attention of the United Nations Security Council, from which Russia, a few days before, had "walked out," thus losing her chance to veto action. The Council requested members of the United Nations to join in military intervention in support of the South Koreans. Sixteen countries sent substantial or token forces, while the United States sent a large force under MacArthur, who was also designated commander of the United Nations force. The force was highly successful, until it suffered a setback due to the military intervention of China on the side of North Korea. To avoid expansion of the conflict into a world war, President Truman ordered General MacArthur, United Nations Commander (yet responsible directly to the United States government), to refrain from crossing over from Korea into Chinese territory or bombing China. When MacArthur opposed these limitations, he was dismissed from his Far Eastern Command. Between 1951 and 1953 the battle was stalemated at around the 38th parallel, while the United States, with United Nations approval, engaged in truce talks with the Communists. On July 27, 1953, a cease-fire was obtained. Slowly the terms of a truce were agreed upon. No plans for re-unification were found acceptable to both sides, and Korea remained segmented in two parts.

WARFARE IN INDO-CHINA

The region of southeast Asia which has been known for some time as Indo-China was under French rule to a greater or lesser degree from 1873. Of the five states which originally were separate from one another, three of them—Annam, Tonkin, and Cochin-China—were united under the name of Vietnam. The other two were Laos and Cambodia. This entire area was administered by France under a governor-general.

In Indo-China violent opposition to French rule came from the Communist forces of Vietnam. Warfare began in 1946, and for seven and a half years the French and pro-French Vietnamese opposed the Vietnam Communists without success. In May of 1954, Dienbienphu, an important French stronghold, fell; and in July of the same year France signed a truce which amounted to defeat. Vietnam was partitioned, like Korea, into a northern communist state and a southern native democratic state. In accordance with the conditions of the truce, Cambodia and Laos also received independence from France shortly afterward.

NATIONALISM IN THE POSTWAR WORLD

One of the greatest map-changing factors in the years following the war was a new spirit of fervent nationalism coupled often with a genuine readiness and ability for self-government among formerly colonized peoples and protectorates or countries under mandate. The United States granted independence to the Philippines in 1946. India was granted independence in 1947, and at the same time Pakistan was made a separate independent state. The British may have postponed granting independence until this time out of a genuine fear that India, lodged so close to Russia, would fall easy prey to Communist infiltration. However, in many cases, it was clear that granting of autonomy would involve economic and political loss to the mother country. Burma and Ceylon received independence from Great Britain in 1947 and 1948 respectively. Malaya received her independence in 1957.

THE DECLINE OF BRITISH POWER

The Second World War had sapped Britain's wealth; the country was no longer able to export sufficiently, and the Empire was diminishing.

Under the Labor Government, which carried the country in 1945 with Clement Attlee as Prime Minister, and under successive governments, the English recognized that their position as a world power had become precarious and that there was a necessity for drastic measures to keep England's economy on a firm basis. A degree of socialism was probably a matter of necessity in a country which found itself obliged to levy the highest taxes of any democracy. The Bank of England, British Railways, the Postal Service, coal mines, and the iron and steel industries were among the interests that were nationalized. The Conservative Government, returned to power in 1951, although it had opposed socialization, saw that it could not turn back the clock. A few nationalized industries, however, were returned to private ownership.

In 1949 the government was obliged to devaluate the pound from $4.03 to $2.82 in acknowledgment of the decreased real value of British sterling. Continental currencies dropped proportionately. Britain hoped thus to increase exports and fill the dollar deficiency. In recognition of its new world position, Britain was obliged to depend on good diplomacy and United States support to retain its influential position in areas of strategic interest.

BRITAIN AND THE MIDDLE EAST

In 1951, Britain's oil interests in the Middle East were seriously threatened when the Iranian government nationalized the industry and appropriated property of the (British) Anglo-Iranian Oil Company. Britain, dependent as she was on both the income and the oil itself, refused to accept the decision. The Iranians were not able to operate the wells, and the government which had appropriated them fell. In 1954, Iran signed a 25-year pact with eight private Western firms, permitting them to resume their management of the oil industry with increased royalties paid to the Iranian government.

Mounting Arab nationalism in the Middle East provided an opening for Soviet interference and aid in the Arab countries. The situation was further irritated by Arab opposition on the part of Egypt, Syria, Lebanon, Iraq, Saudi Arabia, Yemen, and Trans-Jordan to the creation in 1948 of the Jewish state of Israel, in the former British Mandate area of Palestine.

In 1955 a British-dominated Middle East Treaty Organization, also called the Baghdad Pact, was signed by Britain, Iran, Iraq, Pakistan, and Turkey. It was a treaty of mutual defense, similar in language to NATO. The United States sent observers, thus indicating her support, but did not join.

THE SUEZ CANAL CRISIS

In 1954, under some pressure from the United States, Britain agreed to withdraw within twenty months the troops which it had long stationed in Egypt. By 1956 all British troops, including those in the Suez Canal Zone, had departed. Simultaneously, it was becoming apparent that Egypt, under the dictatorship of Colonel Gamal Abdel Nasser, aspired to a position of Arab leadership in the Middle East. She became rapidly anti-Western, and in the summer of 1956, Nasser seized the Suez Canal.

Although on Egyptian territory, the canal was owned by a private company (over fifty per cent European) and had long been under international control. The prospect of this vital thruway being managed to the political interest of one country caused a crisis. The British and the French deliberated with the United States and in the United Nations their claims that Egypt had violated the Convention of 1888, by which the international status of the canal was guaranteed. A few months after the Egyptian seizure of the canal, Israel, citing Egyptian (Arab) attacks into her country, invaded Egypt's Sinai peninsula. Two days later England and France "intervened," as they claimed, in the name of security. The Anglo-French attack upon Egypt was limited, beginning only with aerial bombardment of strategic points; it was not until days later that troops were landed. Only seven days after the British and French intervened, they accepted a cease-fire order of the General Assembly of the United Nations, which had been supported by the United States. The three invading countries withdrew their troops. It remained ostensibly for the United Nations, whose forces began policing the area, to settle the difference over the canal, as well as the Arab-Israeli dispute. Egypt, however, was in full possession of the canal.

THE FRENCH IN NORTH AFRICA

Apart from Indo-China, France's principal foreign possessions were in North Africa and Central Africa. Nationalism was growing in both areas.

Native opposition and demands for autonomy developed in North Africa, where the French ruled Algeria, Tunisia, and French Morocco—all three with Arab populations. Moslem terrorist activities led to open warfare with the French.

Tunisia and French Morocco achieved virtual independence in 1956, and in the same year, Spain granted independence to her section of Morocco. The French, however, insisted on certain conditions of political and economic interdependence with France. She retained troops in both Tunisia and Morocco. Fighting broke out again in the following year.

In Algeria the fighting continued, and was reflected in France, where Algerians at times rioted in the capital. The situation was a very special one, as Algeria was not a colony but politically an integral part of France proper; it was organized politically as three departments of metropolitan France. Thus, when the Algerian question was proposed for discussion in the United Nations, France could claim sincerely that it was an internal affair. By 1957, France had spent large sums of money and suffered heavy casualties in the Algerian fighting, without achieving any success.

At home, the Algerian question was a political issue which reflected France's lack of unity and its inefficient constitution. No government could remain in office if its policies would require the nation to make an all-out effort toward winning the Algerian war, which would also require increased taxes. On the other hand, no government could gain the support of the people if its policy would be to surrender Algeria; French residents in Algeria and business interests were too dependent on its remaining a part of the country.

UNRESOLVED INTERNATIONAL PROBLEMS

The year 1957 saw a heightening of the tension between East and West, particularly in the area of disarmament. The launching by the Soviets of the first artificial satellite and the evidence of their having an intercontinental ballistic missile alarmed Western nations. Soviet peace propaganda stressed the need for top-level meetings outside of the United Nations, but there were grave doubts among Western leaders concerning Soviet sincerity toward establishing rigid disarmament regulations.

The divided status of Germany continued to concern the West, and particularly West Germany; there seemed little likelihood that Russia would permit free elections in East Germany or re-unification. Regarding the other eastern European countries under Soviet domination, the free world seemed to be faced with a grossly unjust situation which it was totally impotent to help to set right.

In the Middle East, the willingness of certain of the Arab states to co-operate with and even support the program of the Soviets, combined with the unresolved conflict between Israel and the Arab countries, had the effect of making the politics of Middle Eastern countries a continuing potential threat to world peace. Overtures of increased economic and, of course, military assistance to certain of the Arab countries on the part of Russia, and in 1957 on the part of Communist China, were a source of further East-West tension in the area.

In North Africa the stalemated fighting between French and Moslem forces was rapidly becoming a struggle of international significance; it was growing increasingly difficult to find a basis for a solution acceptable by both sides.

In the face of these and other complex issues which threatened the peace of the world, the United States, England, and France and the members of NATO based their highest hopes for security on presenting to the Sino-Soviet bloc a unified front, a combined and resolute will to keep the free areas of the world invulnerable to Communist domination through a united and strong defensive force, and an untiring willingness to explore all possibilities of reaching a sincere plan for disarmament and bringing about a rapprochement between East and West. As individual nations and allied blocs continued their efforts to cope with international problems, the United Nations and its various committees were constantly considering the questions of world importance. Secretary-General Dag Hammarskjold was particularly active in seeking to aid members in arranging for new discussions which could lead to a basis for disarmament agreements.

EXAMINATION QUESTIONS

1. In what century was the characteristic life of medieval times coming to a close?
2. What made voyages beyond the seacoast possible and relatively safe?
3. What objective did Columbus have in mind in sailing westward across the Atlantic?
4. What was the greatest impetus to the spread of knowledge during the Renaissance?
5. About what time did the church lose its temporal power?
6. Who was John Wycliffe?
7. Who was the leading spirit of the Reformation?
8. Who was the right-hand man of King Henry VIII of England?
9. When was the Spanish Inquisition?
10. How long did Queen Elizabeth of England reign?
11. What broke the Spanish control of the seas?
12. Who was Cardinal Richelieu?
13. What European republic was formed in 1579?
14. Who was the first monarch of the English Restoration?
15. Which rulers of England were placed on the throne at the request of Parliament?

16. Which French king ascended the throne when he was five years old and reigned for seventy-two years?
17. What was the Edict of Nantes?
18. Which king could not speak English when he ascended the British throne?
19. Who was Marie Antoinette?
20. With what military action is the French Revolution said to have begun?
21. How long did the first French Republic last?
22. Whom did Charlotte Corday assassinate?
23. When and where was Napoleon Bonaparte born?
24. When did Napoleon crown himself emperor?
25. What caused the defeat of Napoleon's Grand Army in Russia in 1812?
26. What effect had Napoleon's campaigns on the tiny principalities and petty kingdoms of Central Europe?
27. When did Fulton's steamboat appear?
28. With what did the industrial revolution begin?
29. When did the modern conflict between capital and labor begin?

30. What was the result of the increase of national wealth?

31. Where were slaves freed first: in British dominions or in the United States?

32. When did Queen Victoria ascend the British throne?

33. When was the second French Republic proclaimed?

34. Who was the president of the second French Republic?

35. Name three leaders of Italy's unification.

36. Who brought about the Franco-Prussian War?

37. When was the famous Triple Alliance formed, and why?

38. Which British prime minister was known as Lord Beaconsfield?

39. What was the land area of the British Empire during the nineteenth century?

40. Who was the last of the tsars of Russia?

41. Who were the Chinese Boxers?

42. What was the result of the Russo-Japanese War in 1904–1905?

43. What countries comprised the Triple Entente during the First World War?

44. When did the First World War end?

45. The invasion of which country began the Second World War?

46. When did the Japanese attack Pearl Harbor?

47. What organization is the successor of the League of Nations?

48. Who was the first chief of NATO?

49. What countries after the Second World War became known as the Russian "satellites"?

50. What event precipitated the Korean War?

FOR FURTHER STUDY

EUROPE SINCE 1914, by Frank Lee Benns. (F. S. Crofts, New York.)

HISTORY OF EUROPE FROM THE REFORMATION TO THE PRESENT DAY, by Ferdinand Schevill. (Harcourt, Brace & Co., New York.)

MODERN HISTORY, by Carl L. Becker. (Silver, Burdett, New York.)

MODERN TIMES IN EUROPE, by J. Salwyn Schapiro. (Houghton Mifflin Co., Boston.)

NEW EUROPE, by Bernard Newman. (The Macmillan Co., New York.)

POLITICAL AND CULTURAL HISTORY OF MODERN EUROPE, by Carlton J. H. Hayes. (The Macmillan Co., New York.)

THE RENAISSANCE, by Frantz Funck-Brentano. (The Macmillan Co., New York.)

WORLD HISTORY AT A GLANCE, by Joseph Reither. (Barnes & Noble, New York.)

IV

A Short History of the United States

THE EARLIEST BEGINNINGS

IN ALL PROBABILITY for many thousands of years before Columbus's great discovery, savage tribes (called Indians because Columbus discovered what he thought was part of India) roamed the continents we know today as North and South America. These tribes differed widely in their local customs and language, and, in some degree, in physical characteristics. Their origin is shrouded in obscurity. They made varied resistance to the advance of the white man (called by them "paleface"), and fought against "white" civilization up to the middle of the nineteenth century. They were eventually subdued and confined to "Indian Territories," until, in 1924, Congress granted American citizenship to all Indians of the United States. The number of Indians in the country today is over a quarter of a million, more than half as many as there were when the white men first appeared. There were probably never, at any time, more than half a million, and these were widely scattered in early days.

The continents of the New World, as the new lands were designated when they were first discovered, had been entirely unknown to the peoples of Europe until the end of the fifteenth century. The Atlantic Ocean was believed by the early navigators to be a terror-infested sea, and they did not care to risk exploring it.

But commerce is a strong incentive to bravery, and in this case it was the need for a western route by water to the Indies that impelled the mariners to their courageous voyages. The Oriental trade was profitable, and as the Turks had taken Constantinople in 1453, they were shutting off many of the routes, both overland and water, that had been followed. Already the Portuguese had sailed around the African continent, but there was a growing belief among navigators that a new route might be found by sailing westward across the Atlantic Ocean.

The superstitious terror of the Atlantic was being cast aside toward the close of the Middle Ages, when the great intellectual movement called the Renaissance broke down so much of medieval custom and thought. This revival of learning and science emphasized the opinion of leading scholars that the world was round, so it was a natural assumption that by sailing westward one could reach India. And if two large continents had not barred the way, the explorers of this period would have accomplished the end they sought.

Columbus, on his epoch-marking voyage in 1492, was looking for the Indies. Believing that he had reached them by a westward route, he applied the name Indies to the territory he had discovered. The islands at which he landed are still known as the West Indies, and the native American savages as Indians. On later voyages, however, Columbus and other navigators gradually confirmed the existence of South America, North America, and Central America. The name of these continents was derived from that of the Florentine navigator Amerigo Vespucci, who claimed that he explored the South American coast in 1497. Most scholars do not believe in this 1497 voyage, but the name America has persisted.

Having financed the voyages of Columbus, Spain took a leading part in the exploration of the interior of the newly discovered lands. Mexico was invaded by Cortez, who conquered the Aztec Indians. Balboa cut his way through Panama, and in 1513 discovered the ocean that was called the Pacific by Magellan when he circumnavigated the world by way of Cape Horn from 1519 to 1522. Ponce de León discovered and named Florida in 1513. The southeastern corner of America from Florida to the lower Mississippi was discovered and explored by De Soto in 1539–1542. The lure that led these explorers on was plunder. They took gold from the Indians and slaughtered them unmercifully. Only a few attempts were made to settle and colonize these regions. Nevertheless, the Spanish claimed the lands over which they roamed.

With the defeat of the Spanish Armada in 1588 by the English navy, Spanish power on the seas was wiped out. Defeat put a quietus on Spain's activity in the New World, and at this point England appeared on the American scene. In the meantime the St. Lawrence River in Canada had been explored by Cartier, a Frenchman, and as a result the lands drained by that river and its tributaries were claimed by France. She also seized the valley of the Mississippi.

The New World from Mexico southward was continuously dominated by the Spaniards. As a result there is a predominantly Spanish strain in those countries today. This includes the greater part of South America, whose people speak Spanish and have Spanish traditions; the one exception is Brazil, whose people speak the Portuguese tongue. Mexico and most of the countries to the south began to shake off the influence of Spain in the eighteenth century. In the nineteenth century, under the leadership of Simon Bolivar, most of Central and South America achieved independence. Cuba stayed under Spanish-European control until 1898.

THE COLONIAL PERIOD

The story of the United States begins with the English colonies on the Atlantic seaboard of North America extending from Florida northward almost to Nova Scotia. The founders and inhabitants of these colonies were chiefly English, but in certain areas there were Dutch and Swedish.

England's chief claim to territory in the New World was founded on the voyage of John Cabot in 1497, although for a long time she made little effort to enforce this claim. During the sixteenth century, the desperate struggle with Spain caused England to direct her attention to America as a means of crippling her rival. Hawkins, Drake, and other freebooters preyed on Spanish shipping. At the same time attempts to found an English settlement in the New World were made by Sir Humphrey Gilbert in 1583 and by Sir Walter Raleigh between 1585 and 1587. These ended in failure. However, Raleigh, who spent his fortune financing several unsuccessful expeditions, popularized the idea of colonizing the New World. Chartered companies now entered the field.

The English came to America for a variety of motives. The victory over the Spanish Armada in 1588 fostered a spirit of pride in England's power and growth. Patriots argued that overseas expansion would contribute to the nation's greatness; statesmen reasoned that colonies would augment the country's foreign trade. The desire for economic improvement was also a powerful stimulus. Many people of small means were anxious to secure a fresh start in the New World, where there was an abundant supply of land. Many wealthy persons, as well, were eager to finance colonial expeditions because of the opportunity for huge profits.

Religious and political factors played an important part in bringing the English to the New World. Seventeenth-century England was torn by religious and political strife. The established church was the Anglican (Protestant Episcopal) Church. There were, however, numerous dissenting Protestant groups—Puritans, Presbyterians, Quakers—who refused to adhere to the Anglican form of worship. Since Dissenters, as well as Catholics, were bitterly persecuted by the government, thousands sought refuge in America. Religious hatred was intertwined with political bitterness. The Puritans were the staunchest supporters of Parliament in its attack upon the "divine right" theory of Charles I. During the stern Puritan regime that followed the overthrow and execution of Charles I in 1649, many Anglican gentry who had supported the King migrated to Virginia. Following the royalist reaction that set in with the restoration of the Stuarts in 1660, numerous Puritans sailed for New England. In an age dominated by intolerance, the New World appeared as a haven of religious and political freedom.

In 1607 the colony of Jamestown, Virginia, was founded. It was named after King James I of England, who chartered the company of gentlemen adventurers who established the settlement; and Virginia was named after Queen Elizabeth, the "Virgin Queen." Jamestown was the first important English settlement in America. The resourceful Captain John Smith rallied the colonists from their early discouragement, caused by disease and famine. Maryland (named after the wife of King James) was founded officially in 1632, by royal charter, under Lord Baltimore; the leading city still bears his name.

A group of Puritans, an English religious sect, who called themselves the Pilgrims, after a brief stay at Provincetown landed at Plymouth (Massachusetts) in 1620. Their ship was the famous *Mayflower*. William Bradford was governor of Plymouth until 1657. The colony grew but slowly. The Pilgrims were Puritans who believed in absolute separation of religion from ceremony: their theology was stern, and their services were conducted within almost bare walls. Europe was in turmoil between Protestants and Catholics throughout this period, and in Massachusetts religious differences were strong among the different groups. Mrs. Anne Hutchinson, a religious radical, was banished from Massachusetts with her followers. Quakers were persecuted. Roger Williams, also expelled from Massachusetts for religious reasons, founded a community that tolerated all sects, which became Rhode Island.

Further settlements arose in Connecticut, on the sites of Hartford, Wethersfield, Windsor, and elsewhere. The settlers mingled with the Dutch of New Amsterdam, who had settled on the site of modern Manhattan (New York). New Haven was founded in 1638. Most of the New England Indians were friendly, but there were some uprisings and massacres. Religious persecutions in Massachusetts drove fugitives northward, where new communities were established in New Hampshire and Maine. Most of the New England colonies finally united in the New England Confederation for mutual protection against Indians and Dutch.

Henry Hudson, an Englishman working for Holland, in 1609 sailed up the river that still bears his name. New Netherland was colonized under the trading monopoly of the Dutch West India Company. The Dutch, too, persecuted rival religious sects. In Delaware Bay, meanwhile, some Swedes had settled.

THE DEVELOPMENT OF THE COLONIES

There was not much supervision of the American colonies during the hundred years from 1660, when, after the Commonwealth under Cromwell, the Stuarts were restored to the English throne. New England was in sympathy with Parliament, and Virginia's bias was toward the Cavaliers and royal authority. This issue was not fought over by the two Colonial groups as they were too far apart. In those days, 250 miles was a long distance.

New activity in English colonization in America followed 1660, for colonization seemed to offer English capital an excellent opportunity for profit. The Quaker William Penn founded Pennsylvania—the name of the state means "Penn's Woods." Carolina, which was named after King Charles I of England, had been settled partly by French Huguenots. New Amsterdam, settled by the Dutch, was captured by the British and renamed New York. Although it passed again into Dutch hands, it became English again after 1674. A narrow strip of the Atlantic coast became English from Maine to Carolina. The Spaniards were in Florida at St. Augustine. As a bulwark between Spanish and English, Georgia grew up, founded by an Englishman, James Oglethorpe, with British convicts from debtors' prisons.

In 1760 the colonies were New England, composed of Maine and Massachusetts united, New Hampshire, Connecticut, and Rhode Island; New York, in which there was a Dutch element; New Jersey; Delaware, which had a Swedish element; Pennsylvania, whither many Germans immigrated at a later date; Maryland, a Catholic colony; Virginia, where wealthy English landowners had settled; Carolina, which was later to be divided into North and South Carolina; and Georgia. The inhabitants of these colonies were of various nationalities, but they were preponderantly British. These British colonists, however, held widely differing religious and political views.

The colonists were gradually drawn together by a common bond of defense against the Indians and French, and eventually against the despotic selfishness of the British king and the greed of British capitalists. In spite of quarrels among themselves, they pooled their efforts toward combating the forces that might have overwhelmed all of them.

The early English settlers laid the foundations of American democratic government under which we are now living. Faced by primitive conditions and far removed from governmental agencies to which they had been accustomed, they proceeded to put into practice principles of self-government. In 1619 the Virginia Company authorized the calling together of an assembly known as the House of Burgesses. This was the first representative law-making body in America. In 1620 the Pilgrims, while on their way to America, signed the Mayflower Compact, an agreement by which they bound themselves to obey whatever laws were passed by the majority for the common good. In 1639 the settlers on the Connecticut River drew up a framework of government, called the Fundamental Orders, which was the first written constitution in the Western Hemisphere. The establishment of town meetings in the New England towns provided an expression of pure or direct democracy. The Zenger Case in 1734, whereby Peter Zenger, a printer, was acquitted after his trial for criticizing the governor of the colony of New York, established the precedent of a free press in America. Roger Williams established complete religious toleration in the colony of Rhode Island. Roger Williams may be considered, because of his liberal views, as the first "modern" American.

The early American colonists, however, may be criticized in some respects. Negro slavery was tolerated and accepted. Indentured servitude was common in most of the colonies. Religious bigotry was the rule in most of the New England colonies; witness the persecution of the Quakers in Massachusetts and of the Catholics in other colonies. Witchcraft was still accredited and condemned witches were burned. Religious and property qualifications for voting and office-holding left the great majority of the colonists in each colony disenfranchised.

The French were missionaries, explorers and traders, rather than colonists. From Canada southward through the Middle West they established trading posts and forts. Notable among the Jesuits who set out to convert the Indians to Catholicism were Marquette and Joliet. La Salle explored the Mississippi. Louisiana, which was named for the French king, Louis XIV, began to be settled in a desultory manner around 1700. Today the city of New Orleans retains its French element.

There were wars with the French and the Indians, including King William's War, fought from 1690 to 1697, the European phase of which was caused by William of Orange's overthrow of James II of England; Queen Anne's War, fought from 1701 to 1713, and in Europe called the War of the Spanish Succession; and King George's War (1745–1748), which the Europeans called the War of the Austrian Succession.

The French and Indian War proper began in 1755 with the defeat of Braddock's expedition from Virginia. Its European counterpart was the Seven Years' War (1756–1763), which involved England and Prussia against France and Austria. The French-Canadian forts of Louisburg and Duquesne fell to the English. James Wolfe, the British general, captured the French stronghold of Quebec; and Montreal was taken in 1760.

Spain obtained Louisiana by the Treaty of Paris. Virtually all of Canada became British as did many of the West Indian islands. France was forced out of North America. Although the English colonies were harassed by further Indian wars, the Indians, because they had no leaders who could unify their forces, never made an effectively united attack. Fighting by groups and tribes, they were unable to hold their own, and gradually they were forced westward until the white men had engulfed them permanently.

The colonial period ended in the struggle of the colonists against the British crown and the rich men in England who controlled Parliament. The royalists wanted to see the colonists subdued, because the king's authority was waning and the colonies appeared to be a good place to exert what remained of royal power. The owners of property were desirous of making money from colonial trade. Against these two groups, the colonists were aroused to armed defiance. However, the British people as a whole did not unite against the colonies, and the Whigs wanted to see them win. The American Revolution was thus only partially opposed in England.

COLONIAL LIFE

In 1760 there were about a million and a half white persons in the American colonies. In a good many details colonial life was much like that in England. Although America had no titled nobility of its own, there were marked social differences between the aristocrats and the poorer laboring classes, with the usual opposition. Some of the former were already wealthy and came to America lured by adventure or by the hope of making more money. Others made fortunes in land speculation, for as the frontier moved westward the land increased in value.

The laboring classes were servants who were bound by indentures to work for a term of years to pay for the cost of their passage to America, after which time they became free. To supply the heavy demand for this labor, both adults and children were kidnaped in England, but in the hope of making their fortunes at the expiration of their servitude, others pledged themselves voluntarily. In addition to these there were the African slaves, in whom a profitable trade was developed from the time they were first brought to Virginia in 1620. They were set to work on the tobacco and rice plantations of the southern colonies.

The daily life of the early colonists was for the most part rigorous. There were few amusements. There were no good roads, and in consequence travel was arduous at best, and much worse in rainy weather.

The chief industry of the colonies was agriculture. In exchange for the sugar of the West Indies, flour, potatoes and other vegetables, and pork, beef, and fish were exported. The South shipped tobacco to all parts of the world, for, having been taught by the Indians, people took up smoking as a popular habit.

All the colonies exported lumber, and its by-products, pitch, tar, and turpentine, were furnished by the Carolinas. South Carolina exported rice and indigo. There had as yet been no development of manufacturing, and for the most part the domestic system of production still held. Capitalists, called entrepreneurs, bought raw materials and had them delivered to the homes of workers who made the finished articles. The entrepreneurs collected them and marketed them at a profit. Colonial artisans made coarse shoes, cloth, tools, nails, and other necessities, but the better goods and the luxuries had to be imported from Europe. There was some iron mining and smelting for export, and rum was distilled in New England.

Fearing the competition of the colonies, England placed various restrictions on American manufactures and other enterprises. England's economic policy toward the colonies was in line with the prevailing theory of *mercantilism* which was accepted and practiced by the European powers of the seventeenth and eighteenth centuries. In accordance with the principles of mercantilism, statesmen held that a nation's wealth depended upon a large supply of gold and silver and that this supply was determined largely by a favorable balance of trade (exports of greater value than imports). Colonies, they argued, would create more wealth. Not only would the Crown receive a share of all the treasure found in the New World, but the government could restrict the trade of the colonies to its own merchants. Since the latter would exchange the more valuable manufactured goods of the mother country for the less valuable raw materials of the colonies, a favorable balance of trade could be created. Colonial trade was thus sharply curtailed by the British Parliament's Navigation Acts, and the British tried to keep the American colonies under a monopoly. These restrictions increased in severity, and the colonists became correspondingly active in smuggling and other evasions of the laws in a manner similar to the "bootlegging" of later prohibition times.

England's mercantile policy toward the colonies and its enforcement after 1763 sowed the seeds that were to grow into the independence movement of the 1770s.

Colleges were founded early in the history of the colonies. Harvard was established in 1636; Yale in 1701; the College of William and Mary, in Virginia, in 1693; the University of Pennsylvania in 1740; Princeton, which was originally the College of New Jersey, in 1746; King's College, later Columbia University, in 1754; Brown University, which began as Rhode Island College, in 1764; and Dartmouth College in 1769. Public schools did not develop nearly so fast, especially in the South. The printing industry was established, and in spite of the fact that the first books in America were brought from England, American culture and American literature gradually came into existence.

THE AMERICAN REVOLUTION

For many years before there was any open act against British governmental authority, the spirit of rebellion in the colonies was slowly growing. The scattered colonies, however, were not united; some were royalist sympathizers, while others had selfish interests in connection with British exploiters of American enterprise.

There were various reasons for dissatisfaction. Some groups of the colonists felt a resentment at the attempts of British capital to make money from American lands, while others of the merchant or trader class were irritated by the restrictions which the British imposed on the American merchant marine and its trade with the rest of the world. The attempt of the British crown to raise royal revenues from American taxation was an added cause for anger. Between the years 1760 and 1775 a succession of grievances brought the situation to a head.

BEGINNINGS OF THE REVOLUTION

It was in 1764 that the British government, under George III, asserted its authority unmistakably. There was now to be a strict enforcement of the Navigation Acts, restricting trade and collecting customs. Ostensibly for defense, but believed by the colonists to be for the purpose of intimidating them and making them pay the customs duties, a British army was quartered in the colonies. Taxes were levied on the colonies by Stamp Acts, by which money was raised to pay royal bills.

New England was particularly affected by hampered trade, and for this reason the first blood of the revolution was spilled there. There was a popular slogan which said, "Taxation without representation is tyranny." Incidentally, this outcry did not originate in America. It had been used for years in England, and had been effective in influencing many Parliamentary reforms. It came readily to the lips of the colonists, most of whom were Englishmen.

Everywhere indignation was aroused by the Stamp Act of 1765. Patrick Henry rose up in the Virginia assembly to speak bitter words against George III, and when cries of "Treason!" were shouted, uttered his famous reply, "If this be treason, make the most of it." So popular were Henry's resolutions against the Stamp Act that they were read throughout Virginia. Patrick Henry and James Otis, having crystallized popular sentiment, were followed by other leaders, and parties who called themselves "Sons of Liberty" were organized.

Such opposition as this resulted in the repeal by Parliament of the Stamp Act of 1765. But the quarrel was soon begun again, and in 1767 the Townshend Acts were passed. These placed new stamp duties on colonial imports, and there were new protests, in which Virginia sided definitely with Massachusetts, which suffered most from the trade restrictions. For the purpose of intimidating the port of Boston into submission, British troops were landed there under General Gage; and to subdue angry mobs who were violently denouncing the soldiery, British guns were fired into a crowd. The fatalities resulted in this being known as the "Boston Massacre" of March 5, 1770. The loud public protest was led by Samuel Adams and John Hancock, who were prominent Bostonians.

The temper of the colonists was shown clearly by other acts of violence which took place within the next few years throughout the colonies. A new British minister, Lord North, had the Townshend Acts repealed, with the exception of a small duty on tea as a test of enforcement. The duty itself was not objectionable, but the principle was. After there had been a failure to sell English tea to the American colonies, the Americans' resistance was crystallized in the "Boston Tea Party," December 16, 1773, when a crowd of Boston residents disguised as Indians went aboard a British vessel and threw its cargo of tea into the harbor.

George III stubbornly insisted that America, particularly Boston, should recognize his authority. The first of a new series of oppressions in 1774 was the official closing of the port of Boston. The colonists appeared to be left a choice between submitting or rebelling—and they chose the latter. The semblance of union was effected in the First Continental Congress of 1774, in which delegates from all the colonies except Georgia argued on behalf of America. This historic congress met at Philadelphia in September 1774. All the delegates were Whigs, which means that they were rebels. The Tories in America were British sympathizers.

With the apparent purpose of taking over some military stores at Concord, but with the earnest purpose of capturing the colonial agitators John Hancock and Samuel Adams, who were thought to be in Lexington, the British General Gage led his soldiers from Boston and along the eleven-mile road to Lexington in the spring of 1775. The movements of Gage and his troops were watched, and signal lights were flashed to waiting messengers—"One if by land and two if by sea" according to Longfellow's poem. The famed Paul Revere and a man named Dawes sprang to their horses and rode to spread the alarm. At Lexington, the colonial "minute men," who were pledged to assemble at a minute's notice, hampered the advance of the British infantry. But under the fire of the British, the minute men were dispersed, and the British proceeded to Concord.

The nineteenth of April is still observed in the vicinity of Boston to commemorate Lexington and Concord. The British were surprised at Concord by musket shots, and their retreat toward Boston was effected only after the colonial riflemen had done deadly work from behind trees, stones, and buildings. When Gage returned to Boston, his casualties included 273 dead, wounded, or missing.

THE REVOLUTIONARY WAR

Once begun, the revolt acquired irresistible momentum. All efforts in behalf of conciliation on the part of Burke, Pitt, Fox, and other Whig leaders in Parliament, failed to turn the king and his advisers from their policy of coercion. The battle of Lexington in April, the capture of Fort Ticonderoga in May, and the battle of Bunker Hill followed one another in quick succession. In October a British captain destroyed Falmouth in Maine; and in November a colonial force under Montgomery and Arnold invaded Canada. It was difficult to maintain an attitude of loyalty in the face of actual warfare. The colonists were stirred to anger by the news that the king had rejected the "olive-branch" petition dispatched by the Second Congress, and that he was hiring Hessian mercenaries for service in America. These facts were clearly stated by the great propagandist of the Revolution, Thomas Paine, in *Common Sense* (1776), a pamphlet which convinced thousands that independence, rather than redress of consequences, should be the logical goal. Paine echoed the attitude of the leading colonists: "Arms, as a last recourse, must decide the contest." The Second Continental Congress took under consideration the declaring of independence formally, and one by one the different colonies authorized their representatives to support this plan. The Declaration of Independence was drawn up in writing by Thomas Jefferson, with minor changes by a committee which included Benjamin Franklin and John Adams. The document was signed by the delegates a few at a time, and was formally adopted by the congress on July 4, 1776, which date is now celebrated as Independence Day. The Declaration was not signed by all the delegates until weeks later.

The American Declaration of Independence stated that "all men are created equal"; that all have the right to "life, liberty and the pursuit of happiness"; that when a government stops guaranteeing these rights, "it is the right of the people to alter or to abolish it, and to institute new government, laying its foundation on such principles, and organizing its powers in such form, as to them shall seem most likely to effect their safety and happiness." To these lofty aims the signers pledged their lives, their fortunes, and their sacred honor.

The Declaration of Independence is recognized as the blueprint for

American democracy. It gave expression to the ideals of liberty and self-government, which were the product, first, of the free environment of the New World, and, second, of a study of the writings of John Locke and Jean Jacques Rousseau. For purposes of analysis we may divide the Declaration into three sections: (1) a summary of political theories and beliefs—for example, that all men are created equal, and that governments rest upon the consent of the governed; (2) a statement of twenty-seven specific grievances or charges against the king—for example, the imposition of taxes without consent of those taxed; (3) the declaration that "these united colonies are, and of right ought to be, free and independent states." The Declaration served as a document of propaganda for the spread of opposition against Great Britain.

General Howe took Gage's place in command of the Boston troops, and after evacuating Boston he proceeded to New York with the help of the British fleet, which was under the command of his brother. In spite of General Washington's attempt at defense, the American army met several reverses in New York and was forced to retreat into New Jersey. The rebel situation was not a happy one, but the sagging American spirits were revived between December 25, 1776, and January 4, 1777, by Washington's military successes in the vicinity of Trenton and Princeton. A real army could not be raised by the Continental Congress, and when their terms of service expired, the troops went home.

The prosecution of the war was desultory on both British and American sides. The British forces failed to work together, and the Americans did not have the resources to throw into an extensive campaign. After an extremely difficult year, in December, 1777, Washington and his troops went into winter quarters at Valley Forge. In the meantime, American troops had been more successful in frustrating attempted British invasions from Canada. In October, 1777, Burgoyne, the British commander, surrendered his army at Saratoga. Lafayette had come from France in the middle of the year to proffer his services to the Americans, and the Americans were also helped by other foreign officers, including the German De Kalb, who had served in the French army, Baron Von Steuben, another German, and Pulaski, a Pole.

Having been pushed out of the New World not many years previously, France had political reasons for wishing to see England humbled in America. In February, 1778, after the defeat of Burgoyne, alliance treaties were signed by the Americans with France, which precipitated fresh enmity between France and England. English troops being occupied elsewhere, the British somewhat neglected the American colonies in the spring of 1778.

A small navy was authorized by the Continental Congress, but America's chief representation on the seas were "privateers"—ships fitted out and armed by private owners. They sold in French ports the enemy merchant ships that they captured, and many of them became wealthy from the disposal of their prizes. John Paul Jones, who won a reputation for bravery and skill as a sea-fighter, was one of the first commissioned captains in the American navy. After alliance with America, the French sent their fleet to meet the British navy.

From 1778 to 1781 the war dragged along with no decisive victories for either side. But the Americans struggled and suffered, confident that ultimately they would win. Aided by the French troops under Lafayette and the French fleet in Chesapeake Bay, Washington surrounded Cornwallis and his troops, and the British general had no choice but surrender on October 19, 1781, at Yorktown, Virginia. Six years and much money had been spent by England in attempting to subdue her rebellious colonies, but the American colonies had won their independence. In the summer of 1783 a formal treaty of peace was negotiated in Paris.

To the north, the boundary of the United States was made very similar to the northeastern boundary of today. To the west it went to the Mississippi River, and southward to a line somewhat north of the Gulf of Mexico. Florida was left to Spain. The new republic was now a land of great territorial extent. There were thirteen states at this time.

THE NEW NATION

Having brought the war to a successful conclusion, each of the thirteen states of the new nation was now concerned chiefly with its own affairs. The states did not immediately see the necessity of giving to their own Congress the powers they had resented in Parliament. But in the following years the need of such a central government became apparent.

In 1777, under the Articles of Confederation, a provisional government was established, which held the states loosely together during the war. It was, however, made plain by these articles that each state was to retain its sovereignty, its freedom, and its independence. After the end of the war, and during the conflict as well, there were disadvantages in these restrictions on a central government. Owing to the fact that Congress could not levy taxes, the soldiers often went unpaid. Each state was jealous of the other, and for ten years there was considerable confusion.

In the meantime the paper money of the Continental Congress, and of the separate states, became nearly worthless—a situation which caused ill feeling, poverty, and actual want. After the war there was a lagging in trade, for the British duties were high, and the lack of a central power in America made it impossible to retaliate in kind. The state leaders gradually realized that a properly constituted central government was necessary. Lacking this, the states, bickering among themselves, might sooner or later fall prey to foreign powers.

Alarmed by signs of domestic anarchy and by the possibility of foreign aggression, thoughtful men sought to strengthen the central government. Yet every attempt to increase the authority of the Congress (for example, a proposal to empower Congress to collect duties on imports) was thwarted by the rule which required unanimous consent of all the states for amendments. The successful movement for revision developed in an indirect way. In 1785 representatives from Maryland and Virginia met at Mount Vernon to settle a dispute over the regulation of shipping on the Potomac River and Chesapeake Bay. After reaching a satisfactory agreement, the commissioners decided to invite all of the states to send delegates to Annapolis for the purpose of considering commercial matters of common interest. Since only five states responded to the call, the Annapolis Convention (1786) was unable to take any definite action. Alexander Hamilton, however, induced the convention to issue another appeal to the states, urging them to send delegates to Philadelphia—this time to consider measures for strengthening the national government. The feeble Congress seconded the proposal by officially calling for a convention "to revise the Articles of Confederation."

After a great deal of agitation, the Constitutional Convention was finally assembled in Philadelphia in 1787. Among those present were such outstanding figures as Benjamin Franklin, Gouverneur Morris, Alexander Hamilton, and Rufus King. Franklin had already been sent to represent the American colonies abroad, especially in France, where he had made the request for French assistance. He was well known in America on account of his printing plant and his annual publication for 25 years of the very popular *Poor Richard's Almanac*. The public had great confidence in these men, and they began to draw up a constitution.

The federal Constitution was not ratified by the thirteen states with any great eagerness. The colonial politicians hemmed and hawed, fearful of the loss of prestige in their native localities, and yet realizing the need for national unity. The Constitution was at first unreservedly opposed by some, and most of the states ratified it with "amendments" or reservations. Delaware was the first to ratify it, on December 7, 1787. New York, which ratified it on July 26, 1788, was the eleventh state to accept the Constitution. The other two late signers were North Carolina, whose ratification came in 1789, and Rhode Island in 1790.

In the Constitution of the United States is set forth the basis of our national government, outlining its form and structure, and designating how its members shall be elected and what shall be their duties and limitations of authority. (For detailed discussion of the Constitution see section entitled "Civics and Government.")

The government under the Articles of Confederation was successful in at least one achievement before it went out of existence. To its credit was the passage of the Northwest Ordinance (1787), which was designed to regulate the newly acquired Northwest Territory, consisting of an area south of the Great Lakes, east of the Mississippi River, and north of the Ohio River. The Northwest Ordinance provided for the administration of the territory by officials appointed by Congress; the election of a territorial legislature as soon as the adult male population reached five thousand; complete religious tolerance and freedom of speech and press; the exclusion of slavery; the reservation of part of the land for encouragement of education; and the ultimate admission of from three to five states on the basis of full equality with the original states of the Union. This famous act proclaimed a new and enlightened principle of colonial administration. The ordinance served as a model for the organization of all other territories on a self-governing basis. It established the principle of admitting territories to full statehood, thus making possible the expansion of the Union from the original thirteen states to its present forty-eight members.

THE FIRST ADMINISTRATION

George Washington was the first person to be elected president of the United States, and John Adams was the first vice-president. Through his successful leadership in the Revolutionary War, General Washington had won the high esteem of the people; and their choice for a president, as provided for in the newly ratified Constitution, was unanimous. A Congress was also elected, and New York became the temporary seat of the government. President Washington's term began in 1789.

With no precedents to guide them, these pioneers in federal government bore a heavy burden. Much depended upon their initial efforts in the launching of this new republic. The eyes of all Europe were upon them, watching the experiment that was being tried; for with the exception of Switzerland, there was almost no republican government in Europe in the eighteenth century, and Switzerland was too small a country to figure prominently in European politics.

The first secretary of state was Thomas Jefferson, who shortly before had been American minister to France. The noted expert in finance, Alexander Hamilton, became the first secretary of the treasury. Through Hamilton's financial genius the national debt was funded. Congress was persuaded to assume the state debts which were incurred during the war, taxes were levied, and the first national bank was established, being opened in 1791.

Congress adopted ten of the amendments which were proposed by the states when they ratified the Constitution, and formed a "Bill of Rights" which outlined the fundamental prerogatives of citizens. Presently three new states were admitted to the Union: Vermont in 1791; Kentucky, where Daniel Boone had become prominent some years previously, in 1792; and Tennessee in 1796.

When opposition to the administration began to result in factions, political parties were formed. The Federalist party was influenced by the policies of Alexander Hamilton, who was a zealous advocate of centralized national government—a man whose beliefs leaned toward aristocracy. The Republicans followed the leadership of Thomas Jefferson, who stood strongly for democracy. Washington, nominally a Federalist, was re-elected for a second term in spite of party opposition.

Shortly after Washington's first election, the national capital, Washington, D.C., named after the president, was established between Maryland and Virginia on the Potomac River.

In 1796 John Adams was elected the second president of the United States, with Thomas Jefferson as vice-president. That year Washington delivered his famous farewell address, and retired to a quiet life at Mount Vernon. He died in 1799.

THE DEMOCRACY'S EARLY PROGRESS

The administration of Adams was forthwith beset by new difficulties with France, where Napoleon Bonaparte was on the way to imperial power. The difficulty was settled by treaty in 1800. The Federalists lost their prestige in the election of 1800. Adams had advocated a strong federal government against "states' rights," and due largely to his politics the Federalists lost the election. The right of nullification of a federal law had been asserted by the states of Kentucky and Virginia, which, in particular, had rejected the "alien and sedition acts" which Congress passed during the period of dispute with France. Therefore Jefferson, a Democratic-Republican, was elected president, with Aaron Burr as vice-president, to take office in 1801. (The early Republican party later became the Democratic party as we know it today; while the Republican party of today may be traced to the early Federalist party.)

It was during the administration of Jefferson that war took place with Tripoli, and with the other Barbary states of Morocco, Algiers, and Tunis. From these countries pirates in the Mediterranean Sea had been carrying on depredations for years. The European powers had been winking at this piracy, so it remained for the youthful United States to take the matter in hand, and the piracies stopped.

Napoleon had acquired the Louisiana Territory from Spain; and fearing that Great Britain might make an attempt to take it, he offered to sell it to the United States in 1803. Congress was persuaded by Jefferson to buy this large region for $15,000,000. In 1804, Lewis and Clark explored the new territory and reached beyond it to what is now Oregon, thus opening up another extensive region which they claimed for the United States, and inaugurating a new era of territorial expansion.

The acquisition of Louisiana was a most important act in Jefferson's administration. It doubled the area of the United States, adding to our country a fertile region that became the granary of the nation. It secured for the United States undisputed control of the Mississippi River. It set a precedent for the acquisition of other territories, thus making possible westward expansion to the Pacific. It increased the power and prestige of the central government, which now had an immense domain to govern directly. The purchase and administration of the territory by Congress added force to the doctrine of "liberal construction," or elastic interpretation of the Constitution. Jefferson's policy of westward expansion, however, was attacked by many Federalists, especially in the northern states. Jefferson was elected again in 1804. An embargo act was passed by Congress to enforce the rights of neutral American ships on the high seas. This aroused the indignation of traders throughout the country, who found that their profits were curtailed. But France and England, who at that time were at war, were not considering the rights of the American merchant marine.

The fourth president was James Madison, who began his term in 1809. The flagrant violation of the rights of American vessels on the high seas made war a keen probability. Inspired by his desire to blockade England, Napoleon had issued a decree against neutral commerce.

Over a period of years warships of Britain had been impressing American sailors into service on the seas, claiming that they were still British subjects. The United States maintained that it was the right of a man to change his allegiance, and that a British subject could become an American through naturalization. Although both France and England had seized American shipping, America was more offended by the British on account of their impressing her seamen.

The United States pressed her grievances against both England and France, but the trend of events led us to war with England. New leaders in Congress, Clay, Sevier, and Calhoun, who were known as "war hawks," clamored for a declaration of war against England. As impetuous nationalists, they were intent on avenging the nation's honor; as ardent expansionists, they were anxious for an opportunity to acquire Canada from Britain and to seize Florida from Spain, as they believed that Spain would be the ally of England in North America as in Europe. Despite the opposition of commercial New England, Congress, in June 1812, declared war on England.

THE WAR OF 1812

Several incidents combined to bring about the War of 1812 with Great Britain. One or two unofficial naval engagements had occurred on the high seas. A British ship was captured by an American vessel in 1811. The Indians had been giving trouble from time to time, and in 1811 there were Indian uprisings in the West that had to be put down. It was believed that the Indians were instigated by British agitation. It is a fact that Indians received arms and ammunition from British Canada.

Failure resulted from the first American military expeditions to Canada, but the naval campaigns were more favorable. In two successful engagements, the frigate *Constitution*—called "Old Ironsides"—distinguished herself, and lesser engagements took place in 1812.

In 1812 Madison was re-elected president. After the defeat of the American ship *Chesapeake,* in 1813, Oliver Hazard Perry conducted his successful campaign on Lake Erie to wrest the control of the Great Lakes from the British. Further land battles followed, particularly with the British and their Indian allies under the famous chief Tecumseh, in which the Americans were victorious. General Andrew Jackson conducted successful warfare against the Creek Indians in the South in 1814.

In September, 1814, there were simultaneous military and naval engagements at Plattsburg and on Lake Champlain, where the Americans were victorious over the forces from Canada. In the meantime, Napoleon had been overthrown in Europe. The English, encouraged by their success, invaded Chesapeake Bay, captured the city of Washington, and burned the Capitol.

From Washington, the British turned to Baltimore, where, though their land forces were driven back, they bombarded Fort McHenry, in the harbor, throughout the day and night of September 13. It was at the end of this night that Francis Scott Key wrote "The Star-Spangled Banner." He was watching the bombardment from the deck of a British ship under a flag of truce, and when, as morning dawned, he saw that the American flag still floated from the ramparts of the fort, he wrote the song that was to become the national anthem of his country. When Fort McHenry refused to capitulate, the British withdrew. On December 24,

1814, the treaty of peace was signed. American shipping on the high seas was not interfered with any more.

On account of the slow means of communication in those days, news of the signing of the peace treaty did not reach America in time to avert the battle of New Orleans, in January, 1815, but the battle was a victory for the Americans under General Andrew Jackson. In 1812 Louisiana had been admitted to statehood in the Union.

THE GROWTH OF THE UNITED STATES

Tried by the fires of both war and peace, the United States expanded and developed. Although some of the states were not in harmony with everything that the federal government did, the union of states held together. There was an increasing number of immigrants from foreign countries; in 1817 there were 22,000. The tremendous war bill had to be paid. The Southern planters had suffered financially by the war's hampering of their trade, for they had been deprived of the British markets for their cotton. Manufacturing developed only in the North; and in the growing divergence of economic interest between the North and South, the subject of Negro slavery was involved.

In 1816, James Monroe had won the presidency on the same Democratic-Republican party ticket as his two predecessors. In the northeastern states the manufacturing interests, which had forged ahead during the war when there was little or no foreign competition, now demanded protective tariffs. The Southern states did not need tariffs because they were mainly agricultural. The manufacturer, and not the consumer, was directly protected by the tariffs. The consumer was more likely to benefit, immediately, at least, from the lower prices of goods from abroad. The seeds of the Civil War were planted in this commercial conflict; sectional differences arose from economic strife as much as from the moral question of slavery in the states as the country spread westward.

Indiana was admitted as a state in 1816, and Mississippi in the year following. The then new steamboat transportation was developing this western territory. There was also a national impetus toward better roads. The Erie Canal was built, stretching 360 miles from the Hudson River to Lake Erie. The postal system was in operation, but the cost of letter postage was extremely high.

Spain had made no attempt to preserve order in eastern Florida, and after depredations from marauding bands, a treaty was effected by which the United States bought that peninsula and adjoining territory from Spain in 1821 for $5,000,000. President Monroe was elected in 1820 for a second term, and was well supported in his administration. The

Monroe Doctrine was stated in 1823. This doctrine asserted that the United States would brook no interference with any independent government in the Americas, and made it plain that European colonization on the American continents could go no further. Thus the United States adopted a protective attitude toward the republics of Central and South America, which Great Britain supported by reason of her interests there. This policy has doubtless since saved these countries from European aggression.

New states were being admitted to the Union two at a time—one of them a state in which slavery was allowed, and the other in which it was not. By 1817 there were ten of each, with the Mason and Dixon line the division point between slave and free territory. This line, originally the southern boundary of Pennsylvania, was drawn by two English surveyors named Mason and Dixon between 1763 and 1767.

The fundamental cleavage between North and South was sharply defined in 1818, when Missouri applied for admission as a slave state. The issue at this time was political and economic in nature, rather than moral. The admission of Missouri would set a precedent for the rest of the immense Louisiana Territory. The North wished to bar slavery from this entire region because emigrants from the free states were unwilling to settle in slave territory. The South, on the other hand, was anxious to extend the field for slavery and the plantation system. The exhaustion of the soil in the older cotton states impelled slaveholders to seek new land suitable for the plantation system. Both sides were alive to the political aspects of the situation. The free states, which had forged ahead in population, controlled the House of Representatives; but in the Senate, North and South were equal in strength (in 1819 there were eleven free states and eleven slave states). Each section was opposed to any move which would upset the balance in the other's favor.

The debate over the admission of Missouri was bitter and prolonged. In the end, largely because of the efforts of Thomas of Illinois and Clay of Kentucky, Congress adopted a compromise measure, which (1) balanced the admission of Missouri as a slave state by the admission of Maine as a free state; and (2) forbade slavery in the rest of the Louisiana Territory lying north of the southern boundary of Missouri (36° 30′).

John Quincy Adams, son of John Adams, was chosen president in 1824. Of the three candidates who opposed him, two were Henry Clay and Andrew Jackson. Because of the fact that no candidate received an electoral majority, the choice was made in the House of Representatives. Clay was appointed secretary of state, and, based on his having influenced Adams's election to the presidency, in the House of Representatives, there was talk of "corruption."

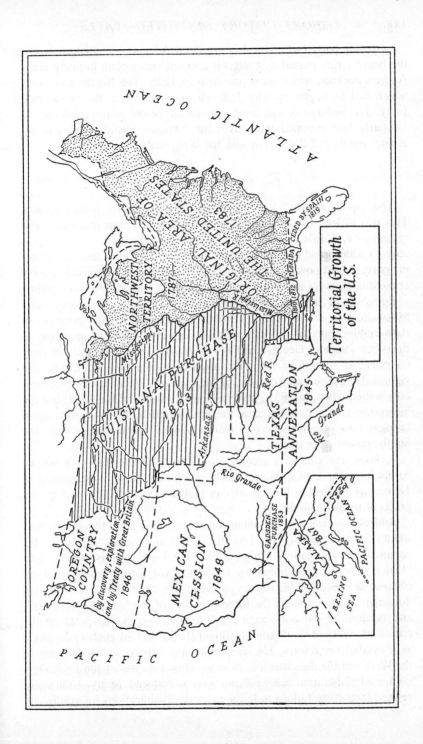

ATLANTIC OCEAN

Territorial Growth
of the U.S.

THE UNITED STATES OF

ORIGINAL AREA OF

NORTHWEST
TERRITORY
1787

Mississippi R.

FLORIDA CEDED BY SPAIN
1819

1810 1812

1783

Mississippi R.

LOUISIANA PURCHASE
1803

Red R.

TEXAS
ANNEXATION
1845

Arkansas R.

Rio Grande

Rio Grande

GADSDEN PURCHASE
1853

OREGON COUNTRY
By discovery, exploration
and by Treaty with Great Britain
1846

MEXICAN
CESSION
1848

ALASKA
1867

BERING
SEA

PACIFIC OCEAN

PACIFIC   OCEAN

Opposing party factions widely criticized Adams's administration, and the heavy tariffs passed by Congress aroused antagonism in many areas. Andrew Jackson was elected president in 1828. The Republican party, which had its beginning with Jefferson, was becoming the Democratic party. The Federalists had nearly passed out of the picture. Adams and his party had renamed themselves the National Republicans, and the greater number of them went with the Whig party in 1836.

THE RISE OF THE WEST

The "spoils system" had its beginning in Jackson's administration. This was to lead to civil service reform much later, but meanwhile this system of removals and appointments for political reasons, and a consequent widespread change in government positions each time an opposing party gained power, resulted in both injustice and inefficiency, for the appointments were not likely to be made from considerations of ability.

Decisions of the federal government were opposed by Georgia and Massachusetts, and by South Carolina, which asserted the principle of state nullification of federal policies. Largely with the approval of President Jackson, Georgia and Massachusetts won their sides of their quarrels. Aroused over the tariff provisions of 1832, South Carolina vigorously opposed the payment of such duties. The quarrel was peaceably settled when, in 1833, Congress passed a revised tariff act; but the increasing antagonism between the North and South was once again brought into prominence. The North wanted "protection," while the South wanted "free trade."

Jackson was elected a second time. He did not approve of federal banks, and the United States Bank, which had been re-established in 1816, was allowed to become extinct in 1836. State banks received deposits of national funds.

Andrew Jackson was the dominant figure of the period. A strong personality, he was greatly loved by his friends and violently hated by his enemies. He was called "King Andrew the First" by his enemies and "Old Hickory" by his followers. He was called King Andrew the First because he conceived his role as president, the chief executive, to be the dominant position among the three branches of the federal government, and because he did not accept the Supreme Court's viewpoint on the constitutionality of the Second National Bank. As Old Hickory he stood as a symbol for reform. He represented the progressive democracy of the West and the discontented, disenfranchised masses of the East. During his administration many reforms were introduced. Many of the states revised their constitutions to lower property qualifications for voting and make provision for rotation in office. In national politics, the convention system of nominating candidates for the presidency replaced the undemocratic caucus system.

The period of Jackson's administration was also noteworthy for its social and humanitarian reforms. Labor unions were first organized. Free, public schooling at government expense was first introduced. The agitation of such people as Dorothea Dix and Frances Wright resulted in the abolition of imprisonment for debt, the introduction of new penal codes, reforms in the administration of prisons and asylums, and the beginnings of the movement for the abolition of slavery.

Other noteworthy features in this period were the beginnings of the "penny newspaper" which has had such a marked influence on our history; movements for the establishment of world peace; agitation for woman's suffrage; the establishment of a number of utopian societies, such as those at New Harmony, Indiana, and Brook Farm, Massachusetts.

The Jacksonian period was noteworthy, too, for the beginnings of the "Golden Age" of American literature. Nathaniel Hawthorne, Ralph Waldo Emerson, Henry David Thoreau, Henry Wadsworth Longfellow, John Greenleaf Whittier, Oliver Wendell Holmes, William Cullen Bryant, and James Russell Lowell were the great literary figures of their day. Edgar Allan Poe first achieved prominence in this period. The great American historians, George Bancroft, William Prescott, Francis Parkman, and William Motley, began their careers in this period.

Martin Van Buren and the Democrats won in the election of 1836. After he was inaugurated in March 1837 there was a financial panic throughout the country in which many of the state banks where federal funds were held on deposit failed, because of large loans to speculators. For this reason, "sub-treasuries" were established as depositories of government funds. This system was to last for about three-quarters of a century, until the establishment of the Federal Reserve System.

The West increased in national importance, and in spite of administrative troubles in Washington, it prospered. There was a constant pioneer movement toward the Pacific Ocean, and an increase in the exploration and settlement of the land. The frontiersmen endured hardship, but they were of the same material as the early American colonists, so they overcame the obstacles that lay before them. With the admission of Arkansas to the Union in 1836, and Michigan in 1837, the total number of states was twenty-six. This was double the number of sixty years before. Through a treaty, the southern Indians of those regions were removed west of the Mississippi River into Indian territory, which later became the state of Oklahoma.

The Western states believed that Van Buren was opposed to them, and they gave their support to William Henry Harrison in the election of 1840. The new party that had arisen out of the Federalist party and other factions opposed to the Democrats was called the Whig party. Harrison, the Whig candidate, was elected, but he died a month after his inauguration and was succeeded by the vice-president, John Tyler.

Tyler pulled away from the policies of his party in his administration. This was particularly marked with regard to the annexation of Texas. Early American settlements in this state had been founded by two Americans named Austin, father and son, who had been granted land from Spanish-Mexican dominions. American immigration increased their settlements, which alarmed Mexico. Texas revolted from Mexico in 1833. In 1836 at the battle of the Alamo, an old Spanish mission, David Crockett and his followers were massacred. Under General Houston the Texans rallied their forces and defeated the Mexicans in 1836 at San Jacinto. For a time Texas became an independent republic, and sought to be annexed by the United States.

A political issue was made of the annexation of Texas in the 1844 presidential campaign. The Democrat, James K. Polk, was elected on a platform favorable to annexation, and therefore Tyler urged congressional influence in this direction before the end of his term in March 1845. Although Mexico had been defeated in Texas in 1836, the boundary line was in dispute. Besides, Mexico made the statement that she would consider it as an unfriendly act if the United States annexed Texas. Texas was admitted to the Union in 1845, and the clouds of war again gathered on the American horizon. In 1845 Florida also was admitted to the Union, and in the following year, Iowa.

THE MEXICAN WAR

In maintaining that the southwestern boundary of their state was the Rio Grande River, Texans based their claim on the terms under which Santa Anna, the Mexican general, had surrendered at the battle of San Jacinto. But the Mexican government insisted that the boundary line was the Nueces River. General Zachary Taylor was sent to occupy the disputed territory with an American force. When some of his men were ambushed and slain by Mexicans, Congress declared in April 1846 that Mexico had started war.

An expeditionary force was led into Mexico by General Taylor; and the Mexicans, though they far outnumbered his army, were defeated in the battle of Buena Vista in 1847. General Winfield Scott also invaded Mexico by way of Vera Cruz, which he captured. He marched toward

Mexico City; and in September 1847 the city surrendered. Subordinate American officers who entered the Mexican capital included Robert E. Lee, Ulysses S. Grant, and George B. McClellan, all of whom were to become important military leaders in the Civil War a few years later. In 1848, by the terms of the treaty of Guadalupe-Hidalgo, Mexico relinquished her claims to all territory north of the Rio Grande, and making a payment of $15,000,000, the United States took over a large region that was later to be divided and become the states of California, Nevada, Utah, Arizona, New Mexico, Colorado, and Wyoming.

SOCIAL AND ECONOMIC DEVELOPMENTS

The progress of the United States to this mid-point in the nineteenth century had been remarkable from the economic, social, and geographical standpoints. For farming, the iron plow came into use in 1855. Only since 1800 had scythes been used, and the reaper since 1831. In the South, Eli Whitney's cotton gin had been used since 1793. Since Fulton's *Clermont* of 1807, steamboats had been increasingly used, and transatlantic steamers were in operation in 1838. Since ocean transportation was aided by a knowledge of wind and weather, the United States Weather Bureau was founded. The appearance of the land also was changing considerably. Several species of American animals and birds had been rendered extinct by advancing pioneers and hunters, and others were on the verge of extinction. The great herds of buffalo, or American bison, that roamed the plains of the West were diminished to a few scattered groups.

There was a rapid gain in population, with the center of population moving slowly toward the west. By the census of 1830 it was shown to be at some point in West Virginia. The majority of inhabitants were in rural districts in 1790, when the first census revealed a total population of about 4,000,000; but by 1850 a much greater proportion of the population was concentrated in towns and cities through the increase of industry and its factories. The population in 1860 was 31,443,321.

It was during the first half of the nineteenth century that anthracite coal came into use for heating and manufactured gas was used for lighting. Among the other inventions that added to the comforts of life were iron stoves and friction matches. In 1844 came the telegraph, and thirteen years later the first Atlantic cable was laid. The Baltimore and Ohio was the first chartered railway, having its beginning in 1827. There were many improvements in printing presses. Anesthetics were first used in surgery in 1842.

There was a marked improvement in education, not only for children, but also for young women, who up to this time had not enjoyed many educational opportunities. Georgia had the first girls' college—Wesleyan Female College, which was founded in 1836 and conferred its first degrees four years later. Oberlin, the first co-educational college in the country, was opened in Ohio in 1833.

THE CIVIL WAR

The great plantations of the South needed cheap labor, and to meet this need Negro slavery had spread. The black men from Africa were then usually regarded as a lower order of human being, but among the more humane Americans—who were outspoken in the North, where slavery was not an economic issue—it was considered that the Negroes were no different from the members of any other race. They believed that, as "all men are created free and equal," the Negroes should be freed.

There were other differences between the North and South. The North wished a protective tariff, while the Southerners wanted free trade with foreign countries. The South produced quantities of cheap raw materials. It was therefore dependent on maintaining a large inexpensive labor force and on being able to compete in a free-trade market to sell all its produce and buy its necessities at the cheapest world-market price. The economic life of the North, however, derived from manufacturing and shipping. More self-sufficient, the North required, nevertheless, protection within American markets. There was a marked contrast between the North and the South from the standpoints of climate, economics, and tradition, and this fact was largely responsible for these sectional differences. A peaceable division of the United States into two independent countries was offered by some as the only solution of the problem.

The slavery issue tended to become the bone of contention. In the North societies for the abolition of slavery grew up, and the agitators for the emancipation of the slaves were called "abolitionists." Years before, the Fugitive Slave Act had been passed by Congress, making it unlawful to give shelter to or aid the escape of a runaway slave; but throughout the Northern states the law was violated generally. Indeed, there were well-organized plans to encourage and help slaves in fleeing to Canada. Carried on with secrecy, this movement was called the "underground railroad."

The acquisition of California and the Mexican Cession as a result of the war with Mexico revived the question of the extension of slavery. Gold was discovered in California in 1848. The following year the "Forty-niners," as they have been called, flocked there to seek their fortunes in the gold fields. Through the influx of prospectors and the people who arrived in their wake, California was rapidly settled, and in 1849 the territory was asking for admission into the Union as a free state (without slavery). In 1848, Wisconsin had been admitted as a free state.

The application of California for admission to the Union as a free state precipitated the issue which steadily widened the breach between the North and South until the outbreak of the Civil War in 1861. The Congress that convened in 1849 had to consider not only the problem of the Mexican Cession, but also the South's demand for a stricter fugitive slave law and the North's demand for the abolition of the slave trade in the nation's capital.

As Congress assembled in December 1849, threats of secession were voiced openly. Keenly aware of the danger, the aged Clay came forward with another of his compromises. This measure carried so many varied provisions that it became known as the Omnibus Bill of 1850. California was to be admitted as a free state, Utah and New Mexico were to be organized as territories on the principle of squatter or popular sovereignty, meaning that the settlers themselves would decide whether or not to bar slavery. The slave trade was abolished in the District of Columbia. To placate the South, a stricter fugitive slave law was enacted. Finally, Texas was to receive $10,000,000 for abandoning her claim to part of New Mexico Territory.

Polk had been succeeded by Zachary Taylor, a Whig, in 1849; but in 1850 Taylor died, and was succeeded by Millard Fillmore, the vice-president. In the campaign of 1852, Franklin Pierce was elected by the Democrats.

THE EVE OF THE CIVIL WAR

Urged by Senator Stephen A. Douglas of Illinois, the Kansas-Nebraska Act was passed by Congress in 1854. By permitting each new state to decide for itself whether it should be slave or free, this bill attempted to settle the slavery question in the vast Nebraska Territory. Rifles appeared in Kansas, and on the border there was bloodshed. "Bleeding Kansas" became the state's nickname. There were fights between those who upheld and those who opposed slavery. Kansas finally voted against slavery, but did not become a state until 1861.

James Buchanan was elected president by the Democrats in 1856. It was in this campaign that the new Republican party—the same party that is in existence today—appeared for the first time, and the following year it arose in its wrath to contest the Dred Scott decision of the United States Supreme Court. This ruling upheld the right of slaveholders to take slave property into any territory, and said in effect that a slave was not a citizen and could legally be held prisoner and made to perform slave labor in any United States territory. The decision thus repealed the Missouri Compromise of 1820. The question was hotly debated by Stephen A. Douglas and a country lawyer of Illinois named Abraham Lincoln. The rights of the slaves were defended by Lincoln.

The threat of secession cast its shadow over the campaign of 1860. The slavery issue, which in 1850 had wrecked the Whig party, now shattered the Democratic organization. Northern Democrats nominated Douglas, while Southern Democrats selected John Breckinridge. In the border states a combination of Democrats and former Whigs launched the Constitutional Unionist party with John Bell as the candidate. The division in the ranks of the Democrats insured the election of Lincoln, who had the solid support of the Republicans.

The South began to perceive that it was losing ground in the "balance of power." In 1858 Minnesota had been admitted as the thirty-second state of the Union, and in 1859 Oregon was admitted—both of them as free states. Kansas, also free, followed in 1861. It was becoming apparent that the slavery question would have to be settled by force, sooner or later.

A Northern writer, Harriet Beecher Stowe, drew attention to the slave question by means of her famous novel, *Uncle Tom's Cabin,* which greatly increased Northern feeling against slavery.

THE WAR BETWEEN THE STATES

The idea of secession was not at this time a new one in the United States, nor did it have its origin in the South. During the early part of the nineteenth century there was talk of secession in the North, particularly in New England, because of objections to federal government policies. As yet it had not been strictly held that the Union could not be dissolved. It was argued that, since the states had broken away from Great Britain, they had an equal right to separate now.

There was talk of secession in South Carolina previous to 1860, and when that year's national election proved to be a Republican victory, a convention summoned by the South Carolina legislature voted that the state's link with the Union was broken.

In October 1859, John Brown, an abolitionist who had already appeared in the course of the troubles in Kansas, seized the United States arsenal at Harpers Ferry, located in that part of Virginia which is now West Virginia, as a first step in an attempt to arm and free the slaves. He had but a handful of men at his command and was speedily overpowered. Half of his party were killed and Brown was tried by a Virginia court and hanged for treason. This event created intense excitement throughout the country. Abolitionists called Brown a martyr, while in the South the incident was regarded as an indication of a Northern campaign to liberate the slaves.

No decisive action was taken by President Buchanan. The burden of decision was left for Abraham Lincoln, who in March 1861 had taken office as president. Upon his election, the Southern states at once proceeded to carry out their threats of secession. South Carolina took the lead, passing the Ordinance of Secession in December. This action was rapidly followed in turn by Mississippi, Florida, Alabama, Georgia, Louisiana, and Texas. Thus far the leaders looked forward to a peaceful compromise, but there were loud arguments and debates that raged throughout the North and South. The right of secession had been recognized by the Northeastern states, but the Northwestern states, where Abraham Lincoln originated, held other views.

It was Lincoln's belief that the Union must be preserved—by force if necessary. Delegates from the seceding states met in convention at Montgomery, Alabama, and formed a provisional government styled the Confederate States of America. Jefferson Davis, of Mississippi, who was secretary of war under President Pierce, was chosen president, and Alexander H. Stephens, of Georgia, vice-president. The constitution of the Confederacy was modeled on that of the United States, but protective tariff and government bounties to manufacturers were proscribed. In his inaugural address, Lincoln took a stand denying the right of secession and arguing that the federal government had a right to enforce the Union. He stated that he would not interfere with existing slavery, nor would he advocate interference.

In April 1861, because a federal garrison at Fort Sumter, South Carolina, refused to surrender, and since the federal government was sending supplies to it, the Confederate forces bombarded the fort, forcing the Union men to capitulate. The firing on Fort Sumter, which had been flying the American flag, aroused the North. On April 15, 1861, President Lincoln issued his first proclamation, calling for 75,000 militia for three months' service—this being the estimate of the strength of the rebellion and of the time that would be required to quell it. As a result of this threat, further Southern states seceded—Virginia, Arkansas, North Carolina, and Tennessee. Only after an internal struggle did Missouri remain in the Union. Kentucky endeavored to remain neutral, but with small success. Delaware was on the fence, approving neither of secession nor of the enforcement of the Union. Maryland sympathized mainly with the Confederates, and many of the inhabitants joined the Southern armies. The nation was indeed divided when, in many instances, brother was to fight against brother, and father against son. It was at first thought that the war would not last long, but it continued for four years.

There were twenty-three states on the Northern side, with a population of 21,000,000; and on the Southern side there were eleven states, with a population of 9,000,000, one-third of whom were Negro slaves. Northern resources were greater, but the Confederates were fighting on their home soil, and they fought desperately.

Early Union successes won some of Virginia's territory, and the western part of the state formed its own government and came into the Union as West Virginia in 1863. On July 21, 1861, a Union force of less than 30,000 men encountered a slightly smaller Confederate force in the battle of Bull Run, a small stream in Virginia about twenty-five miles from Washington. The Union army was defeated, losing nearly 3,000 men, killed, wounded, or missing. Panic-stricken, the Northerners fled in confusion back toward Washington. This was the first serious engagement of the war, and its effect was as disheartening to the North as it was stimulating to the South. Lincoln issued a call for 50,000 additional volunteers.

The Union campaign was based on the general plan of blockading the Southern ports so that they could not receive aid from foreign countries; of capturing the Confederate capital at Richmond, Virginia; and of attacking with the federal fleet from the mouth of the Mississippi River with the purpose of splitting the Confederacy in half. The subsequent battles resulted from this plan of campaign.

The battle of Shiloh (Tennessee), on April 6, 1862, was the first important Union victory. On both sides, a total of about 20,000 men were killed, wounded, or taken prisoner. In the meantime, Commodore Farragut took warships and gunboats up into the Mississippi River; and, after he captured New Orleans, all the towns up the river as far as Vicksburg surrendered to him.

The *Monitor* and the *Merrimac* now appeared on the sea, and engaged in combat after the *Merrimac* had taken the Union fleet by surprise. The Union's *Monitor* could maneuver into action more readily than the *Merrimac* by reason of having its guns in a revolving turret, but though these two vessels bombarded each other for hours neither one was victorious. This event is famous as the first battle between armored war vessels.

After the battle of Fair Oaks, Virginia, when the Union forces were trying to get at Richmond, the Confederate commander, Johnston, was seriously wounded, and Robert E. Lee took command of the Virginian army. A brilliant young commander named "Stonewall" Jackson was now

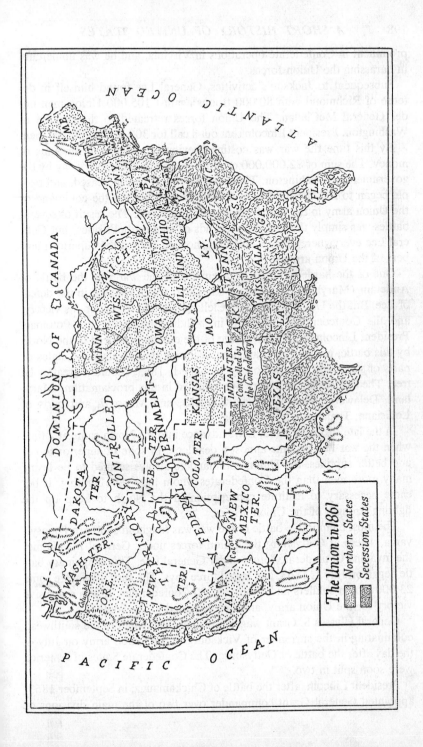

The Union in 1861
Northern States
Secession States

prominent in Confederate operations in Virginia, and he was unmerciful in harassing the Union forces.

Subsequent to Jackson's activities, General Lee found himself in defense of Richmond with 80,000 troops against 105,000 Union men under General McClellan. The Union forces retreated to the defense of Washington. President Lincoln sent out a call for 300,000 additional men.

By this time the war was costing previously unheard-of amounts of money. The sum of $2,000,000 or more was being spent every day by the government at Washington. The protective tariff was increased, and people began to feel the hardships of war. Lincoln shifted the command of the Union army in the East from general to general. The result of several battles was simply the loss of thousands of men on both sides; but General Lee everywhere made a splendid showing against the superior numbers of the Union armies.

One of the hardest fought engagements of the war was the battle of Antietam (Maryland), September 17, 1862, which resulted in the defeat of Lee. But the Union general, McClellan, failed to follow up his victory, and the Confederates succeeded in withdrawing across the Potomac. President Lincoln, taking advantage of the elation produced in the North by this battle, issued a proclamation declaring that all slaves in states or parts of states still in rebellion by January 1, 1863, should thereafter be free. The following states were not included in this proclamation: Maryland, Delaware, West Virginia, Kentucky, and Missouri, and parts of Louisiana, Tennessee, and Virginia.

In the late spring of 1863, Lee's advance into the North came at a time when the war had become almost a deadlock. In spite of superior forces and better supplies, the Union commanders always seemed to be losing many more men than the Confederates whom they were fighting. It became necessary to institute conscription in the North to keep up the fighting strength of the Union armies.

The most memorable battle of the war was fought in southern Pennsylvania, where at Gettysburg the Union forces under General Meade met the invading Confederate forces under General Lee. This sanguinary battle began on July 1, 1863, and lasted three days. The casualties were some 23,000 Union soldiers and about 20,000 Confederates. It was a decisive victory for the Union army, and Lee retreated to the South.

General Ulysses S. Grant waged a brilliant campaign to the southwest, culminating in the surrender of Vicksburg to the Union army on July 4, the day after the battle of Gettysburg. The Confederate States of America were soon split in two.

President Lincoln, after the battle of Chickamauga, in September 1863, appointed General Grant commander over two of the main divisions of

the Union forces. In March of the war's third year, he was made lieu-
tenant-general and virtual commander-in-chief of all the Union forces in
the field. General Lee still commanded the eastern Confederates, but some
of their best officers had been lost in various engagements. These included
the famous "Stonewall" Jackson. In 1865, General Lee became commander-in-chief of the Confederate armies.

Many engagements followed in the East, mostly in and around Virginia, and there was much fighting along the indefinite boundary between
the North and South. In the election of 1864, Lincoln was overwhelmingly returned to the White House for a second term. Nevada was admitted to the Union the same year. The war continued to go on. Much
hardship and suffering was caused in the South by the Union blockade,
but with war vessels purchased abroad the Southerners were able to damage many Northern ships.

In the spring of 1865 the end of the war was in sight. Tired, hungry,
and ill, the soldiers of Lee's army were made desperate by several reverses along the eastern coast. Charleston, South Carolina, was entered
by General Gillmore; the Confederate Congress adjourned; Richmond
was captured; and General Lee surrendered to General Grant at Ap-
pomattox Court House, in Virginia, on April 9, 1865. Grant drew up
the terms of surrender, which were generous and gentlemanly. The total
deaths in the Civil War, either in action or from disease, were 800,000,
half a million of which occurred in the Union army. The cost of the war
ran into the billions, to say nothing of the enormous destruction of
property.

The war between the states is a landmark in American history, both
for the questions it settled and for the problems it created. The Union
victory settled the question of the supremacy of the federal government
over the states, and eradicated the doctrines of nullification and secession.
The war resulted in an expansion of the "unwritten Constitution"
through the exercise of war powers by the President and Congress, and in
the adoption of the Thirteenth, Fourteenth, and Fifteenth Amendments
to the written Constitution. The Thirteenth Amendment provided for the
abolition of slavery; the Fourteenth granted the rights of citizenship to
the Negroes and restricted the powers of the states; the Fifteenth extended the suffrage by eliminating race, color, or previous condition of
servitude as bars to voting.

While the triumphant North emerged from the war strong and prosperous, the defeated South was left broken and destitute. Hundreds of
thousands of lives and a large part of her wealth were lost in the war.
The Northern blockade had caused untold misery; invading armies had
wrought destruction over a vast area. The freeing of the slaves wiped out

two billion dollars' worth of capital and contributed to the ruin of the planter aristocracy and the break-up of the plantation system.

RECONSTRUCTION

Less than a week after General Lee's surrender, the country was horrified and shaken by the assassination of President Lincoln. On the evening of April 14, the President attended Ford's Theatre, Washington, and while sitting in his private box was shot in the head by John Wilkes Booth. He died the following morning. The vice-president, Andrew Johnson, succeeded to the presidency. The war being virtually at an end, the chief work which fell to the administration was that of reconstruction. Johnson's policy with regard to this work led to a serious conflict with Congress.

Johnson attempted to follow Lincoln's plan for restoring the former seceded states to the Union. In December 1863, Lincoln had announced that he would recognize as the legal government in any seceded state any organized group numbering at least ten per cent of the voters of that state in 1860, provided that they take an oath of allegiance to the Union and agree to the abolition of slavery. Congress refused to accept this plan, and, upon the death of Lincoln, proceeded to take matters into its own hands. The Congressional plan of reconstruction centered about the passage of the Freedmen's Bureau Act, which created an organization to advance the general welfare of the Negro; the Civil Rights Bill, which aimed to protect the Negro from being deprived of his civil rights; and the Reconstruction Act, which made acceptance of the Fourteenth Amendment mandatory for readmission to the Union.

Every one of the former Confederate states rejected the Fourteenth Amendment. Congress thereupon abolished the Southern governments which had been recognized by Lincoln and Johnson and proceeded to carry out the provisions of the Reconstruction Act. This was tantamount to imposing military government upon the South and was referred to by the South as the "Crime of Reconstruction." In politics it led to the South's voting "solidly" for the Democratic party in all later elections for many generations.

The administration of the Southern states was taken over by men who had had no previous experience in government. Much progressive legislation was passed in this period. However, because the new men were not experienced administrators, much confusion was evident. The Northern politicians who came to the South to assist in the administration of government were generally well-meaning, but their presence was bitterly resented by sympathizers of the old South, who dubbed them "carpetbaggers" from the bags they carried. A notable feature of this period is that Negroes served in Southern legislatures for the first time.

Johnson was not sympathetic with the more radically minded Republicans; and with the purpose of hampering him, Congress passed an act which forbade the President to dismiss a cabinet officer without the Senate's approval. The President removed Secretary of War Stanton, and a Congressional resolution declared that he had no right to do so. Therefore resolutions impeaching the President for high crimes and misdemeanors were presented by the House to the Senate. The impeachment trial of President Johnson resulted in his acquittal by a vote of thirty-five to nineteen.

It was in Johnson's administration that Alaska was bought from Russia for $7,200,000.

General Grant, in recognition of his decisive role in the Civil War, was the choice of the Republican party in the election of 1868 and was elected. President Grant entered the White House at a time when the South was in a sorry plight. Johnson's administration, controlled by a radical wing of Republicans, had kept many Southern white men in subjection. (The Fourteenth Amendment to the Constitution made it possible to deny the vote to anyone who had participated in rebellion against the United States; thus, temporarily, many white men in the South were disfranchised.) In retaliation against the abuses of the Reconstruction period, a group of Southerners formed the secret society called the Ku Klux Klan, which tried to terrorize Negroes or white men who threatened Southern "respectability." (The Ku Klux Klan of the twentieth century, prominent after the First World War, was modeled after this original band, which met at night and wore sheet-like robes.) The Ku Klux Klan in the South disbanded officially in 1869.

The spoils system, which had been the vice of Jackson's time, was practiced extensively in President Grant's administration. Many of the friends and supporters whom Grant appointed proved to be unscrupulous and corrupt, and there was often misappropriation of government funds for the building up of the West. The period was colored by "crooked politics" and graft, and it was, as well, an era of hard times. The great Chicago fire of 1871 was followed the next year by a conflagration in Boston. Banks and businesses failed in 1873, and financial panic ensued. The paper money of the government depreciated until greenbacks were of little more value than the paper they were printed on. After 1875, Congress provided for their redemption at par value.

There was corruption in other places than Washington. It showed itself throughout the South, and the victims of swindlers included even the tribes of western Indians. There followed Indian uprisings, notably the Sioux War of 1876. It was in this war that General Custer made his celebrated "last stand," in which he and his men were wiped out by the Indians.

The highhandedness of the carpetbaggers came to a climax in the South during the election of 1876. Grant had completed a second term, and the new Republican candidate was Rutherford B. Hayes. Samuel J. Tilden of New York was the Democratic candidate. Following the war, the Southern Negroes naturally voted Republican, but the Southern whites often frightened them from the polls, particularly during the activity of the Ku Klux Klan. Nevertheless, the carpetbaggers returned Republican electors from Southern states even where the votes were Democratic. A crisis was precipitated by this situation, and Congress appointed an electoral commission consisting of eight Republicans and seven Democrats. The commission voted, eight to seven, to give the disputed states to Hayes, and he was elected president. The states abided peaceably by this decision.

The Hayes dispute demonstrated the fact that the electoral system of selecting a president does not always represent the will of the people. Samuel Tilden, the opponent of Hayes, received a popular vote of more than half a million votes over Hayes in the 1876 election.

President Hayes opened his administration by removing federal troops from the Southern states and permitting Southerners to return to self-government. During the ensuing years the North and South slowly became reconciled.

AMERICA'S GROWTH INTO A WORLD POWER

The construction of railroads across the continent was energetically pushed, and bands of steel united the Atlantic and Pacific coasts. There was great activity in the development of cities along these railroads. Mining, especially of silver and gold, developed largely in the West, and in the Middle West agriculture and sheep grazing became important, with the emphasis on the raising of wheat.

James A. Garfield, Republican, was elected president in 1880. Office-seekers clamored against him, and he was loudly criticized by one faction of his own party. Garfield was fatally shot by a disappointed office-seeker named Charles J. Guiteau in 1881, and was succeeded by Chester A. Arthur, vice-president.

A growing movement toward civil service reform was crystallized by the agitation of office-seekers during Garfield's administration, and in 1883 Congress created the Civil Service Commission provided for in the

Pendleton Act. From this time, minor government offices have been filled by persons who have shown their fitness and ability through competitive examinations, thus bringing the spoils system to an end.

After a succession of six Republican presidents, Grover Cleveland, a Democrat, was chosen in the election of 1884. In the election of 1888 a high tariff was a crucial issue, and the Democrats lost the election because they proposed tariff reform and reduction. Benjamin Harrison, who served one term, was elected by the Republicans. Four new states were admitted to the Union in 1889—Montana, North Dakota, South Dakota, and Washington. Idaho and Wyoming were admitted in 1890. Nebraska had been admitted in 1867, and Colorado, the "centennial state," in 1876, just a hundred years after the signing of the Declaration of Independence. Utah was admitted as the forty-fifth state in 1896, after the polygamy sanctioned by the Mormon Church had been abolished.

POLITICAL ISSUES

During the period of the 1870s the farmers had agitated for cheap or inflated currency which would guarantee them higher prices for their products and make it easier for them to repay their debts. An attempt was made to achieve these aims by the organization of the Greenback party in 1876. The Greenback party fought diligently to persuade the government to issue additional paper currency, but despite the impressive showing which the party made in the Congressional elections of 1878, its campaign for cheap money failed.

Meanwhile the advocates of inflation had turned to silver. Until 1873 the government had recognized both silver and gold as legal money and had provided for the free coinage of both metals at a rate of approximately sixteen to one. In 1873, Congress ordered that the coinage of silver dollars be discontinued. By a coincidence, this was followed by the discovery of new silver deposits in the West. The mine owners then agitated for the repeal of the law of 1873 and for a return to free and unlimited coinage of silver at the rate of sixteen ounces of silver to one ounce of gold. In 1878 the pressure resulted in the passage of the Bland-Allison Act, which provided for the purchase of silver by the government for coinage. In 1890, by the Sherman Silver Purchase Act, the amount to be purchased was increased. In 1893 the law was repealed.

Political catchwords in the 1890s were "free silver" and "anti-trust." There was continued agitation by Western miners for the government to coin silver free, or to coin silver at a fixed ratio with gold. The Sherman Anti-Trust Act, which prohibited the amalgamation of large corporations into great trusts for the purpose of "cornering" the market in a particular commodity, was also passed.

Grover Cleveland returned to the White House as a result of the election of 1892. Thus he was the twenty-fourth as well as the twenty-second president of the United States. The administration of the Democrats advocated postal savings, the income tax, the secret or Australian ballot, a limit on immigration, an eight-hour government working day, and the election of senators by direct popular vote. All of these were to be accomplished within the following twenty-five years.

A short time after the inauguration of Cleveland, the financial panic of 1893 was felt throughout the country, but there was a rapid recovery. Through his action in sending troops to protect the United States mails during a railroad strike riot in Chicago in 1894, Cleveland established a precedent of federal action in what had hitherto been regarded as a state affair exclusively.

William Jennings Bryan first appeared as a Democratic candidate for the presidency in the campaign of 1896. He was defeated by the Republican candidate, William McKinley. Bryan advocated the free coinage of silver. The tariff issue again became prominent in politics, and duties were increased in 1897.

THE SPANISH-AMERICAN WAR

The war with Spain, which broke out in 1898, marked the beginning of a new era for the United States. The United States was to emerge from this conflict as a world power with possessions in both the Atlantic and Pacific oceans.

The Spanish-American War developed out of a variety of causes and incidents. The United States was anxious to protect its economic interests in Cuba, particularly sugar. Cuba was in a state of revolt against the Spanish authority, and as a result of the consequent disorders our interests were endangered. Feeling for war against Spain was fomented among the masses of American people because of the exaggerations of certain newspapers, which seized upon the Cuban disorders to increase their circulations. Incidents were distorted and magnified. Most important, the United States had reached a peak of industrialization. There was pressure for the acquisition of new territory for new markets, new sources of raw materials and the investment of surplus capital. There was, in short, a spirit similar to that of the English and continental "imperialism" in this century. It needed but the incident of the blowing up of the battleship *Maine* to plunge us into the war with Spain. This American ship was destroyed by a mysterious explosion while in harbor at Havana, Cuba.

On May 1, 1898, Commodore Dewey, commanding the Pacific squadron of the American fleet, wiped out the Spanish fleet in the harbor of Manila, in the Philippine Islands. Thus the Philippines, which had been under Spanish domination almost since their discovery by the Portuguese Magellan in the early sixteenth century, passed under American control. In 1899 the Philippines revolted under the leadership of Aguinaldo. The rebellion was put down and the leader captured by 1902.

The war began and ended in 1898. The "Rough Riders," under Colonel Leonard Wood and Colonel Theodore Roosevelt, were prominent in the Cuban campaigns. In Cuba more soldiers were killed by disease, especially yellow fever, than by bullets. During the summer Puerto Rico was captured. In December the treaty of peace was signed, and Spain gave up Cuba and ceded Puerto Rico and Guam to the United States as indemnity. There was a consideration by which the United States was to pay Spain $20,000,000 for the Philippines.

RELATIONS WITH LATIN AMERICA

Under the protection of the United States, Cuba became a self-governing republic in 1902. Through the discoveries of United States army surgeons, who isolated the species of mosquito which carried the yellow fever germ, Cuba and other tropical areas in Central America were freed from their great scourge of this malady.

In 1900 McKinley was re-elected, and Theodore Roosevelt became vice-president. President McKinley was shot and killed by an anarchist named Leon Czolgosz at the Pan-American Exposition in Buffalo in 1901, and Theodore Roosevelt succeeded him.

The construction of the Panama Canal was begun during Theodore Roosevelt's administration. The Republic of Colombia, which at the time included the Isthmus of Panama, selected as the best site for the canal, declined the American offers to purchase the needed land. A Colombian revolution in 1903, apparently contesting the refusal of America's offer, succeeded in establishing the Republic of Panama. The independence of Panama was immediately recognized by the United States government, which secured control of a strip of land ten miles wide across the isthmus. Today this is the United States territory called the Canal Zone. Later Colombia was paid an indemnity by the United States.

The construction of the canal and the sanitation of the Canal Zone were directed by the engineer George W. Goethals and the health expert Dr. William C. Gorgas. After surmounting many difficulties, the canal was finished and opened for navigation in August 1914.

THE PERIOD BEFORE THE FIRST WORLD WAR

In the campaign of 1904, Theodore Roosevelt was elected president, and conducted a vigorous second administration. Among his "strenuous" activities were the exposure of corruption and fraud in business combinations. In 1907 another severe financial panic occurred.

An increasingly complex problem was presented by "big business," with its trusts and concentration of huge amounts of capital. The cause of labor was championed by trade unions, and between 1910 and 1920 there were many important labor strikes throughout the land. The commercial scene began to be dominated by oil, steel, public utilities, and power. A gigantic industry was developed through the increasing use of automobiles; and through their manufacture and the distribution of gasoline, a mighty commercial enterprise has grown up. Motorcars have, moreover, influenced the building of splendid roads, often with federal aid, throughout the country.

William Howard Taft, Republican, was elected as Roosevelt's successor, and took office in 1909. In the last month of Taft's administration the Sixteenth Amendment was added to the Constitution, giving Congress power to levy federal taxes on both personal and corporation incomes. Also, by the Seventeenth Amendment, which was ratified in May 1913, it was provided that senators should be elected by direct popular vote instead of by the system of appointment by state legislatures. The establishment of postal savings was effected in Taft's administration, as was the parcel-post system.

The Republican party in the election of 1912 was split by the emergence of the Progressive Republicans under Theodore Roosevelt, who ran against the regular Republican candidate, William Howard Taft. This situation favored the Democrats; and Woodrow Wilson, Democratic candidate, was elected president. Wilson served two terms, which included the period of stress and turmoil of the First World War.

Tariff reduction and the formation of the Federal Reserve System of national banking were early events of the Wilson administration. A further limitation to business combinations was the Clayton Anti-Trust Act, and the Federal Trade Commission became a check against commercial corruption. Added to the pure food acts passed in the Roosevelt administration were the narcotic acts now passed.

THE FIRST WORLD WAR

The policy of the United States when, in 1914, the war broke out in Europe was one of strict neutrality. When, however, the respective blockading activities of both sets of contending powers began to interfere with American shipping, this neutrality was badly strained. In retaliation for Great Britain's effective blockade, Germany began a ruthless submarine warfare which disregarded neutrals and non-combatants. Americans were antagonized by Germany's submarine policy, which destroyed American lives, shipping, and property. Besides, there were bonds of sympathy with the British and French governments.

The United States declared war against Germany in April, 1917. Before there was active participation in the fighting, the country's great resources had to be co-ordinated. This included an elaborate program for a selective draft and the training of more than four million soldiers. The American Expeditionary Forces comprised the largest army the United States had ever placed in the field. In nineteen months some 2,000,000 soldiers were sent overseas, under the command of General John J. Pershing. Between November, 1917 and the close of the war they took part in many military operations on the western front, including the engagements at St. Mihiel in the northeast of France from September 12 to 16, 1918, and the Meuse-Argonne from September 20 to November 11, 1918. The American casualties throughout the war were 126,000 killed, 234,000 wounded, and 4,500 prisoners and missing.

On November 11, 1918, came the Armistice, hastened, no doubt, by the enormous American military, financial, and economic support of the Allied cause. Instead of carrying out the high ideals of President Wilson, the peace treaty signed at Versailles arranged a peace on the basis of military advantages for the victors rather than democratic principles. The Allies tried to cement their victory by strengthening their own countries and weakening the defeated powers, parceling out colonies among themselves and imposing heavy indemnities on the Central Powers. The United States opposed the drastic terms of the treaty, and neither asked nor received territory or indemnity. The main principle championed by Wilson—the League of Nations—was made a part of the treaty in a modified form. Fearing entangling foreign alliances, the United States Senate opposed entering the League. Later, separate treaties of peace were made with the Central Powers, and reconstruction of the havoc of war began.

In the United States the money cost of the World War—about 22 billions—was paid out of the public treasury, and through gigantic Liberty Loans which became the reason for heavy war taxes. A difficult situation was created after the war by the unpaid war debts of the Allies to the United States. In the decade between 1920 and 1930 there was a popular revulsion against war and much agitation for disarmament and world peace.

Problems and Policies During the Years of Peace

Following the public reaction against the terms of the Versailles peace treaty, and on account of the opposition to the League of Nations and its possible entanglements, the voters ousted the Democratic party, and Warren G. Harding, Republican, was elected president by a very large majority. Harding's avowed purpose was to bring the country back to "normalcy" after the strain of the World War. In this era of postwar prosperity there was, in 1922, a national estimated wealth of 321 billion dollars against a national debt of 25 billion dollars and aggregate state and city debts of 6 billion dollars. In the 1930 census the population had increased to 122,775,000.

Calvin Coolidge, the vice-president, became president at the death of Harding in August 1923, and was elected in 1924 for a second term. It was during his administration that oil scandals which had originated during the Harding administration were uncovered. They were concerned with the irregular leasing of public oil lands to private corporations.

Immigration, which early became a national problem, was now restricted by Congress. Out of 92,000,000 inhabitants in 1910, about 12,000,000 were foreign-born, and 19,000,000 more were either foreign-born or of mixed parentage. Immigration restrictions were legislated in 1924 to lessen the number of people coming to these shores, particularly those coming from the countries of eastern Europe. Immigration from many Asiatic countries was for a number of years definitely prohibited; and by a "gentlemen's agreement" the number of immigrants from Japan was limited.

Coolidge's administration was characterized by "economy." Between 1921 and 1929 income taxes were successively reduced, particularly on smaller incomes, and by 1926 the public debt was lowered to about $19,643,000,000. In spite of the country's prosperity, a vital national problem was the unsatisfactory condition of agriculture. The aggregate amount of industrial capital, and the accumulations in both national and state banks, reached unprecedented billions of dollars. There were new labor troubles, especially in the coal industry.

Since the middle of the nineteenth century the railroads had developed steadily, forming a national network of transportation unparalleled anywhere else in the world. During the war they were under government control, but in 1920 they were restored to private management. The government also largely controlled shipping during the war.

A new factor in transportation was the airplane. From 1920 its use in passenger and mail service increased greatly. Charles A. Lindbergh made the first solo airplane flight across the Atlantic in 1927, and in 1933 another American, Wiley Post, made the first solo flight around the world.

In 1928 the presidential election was closely contested. Alfred E. Smith, Democratic candidate, was defeated by Herbert Hoover, Republican. One of the planks in the Republican party platform was the old question of tariff revision, and another important issue was "farm relief." Although not a clearly divided issue, the question of prohibition enforcement came into politics. Enforcement had been an avowed policy of the Coolidge administration, and the Republicans pledged themselves to its continuation. The Twenty-first Amendment, repealing Prohibition (which had become law by the Eighteenth Amendment in 1920), was ratified in 1933.

Tariff revision, chiefly upward, was accomplished during the Hoover administration. To some extent the South has become reconciled to the protection of American industries by tariff. Some farm relief was secured.

After having operated for twenty years on the apportionment of representatives determined by the census of 1910, there was a reapportionment of the House of Representatives according to the results of the 1930 census. Popular government made great gains in the United States—with the use of primaries for selecting party candidates, and in some states with the initiative and referendum, and recall of elected officials by popular demand. The Nineteenth Amendment, ratified in 1920, gave the suffrage to women. The Twentieth Amendment, ratified in 1933, abolished the "lame duck" sessions of Congress (the sessions between election time and inauguration) and set January 20 as inauguration day.

DEPRESSION AND RECOVERY

In October 1929 a crash in the stock market occurred which marked the end of an era of national prosperity. Hard times followed, there was an increase in unemployment, prices fell, and banks failed. The appalling economic condition of the United States in 1932 was attributed by many to the Hoover administration. Franklin D. Roosevelt, a Democrat, won the presidency in a sweeping victory that year. The depression, however, was world-wide. An economic conference of all nations was held in England in 1933, but without effective result. President Roosevelt early called a special session of Congress, which rallied to his support and rushed through remedial legislation to nurse the country back to economic health.

Among the more important emergency measures were those providing for the NRA, or National Recovery Administration; AAA, or Agricultural Adjustment Administration; NLRB, or National Labor Relations Board; PWA, or Public Works Administration; CCC, or Civilian Conservation Corps. These and other federal organizations alleviated distress and unemployment. They frequently operated in co-operation with states and municipalities. To provide work, the administration carried out a program of extensive building of irrigation projects, bridges, and other public enterprises. Laws were passed to strengthen the banks and to secure the money on deposit. Some of the measures taken in this period were later declared unconstitutional by the Supreme Court of the United States, although in the meantime they had in most cases rendered effective service.

The recovery measures involved a great expansion of governmental operations and consequently the expenditure of large amounts of money, all of which resulted in considerable adverse criticism, mostly from political opponents. These policies of the Roosevelt administration became known as the New Deal.

The 1936 campaign for the presidency, with Franklin D. Roosevelt running for re-election against Alfred M. Landon, governor of Kansas, the Republican candidate, was based mainly on the issues arising from the Roosevelt administration's policies dealing with recovery, tariff, and taxation. Roosevelt was re-elected, carrying all states except Maine and Vermont.

In 1937 the country was greatly disturbed by labor strikes and struggles. The Committee for Industrial Organization (C.I.O.), later the Congress of Industrial Organizations, a new factor in the American labor movement, led the workers in the steel, automobile, and other large industries, employing "sit-down" strikes for the first time in this country.

Early in 1937 the United States Supreme Court became an important issue among the people. This was brought about by the proposal of President Roosevelt to enlarge the membership of the Supreme Court because its membership at that time consisted mostly of ultra-conservative men above 70, who were supposedly opposed to the New Deal. Congress refused to adopt this proposal.

THE PERIOD OF THE SECOND
WORLD WAR

When the European war began in the fall of 1939, the United States promptly declared its neutrality, and a special session of Congress was called to consider the amending of the neutrality law, so that munitions might be sold to the belligerents under certain conditions. Meanwhile the president authorized the increase of American military and naval strength to its maximum peace limits.

The international situation in 1940 ended the tradition against a third presidential term. Roosevelt was re-elected, defeating Wendell L. Willkie. Early in 1941, by the device of lend-lease aid to our Allies, the United States had become, in Roosevelt's phrase, an "arsenal of democracy" for the benefit of the European Allies. Practically the entire industrial and natural resources of the country were devoted to the production of ships, tanks, planes, and other war munitions.

AMERICA IN THE SECOND WORLD WAR

Late in 1941, America was drawn into the Second World War. While Japanese representatives were in Washington discussing peace with the President and his secretary of state, Japan treacherously attacked Pearl Harbor and the naval ships there at anchor. This was on December 7, 1941. Within a few days Germany and Italy declared war against the United States.

With the greater part of the American navy in the Atlantic, the United States was unable to prevent the Japanese conquest of the Philippines, despite the heroic defense of Bataan by General Douglas MacArthur and his men. The Japanese also conquered Burma and the British and Dutch East Indies before they were stopped.

In 1943 the American navy defeated the Japanese in several important naval contests in the Pacific, and the American army captured a number of strategic island bases. In Europe the Russians were on the offensive. The Axis powers were expelled from North Africa. And under the leadership of General Dwight D. Eisenhower the Allies successfully invaded Sicily as a base for the invasion of the European continent.

In 1941, while the country was still at peace, Congress hesitated to "freeze" prices, wages, and rents, although all of these were rapidly rising. On January 30, 1942, however, Congress enacted a price control measure. Extraordinary powers were given to the Office of Price Administration. "Black markets" developed, and the fear of a runaway inflation was always present. In October 1942, Congress passed an anti-inflation act authorizing the president to stabilize wages, prices, and salaries in so far as possible at the levels of September 15, 1942.

By the end of 1942, nationwide rationing of sugar, coffee, gasoline, and canned and other goods had become an accepted fact of the war. With the increased intensification of the war, the American people were forced to "do without" their peacetime comforts. America was now concentrating an all-out effort that was soon to show results on all the battle fronts of the world. Labor shortages developed in industry and on the farms as millions of men entered the armed services. At full strength, in 1944, there were about thirteen million Americans under arms all over the world. Millions of women replaced men in industry. Thousands joined the armed forces as nurses, Wacs, Waves, or Spars to release men for combat duty.

Meanwhile American mines, shipyards, factories, and steel mills, under the stimulus of contracts totaling billions of dollars, were turning out prodigious quantities of war materials, which, in spite of German submarines and the Luftwaffe (the German air force), moved in an ever-increasing volume to the fighting fronts. The national debt soared to dizzy heights as Congress appropriated billions upon billions for war materials. Taxes of all kinds were increased, not only to provide necessary revenue, but also to drain off excessive purchasing power and thus keep prices from getting completely out of control. In 1943 Congress approved a pay-as-you-go plan for the federal income tax and ordered employers to withhold part of each employee's wages to apply toward his income tax.

For the first time since the Civil War, the United States went through the process of electing a president in wartime. Governor Thomas E. Dewey of New York became the Republican nominee for president, and Governor Bricker of Ohio the nominee for vice-president. Roosevelt accepted a fourth-term nomination, and Senator Harry S. Truman of Missouri was selected as his running mate for vice-president. Roosevelt and Truman, after a vigorous campaign, won the election, securing 432 electoral votes to Dewey's 99, and 25,600,000 popular votes to Dewey's 22,000,000.

One of the most important features of this election was the activity of labor. The C.I.O., months before the election, organized a Political Action Committee pledged to support Roosevelt and to work for the election of candidates favorable to labor. The P.A.C. was very effectively organized; in many instances it was the decisive factor in the election or defeat of local and Congressional candidates.

An outstanding feature of the war years was the close collaboration between the leaders of the "Big Three," namely, the United States, Great Britain, and the Soviet Union, who met several times during the war. Another outstanding feature was the close collaboration between the United States and England, which was first begun in the Atlantic Conference between Roosevelt and Churchill in August 1941. The Atlantic Conference resulted in the Atlantic Charter. This historic document provided for: self-determination for all nationalities; access to raw materials by all nations; a lasting peace based on freedom from fear and want; freedom of the seas; and the creation of a "permanent system of general security."

Military and economic representatives of both countries met frequently to confer with one another. Anglo-American war activities were co-ordinated through a series of special agencies, such as the Combined Raw Materials Board, Combined Production and Resources Board, Munitions Assignment Board, and the Combined Chiefs of Staff. Later much of this co-ordination was extended into the organization of the UNRRA, the United Nations Relief and Rehabilitation Association.

The precedent established in the Atlantic Conference for the personal meetings of the Chiefs of State was continued at the Casablanca Conference in January 1943. From that meeting there emerged the "unconditional surrender" slogan which became the guiding principle in dealing with the Axis powers. In October 1943 a conference of the foreign secretaries of Great Britain, the United States, and Russia was held at Moscow. At this meeting the governments declared that they would continue their collaboration in the postwar period.

The Moscow Conference of Foreign Ministers (October 1943) laid the groundwork for the successful conferences held later in the year at Cairo, Egypt, and Teheran, Iran. At the Cairo Conference (November 1943), President Roosevelt, Prime Minister Churchill, and Chiang Kai-shek agreed upon future military operations against Japan.

The Cairo Conference was followed by the Teheran Conference (November–December 1943). As a result of this conference, Russia, the United States, and Great Britain announced that they had "reached complete agreement as to the scope and timing of operations which will be undertaken from the east, west, and south." At Bretton Woods, New Hampshire, in July 1944, a conference of the United Nations formulated plans to stabilize international currencies and to establish a world bank to finance foreign trade and economic reconstruction. In August 1944, at Dumbarton Oaks, Washington, D.C., statesmen representing the United States, England, the Soviet Union, and China drafted a preliminary set of proposals for a world security organization to maintain world peace. A second meeting of Roosevelt, Churchill, and Stalin was held at Yalta in the Crimea in early February 1945. At this conference the "Big Three" reached agreement on final plans for the defeat of Germany; common policies for enforcing unconditional surrender terms; a conference of the United Nations, to be held at San Francisco starting on April 25, 1945; and consultation every three or four months by the foreign secretaries of England, Russia, and the United States. On April 12, 1945, two months after President Roosevelt's return from the Yalta Conference, he died of a cerebral hemorrhage at Warm Springs, Georgia. He was succeeded by Harry S. Truman.

Meanwhile, on June 6, 1944, the long-awaited second front had been opened. General Eisenhower, who had been in supreme command of the

Allied operations in North Africa, and General Bernard L. Montgomery, of the British Eighth Army, led the Allied forces in the breaching of "Fortress Europa" on the beaches of Normandy. By the middle of August the Allied armies had swept across France, liberated Paris, and were racing to the German frontier.

In spite of new German weapons—the rocket bomb and the jet-propelled plane—most people believed that the war in Europe might end in 1944. This optimism was short-lived, for on December 16, 1944, a German counter-attack broke through the lines of the American First Army and penetrated deeply into Belgium and Luxembourg. For three weeks the Allied world was kept in a state of tension. The Germans were finally halted, and by the end of January 1945 the territory they had seized in their gamble was reconquered. Toward the end of February 1945, Eisenhower began a final large-scale offensive. The German lines broke. The Rhine River was crossed in April 1945. On May 12, 1945, the Germans signed the documents of unconditional surrender in a schoolhouse in Reims, France. The war in Europe had come to its successful conclusion after almost six years of the costliest, bloodiest fighting in the history of mankind.

In the Pacific the Allies had been on the defensive until August 1942. The first ray of hope came that August, when marines with the help of the navy landed on Guadalcanal in the Solomon Islands. In February 1943 the Japanese evacuated Guadalcanal, and the United States was in position to begin a slow return, lasting more than two years, to the positions it had lost at the opening of the war. The battles of New Guinea, Makin, Tarawa, the Marshalls, Saipan, Guam, Iwo Jima, and Okinawa were fought and won. In these notable victories the United States navy and marines played a major part in assuring the victory.

In October 1944 the navy landed an American army on the island of Leyte in the central Philippines. The Japanese navy suffered serious losses. After the landings had been made, the second naval battle of the Philippines was fought. Once again, as at the Coral Sea, Midway, and Guadalcanal, the Japanese navy was beaten. Admirals Nimitz and Halsey, in command of our navy in the Pacific, were leaders in the victory over the Japanese. By the first of March, 1945, Bataan, Corregidor, and Manila were once again in American possession. After three years of war our forces had not only achieved mastery of the Pacific but were poised for a landing on the shores of the Japanese islands. The climax came on August 6, 1945, when the first atomic bomb was dropped on the city of Hiroshima, followed three days later by the atomic-bombing of Nagasaki. The world felt unmistakably that the war in the Pacific was about to end. This feeling was strengthened when, a few days later, the Russians declared war on Japan and launched a successful invasion of Manchuria.

On August 12, 1945, the Japanese government sued for peace on the terms laid down in the Potsdam Declaration, with the reservation that the Emperor be permitted to remain. After three days of negotiation, while the whole of the civilized world held its breath, the Japanese acceded to our terms, placing General MacArthur as Supreme Commander in Japan, and allowing the Emperor to remain only as a figurehead. On August 14, 1945, President Truman and Prime Minister Attlee simultaneously announced V-J Day. The Second World War was ended.

PEACE AND THE WAR'S AFTERMATH

In accordance with decisions reached at the Yalta Conference, and despite reports that the United Nations Conference would be postponed because of the death of President Roosevelt, President Truman announced that the conference would be held as planned on April 25, 1945, in San Francisco.

After eight weeks of discussion, the delegates from fifty nations succeeded in drafting the United Nations Charter for a world security organization. The charter opens with the phrase, "We, the peoples of the United Nations . . ." It is in a sense an agreement between peoples rather than between governments. The charter as worked out in the conference provides for six principal organs: (1) a General Assembly; (2) a Security Council; (3) an Economic and Social Council; (4) a Trusteeship Council to govern the former possessions of the Axis powers; (5) an International Court of Justice; and (6) a Secretariat. The United States was the first nation to join the United Nations Organization.

Another step in planning for the peace was the Potsdam Conference at the end of July 1945. This conference was held by the "Big Three" powers to determine the specific policies to be followed in working out the formula for surrender terms for Germany, and for Japan when the war in the Far East was ended. Marshal Stalin, President Truman, and Prime Minister Attlee met at this conference. The terms as announced were: (1) complete stripping of Japan and Germany of their war industries; (2) Japanese territory would be restricted to her four home islands; (3) occupation of Germany and Japan.

In accordance with agreements made at the Potsdam Conference, the five foreign ministers met in September 1945. The conference was an utter failure. Its expressed aim of drawing up the basic peace treaties was not achieved. However, Secretary of State Byrnes, Foreign Secretary Bevin, and Foreign Commissar Molotov met again in Moscow in December 1945; this conference met with greater success. In November 1945,

Prime Minister Attlee came to the United States and conferred with President Truman on the problem of the atomic bomb and atomic energy. Their communiqué, as issued, noted that the atomic secret would be retained by the United States and Great Britain until the world had proven that it could be trusted with the secret.

The sudden ending of the war confronted the administration and the country with a host of problems concerning reconversion to peacetime production, the maintenance of full employment, the relaxation of wartime controls over production, and demobilization of our armed forces. The problem of reconversion was made more complex by the wave of strikes that broke out in our mass-production industries, such as in automobile, steel, and electrical manufacturing. The chief demand of the workers was an increase in wages which would maintain their take-home pay at wartime levels. In addition to the problems created by reconversion, the nation was faced with the most serious housing shortage in its history, and also with severe shortages of butter, meat, sugar, clothing, and many other commodities.

POSTWAR AMERICA

The years following the Second World War were difficult ones for the Democratic administration under President Truman. Conservatives in the country hoped for a return to routine government, with an end to New Deal policies and minimum involvement in Europe's reconstruction difficulties. The "Fair Deal" program of President Truman, contradicting the first of these hopes, was designed to raise the living standard of the common man and to increase individual security, through such measures as unemployment relief, more extensive social security, minimum wage requirements, increased price supports for farmers, and government subsidies for improved housing. The Republicans, controlling the Eightieth Congress elected in 1946, vigorously opposed Fair Deal legislation. Waves of strikes beginning in 1945 led to the passage of the Taft-Hartley Labor Act, over the president's veto, in 1947. This bill, although it had some clauses favorable to labor, limited the power of unions to strike and picket, and in other ways restricted the power of organized labor. In the years following, however, labor achieved enormous gains in take-home pay and a considerable reduction in weekly working hours. Slowly, Truman's Fair Deal policies prevailed, at least to the extent that none of the New Deal advantages to labor were reversed.

Meanwhile the country's business was undergoing an unprecedented prosperity boom. Despite minor recessions in 1949 and 1953, the years following the war evidenced far higher production rates in all fields of industry than had ever been known. On the other hand, an inflationary spiral had been set in motion, with wage raises following rising prices and initiating new price raises; the buying power of the dollar declined enormously, and persons living on fixed income suffered badly. This trend continued well into the late 1950s. Few measures to counteract inflation were taken, and they were unsuccessful.

Efforts on the part of Truman's administration to continue the wartime Fair Employment Practices Act and to urge elimination of poll taxes in the South angered Southern Democrats, who were zealously on guard against any infringement of states' rights. The issue of states' rights became increasingly controversial in the middle 1950s.

In 1948, Truman ran for election against the Republican candidate, Thomas E. Dewey. In this election two other parties appeared: the Progressive party, with Henry A. Wallace as candidate, and the Dixiecrats, with Strom Thurmand as their candidate. The Republican campaign was characterized by overconfidence; and Truman was returned to office, although in Congress a coalition of Republicans and Dixiecrats made up a majority.

THE UNITED STATES AND THE FREE WORLD

After the Second World War the United States emerged as perhaps the strongest and wealthiest nation in the world; her position was rivaled only by the Soviet Union. It became evident very early that the Soviets meant by every method possible to strengthen their position on the Continent and in the East and to dominate directly by their military power the smaller nations of Central Europe, while asserting themselves in many other countries through intense propaganda and the international Communist party. Russian troops had remained in many parts of Europe and in Asia after the war, and Russian economy and industry continued to be geared toward achieving military superiority. In Poland, Czechoslovakia, Hungary, Rumania, Bulgaria, Albania, and East Germany—the eastern European states surrounding Russia—Communist regimes had been set up under puppet governments controlled from Moscow; in Italy and France Communist parties for a time increased their memberships considerably. The United States and her allies, particularly Britain, became alarmed by the spread of communism, and feared that in countries impoverished through the war and in underdeveloped countries in other parts of the world the democratic way of life would not be able to withstand the pressures of Russian propaganda and military strength.

Under the Truman Doctrine, stated in 1947, the United States began an important program of economic and technological aid to countries sympathetic to the West but in danger of falling under Soviet domination. Congress voted the necessary funds, and immediately aid was extended to Greece and Turkey. The European Recovery Program, which became known as the Marshall Plan after General George C. Marshall, secretary of state, who outlined and carried it through, was designed to stimulate prosperity in the countries of Western Europe and thus ensure their remaining outside the Soviet orbit. The United States at once pledged and donated or lent to the program many billions of dollars. American aid went also to Yugoslavia; although this country was governed by a Communist dictator, in 1948 it had broken away from Moscow's leadership and given evidence of a sincere desire to co-operate peacefully with non-Communist countries. In 1957, when there were indications that Marshall Tito, president of Yugoslavia, was once more uniting with Russia, aid to this country was reduced and then suspended temporarily.

It soon became evident that economic aid to Europe was not sufficient to check the advances of Russian aggression. Therefore, in 1949, the United States signed with Canada, Great Britain, France, and eight other European countries a defensive pact, declaring that an armed attack upon any one of them would be considered an act of aggression against all. This North Atlantic Defense Pact, which was ratified by an overwhelming majority in the Senate, committed America to a permanent responsibility in Europe. It was a clear sign that isolationism in America was no longer a significant political factor. The United States sent a large number of divisions abroad to serve with those contributed by the other nations under the North Atlantic Treaty Organization. General Dwight D. Eisenhower became supreme commander of NATO's forces.

THE KOREAN WAR

It was also during the Truman administration, in 1950, that a crisis in the Far East was precipitated by the attack of North Korea, a Communist state which had been under Russian control after the war, upon South Korea. South Korea, which was under American control after the war, had been set up as a separate democratic state in 1948, because no arrangement could be reached with the Russians for unifying Korea under a freely elected government. When the North Korean attack took place, the United States took the lead in the United Nations to press military support for the attacked country. The North Korean attack was swift and efficient, weapons and war materials having been supplied by Russia. The vast majority of the troops sent to Korea under United Nations auspices were Americans. General Douglas MacArthur, already Supreme Allied Commander in Japan, commanded the entire United Nations force, but he remained directly responsible to the president of the United States. Several months after the war began, when United Nations forces had pushed the invaders out of South Korea and were advancing well into Communist North Korea, China began to give open aid to the North Koreans.

Following the Second World War, China had entered into civil war. The object of United States diplomacy had been to attempt to unify China under a moderate government. Failing to establish any compromise between the Nationalists under Chiang Kai-shek and the Communist forces under Mao Tse-tung, the United States gave its support intermittently to Chiang. In 1949 the Communist forces had overrun the entire mainland, leaving Chiang Kai-shek and the Nationalists in control of only the island of Formosa (Taiwan). The United States refused to recognize the government of Communist China and consistently opposed its admission to the United Nations.

When China entered the Korean War, General MacArthur strongly urged the military advantages of bombing the Chinese mainland and even recommended an invasion into South China by Nationalist forces from Formosa. He was supported in America by vaguely isolationist leaders, who wished to concentrate America's military efforts in the Far East and leave Europe's protection to Britain and France. President Truman and Dean Acheson, the secretary of state, however, were determined not to allow the Korean War to develop into a world war. Truman decided to limit the fighting strictly to Korean territory; despite the very large numbers of Chinese "Volunteers" in North Korea, the president refused to acknowledge officially that we were at war with the Chinese Communists. When MacArthur openly opposed this policy of limiting the area of war and criticized the administration for it, Truman relieved him of his Far Eastern Command as well as his post in Korea. MacArthur came home an honored hero, but Truman's policy was upheld. The war ended in 1953, and an unsatisfactory peace was worked out. North and South Korea remained disunified.

The Eisenhower Administration and the Changing Political Scene

America's new irrevocable position of responsibility for the continuance and defense of the free world in Western Europe and elsewhere was reflected in the political scene at home. The old guard of isolationist Republicans was losing support, and the younger men in the party were anxious to redefine its policies. Moreover, the achievements of the Fair

Deal were confirmed and there could be little question of turning the clock back.

General Eisenhower had been considered as candidate for the presidency by both parties in 1948, but he was unwilling to be nominated. In 1952, however, he resigned as commander of NATO forces and came home, ready to enter political life. He accepted the Republican nomination for the presidency in the 1952 election, with Richard M. Nixon as the Republican nominee for vice-president. The Democrats nominated Adlai E. Stevenson for president. Eisenhower's victory was a landslide. The Republicans did not have a clear majority, however, in Congress.

As was expected, Eisenhower's administration continued the policy of foreign aid to free countries in Europe and the East. Although the president was extremely popular and was re-elected in 1956, running against Stevenson again, the government was beset with a number of domestic problems, which became increasingly controversial.

Toward the end of Truman's presidency, the issue of Communist infiltration into this country began to loom and developed to unrealistic proportions. The trial of Alger Hiss in 1949, and in the same year the trials of nine Communists charged under the Smith Act of 1940 with advocating overthrow of the government, introduced a succession of Senate investigations into the loyalty of members of the Civil Service. The McCarran-Nixon Bill of 1950 and the McCarran Act of 1952 were designed to protect the nation against subversive elements in the country and against immigration of individuals associated with the Communist cause. Many leaders felt, however, that they were unreasonably strict. In 1950, Joseph R. McCarthy, senator from Wisconsin, began claiming the attention of the nation with drastic charges of Communist infiltration into the State Department and other branches of the government. Later, as head of the Senate Permanent Investigating Subcommittee, he initiated a wave of investigations, the methods of which were very controversial. McCarthy was ultimately censured by the Senate when the vast majority of his accusations had been proved false, and his influence fell rapidly in the middle 1950s.

The issue of Civil Rights, a long-time controversial problem, came to a head again after 1955, the year in which the Supreme Court ruled that segregation of Negro from white students in the public-school system was illegal. The court ordered all the states to integrate their schools as rapidly as was possible. In the South, where the judgment was highly resented, most states, nonetheless, obeyed the court order. The few outstanding cases where local officials resisted integration became national issues.

The economic picture in America throughout these years was a confusing one of increasing prosperity on the one hand and rampant inflation on the other. Although it seemed unlikely that a serious depression, such as the one in 1929, could be on the horizon, the administration began to attempt corrective measures against inflation.

AMERICA'S ROLE IN THE CONTINUING STRUGGLE BETWEEN EAST AND WEST

At the end of the Second World War the United States alone controlled the secret of the atom bomb. In 1949, however, the government announced that the Soviet Union had produced an atomic explosion. This was the signal for an arms race, principally between Russia and the United States. Efforts to regulate or decrease the stockpiling of atom bombs were fruitless. The matter was discussed in the United Nations and at round-table conferences between the major powers, but Russia would never agree to any plan which involved inspection and enforcement of the objectives. In 1952 a hydrogen bomb had been developed with power to wipe out whole cities with one hit. In the middle 1950s America, Britain, and Russia began developing long- and short-range ballistic missiles, anti-atomic weapons, and a whole complex of instruments for fighting atomic war. Yet everyone was aware that the world was not likely to survive an atomic war.

The entire free world relied on America to provide the money, the arms, and the technological advantages needed for survival in the face of possible all-out aggression on the part of Russia. Relations between the United States and her British and French allies were gravely strained in 1956, when the United States supported the resolution in the United Nations to oblige France and England to withdraw troops from Egypt, where the Suez Canal was endangered by Egyptian seizure. Soon after this event, however, America and her allies were making every effort to close the gap between their policies. The closest co-operation between the major Western powers and all the nations of the North Atlantic Pact appeared to be the best protection against Soviet designs. The United States was the undisputed leader of all the free nations.

In the late fall of 1957, NATO held a meeting in Paris attended by chiefs of state. A strong concern over the rapid advances of Russian scientists in the field of ballistic missiles was evident in the discussions. Only a few months before this meeting, the Soviet Union had astonished the world by launching the first artificial satellite to circle the earth in a gravitational orbit. From a military point of view, however, the source of alarm was the development by the Soviets of an intercontinental ballistic missile. President Eisenhower, at the NATO meeting, made every effort to assure the sixteen associated nations that the United States would not lag behind in research and production of necessary defensive equipment. At the same time, the president assured the Western nations that no feasible opening to a renewal of disarmament talks with Russia would be neglected. At the end of the year, although NATO had made plans for installing United States missile defenses on the Continent, there was strong hope that the Soviet Union might be sincerely willing to negotiate disarmament and control of nuclear weapons as a first step toward better understanding between East and West.

EXAMINATION QUESTIONS

1. Why did Columbus apply the name "Indies" to the territory he discovered in 1492?

2. After whom were the continents of North and South America named?

3. What nationalities founded the colonies on the eastern coast of North America?

4. After whom was the state of Virginia named?

5. When did the Pilgrims land in America?

6. Who was Henry Hudson?

7. Who settled New York?

8. When did the French and Indian War begin?

9. What was the chief colonial industry?

10. What well-known American college was founded in 1636?

11. What Act from the British government in 1765 incited Patrick Henry to make the speech in which he said, "If this be treason, make the most of it"?

12. What was the Boston Tea Party?

13. What document states that "all men are created equal"?

14. What celebrated Frenchman offered his service to the cause of the American Revolution?

15. What were American privateers?

16. When did Cornwallis surrender to Washington?

17. Who was the author and publisher of *Poor Richard's Almanac?*

18. Who was the first president of the United States?

19. Why was the war with Tripoli fought?

20. What was the amount involved in the Louisiana Purchase?

21. What battle of the War of 1812 was fought after the peace treaty was signed?

22. What world power supported the Monroe Doctrine?

23. What was the "spoils system" in American politics?

24. What state was an independent republic for a time?

25. When did the Mexican War begin?

26. What issue other than slavery led to the war between the North and the South?

27. What novel of the time drew attention to the slave question?

28. What population did the first census of 1790 show?

29. When was Fort Sumter, South Carolina, bombarded by the Confederate forces?

30. How many states were included on the Northern and Southern sides of the Civil War?

31. What were the first armored war vessels?

32. What were the losses in the battle of Gettysburg?

33. How many men were killed or died from disease in the Civil War?

34. Why was President Andrew Johnson impeached?

35. In what war did Custer make his celebrated "last stand"?

36. What legislation brought the "spoils system" to an end?

37. What was the Sherman Anti-Trust Act?

38. What precipitated the Spanish-American War?

39. During whose administration was the construction of the Panama Canal begun?

40. When were postal savings and the parcel-post system established?

41. Who was president during the First World War?

42. When did the United States enter the war against Germany the first time?

43. Who was in command of the American Expeditionary Forces in the First World War?

44. What American made the first solo flight across the Atlantic Ocean?

45. What name was applied to F. D. Roosevelt's domestic policies?

46. Who were the "Big Three" of the Second World War?

47. What was decided on at the San Francisco Conference of 1945?

48. What was the European Recovery Program designed to do?

49. When did the Korean War end?

50. What did President Eisenhower assure the chiefs of state at the 1957 NATO meeting?

FOR FURTHER STUDY

THE AGE OF JACKSON, by Arthur M. Schlesinger, Jr. (Little, Brown & Co., Boston.)

AMERICA, THE STORY OF A FREE PEOPLE, by Allan Nevins and Henry Steele Commager. (Little, Brown & Co., Boston.)

AMERICAN ECONOMIC HISTORY, by Harold U. Faulkner. (Harper & Bros., New York.)

IRREPRESSIBLE CONFLICT, 1860–1865, by Arthur C. Cole. (The Macmillan Co., New York.)

THE RISE OF THE AMERICAN NATION, by Francis Franklin. (International Publishers, New York.)

THE RISE OF AMERICAN CIVILIZATION, by Charles A. and Mary R. Beard. (The Macmillan Co., New York.)

SHORT HISTORY OF THE AMERICAN NEGRO, by Benjamin G. Brawley. (The Macmillan Co., New York.)

SOCIAL AND ECONOMIC HISTORY OF THE UNITED STATES, by Henry James Carman. (D. C. Heath & Co., Boston.)

TRAGIC ERA, by Claude G. Bowers. (Houghton Mifflin Co., Boston.)

UNITED STATES SINCE 1865, by Louis M. Hacker and Benjamin B. Kendrick. (F. S. Crofts, New York.)

V

Civics and the United States Government

WHAT IS CIVICS?

CIVICS IS THE SCIENCE of civil government, the branch of political science dealing with the rights of citizenship and the duties of citizenship. The citizen is concerned not only with obeying the laws which apply to him, and with the payment of taxes for the support of the government, but also with the election of public officers, with his good behavior, the maintenance of his home and grounds, the organization of charities, and similar activities.

Everyone born in the United States is a citizen of the United States. Aliens (foreign-born persons) may become United States citizens by naturalization. Sometimes entire groups of people are admitted to citizenship by Act of Congress, as were the inhabitants of Puerto Rico and of Hawaii, and, in 1924, all the Indians born in the United States.

The right of expatriation is a fundamental right of the individual; that is, he may choose the country of his allegiance, provided that the country permits him to do so and he fulfills the necessary requirements. This right was inherent in the policy of the United States from the beginning of the country as an independent nation, but was not formally affirmed until 1868. By this right, a citizen of the United States may lose his citizenship by professing allegiance to another country and becoming a naturalized citizen thereof. Under the 1934 law a woman who is a citizen of the United States does not lose her citizenship by marrying an alien, unless she makes a formal renunciation of her citizenship before a court. A naturalized American citizen normally loses his citizenship if he returns to his country of origin and resides there for two years or more, or if he becomes a resident of some other country and resides there for five years or more.

An individual is always under the jurisdiction of the country he resides in, whether or not he avails himself of the privileges of citizenship. He is able to allow some of those privileges to become ineffective simply by not exercising them; as, for example, when a citizen does not exercise his right to vote. He cannot, however, avoid benefiting from the protection of the laws; nor can he avoid the restrictions placed upon his activities by laws in the United States and its lesser political units, and in other countries. Laws apply to residents whether or not they are citizens, except those restrictions meant to apply to citizens exclusively, and privileges arising therefrom (as the right to hold political office).

It cannot be too strongly emphasized that government in the United States is by the consent of the majority and is ultimately subject to the control of the majority; the government and the body of laws are, however, imposed on all individuals, whether they support the politics of the majority or not. It is the right of any citizen to vote (when qualified) for candidates of whom he approves; it is also his right to persuade to his way of thinking as many of his fellow citizens as he can. In practice, minority groups have little power, although they may exercise some influence. It is the duty of every citizen, however, on behalf of himself and his children, to see to it that his rights and privileges are not impaired without a fair consideration of the merits of both sides of the question by a majority of the people.

In a country of 170,000,000 people it would be prohibitively expensive and wastefully slow to refer every question to a popular vote, and it would be well-nigh impossible to initiate legislation by popular demand only. It is for this reason that government by representation (the representatives being elected by the people) is necessary. A government by representation is, strictly speaking, a republic, and not a democracy. True democracy is feasible only when the citizens are few enough in number to be able to convene and express themselves politically on every matter of government. Yet a republic is (in theory, at least) democratic. Most modern governments in the world today are republics, though their political machinery may vary greatly in details.

The United States of America as an independent country was born when the Declaration of Independence (July 4, 1776) and the American Revolution resulted in the 13 original colonies becoming states "free and independent" of Great Britain. Those 13 states have increased in number and extent until there are now 48. When this country became independent, it was necessary to center the government of the United States in a common organization with control of all the states; this was accomplished by drafting a written Constitution, which was finally ratified by all the 13 states in 1789. This Constitution sets forth the powers of the Federal Government and expresses the limitations of the powers of the separate states. The Constitution can be and has been changed by amendment, each amendment becoming effective only after the ratification (approval) of three-fourths of the states. The power of the Federal Government, under the Constitution, was subsequently contested by the states during the first 75 years of its exercise; the federal power was sustained by the Civil War (1861–1865), and has increased in scope and effectiveness ever since.

WHAT IS GOVERNMENT?

Government is the agency which may direct matters of public concern. It seeks to protect our welfare; at the same time it demands that we insure the welfare of others. Our government in so far as possible is an expression of the will of the people. The Declaration of Independence defined it as a "government by the consent of the governed." In the preamble to the Constitution it is "we the people" who "ordain and establish" our basic law. The idea was set down for all time in Lincoln's definition, "government of the people, by the people, for the people."

The United States of America is a republic; its government is federal. When the Federal Government is spoken of, the agency having its central offices in Washington, D.C., is meant. A federal union, like the United States, is made up of units (states) which agree by compact (the Constitution) to "surrender their general sovereignty and consolidate into a new state." Thus, each state of the United States surrenders to the central power its sovereignty in such particulars as the Constitution specifies, but retains its self-government in local matters, as within its own borders —with the exception, always, of the powers delegated to the Federal Government.

The states delegate to the Federal Government power over all those matters which concern the nation as a whole. In the federation of the United States, the central government administers the foreign policy for all the states, regulates commerce between the states, and also regulates currency and coinage. Though a small town may enact its own traffic regulations, its inhabitants are bound, equally with all other inhabitants of the United States, by the federal Constitution and by federal laws passed by Congress. Local or state government may be concurrent with the Federal Government, but cannot be in conflict with it.

THE FEDERAL GOVERNMENT

The Federal or National Government of the United States is headed by the President, who is chief of the executive branch. Congress forms the legislative branch. The third branch is the judicial, headed by the Supreme Court. This arrangement of the Federal Government is specifically provided for in the Constitution, which was ratified by the 13 original states, and was subsequently agreed to by each of the other 35 as each was admitted to the Union. The preamble to the Constitution states its purpose:

"We, the people of the United States, in order to form a more perfect Union, establish justice, insure domestic tranquillity, provide for the common defense, promote the general welfare, and secure the blessings of liberty to ourselves and our posterity, do ordain and establish this Constitution for the United States of America."

The Federal Government has only those powers given to it by the Constitution, including amendments to the Constitution—it has and can have no others. Such powers as are not granted to the Federal Government by the Constitution, or are not expressly denied to the states by the Constitution, remain the powers of the several states, to be administered by them individually, as suits each of them best.

Important powers granted to the Federal Government are the following: (1) the maintenance of an army and navy for national defense; (2) the power to declare war or to make peace; (3) the right to conclude treaties with foreign countries, and to administer other foreign relations; (4) the regulation of immigration and the naturalization of aliens; (5) the maintenance of a postal system; (6) the right to coin money and to issue paper money; (7) the granting of copyrights and patents; (8) the regulation of foreign and interstate commerce; (9) the maintenance of federal courts of justice; (10) the right to tax all the people on an equal basis for the support of the Federal Government, including the right to levy an income tax; (11) the right of Congress to pass laws to enforce the provisions of the Constitution; (12) the exclusive and direct government (by Congress) of the national capital, Washington, D.C., including the city of Washington and the District of Columbia, which are coextensive.

Since the Civil War the Federal Government has steadily extended its power, often at the expense of the states. This has been due to (1) the influence of the elastic clause which enables Congress to "make all laws which shall be necessary and proper for carrying out the foregoing powers"—thus, under the power of Congress to establish an army or navy, it has the power to pass a law conscripting the people of the states; (2) decisions by the Supreme Court which have extended the power of the Federal Government over interstate commerce; (3) the extension of the national domain by the Federal Government; (4) the precedents set by the Civil War and the two World Wars for an expansion of the federal authority. The enactment of amendments to the Constitution has tended to extend the power of the federal authority.

The states may pass laws which do not conflict either with the federal Constitution or with the laws or treaties passed or made by Congress, provided also that state laws do not assume powers expressly forbidden to the states by the Constitution. The judicial branch of the Federal Government, through the Supreme Court, determines, when it is called upon to do so, whether a state law does or does not so conflict. Decisions of the Supreme Court become, in practice, part of the law of the land; they may act as a check, not only upon the legislatures of the states, but even upon the Congress of the United States. As the Constitution asserts:

"This Constitution, and the laws of the United States which shall be made in pursuance thereof, and all treaties made, or which shall be made, under the authority of the United States, shall be the supreme law of the land; and the judges in every state shall be bound thereby, anything in the Constitution or laws of any state to the contrary notwithstanding."

If a conflict arises between a treaty and a federal law, it is generally accepted that the one most recently passed or made shall be binding. However, a treaty always takes precedence over a state law.

The Federal Government, under the Constitution, guarantees that each of the 48 states is independent of the others—that is, that the authority of one state has no effect outside of its own territorial boundaries. But the judicial and other public acts of one state are accepted with "full faith and credit" in the other states. Therefore, a man acquitted of a crime in one state is freed from the consequences of that crime throughout the United States; and a judgment secured against a person in one state can be enforced even if that person moves to another state. Further, the privileges and immunities of a citizen from any state are automatically applicable to the citizen from any other state, whether or not he becomes a resident of that state. For example, no state can tax citizens from other states more than it taxes its own residents. Some of the more important privileges and immunities guaranteed by the Constitution have become so generally accepted that we seldom think of them as such. These include the right to travel in or reside in any state for legitimate purposes; the right to make contracts and to buy or sell or to own property and the right to marry, in any state; equal rights in the courts of any state.

Since the officers of one state have no authority outside the boundaries of that state, a fleeing criminal who manages to cross the state line is, for the moment, beyond capture, unless he is guilty of a federal crime and is being pursued by federal officers. However, such a criminal may be captured by the police of the state in which he happens to be, and by extradition be transported back to the state in which he committed the crime. If the state into which he flees refuses to act, he is safe from molestation.

Though the National Government is a unified central authority, it has three main branches—the legislative, the executive, and the judicial—which act as a check one on the other. This has been accomplished by delegating to each branch of the government some of the powers of the other two branches. Thus, the executive has not only executive powers, but legislative and judicial powers. The legislature or law-making body has executive and judicial powers. The judicial branch has legislative and executive powers. In summary, no one branch of the government can fully exercise its powers without the other two branches exercising their powers. For example, the President ordinarily must approve a bill of Congress before it becomes a law. The President also exercises legislative power by his power of veto. Congress can check the President by the exercise of its judicial power, such as the power of impeachment. The Supreme Court can check Congress by the exercise of its power to declare a law unconstitutional.

Either Congress or a national convention (called by Congress at the request of the legislatures of two-thirds of the states) can propose an amendment to the Constitution. The proposed amendment is presented to the legislatures of the states, or to conventions in the states (whichever Congress designates), and when ratified by three-fourths of the states it becomes a part of the Constitution, and a part of the supreme law of the land. The Supreme Court cannot nullify an amendment to the Constitution.

THE LEGISLATIVE BRANCH

The Congress of the United States forms the legislative branch of the Federal Government. It consists of two "houses," or separate bodies of representatives, the lower called the House of Representatives, or, popularly, simply the House, and the upper called the Senate. The number of members of the House of Representatives is determined on the basis of population, with one representative for about every 300,000 persons. The Senate is made up of two members from each of the states, and contains, therefore, 96 members. To become law, a bill must be passed by both houses of Congress, and (usually) receive the President's signature.

Senators and representatives are elected by popular vote. The essential difference between their apportionment among the states is that the House is elected on a strictly democratic basis, with each state having more or less representatives depending on its population, while the Senate is an embodiment of the federal principle that all the states are equal in their independence and the sovereignty remaining to them. The sovereign power of Rhode Island is equal to that of New York, in spite of the vast difference in population.

Each Congress is designated chronologically by number: the Eighty-fifth Congress was that of 1956–1957. Members of the House of Representatives, each of whom serves for a term of two years, are elected every two years. These elections fall in the even-numbered years; thus, in 1944, 1946, 1948. Any voter who, in his state, may vote for the members of the larger branch of the state legislature may vote for members of the United States Congress. The voting is done by ballot, on the day provided by law. Each state is divided into as many Congressional districts as there are representatives apportioned to that state according to population. Voters in a district mark their ballots only for the election of the representative from that district. To qualify as a representative, a candidate must be at least 25 years of age, must have been a United States citizen for at least seven years, and must reside in the state, and usually, though not necessarily, in the district from which he is sent to Congress.

Members of the Senate serve terms of six years each. These terms are staggered so that the terms of one-third of the senators expire every two years. Consequently, the Senate is at any time made up of at least two-thirds of seasoned members, and one-third of its members may be new. Actually, many old members are often re-elected. Senators are elected by popular vote, by ballot, at the same time as the elections for representatives are held; although in each six-year period, each state will hold only two elections for senator. Senators, however, are elected from each state at large without regard to congressional districts, and only one senator is elected from each state at a time, his choice depending upon a majority of votes in the whole state. To qualify, a candidate must be at least 30 years of age, must have been a United States citizen for at least nine years, and must reside in the state from which he is sent to Congress.

The Senate or House of Representatives has the power, by a majority vote, to expel any objectionable member for any reason. Similarly, it can refuse to grant a seat to any member of whom it disapproves.

Powers peculiar to the Senate include the approval, by a majority vote, of political appointments made by the President (cabinet officers, judges, ministers), the ratification, by a two-thirds vote, of treaties made by the President (usually made with the advice or implied consent of the Senate, secured by conferring with the Senate Committee on Foreign Relations or with influential members of the leading political parties), and the trial after impeachment (by the House) of the President, Vice-President, or any other federal officer who is otherwise beyond the reach of justice.

The Powers of Congress

The powers expressly granted to Congress by the Constitution have been liberally interpreted by the federal courts, so that, in practice, these powers have reached an astonishing magnitude. If any law can be construed as "necessary and proper" for the enforcement or carrying out of the delegated powers, it is held to be constitutional.

In general, the legislative powers of the House and of the Senate are equal, with the exception that revenue acts (bills for raising revenue by taxation or other means) must originate in the House. The power to levy taxes for revenue purposes is practically absolute. Next to the income tax, the chief sources of federal revenue are the customs duties and the excise taxes. The customs duties are the tariff imposed on goods brought into the country. These duties are nominal when they are intended for revenue purposes only. The duties are for "protection" when they are placed at a figure to prevent competition with American products. The tariff rate on different articles is changed frequently, to meet current needs. The tariff must be uniform at all ports or points of entry into the country. Export taxes are prohibited by the Constitution.

The excises are the internal revenue duties. The chief excise taxes are on tobacco in all forms, on playing cards, and on amusement tickets above a certain price; documentary taxes on stock certificates, and bonds. From time to time other articles become subject to tax.

Congress, in addition to its taxing powers, controls both foreign and interstate commerce. Shipping comes under direct federal supervision, including all the laws of navigation, requirements as to wireless (radio) and lifeboat facilities, the quarantine examination of passengers for contagious diseases (before landing). Objectionable articles can be prohibited from importation, by Act of Congress, and the exportation of any article can also be prohibited, if that is desirable. By its control of commerce between the states, Congress regulates all navigable rivers and lakes, and has supervision over all means of transportation (railroads, particularly) and communication (telegraph and telephone). By an extension of this power, Congress controls the "air," and has authorized the Federal Communications Commission to regulate the operations of radio and television stations.

The Interstate Commerce Commission, which was established in 1887 in response to the protests of shippers over the monopolistic practices of the railroads, regulates not only railroads, but buses, trucks, and inland shipping engaged in interstate commerce. Such commissions are formed by Congress, to take over duties too numerous or specialized for Congress itself to handle; they are responsible to Congress, and they exercise their quasi-legislative (that is, partly legislative) and quasi-judicial powers under congressional authority.

Commerce control has given Congress the power to legislate relative to the quality and description of goods (on the label). The Pure Food and Drugs Act is an example of this federal control. Any article sold outside the state of manufacture, or transported across any state boundary, must be honestly labeled as to quality, contents, exact weight or measure. A product labeled "pure" *must* be pure; it cannot be adulterated. The Federal Trade Commission supervises this phase of commerce control. Commerce control has also given Congress the power to legislate relative to working conditions, hours, and wages of labor engaged in manufacturing products sold across state boundaries. It has even extended the application of the term "commerce" to restrict the criminal movements of persons from state to state. This is illustrated in the "Lindbergh Law," which gives the Federal Government the authority to apprehend and prosecute kidnappers. Accordingly, at the instance of a kidnapping, offended parties may call upon the aid of the Federal Bureau of Investigation. The F.B.I., however, as a federal agency, would have no authority to investigate a local crime. State agencies alone are authorized to act in such matters.

Anti-trust legislation, devised to prevent combinations of commercial enterprises to eliminate competition, comes under the commerce control permitted to Congress. In general, Congress has acted to prevent the unfair elimination of small competitors by "big business" on the principle that competition is the life of trade. Prevention of boycotts and intervention in industrial strikes are other aspects of congressional power.

Congress authorizes and superintends the manufacture of the national currency, including coins and paper money. The states are forbidden to coin or issue money. Congress can also borrow money on the credit of the United States. Congress can also pass bankruptcy laws.

Congress engages in business to the extent of enjoying a partial monopoly in the transport of mail. The Post Office Department is headed by the Postmaster-General, appointed by the President, but the ultimate control of the system of mails is in the hands of Congress. Changes in rates, salaries of employees, and erection of new post offices have to come from Congress. No state or private individual or corporation can engage in a business competitive with the United States postal system as respects the carrying of first-class mail (letters). First-class mail is, therefore, a government monopoly. The Post Office Department has competitors, however, in the carrying of parcels, in its money-order business, and other activities (as postal savings).

In time of war, Congress has almost unlimited power to pass whatever laws may be necessary to the national defense. The Constitution expressly makes exceptions to the limitations on Congress at such a time.

Congress controls the establishment of federal courts. Through the federal courts so provided, Congress is able to prosecute and punish offenders against the Federal Government, including violators of federal laws, perpetrators of piracy on the high seas, those guilty of treason, and counterfeiters of the national currency or of other government securities. Congress controls and rules directly all federal forts, arsenals, prisons, post offices, national parks, and reservations, and all government property, including the District of Columbia. These duties, in practice, are delegated by Congress to commissions or departments of the Federal Government, but their authority emanates from Congress.

How Congress Does Its Work

The members of the House of Representatives serve two-year terms. During each two-year term there are normally two sessions of Congress. Each of these sessions commences at noon on the third day of January, and adjourns, ordinarily, in the late spring or early summer. Congress adjourns itself by vote. At other times, Congress can be called into special session by the President. A session of Congress means that both the House and Senate are in session.

The activities of Congress are largely controlled by party politics. The two dominant parties in the United States are the Democratic and the Republican. There are other parties, and occasionally these two parties have split into small groups, but for all practical purposes Congress can be divided into Democrats and Republicans.

The party in power in Congress controls the houses and their committees by means of caucuses. A party caucus is a private and usually secret meeting of the members in Congress who belong to that party; they choose the speaker of the House (who presides while Congress is in session), and nominate the majority in each of the standing committees in both the House and the Senate (the Vice-President presides in the Senate). During congressional session, a party caucus may assemble to decide the policy of the party concerning impending legislation. The decisions of the caucus as to how the members of the party shall vote in Congress are generally accepted as binding. The minority party also holds caucuses, for the purpose of organizing opposition to the party in power. When Congress convenes, the first voting usually confirms the dominant-party caucus for the speaker, and the majority members of committees.

The House of Representatives maintains a chaplain, a clerk, a sergeant-at-arms to preserve order, a doorkeeper, and so on. The House and

Senate each make their own rules of procedure. Owing to the much larger membership of the House, the representatives are limited in the time allowed for debate, so that business may be carried on more swiftly. In the Senate such limitations are seldom made. When the new Congress assembles, it starts with a clean slate, so to speak, for all pending legislation in the previous Congress is dead; any bills not acted upon in the previous Congress must be introduced anew, if they are to be considered. The house rules are usually adopted by each succeeding Congress without change. The first important step is to notify the Senate, formally, that the House is in session. The President is also formally notified that Congress is in session.

A new session of Congress customarily opens with a reading of the President's message, in which he suggests desirable legislation. A careful record is kept of the activities in Congress, including (when demanded by one-fifth of the members) a tabulated list of members and how they voted on a particular question. Although the membership of Congress necessarily changes after each election, many congressmen are returned to Congress term after term by their constituencies. No law limits the number of terms a congressman may serve.

The business of the Federal Government is so complex that even a perpetual session of Congress could not handle all of it unless some provision were made for a separation of duties. Investigation of data and consideration of facts relative to legislation are usually delegated to standing committees, both in the House and in the Senate. There are some 30 standing committees in the Senate, and nearly 50 in the House, ordinarily, although at times there have been many more. A representative or senator may serve on more than one committee. The party caucuses usually see to it that each committee has a majority membership of the party in power. Each committee is permanent throughout each two-year term of Congress. Some of the more important standing committees in the House are as follows: Committee on Rules, on Ways and Means, on Appropriations, on Military Affairs, on Naval Affairs, and on Foreign Affairs. The committees in the Senate usually closely parallel those in the House.

Legislation begins in Congress by the introduction of a "bill," which is a written version of a proposed law, by any member of either house —with the exception that revenue bills must originate in the House. Thousands of bills are introduced during each session of Congress, but comparatively few of them pass both houses and become law. Each bill is given a number by the clerk of the House, as, for example, H. R. 3321, which was the number of the Underwood-Simmons Tariff Bill (named from the chairmen of the House and Senate committees to which it was referred), so that it may be identified, and be recorded in the daily

Journal and printed in the *Congressional Record,* the daily chronicle of what happens in Congress.

A bill introduced in the House or the Senate may receive no attention, and be forgotten; it may be defeated almost at once; it may be subjected to debate; it may be referred for investigation to the proper standing committee. The committee may fail to report on the bill or reject it outright and thus "bury" the bill. The committee may alter the bill, or even write a new bill. The committee may approve the bill, and thus practically assure its passage by the House or the Senate, whichever body is considering it. Despite the fact that both Senate and House have the machinery for "calling out of committee" bills that have been "pigeonholed" or "buried," it is safe to say that in most instances the committee's decision stands. No bill can be passed unless it is acceptable to both houses. Points of disagreement between the two houses are settled by a conference committee made up of members of each house.

When a bill has been approved by both houses of Congress it is sent to the President. He may approve the bill by signing it. He may veto it and return it, with a statement of his objections, to the house in which it originated. The bill may then be dropped or altered, or it may be passed over his veto by a two-thirds vote of each house. A bill may also become a law without the President's signature if he has taken no action on it at the end of ten days (Sundays excepted). If Congress has adjourned while the President has taken no action, the bill is "dead." This course is known as a "pocket veto."

Sometimes one house amends a bill referred to it by the other; then it has to be returned to the house of origin for consideration of amendments. All bills introduced into Congress open with the words: "Be it enacted by the Senate and House of Representatives of the United States of America in Congress assembled, that . . ." Thus is emphasized the concurrent action of both houses. When a bill finally becomes law, it goes into effect either at once or on a date specified within its text. It must then be executed by the proper departments of the Federal Government, and duly enforced as an "Act of Congress."

Revenue bills originate in the House, and, in practice, usually in the Committee on Ways and Means. The ten administrative departments prepare estimates of their probable expenses and present them to the Secretary of the Treasury, who turns them over to the House. Various committees on appropriations consider the demands of the Federal Government (in its executive branch) and recommend that they be met or reduced. Revenue legislation follows, if necessary, the appropriations passed by the House and subsequently approved by the Senate.

Appropriations secured by party persuasion, for local benefit of constituencies, as a play in party politics, have been humorously and somewhat derisively called "pork" out of the public "pork barrel." When members of Congress combine to assist a certain group, in exchange for similar assistance in putting through legislation they themselves desire, their action is termed "logrolling," so called from logrolling in lumber camps, where neighboring groups of lumberjacks are accustomed to unite their efforts.

It is a characteristic of both Congress and our state legislatures that complete independence of judgment on the part of the members has become next to impossible. The average lawmaker is hemmed in on all sides. Pre-election promises, memorials, letters, and petitions always haunt him. He cannot ignore the dictates of his party leaders or of powerfully organized groups and minorities outside of Congress.

The ten original amendments to the Federal Constitution, which are called the Bill of Rights, and our state constitutions protect the right of the people "to petition the government for a redress of grievances." Our concern is not with the right of petition as such. Rather the danger is in the domination of our legislative bodies by pressure groups and their agents in the capitals. Originally, the method lay in approaching the lawmakers in the lobbies of the legislative halls (hence *lobbying*). The methods today are far more comprehensive.

Effective lobbying is carried on by highly trained public relations counsellors, lawyers, politicians, ex-congressmen, and former government officials. They know how to "see the right people," how to attract gigantic sums of money for their purposes. They also know how to stir up public opinion by means of organized pressure on congressmen, by floods of letters, and telegrams. To remedy these alarming conditions it may be necessary to exercise more rigid control over lobbyists and their activities. The ultimate responsibility, however, rests upon the individual citizen. Well-informed, public-spirited citizens are the voices that the congressman most depends upon.

The Executive Branch

The President of the United States is the "chief executive": all powers of the executive branch of the Federal Government emanate from him.

To be a candidate for the presidency (or vice-presidency) a person must be a native-born citizen of the United States, at least 35 years of age, and must have been a resident of the United States at least 14 years. Since it is necessary to acquire national political prestige to be a successful candidate for the presidency, most chief executives have been older than 50 when elected.

Candidates for the presidency are customarily chosen by national conventions of the various political parties. There may be as many candidates as there are parties: there are usually from four to half a dozen, although the minor parties have never elected a President.

The President is actually elected by the people, though, in theory, and in official routine, he is chosen by an antiquated system based on the "electoral college." The Constitution provides for this system, which was designed by the framers of the Constitution to avoid the difficulties of the early days of slow travel and slow communication. Each state has allotted to it in the electoral college as many electors as it has combined senators and representatives in Congress. These electors are chosen by popular ballot in "presidential years" (every fourth year, as 1940, 1944, 1948).

The various parties in each state go through the formality of nominating the number of electors allotted to their state. The names of these candidates are printed on ballots, or placed on voting machines, linked with the names of the candidates for President and Vice-President of the same party. Instead of voting for President and Vice-President, the voter casts his ballot for the electors of the political party he favors, thereby indicating his desire that those electors, if chosen, shall vote for the candidates of their political party.

If a state returns a majority for one party, the electors of that party for that state are elected. As a rule, each state secures a majority for one party and all the other votes (for other party electors) become of no account in the presidential election, for the chosen electors cast all their votes for the candidates of their party. For all practical purposes, since the electors do not go against the choice of their party, the next President and Vice-President are known to the public as soon as the votes in the election are counted. Strictly, according to the Constitution, the chief executive and his "substitute" are not elected until the electors have assembled and officially cast their votes for their party candidates. These votes are then transmitted to the president of the Senate, where they are counted, and the President and Vice-President are then officially announced as elected. If no candidate has a majority of the electoral votes, the House of Representatives decides. Here the representatives from each state vote as a unit, a vote of 25 or more states being required for the choice of the next President (from the three leading candidates). The President and Vice-President take office on the 20th of January following the November elections, each for a term of four years.

At the expiration of the first term, either President or Vice-President or both may be renominated and re-elected for a second term. No President had served a third term until the administration of Franklin D.

Roosevelt. By the Twenty-second Amendment to the Constitution, which was ratified in 1951, no President may serve a third term.

The salary of the President is $100,000 a year. It may not be increased or decreased during the term for which he was elected. In addition to this, he is allowed $50,000 for expenses accruing from his official duties and $40,000 annually for expenses of traveling and "official entertainment." As a rule, this last allowance is not expended in full, any surplus being returned to the federal Treasury. By virtue of his authority as commander-in-chief of the Army and Navy, the President can order for his use any vessel of the United States Navy, expenses thereof being paid by the Navy Department. The upkeep of the Executive Mansion (the White House) and executive offices of the President, with their grounds, is provided for in separate appropriations by Congress.

The duties and powers of the President are many. The Vice-President has but one official duty—to act as presiding officer in the Senate. However, he cannot vote except in the event of a tie vote in the Senate. Although the Vice-President may participate significantly in the Administration in an advisory capacity, he exercises no power in the government unless, through the incapacity or death of the President, he succeeds to the presidency. His salary is $35,000 per year, and he receives $10,000 for expenses.

The powers which have been granted to the President may be classified under the following heads: (1) his purely *executive powers,* which are exercised in connection with the enforcement of federal laws; (2) his *legislative powers,* which give him a share in the making of laws; (3) his *diplomatic powers,* which make him a vital factor in the regulation of foreign affairs; (4) his *military powers,* which are derived from his position as commander-in-chief of the Army and Navy and of the militia of the several states when called into the service of the United States; and (5) his *judicial powers,* that is, powers by which he influences the courts and their processes.

The Constitution imposes upon the President the task of taking "care that all the laws be faithfully executed." He performs this task through thousands of officials ranging all the way from members of the cabinet down to letter carriers, clerks, and laborers. In making important appointments—members of the cabinet, justices of the Supreme Court, ambassadors—he is required to send the name of his choice to the Senate for confirmation. In the matter of senatorial confirmation there has developed the custom of *senatorial courtesy.* According to this usage, if the President obtains the approval of the senators from the state in which the office is to be filled, this is sufficient to insure senatorial approval.

The President is not only the chief executive, but he exercises considerable legislative power. He is not merely a tool of Congress in the carrying out of its laws, but actually originates measures and with the help of administration leaders directs their course through both houses of Congress. He has the power to call special sessions and send annual and special messages to Congress. He thus exerts great influence over legislation. His privilege of patronage or dispensing political favors has influenced many a lawmaker. As leader of his party in Congress he also exerts considerable influence.

In addition to his positive powers in lawmaking, the President has a negative power by which he restrains Congress from doing certain things. By his power of veto, he may prevent a bill from becoming a law. Congress may override his veto by a two-thirds vote.

Another group of presidential powers are those which deal with diplomacy, treaties, and the handling of foreign affairs. The President appoints ambassadors, ministers, and consuls to foreign capitals with the approval of the Senate. Through these agents, who are supervised by the Secretary of State, he carries on the foreign affairs of the nation. He can recognize or ignore foreign nations by receiving their ministers or refusing to do so.

The President now also appoints delegates to the United Nations, the leading delegate having the rank of Ambassador.

The President has derived from his diplomatic powers, through usage, three other powers. First, he may recognize a state of war resulting from the acts of some other power, and take measures accordingly. Second, he may take steps which are technically acts of war, in protection of American rights abroad. An example was the sending of troops to China by President Theodore Roosevelt during the Boxer Rebellion (1900). Third, he may take similar steps to protect our interests abroad, either because of a pending treaty or because of a general diplomatic policy.

As commander-in-chief of the Army, Navy, and Air Force, the President, in time of war, has dictatorial powers. Although he appoints officers to high commands with the advice and consent of the Senate, he may remove them at will during time of war. He has the power to order mobilization, direct the movements of fleets and armies, regulate courts-martial, control conquered territory, and arrange armistices.

The President exercises judicial powers. He may pardon any offense against the federal laws, except in cases of impeachment. He may grant reprieves (the right to stay the enforcement of the penalty) and commute sentences. He may grant an amnesty (a general pardon for a large number of offenders).

The President cannot be arrested, and is not subject to the mandates of any court, high or low, while he is in office. The House can impeach him for just cause, and the Senate must then try him; a two-thirds vote is necessary for conviction. Only one President, Andrew Johnson, has ever been impeached; he was tried but not convicted.

The President's cabinet consists of the heads of the ten departments of the executive branch of the government, whom he appoints (with the approval of the Senate). These are, in the order in which their departments have been created by Congress: (1) Secretary of State, (2) Secretary of the Treasury, (3) Secretary of Defense (originally Secretary of War, Secretary of the Navy, Secretary of the Air Force), (4) Attorney-General, (5) Postmaster-General, (6) Secretary of the Interior, (7) Secretary of Agriculture, (8) Secretary of Commerce, (9) Secretary of Labor, (10) Secretary of Health, Education, and Welfare.

The President meets more or less regularly (at his discretion) with his cabinet, to discuss his policies and projects. They may advise him, but he is at liberty either to follow or ignore their advice, as he may choose. They derive their power from the President, and are directly responsible to him. There are no prescribed qualifications for a cabinet officer. Each receives a salary of $25,000 annually.

The *Department of State* is the senior department of the executive branch of the Federal Government. The Secretary of State, with his assistants, handles all "state correspondence," whether between the Federal Government and the states or between the Federal Government and foreign governments or their representatives. The Secretary of State, under the direction of the President, has charge of all foreign affairs. The diplomatic service is the extended arm of the Department of State to foreign countries; it includes ambassadors and ministers, with their assistants, and consuls. The ambassadors are envoys of the highest rank: they are direct representatives of the President of the United States in the countries in which they reside; their official residences are called embassies. The United States now sends ambassadors or ministers to about 75 countries. The ministers are envoys of the second rank; their official residences are called legations. Consuls are principally commercial representatives in important commercial cities throughout the world; their official residences are called consulates. The diplomatic service, in general, looks after American interests abroad, and watches over American citizens and activities in foreign lands. The Department of State issues passports to American citizens who wish to travel in foreign countries.

The Secretary of State is in charge not only of foreign affairs but performs, as well, certain domestic functions. Among the latter, he publishes federal laws and executive proclamations; proclaims the ratification of amendments to the Constitution; preserves original copies of treaties and all laws enacted by Congress; and conducts all correspondence between the President and the governors of the states.

The *Treasury Department* superintends the collection of revenues and all moneys due the government; holds the federal funds and disburses them at the direction of Congress; has direct charge of the mints and coinage, including the capture and punishment of dishonest taxpayers and of counterfeiters; and supervises, by special bureaus organized for the purpose, the Public Health Service, the Coast Guard Service, the construction and maintenance of public (federal) buildings, and the Federal Reserve System of banks.

The *Defense Department* has charge of the United States Army, the United States Navy, and the United States Air Force, under the direction of the President, who is commander-in-chief of each. The U.S. Military Academy at West Point, the U.S. Naval Academy at Annapolis, and the U.S. Air Force Academy at Denver, Colorado, are administered by the Defense Department. The Secretary of the Army, the Secretary of the Navy, and the Secretary of the Air Force no longer have cabinet status.

The Attorney-General, head of the *Department of Justice,* is legal adviser of the President. In the person of his assistants, he prosecutes violators of federal laws, or represents the United States in cases brought against the government. The Federal Bureau of Investigation, an arm of the Department of Justice, investigates violations of federal laws. The Attorney-General also supervises the federal prisons.

The *Post Office Department,* under the direction of the Postmaster General, manages the great business of the postal system (U.S. Mails).

The *Department of the Interior* concerns itself with certain responsibilities of the Federal Government within the United States, including the supervision of government lands (the public domain, national parks, national monuments, and other reservations), the geological survey, reclamation of waste land, control of mines, patents, pensions, etc. This department also handles matters pertaining to the Indians.

The *Department of Agriculture* oversees farming problems in general, and includes within its jurisdiction and investigation the Forest Service, the Weather Bureau, conquest of injurious insects and of animal and plant diseases, road-building, compiling statistics of markets and farm prices, the publication of bulletins of agricultural information, etc.

The *Department of Commerce* supervises taking of the national census and tabulation of data obtained, controls the standards of weights and measures, supervises government fisheries, maintains lighthouses, has direct administration over navigable waters, conducts the coast and geodetic surveys, supervises aviation and radio, and inspects shipping.

The *Department of Labor* looks after the welfare and improvement of conditions of wage-earners throughout the country, and also supervises certain aspects of immigration and naturalization, which are related to labor statistics and over-all employment conditions.

The *Department of Health, Education, and Welfare* superintends the public education system and public health and welfare measures, including the Social Security Administration, which cares for the unemployed, the aged, and the needy.

The complexity of the activities of the Federal Government has resulted in the creation of a number of *boards* and *commissions*. Heads of boards and commissions are not members of the President's cabinet. Members of boards and commissions are usually appointed because they are experts in their fields, and they serve an indefinite period. The powers of boards and commissions are sometimes very wide; they derive quasi-legislative powers from Congress, which approach the absolute effect of acts of Congress. Decisions of the Federal Trade Commission, for example, so long as they do not conflict with the Constitution or established statutes, are legally binding on the parties concerned.

The Civil Service Commission superintends the examination of candidates for the minor government positions, and recommends qualifying applicants to the proper appointing officials. By far the greater part of the minor federal officers and employees receive their appointments under this commission. The Interstate Commerce Commission controls the regulation of trade between the states. The Federal Reserve Board, of which the Secretary of the Treasury is an *ex officio* member, superintends the Federal Reserve System of national banking. Other banking and loan boards handle other phases of the federal finances. The Federal Trade Commission is the watchdog of business. The Maritime Commission looks after the American merchant marine. The Federal Communications Commission controls the "air," distributing authorized wave lengths to broadcasting stations, and settling disputes that may arise between stations.

Also in the nature of distinct boards or commissions is the management of such federal institutions as the Government Printing Office, the Library of Congress (its duties include registration of copyrights), the National Museum, the Smithsonian Institution (a national institution of learning), and the like.

THE JUDICIAL BRANCH

The third great branch of the Federal Government, the judicial, is headed by the Supreme Court of the United States. The judicial system of the United States includes all the federal courts, with their judges and officers. The federal attorneys, however, are employed by the Department of Justice, which is one of the ten administrative or executive departments, headed by the Attorney-General.

"The judicial power of the United States," says the Constitution, "shall be vested in one Supreme Court, and in such inferior courts as the Congress may from time to time ordain and establish. The judges, both of the supreme and inferior courts, shall hold their offices during good behavior, and shall, at stated times, receive for their services a compensation, which shall not be diminished during their continuance in office."

Unlike other higher government officials, judges of the Supreme Court and lesser courts hold office for life, unless they resign, retire, or are impeached and tried by Congress. For this reason, in its history the United States has had, up to 1957, only 14 Chief Justices of the Supreme Court as against more than 34 Presidents. The Supreme Court consists of the Chief Justice and eight associate justices, all appointed by the President, "by and with the consent of the Senate."

Next in rank to the Supreme Court are ten Circuit Courts of Appeal, distributed throughout the country, as well as the District of Columbia Circuit. Each Circuit Court has at least three circuit judges. Below these are the 85 or so District Courts, also distributed throughout the country, according to need, with 140 or more judges—the number steadily increases with the growing complexity of legal business. There are also a Court of Customs and Patent Appeals, a Customs Court, a Court of Claims, a District of Columbia Court, and federal courts for Alaska, Hawaii, Puerto Rico, and other territories and possessions.

The types of cases which, according to the Constitution, come within the authority or jurisdiction of the federal courts may be classified under two heads. The first class proceeds from the *nature of the case*. It includes matters which arise under the Constitution, laws, and treaties of the United States. It also includes those matters which are related to seizure of vessels, claims, contracts, offenses, etc., in time of war or peace.

The second class is based upon the *character of the parties*. It comprises: (1) cases affecting our ambassadors, other public ministers and consuls sent to foreign countries; (2) cases in which the United States is a party; (3) cases involving two or more states, or citizens of different states; (4) cases between a state (or its citizens) and a different country (or its citizens or subjects). By the Eleventh Amendment, however, suits brought against any state in the Union by citizens of another state, or by citizens (or subjects) of a foreign country, may not be tried in the federal courts.

The federal courts are subject to a number of checks, some of which are imposed by the Constitution and others by act of Congress. The Constitution requires the consent of the Senate in the appointment of judges. It prescribes that federal judges may be removed by impeachment. Congress may also reduce or increase the number of judges in the Supreme Court. It determines what types of cases may be handled exclusively by the federal courts.

Claims against the United States are brought into the Court of Claims, established especially for that purpose. Funds for awards made by this court are appropriated by Congress as a matter of course. Appeals may, if permissible, be taken to higher federal courts. The Court of Customs and Patent Appeals decides all the controversies arising from interpretation or application of the customs laws and duties, and of patents.

One phase of the work of the federal courts, and of the Supreme Court in particular, which has been the subject of argument, is its power to pass upon the constitutionality of the acts of the government, federal and state. The Constitution itself makes no positive, direct reference to the use of this power. It was not until John Marshall's opinion in the case of *Marbury vs. Madison* (1803) that the right of the courts to declare laws passed by Congress unconstitutional was formally asserted. The Constitution, he argued, was the "superior paramount law" of the land, and, therefore, any "legislative act contrary to the Constitution is not law." It is "the very essence of judicial duty," he maintained, for the court to declare what is and what is not "repugnant to the Constitution." Since Marshall's day the power of the courts to invalidate acts of the federal and state governments has been asserted repeatedly.

In the discharge of their duties, the courts are concerned with matters which vitally affect the "liberties" of the individual citizen. Such "liberties" are meant to be the protection of life, liberty, and property.

The courts are required to observe the guarantees offered in the Bill of Rights. These are related to such matters as trial by jury, the use of witnesses and counsel, and so on. The courts also make use of three important decrees or *writs* which likewise affect the fundamental rights of citizens. Foremost is the writ of *habeas corpus* (you shall have the body), which the courts issue to prevent the unreasonable or illegal detention of an individual by the authorities. The Constitution provides that "the privilege of the writ of habeas corpus shall not be suspended, unless when, in cases of rebellion or invasion, the public safety may require it." Another is the writ of *mandamus* (we order). It is commonly used to require a public official, or a lower court, to do something which the law prescribes. Still another is the writ of *injunction*. This forbids the performance of something previously declared illegal.

THE BILL OF RIGHTS

The civil rights of a person are his legal rights. In addition to civil rights, a citizen has two political rights—to vote and to hold public office, provided that he meets the requirements therefor. Generally speaking, anyone can do anything unless he is prohibited from so doing by law. However, laws change, and what is legal at one time may be illegal at another.

Certain fundamental rights cannot be taken away from any person. Under the Constitution, neither the Federal Government (Congress) nor the government of any state in the Union can deprive any person of the right to be free. Nor can the federal or any state government punish a person by a bill of attainder (inflicting punishment without judicial trial) or by an *ex post facto* law (a law which makes criminal an act which was not forbidden at the time it was done: a law, for example, which would make the sale of intoxicating liquor consummated in 1916 a crime under the law passed in 1919). Further, no person may be deprived of "life, liberty, or property, without due process of law." Due process of law includes a judicial trial. An unreasonable law (as may be determined by the Supreme Court) is not recognized as due process of law, and cannot be valid.

The first ten amendments to the Constitution are sometimes called "the Bill of Rights." They forbid Congress to limit the civil rights of anyone in the respects named. The important provisions of the Bill of Rights are as follows: "Congress shall make no law respecting an establishment of religion, or prohibiting the free exercise thereof; or abridging the freedom of speech, or of the press; or the right of the people peaceably to assemble, and to petition the government for a redress of grievances"; "the right of the people to be secure in their persons, houses, papers, and effects, against unreasonable searches and seizures, shall not be violated"; "no person shall be held to answer for a capital, or otherwise infamous crime, unless on a presentment or indictment of a grand jury"; "nor shall any person be subject, for the same offense, to be twice put in jeopardy of life or limb"; "nor shall be compelled, in any criminal case, to be a witness against himself"; "nor shall private property be taken for public use, without just compensation"; "in all criminal prosecutions, the accused shall enjoy the right to a speedy and public trial . . . and to be informed of the nature and cause of the accusation; to be confronted with the witnesses against him; to have compulsory process for obtaining witnesses in his favor; and to have the assistance of counsel for his defense"; "excessive bail shall not be required, nor excessive fines imposed, nor cruel and unusual punishments inflicted"; etc.

Freedom of religion, freedom of speech and of the press, and the like, are subject to legal interpretation. No person may use such liberties to the injury of another person. Though everyone is granted religious liberty, he may commit no act by reason of his religious faith which is harmful to society or other individuals. Freedom of speech and of the press is likewise curtailed by libel laws, to prevent slander and malicious utterance.

The Constitution limits the rights of states in important particulars which concern the civil rights of individuals. No state may legislate to impair the force of contracts (a contract legally entered into is valid, even if a later law prohibits such a contract); no state may authorize legal tender other than gold or silver coin (in practice, paper money of the United States is accepted everywhere in lieu of coin, because it is redeemable in gold or silver, unless otherwise provided in a national emergency); no state may deny to anyone within its jurisdiction the equal protection of its laws. Notice that in such matters aliens and citizens are on an equal basis.

THE AMENDING PROCESS AND THE AMENDMENTS

The Constitution provides two ways for proposing an amendment: by a two-thirds vote of both houses of Congress, or by a convention called by Congress upon petition of two-thirds of the states. No such convention has ever been called. Amendments may be ratified either by the state legislatures or by conventions, as Congress may decide. Congress has preferred the former method, although the Twenty-first Amendment was ratified by state conventions. In brief, the method used in the adoption of the first twenty amendments and the Twenty-second has been proposal by a two-thirds vote of each house of Congress and ratification by the legislatures of three-fourths of the states.

The first ten amendments, or the Bill of Rights, may almost be said to be an integral part of the original Constitution. The Eleventh and Twelfth Amendments were added in 1798 and in 1804, respectively. The Thirteenth, Fourteenth, and Fifteenth Amendments were added during the Civil War and Reconstruction. The Sixteenth and Seventeenth Amendments, providing for a federal income tax and popular election of senators, were added in 1913. The Eighteenth, providing for prohibition of intoxicating liquors, and the Nineteenth, giving the suffrage to women, were added shortly after World War I. The Twentieth, changing the dates for inauguration of the President and the sessions of Congress, and the Twenty-first, repealing the Eighteenth Amendment, were ratified in 1933. The Twenty-second, limiting the length of office of a President to two terms, was ratified in 1951.

STATE GOVERNMENTS AND POLITICS

The Constitution expressly provides that "the powers not delegated to the United States by the Constitution, nor prohibited by it to the states, are reserved to the states respectively, or to the people." The states are equal in legal status in the federal Union. Therefore each of the 48 states governs itself in all particulars not granted to the Federal Government and not forbidden by the federal Constitution.

It is this almost limitless expanse of "reserved" or "residual" power which has made our states "experimental laboratories" for numerous types of political, economic, and social legislation.

"Politics" is the popular name given to any activity designed to control the popular vote in the interest of a certain group with its own public policy. In the United States, voters have become nationally divided into several parties, only two of which are strong enough to control national elections: the Democrats and the Republicans. Others are sometimes able to control local elections, and, occasionally, to send representatives to Congress.

EXAMINATION QUESTIONS

1. What is Civics?
2. How may foreign-born persons become United States citizens?
3. How may a naturalized American citizen lose his citizenship?
4. Who has the ultimate control of the government of the United States?
5. What fraction of the states are necessary to the ratification of a Constitutional amendment?
6. Who administers the foreign policy for all the states within our country?
7. What were the aims stated in the preamble to the Constitution?
8. What happens when a conflict arises between a treaty and a federal law?
9. What are the three main branches of the National Government?
10. How are the House of Represent-
atives and Senate apportioned?
11. How long do members of the Senate serve?
12. What are the chief sources of federal revenue?
13. What body supervises the workings of the Pure Food and Drugs Act?
14. What activity of the Post Office Department is a government monopoly?
15. What are the two dominant political parties in the United States?
16. How does a new session of Congress usually open?
17. In what case does a bill become a law without the President's signature?
18. What are the requirements for a candidate for the presidency?
19. How are candidates for the presidency chosen?

20. When do the President and Vice-President take office?
21. Who chooses the members of the President's cabinet?
22. Can the President be arrested?
23. What are the titles of the President's cabinet officers?
24. Under which department does the diplomatic service come?
25. What service looks after the interests of American citizens abroad?
26. Who is commander-in-chief of the United States Army?
27. What is the function of the Department of Labor?
28. Which federal body supervises appointments to most minor federal offices?
29. What is at the head of the judicial branch of the Federal Government?
30. For how long do the judges of the Supreme Court hold office?
31. How may federal judges be removed from office?
32. What is a writ of *habeas corpus?*
33. What are civil rights?
34. What comprises the so-called "Bill of Rights"?
35. According to the Constitution, to whom are the powers which are not specifically delegated to the United States reserved?

For Further Study

AMERICAN GOVERNMENT AND POLITICS, by Charles A. Beard. (The Macmillan Co., New York.)

THE CONSTITUTION AND WHAT IT MEANS TODAY, by Edward S. Corwin. (Princeton University Press, Princeton.)

ESSENTIALS OF AMERICAN GOVERNMENT, by Falk A. Ogg and Perley O. Ray (Appleton-Century, New York.)

GOVERNMENT AND POLITICS IN THE UNITED STATES, by Harold Zink. (The Macmillan Co., New York.)

HOW TO BE A RESPONSIBLE CITIZEN, by Roydon V. and Elizabeth G. Wright. (Association Press, New York.)

VI

Geography for Everybody

GEOGRAPHY IN GENERAL

THE WORD *geography* is derived from Greek, and signifies the writing about or description of the earth.

In form, the earth is a sphere; astronomically, it is one of the planets which revolve in eternal motion around the sun. The earth itself is made up of: the rocky solid substance, called the lithosphere (envelope of rock); the liquid substance which fills the hollows, called the hydrosphere (envelope of water); and the gaseous substance which surrounds the entire earth, called the atmosphere (envelope of air).

Depending on the conditions of the earth, varied animal and plant life has developed over the earth's surface. Today, with the benefits of modern science, differences in geography matter little to civilized man, who has conquered the globe by discovery and research. The interrelationships of man, in commerce, give rise to the distribution of man's activities, as those have been adapted to local conditions in various parts of the world. The activities of groups of men are further controlled by a man-made system called government, which varies, too, in different localities.

The globe which is the earth revolves around the sun; and at the same time the earth revolves around its own axis. On this compound motion depend the change of the seasons and the daily change from day to night and from night to day. The relative position of the earth as it receives the sun's rays of light and warmth causes the division of the surface into the torrid, temperate, and frigid zones of climate, which vary to some extent with the seasons. The torrid zone, in the region of the equator, is the hottest; the frigid zones, in the region of each of the two poles, are the coldest: North (Arctic region) and South (Antarctic region). The temperate zones are both hot and cold, in a manner of speaking, having marked changes of winter and summer, and they are located between the torrid and frigid regions.

THE CONTINENTS

A *continent* is a large body of land having generally the form of a plain bordered by ridges of mountains and usually surrounded by water. It is customary to regard the land surface of the globe as divided into six continents, namely, North America, South America, Europe, Asia, Africa, and Australia. All land that is continuous with a continent belongs with it, together with all islands immediately adjacent to it. Since Europe and Asia are connected, neither is insular in form; for this reason, both together are sometimes called the continent of Eurasia.

An *island* is a comparatively small body of land entirely surrounded by water. Some of the larger islands, so called, might as well be regarded as small continents, especially Greenland; and owing to modern journeys of exploration, the land mass at the South Pole is called the Antarctic continent, or Antarctica.

It is interesting to note that in a general way the continents tend to the shape of triangles. (This is particularly marked in North and South America, where the tapering is toward the south.) The great mountain ranges not far from the seacoast have a general direction of north and south. Between the mountains and the sea, ideally speaking, a narrow strip of land approaches sea level, and if the land is old (has not changed recently in geological time), there is likely to be a well-developed beach, upon which the waves dash ceaselessly. Africa is connected to Asia by the narrow isthmus which is now split by the Suez Canal, just as the isthmus between North and South America is broken by the Panama Canal. (An *isthmus* is a neck of land, or a narrow strip—comparatively speaking—which connects two continents, or connects a peninsula with the mainland.)

The level of the land is referred to the level of the sea, as a standard of comparison in computing the height of rising slopes and mountains. Any point of land is therefore said to be a certain number of feet "above sea level." Actually, the ideal sea level used in computation is the mean sea level, or the average between high and low water. On the average, the highest point of land above sea level does not exceed six miles, and the lowest point of the rocky envelope below the surface of the sea does not go much below six miles. At first mention, these greatest heights and depths seem like a large variation to us; but if a model of the earth were made eight inches in diameter, the variations of the earth's surface made in proportion would be so slight that the ball would seem merely to be a little rough on the surface. The earth is approximately 8,000 miles in diameter and 25,000 miles in circumference.

THE OCEANS

The ocean, as a whole, is the body of salt water which covers about three-quarters of the surface of the earth. The majority of this water is divided into five oceans separated by the continents and called the Atlantic, Pacific, Indian, Arctic, and Antarctic. The ocean as a whole is often referred to simply as the *sea*.

The sea varies in depth according to the configuration of the lithosphere which forms its bottom. The average depth is about 13,000 feet; the greatest depth is almost seven miles. The sea bottom, however, is for the most part a level plain, covered with clay or ooze. Sea water has an average content of about 3½ per cent of dissolved salts, about three-fourths of which is common salt (sodium chloride). The density of the ocean is therefore greater than that of fresh water.

Lesser bodies of salt water, connected with one of the five oceans, but smaller in size, are called *seas,* as the Mediterranean Sea, the Red Sea, etc. Inland bodies of water, especially if salty, are also sometimes called seas, as the Caspian Sea and the Aral Sea.

The fluid mass of the hydrosphere is pulled by the tides, which are caused by the unequal attraction of the sun and moon. Ocean tides flow and ebb twice daily (or in 24 hours and 51 minutes, so that the hour varies slightly from day to day); high tide or flood tide is the point of greatest influx onto the land, and lower ebb tide is the point of farthest recedence from the land. The oceans are also swept by currents, caused by the conjunction of tides, winds, the earth's rotation on its axis, the alternate heating and cooling in day and night, etc. Some of these currents are steady, some are periodical. The Gulf Stream, one of the best known, is a warm current, sweeping northward in the Atlantic Ocean, and affecting the climate of the eastern United States and the British Isles.

GEOGRAPHICAL LINES

For convenience in referring to its parts, the surface of the earth is divided by imaginary or geographical lines. The chief divisions are the Eastern and Western Hemispheres; North and South America, with adjacent waters, comprising the Western Hemisphere. The surface is also divided into the Northern and Southern Hemispheres.

The *equator* is an imaginary line drawn around the earth, equally distant from both poles; it is a great circle, from which latitudes are reckoned, its own latitude being 0°; it divides the earth into the Northern and Southern Hemispheres. *Latitude* is the distance of a point north or south from the equator; it is measured in degrees of the great circle of any meridian. A *meridian* is a great circle (imaginary) drawn around the earth through the poles; it crosses the equator at right angles. Meridians are now referred to as halves of the great circles; a meridian, therefore, is an imaginary line drawn from the North to the South Pole, at right angles to the equator, following the curvature of the earth's surface. *Longitude* (measured either in degrees or in time, east or west, from a prime meridian, usually the one drawn through Greenwich, England) is the measure of an arc of the earth's curvature between two meridians, or between the meridian of a certain place and the prime meridian. Any place on the surface of the earth can thus be located on a map by its latitude and longitude; the latitude gives its place north or south of the equator, and the longitude gives its position east or west of the prime meridian.

The proper study of a map of the world really requires a globe. Flat maps have to be distorted in some way or other, because, of course, the surface of the earth is not flat. With a globe the lines of latitude and longitude can be readily examined, and their differences noted. The relationship between the continents and oceans can also be readily understood. On a flat map the nearness of Alaska to Siberia, or of Norway to Greenland and Greenland to North America, is not apparent. On the globe, the northern and southern extremities of the continents, as they approach the poles, are represented as dwindling, which is correct. On a flat map, especially on a rectangular projection of the earth's surface, the northern and southern portions are expanded, for the Arctic and Antarctic Circles have to be made equal to the equator.

The *zones* are imaginary belts lying between imaginary circles north and south of the equator and parallel to it. The two parallels of latitude corresponding to parallels used in astronomy are called the tropic of Cancer and the tropic of Capricorn, north and south of the equator, respectively; the region lying between these imaginary circles is commonly called the "tropics." It is in the hot or torrid zone. The frigid zones, north and south, are contained within the area circumscribed by the polar circles, the Arctic and Antarctic Circles, respectively. Between the torrid and frigid zones lie the temperate zones.

GEOGRAPHIC FACTORS AND MAN

The manner in which men make a living and the kind of living they make depend in great part on the resources nature has given them to work with. These include: (1) the supply of arable land; (2) the supply of animals, both wild and domesticated, which can be used as beasts of burden, as a means of providing power, and as a source of food and clothing; (3) mineral resources; (4) forests; (5) bodies of water, which can be used for transportation, for the generation of power, and, through irrigation, as a means of increasing food supply.

A second factor that affects man is topography or the physical features of a region. The most important of these features are mountains, plateaus, valleys, plains, rivers, lakes, and seacoasts. A census of the world's population reveals that the greater part of the human race lives in the plain areas of the temperate and tropical zones.

Climate is among the most important geographic factors affecting man. Climate refers to the normal range of temperature and humidity of a region. Climate is important in determining the productivity of the land. For example, regions with a hot, dry climate do not have dense forests and fertile farms. Climate also has an important effect on the general physical and mental character of individuals. The most enterprising of nations are found in temperate climates.

The factors that determine climate are latitude, height above sea level, distance from bodies of water, prevailing winds, and mountain ranges in the path of prevailing winds. Latitude, the most important control, is the distance from the equator. The nearer we are to the equator, the hotter it is. The reason for this is that at the equator more of the direct, or vertical, rays of the sun strike the earth than at any other point. The further removed a point is from the equator, the fewer direct solar rays it receives, and the colder it is.

For every three hundred feet we rise above sea level, the temperature falls approximately one degree. The reason for this is that the heat of the sun is absorbed by all the things around us, particularly the ground. As one reaches higher altitudes, there is less warm ground to radiate heat. The warm air rising from the lowlands expands and cools as it rises, thus supplying less and less heat as the altitude increases. Mountain tops may be warm when the sun shines, but radiation is so rapid in the thin air that these places cool quickly when the sun ceases to shine.

Large bodies of water tend to have a moderating effect on climate because water absorbs heat more slowly and loses it more slowly than does land. The effect of the sea on climate is further influenced by the currents which circulate through each of the oceans. For example, the waters of the Gulf Stream warm the northwestern coast of Europe; while the cold waters of the Labrador Current have the reverse effect on the climate of northeastern North America.

Winds which blow from water upon land tend to moderate the heat of summer and the cold of winter. In other cases, cold winds may increase the severity of the climate. Winds also influence climate by distributing moisture.

Mountain ranges in the path of prevailing winds may have an important effect on the climate of a region. Thus the western slopes of the Rocky Mountains which receive the moisture-laden winds of the Pacific are well-watered, while the eastern slopes are arid and require irrigation for cultivation. In some regions, mountains act as a barrier to cold winds. Thus the Alps protect the Po Valley of Italy from the cold north winds.

Natural factors do not, of course, entirely determine the manner in which men make a living, but the way in which men use these materials and conditions is also important. For example, despite the lack of many natural resources, Switzerland is able to maintain a comparatively high standard of living because of the exceptional industry of its people.

DISTRIBUTION OF ANIMALS AND PLANTS

The animals normally inhabiting a certain region of the earth are called its *fauna;* similarly, the plants of a specific region are known as its *flora*. The distribution of animals and plants, or of life generally, is a highly technical subject for study, and requires a knowledge not only of geography and climatic conditions but of zoology, botany, and geology. The present distribution depends on former conditions of the earth as well as on the present environment. The distribution has been affected by the wanderings and activities of man; many native species have become extinct, or are approaching extinction, and other species have been carried out of their natural environment. The present distribution is summarized by continents below.

ASIA

The Asiatic fauna and flora are related somewhat to those of Africa and the lands of the Mediterranean region in Europe; land bridges, or nearness of one region to another, have spread the forms of life over this territory. Some of the islands, especially New Guinea, are more related to Australia, which is peculiar in that it was never, in recent geological time, connected by land with any other continent.

The elephant, in particular, is a characteristic animal of Asia (in India), as are also the tapir, rhinoceros, Malayan bear, scaly anteater, lemur, monkey, and gibbon. The orangutan is found in Sumatra and Borneo. The tiger and leopard (panther) are especially widespread through Asia; the lion is found as far east as the Indian desert. The hyena, species of antelopes, and the coney are also found. Deer are found in southwestern Asia, where are also asses, sheep, goats, camels (the one-humped camel is native to Arabia, the two-humped or Bactrian camel belonging farther north), oxen, and buffaloes (not to be confused with the American bison). In central Asia the horse developed. In Tibet is the yak; in north-central Asia, the musk deer; in northern Asia, the ermine, sable, reindeer, lemming, lynx, and glutton, together with seals; in eastern Asia, the raccoon dog, some peculiar moles, etc. Commoner animals abound, with many species of birds, reptiles, etc. Among marine animals, the dugong is peculiar to the Indian Ocean, and the sturgeon is common, with many small and large varieties of fish, both common and uncommon.

Only a few plants can be mentioned. The teak tree is common in India, and also the sandal tree—sources of teakwood and sandalwood; there are, too, many palms and bamboos in southern Asia. The poppy is particularly common in the Orient. Other tropical Asiatic plants include the indigo, pomegranate, mango, fig, banana, tobacco, cotton, coffee, tea, citrus fruits, coconut, betel nut, rice.

AFRICA

Subtropical and tropical Africa are still to a large extent unexplored; the deep jungles contain the particular birds, insects, and plants of the tropics. Insects, incidentally, abound throughout tropical regions, running into many thousands of different species—even thousands of different butterflies and moths alone.

When one thinks of African animals, some come immediately to mind, including the aardvark (Cape anteater), scaly anteater, lemurs of various kinds, many monkeys and apes, gorilla, chimpanzee, lion, leopard (panther), hyena, African elephant (different from that of India), hippopotamus, giraffe, rhinoceros, antelope, zebra, Cape buffalo, ostrich, crocodile, chameleon, python, puff-adder, monitor lizard, etc. The tsetse fly is found native only in Africa. The one-humped camel of the Sahara Desert was imported from Arabia. South of the desert there are no deer, no bears, no wolves; pigs, cattle, goats, sheep, and camels were absent until introduced by man.

Madagascar is strikingly different from Africa proper. Few mammals common in Africa are found in that island; Madagascan carnivores (meat-eating animals) are highly primitive. There are, however, lemurs, a river hog, chameleons in great numbers, and several amphibians.

As to flora, northern Africa is not tropical, the desert region of the Sahara is almost without plant life, and the jungle regions of the tropics are luxuriant with vegetation. In the north, of course, the plants are much like those of southern Europe. In the desert are the date palms; south of the desert, the baobab, shea butter tree, the fan palm; of timber, the African mahoganies are most important; beautiful orchids are present in variety. Plants common to other parts of the world are abundant.

AUSTRALIA

The fauna of Australia are peculiar, in that this island continent has been separated for geological eons from the rest of the world. A more ancient form of animal life characterizes the region. The lungfish is found only in Australia. Crocodiles and tortoises abound, together with many lizards and snakes. Typically Australian are the wingless birds, the emu and cassowary, and the odd lyrebirds, bower builders, and honeyeaters. Australian mammals include those called marsupials, because they carry the young about in a kind of pouch on the mother for some time after birth; the best known are the kangaroos. The dingo or the wild dog may have been introduced by man, though some authorities think not. Bats and rodents abound, like those in the rest of the world, but they fly or swim, so could have reached the continent from elsewhere. The wombat is an Australian marsupial. Insects are numerous, especially ants. The echidna is a primitive egg-laying mammal.

Many grasses and shrubs are found in Australia: it is a grazing country. There are some luxuriant forests. Eucalyptus trees are confined mostly to Australia; there are many species. Acacias abound.

EUROPE

The fauna of Europe have necessarily been greatly reduced by the concentration of human population. Wild horses on the eastern steppes survived until recently. Modern survivors include the brown bear, wolf, fox, otter, badger, and a few wild cats; also typically European deer; the chamois in the higher Alps; the muskrat in a few regions; many moles, and some rabbits. Domesticated varieties include the familiar dogs, cats, horses, swine, cattle, sheep.

Southern Europe, in the Mediterranean region, is noted for the olive; somewhat more to the north is a zone of beeches and, going north, oaks, then the ash; farther north, the pines and other evergreens and conifers, together with birches, which extend throughout the world in similar regions (i.e., similar in climate and soils). With the olive in the south are also found the myrtle, oleander, and laurel; typically European are heather, arbutus, pistachio, and vines (grapevines, the source of fine wines); also, introduced, are citrus fruits, almonds, figs, pomegranates.

NORTH AMERICA

The fauna and flora of North America are similar to those of Europe and Asia in their northern parts. The fauna include the reindeer (caribou), polar bear, and beaver, in both regions; and the related moose, wapiti, bison, and grizzly bear, corresponding respectively to the elk, red deer (stag), bison, and brown bear of Europe and Asia. Also in both regions are found cats, lynxes, weasels, bears, wolves, seals, hares, foxes, marmots, lemmings, sheep, deer, and squirrels in considerable variety. Typically North American are some rodents such as the prairie dog, gopher, porcupine, muskrat; carnivores, the raccoon and skunk; ungulates, the musk ox, the big horn, the Rocky Mountain goat, the pronghorn; and one marsupial, the opossum. Birds are much like those of Eurasia, including flycatchers, wood-warblers, the Baltimore oriole, bobolink, cowbird, quail, grouse, wild turkey, turkey buzzard, thrushes, owls, hawks, eagles, etc., and both in North and South America, hummingbirds. Among other animals are many insects, turtles, salamanders, reptiles.

Conifers, birches, poplars, maples, occur in the northeast; oaks, hickories, plane and tulip trees, walnuts, etc., appear southward; in the west, especially in California, are the redwoods (Sequoias). Other trees and plants are too numerous to mention.

SOUTH AMERICA

Many monkeys leap among the trees of the great Amazon valley in Brazil, including red howlers, spider, marmoset, etc.; there are also the jaguar, puma (cougar), ocelot, kinkajou, otter, ferret, weasel, capybara, agouti; many squirrels, rats, mice, porcupines, tapirs, peccaries, armadillos, anteaters, sloths, deer, opossums, millions of bats (including vampires), sea cow (manatee); hundreds of kinds of birds, many of brilliant plumage, including vultures, parrots, macaws, toucans, doves, hawks, eagles, whip-poor-wills, woodpeckers, hummingbirds, parakeets, egrets, ducks, geese, herons, gulls, cormorants, spoonbills, ibises, and ostriches. Many of these are common to both North and South America, and are found, too, in Central America. The more tropical and native varieties are easily recognizable. Turtles, lizards, snakes (especially the boa constrictor), frogs, toads, etc., abound, as do also fish. Insects are there by millions, especially giant ants, termites, fireflies, bees, hornets, wasps, cicadas, beetles; and their relatives, scorpions, spiders, centipedes, etc. Life is rich and varied in the South American tropics; in the southern temperate zone, it is similar to the northern, in North America. Llamas are peculiar to South America.

The flora of South America, especially in the tropical jungle, are much too varied to describe fully. The principal trees are palms, myrtles, Brazil nuts, acacias, bignonias, cecropias, rosewoods, rubber trees, figs, etc. There are many orchids, ferns, vines, etc. The jungle is a tangle of massed vegetation. Native to the north central part of South America are such valuable plants as the quinine, cacao, cassava (source of tapioca), sarsaparilla, guava, calabash, coca (source of cocaine), tonka beans, ipecacuanha (source of ipecac), etc.

THE COUNTRIES OF THE WORLD

Europe consists of: the British Isles (England, Scotland, Wales, and Ireland) comprising the United Kingdom of Great Britain, Scotland, and Northern Ireland, and the Republic of Ireland; Portugal, Spain, France, Monaco, Belgium, Netherlands, Luxembourg, Germany, Switzerland, Italy, Austria, Liechtenstein, Czechoslovakia, Hungary, Yugoslavia, Poland, Finland, Denmark, Sweden, Norway, Rumania, Bulgaria, Albania, Greece, Turkey in Europe, Russia (now the Union of Socialist Soviet Republics), including Russia proper and also White Russia, the Ukraine, Lithuania, Latvia, Estonia, Armenia, Georgia, and Azerbaijan. Iceland is an island to the northwest, in the Atlantic.

Asia includes the following countries or regions: Turkey, Syria, Israel, Jordan, Saudi Arabia, Yemen, and the dependent Arabian states, Iraq, Iran, Afghanistan, Siberia (part of the Russian or Soviet territory of Europe), Mongolia, China, Tibet, Ceylon, India, Pakistan, Nepal, Burma, Thailand, Vietnam, Cambodia, Laos, Korea, Malaya. Adjacent island groups include Japan, the Philippine Islands, and Indonesia, the latter comprising Sumatra, Borneo, Java, Celebes, etc.

Africa includes the following countries, many of which are the colonies and possessions of Western powers: Egypt, Libya, Algeria, Morocco, Tunisia, Rió de Oro, French West Africa (Senegal, Dahomey, Ivory Coast, French Guinea, French Sudan, Territory of the Niger, Upper Volta, and Mauretania), French Equatorial Africa, Gambia, Portuguese Guinea, Sierra Leone, Liberia, Ghana Nigeria, Belgian Congo, Angola, Union of South Africa (Cape of Good Hope, Natal, Transvaal, Orange Free State), Southwest Africa, Northern and Southern Rhodesia, Tanganyika Territory, Mozambique, Uganda, Kenya, Italian Somaliland, British Somaliland, Ethiopia, Eritrea, and the adjacent island of Madagascar. Near the western coast are the Madeira and Canary islands.

The countries of *North America* are Alaska (U.S.), Canada, the United States, Mexico, and Central America (British Honduras, Guatemala, Honduras, Costa Rica, El Salvador, Panama, Nicaragua). Northeast is the great island of Greenland. South of Florida are the West Indies, including Cuba, Haiti, Dominican Republic, Jamaica, Puerto Rico, etc. Not far away are the Bahama Islands and the Bermudas.

The countries of *South America* are Colombia, Venezuela, British Guiana, Dutch Guiana, French Guiana, Ecuador, Peru, Brazil, Bolivia,

Chile, Argentina, Uruguay, Paraguay, and the adjacent island of Trinidad (north) and the Falkland Islands (south).

The divisions of *Australia* (the entire continent is part of the British Commonwealth) are Western Australia, Northern Territory, South Australia, Queensland, New South Wales, Victoria, and the adjacent island of Tasmania.

In the Pacific Ocean are many islands and island groups, chief among them New Zealand (North Island and South Island), the Hawaiian Islands, the Caroline Islands, the Marshall Islands, the Samoan Islands, the Fiji Islands, Tahiti (in the Society Islands), and the New Hebrides. Antarctica, not populated, has recently been extensively explored.

THE UNITED STATES OF AMERICA

The United States of America is the principal country of the continent of North America, and one of the leading powers of the world. It is bounded on the north by Canada (excepting the state of Alaska at the extreme northwest of the continent), on the east by the Atlantic Ocean, on the west by the Pacific Ocean, and on the south by Mexico and the Gulf of Mexico. Its total land *area* (continental United States, including territories and possessions) is 3,026,789 square miles. The *population,* according to the census of 1956, runs to 171,200,000 people, including armed forces abroad. Politically, the United States is a federal republic, divided into 49 states and the District of Columbia, the *capital.*

PHYSICAL FEATURES

The northern boundary between Canada and the United States is, along its western part, the 49th parallel of latitude, and, in the east, partly the natural boundary formed by the Great Lakes and partly an arbitrary boundary settled by treaty. The boundary between Mexico and the United States is, in its eastern part, the Rio Grande, and, in its western part, an irregular line established by treaty.

The topography of the United States is in general that of a great central plain, drained by the Mississippi River and its tributaries, with the range of Rocky Mountains on the west, and west of them a highland sloping to the Pacific coast; and with the Appalachian system of mountains on the east, and east of them a highland sloping to a coastal lowland region.

The Great Lakes, of which there are five (Superior, Michigan, Huron, Erie, and Ontario), are part of the northerly drainage system of the St. Lawrence River, which flows through eastern Canada to the Atlantic Ocean. Eastern rivers of the United States include the Hudson, which joins the Atlantic at New York harbor; the Delaware, joining the Atlantic at Delaware Bay; the Potomac, emptying into Chesapeake Bay; the Connecticut, draining Vermont, New Hampshire, western Massachusetts, and central Connecticut, and emptying into Long Island Sound; the Susquehanna, flowing through New York, Pennsylvania, and Maryland, to Chesapeake Bay.

The Mississippi is formed by the conjunction of three main streams: the upper Mississippi, rising in Minnesota; the Missouri, rising in the Rocky Mountains; and the Ohio, rising in Pennsylvania. The Mississippi proper is some 2,500 miles long; from the headwaters of the Missouri River to the Gulf of Mexico, into which the Mississippi empties, the distance is about 4,200 miles. The Cumberland and Tennessee rivers swell the Ohio; the Arkansas and Red rivers, no small streams in themselves, flow into the lower Mississippi. The Mississippi deserves its popular name, borrowed from the Indians, of the Father of Waters.

Other rivers entering the Gulf Stream are the Alabama, which is swelled by the Tombigbee; and the Rio Grande, which rises in southwestern Colorado and forms part of the boundary between the United States and Mexico. The Colorado River, which flows through the magnificent Grand Canyon, empties into the Gulf of California, which is between the peninsula of Baja (Lower) California and Mexico proper. The greatest river of the Pacific coast is the Columbia, which for a considerable distance forms the boundary between Oregon and Washington.

The United States has such varied topographical features that it is like many countries in one. Prairies, forests, deserts, low-rolling hills, high mountains—all these are within the continental limits of the United States. Something like five-sevenths of all the fresh water in the world is inclosed in the lakes and rivers of the United States. The climate ranges from the coldest winters to the hottest summers, from icy mountain tops to sunny beaches of California and Florida. Wind-chilled Chicagoans can take a train for Palm Beach, and, traveling many hundreds of miles within the country, arrive at a region of temperate winters and hot summers. Crossing the American continent, one can view corn fields, wheat fields, tobacco fields, and cotton fields; apple orchards and orange groves; coal mines and oil wells; steel mills and cattle ranches; textile factories and sheep herds.

EDUCATION

About 90 per cent of the children of school age in the United States attend either the public or private schools, an aggregate of more than 34,000,000 children between the ages of five and seventeen. The property of public schools, elementary and secondary, has been estimated at more than $5,000,000,000 in value; of public elementary and high school

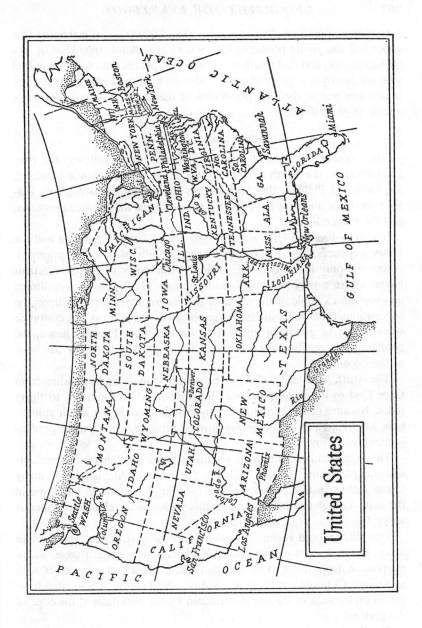

United States

(secondary) buildings, there are more than 300,000. It is estimated that about half the young people of high school age attend some kind of secondary school, and that a little more than two people out of each hundred who are twenty-one years of age or older are college graduates. Not more than 6 per cent of the total population of the United States, ten years of age or older, is illiterate.

Resources and Industries

The physical divisions of the United States are as follows: the New England Hills, the North Atlantic Lowland, the South Atlantic Lowland, the Piedmont Plateau, the Appalachian Mountains, the Allegheny Plateau, the Lake and Prairie Plains, the Great Plains, the Rocky Mountains, and the Pacific Slopes.

The New England Hills is the region east of Lake Champlain and the Hudson River Valley. The country is rugged, hilly, with a thin, poor soil. About the only lowland in this region is the valley of the Connecticut River, where a very rich soil is to be found. This entire region affords an excellent example of the effect of the geography of a region upon the occupations of its inhabitants. No single, rich, staple crop like cotton or wheat could be grown in this section for export to Europe; hence, the people of this region turned to manufacturing and fishing for the basis of their economy.

The North Atlantic Lowland is the narrow strip of land extending from Cape Cod to the Potomac River. It varies in width from ten to thirty miles. Because of the sandy and marshy soils there is not much cultivation. Maryland and Delaware are devoted primarily to extensive gardening and fruit growing.

The Appalachian Mountains region includes the range of mountains extending from the Hudson Valley to Georgia and Alabama. The many fertile valleys in this region are due to a large amount of limestone in the soil. An outstanding feature of this region is an almost continuous valley from New York to Alabama.

The hilly, rugged region immediately to the east of the Appalachian Mountains is known as the Piedmont Plateau. The eastern edge, where the plateau drops down to the coastal plain, is the site of many cities such as Atlanta, Columbia, Raleigh, Richmond, and Trenton. These cities have grown up because of the power furnished by the waterfalls at the edge of the plateau.

The line from the southern part of Texas, northeastward to Kentucky and then southeastward through Alabama and Georgia and northward along the Atlantic Coast to the Potomac River, describes the region commonly called the South Atlantic Lowland. These rich, level plains, easily worked and abundantly productive, led to the plantation type of farming with cotton as the chief crop. There it was that slavery first took root.

The Lake and Prairie Plains, north of the Ohio River and east of the Mississippi River, constitute one of the important agricultural regions in the United States. Endowed with navigable rivers and level plains, it is well adapted to the needs of commerce.

The Great Plains is the area west of the Mississippi River to the Rocky Mountains. Because of a slight rainfall, agriculture in some parts of this region is dependent on irrigation or the cultivation of drought-resistant plants. Much of this region is a natural pasture land, but overgrazing has changed large areas of grass regions to almost barren deserts.

The Rocky Mountains cover for the most part the states of Idaho, Montana, Utah, Wyoming, Nevada, Colorado, and parts of Arizona and New Mexico. This region is little changed from its natural condition. Aside from the production of minerals, this section plays a comparatively small part in the commerce of the country.

The Pacific Slopes region, west of the Rockies, contains many rich valleys suitable for fruit growing. The northern slopes have an abundance of rainfall and a climate splendid for agriculture. The southern section is drier and must depend on irrigation.

THE NEW ENGLAND REGION

Despite the relatively thin soil and harsh climate, there are a few favored sections for farming in New England. Special crops, such as tobacco and onions, are grown in the Connecticut Valley. The abundance of pasturage and water also makes this region advantageous to dairy farming, which is the most important branch of agriculture in New England.

The peculiarity of the continental shelf along the coast of New England gives New Englanders an advantage for fishing. Herring, halibut, cod, mackerel, and lobsters thrive here in abundance. The cities leading in the fishing industry are Boston and Gloucester.

New England has favorable factors for manufacturing. It has an adequate supply of cheap power, a labor supply, and a market in which to dispose of the commodities it manufactures. The industries that have settled in this region are the manufacture of cotton and woolen products, shoe manufacturing, tanning of leather, the manufacture of silver-plated ware, men's hats, brass goods, hardware, wire screens, and paper. During the Second World War, the New England region was one of our most important arsenals in the struggle for democracy. Its chief manufacturing cities are Fall River, Manchester, Lynn, Lowell, Meriden, Danbury,

Springfield, Bridgeport, Worcester, and Holyoke. Boston is the major city. It is the capital of Massachusetts and the most important seaport of New England. Were the metropolitan sections of Boston to combine into one great city, as have the boroughs in New York and the counties in Chicago, Boston would probably rank as the third city in population in the United States. Augusta, the capital of Maine, is on the Kennebec River, and contains important cotton mills.

THE MIDDLE ATLANTIC REGION

The Middle Atlantic region includes most of the states of New York, New Jersey, Pennsylvania, Delaware, and Maryland. From a commercial and industrial point of view, this is one of the most energetic regions in the United States. Excellent harbors and valleys, combined with a wealth of natural resources, explain the large number of cities with over 100,000 inhabitants.

A few sections are especially favored for farming. The plain around Lakes Ontario and Erie, together with the Finger Lake and Hudson Valley areas, are important fruit sections. The area along the coastal plain of Delaware and Maryland is especially important for truck farming. The abundant rainfall and the hilly country of the plateau area make it an important dairying area.

While fishing does not play as important a part as in the New England area, the harvest of the sea is quite abundant. The most important fishery product is the oyster, the most productive beds being located in the Chesapeake Bay and Long Island Sound areas.

An abundance of coal and water power, combined with an adequate labor supply and a rich and populous market, cause a concentration of manufacturing in this region. The characteristic manufactures of this region are textiles in Utica (N.Y.) and Philadelphia; gloves in Johnstown and Gloversville (N.Y.); collars in Troy (N.Y.); clothing in New York and Rochester; cameras and films in Rochester; silk in Paterson (N.J.); iron and steel in Pittsburgh; electric machinery in Schenectady (N.Y.); potteries in Trenton (N.J.); canned goods in Baltimore; radio products in Camden (N.J.).

The Middle Atlantic states are better favored by nature for commercial centers than New England. This is due to the fact that the general direction of the valleys of this region is east and west. The most important center is New York City, which ranks not only as the leading seaport of the United States but also as the financial center of the country. Other cities of importance are Philadelphia, Buffalo, Pittsburgh, and Syracuse.

The Southern Region

South of the Potomac and westward through Oklahoma and Texas are the states usually called the Southern states. The region includes all the broad, coastal plain stretching southwest from North Carolina, through Texas, and north to the junction of the Ohio and Mississippi rivers.

The regions around the Mississippi River contain rich, alluvial soils that made large plantations feasible. The South has a variety of climate ranging from the subtropical climate of Florida and the Gulf Coast to the temperate climate of the uplands.

The industries of the Southern states are derived from their forests, soil, water power, coal, and iron ore. The largest body of hard woods in the United States, including oak, hickory, sycamore, and black walnut, is found in the Appalachian highlands. From the sap of the long-leaf pine trees found on the sandy plains and the swampy lands, two valuable by-products, rosin and turpentine, are processed. This region produces over 60 per cent of the world's supply of turpentine.

The South is especially favored for livestock raising and agriculture. In the upland valleys of Kentucky and Tennessee, many cattle, especially horses, are raised. Kentucky, in particular, has long been noted as the favorite breeding place of race horses. Texas, with its vast, semi-arid grassy plains, affords an excellent pasturage for cattle.

Cotton and tobacco have become the leading money crops of the South. Over 70 per cent of the world's supply of cotton is produced in the United States. Cotton grows in all the Southern states, from Texas to Virginia. The leading states in order of cotton production are Texas, Mississippi, Alabama, and Georgia. The principal ports for the shipping of cotton are Galveston (Texas) and New Orleans (Louisiana).

The supply of minerals in the South is not very large. Iron is mined and smelted at Birmingham (Alabama). Phosphate, a mineral of considerable economic value, is found in the South. It is especially valuable as a natural fertilizer. Rock salt and sulphur are mined in Louisiana. These deposits have enabled the United States to produce over 80 per cent of the world's supply. Texas and Oklahoma hold an important place in the production and refining of petroleum products.

The South has become industrialized to a large extent. There are two important factors in the development of manufacturing; namely, raw materials and power in the form of coal and water. Thus we find lumbering industries, iron and steel manufacturing, furniture manufacture, and tobacco products.

The metropolis of the South is New Orleans, its most important seaport and commercial and financial center. Other important cities include Houston and Galveston, Texas; Charleston, South Carolina; Memphis, Tennessee; Louisville, Kentucky; Atlanta, Georgia; and Tampa, Jacksonville, and Miami in Florida.

THE CENTRAL STATES

The Middle West is the name often given to the Central states. This section comprises about 25 per cent of the area, about one-third of the population, and nearly 60 per cent of the agriculture of the country. The physical nature of this region naturally turned the attention of its early settlers to farming.

The area is endowed with level, rolling prairies topped with deep, rich soil. The climate of this region is largely of the continental type, the winters being very severe and the summers long and hot.

It is in farming products that the Central states have acquired first place. The topography of the region makes possible the use of farm machinery, and, because of climate and soil, grain is the principal staple crop. Much corn from this section goes to the market in the form of beef, pork, mutton, horses, and mules.

Another commodity of this region is the sugar beet. Sugar beets are usually cultivated in those regions where it is too cool for corn to mature. Meat-packing plays an enormous part in the economic life of the people of this section. The center of the meat-packing industry is in Chicago. In point of meat production, Illinois is first and Kansas second.

About one-third of the value of manufactured products comes from the Central states. An abundance of fuel, plenty of water power, a large population, and the most extensive of transportation facilities make the Middle West one of the greatest manufacturing centers of the world. The lumbering industries, automobile manufacturing, the manufacture of farm equipment, the manufacture of rubber products, ready-made clothing, and iron and steel milling are some of the leading industries in this area.

No other region in the United States has such an extensive network of railroads as the Central states. Nearly all the larger cities are railroad centers, notably Chicago, Indianapolis, St. Louis, and Kansas City. Chicago is the largest city in this region, with a population of over 3,000,000; it is the second largest city in the United States. There are five cities in this section with a population of well over 500,000: Chicago, Detroit, Cleveland, St. Louis, and Milwaukee. In all, there are twenty-four cities in this Middle West area which have a population of over 100,000—

among them, Minneapolis, St. Paul, Des Moines, Duluth, Columbus, Toledo, Akron, and Omaha.

THE WESTERN STATES

The Western states area comprises all the territory lying west of the 100th meridian of longitude (which runs through the center of the Dakotas and through Texas in the South). The area is a gradually rising plain which extends some twelve hundred miles to the Rockies, followed by a series of ranges to the coast. All of this section, with the possible exception of the strip along the northwest coast of the United States, is of a semi-arid and arid character. Most of it has less than twenty inches of rainfall per year, and some areas have under ten inches of rain per year. The high altitude and lack of rainfall coupled with high winds make large portions of this region virtual deserts.

The climate of the eastern section is of an extreme continental type, very hot in summer and cold in winter. In the extreme northwest, one finds a comparatively warm climate both summer and winter. Southern California, however, has a subtropical climate with almost rainless summers. Irrigation is needed for most of the farming done south of San Francisco.

Despite the lack of rainfall, agriculture has been developed to a comparatively high degree by means of irrigation. Irrigation, or the artificial application of water to land, has been practiced since very ancient times by peoples dwelling in dry lands. The first white people to practice irrigation in this country were the Mormons in Utah.

The arid and semi-arid territory of the United States includes nearly all of the states of Arizona, Nevada, and New Mexico, and portions of California, Colorado, Idaho, Kansas, Montana, Nebraska, North Dakota, South Dakota, Oklahoma, Texas, Utah, Washington, and Wyoming. Irrigation is practical to a greater or lesser extent in all of these states. Irrigated land, in many ways, is much more valuable than other kinds of agricultural land, because the irrigation water contains so much of mineral plant foods and fertilizer in solution. Also, the farmer, by having control of his water supply, does not run the risk of drought or of too much rain, which are the two greatest hazards of the average farmer.

Following out the Reclamation Act of 1902 and the Carey Act, Congress has appropriated millions of dollars for irrigation projects in this entire area. Most noteworthy of these projects are: the Boulder Dam on the Colorado River, the Grand Coulee Dam on the Columbia River, the Elephant Butte Dam on the Rio Grande, the Gunnison Tunnel in western Colorado, the Roosevelt Dam in central Arizona, and a number of irrigation projects in Wyoming and other states. The irrigated lands yield wheat, a variety of fruits, and vegetables.

This section is most important for its mineral products. Gold, copper, silver, petroleum, salt, and borax abound in the Western states. Semi-precious stones like turquoise, amethyst, and topaz are found in New Mexico, Arizona, and Montana. Another great part of the wealth of this region is in its forests. Much of our timber supply comes from the forests of the Northwest.

Manufacturing on a large scale has not been developed in this region. Most of the products manufactured here are for local consumption. The remoteness of markets and the lack of an adequate labor supply have retarded the large-scale development of industry in the West. Such manu-facturing as one finds here is largely of equipment for smelting ores, mining machinery in Los Angeles and Denver, shipbuilding on the West Coast, and sugar refining in San Francisco. The production of films in Hollywood and the manufacture of aircraft (greatly increased with the Second World War) have added two large-scale industries to the West Coast.

With the exception of Denver and Salt Lake City, most of the large centers of population are on the Pacific slope. The chief metropolis of the coast is Los Angeles, the third largest city in the United States. San Fran-cisco, Seattle, Portland, Spokane, and San Diego are important cities in this area. Nevada is the most sparsely populated state in the Union.

ALASKA

Alaska, which was proclaimed a state in 1959, is located in the far northwest of North America; it is in about the same latitude as Scandina-via, and, in places, has about the same kind of climate. The size of Alaska usually astonishes the average person. In actual square miles, it is nearly the size of the eastern section of the United States from the Mississippi River to the Atlantic Ocean (586,400 square miles), and the length of its coast line exceeds that of continental United States.

Alaska was first noted for its supply of furs. Furs are still of some im-portance and the fur industry is now established on fur farms, where scientific methods of raising fur-bearing animals are used. Another rich resource is its fisheries. Over 50 per cent of the salmon used in the United States is caught and canned in Alaska.

At the present time, Alaska's mineral resources are its chief source of wealth. Here are important gold fields, located near the city of Nome, and vast untouched coal fields of both bituminous and anthracite variety. There are also large deposits of copper on the Prince of Wales Island.

The great lack in this territory has been transportation facilities; until quite recently dog teams were the most common means of transportation both in summer and winter. The lack of roads, however, was eased at the time of the Second World War. In co-operation with Canada, a broad highway was built which connects Seattle with Fairbanks, Alaska. This highway is known as the Alaska-Canada (Alcan) highway. Air transportation has been greatly developed since the war. Fairbanks, as the northernmost air center on the continent, is served by eleven lines.

The largest city, by population, is Anchorage. Other towns include Juneau, *capital* of the state, Fairbanks, Ketchikan, Sitka, and Nome.

Territories and Possessions of the United States

HAWAII.   The Hawaiian Islands (twenty in number) are located far out in the Pacific Ocean at the crossroads of the ocean traffic. This little group of islands forms a most important possession of the United States. It not only furnishes an important mid-ocean supply station, as it did during the Second World War, but, in a sense, is the western gateway to the Panama Canal. The great commercial crop of these islands is sugar. Pineapples are a most important crop for export. Honolulu is the *capital*. Pearl Harbor is our most important naval base in the Pacific. Hawaiians voted in 1940 for statehood and await action of the United States Congress.

PUERTO RICO.   An island somewhat smaller than our state of Connecticut, Puerto Rico is one of the most densely populated islands in the West Indies. It has more than 643 inhabitants per square mile, although some 35,000 persons migrated annually to the United States in the ten years following World War II. The climate is tropical. The population is Spanish in origin, with mixtures of Negro and Indian blood. The chief commercial products of this island are coffee, sugar cane, and tobacco. The chief cities are San Juan (the *capital*) and Ponce.

Puerto Rico, according to a United States Congressional Resolution signed by President Truman in 1952, is a free commonwealth associated with the United States. It is not, therefore, strictly speaking a possession of the United States.

GUAM AND SAMOA.   Guam and American Samoa are important as shipping and air stopovers en route to the Far East. They have increased in importance as defense bases as a result of the Second World War. Guam has an *area* of 206 square miles; its *capital* and leading city is Agana. In American Samoa (76 square miles) is the port of Pago Pago.

VIRGIN ISLANDS.   The Virgin Islands are located in the Caribbean region, just east of Puerto Rico. They are noted for their pleasant climate and are important as air and naval bases in guarding the Panama Canal. The *capital* and leading city is Charlotte Amalie.

CANAL ZONE.   Located on the Isthmus of Panama, the Canal Zone is a strip of land ten miles wide through which the Panama Canal runs. It has tremendous commercial and strategic importance to the United States. The Canal Zone is 553 square miles in *area;* its chief cities are Balboa, Ancon, and Cristobal.

WAKE AND MIDWAY ISLANDS.   Wake and Midway islands are important landing stages for airplanes and are located in the Pacific Ocean. Wake Island, combined with Wilkes and Peale islands, has an *area* of about 2,600 acres, lying 1500 miles northeast of Guam. Midway Islands (*area* 28 square miles) are 1325 miles northwest of Honolulu.

TRUST TERRITORIES.   There are 625 islands in the Pacific Ocean administered by this country as the Trust Territory of the Pacific Islands—established by the United Nations in 1947. The chief groups are: Caroline, Marshall, and the Mariana islands (excluding Guam).

THE BRITISH COMMONWEALTH
OF NATIONS

The British Empire is more accurately named the British Commonwealth of Nations, for many of the units are nationally independent in all matters except foreign policy. Some members admit only a loose relationship with all the others. India, for instance, elected in 1950 to remain in the Commonwealth of Nations, with the word "British" expressly not mentioned. In Europe, the British Commonwealth has its head in the British Isles, northwest of France, bounded on the north and west by the Atlantic Ocean, on the south by the Atlantic and by the English Channel (the strip of salt water between England and France), and on the east and north by the North Sea. The islands consisting of the United Kingdom of Great Britain and Northern Ireland include England, Wales, Scotland, and Northern Ireland. (Southern Ireland—the Republic of Ireland—is a separate country, not associated with the Commonwealth.)

Excluding the Arctic and Antarctic regions, the Commonwealth of Nations dominates about a fourth of the habitable land of the globe, aggregating 12,021,522 square miles, and controlling over 600,000,000 people. There are some 50,000,000 people in the British Isles. The independent nations (officially termed Dominions) within the Commonwealth are Canada, the Commonwealth of Australia, the Dominion of New Zealand, the Union of South Africa, the Dominion of Ceylon, Republic of Pakistan, the Republic of India, and Ghana. The Commonwealth also includes colonies, protectorates, protected states, and trust territories, all of which are ruled more or less directly by the British Government. All the units of the British Commonwealth profess allegiance to the Crown and are thus fraternally united.

The British Commonwealth in the Americas includes: Bermuda, (British) West Indies, consisting of Jamaica, Trinidad, Tobago, Barbados, Windward Islands and Leeward Islands; the Bahama Islands, British Honduras, British Guiana, and the Falkland Islands. Gibraltar and Malta are important British European possessions. British possessions in Asia include: Aden, Cyprus, British North Borneo, Hongkong, and Singapore. Territories of the British Commonwealth in Africa are: the Central Africa Federation, including Northern Rhodesia and Southern Rhodesia; British South Africa, and British East Africa, including Kenya and British Somaliland. A number of islands in the Pacific Ocean are British controlled.

The capital of the British Commonwealth is London, England. The United Kingdom, which is the mother country of the Commonwealth, is a monarchy; but in practice the country is a republic, for the popularly elected House of Commons controls Parliament, and the Prime Minister heads the government.

THE COUNTRIES OF NORTH AMERICA

THE UNITED STATES

(see page 259)

CANADA

Canada, an independent member of the British Commonwealth, sprawls across the northern portion of North America, north of the United States, exclusive of Alaska. It includes Prince Edward Island, Nova Scotia, New Brunswick, Quebec, Ontario, Manitoba, Saskatchewan, Alberta, British Columbia, Yukon, and Northwest Territories; the total *area* is 3,845,774 square miles; *population,* 15,861,000. Canadian trade with the United States is huge. The *products* are much like those of the northern part of the United States, and, in the far north, like those of Alaska. Much of the far north is a frozen waste. In north-central Canada, in recent years, large deposits of uranium ore and other metals and oil have been discovered, adding substantially to the wealth of this huge country. The *capital* is Ottawa; *largest cities,* Montreal, Toronto,

Winnipeg. Canada is bounded: north, Arctic regions; west, Alaska, Pacific Ocean; south, the United States and Great Lakes; east, Atlantic Ocean.

For many years, Newfoundland, an island on the extreme east of the mainland, with Labrador, a bleak east coast region, was a separate political entity. In 1949, by referendum vote, Newfoundland (including Labrador) merged with Canada and became the tenth province; *area,* 155,364 square miles.

MEXICO

Mexico is mostly a mountainous plateau which is partly desert and semi-desert. It has an area approximately fifteen times as great as New York State. A large part of the country has a mild climate, although the lowlands and the deserts are very hot. Mexico has a climate which is both temperate and tropical, and a great variety of crops, such as corn, beans, wheat, coffee, sugar, cotton, tobacco, and henequen. Agriculture and stock raising are the chief industries of the country.

Because of the mountainous character of the country, there is a lack of suitable transportation facilities. Although no longer important as a gold-producing country, Mexico is still among the leading producers of silver, copper, lead, pyrites; more than 91,000,000 barrels of petroleum are produced annually. Mexico is somewhat backward industrially, although since World War II manufacturing has greatly increased. The tourist trade is of enormous national importance. Mexico City is the *capital*. Monterey, Vera Cruz, and Tampico are other important cities. The total *area* of Mexico is 763,944 square miles, and the estimated *population* is 29,679,000.

THE COUNTRIES OF CENTRAL AMERICA AND THE CARIBBEAN

GUATEMALA

The republic of Guatemala is in the northern part of Central America below Mexico. Bananas, chicle gum, coffee, sugar, and grains are produced; mahogany and important dyewoods are also exported. The *area* is 42,042 square miles, and the estimated *population* is 3,263,000. Guatemala City (the *capital*), Quezaltenango, and Zacapa are important cities.

HONDURAS

The Central American republic of Honduras is bounded chiefly by the Caribbean Sea and the Gulf of Honduras on the north, and Nicara-

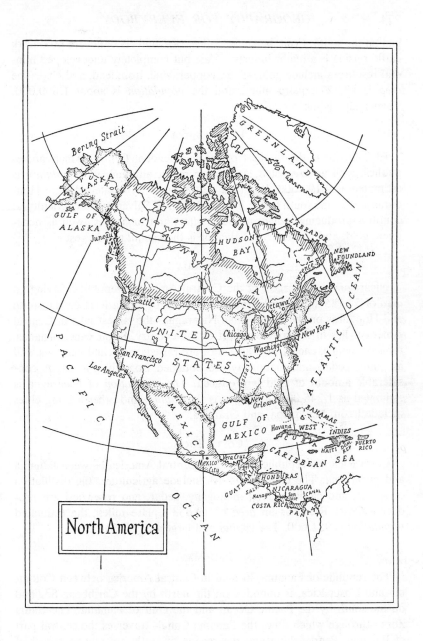

Bering Strait

GREENLAND

YUKAN
ALASKA
GULF OF
ALASKA
Juneau

HUDSON
BAY

LABRADOR

NEW
FOUNDLAND

Seattle

St. Lawrence R.

Ottawa

ATLANTIC OCEAN

UNITED

Chicago

Washington

New York

San Francisco

STATES

Los Angeles

MEXICO

MISSISSIPPI

RIO GRANDE

New
Orleans

GULF OF
MEXICO

BAHAMAS

Havana

WEST - INDIES

CUBA

HAITI
DOM.
REP.

PUERTO
RICO

CARIBBEAN SEA

PACIFIC

Vera Cruz

Mexico
City

GUATEMALA

HONDURAS

SAL.

Managua

NICARAGUA

San
Jose

CANAL

COSTA RICA

PANAMA

OCEAN

North America

gua on the south. Fruit, bananas, coffee, rice, and coconuts are produced; cattle raising is a major industry. Vast but completely undeveloped mineral resources include gold, silver, copper, zinc, iron, lead, and coal. The *area* is 43,227 square miles, and the *population* is about 1,660,000. Tegucigalpa is the *capital*.

EL SALVADOR

El Salvador is the smallest of the independent Central American republics, with an *area* of 8,259 square miles, although its *population* is estimated as 2,193,000. Bounded on the north by Guatemala and Honduras and on the south by the Pacific Ocean, El Salvador is an agricultural country—producing indigo, rubber, coffee, and tobacco as well as henequen, gold, and balsam. San Salvador is the *capital* and largest city.

NICARAGUA

Nicaragua is the largest of the Central American republics, having an *area* of 57,145 square miles, and is bounded by Costa Rica on the south and Honduras on the north. Lake Nicaragua—the largest lake in Central America—lies in the southern part of the country. Sugar cane, bananas, tobacco, coffee, cacao, rice, and corn are raised; medicinal herbs as well as gums, cedar, and mahogany are obtained from the forests. A considerable amount of gold is produced. The *population* of Nicaragua is estimated as 1,245,000. Managua is the *capital,* and other leading cities include León, Matagalpa, and Granada.

COSTA RICA

Costa Rica is a republic, located in Central America between Panama and Nicaragua. The chief industries include agriculture, the distillation of spirits, and cattle raising; mahogany, cedar, and rosewood are produced. Costa Rica has an *area* of 19,653 square miles; the estimated *population* is 951,000. The *capital* and largest city is San José.

PANAMA

The republic of Panama, located in Central America between Colombia and Costa Rica, is bounded on the north by the Caribbean Sea and on the south by the Pacific Ocean and the Gulf of Panama. The Canal Zone—through which flows the Panama Canal—traverses the central part of Panama. Pearl fishing and the raising of cattle are among the chief industries. Coffee, bananas, sarsaparilla, sugar cane, and similar products are exported. The *area* is 29,133 square miles; the estimated *population* is 2,193,000. Panama (the *capital*) and Colón are the leading cities.

CUBA

About half of Cuba is level land, on which the planting, cultivation, and harvesting of sugar and tobacco is relatively easy. Climate and rainfall are also favorable for the cultivation of these crops. The economic life of the island is derived almost uniquely from the production of sugar. Havana, the *capital,* is the most important city and port; other cities are Santiago and Matanzas. Cuba has an *area* of 44,164 square miles; the *population* is 5,832,277.

DOMINICAN REPUBLIC

The Dominican Republic, occupying the eastern part of the island of Hispaniola, in the Greater Antilles, has an *area* of 19,333 square miles; *population,* 2,404,000; *capital,* Ciudad Trujillo. Agriculture and cattle raising are the two main industries of this very fertile country; chief products include sugar, molasses, cacao, coffee, corn, and tobacco. There are deposits of platinum, silver, copper, iron, and salt; the mining industry is being developed. Exports include rum, alcohol, molasses, chocolate, and textiles.

HAITI

The western part of the island of Hispaniola is occupied by the republic of Haiti: *area,* 10,714 square miles; *population,* 3,305,000; *capital,* Port-au-Prince. Mineral deposits are largely undeveloped but include copper, silver, gold, iron, antimony, sulphur, tin, nickel, coal, porphyry, and gypsum. Agricultural products include rice (grown for domestic consumption), coffee, sisal, cotton, raw sugar, bananas, tobacco, and cocoa. Logwood is exported, along with other valuable hardwoods, and lately cattle breeding has become a growing and important industry.

POSSESSIONS OF EUROPEAN COUNTRIES IN NORTH AMERICA AND THE CARIBBEAN

British Possessions

BERMUDA, the oldest self-governing British colony, lies about 600 miles east of North Carolina; it has an *area* of 21 square miles, a *population* of 40,434, and its *capital* is at Hamilton. It is a very popular winter resort.

A number of British colonies in the West Indies, southeast of the United States, are in the process of becoming an independent nation to be called the British Caribbean Federation. TRINIDAD, which will be the

Federal capital, lies almost directly off the coast of eastern Venezuela: *area,* 1,864 square miles; *population,* 678,000; *capital,* Port-of-Spain. TOBAGO, *area* 116 square miles, lying close to the northeast coast of Trinidad, is usually considered together with the larger island; both export sugar, rum, and asphalt products from the great asphalt lake, 114 acres in size, on Trinidad. JAMAICA lies south of the eastern end of Cuba: *area,* 4,411 square miles; *population,* 1,503,047; *capital,* Kingston; it has tropical climate and products. Northeast of Venezuela are the (British) WINDWARD ISLANDS (Grenada, the Grenadines, Dominica, St. Vincent, and St. Lucia): *total area,* 810 square miles, and BARBADOS to the east of them, with an *area* of 166 square miles, a *population* of 222,942, and its *capital* at Bridgetown. The LEEWARD ISLANDS are north of the Windward group: *area,* 422 square miles; *population,* 122,884; *capital,* Antigua. The BAHAMA ISLANDS, lying northeast of Cuba, export sponges and sisal hemp: *area,* 4,404 square miles, *population,* 86,659, *capital,* Nassau.

BRITISH HONDURAS is a small colony on the east coast of Central America, due east of Guatamala, south of Yucatan: *area,* 8,867 square miles; *population,* 73,171; *capital,* Belize.

French Possessions

Two barren fishing islands off the southwestern coast of Newfoundland in Canada, ST. PIERRE and MIQUELON, are French possessions, with a combined *area* of 93 square miles and a combined *population* of 4,600; *capital,* St. Pierre.

In the Caribbean area, France possesses two islands in the West Indies: GUADELOUPE (Basse-Terre and Grande-Terre): *total area,* 583 square miles; *population,* 229,120; *capital,* Basse-Terre; and MARTINIQUE: *area,* 380 square miles; *population,* 239,130; *capital,* Fort-de-France. Both Guadeloupe and Martinique are represented in the French Parliament, but they are not treated as an integral part of France. Their chief products are sugar, coffee, rum, cocoa, and bananas.

Possessions of the Netherlands

The NETHERLANDS ANTILLES in the West Indies, comprising the islands of CURAÇAO, ARUBA, and BONAIRE, all part of the Windward Islands, and the islands of ST. EUSTATIUS, SABA, and part of ST. MARTIN, all in the Lesser Antilles, enjoy an equal status with the Dutch homeland in the Kingdom of the Netherlands. The *area* of the Netherlands Antilles is about 285 square miles; *population,* 181,100; *capital,* Willemstad (on Curaçao); *chief products,* corn, salt, phosphates, oil.

THE COUNTRIES OF SOUTH AMERICA

VENEZUELA

The republic of Venezuela is in northern South America above Brazil, and has a long, irregular coast line on the Caribbean Sea. A large part of Venezuela is drained by the Orinoco River. The country is one of the world's leading producers of petroleum. It also produces rubber, coffee, tonka beans, cereals, and other important exports. The Venezuelan state of Nueva Esparta is a valuable pearl center. Venezuela covers an *area* of 352,170 square miles; the *population* is about 5,774,000. Caracas is the *capital,* and other important cities include Maracaibo and Valencia.

COLOMBIA

Colombia is a republic in northwest South America, and has an extensive coast line both on the Pacific Ocean and the Caribbean Sea. The Andes mountains in the west rise to a height of 18,320 feet at Tolima volcano. Panama hats and iron are manufactured, and coffee, bananas, cocoa, sugar, and tobacco are among the chief agricultural products. Important emerald mines and the production of many other minerals are also leading industries. The *area* of Colombia is 448,794 square miles; the *population* is 12,657,000. Bogotá is the *capital,* and other notable cities include Medellín, Barranquilla, and Cali.

ECUADOR

The republic of Ecuador, in northwest South America, lies mainly between northern Peru and the Pacific Ocean. Traversed by the Andes mountains, Ecuador contains the great peak of Chimborazo (21,424 feet). Cereals, balsa wood, coffee, cocoa, and fruit are among the chief agricultural products; and Panama hats are manufactured. The minerals include silver, petroleum, gold, and copper; and the petroleum industry is being expanded. The use of modern farming methods is vastly increasing agricultural production. Ecuador has an *area* of 116,270 square miles; the *population* is 3,567,000. Quito is the *capital,* and other important cities are Guayaquil and Cuenca.

PERU

The republic of Peru, on the Pacific coast of northern South America, contains some of the loftiest peaks of the Andes mountains. Peru has numerous rivers, including the Napo, Ucayali, and Huallago. Sugar cane,

South America

cotton, grains, and coffee are among the agricultural products, but manufacturing is also an important industry in Peru, and furniture, glass, copper bars, and petroleum derivatives are made. The *area* is 532,000 square miles; the *population* is about 9,396,000. Lima is the *capital,* and other large cities are Callao, Arequipa, and Cuzco.

BRAZIL

Brazil lies mostly in the tropics. The northern areas are lowlands and are hot, swampy jungles. Most of the industry and population are to be found in the plateau and highland, within a limited distance from the coast. Brazil is favored, moreover, by a long coast line which has some good harbors, such as Rio de Janeiro and Santos. The Amazon is the chief river of Brazil and is navigable for over 2,000 miles.

The temperature, rainfall, and soil of Brazil are well suited to agriculture. Grazing is increasing in importance. Brazil also has vast mineral resources such as gold, black diamonds, coal, manganese, and iron ore. The mineral wealth of the country is as yet only partially exploited. Manganese is now exported in large quantity; huge deposits of monazite, used in the production of fissionable material, have been discovered.

Coffee is the most important product of Brazil, constituting about 60 per cent of the value of all exports. Cotton is an industry of growing importance. Despite the fact that Brazil lacks fuel for manufacturing, the factories of Brazil produce about 90 per cent of the cotton goods and a large percentage of the woolen goods, boots, shoes, hats, and furniture used within the country.

Brazil exports coffee, cacao, castor beans, Brazil nuts, sheep and goat skins, balsam, ipecac, and manganese ore. Brazil imports a variety of manufactured products and canned products. The *area* is 3,275,510 square miles; the *population* is 58,456,000. Rio de Janeiro is the *capital,* and other important cities include São Paulo, Recife, São Salvador (Bahia), Pôrto Alegre, Belém (Pará), Belo Horizonte, and Fortaleza.

BOLIVIA

The republic of Bolivia is in the west-central part of South America, north of Argentina and Paraguay. Bolivia contains a section of the lofty Andes mountain range, and the country's highest peak is Sahama (22,349 feet). Among the agricultural products are coffee, cacao, rubber, grains, and potatoes; wool and hides are also produced. The chief minerals are copper, tin (15 per cent of the total output of the world), zinc, and silver. The oil industry is being greatly expanded and oil is now exported. Bolivia covers an *area* of 416,040 square miles; the estimated *population* is 3,198,000. The *capital* is La Paz; other important cities are Cochabamba and Potosí.

The center of Bolivia's population lies on a high plateau in the Andes.

PARAGUAY

Located in the southern part of South America, the republic of Paraguay lies north of Argentina and south of Bolivia and Brazil. The chief exports include beef products, hides, tannin, and lumber; yerba maté (Paraguay tea), cotton, tobacco, and oranges are also produced. The *area,* including El Chaco, is 157,000 square miles; the estimated *population* is 1,565,000. Asunción is the *capital* and largest city.

URUGUAY

Uruguay is the smallest independent country in South America, located on the Atlantic coast east of Argentina and south of Brazil. Grains, olives, citrus fruit, rice, tobacco, and linseeds are produced; hides, wool, textiles, and wine are among the principal exports. A large number of minerals, including gold and silver, are found in Uruguay, which covers an *area* of 72,172 square miles and has an estimated *population* of 2,525,000. Montevideo is the *capital;* Paysandú and Salto are also important cities.

ARGENTINA

Argentina occupies most of southern South America. The northern part of the country touches the tropical zone and the southern part extends almost to the frigid zone. The climate, therefore, is varied, but predominantly moderate. The temperature is favorable to agriculture and makes possible the cultivation of a variety of crops.

The coast of Argentina is indented with many gulfs and bays. The chief port is Buenos Aires, which is the *capital* of the country and the largest city in South America. Argentina is largely a country of plains. The Andes mountains to the west separate Argentina and Chile.

Agriculture and stock raising are the most important industries. Wheat, flax, corn, oats, and alfalfa are the most important crops. The wine industry is also important. The quebracho, the most valuable tree of the Argentine forests, is used to extract tannin. Tannin is the chief source for tannic acid and very valuable in tanning leather.

Argentina has the largest foreign trade of all the South American countries. The leading exports are wool, hides, chilled meat, tallow, wheat, corn, and flaxseed. The leading imports are coal, railroad equipment, and agricultural machinery. The *area* of Argentina is 1,078,769 square miles; the estimated *population* is 19,108,000. Other large cities besides Buenos Aires are Rosario, Córdoba, and La Plata.

CHILE

Chile is located on the west coast of South America. It is a center rich in mineral resources, such as natural nitrates, copper, coal, iron ore, and gold.

In northern Chile, in the region of the Atacama Desert, natural nitrates and copper are mined extensively. South of the desert lands is the region known as the "Vale of Chile," a wide, irrigated valley with a moderate climate. Here most of the country's food products are grown. These include wheat, corn, vegetables, grapes, and other fruits. In recent years manufacturing facilities have grown tremendously. The Huachipato steel mills near Concepción are second in South American production only to the Volta Redonda plant in Brazil.

The chief handicaps to the development of Chile are its regular coast line, lacking natural harbors, and the barrier of the Andes in the east. Chile has, however, a few good harbors, such as Valparaiso, which is the port for Santiago, the *capital* of the country. The construction of the Panama Canal and the increasing use of air travel has benefited Chile considerably in expanding her foreign trade, especially with the United States. The *area* of Chile is 286,377 square miles; the *population* is 6,774,000. Other large cities in Chile are Concepción, Antofagasta, Iquique, Talca, Chillán, and Valdivia.

POSSESSIONS OF EUROPEAN COUNTRIES IN SOUTH AMERICA

British Possessions

BRITISH GUIANA is on the north coast of South America between Venezuela and Netherlands Guiana, north of Brazil: *area*, 83,000 square miles; *population*, 465,416; *capital*, Georgetown; *resources*, gold, diamonds, manganese, and mica. The FALKLAND ISLANDS and SOUTH GEORGIA are east of the Strait of Magellan, at the southern end of South America. The Falkland Islands, with an *area* of 4,618 square miles and a *population* of 2,230, have a strategic and economic importance.

French Possessions

FRENCH GUIANA, a department of France, with representation in Parliament, comprises an *area* of about 34,740 square miles on the northern coast of South America, east of Netherlands Guiana, west and north of Brazil: *population*, 27,863; *capital*, Cayenne. The land is mostly uncultivated. Lumber is an important product; rice, corn, cocoa, bananas, and sugar cane are grown; gold deposits are exploited.

Possessions of the Netherlands

SURINAM (NETHERLANDS GUIANA), on the northern coast of South America, is bounded by French Guiana on the east and British Guiana on the west and has an *area* of about 55,400 square miles: *population,* 240,000; *capital,* Paramaribo. The region enjoys equal status with the Dutch homeland in the Kingdom of the Netherlands. Netherlands Guiana is an important producer and exporter of the aluminum ore, bauxite; it also exports citrus fruits, rice, and coffee.

THE COUNTRIES OF EUROPE

THE UNITED KINGDOM

The United Kingdom occupies most of the British Isles. ENGLAND, comprising the greater part of the larger eastern island, has an *area* of 50,874 square miles and a *population* of 41,147,938. Its *capital,* London, is the capital of the United Kingdom and of the British Commonwealth of Nations; the *population* of greater London is about 51,221,000 and it has an *area* of 94,279 square miles. In the middle southwest is WALES, with an *area* of 7,466 square miles and a *population* of 2,596,986. In the north is SCOTLAND, with an *area* of 30,405 square miles and a *population* of 5,213,000; its *capital* is Edinburgh. NORTHERN IRELAND is a part of the United Kingdom and has an *area* of 5,237 square miles and a *population* of 1,387,000; its *capital* is Belfast. The ISLE OF MAN (between England and Ireland) and the CHANNEL ISLANDS (just north of Britanny, France) are British; their combined *area* is 296 square miles.

Agriculture, manufacturing, and trade are all great activities of the United Kingdom; products include wheat, livestock, and other agricultural products; coal, textiles, iron and steel products, cutlery, vehicles, and liquors. The climate is temperate. The islands have irregular coast lines, providing excellent natural harbors; numerous navigable rivers permit shipping to go far inland. Chief industrial cities include Birmingham and Glasgow.

IRELAND (EIRE)

The Republic of Ireland (Eire) occupies most of the island known as Ireland. (It is not part of the British Commonwealth.) Its *capital* is

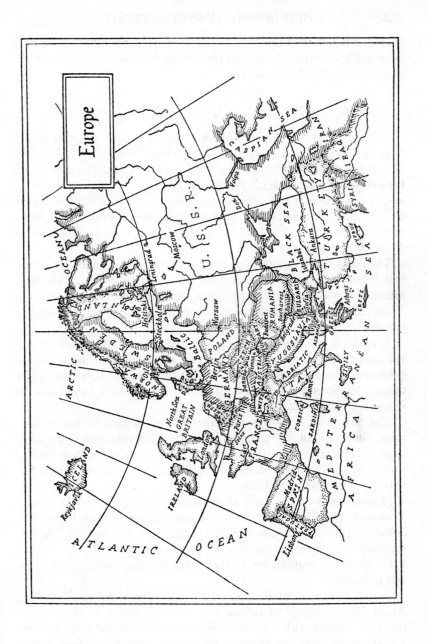

Dublin. *Area,* 27,137 square miles; *population,* 2,909,000. The country is largely agricultural, with food processing, tobacco, clothing, and distilling among the chief industries.

FRANCE

The topography of France is divided about equally between mountains or hilly regions and plains. The large level stretches of the country have facilitated the construction of roads and railroads. The diversity in the topography of France has favored the development of a well-balanced nation engaged in many different occupations and producing a variety of agricultural products and manufactured goods. France has about the same *area* as Texas, 212,659 square miles, with a *population* of 43,300,000; the *capital* is Paris.

The coast line is regular and extensive and has the added advantage that it fronts on two of the most important bodies of water for commerce, the Atlantic and the Mediterranean. Moreover, the location of France on the continent encourages an extensive trade with the leading countries of Europe.

In addition to her good commercial location, France possesses the advantages of having natural boundaries on all sides except the north and northeast (the Belgian frontier). Past experience, however, especially during the Second World War, has proved that such boundaries no longer are effective barriers against invasion.

The climate of France ranges from oceanic to Mediterranean—from rainy winters to hot, dry summers along the Mediterranean. Contrasting types of climate, combined with a variety of soil conditions, have enabled France to produce many different kinds of crops, including wheat, rye, oats, potatoes, and sugar beets.

Mining and manufacturing play a comparatively secondary role in France. A lack of coal has retarded the manufacture of steel. France has, however, deposits of salt, potash, fine pottery clay, and bauxite. The outstanding manufacturing districts are centered about Lille, Lyons, and Paris. Important seaports are Le Havre, Cherbourg, Boulogne, Marseille, and Bordeaux.

France is dependent on possessions and former colonies in North Africa for her supply of certain raw materials and a market for her products. Algeria, with a Mediterranean coast line of 650 miles, between Tunisia on the east and Morocco on the west, consists of four departments (Algiers, Oran, Constantine, and Bône), which are an integral part of metropolitan France. It has an *area* of 80,117 square miles; *population,* 9,530,500; *products,* wheat, barley, oats, corn, potatoes, olive oil, wine; iron, zinc, lead, mercury, and copper. Morocco (see page 302) and Tunisia (see page 304), former French Protectorates, are now virtually independent. From these and other former colonial territories France imports sugar, coffee, rice, silk, gold, and forest products such as rubber and tannin.

The island of CORSICA, near the southwest coast of Italy, belongs to France.

MONACO

On the Mediterranean coast of France is the principality of Monaco, about 8 square miles in *area,* and having a *population* of 20,422. Monaco derives much of its revenue from the famous gambling casino for which the city of Monte Carlo has been noted since 1860.

THE NETHERLANDS (HOLLAND)

One-fourth of the Netherlands has an altitude of below sea level. This land was reclaimed from the ocean at tremendous cost. The fertile soil is about the only natural resource of the Netherlands. Approximately one-fourth of the land is devoted to the cultivation of wheat, potatoes, sugar beets, and the great money crop of bulbs for tulips. Dairying is another important industry.

Shipbuilding, brewing, distilling, the manufacture of cotton goods, and wooden shoes are outstanding manufactures. Amsterdam, the *capital,* The Hague, and Rotterdam, its seaport, are the most important cities. The *area* of the Netherlands is 12,862 square miles; the *population* is estimated at 10,808,576.

BELGIUM

Belgium is a country of great density of population, intensive agriculture, and extensive foreign trade. Belgium has been able to support a population which is larger than that of the whole continent of Australia because of its concentrated farming, rich coal mines, access to nearby iron deposits, and her central location.

The crops produced in Belgium include potatoes, sugar beets, flax for linen, and many grains. The most important manufactures are metal goods, textiles, laces, and linens. As in France, there is a good balance between agriculture and manufacturing.

Important cities are Brussels, the *capital;* Antwerp, the chief port, located at the mouth of the Scheldt River; Ostend, and Bruges. The *area* of Belgium is 11,775 square miles; the *population* is about 8,868,000.

LUXEMBOURG

An agricultural country, the Grand Duchy of Luxembourg lies in a strategic spot in northern Europe. *Boundaries:* north, Belgium; west, Belgium; south, France; east, Germany. *Area,* 999 square miles; *population,* 309,000; *capital,* Luxembourg. Although the country is very small, its mineral resources are huge, among them being pig iron, iron, and steel. Luxembourg's agricultural products include oats, wheat, barley, rye, and potatoes.

SWITZERLAND

Switzerland, which is almost entirely mountainous, attracts a great number of tourists. The Swiss Alps reach an altitude of 15,217 feet. Dairy farming is an important industry. Such products as Swiss cheeses and milk chocolate are known the world over.

Important products are clocks, watches, machinery, wood carvings, and musical, optical, and scientific instruments. The manufacture of embroidered textiles is an industry in which Switzerland leads the world. Switzerland has a large foreign commerce for her size; and her people enjoy a higher standard of living than is to be found in many of the larger and more powerful nations of Europe. Berne is the *capital.* Geneva, Zurich, Basel, and Lucerne are other important cities. The *area* of Switzerland is 15,737 square miles; the *population* is 4,978,000.

ITALY

As Italy is mostly a mountainous country, there is a limited amount of land available for agriculture. The valley of the Po River is the most fertile region as well as the center of manufacturing.

Italy, despite its mountainous character, lacks the basic mineral resources of iron ore and coal. Lack of coal has been overcome by the extensive use of water power. The most valuable mineral product of Italy is sulphur. In northern Italy there are also quarries of fine white marble. There are some good harbors on the long coast line which have enabled Italy to develop a merchant marine and a carrying trade. A large fishing industry has been encouraged as well.

The climate in most parts of Italy is Mediterranean—hot, dry summers and rainy, mild winters. Wheat, grapes, olives, and citrus fruits are grown.

A supply of cheap labor has favored the manufacture of low-priced textiles and the culture of silk. The principal cities are Rome, the *capital;* Milan and Turin, important manufacturing centers in the north; Naples, the most important seaport on the Mediterranean; Trieste, an important seaport on the Adriatic; Florence and Venice, among the many great cultural centers.

The *area* of Italy is 119,800 square miles; the *population* is 48,001,000. Sicily (to the south) and Sardinia (to the west), islands in the Mediterranean Sea, are part of Italy; also the small island of Elba, off the west coast of the country.

VATICAN CITY

Vatican City, the world's smallest independent state, is located near Rome in western Italy, and is governed by the Pope. Within the boundaries of this state are the Vatican Palace and Museum, St. Peter's Cathedral, and other important buildings. The *area* is .16 square miles (108.7 acres); the *population* is 1,025.

SAN MARINO

San Marino is the smallest republic in the world, lying on the slope of Mount Titano near Rimini in Italy: *area,* 38 square miles; *population,* 13,500. Stock raising and agriculture are its main industries, and exports include cattle, wine, and building stone.

SPAIN

Despite a scarcity of agricultural land, farming is the occupation of a majority of the Spanish people. Only about one-fourth of the land produces crops. Wheat, olives, oranges, lemons, and figs are the principal crops. Sheep raising is a leading industry.

Spain is rich in mineral resources, most of which are worked by foreign capital and engineers. Bilbao is the leading iron-ore exporting city. Other important minerals are copper, lead, zinc, and mercury. Barcelona is the leading manufacturing city. Leading exports are minerals, wood, olive oil, wine, fruits, cork, and some cotton goods. The Balearic Islands in the Mediterranean, east of the Spanish mainland, form a province of Spain; among them is the tourist mecca, Majorca. Madrid is the *capital* of Spain. The *area* of Spain is 196,607 square miles; the *population* is 28,976,000.

PORTUGAL

Portugal, one of the smallest nations in Europe, is situated in the western part of the Iberian Peninsula (with Spain constituting the eastern and southern part of the peninsula). The most important occupation is fishing, and the catching and canning of sardines is an important industry. Portugal is the world's leading producer of cork. There is considerable mineral wealth in Portugal which as yet has not been fully exploited. The Azores, a small group of islands about 800 miles off the southwestern coast of Europe, are a possession of Portugal. Lisbon, the *capital,* is the most important city of Portugal. The *area* of Portugal is 35,582 square miles; the *population* is 8,765,000.

EAST AND WEST GERMANY

Germany is situated in the central part of Europe and faces on both the North and Baltic seas. The climate in the western part of Germany is oceanic; in the east it is continental. In the southwestern part of Germany, along the Rhine River, the climate is mild enough for the cultivation of wine grapes.

The greatest handicap of Germany is the limited amount of fertile land. The problem of food supply is therefore a difficult one. Germany has three navigable rivers, which flow northward through the country: the Rhine, the Elbe, and the Oder. All of these rivers rise in other countries, and the Rhine also has its mouth in Holland.

Germany's mineral resources made her great industrial development possible. She has vast coal resources and the most productive iron mines in Europe. Germany also produces some copper, lead, potash, zinc, and silver. Potash laid the foundation for Germany's great chemical industries. Germany is important for the manufacture of steel and steel products, dyes from coal, and optical instruments.

EAST GERMANY became a separate political entity under Soviet control in 1949, with an *area* of 42,112 square miles; *population,* 17,600,000; *capital,* Berlin (Soviet Occupied Zone).

WEST GERMANY, the remainder of the country, has an *area* of 94,723 square miles; *population,* 49,995,000; *capital,* Bonn. The SAAR, a rich industrial and mining area between France and Germany, is part of West Germany, although France has a treaty concerning the coal mines there. *Important cities:* West Germany: Hamburg and Bremen, its great seaports; Frankfurt, Düsseldorf, Cologne, and Essen, formerly known as the "Pittsburgh of Germany"; East Germany: Dresden and Leipzig.

AUSTRIA

Austria is a republic located north of Italy and south of Germany and Czechoslovakia. Among the lofty Austrian mountain ranges are the Rhaetian and Noric Alps, containing peaks more than 12,000 feet in altitude. The principal river is the Danube, which flows through the northeastern part of the country. Since World War II, Austria's economy has become mainly industrial. There are also mineral and metal deposits, such as magnesite, iron ore, graphite, and talc. Timber is an important natural resource. Agricultural products include cereal grains, potatoes, corn, wine, livestock, and fruit. Chief industries are textiles, iron and steel, building materials, aluminum, and machine tools. Agriculture is the leading industry. The *area* is 32,369 square miles; the *population* is about 6,974,000. Vienna is the *capital,* and other large cities include Graz, Linz, Innsbruck, and Salzburg.

LIECHTENSTEIN

Lying on the Upper Rhine between Switzerland and Austria is the tiny principality of Liechtenstein: *area,* 62 square miles; *population,* 13,571; *capital,* Vaduz. Tax-exempt, like Monaco, it is the home of many large corporations which headquarter there. Stock raising is a highly developed industry in Liechtenstein.

DENMARK

The kingdom of Denmark occupies several islands and a peninsula extending north of Germany, between two seas—the Baltic and the North. Denmark is composed chiefly of low-lying plains, and the principal industries include agriculture, dairying, and fishing. The *area* is 16,575 square miles; the estimated *population* is 4,439,000. Copenhagen is the *capital,* and other large cities are Aarhus, Odense, and Aalborg.

Denmark owns the FAROE ISLANDS in the North Atlantic, and GREENLAND, a large island near the North American continent; *area,* 827,300 square miles; *population,* 24,159; *capital,* Godthaab. The deposits of cryolite on Greenland are the largest in the world. Greenland also supports weather stations and airports vital to the North Atlantic air routes.

NORWAY

Located in the western part of the Scandinavian peninsula in northern Europe, the kingdom of Norway has an extensive coast line indented by many fiords. Norway contains numerous lakes and rivers, and is separated from Sweden on the east by the lofty Kjölen mountains. Fishing, agriculture, and dairying are the chief industries; the manufactured products include textiles, machinery, soap, and paper. Metals such as iron, silver, and zinc are mined. The *area* is 124,556 square miles; the estimated *population* is 3,450,000. Oslo is the *capital* of Norway, and among other leading cities are Bergen and Trondheim.

SWEDEN

Sweden is a kingdom occupying the greater portion of the Scandinavian peninsula in northern Europe and containing many rivers and lakes. With northern mountainous parts, Sweden has numerous high peaks, such as Sylfjallen (15,781 feet) to the west near Norway. The southern part is largely a plain. The chief industries are agriculture, iron mining, and the production of lumber, paper pulp, textiles, porcelain, and glass. Sweden covers an *area* of 173,347 square miles; its *population* is about 7,290,112. The *capital* is Stockholm, and among the other leading cities are Göteborg, Malmö, Norrköping, and Hälsingborg.

FINLAND

Finland has a relatively small amount of productive land; and because of the short growing season, only the hardiest crops can be cultivated. The lumbering industry is the most important source of employment. Helsinki, the *capital,* is Finland's most important city. Consisting of a rugged plateau, the country contains many navigable lake and canal waterways, and is located east of Sweden and north of the Gulf of Finland. The *area* is 130,165 square miles; the *population* is 4,240,000.

ICELAND

Lying close to the Arctic Circle in the North Atlantic is the Republic of Iceland: *area,* 39,758 square miles; *population,* 154,000; *capital,* Reykjavík. An island of volcanic origin, with many hot springs and geysers, Iceland was formerly a colonial possession of Denmark. Keflavik, on the North Atlantic air route, is an important civilian airport.

GREECE

Greece is relatively small in size, mountainous in topography, and has scanty summer rainfall. Currants, olives, figs, and tobacco are among the leading exports. Athens is the *capital.* The *area* of Greece is 50,257 square miles; its *population* is about 8,050,000.

TURKEY

A small part of western Turkey (including Istanbul, formerly Constantinople) lies in Europe; the large part of the country is in Asia. Turkey is discussed in the section "Countries of Asia" (page 293).

YUGOSLAVIA

Yugoslavia, in southern Europe, is located north of Greece and is bounded on the west by the Adriatic Sea, Italy, and Albania. The chief industries are dairying, fruit raising, and lumber production; grains and minerals are also produced. The nation covers an *area* of 98,766 square miles, and its estimated *population* is 17,555,000. Belgrade is the *capital;* Zagreb, Subotica, and Sarajevo are also large cities.

ALBANIA

The republic of Albania is a mountainous country lying on the east coast of the Adriatic Sea: *area,* 10,629 square miles; *population,* 1,250,000; *capital,* Tirana. The country has large forest resources and a mineral wealth as yet not fully developed. Chief products include tobacco, timber, wool, hides, furs, dairy products, olive oil, cattle, and bitumen.

BULGARIA

Bulgaria, in southeastern Europe, lies between the Black Sea on the east and Yugoslavia on the west, and contains two high mountain ranges —the Balkan and the Rhodope. The chief industries include agriculture, silk manufacturing, and the mining of coal and copper. Sofia is the *capital;* other leading cities are Plovdiv, Varna, Ruse, Burgas, and Pleven. The *area* of Bulgaria is 42,808 square miles. The *population* is about 7,160,000.

RUMANIA

Rumania has the largest area and population of any of the countries of southeastern Europe. Her greatest assets are her fertile farm lands and numerous forests and productive petroleum fields, such as those at Ploesti. Bucharest, the *capital,* is its most important city. Constanta is an important port on the Black Sea. The *area* is 91,584 square miles; the *population* is 17,300,000.

HUNGARY

Hungary is in southeastern Europe, south of Czechoslovakia and north of Yugoslavia. Farming and wine-making are the chief industries, and the manufactured products include sugar, iron, and steel. Bauxite, coal, and lignite are among the minerals produced. The *area* of Hungary is 35,902 square miles; the *population* is about 9,808,000. Budapest is the *capital,* and other leading cities are Szeged, Debrecen, and Kecskemet.

CZECHOSLOVAKIA

Czechoslovakia is endowed with many natural resources, including forests, coal mines, rich sugar-beet lands, and a rich and varied industrial development. Czechoslovakia produces large quantities of shoes, munitions, beer, glass, textiles, and other manufactures. Prague is the *capital* city. Pilsen is the most important manufacturing city. The *area* of Czechoslovakia is 49,381 square miles; the *population,* 13,089,000.

POLAND

Poland is one of the leading agricultural nations of Europe. It ranks high among the European producers of potatoes and sugar beets. Poland is self-sufficient in lumber and has valuable mineral resources, including zinc, lead, coal, petroleum, and nickel. Manufacturing has reached a high degree of importance. Lodz, the "Manchester of Poland," is noted for its cotton mills. Warsaw, the *capital,* is also a textile center. Sugar refining has also become an important industry. The *area* of Poland is 120,355 square miles; the *population* is about 27,500,000.

THE UNION OF SOVIET SOCIALIST REPUBLICS (RUSSIA)

The Union of Soviet Socialist Republics covers one-sixth of the earth's surface. It occupies eastern Europe and northwestern Asia. However, despite its tremendous size, the nation does not have a good outlet for trade, for a large part of her seacoast lies in cold regions. The important ports of Archangel, Leningrad, and Vladivostok are icebound for some part of the year. Odessa, the leading port on the Black Sea, is open the year round.

Much of the land, even as far south as Moscow, the *capital,* is not very good for farming. The leading agricultural area is the so-called "fertile triangle of black earth" in southwestern Russia, the Ukraine. Another handicap to Russia is the fact that her rivers flow north and south, and are icebound during the winter. The size of Russia has actually handicapped her trade. It has been difficult to ship products from the interior to the world markets. The development of transportation is one of modern Russia's greatest tasks.

The climate of Russia is mainly continental. The temperature in different regions varies from frigid to subtropical. It has been said that the U.S.S.R. contains nearly every natural resource of modern civilization—minerals of all kinds, every variety of timber, every character of cereal, vegetable, and fruit, in addition to vast resources of coal and petroleum.

The exports of Russia are exceeded by her imports, which include such products as industrial machinery, iron and steel products, wool, and cotton. The principal exports are petroleum products, lumber and forest products, grains, textiles, and furs.

The peoples of Russia are of many races and nationalities, including Russians and Ukrainians to the west, Tatars and Mongolians farther to the east. The three Baltic states—Lithuania and Latvia of Lettic race, and Estonia of Finnish background—are now part of the Soviet Union. The total *area* is 7,877,598 square miles, and the population is about 200,200,000. Russia is the leading Communist country in the world.

ESTONIA

Estonia is an agricultural country on the Baltic: *area,* 18,353 square miles; *population,* 1,134,000; *capital,* Tallinn. In addition to agriculture and dairy farming, there are large forest lands exploited especially by the important furniture and match industries. Other natural resources are phosphorites, peat, and shale.

Estonia was annexed by Russia in 1940, becoming the Estonian Soviet Socialist Republic.

LATVIA

Latvia lies north of Lithuania and south of Estonia: *area,* 25,305 square miles; *population,* 1,994,506; *capital,* Riga. Its largely agricultural aspect is becoming more and more industrial. Among Latvia's natural resources are large deposits of gypsum and peat.

In 1940 Latvia was annexed to the Soviet Union, becoming one of the Soviet Socialist Republics.

LITHUANIA

Lithuania lies on the Baltic Sea, bounded by Latvia, Poland, and White Russia: *area,* 24,500 square miles; *population,* 2,879,000; *capital,* Vilna. Among the chief crops of the country are rye, barley, oats, wheat, potatoes, and flax.

In 1940 this country was annexed by Russia, becoming one of the Soviet Socialist Republics.

BRITISH POSSESSIONS IN EUROPE

GIBRALTAR, the southernmost tip of Spain, at the gateway to the Mediterranean Sea, is an armed fortress: *area,* 2 square miles; *population,* 24,736; a British crown colony. MALTA, including two adjacent islands, is a self-governing colony in the Mediterranean, just south of Sicily: *area,* 122 square miles; *population,* 320,613.

THE COUNTRIES OF ASIA

TURKEY

The greater part of Turkey is located in Asia Minor; the European section of the country lies east of Greece and is separated from Asiatic Turkey by the Dardanelles, the Sea of Marmara, and the Bosporus. Turkey's *area* is 294,416 square miles, and the *population* is 24,111,778. Among the chief products are tobacco, fruit, and cereals. The principal cities are Istanbul in European Turkey, Ankara (the *capital*), and Smyrna.

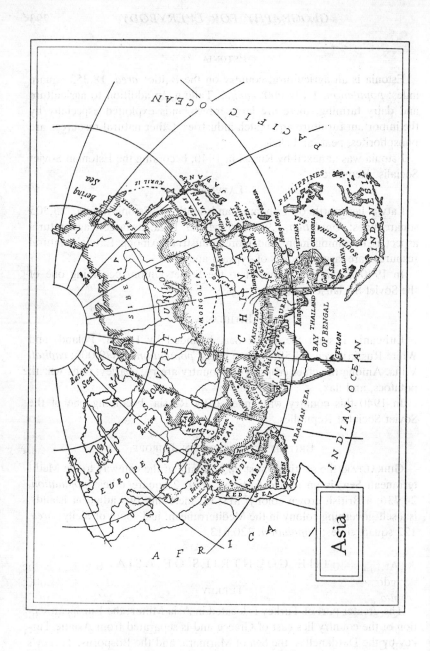

Asia

SYRIA

North of Jordan, south of Turkey, bordered by Lebanon and the Mediterranean on the west and Iraq on the east, is the republic of Syria: *area,* 72,334 square miles; *population,* 3,906,000; *capital,* Damascus.

LEBANON

Lebanon, at the southwest tip of Syria and on the Mediterranean, is a republic with an *area* of 4,000 square miles; *population,* 1,425,000; *capital,* Beirut.

JORDAN

Northwest of Saudi Arabia and bordering the Mediterranean Sea is the kingdom of Jordan, formerly known as Trans-Jordan: *area,* 37,500 square miles; *population,* 1,500,000; *capitals,* Amman and Jerusalem. Except for a narrow fertile portion in the west, the country is largely desert, with phosphate and potash mines.

SAUDI ARABIA

Located in southwestern Asia, Saudi Arabia occupies most of the peninsula between the Persian Gulf and the Gulf of Oman on the east, and the Red Sea on the west. Large deserts such as the Nefud and Rub El Khali cover a great portion of Arabia. The river beds are usually dry, but streams are formed during the rainy season. Mount Manar, which has an altitude of 10,561 feet, rises in the southwest and is the highest peak on the Arabian peninsula. Saudi Arabia has an *area* of 870,000 square miles; *population,* 6,500,000; *capitals,* Mecca and Riyadh. The chief industries include the production of petroleum, coffee, grain, dates, and Arab clocks. Hides and wool are also produced.

SMALL ARABIAN STATES

At the southwestern tip of Saudi Arabia and on the Red Sea is the kingdom of YEMEN: *area,* 75,000 square miles; *population,* 4,500,000; *capital,* Sana.

Occupying a strip of land about one thousand miles long along the southeast portion of the Arabian peninsula is the Sultanate of MUSCAT AND OMAN.

The BAHRAIN ISLANDS, off the Arabian coast in the Persian Gulf, comprise an independent Arab state under British protection: *area,* 250 square miles; *population,* 120,000; *capital,* Manamah.

IRAQ

Iraq is a kingdom located north of Saudi Arabia in southwestern Asia, and bounded on the east by Iran. The Tigris and Euphrates rivers flow through the central part of Iraq, and the soil is unusually fertile. Great quantities of oil are produced. Other products are grains, dates, tobacco, wool, and hides. The *area* is 171,000 square miles; *population,* 5,200,000. Baghdad is the *capital.*

ISRAEL

Israel is bounded on the west by Egypt and the Mediterranean Sea, and the River Jordan and the Dead Sea form a large part of the eastern boundary between Israel and Jordan. In the west is a fertile coastal plain, while a range of limestone mountains in the east rises to an altitude of almost 4,000 feet. The country is agricultural. Among the chief products are grains, fruit, olives, melons, rock salt, and sulphur; the making of wine is an important industry, and the principal minerals are gypsum, limestone, and sandstone. The *area* of Israel is 8,048 square miles; the estimated *population* is 1,850,000. Jerusalem is the *capital,* and other cities include Tel Aviv, Haifa, and Beersheba.

IRAN (PERSIA)

The kingdom of Iran is in southwestern Asia, east of Turkey and Iraq, and bounded on the south by the Persian Gulf and the Gulf of Oman. Much of Iran is mountainous, but in the north-central portion is a vast desert called the Dasht-i-Kavir. Among the chief products are oil, grains, fruit, gums, cotton, tobacco, and rice; wool, hides, and carpets are also produced. The richest single oil field in the world is located in southwestern Iran near the Persian Gulf. Iran covers an *area* of 628,000 square miles; the estimated *population* is 21,146,000. Teheran (Tehran) is the *capital,* and other leading cities are Tabriz and Isfahan.

AFGHANISTAN

Afghanistan is a kingdom located east of Iran. Fruit, grains, corn, tobacco, and sorghum are raised; hides and wool are produced, and other exports are carpets, felts, silks, drugs, copper, lead, and iron. The *area* is 245,000 square miles; the estimated *population* is 12,000,000. Kabul is the *capital.*

INDIA

India, one of the world's largest countries, is an independent member of the (British) Commonwealth of Nations. The country has an *area* of 1,221,880 square miles; *population,* 337,000,000; *capital,* New Delhi. *Boundaries:* north, China, disputed area of Kashmir, Pakistan; west, Pakistan, Arabian Sea, Indian Ocean; south, Arabian Sea, Indian Ocean, Bay of Bengal; east, Bay of Bengal, island of Ceylon, eastern section of Pakistan, Burma, China.

Two great rivers on the Indian peninsula are famous: the Indus and the Ganges. The climate is tropical except in the cooler northern mountains of the Himalayas. Indian agricultural products include rice, wheat, sugar cane, cotton, jute, tea, and rubber. The lumber and textile industries are important. Among the natural resources are coal, tungsten, iron ore, and gold. Calcutta and Bombay are large and important cities.

PAKISTAN

Pakistan, formerly part of the British Indian Empire, is divided into two zones, one on the western boundary of India, the other much smaller at the northern corner of the Bay of Bengal, 1,000 miles from the larger section. Pakistan has a *total area* of 364,737 square miles; *population,* 75,842,165; *capital,* Karachi. *Boundaries* of the western zone of Pakistan: north, Afghanistan and Iran; west, Iran and the Arabian Sea; south, Arabian Sea and India; east, India. The eastern zone is bounded on the east, north, and west by India; on the south by the Bay of Bengal; and the southeast tip touches Burma.

Like India, Pakistan is largely an agricultural country with much the same products. Pakistan is the largest producer of raw jute in the world; the textile industry is next in national importance. The country has huge iron-ore deposits as well as sulphur, chromite, petroleum, gas, and coal.

NEPAL

North of India, on the southern slope of the Himalayas, lies the constitutional monarchy of Nepal: *area,* 54,000 square miles; *population,* 8,431,547; *capital,* Katmandu. The fertile valley in which Katmandu lies, although only 15 miles long and 20 miles wide, supports 450,000 inhabitants. There are rich forests throughout the country and deposits of quartz. Exports include rice, jute, grain, hides, cattle, drugs, and wheat.

CEYLON

Ceylon, a large island in the Indian Ocean, just east of the southern tip of India, is an independent member of the British Commonwealth of Nations. This country has recently begun to be industrialized; mineral resources, metals, semiprecious stones, and precious stones are mined.

The agricultural products are tropical and include tea, rubber, coconuts, rice, cacao, cinnamon, and tobacco. Ceylon has an *area* of 25,332 square miles and a *population* of 5,383,000. The *capital* is Colombo.

BURMA

The Union of Burma is a republic located on the Bay of Bengal, south of China, east of India and Pakistan, and west of Thailand. Burma, in large part, lies in the valley area of the Irrawaddy River, which is navigable for nearly one thousand miles. The country produces rice, cotton, maize, and tobacco. Resources include silver and petroleum; high-grade rubies, sapphires, and jade are found. Burma has an *area* of 261,789 square miles and a *population* of 19,434,000. The *capital* is Rangoon.

THAILAND (FORMERLY SIAM)

The kingdom of Thailand, located in southern Asia, is bounded on the east by Indochina and on the west by Burma, and lies to the north of the Malay Peninsula. The most important products include teakwood, rice, tobacco, pepper, and para rubber; among the chief minerals are coal, iron ore, tin, and manganese. Thailand covers an *area* of 200,148 square miles, and the *population* is 20,300,000. Bangkok is the *capital*.

LAOS

Formerly a part of French Indo-China, Laos is a constitutional monarchy of Thai origin, lying south of China and east of Thailand. *Area,* 69,480 square miles; *population,* 1,300,000; *capital,* Vientiane. Agricultural products are rice, tea, coffee, maize, citrus fruits, and tobacco.

CAMBODIA

Cambodia, formerly a part of French Indo-China, is a constitutional monarchy in southern Asia, lying south of Thailand. *Area,* 88,780 square miles; *population,* 4,073,967; *capital,* Phnom Penh. A predominantly agricultural country, Cambodia devotes over 75 per cent of her cultivated land to rice. The country possesses forests of valuable hardwood trees and a flourishing cattle industry. Some ore and mineral deposits are present, including iron, copper, gold, and manganese.

VIETNAM

Formerly a part of French Indo-China, Vietnam is now divided into two zones, north and south, the north being a Communist state and the south a separate republic. *Total area,* 127,380 square miles; *population,*

22,614,000; *capitals:* Saigon (South Vietnam), Hanoi (North Vietnam). Vietnam is largely agricultural, and both zones have mineral deposits. In the north the principal products are rice, coffee, maize, tea, tobacco, sugar cane, and shellac; in the south, tea, coffee, and quinine. Exports from the combined zones include rice, rubber, coal, fish, lumber, pepper, hides, zinc, and tin.

MALAYA

Malaya, consisting of the four former Federated Malay States (PERAK, SELANGOR, NEGRI SEMBILAN, and PAHANG), the five former Unfederated States, and the two British Settlements of MALACCA and PENANG with PROVINCE WELLESLEY, became the tenth independent member of the British Commonwealth. It has a *total area* of 50,690 square miles; *population,* 5,750,000; *capital,* Kuala Lumpur. Malaya is the world's largest supplier of tin and an important source of rubber.

SINGAPORE

Singapore, an island off the Malay Peninsula, is a member of the British Commonwealth: *area,* 217 square miles; *population,* 1,165,129. It is the chief port of the former Straits Settlements (Penang), now part of Malaya.

CHINA

China is located in the east-central part of Asia. Its territory extends from the temperate zone to the tropics. The temperature, therefore, is very well suited to agriculture. China, moreover, is located in the belt of monsoon winds which blow over the Indian Ocean in the summer and bring abundant rainfall for the crops.

The topography of China is varied, with great flood plains along the Yangtze River and the Hwang-ho or Yellow River. The Yellow River carries down from the plateaus in the northwest a large amount of rich yellow soil, which annually renews the fertility of the earth when the river overflows. Much of the soil of northwestern China is *loess,* a fine rich soil which is carried by the winds from the deserts of Central Asia.

Many people wonder why China has not achieved a development in accordance with her size, her resources, and her vast population. Her retarded development is due to the poverty of her people, the constant civil wars, the lack of a strong, stable government, the feudal system of land tenure that prevails in many provinces, the lack of capital, and the paucity of transportation facilities.

The per capita foreign trade of China is not very large. Among the leading exports are tea, raw silk, furs, hides, bristles, cotton piece goods, tung oil, soybean products, tin, and antimony. The chief imports are cotton goods, sugar, rice flour, petroleum products, iron and steel goods, and railway equipment.

The *area* of China proper is 2,279,134 square miles; *population,* 601,912,371. The *capital* of the People's Republic of China (Communist), which controls the entire mainland, is Peiping. Other leading cities include: Nanking (former capital), Shanghai, Tientsin, Kwangchow (Canton), Hankow, and Wenchow.

TAIWAN (Formosa), an island 110 miles off the mainland, is administered by the Chinese Nationalists. Known as the Republic of China, the Nationalists claim the mainland also. The *area* of Taiwan is 13,800 square miles; *population,* 9,000,000 (provisional); *capital,* Taipei. Taiwan and thirteen nearby islands contain United States naval and air bases and are protected by the United States Navy.

Under the control of the People's Republic of China (Communist) are INNER MONGOLIA, SINKIANG, TIBET, MANCHURIA, and KWANTUNG.

MONGOLIA (OUTER MONGOLIA)

Formerly the Chinese province of Outer Mongolia, the People's Republic of Mongolia is bounded on the north by Siberia, on the east by Manchuria and the Tarbagatai Mountains, on the south by Sinkiang, and on the west by Turkestan: *area,* 1,750,000 square miles; *population,* over 1,000,000; *capital,* Ulan Bator. Small areas of Mongolia in the southern and southeastern portions are covered by the Gobi Desert. The principal industry is livestock raising; wool cleaning, tanning, and shoemaking are other occupations. Coal, gold, and marble are mined, and oil was discovered recently.

UNION OF SOVIET SOCIALIST REPUBLICS

Although Siberia, in the U.S.S.R., lies entirely in Asia, the U.S.S.R. is described in the section "Countries of Europe" (page 292).

JAPAN

The islands of Japan are located in the Pacific Ocean off the coast of Asia. The climate is varied, although predominantly of the modified, humid continental type, such as in our New England and Middle Atlantic states. The location of the islands is favorable from a commercial point of view. They are in an excellent position for trade with China, India, Indonesia, Australia, and New Zealand. Her well-indented coast line provides many harbors and facilities for shipbuilding.

Japan made effective use of her limited water-power resources and has abundant coal and copper deposits. The forests of Japan are extensive and yield the raw materials for making lacquer; camphor, and mulberry leaves, which are essential in the silk industry. Until recently, much manufacturing was done by hand in Japan, especially in the homes of the workers. The most important of these domestic industries is sericulture, the production of silk. Before the Second World War, control of Japanese industries was in the hands of the Zaibatsu, a group of five powerful families that ran the iron- and steel-milling, the chemical and textile industries, banking, shipbuilding, transportation, and foreign trade.

The important cities of Japan are Tokyo, the *capital;* Yokohama, the most important seaport; Kobe and Osaka, great manufacturing centers. Japan covers 146,690 square miles; the *population* is 89,269,278.

KOREA

Korea is divided into two states, the Republic of Korea in the south and the People's Democratic Republic of Korea (Communist) in the north: *total area,* 85,266 square miles; *population,* 21,526,000; *capitals,* Seoul (south) and Pyongyang (north). The country as a whole is mountainous but has a cultivated agricultural area of approximately 11,000,000 acres, producing rice, barley, tobacco, wheat, and beans. The northern section contains about 80 per cent of the country's heavy industry. Among Korea's natural resources are gold, silver, zinc, copper, lead, iron, tungsten, graphite, timber, kaolin, and coal.

INDONESIA

Indonesia, a republic, formerly the Dutch East Indies, comprises a group of some three thousand islands lying south of the mainland of Asia and the Philippines and north of Australia. The largest islands are West Borneo, Sumatra, Java, and Celebes. The *total area* of Indonesia is 905,522 square miles, and the *population* is estimated at 82,450,000. Indonesians are of a number of races. The islands are extremely rich in natural resources, including tin, oil, coal, aluminum ore, manganese, copper, nickel, silver, and gold. The chief agricultural products are rice, maize, ground nuts, soya beans, tobacco, coffee, rubber, tea, sugar, and indigo. The *capital* of Indonesia is Jakarta on the island of Java.

PHILIPPINE ISLANDS

The Philippines are a large archipelago of over three thousand islands near the coast of Asia. The principal commercial products are its raw materials, the chief of which are sugar cane, hemp, tobacco, coconut, rubber, gold and copper deposits. Much of its trade is with the United States. The people are mainly of Malay and Spanish blood. Manila is the *capital,* and other leading cities are Cebu, Zamboanga, and Davao. The *area* is 115,600 square miles; the *population,* 21,849,000.

BRITISH POSSESSIONS IN ASIA

The following territories in Asia are British colonies or dependencies.

CYPRUS, an island in the Mediterranean just south of Turkey and Asia Minor, is a large British colony: *area,* 3,584 square miles; *population,* 509,000; *capital,* Nicosia.

ADEN, a tiny peninsula on the southern Arabian coast, includes 75 square miles in Aden itself, plus 112 square miles of protectorate area, with a *total population* of 800,000; attached to Aden is the island SOKOTRA, under British protection, with an *area* of 1,400 square miles and a *population* of 12,000.

BRITISH NORTH BORNEO is a northern piece of the island of Borneo, in the East Indies: *area,* 29,500 square miles; *population,* 333,752. Adjacent, also on Borneo, is the protectorate of BRUNEI, and also SARAWAK, the latter having an *area* of 50,000 square miles and a *population* of 605,000.

HONG KONG, an island, is a crown colony on the southern coast of China: *area,* 391 square miles; *population,* 2,250,000.

COUNTRIES OF AFRICA

MOROCCO

Formerly a French protectorate, the kingdom of Morocco lies on the northwestern tip of Africa, bordering the Mediterranean. *Area,* 172,104 square miles; *population,* 8,033,985; *capital,* Rabat. Five natural zones make up the country: a series of mountain ranges (Riff, Middle Atlas, Upper Atlas, and Anti-Atlas); in the west a series of rich plains; in the southwest alluvial plains; in the center the "meseta," or well-cultivated plateaus; in the south a Saharan zone. Agriculture and pastoral industries are the main occupations in Morocco, though modern industry is being developed rapidly. The most important agricultural products are cereal grain; fruit orchards and vineyards are also numerous. Manufactures include carpets, leather goods, woolen and silk stuffs; chief natural resources are copper, tin, oil, phosphate, manganese, lead.

ALGERIA

Algeria consists of four departments treated as an integral part of metropolitan France. It is discussed in the section on France (page 284).

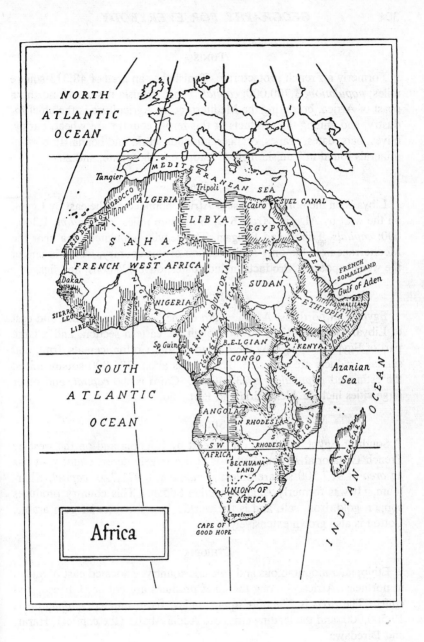

NORTH
ATLANTIC
OCEAN

MEDITERRANEAN SEA

Tangier

MOROCCO
RIO DE ORO
ALGERIA
Tripoli
LIBYA
Cairo
SUEZ CANAL
EGYPT

SAHARA

FRENCH WEST AFRICA

Dakar

SIERRA
LEONE
LIBERIA

NIGERIA
GHANA

FRENCH EQUATORIAL AFRICA
CONGO
Sp Guinea
B.ELGIAN
CONGO

SUDAN
ETHIOPIA
FRENCH
SOMALILAND
Gulf of Aden
BR.
SOMALILAND
UGANDA
KENYA

SOUTH
ATLANTIC
OCEAN

ANGOLA
N RHODESIA
S RHODESIA
SW
AFRICA
BECHUANA
LAND
UNION OF
S AFRICA
Capetown
CAPE OF
GOOD HOPE

TANGANYIKA
MOZAMBIQUE
Azanian
Sea
MADAGASCAR
INDIAN OCEAN

RED SEA

Africa

TUNISIA

Formerly a French protectorate, Tunisia has an *area* of 48,313 square miles; *population,* 3,700,000; *capital,* Tunis. Tunisia lies on the northern coast of Africa, bordering the Mediterranean. Agriculture is the chief industry, and among the products of this fertile country are wheat, barley, olives, oats, dates, grapes, oranges, almonds, cork, and henna. Important minerals found in Tunisia include lead, iron, phosphate, and zinc.

LIBYA

Libya is on the northern coast of Africa, bounded on the east by Egypt, on the west by Algeria. *Area,* 679,358 square miles; *population,* 1,340,-000; *capitals,* Tripoli and Bengazi. The heavily populated area near the Mediterranean is the only fertile section of this country, which is one of the world's poorest. Products include dates, olives, lemons, and figs.

EGYPT

Egypt is in northeast Africa, south of the Mediterranean Sea and east of Libya. The Nile River flows through the eastern section, and a large part of Egypt is covered by the Libyan Desert. Cotton, cereals, fruit, and similar products are exported. The *area* is about 386,000 square miles; the estimated *population* is 23,240,000. Cairo is the *capital,* and other large cities include Alexandria and Port Said.

SUDAN

South of Egypt, bordered on the east by Ethiopia and on the west by French Equatorial Africa, Sudan is also a largely desert country. It has an *area* of 967,500 square miles; *population,* 8,971,720; *capital,* Khartoum. (It was formerly Anglo-Egyptian Sudan.) This country produces copper, gold, iron, salt, and is the world's largest source of gum arabic. Cotton is also grown extensively.

ETHIOPIA

Ethiopia, a mountainous and volcanic country, is located east of Sudan in northeast Africa. Among the chief products are cotton, tobacco, and coffee. The *area* is 350,000 square miles; the estimated *population* is 19,500,000, and the leading cities are Addis Ababa (the *capital*), Harar, and Diredawa.

LIBERIA

Liberia is an independent republic on the coast of southwestern Africa, bounded on the northwest by Sierra Leone and on the north and east by French West Africa. Tropical forests cover most of the country, which has an *area* of 43,000 square miles and a *population* estimated at 2,750,-000. Liberia produces fibres, crude rubber, rice, coffee, cocoa, and sugar. Gold and iron ore are among the resources, the latter being mined in great quantity. Monrovia is the *capital*.

GHANA

Ghana is an independent member of the British Commonwealth, composed of four former British colonies (Gold Coast, Ashanti, Northern Territories, and Togoland), lying on the southern or under side of the bulge of West Africa. The *area* of Ghana is 41,843 square miles; *population,* 4,125,000; *capital,* Accra. There is enormous mineral wealth in Ghana, including manganese, gold, aluminum, and diamonds. Forests are extensive and profitably cut. Exports include diamonds, gold, and cacao.

THE UNION OF SOUTH AFRICA

The Union of South Africa, in the British Commonwealth, occupying the southern end of the continent of Africa, includes the former colonial area of the Cape of Good Hope, Natal, the Transvaal, and the Orange Free State. The country has an *area* of 472,733 square miles and a *population* of 13,915,000; its *capital* is at Pretoria, although the legislature meets in Cape Town.

The Union has great wealth in gold and diamonds and is also a large producer of uranium. The natural resources include coal, copper, tin, iron, lead, lime, manganese, and platinum. Farm crops are wheat, tobacco, tea, sugar cane, citrus fruits, butter, and cheese. Merino wool is exported in great quantities. Johannesburg is a large and important city.

Associated with the Union of South Africa is South-West Africa (formerly German territory): *area,* 317,725 square miles; *population,* 447,000; *capital,* Windhoek.

POSSESSIONS OF EUROPEAN COUNTRIES IN AFRICA

British Possessions

THE CENTRAL AFRICAN FEDERATION, including NORTHERN RHODESIA and SOUTHERN RHODESIA (both largely self-governing) and NYASALAND (protectorate), is under British administration: *area,* 488,060 square miles; *population,* 6,876,600. The *capitals* are Salisbury and Lusaka.

BASUTOLAND is a colony northeast of the Cape of Good Hope. BECHUANALAND is a protectorate: *area,* 294,020 square miles; *population,* 294,000. SWAZILAND, near the east coast, is a small protectorate: *area,*

6,704 square miles; *population,* 184,000. These territories, administered by three Resident Commissioners, form BRITISH SOUTH AFRICA.

NIGERIA, in the southern part of the western bulge of Africa (northern half of the continent), is the largest British colonial territory in Africa: *area,* 373,250 square miles; *population,* 31,800,000; *capital,* Lagos; *products,* tin, lead, iron, and other metals. BRITISH CAMEROONS (formerly German Kamerun) is a small addition to Nigeria. GAMBIA, a tiny section around the mouth of the Gambia River, is a crown colony: *area,* 4,010 square miles; *population,* 250,160; exports large quantities of peanuts. SIERRA LEONE is on the west coast: *area,* 30,000 square miles; *population,* 2,000,000; *capital,* Freetown; *products,* iron ore, gold, and diamonds.

In the east is BRITISH EAST AFRICA: KENYA, a crown colony, is bounded by the Umba, Juba, and Uganda rivers; *area,* 224,960 square miles; *population,* 6,150,000. To the south is TANGANYIKA TERRITORY (formerly German East Africa); *area,* 362,688 square miles, *population,* 8,069,000. West of Kenya is the UGANDA PROTECTORATE; *area,* 93,981 square miles; *population,* 5,593,000.

Other British African possessions are: ZANZIBAR, an island east of Tanganyika; MAURITIUS, an island in the Indian Ocean; the SEYCHELLES, some 90 islands; BRITISH SOMALILAND, on the northeast coast, south of Arabia, *area,* 68,000 square miles, *population,* 640,000; ST. HELENA, 1,200 miles west of Africa in the Atlantic.

French Possessions

FRENCH WEST AFRICA, with an *area* of 1,821,600 square miles, *population,* 18,777,163, has been formed by the integration of seven colonies. Its *capital* is Dakar. It exports fruits, palm nuts, oil, rubber, cotton, cocoa, coffee, and peanuts, mostly to France. Other French possessions in Africa include FRENCH EQUATORIAL AFRICA, FRENCH CAMEROONS, and TOGOLAND; FRENCH SOMALILAND and MADAGASCAR.

Belgian Congo

THE BELGIAN CONGO is located in the southern part of Africa and is bounded on the north by French Equatorial Africa and Sudan, on the east by Tanganyika and Uganda, on the south by Northern Rhodesia and Angola, and on the west by Angola, the South Atlantic, and French Equatorial Africa. The region covers an *area* of 904,757 square miles, has a *population* of 12,264,000, and is administered by a Belgian governor-general at Leopoldville. Palm oil, cotton, palm nuts, coffee, cocoa, rubber, sugar, and ivory are among the products of the Belgian Congo. The land is rich in ores, including copper, silver, gold, and radium.

Spanish Possessions

Spain's possessions in Africa are SPANISH GUINEA, on the west coast, jutting inland into French Equatorial Africa; RÍO DE ORO, on the northwest coast, and extending into French West Africa. Spanish Guinea has an *area* of 10,852 square miles; *population*, 198,663; *capital*, Santa Isabel. Río de Oro has an *area* of 73,362 square miles.

Portuguese Possessions

Portugal possesses two large areas in Africa. ANGOLA is on the west coast, south of French Equatorial Africa and Belgian Congo, and north of South-West Africa: *area*, 481,351 square miles; *population*, 4,243,-000; *capital*, Luanda. MOZAMBIQUE is on the east coast, north and east of the Union of South Africa and Rhodesia, and south of Tanganyika: *area*, 297,731 square miles; *population*, 5,975,000; *capital*, Lourenço Marques. Chief products of Angola are coffee, rubber, sugar, coconuts, ivory, tobacco, cotton, and wax. Mozambique produces sugar, coconuts, and cotton. Both regions have considerable mineral deposits.

The islands of SÃO TOMÉ and PRINCIPE, off the coast of western Africa, are Portuguese territory under a governor.

AUSTRALIA AND THE PACIFIC ISLANDS

AUSTRALIA

Australia, a member of the British Commonwealth, comprises the entire Australian continent. To the southeast of Asia, between the Pacific and Indian oceans, it includes the states of New South Wales, Victoria, Queensland, South Australia, Western Australia, and Northern Territory, and the island of Tasmania. The *area:* 2,974,581 square miles; the *population* is estimated at 9,400,000; the *capital* is Canberra.

There are mountains rising as high as seven thousand feet. The climate is temperate in the south and tropical in the north. Australia is one of the world's important producers of wool, and exports various agricultural products, notably wheat. Other products: sugar, wine, fruit, vegetables, beef, and minerals (uranium, gold, coal, copper, iron, silver, tin, zinc).

Administered by Australia is the recently combined territory of PAPUA and NEW GUINEA, the former with an *area* of 90,540 square miles and a *population* of 488,396, and the latter having an *area* of 93,000 square miles and a *population* of 1,206,749.

NEW ZEALAND

Southeast of Australia is New Zealand, consisting of North Island and

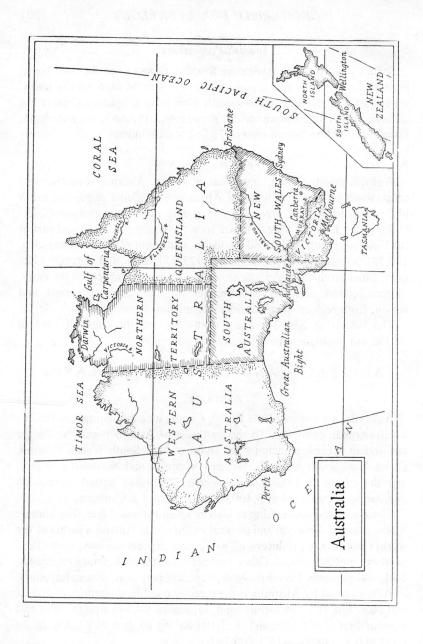

Australia

South Island and adjacent smaller islands. The country is a member of the British Commonwealth. It has an *area* of 103,736 square miles and a *population* of 2,164,755; the *capital* is Wellington.

With an unusually diverse topography, New Zealand is agricultural, with a variety of products and livestock. Like Australia, it is a great producer of wool. Natural resources include coal, petroleum, gold, and silver.

WESTERN SAMOA is administered by New Zealand under United Nations trusteeship. It includes Savaii and Upolu, the two largest islands in the western Pacific, with a *total area* of 1,133 square miles, *total population* of 96,678. The chief exports are copra, bananas, and cocoa.

UNITED STATES POSSESSIONS IN THE PACIFIC

United States' Pacific islands are discussed in the section on the United States (pages 269–270).

BRITISH POSSESSIONS IN THE PACIFIC

Important British Pacific islands are the following:

The FIJI ISLANDS lie east of northern Australia, number about 320, have a *total area* of 7,036 square miles. The *population* includes 320,800; the *capital* is Suva. The principal products are sugar, coconuts, gold, and tobacco. The TONGA ISLANDS, or FRIENDLY ISLANDS, are a protected state. The Polynesian kingdom has an *area* of 269 square miles; a *population* of 54,342. THE BRITISH SOLOMON ISLANDS, a protectorate, include the famed Guadalcanal. The *total area* of the Solomon Islands is 12,400 square miles; *population,* 100,300.

FRENCH POSSESSIONS IN THE PACIFIC

Numerous far-flung French Pacific islands which are governed as a unified overseas territory (*capital,* Papeete) include TAHITI (one of the Society Islands), a picturesque and fertile island; *total area,* 1,520 square miles. The *population* is 63,000. NEW CALEDONIA, with an *area* of 8,548 square miles, is about halfway between Australia and the Fiji Islands, has a *population* of 63,000, and is administered by France along with a number of other dependencies. The chief industry is mining, with an abundance of chrome, cobalt, nickel, and manganese. Agricultural products are coffee, copra, cotton, corn, tobacco, bananas, and pineapples.

EXAMINATION QUESTIONS

1. What does the Greek derivation of the word geography signify?
2. What is the lithosphere?
3. To what general shape do all continents tend?
4. What is the earth's circumference?
5. What is the ocean's average depth?
6. Why does the hour of ocean tides vary from day to day?
7. What is the equator?

8. What is latitude?
9. What does the term "fauna" mean?
10. Name the wingless birds of Australia.
11. Of what continent are the prairie dog and porcupine typical?
12. In what continents are the following: Czechoslovakia, Afghanistan, Costa Rica, Panama, Dutch Guiana, Tasmania?
13. What is the area of the United States including territories and possessions?
14. Name the five Great Lakes.
15. What three main streams join to form the Mississippi River?
16. What are the leading money crops of the South?
17. Which U.S. city is the center of the meat-packing industry?
18. What United States region has the greatest network of railroads?
19. Name five cities in the Central states with a population of more than 500,000.
20. What is the most sparsely populated state in the Union?
21. Where does more than one-half of the salmon used in the United States come from?
22. What are the chief cities of Puerto Rico?
23. Where are the Virgin Islands?
24. How many people does the British Commonwealth include?
25. What is the capital of Canada?
26. Which is the largest Central American republic?
27. What is Cuba's chief product?
28. Name two French possessions in the Caribbean.
29. Which South American country leads in producing petroleum?
30. Name Brazil's leading product.
31. Which South American country has the largest foreign trade?
32. What is the capital of Chile?
33. Where is the Isle of Man?
34. To what country does the island of Corsica belong?
35. Which European country is partly below sea level?
36. What is Italy's most valuable mineral product?
37. Name the world's smallest state.
38. Name Germany's three navigable rivers.
39. What form of government has Sweden?
40. What is Russia's official name?
41. Give Russia's population.
42. What is the capital of Israel?
43. Where is Iraq located?
44. Where is the richest single oil field in the world?
45. Is the population of China more or less than 500 million?
46. What is Japan's leading industry?
47. The Philippines consist of how many islands?
48. Where is Ghana?
49. What is the capital of Australia?
50. The Fiji Islands are the possession of what country?

For Further Study

Economic Geography, by R. H. Whitbeck and V. C. Finch. (McGraw-Hill, New York.)

Industrial Geography, by Charles E. London. (Prentice Hall, New York.)

Introduction to World Geography, by P. A. Knowlton. (The Macmillan Co., New York.)

Trade Centers and Trade Routes, by Eugene van Cleef. (Appleton-Century, New York.)

VII

Economics for Everybody

ECONOMIC WEALTH

MANKIND LIVES in an environment which gives him some of the things necessary for his existence and conducive to his well-being generally; such things as air, water, and natural beauty. These things are known as "natural wealth." But in order to live and in order to enjoy life, man must have a great many more things than we include in the phrase "natural wealth." From the earliest times, he has had to find his food by hunting, by growing crops, by fishing; the food must be prepared; some of it must be preserved to serve him when fresh food is scarce; he must make dwelling places, clothing; he must protect himself from contagion by various sanitary measures. If he wishes to live well he must have, in addition to all these, pleasing things, beautiful objects, music, interesting books, means of transportation, desirable things without end.

Wealth consists of material goods and services. When making an estimate of the wealth of a country, only the material wealth or goods is customarily included. Economic wealth may be divided into two great classes: consumers' goods and producers' goods. Consumers' goods are those in the possession of consumers which thus satisfy them directly. Producers' goods consist of raw materials, partly finished goods, buildings, machinery, etc., which satisfy our wants indirectly. Another name for producers' goods is capital or capital goods.

We must learn to view wealth not in terms of money or merely as economic goods capable of satisfying wants. To quote John Ruskin, a great Englishman, "there is no wealth but life." By this he meant that nothing that does not make human life better, happier, and spiritually richer is really wealth. Economics is therefore the social science which seeks to promote our well-being by studying scientifically the best possible ways of producing desirable goods and using them to the best advantage for all.

PROPERTY

The term *property* as used in everyday speech often is synonymous with wealth. In economics, however, it is useful for clear thinking to see the distinction between wealth and property and in turn how they differ from income. Property can best be defined as any wealth or income which is owned by legal right and may lawfully be used, accumulated, or given away. An attitude indicative of a feeling for property rights has developed in many animals as well as in man. The dog certainly is aware of what belongs to his master, and will protect it; he will protect his own kennel or his own bone against any other dog. This same attitude is found in the wild animal defending its food, its den, or its hunting range. But with animals, and also with primitive man, the nature of property ownership is immensely more simple than it is in our present system; therefore, it will be easier to understand our conception of property by considering the more primitive practices first, and then seeing how our system developed from the simpler forms.

Primitive man had property rights to that which he made. The man who chipped a stone tool for his use undoubtedly felt that he had the primary right to use the tool which he had produced, and likewise the club he found belonged to him as long as he could use it. Property rights are quite generally determined not merely by creation or by discovery, but by use: when property ceases to be used by its former owner, he loses interest in it, and anyone may then take it, and claim the rights of ownership as long as he, in turn, makes use of it. Ownership through use is most widely found in connection with land, where most primitives feel that they have certain rights to the land which they have built on, hunted over, or grown crops on; but which ceases to belong to them once it is demonstrated that they no longer use it. We find the conception of property amongst primitives extends to food, weapons, clothing, ornaments, land, and a great variety of other objects, including such intangible things as names, rituals, and precedence.

In many circumstances, different communities, or different individuals in the same community, may possess surpluses of certain forms of wealth; and it becomes mutually advantageous to exchange them. For example, a community living on the shores of the ocean may have more than enough fish but very little meat, while a community living near them but inland has no fish but a surplus of game. In such a case, informal exchange or barter is apt to occur. Exchange of products becomes very much more common when extensive division of labor develops within any group. Thus, in one community there may be a certain individual who makes better weapons than anyone else, but whose hunting ability is poor. It is to the advantage of the community at large that this man should spend most of his time in making weapons, while others do the hunting; and therefore an exchange of property within the community takes place: the specialist in the production of weapons selling or bartering these weapons for the food which the hunters bring in. It is important to notice that the food that is brought in is actually a form of economic wealth produced by the joint efforts of the hunters and the manufacturer of weapons, and instead of considering the food used by the manufacturer to be something purchased by him, it is just as easy, and perhaps fundamentally more correct, to consider this food to belong to him by virtue of his contribution to its production. This same principle applies to any goods produced in our own society, in the production of which not only labor has been contributed, but also that which we know as "capital."

In extremely simple forms of society there is probably little or no exchange of wealth, or change of ownership for any reason. Upon the death of a man his whole property, consisting perhaps of a few stone tools, a few clubs, and bits of clothing and ornaments, would be buried with him, this constituting very little loss to the rest of the community since his whole wealth could be duplicated in a day's time by anyone who cared to make the effort. But with communities having slightly more elaborate cultures, this disposal of the dead man's property is no longer feasible. It may be the product of several years' work, in which case the other members of the community would dislike to see it lost; furthermore, if any of this wealth is in the form of large articles, as, for example, a permanent dwelling place, it may be quite impossible to dispose of it by burial. The property then passes to another individual by a process that we know as inheritance. With the institution of inheritance it becomes possible to build up huge accumulations of wealth that could not occur otherwise.

Capital

Wealth, as we have seen, consists not only of that which is directly used, but also of that which is used indirectly in the production of usable goods. Thus the specialist in the making of weapons creates a commodity which is not directly useful to mankind, but which enables man to produce a more directly useful form of wealth: in this case, game. In the production of wealth, therefore, we find that three factors may co-operate: first, labor, which is the work required to produce the desirable result; second, the raw material; and third, capital.

Capital consists intrinsically of all goods required to assist in the production of wealth. In modern factory production, capital consists of: the factory buildings; the machines used in the production, packing, and labeling of the product; whatever objects may be necessary for the proper care and maintenance of the factory and machinery; the railroad used in bringing to the factory the raw materials and in taking from the factory the finished product; the newspapers, magazines, or billboards that may be used in advertising the product of the factory; and many other items. Of course, at the present, these factors of capital are represented purely in monetary terms. The capital needed to run a factory is, generally, the money required to buy the land, to build the factory, purchase and care for the machinery, pay the cost of transportation, advertising, and taxation, and also to pay the laborers in advance for their share of the final product or wealth. For labor, as a participant in the production of wealth, would be entitled to be paid only after the wealth produced has been sold, and payment for it received; but in our system the laborer is paid on a wage or salary basis, receiving his pay before the wealth which he helps to create has produced any return. Thus capital, in our system, must provide not only that which is specifically capital goods, but also must provide for the hire of labor for the period which elapses from the beginning of work until the receipt of payment for the produce of the work.

Capital goods, or the instruments of production, may be classified into fixed, circulating, specialized, and free capital goods. Fixed capital goods are producers' goods which last a relatively long time. Factory buildings, machinery, and tools are examples of fixed capital goods.

Circulating capital goods are producers' goods, which are used up or converted into other products in a comparatively short time. Textiles, fuels, and chemicals are examples of circulating capital goods. Wholesale and retail stores are examples of enterprises that have a large proportion of their capital in the form of circulating capital goods.

Specialized capital goods are producers' goods which have only certain specific uses. Most kinds of machinery, some tools, and buildings such as storage plants are examples of specialized capital goods. Note that specialized capital goods may be of the "fixed" type, such as railroad tracks, or of the "circulating" type, such as coal.

Free capital goods are producers' goods which can be used without trouble (freely) for many different purposes, such as many kinds of raw materials and some kinds of buildings. Free capital goods may be of the "fixed" type, such as loft buildings, or of the "circulating" type, such as raw woolens.

Part of the outlay of capital is used up in the creation of wealth, i.e., in the form of free capital goods: that part which goes for the purchase of raw materials, for the payment of transportation costs, for advertising and for many other factors in production. The price of the finished article must include the cost of the labor that goes into its production, and also that fraction of the capital outlay which has been expended on it. In addition, there will be included in its price a return on the unexpended capital, or fixed capital goods, and a profit.

Certain parts of the capital used in running a business, such as those for land and factory, are not used up in production, and these parts are known as the "capital investment," or "capital" in the narrower sense. When "capital" is spoken of in contradistinction to labor, this is the sense in which it is meant; and a person popularly referred to as a "capitalist" is one whose income is derived primarily from this source. A certain price must be paid to the owner of this capital, even though at the conclusion of the work the capital remains intact. This payment for the use of wealth, known technically as "economic rent," exists for the following reasons, which justify the practice of paying interest.

The first justification lies in the factor of deterioration, or depreciation. Although the factory remains after it has been used for a year, it is not worth quite as much as it was at the beginning of the year. It may require the expenditure of more capital to keep it in good working order; older types of machinery may have to be replaced; the building itself may have to be repainted; and in any case taxes must be paid on the building and on the land which it occupies. This deterioration must of course be included in the price of the finished article.

Not all capital expenditures are subject to deterioration, but all are subject to risk. The factory owner, during the year of the factory's operation, has either taken the risk of losing the factory by fire, earthquake, or through legal means, or he has had to spend money for fire insurance, title guarantee, and so forth. Risk is apparent in any expenditure of capital; and to justify one in taking a risk there should be a possibility of gain. Let us take as an example a bank whose business it is to lend money. Not all of the loans a bank makes will be repaid. Some of the individuals or corporations to whom the bank lends money will never be able to make repayment, and will go through bankruptcy or otherwise disappear from the picture, while others may refuse to make repayment and either succeed in evading their indebtedness or force the bank to spend money in an effort to collect. For these and other reasons, only a certain percentage of the total loans made may be expected to be repaid. Simply in order to break even, then, the bank will have to receive, from those who do repay, sufficient additional money in the form of interest to compensate for that fraction of the total loans made that cannot be recovered. Thus if we figure that one loan out of every hundred will prove unsound, the rate of risk would be figured at one per cent, and by charging one per cent on its loans the bank would maintain its capital intact.

Now let us take a slightly more complex case: that of a man engaged in selling books at retail. He must recognize that there is a possibility that he may lose some of this stock of books; that some of them may be destroyed by fire or water; that some may be stolen; that some buyers may never pay for the books, or that he may be unable to sell some of them. In order to cover these possibilities he would have to sell the books for more than he pays for them, simply to come out even on the entire transaction. The amount of risk varies enormously, according to the type of transaction involved: the more risky the transaction is, the greater the differential between cost and selling price must be. This differential in the case of perishable goods, such as bread, and also in the case of style articles, where there is a risk of going out of fashion, must be very much greater than in the case of goods where the risk is less. The greater risk involved is also the reason why the rate of return on stocks is greater than on bonds, on second preferred stocks greater than on first preferred, and on dubious investments greater than on those of better quality.

If the bank has fixed a rate of interest, and the bookseller has fixed a selling price, that covers all the risks that they encounter, it would still be pointless for them to engage in business. Men engage in business in order to gain something from it, and therefore they must get not merely enough increment to keep them from losing, but sufficient in addition to give a profit. Our economic society is organized on the basis of the voluntary co-operation of individuals for the sake of profit.

Let us consider this example: when you buy a book in a retail store for three dollars, the owner of the store has perhaps paid one dollar and eighty cents for the book. The dollar and twenty cents additional which he receives covers part of the rent of the store; heat, light, upkeep, and taxes; the value of the time of the owner or of a clerk whom he has hired; payment for the risk of damage to the store and to the books by fire, water, theft, and for all other possible mischances; payment for the chance that the book would never be sold, but would remain on the shelf until it fell to pieces; and the payment of a profit upon the money spent for the book and for the money paid for the store. The publisher of the book has received one dollar and eighty cents from the retailer; this covers the cost of the setting of type, the making of plates, the payments to the author, and the cost of paper and other materials that went into the production of the book; the profits that he has taken; the risks that he has run of not selling the book and of damage to his offices by fire, etc.; the payment of the workers; payment of taxes; and costs of advertising and shipping. The fraction of the one dollar and eighty cents that was spent for the paper went to the paper concern, where it in turn was distributed between labor and other costs, interest on capital, and profit. Each person who has handled the merchandise which goes into the article which you use has received for it not merely what it cost him to produce it, but an additional amount to cover risks and a further fraction to give him a profit.

In summary, we might note that our economic system today differs from that of years ago in that the chief factor of production is capital. As a result of this change brought about by the Industrial Revolution, we have what is called roundabout production. Roundabout production may be defined as production in anticipation of demand, particularly where there is a tremendous gap in communication between producer and consumer. This is in direct contrast to direct production. Direct production occurs where labor is the chief factor. Goods are made on order only, and the producer takes a long time to satisfy the demand.

MONEY

When the exchange of goods is frequent, it is possible to evaluate one commodity in terms of another. If, for example, an ordinary principle of exchange is to barter two oranges for three apples, then each orange is worth one and a half apples. In this fashion every commodity could be evaluated in terms of any other commodity. For ease of reference, it becomes useful to state the value of any commodity in terms of one preferred commodity. This preferred commodity, used to evaluate all the others, is "money."

Money may thus be defined as any commodity which is readily accepted in exchange for goods and services. Any commodity could be used as money. However, only those commodities which have the following qualities make good money:

(1) *Uniformity*—Every piece of the commodity must be the same as every other piece. This would eliminate diamonds, for example, because the quality of diamonds varies.

(2) *Portability*—It must be easy to carry from place to place.

(3) *Small bulk*—It must have high value in small bulk. This would eliminate coal, for example, because it takes a good deal to make it an appreciable value.

(4) *Recognizability*—It should be easy to recognize and should not require the services of an expert to see whether or not it is genuine.

(5) *Divisibility*—It should be readily divisible into smaller units.

(6) *Stability*—Its price should not change frequently.

(7) *Durability*—It should be able to stand long, hard wear without losing its identity.

In highly commercial communities, whatever commodity is used as money is largely withdrawn from other uses in favor of its use as currency; hence it is advantageous to use as money a commodity which is intrinsically of no great importance to the community.

Gold, which has been the basis of our monetary system for thousands of years, has all these advantages. It lasts practically indefinitely; although, of course, when gold coins are passed from hand to hand there is a wear on the coin; it is no commoner in winter than in summer, and no more valuable at any time than at any other; it is useful for no practical purpose of importance, other than the one for which it was originally desired, namely, for personal adornment; so that no loss is incurred by its withdrawal from practical service. For if gold utterly disappeared from the world today, mankind would be no worse off, except, of course, for whatever disruption of the monetary system would ensue. In this respect gold differs notably from silver, which, but for its monetary value, would be widely used in electrical instruments.

Some critics of our monetary system consider this lack of real value in gold to be a disadvantage rather than an advantage of the system, and have suggested the substitution of electrical power or human labor as the standard. But such standards would be actually much inferior to gold. They fluctuate more than gold does; they would be subject to a certain amount of seasonal variation; their value might change from generation to generation, as, in fact, the value of electrical energy has changed with the development of new methods of producing it; and it would be almost impossible to preserve them as an indication of savings, while gold can be preserved in the vaults of banks and governments.

In the history of the United States, many types of money have been in use. During the Revolutionary and Civil wars we had *fiat money*. Fiat money is paper money with no backing behind it except the credit of the government. It cannot be redeemed for metal. Although the *continentals* of the Revolutionary War period and the *greenbacks* of the Civil War period could not be redeemed, they were legal tender. Legal tender is money which must be accepted by all citizens of a country in payment for debts. All money in the United States today is legal tender.

In the period following the Civil War, the United States was on a bimetallic standard. This is a system where there are two types of standard money, gold and silver. All paper money may be redeemed in either of these metals.

Money may be classified into various types. Standard money is a metal whose face value is equal to its bullion value. The paper equivalent of standard money is called representative money. This is paper money that can be converted into bullion, equal in value to the face value on the paper. Subsidiary money is all money whose bullion is less than its face value. Another characteristic of the standard coin is that the government permits free coinage.

The use of money is governed by two laws. One, Gresham's Law, points out that when two kinds of money with the same face value but different commodity value circulate under a bimetallic system, the cheaper money will tend to drive the more valuable money out of circulation. This indicates simply that if one of two pieces of money, each legally worth the same amount, is more valuable because it is backed by and represents a larger commodity value in gold or silver, individuals will naturally prefer to spend the cheaper money and save or keep out of circulation the more valuable money. The other law, the quantity theory of money, holds that other things being equal, (1) prices vary directly with the quantity of money in circulation; (2) the value of money varies inversely with the quantity in circulation. This law points out the fact that money is more valuable when it is scarce; it is less valuable—since prices rise—when a great deal of it is in circulation. Money, like any commodity, is subject to the law of supply and demand, to be discussed in this chapter.

SAVING

A person who, through the use of his labor or the use of his capital, has produced wealth for himself need not utilize this wealth at once. He may, if he prefers, save it in the form of money or some equivalent, for his consumption at a later time. This saving is, of course, necessary to the individual in our society: without it he could not at any time take a vacation, retire, support himself when ill, nor could he ever indulge in luxuries costing more than his current earnings. An individual may have savings in the form of money, but more frequently in the form of bank deposits and interest-bearing loans such as savings-bank deposits, notes, mortgages, and bonds; or he may invest his savings in forms of wealth less directly convertible into money, as in real estate, buildings, shares in business ventures, or common stocks of any variety. The possibility of using these forms of wealth at any time by converting them into goods for immediate consumption is the main attraction of any program of saving, and its importance to the individual can hardly be overstressed.

But there is not a corresponding importance to savings, considered nationally or from a world-wide point of view. The savings of one individual are convertible into consumer's goods only as long as there are other individuals producing consumable wealth and willing to convert that wealth into savings (money). Thus monetary wealth is not real wealth, and only represents on the part of the community generally a promise to pay by its conversion into real wealth or consumer goods. For any large part of the community, and for the world in general, this conversion is, of course, impossible. If for some reason the production of food were to cease today, it would be impossible for our national wealth, expressed in terms of money, stocks, bonds, bank credits, and so forth, to be converted into food. This means that in the monetary sense it is impossible for a nation or for the world at large to save. All monetary savings are in a general sense only temporary; the real value of such savings exists only when they are no longer savings but are converted into wealth; that is, when the money is spent on consumer (or capital) goods.

The problem arises when unemployment and old age insurance is put into effect, involving the saving by the government of a huge reserve fund for future use. It is quite impossible for the government to save such huge quantities of wealth since there would be no way to convert it into consumer goods at any one time. Actually, therefore, this so-called reserve fund of the government consists, and can consist, only of government promises to pay. In a rather different sense, the community at large saves by piling up either capital goods or consumer goods which are not subject to rapid deterioration. Thus the highway and railroad systems of this country, the buildings, factories, machines, farm equipment, power plants, and even stocks of non-perishable foods, may be considered to be a real saving on the part of the country. The true national wealth is thus increased by the piling up of preserved consumer goods and by the provision of means for the future production of consumer goods.

The value of money is therefore dependent upon one's ability to convert it, on demand, into consumer goods. At different times in the world's history, the possibility of converting monetary wealth into consumer wealth has been subject both to long-term changes and to periodic fluctuations. To buy an automobile when automobiles were first produced cost tremendously more for a much inferior product than it would cost today. Generally speaking, the increase in our ability to produce manufactured goods has lowered the cost and increased the quality of what each unit of money can buy. On the other hand, the prices of certain things such as rare manuscripts and hand-made materials of many kinds, of antique articles of various sorts desired for their antiquity, works of art, land, and labor have increased in price.

As during this whole period the ability of an individual to procure monetary wealth has also varied, the amount and kind of goods that a worker can consume as the result of his labor is considerably changed. The amount and quality of goods consumed by the average member of a community, including both necessities and luxuries, is known as its "standard of living." The worker today earns a hundred times as much money as he did some seven or eight centuries ago, and considerably more than was the rule even fifty years ago. Dollar for dollar, his earnings will buy for him less in terms of necessities than in that former period; but, day's work for day's work, he is able to buy much more. In addition he can purchase many articles, some of them necessities but most of them luxuries, which were completely unknown to his ancestors. An additional factor which has appeared only in recent times is the possibility that, being unable to find work, he will be unable to earn anything at all and his very living may be endangered. But considered on the average, the standard of living today has risen fairly steadily from the standard of several centuries ago. This improvement represents real progress in the economic development of civilization.

There is a further problem, however, which arises because of the variations in the standard of living within relatively short periods, periods of prosperity and of depression. Quite apart from any governmental tinkering with the currency, the real value of money and the real value of labor, both expressed in terms of what they will buy, are considerably higher in one of these periods than in the other. The value of money may thus be expressed in terms of a more fundamental standard of living, which itself is the most real index of prosperity and standard of wealth. Many economists have therefore sought to achieve a monetary basis, other than gold, which would be subject to less fluctuation in terms of the standard of living; that is to say, in terms of what the monetary wealth will buy. There would obviously be a real advantage in being able to save with a definite knowledge of exactly what one's savings would buy at a future time, instead of being to some extent engaged in a speculation as to the future value of one's monetary wealth; but there are serious practical difficulties in the creation of any such monetary system.

CREDIT

In a rather primitive community where only a small number of commodities are used and where exchange of these commodities is rather infrequent, it would doubtless be possible to pay for every article which changes hands, in terms of the commodity selected for use as money. But as the number of commodities produced and the frequency of exchanges becomes greater, this possibility no longer exists. All the gold in the world would hardly suffice to conduct the normal business of one month in New York. If credit disappeared, the lack of money would make it difficult to buy or sell at all, and practically impossible to consummate any deals involving large sums, except, of course, by the primitive and inelastic method of barter. Consequently, gold is not used by us as currency but only as a basis for our whole system of monetary credit.

Credit is a promise to pay in the future in exchange for commodities, services, or money. Credit, therefore, is a substitute for money. We are living in a credit economy; that is, most of the business transactions in a country like the United States are made, not with money, but with promises to pay.

There are two great classes of credit: *consumer's credit* and *producer's credit*. Consumer's credit is a promise to pay made by a consumer in exchange for commodities, services, or money which he wishes to acquire at once. Producer's credit is a promise to pay made by a producer in exchange for commodities, services, or funds which he wishes to employ in his enterprise in order to carry forward his business activities.

The credit economy carries with it certain advantages and disadvantages. It has made saving and investment a source of profits. Nevertheless, every loan and investment carries with it the risk of changes in purchasing power which may adversely affect the lender or the borrower.

Credit to producers has made possible greater production and trade. Under our system of production it requires large amounts of capital to make goods in anticipation of demand. Credit makes such production easier. In addition, the use of borrowed funds enables the producer to gain a higher rate of return on his own investment. There are, however, disadvantages to offset the above benefits. In times of falling prices, fixed interest charges may become a very heavy burden. In case of default of interest or principal when due, the creditors may legally seize and sell the property, or the control of the business may pass into other hands.

Installment buying and other forms of consumer's credit make possible a higher standard of living. Although the purchase of goods on credit makes possible the use of the goods while paying for them, it must be recognized that goods bought on credit may lead to extravagance. Then, too, goods bought on credit usually cost more than the same goods when bought for cash. There is, moreover, the risk of losing goods purchased on credit because of the non-payment of one or more installments.

The use of credit by governments can avoid the imposing of heavy taxes on the people. There is, at the same time, the danger of extravagance on the part of the government when its power to borrow is unlimited. Government borrowing may become a major factor in creating booms and financial crises.

Our government, as that of any other country, has the exclusive privilege of producing money in any form. It may issue, and has often issued, gold in the form of coins, but even where this occurs it is only an unimportant part of the monetary system. The government issues bills of various denominations from one dollar up, which are equivalent to gold in the sense that they were originally redeemable in gold or, in some cases, redeemable in silver or other money which was in turn exchangeable for gold. If the government issued bills solely to the extent of its own supply of gold, the effect of the circulation of paper currency would be practically negligible. But the government is not limited in this way: it actually issues bills to a value far in excess of the supply of gold which it promises to pay for their redemption, a procedure which is possible only because it will not normally happen that many people may simultaneously demand payment for the government's bills. There may therefore exist governmental promises to pay to the quantity of about two and a half times the value of the total amount of gold available in the country.

Governments may use commodities other than gold as the basis, or part of the basis, of their own currency; silver is sometimes so used, and also government bonds and the currency of foreign nations. In the last case there is a noticeable further expansion of the quantities of money available, as a smaller nation may have issued two promises to pay on the basis of one equivalent promise to pay of the British or American governments, the latter promises to pay being in turn only fractionally covered by metals in the treasuries of the respective countries. We do not ordinarily realize that the small coinage of this country, made of silver, nickel, and copper, is also an illustration of governmental credit; for the value of the metals in any of our minor coins is very much less than the face value of the coin. The reason for the acceptance of coins and bills has been in general the reliance upon the government's willingness and ability to redeem any part of the currency. Its willingness is expressed in the honesty of the government's conduct; its ability is evident in the fact that the government is able to levy taxes to whatever extent may be necessary.

The total amount of government currency outstanding, even after this expansion, is still wholly inadequate to satisfy the needs of our highly organized commercial system. Most business is done with the aid, not of government credit, but of bank credit. The bank is an institution for the handling, and sometimes for the issuance, of money, receiving money from its original capital, and from deposits, and lending that money, plus a good deal more that it does not really possess, to anyone who needs it and gives evidence of being able to repay. A bank, in the normal course of its operations, will have promised to pay others very much more than it actually has; this extension of credit being possible only because the great majority of these promises to pay will never be actually converted into currency.

A bank, for example, establishes a credit of ten thousand dollars in the account of John Smith. Technically, the bank has lent John Smith ten thousand dollars for the needs of his business, and will receive from him interest on that amount. But John Smith may never use more than eight or nine thousand dollars of this credit, and that part which he does use may never leave the bank. He may owe Henry Brown a thousand dollars for merchandise which he has received. This he pays for, ordinarily, not by going to the bank, getting United States currency, and making a payment in cash, but by writing a check on the bank and sending it to his creditor. So Henry Brown has now received a check for one thousand dollars from John Smith. This check he deposits in the bank to his own credit. The bank now is engaged to pay John Smith nine thousand dollars and Henry Brown one thousand dollars. But Henry Brown, in turn, is apt to use this money only in the form of checks; and consequently little if any of the original ten thousand dollar credit of John Smith's may ever leave the bank. Thus a bank having resources of a million dollars might conceivably lend ten million dollars.

But what happens if Henry Brown does not use the same bank that John Smith uses? Then his check will be deposited in his own bank, which will call upon John Smith's bank for one thousand dollars. A great many such transactions take place every day, and a great many of them normally cancel each other. A number of clients of Henry Brown's bank will deposit checks on John Smith's bank, but at the same time there will be a similar number of clients of John Smith's bank depositing checks on Henry Brown's. These transactions, therefore, need not be completed by any actual transfer of cash. Through the medium of a clearing house, the credits and debits resulting from each bank's daily transactions are paired with one another and the small differential between the outgoing and incoming amounts is the only fraction of the huge mass of credit that need be paid in cash.

What would happen if the persons having credit at one bank all demanded payment at once? Although this, as we have said, will not occur normally, something very like it will occur if there is a panic and a question arises as to the ability of the bank to meet its obligations. In such cases a lone bank, not connected with other financial institutions, might be forced to close its doors; but with conditions as they are today, each bank is protected by the resources of the whole banking system. When a bank finds itself endangered by a run, it sends the notes, received in evidence of its loans to corporations or individuals, to another bank, and receives from this bank an amount slightly less than the face value of the obligation. This credit it then uses to pay off its own obligations. This process, known as rediscounting, is carried on not merely as an emergency measure but as a normal banking function. Suppose a bank contracts to lend one hundred dollars for two months at six per cent interest. What actually happens is that the borrower gives the bank a promise to pay one hundred dollars in two months' time, and the bank establishes a credit for the borrower of ninety-nine dollars, the discount of one dollar representing two months' interest on the total amount. Now the bank has contracted to pay ninety-nine dollars, but it may turn the note that it has received over to a rediscount bank, usually in the Federal Reserve System, for ninety-nine dollars and some odd cents. In this way the bank assumes the risk of the loan but does not actually expend any capital.

Besides the use of checks and promissory notes as credit instruments, *drafts, bills of exchange,* and *trade acceptances* are in common use. A bank draft is a written order drawn by one bank upon another bank to pay a third person a specified sum of money. A bill of exchange is a draft that is used in foreign exchange. A trade acceptance is a draft which has been received by the drawee or debtor and which he has acknowledged by writing across the face of the order the word "Accepted" and has designated the place of payment, either his bank or place of business. Credit instruments may be transferred from one person to another by means of an endorsement; that is, the placing of his signature on the back of a credit instrument made payable to him. Such instruments are said to be negotiable.

MANAGED CURRENCY

We have seen that the monetary system of a country is of very little intrinsic value: that it consists only of promises to pay gold in such quantities that it would be impossible to pay if called upon to do so. The value of the currency in terms of gold thus continues only as long as the credit of the country remains good. We may furthermore recall that gold itself has no real value, and that its actual value is predicated upon the willingness of other people to receive it in exchange for commodities. Now, if the gold reserve wholly disappears, and the people in general do not know about it, the effect would be the same as if the gold reserve remained. The value of gold is therefore wholly psychological, and under proper circumstances it might be eliminated from our economy.

These circumstances do occur whenever the people of a country become so accustomed to a paper currency that they accept this currency without considering whether or not it is convertible into gold. It becomes possible, therefore, for a country to "leave the gold standard," and simply issue paper currency not redeemable in anything else. Fundamentally this situation is no different from the system of the gold standard, since it merely substitutes the habitual willingness to accept paper currency for the habitual willingness to accept gold, neither paper nor gold being of sufficient intrinsic value. The situations, however, do differ radically in one respect: that while the production of new gold is limited by the output of mines, the output of paper currency is limited only by the discretion of the government. If the government issues paper currency in very large quantities, it will gradually destroy the willingness of the people to accept the currency. To some extent this is a simple result of the law of supply and demand: if the supply is apparently unlimited, an object can have little value; but it would also be due in part to the fact that the psychology of paper money cannot be wholly divorced from the traditional tie with a quantity of gold.

When the government increases the supply of currency, this action is known as currency or monetary inflation: when the government decreases the supply of currency, we have monetary deflation. Either effect can be produced when on the gold standard by varying the rate at which the government will redeem its currency; and when the government fixes the value of its currency, not by redemption in gold, but by controlling the foreign exchange market, it may produce inflationary or deflationary effects through the sale of its own currency at a calculated price or in calculated amounts in the open market. Particularly in the case of a currency not tied to gold, it is possible for the government to vary at its discretion the value of the currency in terms of gold. It might, for example, attempt to control the value of the currency in such a way that not its value in gold but its value in commodities would remain constant. This inverse control of the value of money is actually effected by a direct control of commodity prices, such as occurred during the war under the charge of the Office of Price Administration in this country. A belief in the permanent desirability of such control is held by some economists.

Besides monetary inflation, it is possible to have credit inflation. As we have said before, the supply of gold is expanded by the government into a larger supply of currency, and this supply of currency is further expanded through the use of bank credit and of other devices into a very much greater volume of credit; and that business itself is run upon this bank credit. Now, in time of panic and depression, banks hesitate to extend credit, and the total amount of credit in our system becomes considerably lower. During enormous prosperity many persons' credit is good, and the supply in the country is greater. These conditions of credit inflation and deflation may be, to some extent, controlled by government: the government may produce credit inflation by loaning money or by encouraging or forcing banks to do so. It is much easier for the government to produce credit deflation than inflation, as it can do this simply by restricting by legal means the extent to which a bank may extend credit. Furthermore, when the credit base of the banks is determined by national bonds, the government is able to affect that base by distributing or calling in these bonds or by legally varying the credit base. By controlling credit inflation and deflation, the government may be able to have command, to some extent, of business cycles.

The effect of monetary inflation is much more severe than that of credit inflation, and it is intrinsically much more dangerous. Currency inflation, in the history of the world, has usually been extended until the point has been reached when the value of the currency and the credit of the country totally disappear. Under such circumstances we have conditions of economic disaster to almost everyone concerned. Business is destroyed, the small wage earner suffers, most owners of securities lose the greater part of their wealth, and only a few fortunate speculators gain by the losses of other members of society.

PRICE

The price of any article which is exchanged in an open market depends upon supply and demand. If an article would sell normally for the price of one dollar and something happens to increase the supply, the extra quantity of the article on the market will cause the sellers to reduce the price until the reduced price will entice sufficient extra buying so that the demand at the new low price will equal the supply. If the supply is suddenly lowered, the ability of the sellers to get higher prices will allow them to raise the price until the new high price levels reduce the demand to the point where it is only sufficient to be equivalent to the reduced supply. If, on the other hand, there is an increased demand for a given article, the price will be raised until the demand is again reduced to the quantity determined by the existing supply. If the demand is reduced, the price will be lowered to bring back the demand once more to its previous levels. Price may be defined as value expressed in terms of money. Demand may be defined as the desire that a person has for a commodity plus his ability to pay for it. There are certain laws of demand which are characteristic of the economic system. Demand varies directly with "marginal utility."

Let us consider as an example the price of chromium; if for any reason the demand for chromium is increased, the price of the metal would be raised, as determined by the law of supply and demand. But if chromium commands a higher price on the general market, it becomes financially profitable to work mines for the production of chromium that were previously undeveloped or abandoned because the cost of production was greater than the price of the produced metal. The cost of producing a further unit quantity of any product beyond the quantity already produced is known as the "marginal cost," or "marginal productivity." In this case the price of chromium will never rise, except for short periods, above the marginal cost of the production of chromium. Instead the supply will be increased. A further factor in this equalization is "marginal utility." The marginal utility of a given product to any person is the price that he would be willing to pay for one more unit of the product than he already possesses. The price of any article in the long run will be such that the marginal cost equals the marginal utility, and all variations in price and all transactions in the open market tend to bring the actual conditions to the stated results. In other words, at a certain equilibrium price the supply will equal the demand.

To take another illustration, let us suppose that the supply of housing in a given community for the moment is less than the demand for housing. The general level of rents in that community will rise until the profits made by landlords are sufficiently great to attract investments in apartment house construction; and new building will then occur, continuing until a time arrives when the increased supply brings the normal rent down to such a point that it is no longer attractive to build. The point around which rents will actually fluctuate is determined by the normal interest rates on capital in the community. On the other hand, if taxes in the community are increased, the landlord no longer makes a profit at the old rent. For this reason no new building occurs, and buildings which are destroyed by accident or which become too old to be used are allowed to remain out of service, thus reducing the housing supply. This reduction continues until the demand overtakes the supply, rents rise once more, and the point of normal return upon investment is again reached.

Demand also varies inversely with price. Thus, if the price of a commodity goes down, the demand for the product will increase. Demand also varies directly with purchasing power. If purchasing power declines, then the demand for commodities will decrease. Some goods, however, react differently with a change in price. A change in the price of bread will not seriously affect the demand for it. Thus necessities are said to be subject to inelastic demand.

INEQUITABLE PRICES

Prices normally fluctuate around a point which will give a return approximately equal to the prevailing rate of interest. This is usually called the "normal price" or the "law of adequate returns." The law of adequate returns works successfully only in a situation where there is a freely fluctuating supply and a freely fluctuating demand, without any great time lag between the variation in either of these factors and the resultant characteristic responses to them. One common exception to the law occurs when the supply of an article is constant. An example of this is in the supply of land available within a given community. If the community is not able to expand outwardly into neighboring territory, the price of land, when in great demand, will increase at a much more rapid rate than would commodities which have a fluctuating supply.

When the demand is constant, as it is in large measure for basic foods, any considerable variation in the supply causes violent fluctuations in price. Thus, when there is an extremely good year in wheat production, the income of the farmer is apt to be inequitably reduced, since the excessive wheat supply hangs over the market and forces a tremendous reduction in price, a reduction which would not take place with an article such as fruit, where the amount consumed varies inversely as the price.

The extreme case of the breakdown of the law of adequate returns occurs when both the supply and the demand are constant. Take the case of a besieged city when food begins to be lacking. Up to a certain point it is possible for the citizens to cut down upon the amount they eat, but there is a definite limit to the extent to which they can cut down. The supply, meanwhile, is constant and not sufficient. In such a case the price of any article of food, let us say of bread, will rise indefinitely, until a single loaf of bread might be sufficient to purchase all the real estate and metallic wealth in the city. The same is true of the services of a doctor in times of plague, or of the price of shelter or gas masks in wartime, and of the prices of other articles in various unusual situations.

A further factor that causes the law of adequate returns to work improperly is the delay in equalization of supply and demand. When a change occurs in one factor of the equation involving supply and demand, a chain of causes is set in motion which will eventually result in an equilibrium at a just figure, but some considerable time may elapse before this condition is achieved. In the case of dwellings mentioned above, after any considerable variation in demand, the rents will be too high or too low according to the standard of adequate returns, and will entail profiteering or capital loss until such times as conditions can be equalized. In the former case, assuming that it takes ten months to build apartments, rents will remain too high for a period of at least ten months. In the other case, where demand is too low and rents drop to levels that do not cover expenses, apartment houses will not become uninhabitable from accidents or obsolescence for a much longer period, and landlords will receive an insufficient return in rents for a period which will be measured in years.

There are, in addition, a good many cases where the delay in equalization is much greater than in this case. Take, for example, the supply of trained labor, particularly in the higher categories such as the professions. If there are not enough doctors for the needs of the community, it will require not less than ten years to attract into the medical profession an increased supply of practitioners. Thus the supply of doctors, and likewise the supply of lawyers and teachers, is determined not by the demand for their services that exists at the moment but by the demand that existed ten years or more before. If the demand for lawyers were suddenly cut in half, it would take a period equal to half the average life span of a lawyer's working life, perhaps a matter of fifteen or twenty years, before the supply would be adjusted to the reduced demand, even supposing that no new lawyers were created during the period of adjustment. Of course this situation would be avoided if lawyers prepared themselves for the practice of other trades when confronted with unfavorable conditions in their own profession, but after a man has spent six to ten years of his life, as well as a good deal of money, in preparation for a particular mode of living, he is extremely reluctant to make any changes in it; and, in fact, it might be impossible for him to make any changes except by becoming a laborer.

The conditions described as true of the professions are also true of skilled labor, and even more so of unskilled labor. The amount of labor available is obviously a fairly constant factor. There are, indeed, well-to-do persons who will work only when the returns for working are high, and there are a number of other individuals who will work overtime under the same conditions. But the variation in the total amount of labor on the market under the very best and under the very worst conditions of our economic system is never very great. If the supply of labor is, then, excessive, the effect of the law of supply and demand is to reduce the level of wages to a point where labor is just able to support life or, rather, to the lowest level at which a workman in a given community is willing to exist.

MONOPOLY

A further difficulty with the operation of the law of adequate returns occurs when the supply or demand of a commodity is controlled by one concern, or by any group of concerns that agree to fix prices rather than to have open competition. Such a group could demand and receive any price whatsoever for any necessities that it has to sell.

There are various classes of monopolies. Individuals, because they are peculiarly talented in some valuable way, can command a remuneration to suit themselves. Examples would be highly talented actors, radio performers, or professional athletes. Legal monopolies are those granted by the government either to itself or to someone else; for example, the post office, the coining of money, or the granting of patents, copyrights, and trademarks. Natural monopolies may be of two types, either of location or the nature of the business. Natural monopolies of location are those which arise from the control of some one commodity to be found exclusively in only one region. Examples are the diamond mines in South Africa and the anthracite mines in Pennsylvania.

Those enterprises which, by the nature of their business, must have a monopoly of the business in a given territory in order to carry on profitably are called natural monopolies of organization. Examples are public utilities and railroads. Such enterprises necessitate the investment of huge sums of capital. If a competitor should step in and take away part of the business, both would incur heavy losses and might face ultimate ruin. That is why a public utility, before it decides to start in business, gets a written agreement from the government, called a franchise, granting the public utility a monopoly for a long period of years. Other monopolies are those which companies form by huge mergers or consolidations through their control of huge funds of capital.

The monopolist will fix that price for his commodity which will yield him the greatest net return. The monopolist takes the following facts into consideration: (1) the number of units that can be sold at a given price; (2) the cost per unit when producing a certain number of units; and (3) whether a lower price will bring a larger net return than higher prices do.

In practice, however, there are other limitations on monopoly prices. If the monopolist is too greedy, sooner or later competitors attracted by the large profits will attempt to break into the industry. High prices will cause more and more consumers to look for adequate substitutes. Public opinion will force the government to seek means to break up a greedy monopoly or to curb its greed in some way; for example, by regulation or competition from government-owned enterprises.

Besides monopoly of products, we have monopoly of consumption. If one company, or a group of companies or individuals, constitutes the whole market for a given product, it can dictate the price of any article purchased, short of throwing the seller of the article out of business. Thus various small companies producing automobile parts for concerns such as Chrysler, General Motors, and Ford are practically at the mercy of these larger companies. If the automobile manufacturers, in agreement, or sometimes individually, cut down the price that they offer for the smaller company's products to a point where the price covers the general cost of production but not sufficient return on capital investment, the small company can do nothing but accept. Consequently the rate of return on articles manufactured by companies dependent upon a small number of large consumers tends to be less than the average rate of return. In other business ventures the extreme case occurs when one company has a monopoly in the production of a given article but a second company has a monopoly in its consumption. In such cases, the price at which the article is to be sold must be determined by an arbitrary agreement, reached usually by a bargaining process between the two companies.

What is true of the purchase of commodities is also true of the purchase of labor. In communities where laborers are unorganized and are hired by a large number of independent small capitalists, the wages of labor will be determined by the normal workings of the law of supply and demand. But where one company uses the greater part of the labor of a single town, it is largely able to dictate the wage level, and the results are frequently less satisfactory from the point of view of labor and from the point of view of society. Where strongly organized labor exists in a community of small capitalists, the reverse situation takes place. When both capital and labor are organized, the wage level is fixed by an arbitrary bargaining process just as is the price of a commodity sold by a monopoly producer to a monopoly consumer.

THE BUSINESS CYCLE

The factors that control price are such that we may say that the price of any single article is in stable equilibrium. In other words, any fall of the price immediately sets in motion factors that will tend to raise the price and re-establish the level near where it was before. Purely economic factors would control the whole system of prices in the same way were it not for the existence of psychological factors which, within certain limits of range, produce the reverse effect. When, for any reason, the price level of all commodities decreases, it is apt to cause a fear, in the minds of all the members of the community, of a further fall; and those persons who own commodities not for their own immediate use but for speculation, reserve, or business purposes will then attempt to sell their holdings before the price level sinks too far. This throwing of old stocks upon the market further depresses the price level, which, in turn, reinforces public fear.

The psychological factor of panic thus tends to convert a minor fall in prices into a major depression, the duration and nadir of which will generally depend, among other factors, upon the quantity of stocks on hand at the time the depression begins. The seriousness of a depression results from the fact that it is quite impossible for the country as a whole to convert commodity goods into cash, and while the public is trying to do so, the result is simply the continual exchange of the ownership of commodities at ever-decreasing price levels. Finally, when the restricted consumption of commodities in the depression period has become greater than the restricted production, stocks of commodities are reduced to a point where their overhang upon the market is less important than the public demand for new goods.

When the general price level tends to rise, there may be an optimistic public reaction producing the feeling that prices both of commodities and of capital investments will continue to rise indefinitely. Everyone then seeks to convert his cash or monetary credit into commodities, in this way raising the price level still more and intensifying the psychological demand for goods. This process likewise continues until the increased production that occurs in prosperous times overtakes the increased consumption, and results in the piling-up of huge stocks of consumer goods.

Thus we see that a not uncommon situation in our type of economic organization is the alternation of periods of prosperity and depression. This alternation is characteristic not merely of capitalism but of all systems where goods are exchanged in terms of money.

A depression in a simple community is not such a serious matter as it is for a more complex one. With the improvement of our material culture has come an intensification of the hardships felt in periods of depression. The more advanced culture has larger stocks of commodities, and the total amount of monetary credit becomes greater. Furthermore, division of labor has progressed further in the industrial community, so that there are many individuals who rely for their whole living upon the normal operation of commerce. In primitive society, after all, it did not matter greatly if one's holdings lost value: one simply dug in and lived on the production of the land, either agriculturally or industrially. Even in a more complex culture, where persons might be engaged as laborers, it was possible until recently for any laborer who had no work to leave the city and strike out into new territory, either reaching farming land where there was always room for additional farm labor, or going into the woods and carving out a homestead for himself. This solution to the problem becomes impossible as frontiers cease to be but a few miles away; when even the demand for farm labor is cut down by the development of mechanical aids to the farmer; and when, in particular, great cities come into existence with their populations running into millions, who are dependent for food upon the exchange of their industrial products and services for the products of the agricultural communities around them.

Another factor which has contributed to the intensification of depressions is the increase in efficiency of our methods of production, so that one man's labor will do what dozens or hundreds would be required to do in earlier times. This has freed a large proportion of the population for the production of luxuries. When ninety per cent of the population was engaged directly or indirectly in the production of food, housing, and necessary clothing, a depression could never be of great intensity, since the demand for these products could never cease for any considerable period of time. But today, when the majority of our population is engaged in the production of articles it does not directly consume, the situation for the workers becomes acute in times of depression. For while the sale of agricultural implements or food can never fall off tremendously in quantity, nor remain exceptionally low for more than short periods, the consumption of "luxury" articles (television sets, for example) can be reduced to practically nothing and remain at that low level for as long as the psychological factors of depression continue. The great majority of our population today is thus dependent upon the consumption of goods which give no guarantee by their nature that the demand for them will continue; and the livelihood of the major part of our population is thus directly dependent upon the psychological factors of the business cycle.

After a depression, the normal cycle seems to run something like this: the demand for goods makes business pick up and conditions improve for a few years. Before business has reached halfway to the peak of prosperity there is a secondary depression; which does not, however, reach the low levels of the preceding one. Then there is a further rise, interrupted only by minor price fluctuations, which takes business to the height of prosperity. Then prices tumble. Before they have fallen halfway to depression levels, there is a secondary recovery followed by a further trend toward depression.

When depression is not of great severity or long duration, it is possible to view its occurrence merely as an interesting phenomenon in the economic sphere, which a business man should study. But more and more, in modern times, depression has come to mean starvation for many. We therefore find it imperative to arrive at some solution that will either eliminate or modify the business cycle with its attendant hardships.

Many people believe that by giving the workers and farmers, who are by far the largest portion of the population, a more equitable share of the annual income, mass purchasing power will increase and thus stimulate the production of our farms, factories, and mines. Another suggested remedy has been a more extensive program of social insurance which would provide purchasing power during periods of unemployment.

Some economists believe that the government and big business organizations should postpone all major construction until a recession in business sets in. The construction of public works, such as roads, buildings, dams, and grade crossings by the government, and the building of additional plant capacity by private enterprise during a period of prosperity only intensify competition for labor, raw materials, and capital. This competition aggravates speculation and leads to ultimate collapse.

A better housing program, with government aid, may be made a powerful means of overcoming business depressions. As Franklin D. Roosevelt once said, "From the point of view of widespread and sustained economic recovery, housing constitutes the largest and most promising single field for private enterprise."

It is felt by organized labor and others that the only solution to the problem of unemployment caused by improvement in machines is a reduction in working hours. It is therefore urged that the time has come to establish a shorter work week. Wage rates, of course, would not be lowered in proportion to the reduction of hours, so that the workers will not be deprived of their former purchasing power. It has also been proposed that the Federal Reserve System tighten control over credit to curb speculation in boom times and stimulate recovery in times of depression.

The two main elements in any answer to this problem, involving, as it does, a theoretical revision of our whole economic system, are regulation of production and regulation of distribution and consumption: the problem of the creation of wealth, and the problem of the distribution of wealth. Besides the present manner of distribution, there are two other forms of distribution which we shall briefly consider.

ECONOMICS AND STATE CONTROL

SOCIALISM

Socialism believes in the distribution of wealth to each individual in accordance with his merits; that is, the individual who creates more, either because of greater ability or greater willingness to work, should be rewarded by a greater share of commodities than that person who does less work or work of less value. Of course neither capitalism nor socialism would fail to care for the mentally or physically crippled, for orphans or for aged persons who are not able to provide for themselves.

In what specific ways does the socialist wish to see our economic system modified? Primarily, he is opposed to the private ownership of wealth whenever it is owned by someone who has not earned it by contributions to the public good. He therefore objects to the possibility of making money by market manipulations when such manipulations are not definitely in the public interest; he objects to the fact that the present system to some extent makes it possible for the wealthy to grow more wealthy, at a rate wholly inconsistent with any services rendered to the community; and he objects to the possession of wealth by individuals or families purely as a matter of inheritance on the part of the individual receiving the wealth.

Socialism, then, tends to propose these modifications of the capitalistic system: first, wealth must not be inherited in such a way as to remove the beneficiary from economic competition with his fellows. This aim may be achieved by semi-confiscatory tax on inheritance, especially by inheritance taxes which run into tremendous percentages in the upper brackets.

Second, there should be a more even distribution of wealth, thus preventing extremes both of wealth and poverty within a community. This aim would be largely achieved by the reduction of inheritances as mentioned above.

Third, wealth should not beget wealth. To achieve this result completely, it would be necessary for the state to take over the function of providing capital, so that it would become impossible for the individual to make money by lending or investing. One objection to this scheme is that it would tend to an enormous amount of governmental control of private initiative, with the resulting evils of bureaucracy. In addition, the distinction between capital goods and consumer goods fails in practice, since most consumer goods can also be used as capital goods; thus, land and buildings may be used either for production or for living purposes, and food may be eaten fresh or be manufactured into a more complex variety of food. But the aim of the socialist in this respect may be largely achieved by the reduction of great accumulations of wealth, so that the proportion of a person's income due to capital return on investments would remain moderate. If, in fact, the capital owned by any individual was limited to the money that he earned and saved in his lifetime, there would be no particular objection to his enjoying an income of this type.

Socialism proposes, fourthly, that it should be impossible to make money by any means that do not actually benefit society. This would mean the prohibition or strict regulation of all forms of gambling, especially of gambling in capital goods such as grain futures and stocks and bonds; the prohibition of improper advertising; of the sale of harmful or useless products; of the sale of any product under false pretenses; and, in extreme socialistic systems, the severe restriction of any form of activity which does not either produce or distribute consumer goods, or contribute to such intangible things as education, travel, and entertainment.

Fifth, socialism demands that there should be sufficient regulation of market conditions that the injustices in price levels, which we discussed in the section on price, should be avoided.

And sixth, whatever other steps may be necessary to reduce human suffering and add to human enjoyment should be undertaken by the government. This would include not only action to control the business cycle but also governmental entrance into the business field whenever the government is able to perform needed services that would otherwise not be performed, or be performed less efficiently or less economically by private individuals. It would also include governmental care for future generations by the conservation of national wealth, by the protection of national health, and by whatever eugenic control may be necessary or desirable.

There are, of course, varying degrees of socialism in both theory and practice. Although the United States is not socialistic, the government intervenes in the control of monopolies, in the building of highways and operation of postal services, in the imposition of taxes for social security, in the regulation of the exchange of securities, and in the supervision of advertising and numerous other business activities. All such governmental actions may be considered as certain specific features of a modified socialism operating in a characteristically free-enterprise economy. On the other hand, countries that have predominantly socialistic economies have found it necessary to retain or reinstigate certain features more characteristic of free enterprise, notably a degree of free competition and the opportunity of profit and some private accumulation of capital.

COMMUNISM

Communism, unlike socialism and capitalism, proposes that wealth should be distributed not in accordance with merit but according to need. Under such circumstances, society as a whole—represented by the government—controls all production and in turn all distribution.

The communist slogan, "From each according to his ability, to each according to his need," is based upon the theory that in a co-operative society it will not be necessary to offer individuals the lure of large money gains. The theory communism holds is that such incentives as the esteem of one's fellow men, pride in one's work, and striving for the social good can be relied on to stimulate all classes of workers to a greater degree than the pursuit of money. For this reason, communists urge equality of pay.

Turning to the more objective consideration of communism as it has existed in the world, we notice that in actual practice there has never been any extensive adherence to the communistic theory of distribution. Communism, in the sense of distribution according to need, does not exist in the Soviet Union. Aside from the Russian venture there have been many cases of small societies in England and the United States that have lived on a communistic basis: all of them have disappeared after a longer or shorter period, and none of them has consisted of large groups.

Communism as an economic system, then, has failed when attempted by small communities and has not been followed in the only large experiment. However, communists, who take their cue from the writings of Karl Marx, maintain that communism is an inevitable development from capitalism and that in time the entire world's economy will be communist in nature.

FASCISM

Fascism developed as an outgrowth of two causes: one, political and economic limitations of the capitalistic system; the other, the reaction to the threat of communism. Its general characteristics include: a glorification of the state; the abolition of democracy; an attempt to make a nation self-sufficient by complete regulation of its economic life; and continued emphasis on militarism. World War II put an end to the fascist governments in Italy and Germany and their satellites, although there are still some others in existence.

PRODUCTION

Although economic theorists have concerned themselves especially with the manner in which wealth should be distributed, there are many important problems affecting its production. Consider first the production of the food supply. The quantity of food produced by the cultivation of a given area has been increasing with the development of modern methods of agriculture, but, as Malthus pointed out many years ago, the population also increases at a rate which will make it overtake any conceivable level of food supply. The mathematics of Malthus were not entirely correct, for he failed to properly take into account the death rate and the tendency of peoples to reproduce less with the extension of education to the masses. There is, nevertheless, constantly facing the world the prospect of lowered standards of living, starvation, lowered resistance to disease, plagues, and floods, all directly or indirectly resulting from the too large growth of the human population. At some time it could become necessary to restrict this growing population, either by a sort of voluntary birth control or by a government-sponsored program of eugenics. That the voluntary limitation may be sufficient in point of numbers is indicated by the declining birth rates in most civilized countries, but a danger is pointed out in that the declining birth rate has been affecting the presumably better individuals rather than those of lower intelligence. However this may be, the economist, as opposed to the sociologist, is only concerned to point out that the food supply of the world today is far from exhausted, and that no danger from Malthusian principles need be apprehended for another two centuries at least.

With the improved methods of creation of wealth that have been progressively displacing the cruder methods of the past, the number of hours per citizen needed for the production of necessities has constantly declined. It would be possible for the community today to live if each individual worked only an hour a day. The improvement in methods of production allows an ever-increasing part of man's activity to be devoted to the enjoyment of leisure, and to the production of luxuries to be enjoyed in that leisure. A certain proportion must be maintained between these two factors: the production of luxuries would be useless were there no leisure in which to enjoy them; and leisure itself would become monotonous were no luxuries provided for the entertainment of leisure time. The average number of hours in the day's work has therefore been gradually decreasing, and while our ancestors may have worked fifteen or sixteen hours a day for six (or sometimes seven) days a week, making, perhaps, a working week of about one hundred hours, the average working week has progressively dropped to the level of forty or thirty-five hours, with a level of even twenty hours per week regarded as not improbable for the near future.

If the average number of working hours per week is not in proper proportion to the community's ability to produce, certain evil results will follow. If the hour level is too low, there will be extra leisure time beyond that which can be satisfactorily utilized; which may lead to dissatisfaction, and, in the economic sphere, to an increased demand for luxuries. This in turn brings a further demand for labor to be used in the production of luxuries, and results in an increase in pay and in the hours of labor per week. If legislation makes this last development impossible there will be a general increase in prices and wages of labor, which will, however, under these circumstances, bring about dangerous sociological results.

A greater danger occurs when the number of working hours per week is too great in proportion to the community's rate of consumption. In such a case, production will proceed at a more rapid rate than consumption until a depression results, during which increased production will throw huge numbers of the working population out of their ordinary occupations. If the working hours remain high, this depression may not lead to a period of prosperity, as would be the case according to the normal business cycle, but may lead to a condition of chronic unemployment.

If women enter business fields, their labor either increases the general production or replaces that of men. In either case the resulting condition can only be corrected by a decrease in the average working hours. Whether it is desirable for women to work is a sociological problem and not an economic one; but, whatever labor is performed by women, it must be compensated for by a decrease in general working hours or else the evil effects mentioned in the last paragraph will follow.

With regard to child labor: in so far as it replaces the labor of adults, it must be compensated for by decreased working hours. But here, at least, there is no difference of opinion as to the desirability of the procedure; from almost every point of view, child labor is undesirable.

It is difficult for a small community to legislate against child labor, or in any way to attempt to improve the working and living conditions of the general population. For, in so far as this is done, the cost of production within that community increases and the community suffers in competition in the world markets. Any great reform must be a universal reform, or else it will militate to the disadvantage of the most advanced community. A community may be able to protect itself from the effects of competition due to other communities having lower standards, if it is able to erect tariff barriers against those communities; and if it is possible for the first community to live—to some extent—on its own production. This resource is available, in our political system, only to a whole nation. It is possible for a country such as the United States to improve its sociological and working conditions, but a state or community cannot do this without considerable difficulty.

Thus, as long as cheap labor exists in any part of the United States, it will be impossible for labor organizations to procure great benefits in the most advanced states. To take an example: as wages of labor in New York City increase, as union contracts force upon the employer the retention of labor that he might otherwise dispense with, it becomes increasingly hard for the employer of labor to compete with other producers of the same products whose labor costs are determined by the poorer conditions in some of the other states. A point will be reached when the New York employer loses money by producing: when he will be forced either to move to a more advantageous region or else to abandon his business.

The same consideration applies to the regulation of capital: strict regulation of corporate practices in New York State would be of no avail as long as Delaware and Maryland offer an almost unregulated haven for corporate management. There is, within the United States, a constant competition for industry, with each community attempting to outbid the others in terms of cheap labor, tax exemption, and freedom for corporate activities. Doubtless the tendency, on the whole, has been for improvement; but no rapid improvement can ever be obtained except on a nation-wide scale.

WASTE

Another objection that economic theorists frequently make to the present form of capitalism is that the system is dependent upon the existence of scarcity. The existence of too much wealth may actually lead to conditions where the existing wealth is hardly utilized, and the community is worse off than it would be if it were less wealthy. Thus, if too much grain is produced in a given year, the price of grain sinks, and the actual income of the farmer is lowered. Just as the farmer finds himself in difficulties, so the distributor, retailer, and all those concerned in the processing of grain find that their plans are upset, their price system demolished, and their normal profits lacking. In order to avoid the evils of this situation, it is not uncommon to find producers attempting to withhold their produce from the market, and thus artificially to create a scarcity. Many countries have participated in such attempts, from our depression endeavors in plowing-under agricultural land, to Brazil's long-standing efforts to get rid of excess coffee by burning half the coffee produced. Outside of the fact that such efforts toward the creation of artificial scarcity have been uniformly unsuccessful, it seems to be a terrible waste of wealth that should be devoted to public enjoyment.

Economic radicals have maintained that, although an economy based upon scarcity may have been necessary when most commodities were actually scarce, such a system is an anomaly when we have the instruments which will enable us to produce enough for all. The socialist, in particular, objects not only to the destruction of wealth, but to the fact that the production of commodities is restricted by denying the worker access to the tools of production.

One of the most common objections to our present form of economic system concerns its enormous waste of both finished and raw materials and of effort. Many concerns are competing to sell similar objects, and if the object is one that will deteriorate, as is the case with most agricultural produce, or if it is an article of fashion which must be sold immediately or else not at all, then competition to sell may pile up huge stocks of manufactured articles and agricultural produce which are never sold and which either rot on shelves or must be destroyed. That, of course, means a waste not only of finished goods but of the material and labor that have gone into its creation. Competing manufacturers each may sell a small fraction of the total consumption, and provide marketing facilities for their products all over the United States. If an agreement could be reached whereby each manufacturer would have an exclusive territory, the cost of distribution would be cut to a small percentage of its former level. The competition for markets is responsible for other costs than those of distribution itself. It is responsible for the expenditure of great amounts in advertising. Competition for markets may also result in lowering the standard of quality of the goods sold, if such lowering of standards is not detectable by the purchaser and is reflected in lower production costs.

The waste of national resources and raw materials is still more serious. In the early days of this country, great forests were cut down without regard to any replenishment of the supply. The same is largely true of our mineral resources, especially oil. The cotton planting of the South resulted in immediate profits, at the expense of complete exhaustion of the soil; and likewise the intensive cultivation of the Mississippi Valley has resulted in soil erosion, floods, and "dust bowl" areas where the value of the land has almost completely disappeared. But it must be said, in answer to this very serious complaint against capitalism, that it is not at all certain that any system would be better, or that capitalism itself is responsible for the results produced. That capitalism can conserve resources is indicated by the large-scale reforestation programs that have been carried on by private resources, and by the rational development, according to the capitalistic scheme of things, of large projects of all sorts. That errors have been made under capitalism is undoubtedly true, but capitalism need not continue to make the errors that it has made, and it is not to be supposed that governments themselves are so constituted that they are immune to the making of serious blunders. As for the losses involved in marketing, no capitalistic enterprise intends to incur such losses, and when it does incur them, it does so through the failure to anticipate conditions correctly. Again, it is not at all certain that a government bureau would be any more accurate in forecasting consumer demands than the managers of modern industry.

Alternate approaches to these problems are offered in the socialistic and communistic schemes that we have already mentioned, ranging from the social ownership of the instruments of production to production and distribution by the state itself. We have already mentioned that the lack of a clear distinction between capital and consumer goods makes the socialist's suggestion of public ownership impractical. Another answer is offered in social control through legal regulation of methods of competition, prices, and profits. The main difficulties here are difficulties of detail: a certain amount of regulation is obviously necessary, and the necessity for such regulation is recognized by everyone. But there is no agreement as to the amount of regulation that is necessary or desirable, and as to the particular ways in which such regulation should take place.

The extreme form of public regulation is known as "planned economy," wherein governmental agencies determine how much of each commodity will be consumed, and, on the basis of this estimate, regulate production so that there will be no large discrepancy between supply and demand. Planned economy can exist either with or without public ownership.

DIMINISHING RETURNS

There is, in economics, a universal principle of "diminishing returns." In its simplest form this may apply to the production of wealth by farming. As applied to land, the law of diminishing returns may be stated as follows: Given a certain piece of land, additional investments of labor and capital, after a certain point is reached, will yield less than proportional returns, if the methods of production remain the same. Up to the point where diminishing returns appear, the yield or returns may increase in proportion to cost or the returns may remain constant.

Thus, a given area will produce a certain amount of grain by one man's efforts: with two men working the land, more will be produced, but not twice as much; and as the number of laborers is increased, the average amount produced by each laborer diminishes. This same law holds true for production by a factory and for return on capital investment. For if a small concern makes a profit out of the sale of certain merchandise, the increase of the size of the concern, beyond a certain point, means that it sells to marginal consumers, that it must market its products in unfavorable territories as well as in favorable ones. The law of diminishing returns holds true for the production of mineral resources: as the amount produced is increased, ores must be worked that are less rich. Similarly, as a nation increases its production of agricultural commodities, marginal land, intrinsically unsatisfactory for agricultural processes, must be farmed.

Now, the economic radical applies this law of diminishing returns to capital itself. After a certain amount of production has taken place, the demand of a nation for automobiles, television sets, and for luxuries of all sorts diminishes until the point is reached where the principal demand is the demand for replacement. The amount of capital in a country increases at least as rapidly as the total increase of wealth, but the opportunities for its employment are restricted. In seeking employment, therefore, capital tends to leave the more advanced nations and become invested in the development of the resources of the more backward countries. But as the opportunity for the exploitation of backward countries exists only as long as there are such backward countries, and as the opportunity for an industrial nation to sell its produce to a nation of farmers exists only as long as the latter nation remains non-industrial, a time must come when the opportunities for capital are largely exhausted.

The premises of this argument are, however, highly speculative. It is not altogether certain that the market of a given country will ever become saturated, for the invention of new products continually increases the demand, quite apart from any resort to foreign markets. Also, it is a curious fact that the best markets of industrial countries are, contrary to general opinion, other industrial countries rather than the less highly developed communities. And finally, if the possibility of exporting to other countries is completely destroyed, and if the internal market is not improved by further inventions, it still would not follow that any disruption of our economic system would result. What would in all probability happen is simply this: that the general rate of return on invested money would sink to an indefinite extent, approaching, in fact, without ever reaching it, a point where the return on investment would only equal the risk in making the investment. To this extent the law of diminishing returns undoubtedly does apply; and it has, in fact, already been noticed in operation. When the industrialization of a country is completed, the average rate of return on capital investments becomes lower. But this in itself is hardly an objection to the capitalistic system and certainly not a reason to expect its dissolution.

The effects of the law of diminishing returns may be postponed without risk to the capitalistic system of production. Improvements in the methods of agriculture, such as rotation of crops, improved fertilizers, and the adoption of more scientific agriculture, have retarded the operation of diminishing returns. The increasing use of synthetic products and discoveries in chemurgy have still further slowed up its operation. The discovery of new methods, materials, and processes in manufacture combined with an extensive program of conservation have also retarded the law of diminishing returns. Science and invention, particularly in the field of atomic energy, hold out greatest promise for the future of man in maintaining a constantly improving economic society.

EXAMINATION QUESTIONS

1. What is "economic wealth"?
2. What are the factors which originally determined ownership?
3. What other factors are involved in ownership in modern societies?
4. What is capital?
5. In what sense is it true that labor is prepaid?
6. What part of the capital used in business is known as "capital investment"?
7. How is deterioration a factor in price?
8. If the John Doe Company has issued two series of Preferred Stock, one called "A" and the other "B," both paying $6 per annum, how could you account for the conditions if "A" stock sold for $80 a share when "B" stock sold for $65?
9. Is money a commodity?
10. What are the possible advantages of gold as a monetary base?
11. What justification is there for saying that gold or money is not real value?
12. What is meant by a "standard of living"?
13. Could you buy more or less with a dollar in 1946 than in 1846?
14. Justify the statement that modern business is run on credit.
15. Why is it possible for a bank to lend more money than it possesses?
16. In what way does a managed currency resemble a gold-standard currency?
17. What is monetary inflation?
18. What are two ways of causing monetary inflation?

19. What are the differences between currency and credit inflation?
20. Is the law of supply and demand inconsistent with the law of adequate returns?
21. Which of these two laws is the fundamental one?
22. What is "marginal cost"?
23. How is marginal cost related to marginal utility?
24. How is this law related to the law of supply and demand?
25. When does profiteering occur?
26. Why doesn't the law of adequate returns work as well for labor as for commodities?
27. Why doesn't a monopoly establish prices for its products at extremely high levels?
28. What is a monopoly of consumption?
29. How are wages fixed where capital and labor are organized?
30. Why do inventories on hand at the beginning of a depression have some bearing upon its duration?
31. Are depressions really more serious now than they used to be?
32. What bearing upon this has division of labor?
33. Are depressions in an undeveloped country different from those in a developed one?
34. What is socialism?
35. How would socialism treat inheritance?
36. What is the economic creed of communism?
37. Would there be differences in pay under true communism?
38. Who said that communism is an

inevitable development of capitalism?

39. What are the characteristics of fascism?

40. Can the world produce enough food for its growing population?

41. Why does the length of the working week tend to diminish?

42. How is chronic unemployment related to the working week?

43. What is the result of women entering industry?

44. What is one remedy for overproduction?

45. How does a low standard of living in one region affect workers in another?

46. Why does Brazil destroy coffee?

47. What raises costs of distribution?

48. What is "planned economy"?

49. What is the law of "diminishing returns"?

50. How may diminishing returns be retarded?

FOR FURTHER STUDY

BASIC TEACHINGS OF THE GREAT ECONOMISTS, by John W. McConnell. (Barnes & Noble, New York.)

COMPARATIVE ECONOMIC SYSTEMS, by William N. Loucks and John W. Hoot. (Harper & Bros., New York.)

ECONOMICS IN EVERYDAY LIFE, by Kennard E. Goodman and William L. Moore. (Ginn & Co., Boston.)

ECONOMIC PROBLEMS IN A CHANGING WORLD, by Willard L. Thorp.

(Rinehart & Co., New York.)

ELEMENTARY ECONOMICS, by F. R. Fairchild, E. S. Furniss, and N. S. Buck. (The Macmillan Co., New York.)

HISTORY OF ECONOMIC DOCTRINES, by Charles Gide and Charles Rist. (D. C. Heath & Co., Boston.)

PRINCIPLES OF ECONOMICS, by Frederick B. Garver and Alvin H. Hansen. (Ginn & Co., Boston.)

VIII

Good English Self Taught

WHAT DETERMINES "GOOD ENGLISH"?

GOOD ENGLISH is determined by the practice of the best writers and speakers. The precedent of *use* cannot be influenced or altered by any one person or any separate group of persons. In English what is *used most often* by the "best users" of the language is *right*.

Grammars and dictionaries are valuable aids to good English, because they record and explain *good usage*. Few people have the time or the inclination to compile their own tabulations of the forms employed by good writers and speakers. They can rely upon a good dictionary, which will inform them accurately concerning correct spelling, grammar, and meaning. Everyone who wishes to use good English should own a good dictionary and learn how to use it.

Tradition has a powerful influence on good English. From Chaucer's time to the present day, the great figures in literature have left their mark upon our language. Usage, once established, is slow to change. But our mother tongue does change, and writers and speakers sooner or later accept the changes. The trend of our language today is toward simplification in spelling and punctuation; the irregularities and inconsistencies of grammar and syntax tend to disappear; the English language is constantly becoming more mobile, more adaptable to the needs and moods of its users.

Good English may be further defined as English which is most widely and most enduringly *understood*. Only those forms of English which have been widely accepted and which have been long established can be certain of being comprehended wherever English is spoken or read.

Good taste in speaking English does not demand pedantic adherence to all rules of grammar. Such studied speech would sound stiff and unnatural. In conversation, it is quite permissible for one to be informal, to speak more spontaneously than one would write. Many words and expressions are acceptable colloquially (which is to say, in ordinary speech) which would not be suited to formal writing. Making these distinctions becomes more or less second nature after study and extensive reading.

In speech, you must particularly watch pronunciation. Do not trust too implicitly pronunciations which you hear, or pronunciations which you use daily. It is worth while to check your pronunciations with the recommended versions in a good dictionary. Listen to good public speakers and note how they pronounce certain words. Note too their general pattern of speech and try to model yours on theirs.

In writing, you must particularly watch spelling and punctuation. Correct spelling is very important. Try to develop a "spelling conscience," that is, a constant awareness of spelling while writing. Check all doubtful spellings in the dictionary. Keep a list of words you misspell frequently and drill on the correct spelling of these words. Punctuation is important too, for it helps you to express your meaning clearly in writing.

In both speech and writing, the fundamental principles of grammar must be followed. The practical reason for this is that only by being grammatical can you be sure of being clear and persuasive. A few words, well spoken or well written, are far more compelling—in social life or in the commercial world—than thousands uttered carelessly, dashed off in slipshod haste, or poured out in ignorant confusion.

GRAMMAR

Scholars have analyzed not only the English language, but all other known languages, and have reduced the uses and forms of words and their combinations to a set of rules—rules derived from usage. The manner in which words may be put together to form sentences is called *grammar*.

THE PARTS OF SPEECH

Any word, depending on how it is used in a sentence, may be classified as one of eight parts of speech, which are known by the following names: noun, pronoun, adjective, verb, adverb, preposition, conjunction, interjection. In order that later explanations may be thoroughly understood, it is necessary to know these parts of speech and their uses.

A NOUN is the name of something: an object, a group of objects, a person or place, a quality. Examples: *book, table, house, truth, people, France, light, Ethel, discrimination, kindness, history, relativity, mountain.*

A PRONOUN is a word which stands for a noun (the prefix "pro" is Latin, meaning "for"). A pronoun is not a definite name of anything; its identity with some noun is determined by its position in a sentence or paragraph, or its meaning may remain indefinite. Examples: *he, she, it, I, we, they, this, that, who.*

An ADJECTIVE is a word used to modify or describe a noun or pronoun, or other substantive (a *substantive* is any word or group of words used, grammatically, like a noun). Examples: *blue, long, beautiful, wondrous, dependable, precise, wicked, kind, lovable, comic.*

A VERB expresses an action or mode of being; no sentence is grammatically complete without a verb. Examples: *is, do, have, laugh, fly, leap, eradicate, respond, analyze, discriminate, sweep, think, love.*

An ADVERB is a word used to modify or describe an adjective, a verb, or another adverb. Examples: *beautifully, loudly, dependably, precisely, here, there, frequently, often, soon, surely.* Note that many adverbs end in *ly.* Adverbs express particularly matters of time, manner of acting or doing, place, and the like.

A PREPOSITION is a word used to connect a noun or pronoun (which usually follows the preposition) with some other word or words, in such a way that the preposition and its following noun or pronoun (with modifiers, if any) are related to the other word or words. Prepositions usually express position, direction, time, means, or a similar abstract relation. Examples: *to, by, of, from, at, under, over, between, among, in, against, with, for, on, across, around, before, during, except, through, upon.*

A CONJUNCTION is a joining word: it connects two words, two phrases, two clauses, or more, into one sentence. A co-ordinating conjunction (*and, but, or, nor*) connects parts of equal grammatical rank, like two nouns or two independent clauses. A subordinating conjunction (*as, though, if, since, because, unless*) connects a subordinate part of the sentence to the main part.

An INTERJECTION is a word "interjected" among other words, without having any grammatical relation to them; an interjection is usually followed by an exclamation point (!). Examples: *Oh! Ouch! Alas! Ah!*

The same word, without change of form, may be used as two or more different parts of speech, depending on its relation to other words in the sentence. *But* has been used so interchangeably as preposition and conjunction that it is often difficult to classify it strictly as one or the other part of speech. In the following sentence the word *poison* is a noun, used as object of the preposition *with:* "They kill mice with poison," and in this sentence it is a verb: "People poison mice." Used as an exclamation of surprise, it may be an interjection: "Poison! Was it that?"

Strictly, here *poison* is a noun used with the force of an interjection; it explains the identity of the pronouns *it* and *that*. The adjective formed from the noun *poison* is *poisonous,* though *poison,* itself, may be used with the force of an adjective: "He swallowed ten poison pills."

The three *articles* are really adjectives: *a* and *an* (indefinite), and *the* (definite). Notice the difference between *a book* (any book) and *the book* (a particular book). Before nouns beginning with a vowel sound, *an* is used; before all other nouns, *a* is used. In America, it is usual to say *a history* or *a hospital,* although in England *an history* and *an hospital* are common. This is a question purely of pronunciation.

Test your knowledge of the parts of speech by naming each word in the following sentence; then check your list with the explanation in the paragraph below:

> What! You say the old bridge over the river collapsed just as the train reached it?

What is used here as an interjection, or exclamation of surprise. *You* is a pronoun, referring to the person spoken to. *Say* is a verb, indicating the action which has been performed by *you. The* is a definite article, modifying the noun *bridge. Old* is an adjective, also modifying *bridge. Over* is a preposition, having for its object the noun *river,* which is modified by the article *the. Collapsed* is a verb (it expresses the action performed by the bridge). *Just* is an adverb telling the time of the accident. *As* is a conjunction introducing a subordinate clause, made up of the words that follow. *Train* is a noun (modified by *the*), being the doer of the action of the verb *reached,* which has for its object the pronoun *it.*

THE SENTENCE

On the structure of the sentence depend clarity, coherence, and style itself. So varied are the possibilities of sentence structure in English that the same words may be combined in several different arrangements, each expressing the same idea. Different combinations offer different points of emphasis, and vary in strength and smoothness. In choosing the sequence of words which best expresses his thought, the master of English reveals his skill.

A sentence is *a combination of words expressing a complete thought.* For convenience in reading, each sentence ends with a "full stop," namely, a period (.), an interrogation point (?), or an exclamation point (!). The first word of each new sentence is capitalized. Every group of words in this book which begins with a capitalized word and ends with a full stop is a sentence, with the possible exception of lists of words or illustrations preceded by *for example,* or a similar introductory phrase.

A sentence may be as short as one word: "Go!" This one-word sentence expresses a complete thought or idea: it is a command to depart. A qualifying word may be added, explaining where one is to go ("Go away." or "Go downstairs."), how one is to go ("Go quickly."), when one is to go ("Go immediately." or "Go tomorrow."); these qualifying words modify, in each example, the verb *go,* so they are adverbs.

A word of emphasis may be added, to make the command stronger ("Please go." or "Do go.") A pronoun may be inserted, making the subject of the command unmistakable ("You go."), or a person may be called by name ("John go."). Thus may the sentence be lengthened; as words are added, a more definite or limited thought is expressed. If the thought is highly defined, it may require many words to express it, as, for example: "Ethel, please go downstairs and tell your sister that it is almost time for her to leave for school."

The Three Kinds of Sentences

There are three kinds of sentences: the *declarative,* the *interrogative,* and the *imperative.* The declarative sentence makes a statement:

Boswell was Johnson's biographer.
The Secretary of Labor indicated that he approved of the bill.

The interrogative sentence asks a question:

What time is it?
Whom do you expect to see on this program?

The imperative sentence gives a command:

Clear out of here.
Keep off the grass.

A Verb Essential to Every Sentence

An old precept of good English is that every sentence must contain at least one verb. Although, in much modern writing, groups of words are allowed to stand as sentences without verbs, it is best for the inexperienced writer of English to follow the rule carefully. In conversation, naturally, the rule need not be stringently observed. Conversation is often unavoidably chopped up, and phrases do quite as well as sentences, particularly in replying to questions, or in hasty dialogue. For example, consider the following:

"Going to the theater?"
"Yes. Want to come?"
"Sure. What's on?"

Expressed in formal sentences, this dialogue would sound something as follows:

"Are you going to the theater?"
"Yes. Do you want to come?"
"Surely. What is being presented tonight?"

When conversation is recorded in writing, its original phrasing is preserved. You have noticed this in sketches and stories; even intricacies of dialect are sedulously followed. When the words of some careless or illiterate speaker are not being quoted, however, the writer must be more particular in his choice of words and in his phrasing. In such writing, even today, the use of correct sentences far exceeds the use of incomplete and verbless sentences. A sound principle reasserts itself: the more sincerely a writer strives for good English, the more likely is he to be understood.

Distinguishing Sentences from Fragments

Tests may be applied to combinations of words to determine whether they may stand as grammatical sentences. The simplest test is to judge, if you can, whether the combination states a complete thought. If the thought is incomplete—if more words must be added to complete it—then the words as they stand are not a sentence.

Which of the following would you consider complete sentences, remembering that a sentence must express a complete thought?

1. Which I have always liked.
2. The rain came down in torrents.
3. We were late because we had a flat tire.
4. Running a race.
5. That Einstein's theories are now being put to practical use.

The first example is not a complete sentence because you do not know what *which* stands for. The second gives a complete thought and so is a sentence, as is the third example. The fourth is merely a group of words hanging in mid-air. The fifth example is not a complete sentence. While it is more definite than the previous example, it would require such an introduction as *We understand* or *We have been told* to be a real sentence.

THE PARTS OF THE SENTENCE

There is a further and more systematic way of distinguishing a sentence fragment from a complete sentence. That is by looking for the essential parts of the sentence. Every sentence must contain a *subject* and a *predicate verb*. The predicate verb indicates the action or state of being of the sentence.

>Time *passes* quickly in the summer.
>He *is* tired.

The subject is what is spoken about in the sentence. It is the doer of the action that is indicated by the predicate verb. It may be found by asking "Who?" or "What?" before the predicate verb. In the first sentence above, for example, we ask, "What passes quickly in the summer?" The answer, *time,* is the subject. In the second sentence we ask, "Who is tired?" The answer, *he,* is the subject. The subject may be a noun, a pronoun, or a group of words acting as a pronoun.

In addition to the subject and the predicate verb, a sentence may have *predicate complements.* Predicate complements are words which add meaning to the predicate verb. We shall describe the four predicate complements here: the *direct object,* the *indirect object,* the *predicate noun and pronoun,* and the *predicate adjective.*

The direct object is a noun or pronoun that receives the action of the verb directly. It may be found by asking "Whom?" or "What?" after the verb.

>The ball hit the *fence.*
>I stubbed my *toe.*
>We all like *him.*

The indirect object is a noun or pronoun that receives the action from such verbs as *offer, give,* and *send,* which leave the word *to* understood.

>We sent *him* a large package.
>The engineer gave the *dispatcher* his number.
>I offered *Neil* a cigarette.

The predicate noun and pronoun are used with copulative verbs (parts of *to be*) and rename the subject of the verb.

>Carl is the *leader* of the troop.
>He was *president* for one term.
>It is *I.*

The predicate adjective follows a copulative verb and describes the subject.

>I am *happy* tonight.
>He was *tall, dark,* and *handsome.*

THE CLAUSE

A clause is a group of words which contains a subject and a predicate verb but which is not in itself a complete sentence. A clause may be a main or *independent* clause, which means that it does not depend on any other group of words for its meaning; or it may be *dependent* or *subordinate,* which means that it makes no sense or makes incomplete sense when read by itself.

MAIN CLAUSE: (*in italics*)	*The car stopped at the corner* and *we got out.* If I had time, *I would see the show.* *I don't know* when we shall meet again.
SUBORDINATE CLAUSE: (*in italics*)	*If I had time,* I would see the show. I don't know *when we shall meet again.* I know *what you are thinking of.*

Main clauses may be joined by *co-ordinating conjunctions* such as *and, but, or, neither . . . nor.* Subordinate clauses may be joined to main clauses by *subordinate conjunctions* such as *where, when, why, because, since,* or by *relative pronouns* such as *what, who, whom, that, which.*

Subordinate clauses may be used either as modifiers of certain words in the main clause or as nouns.

AS MODIFIERS:

OF THE VERB:	The sun came out *when we were ready to leave.* He was working *where the agency had sent him.*
OF THE SUBJECT:	The clock *that I have just bought* has radium dials. The tall oak tree, *which is more than two hundred years old,* is to be cut down.
OF THE COMPLE- MENT:	He is the officer *who caught the runaway horse.* I like stories *that have a happy ending.*

Clauses which modify nouns and pronouns are called *adjective clauses.* Clauses which modify verbs, adverbs, or adjectives are known as *adverbial clauses.*

AS NOUNS:

AS SUBJECT:	*What you don't know* won't hurt you.
AS OBJECT OF THE VERB:	We like *what we have seen so far.*
AS PREDICATE NOUN:	This is just *what you want,* Marie.

AS OBJECT OF A PREPOSITION: Give the books to *whoever wants to read them.*

THE PREPOSITIONAL PHRASE

A prepositional phrase is a group of words introduced by a preposition. The preposition links the object of the preposition to another word in the sentence. Some phrases are:

> to me, for the cat, in the house, without money,
> from morn, till night, above the horizon.

A phrase which modifies a noun or pronoun is an *adjective phrase:*

> The crowd *in the theater* rioted.
> This is *for Mr. Edwards.*

A phrase which modifies a verb, adverb, or adjective is an *adverbial phrase:*

> I have just come *from my office.*
> The bird jumped *from one limb to the other.*

PROBLEMS OF NOUNS

Nouns may be classified on the basis of certain properties. These properties are called *gender, number, person,* and *case.*

Gender of Nouns

Nouns have gender according to the sex of the object they name. In English nouns may be of *masculine gender* (*boy, man, father, son*), *feminine gender* (*girl, woman, mother, daughter*), *neuter gender* when they refer to objects having no sex (*book, clock, table, Chicago*), or *common gender* when they may refer to objects of either masculine or feminine gender (*child, teacher, doctor, neighbor, friend*).

Number of Nouns

Nouns are of *singular number* when they refer to one person or thing (*rock, house, army, theater, lady*). They are of *plural number* when they refer to two or more persons or things (*rocks, houses, armies, theaters, ladies*).

Most nouns form their plurals by adding *s* or *es* to the singular:

> cigar, cigars; bench, benches; hat, hats; pencil, pencils; match, matches; fox, foxes; Negro, Negroes; potato, potatoes; studio, studios; piano, pianos; sister-in-law, sisters-in-law; spoonful, spoonfuls.

Singular nouns which end in *y* preceded by a consonant sound change the *y* to *i* and add *es*.

> lady, ladies; baby, babies; colloquy, colloquies; rally, rallies; lily, lilies.

But

> valley, valleys; trolley, trolleys; chimney, chimneys.

Some nouns ending in *f* or *fe* form plurals by changing the *f* to *v* and adding *es* or *s*.

> calf, calves; knife, knives; life, lives.

But

> belief, beliefs; proof, proofs; handkerchief, handkerchiefs.

The plural of numbers and letters is formed by adding *'s*.

> one *8*, two *8's;* one *a*, two *a's*.

Certain nouns form their plurals in special ways.

> child, children; man, men; ox, oxen; foot, feet; tooth, teeth; mouse, mice.

These words make no change at all for the plural: *sheep, deer*.

Plurals of foreign words and of words which retain much of their foreign quality are sometimes hard to remember.

> alumnus, alumni (men); alumna, alumnae (women); appendix, appendices; axis, axes; bacillus, bacilli; bacterium, bacteria; crisis, crises; criterion, criteria; hypothesis, hypotheses; memorandum, memoranda; oasis, oases; parenthesis, parentheses; phenomenon, phenomena; synopsis, synopses.

Person of Nouns

Person of nouns refers to the fact that a noun may represent the speaker (*first person*), the person spoken to (*second person*), or the person spoken about (*third person*).

> FIRST PERSON: I, your *brother*, insist on it.
> SECOND PERSON: *Charlie*, hurry up.
> THIRD PERSON: He, the other *man*, has left.
>   The *time* to act is now.

Case of Nouns

The cases of nouns are determined by their use in the sentence. There are three cases of nouns: *nominative, possessive,* and *objective*.

The nominative case is the case of nouns that are used as the subject of a verb or as the predicate nominative.

The *game* was scoreless for two innings.
The newly elected *president* is her *fiancé*.

The objective case is the case of nouns that are used as the object of a verb or object of a preposition.

He wrote a long *letter*.
The ride to my *house* takes about twenty *minutes*.

In neither the nominative nor the objective case does a noun change its form. The only case in which it does change its form is the possessive case, which, as its name implies, indicates ownership.

Walter's sister is downstairs.
I saw *Edna's* daughter.
Franklin D. Roosevelt's tenure in office ended with his death.

Normally possessives are formed by adding *'s* to singular nouns, and the apostrophe alone to plural nouns ending in *s: the lady's hat* (singular), *the ladies' hats* (plural); *the dog's food* (singular), *the dogs' food* (plural); *Margaret's husband* (singular); *a laborer's wages* (singular), *laborers' wages* (plural).

If the singular noun already ends in *s*, add *'s* according to the rule: *the lass's sweetheart* (singular); *the lasses' sweethearts* (plural).

If a plural noun does not end in *s*, add *'s* according to the rule: *the children's playground, the people's rights, men's furnishings.*

If a proper name ends in *s*, either *'s* or the apostrophe alone may be added: *Jones' book, Jones's book* (both singular).

PROBLEMS OF PRONOUNS

Because pronouns in English change their forms more than nouns, depending on their grammatical relations to the rest of the sentence of which they may form a part, they often cause errors. Like nouns, pronouns have person, number, gender, and case.

Person and Number of Pronouns

Pronouns have three *persons*. The first person is the person speaking; first person pronouns are *I, me, we, us, my, our, myself, ourselves*. The second person is the person spoken to; second person pronouns are *thou, thy* (seldom used in modern English), *you, your, yourself, yourselves*. The third person is the person spoken of; third person pronouns are *he, his, him, she, her, hers, it, its, they, their, them, theirs, himself, herself, itself, themselves, one, oneself, everybody, everyone, who, whose, whom, someone, somebody, each, none*, etc.

Pronouns have two *numbers*, singular and plural. Pronouns in the singular number are *I, me, my, myself, thou, thy, you, your, yourself, he, his, him, himself, she, her, herself, it, its, itself, one, oneself, everybody, everyone.* Pronouns in the plural number are *we, us, our, ourselves, you, your, yourselves, they, them, their, themselves.*

A pronoun agrees with its antecedent in person and number. The *antecedent* of a pronoun is the noun which reveals the identity of the pronoun. In the sentence "The woman went to the meeting, where she voiced her opinions," the antecedent of the pronoun *she* is *woman. Woman* is in the third person singular; therefore *she* is also in the third person singular. Consider the following:

> The girl is upset. She is angry. Her pride is hurt. The boy is confused. He is angry also. But his pride is not hurt. You see, my friends, they love each other deeply, these two, but neither dares to believe that the other has any feelings in the matter at all.

The antecedent of *she* and of *her* is *girl;* they agree in being third person singular. The antecedent of *he* and of *his* is *boy,* also third person singular. The antecedent of *you* is *friends,* which, being used in address, is second person plural. The antecedent of *they* is *two,* or, by the context, *girl* and *boy,* making the pronoun third person plural.

Difficulty with antecedents increases with such indefinite pronouns as *everyone, someone, each, none.* Remember that these pronouns are singular in number, so that if they serve as antecedents for personal pronouns, the personal pronouns must be singular to correspond.

> RIGHT: Everyone must keep his place.
> WRONG: Everyone must keep their place.
> RIGHT: Each of us has his chance.
> WRONG: Each of us has their chance.
> RIGHT: Someone is going to miss his train.
> WRONG: Someone is going to miss their train.
> RIGHT: No one can be denied his right to vote.
> WRONG: No one can be denied their right to vote.
> RIGHT: Everyone should be told what he ought to do.
> WRONG: Everyone should be told what they ought to do.

Careless writing may allow pronouns to be confusing or ambiguous. Arrange your sentences so that a pronoun is near its antecedent—unmistakably near. If you cannot place pronoun and antecedent near together, then repeat the antecedent or insert a noun meaning the same thing as the antecedent. Study the following:

> NOT CLEAR: I ran from the hut into the field and watched it burn. (The antecedent of *it* might be either *hut* or *field.*)

BETTER: I ran from the burning hut into the field, and I watched the shack burn. (This, or a similar rephrasing, makes the statement clear.)

NOT CLEAR: Jack and John were walking past the house, when he said to him that he was leaving town. (Who said to whom that who was leaving?)

BETTER: As the two men were walking past the house, John said to Jack that he was leaving town. (There is now but one pronoun, *he,* of which the antecedent is logically the noun *John,* which names the speaker.)

ALSO CORRECT: Jack and John were walking past the house, when John said to him that he was leaving town.

Perhaps more misleading are pronouns with antecedents which are hidden away in long sentences. Notice the disagreement in the following example, and the two possible ways of correcting it:

WRONG: According to Margaret, a husband is valuable for one thing, and that is, they pay the bills. (*They* is plural, but its antecedent *husband* is singular.)

RIGHT: According to Margaret, husbands are valuable for one thing, and that is, they pay the bills. (*They* and its antecedent *husbands* are now both plural, which is correct.)

ALSO RIGHT: According to Margaret, a husband is valuable for one thing, and that is, he pays the bills. (*He* and its antecedent *husband* are now both singular, which is correct.)

Gender of Pronouns

Pronouns in the third person singular may be one of three genders. *He* is masculine, *she* is feminine, and *it* is neuter. Pronouns in the other persons and in the plural may be of any gender, depending on the sense of the sentence.

One problem of proper gender of pronouns occurs when a mixed group is referred to as a whole, though it contains both men and women. Masculine pronouns alone are used in such a case, except in legal documents (wherein "he or she" and "he and she" are laboriously repeated throughout). Notice the following:

UNNECESSARILY PRECISE: Each member of our class must report his or her tardiness himself or herself.

QUITE CORRECT: Each member of our class must report his tardiness himself. (This statement refers to both males and females, if both genders are represented in the class.)

Case of Pronouns

As we have seen, nouns do not generally change their form to show cases, but personal pronouns do, as follows:

NOMINATIVE:	I, we	you	he, she, it	they	who
POSSESSIVE:	my, our	your	his, her, its	their	whose
OBJECTIVE:	me, us	you	him, her, it	them	whom

The nominative case of pronouns is used for the subject of the verb and the predicate nominative.

> *We* likè to play baseball.
> *We* boys like to play baseball. (Not "*Us* boys like to play baseball.")
> It is *he*. (Not "It is *him*.")
> Happy men are *we*. (Not "Happy men are *us*.")
> Those who are to go will be *you, she,* and *I*. (Not "Those who are to go will be *you, her,* and *me*.")

Note that although the form *It is I* must be used in formal English, the form *It is me* has become frequent in colloquial English, even though it violates the rule of the use of the nominative case in the predicate nominative. It should be avoided.

The objective case of pronouns is used for the object of the verb and the object of the preposition.

> Mr. Tate congratulated *me*.
> Mr. Tate congratulated *him* and *me*. (Not "Mr. Tate congratulated *he* and *I*.")
> Take John and *me* with you. (Not "Take John and *I* with you.")
> Against *them* are a hundred foes. (Not "Against *they* are a hundred foes.")
> Between *you* and *me*, they can't win. (Not "Between *you* and *I* they can't win.")

The pronouns *who* and *whom* follow the same rules. Either form may begin a question, depending on whether the nominative or the objective case is required. Examples of the nominative case:

> *Who* is going?
> *Who* stands in the doorway?
> I asked *who* was standing in the doorway.
> *Who* did you say was standing in the doorway?
> This is the person *who* Ethel says was standing in the doorway.

In all these sentences, *who* is in the nominative case, used correctly, because it is always the subject of a verb. First, *who* is the subject of *is going;* second, *who* is the subject of *stands;* third, *who* is the subject of *was standing;* fourth, *who* is still the subject of *was standing;* fifth, *who* is again the subject of *was standing.* In the next to the last sentence, you can prove that *who* should be nominative by substituting *he;* thus: "Did you say he was standing in the doorway?"

Used with the verb *to be, who* must be governed by the rule for the predicate nominative.

> Can you tell me *who* the girl is?
> I asked *who* she was.

To show that *who* is the predicate nominative, you must make an awkward rearrangement, "she was who," or, "the girl is who."

When used as the object of a verb or a preposition, *whom* is required.

> I asked the girl *whom* I saw standing in the doorway.
> *Whom* do I see standing in the doorway?

In the first example, *whom* is the object of *saw;* in the second, *whom* is the object of *see.* Rearranged, these sentences might read:

> I asked the girl I saw *whom* standing in the doorway.
> I see *whom* standing in the doorway?

Examples of *whom* used as the object of prepositions:

> To *whom* did you refer?
> *Whom* are you giving that to?
> *Whom* he asks for is none of my affair.

Usually, such sentences can be rearranged so that the preposition comes directly before its object, showing that the objective case is required; thus:

> To *whom* are you giving that?
> For *whom* he asks is none of my affair.

Simple pronoun possessives are *my* life, *your* coat, *her* gloves, *his* cane, *their* courage. The possessive of the neuter pronoun *it* is *its* (no apostrophe). Examples:

> A cow chews *its* cud.
> This chair does not stand firmly on *its* legs.
> Give me *its* number.

Note: The form *it's* is the contraction of "it is," the apostrophe indicating the omission of the letter *i.* Examples:

> *It's* going to rain.
> Wherever you go, *it's* equally expensive.

Some possessive pronouns are used with substantive force (without a noun following). When so used, they replace the noun. These include *mine, ours, yours, hers, his, theirs* (notice that there is no apostrophe with the forms ending in *s*). The possessive of *who* is *whose*. Examples:

> *Whose* part are you taking?
> I do not know *whose* shoe this is.

Note: The form *who's* is the contraction of *who is*, the apostrophe indicating the omission of the letter *i*. Examples:

> *Who's* going?
> I'd like to know *who's* the boss.

Possessives of compound pronouns usually add *'s* to the last part of the compound. Examples: *somebody else's, anyone else's, everybody else's*.

Possessives of compound nouns are formed by adding *'s* to the last syllable of the compound. Examples: *mother-in-law's* (singular), *mothers-in-law's* (plural); *editor-in-chief's* (singular), *editors-in-chief's* (plural).

Avoid forming possessives of the last word of phrases. The possessive can also be indicated, when desired, by the preposition *of*. Thus, you can say either *the captain's sword* or *the sword of the captain;* both mean the same. Avoid the possessive case of the last word of a phrase by substituting an *of*-phrase. Examples:

> AWKWARD: The wind blew the mayor of New York's hat into the street.
> BETTER: The wind blew the hat of the mayor of New York into the street.

PROBLEMS OF VERBS

As we have seen, verbs are the action words of a sentence (*smile, grumble*) or the words that express state of being (*be, seem*). We shall discuss in this section some of the ways verbs are classified, the forms of verbs, the question of agreement with the subject, and the problem of tenses of verbs. With this information you will be able to use verbs more effectively and to avoid certain common errors.

Transitive and Intransitive Verbs

Verbs of action are either *transitive* or *intransitive*.

If a verb is *transitive,* it requires an object to complete its meaning, and that object must be a noun or pronoun, or words used as such, in the objective case. An *intransitive* verb does not require an object. The same verb may sometimes be used transitively or intransitively, as desired, or according to the meaning employed.

If the subject of a verb cannot by itself perform the action expressed, the verb is logically transitive (that is, its action is carried over from the subject to an object), and must have an object to complete its meaning. For example, "The day closed" is complete, for the day can close by itself; *closed* is intransitive. But you cannot say, *The boy closed,* for this does not express an understandable idea; the boy cannot close himself— he must close *something,* as "The boy closed the door." The verb *closed* is now transitive, taking the object *door.*

Similarly, if you wish simply to state that a man fired a gun, you can say, "The man shot," which is complete, since a man can shoot without necessarily shooting anything, *shot* being intransitive; but if you wish to go farther, and state what the man shot, the verb becomes transitive and takes an object; thus: "The man shot a tiger."

In English considerable variety of sentence structure is possible. However, reversing the order of subject and object may reverse the meaning. The following apparently mean substantially the same thing:

> The man shot a tiger.
> The man a tiger shot.
> A tiger the man shot.

But notice that you cannot say, "A tiger shot the man," and retain the same meaning. Now *tiger* has become the subject, and *man* has become the object of the verb *shot.* However, this new sentence permits the same variations as the first:

> A tiger shot the man.
> A tiger the man shot.
> The man a tiger shot.

The Copulative Verb

A third class of verbs is the *copulative* verb. A copulative verb is a linking verb; that is, it links the subject with a predicate complement. The most common copulative verb is *to be.*

> The Henrys *are* newcomers to the city.
> My name *is* William.
> They *were* very wealthy at one time.
> I *have been* here before.

Certain other verbs are also used as copulative verbs.

> The weather *seemed* bright.
> His conclusion *proved* incorrect.
> This *tastes* good.

Notice that each of the complements after these copulative verbs is an adjective, rather than an adverb, as might seem to be needed. To use an adverb in the third sentence, for example, would give an entirely different meaning to the sentence. "This tastes well" does not mean that the speaker likes the taste of the food in question; it would mean that the food itself had a good sense of taste—a sensitive palate—which would be absurd.

The Infinitive of a Verb

An infinitive, which is a part of a verb expressed with *to,* as *to be, to laugh, to swim, to have laughed, to have been loved,* etc., may be used as the subject of a verb, as in this example: "To love and lose has compensations." *To love* and *(to) lose,* two infinitives connected by the conjunction *and,* form a double or compound subject of the verb *has.*

An infinitive may also be used as a complement of a verb.

> As OBJECT: I like *to play* tennis.
> He plans *to leave* Sunday.
> As PREDICATE COMPLEMENT: To know her is *to love* her.

An infinitive also has these uses:

> As ADJECTIVE: This is a meeting *to decide* on future policies.
> As ADVERB: He stayed here *to study.*

The Participle of a Verb

The present participle is formed by adding *ing* to the present tense of the verb: *hope, hoping; laugh, laughing.* The participle may be used as part of the verb.

> He *was laughing* all the way home.
> It *has been raining* for an hour.
> The wind *was howling* all night.

The participle often takes on the attributes of an adjective, modifying a noun or pronoun.

> The room has *running* water.
> The *falling* plaster glanced off my shoulder.
> He was struck a *stunning* blow.

As an adjective, the participle may introduce a group of words known as a *participial phrase.*

> *Turning the corner,* the car skidded.
> *Trotting gracefully,* the horse crossed the finish line first.
> *Pointing to the clock,* he gulped down his last sandwich and ran off.
> He, *glancing to his left,* stepped into the street.

A common error known as a *dangling participle* sometimes arises with participial phrases. You may see a sentence like this:

Breathing heavily, the top of the mountain was reached.

Analyzing this sentence logically, we can find the error of this sentence. As it stands, it leads us to believe that the top of the mountain was breathing heavily, an obvious absurdity. We can correct the sentence by saying "Breathing heavily, we reached the top of the mountain." In using participial phrases always make sure that your phrase modifies the word you want it to modify.

WRONG: Opening his fist, a tiny insect was visible.
BETTER: Opening his fist, he showed us a tiny insect.
WRONG: Being fully toasted, I took the bread from the stove.
BETTER: Being fully toasted, the bread was taken from the stove.

When a participle is used as a noun it is called a *gerund*.

As SUBJECT: *Swimming* requires long practice.
As OBJECT OF VERB: I don't like *swimming*.

Agreement of Verb and Subject

The choice of the particular form of a verb is determined to a large extent by the subject of the verb—specifically by its number. We would not, for example, say "We goes home today." We know that when we have *we* as a subject, the verb must be *go* or *do* or *gather,* etc. This correspondence between verb and subject is known as *agreement.*

If the subject of a verb is singular, the verb must be singular in form. If the subject is plural, the verb must be plural in form.

RIGHT: The boy is good.
WRONG: The boy am good. (The verb is first person, the subject third person.)
WRONG: The boy are good. (The verb is plural, the subject singular.)
RIGHT: The boys are good.
WRONG: The boys is good. (The verb is singular, the subject plural.)

Collective nouns (by which are meant nouns which are singular in form, but plural in meaning) may take either a singular or plural verb, depending on whether the subject is regarded as a unified whole or as made up of its several parts.

The crowd is wildly cheering.
The crowd are being greeted one by one.

The crowd, in the first sentence, is thought of as cheering as if with one Gargantuan throat. In the second sentence, the crowd is thought of as a number of individuals being greeted separately. Many nouns which are plural in form but singular in meaning require a singular verb; these include *news, politics, mathematics,* etc. The following uses are correct:

> Mathematics is a hard subject for me.
> Politics does not interest me.
> The latest news is startling.

Compound subjects usually take a plural verb. A compound subject may be two nouns or two pronouns, connected by the conjunction *and.*

> RIGHT: Jack and Jill are going up the hill.
> WRONG: Jack and Jill is going up the hill.

Jack and Jill are *two* people, therefore the plural verb *are going* is required. On the other hand, the conjunctions *or* and *nor* do not make two singular subjects plural.

> RIGHT: Jack or Jill *is* going up the hill.
> WRONG: Jack or Jill *are* going up the hill.

The singular verb is required, because *or* means that the two parts of the subject are to be taken separately; thus: "Jack is going up the hill, or Jill is going up the hill." The conjunction *or* implies that you may take your choice, one at a time; the conjunction *and* implies that the parts which it connects must be taken together.

Two infinitives or clauses may be joined by *and* into a compound subject, requiring a plural verb, although sometimes a singular verb may be used:

> To aspire and to achieve *are* admirable ambitions.
> To have loved and lost *is* better than not to have loved at all.

In the first sentence, *to aspire* and *to achieve* are regarded as two different ambitions, profitably united. In the second sentence, because *to have loved* and (*to have*) *lost* are regarded as expressing the same or an indivisible action, they take a singular verb. Occasionally, two nouns of a compound subject are used with a singular verb. If you say, "Living and loving is all of life," you mean that loving is an inseparable part of living; but if you say, "Living and loving are all of life," you are thinking of loving as a separate activity from living.

Do not let a plural noun or pronoun near the verb draw it incorrectly into the plural number. In long sentences, this confusion may arise. Notice carefully the actual subject of the verb, and see to it that the verb agrees with its subject in person and number.

RIGHT: The weakness of the Brown sisters *is* their no-trump hands.

WRONG: The weakness of the Brown sisters *are* their no-trump hands.

The subject is *weakness,* which is singular. Do not let the nearness of the plural *sisters* confuse you; *sisters* is the object of the preposition *of.* Nor can a plural predicate affect the number of a verb with a singular subject. The fact that *hands* is plural does not alter the verb.

Sentences beginning with the adverb *there* seem to be exceptions. In such constructions, the number of the verb is determined by the predicate, which contains the real subject that has been thrown out of its normal position by the inverted order of the words.

There *have been* no storms this spring.

There *has been* no severe storm this spring.

In the first sentence, the plural *storms* controls the verb; in the second, the singular *storm* controls the verb.

Tenses of Verbs

From the principal parts of verbs are formed their various *tenses,* which differ as to the time of the action expressed. The principal parts of a verb are the present infinitive (*to walk*), the past tense (*walked*), and the past participle ([*have*] *walked*). Most verbs form the past tense by adding *d* or *ed* to the present tense; the past participle is often identical in form with the past tense. The principal parts of three regular common verbs are: *love, loved, loved; talk, talked, talked; marry, married, married.*

The three *moods* of verbs are the indicative, the subjunctive (conditional), and the imperative. The *indicative* mood states that an action really takes place, took place, or will take place. The *subjunctive* mood supposes that, or states conditions under which, an action may take place. The *imperative* mood commands or requests that an action take place.

To illustrate the tenses of each mood, following is a summary of the third person singular of the verb *wish:*

Present Infinitive: to wish.

INDICATIVE MOOD

Present Tense: he wishes.

Past Tense: he wished.

Future Tense: he will wish.

Present Perfect Tense: he has wished.

Past Perfect Tense: he had wished.

Future Perfect Tense: he will have wished.

Present Tense: (if) he wish.

Past Tense: (if) he wished.

Present Perfect Tense: (if) he have wished (rarely used).

Past Perfect Tense: (if) he had wished.

Present: wish.

The following examples and explanations make clear the common uses of these tenses and moods of the verb *call:*

Present Indicative: he calls (action happening now).

Past Indicative: he called (action happening yesterday, or any time before the present; most stories are written in the past tense).

Future Indicative: he will call (action that has not yet taken place, but may take place in the next second, or tomorrow, or any time in the future).

Present Perfect Indicative: he has called (action that is repeated often: *He has called me many times;* or action that begins in the past and continues in the present: *He has called me for the past month;* or action that was recently completed: *I have just called home*).

Past Perfect Indicative: he had called (action that was completed in the past, before another past action, as in the sentence: *He had called by the time I reached home*).

Future Perfect Indicative: he will have called (a statement in future time, implying that a condition, to be expressed, will exist when the action has been completed in the future: *He will have called by nine in the evening*).

Present Subjunctive: if he call (action that has not and may not take place; it is conditional on something to be expressed).

Past Subjunctive: if he called (conditional action in the past).

Present Perfect Subjunctive: if he have called (rarely used).

Past Perfect Subjunctive: if he had called.

Imperative: call (action that is commanded, requested, or urged to take place).

Progressive and intensive verb forms are formed with auxiliary verbs; for example:

Present: is calling; does call.

Past: was calling; did call.

Future: will be calling.
Present Perfect: has been calling.
Past Perfect: had been calling.
Future Perfect: will have been calling.

Notice that *he calls* makes a simple statement in present time, though the calling may not be continuously going on. But *he is calling* is a progressive statement in present time: the calling is now going on. *He does call* is an emphatic statement in present time. The imperative may have other forms, similarly; thus: *call, be calling, do call.*

Weigh carefully the sense differences expressed by the following sentences:

> He runs. He is running. How he does run!
> Men smoke because they enjoy tobacco.
> Men are smoking in the anteroom.
> Men do smoke more than they should.

The historical present, so called, is employed to describe past action vividly. For example, events in a story may, to suggest quick action, be related in the present tense. Compare these two examples:

Simple Past: The girl went to the table. She picked up the paper knife. Her fingers tested its sharpness. A sudden glint appeared in her eyes. With determination in every feature and motion, she moved to the door.

Historical Present: The girl goes to the table. She picks up the paper knife. Her fingers test its sharpness. A sudden glint appears in her eyes. With determination in every feature and motion, she moves to the door.

Throughout one article or story, you must maintain a proper *sequence of tenses.* That is, do not mix the present with the past tense; it would be careless English to write the first two sentences of the preceding example thus: "The girl went to the table. She picks up the paper knife." Study carefully the stories you read, and notice how the tenses are kept in harmony. Use the present perfect with the present tense, the past perfect with the past tense, and so on. It is correct to use the following two sentences in the same composition: "The girl went to the table. She had remembered something." Or these two: "The girl goes to the table. She has remembered something."

The Passive Voice

The verb forms so far mentioned have all been in the *active voice.* In each instance, the subject of the verb actually performs the action indicated. Some verbs have also what is called the *passive voice,* in which the subject does not act, but is acted upon. Tenses of the passive voice are formed with the past participle in combination with forms of the verb *to be*. The present indicative active voice is *he calls;* the present indicative passive voice is *he is called*. And so on through the various tenses.

Compare the following:

ACTIVE VOICE: The detective *killed* the criminal.
PASSIVE VOICE: The criminal *was killed* by the detective.

In the passive voice, what had been the object of the action in the active voice (here, *the criminal*) becomes the subject of the verb, and what had been the subject in the active voice (here, *the detective*) becomes the agent of the action, usually expressed with the preposition *by* or *with*.

ACTIVE VOICE: The razor *cut* his cheek.
PASSIVE VOICE: His cheek *was cut* by the razor.

Generally speaking, the passive voice is to be avoided when the active voice can be used. The active voice is much the stronger and the more vivid medium of expression. Notice the difference in intensity of these brief statements:

ACTIVE VOICE: They *heard* a shot.
PASSIVE VOICE: A shot *was heard* by them.

Irregular Verbs

Irregular verbs are bugbears. They are the verbs that form their past tense and past participle by some method other than by adding *d* or *ed*.

Lie and *lay* are often confused. The principal parts are: *lie, lay, lain; lay, laid, laid. Lie* indicates a position assumed by its subject; *lie* never takes an object. *Lay* indicates that its subject gives a position to its object; *lay* always takes an object.

For example, you *lie* in your bed (no object: you assume a reclining position in bed), but you *lay* a pillow on the bed (*pillow* is the object of *lay:* you place the pillow on the bed). But you *lay* in your bed yesterday (no object: you assumed a reclining position in bed, in past time); and you *laid* a pillow on the bed (*pillow* is the object of *laid:* you placed the pillow on the bed, in past time). *Lay* is nearly synonymous with *put*. That a hen *lays* eggs is a common use of the verb *lay;* it may help your memory, indeed, to recall that *a hen lays eggs,* and to realize that you cannot say that *a hen lies eggs.* Some examples:

Robert *has lain* in bed for hours at a time. He *is lying* there now.
Robert *laid* the book on the table in a conspicuous position. It *is lying* there still.
I must *lie* down at once.
I must *lay* the clean towels in the drawer.

The verb *lie,* of which the principal parts are *lie, lied, lied,* meaning to tell a falsehood, has no relation to the pair of verbs just discussed. This *lie* is regular in form, and its meaning is well understood, so you no doubt always use it correctly without thinking about it.

Sit and *set* are another bothersome pair. The principal parts of *sit* are *sit, sat, sat; sit* never takes an object. The principal parts of *set* are *set, set, set*—all the forms are alike; *set* takes an object as a general rule, although it may be intransitive in certain special uses. To *sit* is to assume a sitting position; to *set* is to place or put. You *sit* on a chair, but you *set* a kettle on the stove (*sit* has no object; *kettle* is the object of *set*). You *sat* on the chair yesterday, but you *set* the kettle on the stove yesterday. You have *sat* for hours at a time, but you have *set* the kettle on the stove frequently. A familiar intransitive use of *set* is in referring to a heavenly body: *the sun sets, set,* or *has set.*

LIST OF PRINCIPAL PARTS OF IRREGULAR VERBS

Here are the principal parts of some of the more commonly used irregular verbs. Memorize this list and avoid such errors as *he drunk, the station broadcasted, I seen, I have went,* and other common errors arising from misuse of the principal parts.

PRESENT	PAST	PAST PARTICIPLE
abide	abode	abode
arise	arose	arisen
be	was	been
bear	bore	borne, born
beat	beat	beaten
become	became	become
begin	began	begun
behold	beheld	beheld
bend	bent	bent
beseech	besought	besought
bet	bet	bet
bid	bid (bade)	bid (bidden)
bind	bound	bound
bite	bit	bitten
bleed	bled	bled
blow	blew	blown
break	broke	broken
breed	bred	bred
bring	brought	brought
build	built	built

PRESENT	PAST	PAST PARTICIPLE
burst	burst	burst
buy	bought	bought
cast	cast	cast
catch	caught	caught
choose	chose	chosen
cling	clung	clung
come	came	come
cost	cost	cost
creep	crept	crept
cut	cut	cut
deal	dealt	dealt
dig	dug	dug
do	did	done
draw	drew	drawn
drink	drank	drunk
drive	drove	driven
eat	ate	eaten
fall	fell	fallen
feed	fed	fed
feel	felt	felt
fight	fought	fought
find	found	found
flee	fled	fled
fling	flung	flung
fly	flew	flown
forget	forgot	forgotten
forsake	forsook	forsaken
freeze	froze	frozen
get	got	got (gotten)
give	gave	given
go	went	gone
grind	ground	ground
grow	grew	grown
hang	hung	hung
hang (a person)	hanged	hanged
have	had	had
hear	heard	heard
hide	hid	hidden
hit	hit	hit
hold	held	held

PRESENT	PAST	PAST PARTICIPLE
hurt	hurt	hurt
keep	kept	kept
know	knew	known
lay	laid	laid
lead	led	led
leave	left	left
lend	lent	lent
let	let	let
lie	lay	lain
lose	lost	lost
make	made	made
mean	meant	meant
meet	met	met
pay	paid	paid
read	read	read
rid	rid	rid
ride	rode	ridden
ring	rang	rung
rise	rose	risen
run	ran	run
say	said	said
see	saw	seen
seek	sought	sought
sell	sold	sold
send	sent	sent
set	set	set
shake	shook	shaken
shine	shone	shone
shoe	shod	shod
shoot	shot	shot
show	showed	showed (shown)
shut	shut	shut
sing	sang	sung
sink	sank	sunk
sit	sat	sat
slay	slew	slain
slide	slid	slid
sling	slung	slung
slink	slunk	slunk
smite	smote	smitten

PRESENT	PAST	PAST PARTICIPLE
sow	sowed	sowed (sown)
speak	spoke	spoken
speed	sped	sped
spend	spent	spent
spin	spun	spun
split	split	split
spread	spread	spread
spring	sprang	sprung
stand	stood	stood
steal	stole	stolen
stick	stuck	stuck
sting	stung	stung
stink	stank (stunk)	stunk
stride	strode	stridden
strike	struck	struck (stricken)
string	strung	strung
strive	strove	striven (strived)
swear	swore	sworn
sweep	swept	swept
swim	swam	swum
swing	swung	swung
take	took	taken
teach	taught	taught
tear	tore	torn
tell	told	told
think	thought	thought
thrive	throve (thrived)	thrived (thriven)
throw	threw	thrown
thrust	thrust	thrust
tread	trod	trodden (trod)
wake	woke (waked)	woke (waked)
wear	wore	worn
weave	wove	woven
weep	wept	wept
win	won	won
wind	wound	wound
wring	wrung	wrung
write	wrote	written

Some Troublesome Modifiers

Agreement of Adjectives

The following four words are sometimes demonstrative adjectives: *this, that, these, those. This* refers to something at hand; its plural is *these. That* refers to something at a distance, relatively considered; its plural is *those.* (*Note:* These four words are also used as pronouns. As pronouns, they stand for nouns. As adjectives, they modify nouns.)

An adjective, when it changes form as do these four demonstratives, must agree in number with the noun it modifies, so you must always say, "this kind" (not, "these kind"), or "that kind" (not, "those kind").

I prefer *these kinds* of cloth.
She likes *this kind* of teacups.

Adjectives Misused for Adverbs

Remember that an adjective must be used if you wish to modify a noun or a pronoun; an adverb must be used if you wish to modify a verb, an adjective, or another adverb. *Beautiful* is an adjective; *beautifully* is an adverb. If you say, "She looks beautiful in that dress," you are using good English, for *beautiful* is an adjective modifying the pronoun *she.* If you say, "She looks beautifully in that dress," you are not using good English, unless you mean that the act of looking is beautifully done, which is absurd. Study the following cases:

The runner sped rapidly to his goal. (The adverb *rapidly* modifies the verb *sped.*)

His step was heavy on the stairs. (The adjective *heavy* modifies the noun *step.*)

He stepped heavily on the stairs. (The adverb *heavily* modifies the verb *stepped.*)

The stars gleam brightly. (The adverb *brightly* modifies the verb *gleam.* In the line of the song, "The sun shines bright," for poetic reasons the adjective *bright* is used adverbially to modify the verb *shines.*)

Go slow. (This is a modern traffic idiom; grammatically, it should be: "Go slowly." Modern use has made *slow* a permissible adverb. Adverbs and adjectives are sometimes the same in form, quite correctly; examples: *fast, less, well,* etc.)

"How are you feeling today?" "Very well, thank you." (*Well* is an adjective, modifying the pronoun *I,* understood, as: "I am feeling very well." It is poor English to say "very good" here, not because *good* is the wrong part of speech, but because *well* is the logical adjective to use when describing one's health, *well* being the opposite of *sick.* Notice, however, that *ill* health and *good* health are opposites. *Well* today seldom precedes the noun it modifies, nearly always being a predicate adjective.) "How did you sleep last night?" "Very well, thank you." (*Well* is here an adverb, modifying the verb *slept*, understood, as: "I slept very well." It is poor English to say "very good" because *good* is in this example the wrong part of speech. *Well* is the adverbial form of the adjective *good*. The adverb is required because it is the manner of sleeping that is described, not the sleeper. Notice that you would say, correctly, "I slept soundly," not, "I slept sound.")

Position of Modifiers

Modifiers should be placed as near as possible to the words they modify. Be enlightened by this horrible example: "I bought a cane from the blonde salesgirl with an ebony head." The prepositional phrase, *with an ebony head,* seems to modify *salesgirl,* but properly modifies *cane.* Rearrangement corrects the error; thus: "I bought a cane with an ebony head from the blonde salesgirl."

CONTRACTIONS

In colloquial English many contractions are permissible. Words are likely to be clipped somewhat in conversation, for tongues are both lazy and resourceful. These contractions are good English if they are used correctly. Such contractions as *'d* for *would* (and sometimes *should*), *'ll* for *shall* or *will,* *'ve* for *have,* *'re* for *are,* *'s* for *is,* are common. Some of the current contractions are *you'd, they'd, I'll, we'll, we're, you're, you've, he's, the dog's running.* Warning: Do NOT write *of* when you mean *'ve,* in such expressions as "He could not've helped."

Contractions of verbs with the negative adverb *not* require some discrimination. The apostrophe in each contraction indicates the omission of one or more letters; in *don't,* the apostrophe shows that *o* has been omitted. *Shan't,* it should be pointed out, is not a common contraction, even colloquially, except in certain sections of the country. Always avoid the vulgarism *ain't;* although there is no recognized contraction for "am not," and although *ain't* might serve in this capacity—"ain't I?" meaning "am I not?"—it has yet to receive the sanction of the best usage. Never say, "he ain't," but rather say, "he isn't," or "he is not."

Remember that a verb must agree with its subject in person and number. Do not say, "he don't," when you mean, "he doesn't," any more than you would say, "he do not," when you mean, "he does not." Avoid the forced "aren't I?" which violates the rule just stated; if fully expressed, this is impossible grammatically, for it becomes, "are I not?"

Can't is an acceptable colloquial contraction of *cannot.* Do not use *can,* however, when *may* is the verb required, as in asking permission. The verb *can* expresses ability or lack of it; *may* expresses permission, liberty, or sanction. Examples:

RIGHT: May we take our dog into the park?
WRONG: Can we take our dog into the park?

RIGHT: The children may go if they can get ready in time.
WRONG: The children can go if they can get ready in time.

The Uses of "Shall" and "Will"

Shall and *will* are daily interchanged, without discrimination, by otherwise careful writers and speakers. So widespread has this confusion become that the distinction between the two words is gradually being lost.

Primarily, *shall* and *will* are used as auxiliary verbs to form the future tenses of other verbs. The future tense of the verb *love* is as follows:

I shall love	we shall love
thou wilt love	you will love
he will love	they will love

Notice that *shall* is used with the first person, and *will* with the second and third persons. Always, when simple future time is expressed, *shall* must be used with the first person, and *will* with the second and third persons. Study the following examples:

RIGHT: I shall pay this bill on the first of the month.
WRONG: I will pay this bill on the first of the month.

RIGHT: We shall return tomorrow.
WRONG: We will return tomorrow.

Just the opposite of the simple future tense is the expression of determination or resolve with *shall* and *will.* Expressing strong purpose, *will* is used with the first person, and *shall* with the second and third persons. Study the following examples:

SIMPLE FUTURE: I shall drive dad's car.
DETERMINATION: I will drive dad's car. (I am determined to drive dad's car.)
SIMPLE FUTURE: She will marry me.
DETERMINATION: She shall marry me. (She shall marry me whether she wants to or not.)
SIMPLE FUTURE: They will be killed. (A prediction.)
DETERMINATION: They shall be killed. (It has been decided that they must be killed, come what may.)

The Uses of "Should" and "Would"

Just as with *shall* and *will, should* is used with the first person, and *would* is used with the second and third persons.

Should and *would* are used to conclude statements which are introduced by clauses which are conditional or contrary to fact.

If I had consented, he would have used his own judgment.

If you were strong enough, you would help.

If I could, I should be glad to accompany you.

Should is also used as an auxiliary of other verbs in the conditional expression of uncertainty or withheld thought.

Should you decide to help, let me know.

Should our wives come with us, we shall be well escorted.

Should is also used in requests gently phrased, as: "Should you care for dessert?"

Should may have an emphatic implication, in the sense of "ought to."

You should be ashamed. (You ought to be ashamed.)

Anyone should do the right thing. (Anyone ought to do the right thing.)

Would has three special uses that may be mentioned here. It may express a desire or wish, as in this example: "I would I were a bird." *Would* may also suggest that something might be expected to happen; for example: "Running away would arouse suspicion." It may also be used to express a customary action: "Occasionally, Alvin would meet me at the club."

COMPARISON

Adjectives and adverbs are compared when their degree is increased or lessened. The simple form is called the *positive* degree, next is the *comparative* degree, and finally the *superlative*. Regular adjectives add *er* to the positive to form the comparative, and *est* to the positive to form the superlative. If these suffixes make awkward or unpronounceable words, the adverbial modifiers *more* and *most* are used to form the comparative and superlative degrees respectively. *Good* and *bad* are irregular adjectives, as may be seen from the following examples of adjectives compared:

POSITIVE	COMPARATIVE	SUPERLATIVE
black	blacker	blackest
slow	slower	slowest
great	greater	greatest
beautiful	more beautiful	most beautiful
good	better	best
bad	worse	worst

Comparison may be made in a minimizing direction also, with the adverbial modifiers *less* and *least;* examples: *dark, less dark, least dark; intelligent, less intelligent, least intelligent; good, less good, least good.*

Adverbs are compared with *more* and *most,* or *less* and *least;* thus: *swiftly, more swiftly, most swiftly; swiftly, less swiftly, least swiftly.* A few adverbs which have the same form as adjectives are compared like the adjectives; as: *fast, faster, fastest.*

Comparisons with the Conjunctions "As" and "Than"

As and *than* are conjunctions: do not confuse them with prepositions and allow them to draw following pronouns unjustifiably into the objective case. The case required can be determined by completing the unexpressed subordinate clause. You must say, "He is taller than I," and not, "He is taller than me," because the complete sentence would be, "He is taller than I am" (the nominative case is required as the subject of *am*).

> RIGHT: Albert cannot do so well as he.
> WRONG: Albert cannot do so well as him.
> COMPLETE: Albert cannot do so well as he can do.

> RIGHT: My brother has more money than I.
> WRONG: My brother has more money than me.
> COMPLETE: My brother has more money than I have.

> RIGHT: We were luckier than they.
> WRONG: We were luckier than them.
> COMPLETE: We were luckier than they were.

Notice, incidentally, the spelling of *than,* the conjunction used in comparisons; do not confuse it with *then.* The objective case is correct when you find by completing the unexpressed subordinate clause that it is required:

> RIGHT: George likes Doris better than he [than William does].
> WRONG: George likes Doris better than him.
> COMPLETE: George likes Doris better than he likes her.

However, if the meaning were different, the preceding example would be correct with the nominative case:

> RIGHT: George likes Doris better than him.
> COMPLETE: George likes Doris better than he likes him.

Study the following additional examples:

> UNEXPRESSED: I'd rather take it from you than him.
> COMPLETE: I'd rather take it from you than from him.

UNEXPRESSED: She'll mislead you as readily as me.
COMPLETE: She'll mislead you as readily as she does (*or* did) me.
UNEXPRESSED: I love you less than him.
COMPLETE: I love you less than I love him.

The Comparative Degree

When comparing two persons or things, one with the other, use the comparative degree. Examples:

RIGHT: Esther is the prettier girl of the two.
WRONG: Esther is the prettiest girl of the two.
RIGHT: Which of this pair do you think the more appropriate?
WRONG: Which of this pair do you think the most appropriate?

Warning: Never use *more* with an adjective already in the comparative degree. Examples:

RIGHT: This bag is more heavy than that.
BETTER: This bag is heavier than that.
WRONG: This bag is more heavier than that.

Use the superlative degree when comparing more than two persons or things. Examples:

Muriel is the tallest of the three sisters.
Get the reddest hat you can find.
Faith, hope, and charity—and the greatest of these is charity.

CAPITALIZATION

Capitalization, like so many other phases of good English, is mainly a matter of form that has been solidified by use. The basic idea of capitalization is that a word beginning with a capital is accorded special importance.

FIRST WORD OF A SENTENCE

The first word of every sentence always begins with a capital letter. The first word of every direct quotation begins with a capital letter (exceptions are single words, short combinations, or phrases enclosed in quotation marks for emphasis or to set them apart from the rest of the sentence.)

PROPER NOUNS AND PROPER ADJECTIVES

A proper noun is the name of a particular person or place: *John Jones, Alabama, New York City, Africa, Betty.* Other proper nouns are *Bible* and the names of languages or of natives of countries or sections: *English, Englishman, American, French, Frenchman, Bostonian, Latin, Roman, Greek*. Proper adjectives are capitalized because they are directly derived from proper nouns: the *German* language, the *British* crown, *South American* gold, *Chinese* silk. Names of the deity are capitalized, and also, usually, pronouns standing for Him: *God*, the *Father*, the *Holy Ghost*, in *His* image. Names of the seasons are not capitalized in modern English; write *spring, summer, autumn, winter*.

Titles are capitalized when they refer to a particular person, or when they precede or follow a proper name; examples: *Sir* Walter Scott, *Judge* Taylor, *Captain* Smith, *Mr.* Henry W. Black, *Miss* Dorothy Grove, *Chief Justice* Holmes, *President* Lincoln, *Lord* Beaconsfield. When standing alone, titles are capitalized only when a particular person is meant; examples: the *President* of the United States (the present one), the president of the United States (any president).

Names of days of the week and months of the year are capitalized. Names of geographical sections are also capitalized; examples: the *Middle West*, the *Orient*, the *East*. Points of the compass are not capitalized when spelled out; examples: *north, south, northwest*. Abbreviations of points of the compass are capitalized; examples: *N., S., N.W.*

Parts of place names, such as *street, river, avenue*, etc., are sometimes capitalized and sometimes not. Publishing houses select one style and follow it consistently. The preference seems to be for *Main Street, Mississippi River*. If the common noun precedes, and is to be taken generally, it is not capitalized; examples: the *rivers* of the United States, the *streets* of Chicago. But if the meaning is particular, the common noun is capitalized; examples: *Lake Geneva*, the *River Hudson*.

Names of holidays, historical events, and the like, are capitalized: *Valentine's Day*, the *Revolutionary War*, the *Battle of Gettysburg*.

Titles of Books and Names of Organizations

Important words of the titles of books, plays, and organizations are capitalized.

By important words in titles are meant all except prepositions, conjunctions, articles. The first and last words are always capitalized: *A Tale of Two Cities, The Last of the Mohicans, The Cloister and the Hearth*.

PUNCTUATION

FULL STOPS

Every sentence must end with a period (.), an interrogation point (?), also called a question mark, or an exclamation point (!).

> Spring is a season of rebirth.
> What time is it?
> Hurry over there!

A period must be placed after abbreviations; examples: *St., a.m., i.e., etc., dept.* An exception may be made in the case of such abbreviations as *NATO, AFL-CIO, NBC.*

THE COMMA

The comma (,) is the most frequent mark of punctuation, yet it is used much less today than formerly. Follow the usage of current magazines and recent books, rather than that of works written many years ago. The modern tendency is to use only enough commas to avoid ambiguity and make easy reading. In general, a comma indicates a slight pause or a break in the continuity of the thought expressed by the sentence.

Separating Parenthetical Words

Parenthetical words or phrases (that is, words or phrases inserted in the sentence for purposes of description or explanation, but not forming an integral part of the simple sentence itself) are customarily set off by commas:

> The result, *therefore,* is negligible.
> *No,* I do not think so.
> *On the contrary,* I believe you.
> Anton, *the barber,* is a good citizen.
> The man, *however,* is not responsible.

Note: When *however* is used parenthetically, as in the last example, it is correctly set off by commas. But if *however* is used as a direct adverbial modifier, it must not be separated by a comma from the word it modifies: "However much you love her, she does not return your love."

In the next to the last example, preceding, *barber* is in apposition to *Anton.* Words in apposition are set off by commas unless the connection in thought is very close. The following examples are all correct:

John, *the piper's son,* stole a pig.
My brother John left yesterday.
John, *my brother,* went yesterday.
My friend Smith lives across the street.

Separating Elements of a Series

Series of nouns, lists of things, or series of modifiers, phrases, and the like, are separated into units by commas. Although some modern writers omit the comma before *and* in a series, it may save confusion to insert it:

The colors of the American flag are *red, white, and blue.*
To live, to love, and to die are all of life.
I *sandpapered the board, applied a coat of enamel, and let it dry.*
The modern drugstore is an emporium of *sodas, drugs, cosmetics, knickknacks, furniture, confectionery, and other miscellany.*
Her ideal is a *strong, healthy, handsome, trustworthy* young man.

Note in the last example that *young man* has the force of a single noun, so no comma is needed between the adjectives *trustworthy* and *young.*

When two adjectives modify the same noun, the comma may be omitted if the sense is clear without it. Commas need not be used with more than two adjectives if they are short and can be spoken smoothly:

Her beautiful blonde head fairly shone.
A clever old fellow was he.
The boy had a bright new penny.
Her large clear blue eyes stared into mine.

Notice, however, that commas are sometimes necessary:

These are bright, fast colors.
I have seldom seen such exquisite, delicate lace.
She was a damsel forgotten, forsaken, and forlorn.

Some Special Uses of Commas

In addition, commas should be used in the following situations.

Between a proper name and a following title or academic degree: *Harold Gray, A.B.; John Doe, Esquire; E. H. Robinson, M.D.*

Between repeated words, if they are in the same construction in a sentence: "I could *cry, cry, cry,* of vexation"; "He speaks only *words, words, words."*

Separating an interrogative sentence from a directly preceding declarative sentence which completes its meaning: "You'll do as I ask, won't you?"

Indicating the omission of a word or words which are not repeated but which are understood from what precedes: "Eyes are to see with; ears, to hear with; fingers, to feel with"; "Johnny ordered apple pie; Ethel, mince."

Setting off contrasted words or phrases ("Money, not fame, is what everyone really desires"), or words or names of people spoken in direct address ("Come, dear, we must be going home"; "Gather round, my friends, and listen").

THE SEMICOLON

In general, the semicolon (;) indicates a somewhat greater pause, a somewhat greater break in thought, than the comma. It is used to separate two independent clauses which are not joined by a co-ordinating conjunction: "The site of the battle was a small Pennsylvania town; it is now a great attraction for tourists." Two or more sentences may be written together as one sentence, if they are closely related in thought, and separated one from another by semicolons: "This gauge measures humidity; the other calculates the density of the liquid." The semicolon is used sometimes in order to make clear the separate elements of a series which themselves contain commas: "We stopped at Miami, Florida; New Orleans, Louisiana; and Tucson, Arizona."

THE COLON

A colon (:) generally indicates a gap in the thought, but a gap that is to be completed by something immediately following. Notice its use before a series, following words like *example, for example, the following,* and so on. (*Large cities, for example: New York, Chicago, San Francisco.*)

QUOTATION MARKS

All direct quotations must be enclosed in quotation marks (" "). Direct quotations may be the exact spoken words of some person, exactly recorded in writing, or may be one or more words directly quoted from some other work or book. "To be or not to be, that is the question," is a quotation from Shakespeare's *Hamlet* and is properly enclosed in quotation marks. Other examples are:

> "To be or not to be," if I may quote Shakespeare, "that is the question."
>
> "Darling," he said, looking up into her eyes, "you must forgive me."
>
> "Go," the man called, "and don't come back."

Note that when a direct quotation is interrupted by such words as *I said, he explained,* or *she replied,* a comma surrounds these words. However, when these words come at the end of a quoted sentence and are followed by another quoted sentence, a period follows these words:

> "Yes, we've just returned from Mexico," she explained. "We had a wonderful time."

When a quotation is a question, the quotation is terminated by a question mark:

> "Is this a dagger I see before me?" Macbeth cried.

Similarly, when a quotation is an exclamation, the quotation is terminated by an exclamation point.

When a quotation comes within a quotation, the inside quotation is put in single quotation marks (' '):

> "Caesar said, 'I came, I saw, I conquered,' didn't he?" Mary asked.

WORDS FREQUENTLY MISSPELLED

The following words are among the most frequently misspelled words in the English language. In order to learn to spell them correctly, it is advisable that you write each word on paper. Then compare your spelling with the one given here. If you are correct, pass on to the next. If you have made an error, practice writing it correctly several times until it is fixed in your mind.

absence	among	beginning
absurd	amount	believe
accept	analyze	benefited
accidentally	annual	brilliant
accommodate	answer	bulletin
accompanying	apology	burglar
accomplish	apparatus	business
accumulate	apparent	busy
achievement	appearance	calendar
acknowledgment	appropriate	candidate
acquaintance	Arctic	carrying
across	argument	ceiling
address	assistance	cemetery
advice	athletics	certain
aggravate	attendance	changeable
all right	audience	characteristic
almost	awkward	choose
already	barbarous	chosen
always	becoming	clothes
amateur	before	column

coming	divine	harass
committee	doesn't	having
comparative	dormitory	height
compel	dying	hindrance
competition	eighth	hoping
concede	eligible	hopping
conceivable	embarrassment	illegible
conceive	eminent	imagination
conferred	envelope	immediately
confidently	environment	incidentally
conquer	equipped	incredible
conqueror	especially	independence
conscience	exaggerated	indispensable
conscientious	exceed	infinite
conscious	excellent	ingenious
continuous	exercise	intelligence
control	exhaust	interesting
convenient	exhilarate	interfere
courteous	existence	interrupted
courtesy	expense	irrelevant
criticism	experience	irresistible
decide	explanation	its
decision	familiar	it's
definite	fascinate	itself
dependent	February	judgment
depth	fiend	knowledge
description	finally	laboratory
desirable	forcible	laid
desperate	formally	lead
develop	formerly	led
development	forty	leisure
dictionary	fourth	library
difference	frantically	license
dining	friend	lightning
disappear	gauge	loneliness
disappoint	generally	loose
disastrous	government	lose
discipline	governor	losing
disease	grammar	lying
dissatisfy	grievous	meant
dissipate	guard	medicine
divide	handkerchief	miniature

minute
miscellaneous
mischievous
misspell
murmuring
muscle
naturally
necessary
nevertheless
nickel
niece
nineteen
ninety
ninth
noticeable
obstacle
occasionally
occur
occurred
occurrence
o'clock
operate
opportunity
original
outrageous
paid
pamphlet
parallel
parliament
particularly
partner
pastime
perform
perhaps
permissible
perseverance
persuade
pertain
physical
piece
planned
pleasant

poison
possession
practically
prairie
precede
preference
preferred
preparation
presence
principal
principle
privilege
probably
procedure
proceed
professor
prominent
psychiatry
psychology
pursue
quiet
quite
really
receive
recognize
recommend
religious
remembrance
repetition
restaurant
rhyme
rhythm
ridiculous
sacrilegious
schedule
secretary
seize
sense
separate
sergeant
severely
sheriff

shining
siege
sieve
similar
sincerely
solemn
soluble
sophomore
species
specimen
stationary
stationery
stopped
stretch
studying
succeed
successful
superintendent
supersede
surprise
temperament
than
their
then
there
they're
together
too
tragedy
tries
truly
until
usually
village
villain
vinegar
weather
weird
where
whether
wholly
whose

women   written   you're
writing   your

WORDS FREQUENTLY MISPRONOUNCED

Key to Pronunciation. In order to indicate the exact pronunciations of words, we have used a system of symbols which should be understood before proceeding. We give here the symbol used and a common word in which the sound is used: ā, as in *late;* ă, as in *bat;* â, as in *dare; a,* as in *comma* and *normal;* ah, as in *father;* aw, as in *fall;* ē, as in *plead;* ĕ, as in *let;* ê, as in *mere* and *sphere; e,* as in *dozen* and *river;* ī, as in *pile;* ĭ, as in *bit; i,* as in *habit* and *satin;* ō, as in *note;* ŏ, as in *cot;* ô, as in *north; o,* as in *actor* and *random;* ōō, as in *noon* and *food;* ŏŏ, as in *wood* and *good;* oi, as in *boil;* ow, as in *now;* ū, as in *cue* and *union;* ŭ, as in *but;* û, as in *turn* and *cur; u,* as in *lettuce* and *circus; ū,* as in *picture;* ŭ, as in *talcum;* N, nasalized, as in the French words *bon* and *bien; th,* as in *thought;* TH, as in *than;* zh, like the z in *azure* and the s in *pleasure.* The accent mark (′) indicates that the syllable it follows receives the main stress in the word. The accent mark (″) indicates that the syllable it follows receives the secondary stress in the word.

ABSOLUTELY ăb′-so-lŭt-li
ABSORB ăb-sôrb′
ACCLIMATE a-klī′-mit
  or ăk′-li-māt
ACOUSTIC a-kōōs′-tĭk or
  a-kows′-tĭk
ACUMEN a-kū′-mĕn
ADAGE ăd′-ĭj
ADDRESS a-drĕs′
ADMIRABLE ăd′-mĭ-rab'l
ADOBE a-dō′-bĭ
ADULT ă-dŭlt′
ADUMBRATE ăd-ŭm′-brāt
ADVERSARY ăd′-vûr-sĕ″-rĭ
ADVERTISEMENT ăd-vûr′-tĭz-ment
  or ăd″-vûr-tīz′-ment
AERIAL ā-ēr′-ĭ-al or âr′-ĭ-al
AFFLATUS a-flā′-tŭs
AGAIN a-gĕn′

AGED ā′-jĕd (*old*)
  ājd (*of a certain age*)
AGGRANDIZEMENT a-grăn′-dĭz-ment
AGILE ăj′-ĭl
AGUE ā′-gū
ALBEIT awl-bē′-ĭt
ALBINO ăl-bī′-nō
ALIAS ā′-lĭ-as
ALLIED a-līd′
ALLOY a-loi′
ALMA MATER ăl′-ma mā′-tûr
ALMOND ah′-mŭnd
ALTERNATE *verb:* awl′-tûr-nāt *or*
  ăl′-tûr-nāt
          adjective: awl′-tûr-nĭt
  or ăl′-tûr-nĭt
ALUMNA a-lŭm′-na
ALUMNAE a-lŭm′-nē

ALUMNI a-lŭm'-nī
AMATEUR ăm'-a-tûr
AMENABLE a-mēn'-a-b'l
ANCILLARY ăn'-sĭ-lĕr"-ĭ
ANESTHETIST ăn-ĕs'-thĭ-tĭst
ANNEX verb: a-nĕks'
   noun: ăn'-nĕks or a-nĕks'
ANOMALOUS a-nŏm'-a-lŭs
ANTIPODES ăn-tĭp'-o-dēz
APATHY ăp'-a-thĭ
APOSTASY a-pŏs'-ta-sĭ
APOTHEOSIS ăp"-o-thē'-o-sĭs or
  a-pŏth"-i-ō'-sĭs
APPLICABLE ăp'-lĭ-ka-b'l
APPRECIATION a-prē"-shĭ-ā'-shun
APROPOS ăp"-ro-pō'
ARCHANGEL ahrk'-ān'-jel
ARCHIPELAGO ahr"-kĭ-pĕl'-a-gō
ARCTIC ahrk'-tĭk
ARRAIGN a-rān'
ATHLETIC ăth-lĕt'-ĭk
ATROPHY ăt'-ro-fĭ
ATTRIBUTE verb: a-trĭb'-yūt
   noun: ăt'-ri-byūt
AUTOBIOGRAPHY aw"-to-bī-ŏg'-ra-fĭ
AUTOGYRO aw"-to-jī'rō
AUTOMOBILE ô"-to-mo-bēl' or
  ô"-to-mo'-bĭl
AVIATOR ā'-vĭ-ā"-tôr
AWRY a-rī'
AYE, AY ā (always)
   ī (yes)

BADE băd
BANAL ba-năl' or bā'-nal
BANQUET băng'-kwĕt
BAS-RELIEF bah"-ri-lēf'
BASS bās (musical term)
  băs (fish)
BECAUSE bi-kawz'

BESTIAL bĕst'-yal
BITUMEN bĭ-tū'-men
BIVOUAC bĭv'-ŏŏ-ăk or bĭv'-wăk
BLACKGUARD blăg'-ahrd
BLASÉ blah-zā'
BLASPHEME blăs-fēm'
BLASPHEMY blăs'-fi-mĭ
BOUILLON bŏŏ"-yôn' or bŏŏl'-yŭn
BOUQUET bŏŏ-kā'
BOURGEOISIE bŏŏr"-zhwah"-zē'
BOW bow (to bend or yield)
  bō (anything bent or curved)
  bow (forward part of ship)
BRAVADO bra-vah'-dō
BREECHES brĭch'-ĭz
BRIC-A-BRAC brĭk'-a-brăk"
BRIGAND brĭg'-and
BROCHURE brō-shŏŏr'
BROOCH brōch or brŏŏch
BUFFET bŏŏ-fā' (sideboard)
  bŭf'-et (a blow)
BULLION bŏŏl'-yon
BULWARK bŏŏl'-wûrk

CACHE kăsh
CALDRON kawl'-drun
CALUMNY kăl'-um-nĭ
CANDELABRA kan"-di-lah'-bra
CANON kăn'-un (law)
  kăn'-yun (valley, preferred spelling is canyon)
CARIES kā'-rĭ-ēz
CELLO chĕl'-ō
CENTENARY sĕn'-ti-nĕr"-ĭ or
  sĕn-tĕn'-a-rĭ
CERAMICS sē-răm'-ĭks
CEREBRAL sĕr'-ē-bral
CHAFE chāf
CHAMELEON ka-mē'-lē-un or
  ka-mēl'-yun

CHAMOIS   shăm'-ĭ
CHARADE   sha-rād' *or* sha-rahd'
CHARLATAN   shahr'-la-tan
CHASM   kăzm
CHASSIS   shăs'-ĭ *or* shăs'-ĭs
CHASTE   chāst
CHASTISEMENT   chăs'-tĭz-ment
CHEROOT   she-rōōt'
CHIMERA   kī-mē'-ra *or* kĭ-mē'-ra
CHIROPODIST   kī-rŏp'-o-dĭst
CHOCOLATE   chŏk'-o-lĭt *or*
   chŏk'-lĭt
CHOLER   kŏl'-er
CHORUS   kō'-rus
CINEMA   sĭn'-i-ma
CLANDESTINE   klăn-dĕs'-tĭn
CLIENTELE   klī''-en-tĕl' *or*
   klē''-an-tĕl'
CLIQUE   klēk
CLOTHES   klōTHz
CLOTHS   klôthz *or* klôTHs
COALESCE   kō''-a-lĕs'
COGNIZANT   kŏg'-nĭ-zant
COIFFURE   kwah-fyūr'
COLLOQUIAL   ko-lō'-kwĭ-al
COLONEL   kûr'-nel
COLUMNIST   kŏl'-um-nĭst
COMBATANT   kŏm'-ba-tant *or*
   kŏm-băt'-ant
COMELY   kŭm'-lĭ
COMMUNAL   kŏm'-yū-nal *or*
   ko-myū'-nal
COMPARABLE   kŏm'-pa-ra-b'l
COMPLACENT   kŏm-plā'-sent
COMPLAISANT   kom-plā'-zant
COMPTROLLER   kŏn-trōl'-er
CONCERTO   kŏn-chĕr'-tō
CONDIGN   kŏn-dīn'
CONGERIES   kŏn-jēr'-ĭ-ēz
CONJUGAL   kŏn'-jōō-gal
CONNOISSEUR   kŏn''-i-sûr'

CONSULTATIVE   kŏn-sul'-ta-tĭv
CONSUMMATE   *verb:* kŏn'-su-māt
   adj.: kon-sŭm'-it
CONTEST   *verb:* kon-tĕst'
   noun: kŏn'-tĕst
CONTESTANT   kon-tĕs'-tant
CONTUMELY   kŏn'-tyū-mē''-lĭ
CORNUCOPIA   kôr''-nū-kō'-pĭ-a
CORPOREAL   kôr-pō'-rē-al
COUP   kōō
COUPON   kōō'-pŏn
COURTIER   kōr'-tĭ-er
COVEY   kŭv'-ĭ
COYOTE   kī'-ōt *or* kī-ō'-ti
CREEK   krēk
CRESCENDO   kre-shĕn'-dō *or*
   kre-sĕn'-dō
CREVASSE   krē-văs'
CREVICE   krĕv'-ĭs
CUISINE   kwē-zēn'
CULINARY   kyū'-lĭ-nĕr''-ĭ
CUPBOARD   kŭb'-erd
CURATOR   kyū-rā'-ter

DACHSHUND   dahks'-hōōnt'' *or*
   dăsh'-hŭnd''
DAIS   dā'-ĭs
DATA   dā'-ta *or* dah'-ta
DEAF   dĕf
DEBRIS   dĕ-brē' *or* dĕb'-rē
DEBUT   dā'-byū *or* dĕ-byū'
DEBUTANTE   dĕb''-ū-tahnt'
DÉCOLLETÉ   dā-kŏl'-tā *or*
   dā-kôl''-tā'
DECORUM   di-kō'-rum
DEFICIT   dĕf'-i-sĭt
DEMONIAC   de-mō'-nĭ-ăk
DEMONIACAL   dē''-mo-nī'-a-kal
DENOUEMENT   dā-nōō'-mawN
DEPOT   dē'-pō *or* dĕp'-ō
DERISIVE   di-rī'-sĭv

DESHABILLE dĕz″-*a*-bēl′

DESPICABLE dĕs′-pĭ-k*a*-b′l

DESULTORY dĕs′-ul-tō″-rĭ

DIABETES dī″-*a*-bē′-tēz

DILETTANTE dĭl″-*e*-tăn′-tĭ

DIMINUTION dĭm″-ĭ-nyū′-sh*u*n

DINGY dĭn′-jĭ

DIRECT d*i*-rĕkt′ *or* dī-rĕkt′

DIRIGIBLE dĭr′-ĭ-j*i*-b′l

DISCERN dĭ-zûrn′ *or* dĭ-sûrn′

DISHEVEL dĭ-shĕv′-*e*l

DISPUTANT dĭs′-pyū-t*a*nt

DIVERS dī′-v*e*rz

DIVERSE dī-vûrs′ *or* dī′-vûrs

or d*i*-vûrs′

DOLOROUS dŏl′-*e*r-*u*s *or* dō′-l*e*r-*u*s

DONKEY dŏng′-kĭ

DOUR dōor

DRAUGHT drăft

DROUGHT drowt

DUCAT dŭk′-*a*t

DURESS dyū′-rĕs *or* d*u*-rĕs′

ECLAT ā-klah′

ECLECTIC ĕk-lĕk′-tĭk

ECZEMA ĕk′-z*i*-m*a or* ĕk′-s*i*-m*a*

EIGHTH āt'th

ELEEMOSYNARY ĕl″-*i*-mŏs′-*i*-nĕr″-ĭ

or ĕl″-*i*-ē-mŏz′-ĭ-nĕr″-ĭ

ELITE ā-lēt′

ELIXIR *i*-lĭk′-s*e*r

EMACIATE *i*-mā′-shĭ-āt

ENCORE ahN′-kōr *or* ahn-kōr′

EN ROUTE ahn-rōot′

ENSEMBLE ahN-sŏm′-b'l

ENTENTE ahN-tahNt′

ENTREE ahn′-trā

EPAULET ĕp′-*o*-lĕt

EPISTLE *i*-pĭs′-'l

EPITOME *i*-pĭt′-*o*-mĕ

ERE âr

ERR ûr

ESCHEW ĕs-chōō′ *or* ĕs-chyū′

ET CETERA ĕt sĕt′-*e*r-*a*

EVIDENTLY ĕv′-*i*-dĕnt-lĭ

EXIGENCY ĕk′-s*i*-jĕn-sĭ

EXTANT ĕks′-t*a*nt *or* ĕk-stănt′

FACET făs′-ĕt

FAUCET faw′-sĕt

FECUND fĕk′-*u*nd *or* fē′-k*u*nd

FETE fāt

FIANCE fē″-ahn-sā′ *or* f*i*-ahn′-sā

FINIS fī′-nĭs

FLACCID flăk′-sĭd

FORBEAR fôr-bâr′

FOREBEAR fōr′-bâr

FOREHEAD fŏr′-ĕd

FUNEREAL f*u*-nêr′-*i*-*a*l

FUNGI fŭn′-jī

FUNGUS fŭng′-g*u*s

GALLANT *adj*. and *noun:* găl′-*a*nt

or g*a*-lănt′

GAOL jāl

GAUGE gāj

GENEALOGY jĕn″-*i*-ăl′-*o*-jĭ

GENUINE jĕn′-y*u*-ĭn

GESTICULATE jĕs-tĭk′-y*u*-lāt

GESTURE jĕs′-tyūr

GEYSER gī′-z*e*r *or* gī′-s*e*r

GIST jĭst

GLAZIER glā′-zh*e*r

GONDOLA gŏn′-d*o*-l*a*

GOSLING gŏz′-lĭng

GOVERNMENT gŭv′-*e*rn-m*e*nt

GYROPLANE jī′-r*o*-plān″

HARBINGER hahr′-bĭn-j*e*r

HAUTBOY hō′-boi *or* ō′-boi

HEARTH hahr*th*

HEGEMONY he-jĕm'-o-nĭ *or*
  hĕj'-e-mō''-nĭ
HEIFER hĕf'-er
HEINOUS hā'-nŭs
HELICOPTER hĕl''-ĭ-cŏp'-ter
HERB ûrb *or* hûrb
HERESY hĕr'-e-sĭ
HIATUS hī-ā'-tŭs
HICCOUGH hĭk'-ŭp
HIERARCHY hī'-er-ahr''-kĭ
HOMAGE hŏm'-ĭj *or* ŏm'-ĭj
HORIZON ho-rī'-z'n
HOSPITABLE hŏs'-pĭ-ta-b'l
HYPERBOLE hī-pûr'-bo-lē

IDEA ī-dē'-a
IDIOSYNCRASY ĭd''-ĭ-o-sĭng'-kra-sĭ
IGNOMINY ĭg'-no-mĭn-ĭ
IGNORAMUS ĭg''-no-rā'-mŭs
ILLUSTRATE ĭl'-ŭs-trāt'' *or*
  ĭ-lŭs'-trāt
IMPIETY ĭm-pī'-e-tĭ
IMPIOUS ĭm'-pĭ-us
IMPOSTOR ĭm-pŏs'-ter
IMPUGN ĭm-pūn'
INCOGNITO ĭn-kŏg'-nĭ-tō
INCOMPARABLE ĭn-kŏm'-pa-ra-b'l
INDICT ĭn-dīt'
INDIGENOUS ĭn-dĭj'-i-nŭs
INEBRIETY ĭn-i-brī'-e-tĭ
INEXORABLE ĭn-ĕk'-so-ra-b'l
INGENIOUS ĭn-jēn'-yŭs
INGENUOUS ĭn-jĕn'-ū-ŭs
INTEGRAL ĭn'-ti-gral
INTESTATE ĭn-tĕs'-tāt
INTREPID ĭn-trĕp'-ĭd
INUNDATE ĭn'-un-dāt
INVEIGH ĭn-vā'
INVIOLATE ĭn-vī'-o-lāt
IRATE ī'-rāt *or* ī-rāt'
IRON ī'-ern

IRREPARABLE ĭ-rĕp'-a-ra-b'l
IRREVOCABLE ĭ-rĕv'-o-ka-b'l
JOCOSE jo-kōs'
JOCUND jŏk'-ŭnd *or* jō'-kŭnd
JOUST jŭst *or* jowst

KHAKI kah'-kĭ

LAMENTABLE lăm'-en-ta-b'l
LATH lăth
LATHE lāth
LENITY lĕn'-i-tĭ
LETHAL lē'-thal
LICORICE lĭk'-o-rĭs
LINEAGE lĭn'-i-ĭj
LIVELONG lĭv'-lŏng''
LOATH lōth
LOATHE lōth
LOCALE lō-kăl'
LONGEVITY lŏn-jĕv'-i-tĭ
LONG-LIVED lŏng'-līvd'

MACHINATION măk''-ĭ-nā'-shŭn
MAELSTROM māl'-strom
MAGNETO măg-nē'-tō
MALIGN ma-līn'
MALINGERER ma-lĭng'-ger-er
MANGE mānj
MANGER mān'-jer
MANKIND măn''-kīnd' *or* măn'-kīnd
MARITAL măr'-i-tal
MARTIAL mahr'-shal
MASSACRE măs'-a-ker
MATERIEL ma-têr''-ĭ-el'
MAUSOLEUM maw-so-lē'-ŭm
MAUVE mōv
MEDICINAL me-dĭs'-i-nal
MEMOIR mĕm'-wahr *or*
  mĕm'-wôr
MERINGUE me-răng'
MESA mā'-sa

MIEN   mēn

MINERALOGY   mĭn''-er-ăl'-o-jĭ

MISCEGENATION   mĭs''-i-ji-nā'-shŭn

MISCELLANY   mĭs-e-lā''-nĭ *or* mĭs'-e-la''-nĭ

MNEMONICS   ni-mŏn'-ĭks

MODISTE   mo-dēst'

MONSIEUR   me-syû'

MORAL   mŏr'-al

MORALE   mo-rahl'

MUNICIPAL   myū-nĭs'-i-pal

MUSEUM   myū-zē'-um

MUSICALE   myū''-zĭ-kăl'

NAIVE   nah-ēv'

NAPHTHA   năf'-*tha*

NICHE   nĭch

ORCHESTRA   ôr'-kĕs-tra

ORGIES   ôr'-jĭz

OTIOSE   ō'-shĭ-ōs

PALSY   pawl'-zĭ

PANACEA   păn''-a-sē'-a

PATHOS   pā'-thŏs

PECAN   pi-kăn' *or* pi-kahn'

PENALIZE   pē'-nal-iz

PERSONNEL   pûr''-so-nĕl'

PERSPIRATION   pûr-spi-rā'-shŭn

PHARYNX   făr'-ĭngks

PHILATELY   fĭ-lăt'-e-lĭ

PIQUE   pēk

PLAQUE   plăk *or* plahk

PLEBEIAN   pli-bē'-yan

POSITIVELY   pŏz'-i-tĭv-lĭ

POSSE   pŏs'-ē

PRECEDENCE   prē-sēd'-ens

PREFERABLE   prĕf'-er-a-b'l

PROPHECY   prŏf'-e-sĭ

PROPHESY   prof'-e-sī

PSYCHIATRY   sī-kī'-a-trĭ

PUERILE   pū'-er-ĭl

PULMONARY   pŭl'-mo-nĕr-ĭ

QUAY   kē

RADIO   rā'-dĭ-ō

RANCID   răn'-sĭd

RECIPE   rĕs'-i-pē

RECONNAISSANCE   re-kŏn'-i-sans

RECONNOITER   rĕk''-o-noi'-ter

REDOLENT   rĕd'-o-lent

REFERABLE   rĕf'-er-a-b'l

REMEDIABLE   re-mē'-dĭ-a-b'l

REMONSTRATE   re-mŏn'-strāt

REPARABLE   rĕp'-a-ra-b'l

RESOURCES   re-sōr'-sĕz *or* rē'-sōr-sez

RESPITE   rĕs'-pĭt

REVOCABLE   rĕv'-o-ka-b'l

RIBALD   rĭb'-ald

ROBOT   rō'-bot

ROUT   rowt

SALINE   sā'-līn

SCHEDULE   skĕd'-yūl

SCHISM   sĭz'm

SCION   sī-un

SCYTHE   sīTH

SECRETIVE   se-krē'-tĭv

SEMESTER   se-mĕs'-ter

SIDEREAL   sī-dêr'-e-al

SIEVE   sĭv

SIMILE   sĭm'-ĭl-ē

SLEIGHT   slīt

SOLDER   sŏd'-er

SOVIET   sō'-vi-et *or* sō-vĭ-ĕt'

STALWART   stôl'-wert

STATUS   stā'-tus

SUBTLE   sŭt'l

SUITE   swēt

SUPERFLUOUS sū-pûr'-flōō-ŭs
SWATH swah*th*
SWATHE swāTH
SYCOPHANT sĭk'-o-f*ant*
SYRINGE sĭr'-ĭnj

TELEVISION tĕl'-e-vĭ"-zhŭn
THEATER *th*ē'-a-ter
THITHER THĭTH'-er

ULTIMATUM ŭl"-ti-mā'-tŭm
USURP yū-zûrp'

VEHICLE vē'-*i*-k'l *or* vē'-hi-k'l
VICTUALS vĭt'lz
VISCOUNT vī'-kownt
VITALS vī'-t*a*lz

WITH Wĭth

YEOMAN yō'-m*a*n

ZOOLOGY zō-ŏl'-o-jĭ

WORDS FREQUENTLY MISUSED

ACCEPT, EXCEPT	*Accept* means "to receive"; *except* means "to leave out."
AFFECT, EFFECT	As verbs, *affect* means "to influence," *effect* means "to bring about"; as a noun, *effect* means "a result."
AGGRAVATE, IRRITATE	Means "to make worse"; should not be used in place of *irritate*.
ALL RIGHT, ALRIGHT	*Alright* is not recognized as a word.
ALLUSION, ILLUSION	*Allusion* is "a reference"; *illusion* is "an unreal or misleading image."
ALREADY, ALL READY	*Already* is an adverb and means "before some specified time"; *all ready* means "completely prepared."
ALTERNATIVE	Should be used only when referring to a choice between two things or courses.
ALTOGETHER, ALL TOGETHER	*Altogether* is an adverb and means "completely or thoroughly"; *all together* means "all at once" or "all at the same time."
AMONG, BETWEEN	*Among* refers to three or more; *between* refers to two.
ANGRY, MAD	*Angry* refers to anger; *mad* refers to insanity. Say "angry with," not "angry at."
BESIDE, BESIDES	*Beside* means "at the side of"; *besides* means "in addition to."

BLAME IT ON	Say, instead, "Blame someone *for* something."
BRING, TAKE	*Bring* is action toward the speaker; *take* is action away from the speaker.
CAN, MAY	*Can* refers to ability; *may* refers to permission.
CENSOR, CENSURE	*Censor* means "to examine"; *censure* means "to blame."
CONTINUAL, CONTINUOUS	*Continual* refers to frequent repetition; *continuous* refers to something that goes on without a stop.
COULD OF	Do not use in place of *could have.*
COUNCIL, COUNSEL	A *council* is a body of people; *counsel* refers to advice or an advisor.
COUPLE, PAIR	*Couple* refers to things that are united; *pair* refers to things that may be considered together.
DIFFERENT THAN	Use *different from.*
DUE TO, BECAUSE OF	*Due to* must follow the verb *to be; because of* should be used in other situations.
EACH OTHER, ONE ANOTHER	*Each other* refers to two people or things; *one another* refers to more than two.
ETC.	Use sparingly; do not say *and etc.*
FEW, A FEW	*Few* refers to a limited number; *a few* means some or several.
FEWER, LESS	*Fewer* refers to number; *less* refers to quantity.
FIX, REPAIR	*Fix* is colloquial for *repair.* It is best used to mean "fasten."
FORMER, LATTER	Should be used only when referring to one or another of two objects.
HEALTHY, HEALTHFUL	*Healthy* is a condition of health; *healthful* means "imparting health." Persons are healthy; the food they eat may be healthful.
HUMAN, HUMANE	*Human* refers to people; *humane* refers to benevolence and kindness.
IN BACK OF	Use *behind* instead.

INGENIOUS, INGENUOUS	*Ingenious* means "clever"; *ingenuous* means "frank or naïve."
ITS, IT'S	*Its* is the possessive of *it; it's* means "it is."
KIND OF A, SORT OF A	Eliminate the *a*.
LAST, LATEST	*Last* means "final"; *latest* means "most recent."
LAY, LIE	*Lay* means "to place"; *lie* means "to rest." See the list of irregular verbs on page 373.
LEARN, TEACH	*Learn* means "to receive instruction"; *teach* means "to give instruction."
LEAVE, LET	*Leave* means "to depart or abandon"; *let* means "to allow."
LEND, LOAN	*Lend* is the verb; *loan* is the noun.
LIKE, AS	*Like* is a preposition; *as* is a conjunction. "Say it *like* me," "Say it *as* I do."
MOST, ALMOST	*Most* means "the greatest part"; *almost* means "nearly."
PRINCIPAL, PRINCIPLE	*Principal* means "chief or main" when used as an adjective and "leader or sum placed at interest" when used as a noun; *principle* means "a guiding rule or a fundamental truth."
SET, SIT	*Set* is a transitive verb and means "to place"; *sit* means "to be in, or to change to, a sitting position."
SOMEWHERES	Eliminate the *s*.
THIS KIND, THOSE KIND	*This kind* is correct because *this* is an adjective that should modify a singular noun; *kind* is a singular noun. *Those kinds* would be correct.
TRANSPIRE, HAPPEN	*Transpire* means "to leak out or to become known gradually." Do not use it in place of *happen*.
UNINTERESTED, DISINTERESTED	*Uninterested* means "not interested"; *disinterested* means "impartial."

EXAMINATION QUESTIONS

Each of the following sentences contains one error in grammar, spelling or punctuation. Rewrite each sentence, correcting the error.

1. We visited my two sister-in-laws last night.
2. Two calfs occupy the rear stalls in the barn.
3. Some bacteria is helpful to man.
4. Charle's books arrived.
5. Someone has lost their coat.
6. Everyone had better hold on to their tickets.
7. The rain got into our very bones, which is something that is very annoying.
8. Us girls were the first ones here.
9. It is him I like most.
10. We greeted Ed, the lawyer's son, and she.
11. Between you and I, he is completely wrong.
12. Do you know whom she was?
13. Who did you give it to?
14. Choose whomever wants to go.
15. The book is losing it's interest for me.
16. Whose going to the party?
17. He feels badly after eating the green apples.
18. Running at full speed, the chair tripped him.
19. My brother and cousin, whom I haven't seen in several months, is coming for dinner.
20. Mathematics are one subject that I find uninteresting.
21. The committee was in violent disagreement.
22. There is a chair with a straw seat and a day bed in my room.
23. He is in this country for two years now.
24. Norman lay the book on the table.
25. I laid in bed all day because I had a sore throat.
26. He has layed there since early afternoon.
27. Won't you set down?
28. The water main has busted.
29. The prisoner flew from the jail in the confusion.
30. The picture was hanged in the living room.
31. Have you ever treaded the light fantastic?
32. I'll take two of these kind.
33. Did you sleep good last night?
34. Which pair do you like best—the black or the brown?
35. I think that my typewriter is better then his.
36. You should read Anthony Trollope's *Barchester towers*.
37. Theodore Dreiser is I believe a powerful writer.
38. We are coming home tonight, we will leave tomorrow.
39. "I'm so tired," Ellen cried. "that I think I shall be very bad company."
40. Do you feel alright?
41. His remarks were sacreligious.
42. Don't loose your temper now.
43. Keep a steady ryhthm while dancing.
44. A mirage is an optical allusion.
45. You will have to choose among him and me.
46. What makes you so mad at him?
47. Beside, I have nothing to do now anyway.

48. Blood from a person of one color or religion is no different than blood from a person of another color or religion.

49. Most all of us ski in winter.
50. The accident transpired on the busiest street in town.

FOR FURTHER STUDY

COMMON ERRORS IN ENGLISH AND HOW TO AVOID THEM, by Alexander M. Witherspoon. (Barnes & Noble, New York.)

CONCISE ENGLISH GRAMMAR, by Kittredge and Farley. (Ginn & Co., Boston.)

DICTIONARY OF MODERN ENGLISH USAGE, by Henry W. Fowler. (Oxford University Press, New York.)

GOOD ENGLISH FOR EVERYDAY USE, by Leo J. Henkin. (New Home Library, Doubleday & Co., Garden City.)

GRAMMAR, RHETORIC, AND COMPOSITION, by Richard D. Mallery. (Barnes & Noble, New York.)

HOW TO ENLARGE AND IMPROVE YOUR VOCABULARY, by Richard D. Mallery. (New Home Library, Doubleday & Co., Garden City.)

IX

Effective Speaking

FUNDAMENTAL PRECEPTS

AT ONE TIME or another almost every man and woman is called upon to speak in public. At a formal banquet, at an informal dinner, at a club meeting, at a party caucus, at a meeting of parents and teachers, at a school picnic, at a church school, a fundamental knowledge of public speaking may be helpful in seeing you through and making less terrifying the task of expressing yourself. As a profession, public speaking takes the form of lecturing or political oratory. It is rather for the occasional, non-professional speaker that the pointers given here are intended.

If you are called upon to speak, without being forewarned, you can hardly have a speech prepared. You must stand up and do your best on the spur of the moment. But you will do better if you have some knowledge, however slight, of the principles of public speaking. The person who has never made a speech, or who has never anticipated being asked to make one, is usually in a sad dilemma when he rises to an unexpected summons. He may have stage fright, and stammer; his stammering is made worse by the fact that he probably has nothing whatever to say. On such an occasion, lacking any prepared speech, one does well to say a few words of thanks, of appreciation of the occasion, or something equally courteous and appropriate—and sit down. Sitting down at the proper moment is something which few impromptu speakers learn to do.

PERSONALITY

The good speaker has, perforce, a pleasing personality. If he is well liked in nearly any company, if he can mingle readily with various classes of people, then he is almost sure to be a success on the platform. The speaker must first of all try to develop this pleasing presence.

As you learn to be cheerful in your daily social life, and perhaps to tell a few good funny stories and tell them well, you are acquiring fundamental principles of appeal which will stand you in good stead on the rostrum. No matter how serious may be the subject you are discussing from the platform, a pleasing personality—which is one that is serious and convincing, as well as one that is cheerful and happily sympathetic—cannot do otherwise than give your assertions weight.

Next to your personality and character comes your mental equipment. You ought to be as well read as your time permits. And of course good English and all that it implies must have its place in your schedule.

SELF-CONSCIOUSNESS

Few persons are entirely immune to stage fright. Let this fact console you if stage fright is one of your worries. As a person steps up on the platform for the first time, or even as he rises beside his place at a dinner, he feels all eyes upon him—and he fears that those eyes are searching him critically, that they dislike him, that they are looking through him with cruel contempt. This fear of criticism, of being a "flop," may lead to what is most feared—a miserable failure. The victim has a sensation of his knees shaking or knocking together, he seems to perspire unduly, his throat and lips are dry, he cannot find any suitable place to put his hands, he forgets what he was going to say, he stammers and stutters helplessly. Probably he grows red in the face, or else exceedingly pale, and finally has to sit down in discomfiture.

The real cause of stage fright is self-consciousness, which may be defined as the consciousness of oneself, or ego, "as the subject, or subjective element of experience." The self-conscious person is acutely "aware of being the subject of any given alteration in experience." He is thinking too much of himself, up there on the stage, or standing there before so many staring eyes. But even the speaker before a radio microphone may be self-conscious if he dares to let himself think of the many thousands of ears which are listening to his voice. If he lets himself become a victim of that feeling, however, those thousands of ears, by twirls of little dials, will soon be reduced in number. There is no discourtesy in twirling the radio dial as there is in walking out on a public speaker in a public place.

Paradoxical though it may seem, the would-be speaker must first make himself aware of his audience by cultivating the social amenities; and then, when he is on the platform or before the microphone, he must remember only that they are humanly interested in what he is saying—or rather he should take that smugly for granted, and forget that anyone is going to criticize—until it is all over. The speaker must forget himself— he must cease to be aware that he is himself, human and fallible and weak. Carried away by what he is saying, the good speaker does not stop to think whether he is standing in the right position, whether his tie is straight, or whether his hands are out of place. He goes right ahead, uttering his words and sentences convincingly, and, if humorous, entertainingly.

The speaker who has time to prepare what he is going to say has ready in his hand the best cure for stage fright—he can prepare himself so thoroughly that he has self-confidence instead of self-consciousness. Anyone who knows what he is going to say, and is confident that he can say it well, need never be struck with stage fright.

Stage fright always grows less with experience and practice in speaking in public. So the next step in the cure is to seize eagerly all the opportunities for speaking that may come your way. Do not avoid such chances —seek them. Force yourself to ignore your own fear, and you will find its terrors much diminished. As you "get through" one speech after another, and "get away with it," you will grow more self-confident. Just a word of warning here: do not permit that new-found self-confidence to defeat itself by becoming blustering bravado and overweening egotism.

As for poise and a good stage presence, these come with practice and experience. Poise is a combination of self-confidence and the easy social grace that comes with it. Even a physically awkward and ungainly man can have poise if he knows that he has something worthwhile to say, and if past experience has shown him that he knows how to say it convincingly and well. He can ignore the first impression of his audience, which may be quite unfavorable, being assured that they are human and that he has the key to their human interest, and that those who think they are going to scoff may yet applaud him.

There is such a thing as *audience sense*, which many speakers appear to have naturally, or which they acquire with experience. This sense enables a speaker to know whether his audience is interested or bored, sympathetic or antagonistic. Such a sense, too, enables a speaker to know when he has spoken long enough, and helps him to judge the proper moment to conclude his remarks and sit down. It is a valuable sense; if you have glimmerings of it, strive to increase it. No greater mistake can be made than to go too strongly against the feelings of your audience, either as to the tenor of your remarks, or as to their length.

PREPARING THE SPEECH

For a speech to be good, it must take into account the occasion, the audience, and the most fitting language and arrangement for speaking on that occasion to that audience. These requirements can usually be met only by careful thought and conscientious preparation. Even a man who speaks well without the assistance of either manuscript or notes has his speech well outlined in his mind, point by point, step by step, from introduction to conclusion.

A speech may be readily divided into three important parts: introduction, body, and conclusion. The *introduction* is obviously the beginning; it consists of the opening remarks, which serve several purposes. These first sentences call for the attention of your hearers, get them settled to listen to what you have to say, and give them an inkling of what you are going to talk about. If you gain the attention of your audience at the start, and convince them by your introduction that what you are about to say is interesting, you have already won more than half the battle. And you have also taken a firm grip on yourself, and should find yourself ready to go on with the body of the speech.

One of the easiest and most popular ways to get the good will of an audience is to open with an amusing anecdote (appropriate to the occasion and the subject) or a humorous reference with local application. A famous speaker a generation or so ago, when Latin was studied more widely than it is today, opened a college commencement address by mentioning the first words of Caesar's "Gallic War," which, translated into English, are "All Gaul." He said that those words expressed his own temerity—"all gall"—in coming before those college men to give them words of wisdom ere they went out into the world. With this imaginative jest he gained immediate attention, a sympathetic laugh, and a hearty enthusiasm—for, of course, everyone got the idea that this address was not going to be dull after all!

Too much stress cannot be laid on the fact that the introductory remarks must be apt, they must be very much to the point, and they must be adequate without being overdone. The funniest joke will not serve the purpose if it has no bearing on the occasion, the place, or the subject. Humor should never be injected into any part of the speech for its own sake exclusively; a miscellaneous recounting of comic experiences and funny incidents is not a speech, although it may make very good table conversation. Praise of the audience—as intelligent, forward-looking, and the like—may also form part of the opening of the speech, but it is most important that this should not be overdone, for extravagant praise will arouse the suspicion of even an uninformed audience, and make the people take all the speaker's subsequent statements at a large discount.

Following the praise and the humor, there should be a clear statement of the speaker's thesis—what he is going to demonstrate, what he is desirous of getting across to his listeners.

The *body* of the speech is its main substance. It is on this that the success of the speech as a whole will depend. If the speech is an argument, the body of it must present the points in logical order, leading from the lesser to the more important, and proving them one by one. The cumulative effect of such logical procedure will be to lend weight to the *conclusion,* which will sum up the argument and state with finality what has been shown. If the speech is light and amusing, intended simply to entertain, the body will be composed of those incidents which fit into the general scheme, and those only. Rambling discourse is all very well in conversation, but in a continuous talk, no matter how informal or how short, unrelated anecdotes are a mistake. Even the entertaining speech should have a unity of subject matter so that the speaker may conclude with a witty summary. A man in the legal profession might try a remark such as, "I hope I have made it clear that even though a lawyer's business is a serious one, it is not all trial and tribulation, for there is many a smile at this bar as well as before the more convivial one of another kind!"

Let there be no doubt expressed in your conclusion. Assume, for the sake of emphasis, that you have proved what you set out to prove, and that your audience cannot do otherwise than be convinced. Self-assurance in the conclusion is a strong psychological weapon which every great orator has used with telling effect.

In preparing the speech, then, you should build it carefully, starting with the introduction. Taking the introductory statement of your subject as your cue, proceed to enumerate, on paper, in the privacy of your room or study, the points you are going to try to make or the incidents you are going to describe. These points or incidents or both are the essential parts of the body of your speech. Even in argument, or in any speech which requires points to be proved, appropriate incidents, serious or humorous, can be inserted at proper places for purposes of illustration.

Write out your speech. Whether or not you intend to be guided by your manuscript when on the platform, writing out the speech is excellent training, helping you to clarify your ideas and also aiding your memory in presenting them logically and effectively. When you become more experienced, you may dispense with this. In olden days speakers were supposed to put reminders on their cuffs, but in these days of soft-laundered cuffs the practice is impossible. Speeches are sometimes even read in their entirety from manuscript, especially if they are of a nature as to make precise accuracy important, or if the speaker is inexperienced. Unless the speaker glues his eyes to the paper or card, the audience is not likely to object.

SPEECH MATERIAL

The public speaker can obtain his material from a variety of sources. His first and most important source, of course, is his own experience—

his own life. Those events which have most deeply affected him will provide the most effective material with which to build convincing speeches. It is for this reason that the speaker who is older in years and experience, if he is a good speaker at all, will usually be a better and more persuasive speaker than a younger person. However, he who begins young will improve (it is to be hoped!) with the years, and will find his life's experiences ever more ready to his hand (when writing) and to his tongue (when speaking).

Speech material must be selected with careful judgment, and with constant attention to appropriateness for the occasion. A speech, or various parts of it, may be argumentative (purposeful), entertaining (amusing), or sympathetic (as in a reference to a sad occurrence). You can make the most of the difference in the audience's response to an incident that is amusing and to one that is dramatically illustrative of a point in argument. The whole secret of carrying your audience with you—of making them laugh or cry at your bidding—lies in this ability to distinguish between the emotional effect of the various elements which are put into a speech.

Make up your mind what your speech is to do—whether it is to entertain, to praise, to appeal, to encourage—and then you can set about selecting your material with sound judgment. If you are fairly well read, and to some extent, at least, acquainted with life, you can assume that what appeals to you as dramatic or amusing will appeal to your audience in much the same way, although there may be a difference in degree among individuals.

Your own life and experiences are by no means your only source. You should keep up with the times by reading at least one good newspaper every day. This does not mean that you must read it through; but you should look through it, reading what appeals to you, and what seems to you to be relevant and important. It is also a good idea to supplement the newspaper with a good weekly news magazine, not only to refresh your memory but to supply you with a more rounded view of the happenings of the past week. You will provide yourself with much good speech material this way; and if you expect to give many speeches, it will be an excellent plan for you to clip suitable articles to keep them handy for future use.

Then there is the whole field of the world's literature to choose from— history, biography, poetry, drama, fiction. You should not only keep up with the times, but you should acquaint yourself with the past, by extensive readings in history and biography; and with literature, by reading as much of the work of the great masters as you find time for. You should not deface books by clipping from them, but you can copy into a notebook such quotations or references as seem to you to be suitable speech material. When you use such material in a speech, you should always give its source, as by saying, "There is a most appropriate statement in a novel by Charles Dickens, which is, etc."

Humorous stories, anecdotes, and apt quotations may be found everywhere—in the daily press, in magazines, and in special collections made for the use of writers and speakers. There will be many such collections, no doubt, in your local public library or neighborhood book store. Many are conveniently arranged according to subject matter.

A word should be said here about "prepared speeches," books or selections of speeches already prepared for various occasions. Such stereotyped speeches are sometimes used by people who assume that they cannot prepare a speech of their own, and who are called upon to speak so seldom that they can afford to take that easy way out of what they see as a difficulty and not as an opportunity. The reader of this book who is really desirous of becoming at least a good amateur public speaker should remember that his personality can give originality to what he says, and his personality will only come through if he gives his speeches in his own words. If he makes use of such already prepared speeches, verbatim, contributing nothing that is truly his own, he is merely acting the part of a parrot, and his audience is not likely to be especially thrilled, or even interested.

A book of model speeches can serve a useful purpose, however, if studied as a kind of textbook. The speeches illustrate for the beginner what the elements of different sorts of speeches are, and he can find some that appeal to him and which he may follow in planning his own speeches.

SUBJECT MATTER

The lecturer or professional platform speaker must be guided by what people are naturally interested in. Even if his main subject is rather far removed from those natural interests, he can bring it home to the average listener by treating it in terms which are of universal appeal.

There was a speaker who had lived many years in Guatemala, in Central America, and who made up a splendid talk on that subject. He was particularly desirous of telling his audiences about business and political conditions in Guatemala, but if he had confined his talk to those aspects, he would have lost the attention of many of his hearers. To limit his speech to such specific phases would have been fitting, perhaps, if he had been talking exclusively to businessmen interested in that part of the world, or to statesmen concerned with Pan-American affairs. But to the general public he had to make a more human approach, so, sandwiched in between data about trade and politics, he told of the young natives, of how the girls were wooed and won by their lovers, of their marriage customs, of what the people ate, of their religion, and so on. The resulting talk was of universal appeal, and held the attention of his audience from the first word to the last. Guatemala and its people were made alive to them, because they were given a word picture of the way natives lived and died, loved and lost.

Of primary interest to any audience is the subject of sex—the relations between men and women. To different groups of people, of course, different approaches to the subject must be made, but everyone is fundamentally interested in the subject itself—in love, romance, courtship, marriage, relations of the sexes, and so on.

Also of wide interest is self-improvement, in education, in health, in business, and in sports. Everyone aspires to be better than he is, and he is glad to hear about ways in which others have succeeded—others who had no better chances than he has himself.

Then there is money. Under our economic system, money—its possession and earning power, how to get it and invest it—tends to be exaggerated, but the student interested in appealing to human nature must not belittle it on that account. It may be very true that the worship of Mammon is pernicious and stultifying, so far as "the better things of life" are concerned, but it is also true that most people pay some tribute to the god of wealth, and try in various ways to propitiate him and win his favor.

The speaker who would meet his audience on common ground, must approach them on this human level—and meet them within the range of their experience. By linking their experience to his, he can carry them as far afield as he may wish.

STRAIGHT THINKING

A talk consisting of ideas strung along will be ineffective unless you present them in some kind of order. The sequence of ideas should be logical—one part should follow another naturally, building up a strong argument or a persuasive plea. Straight thinking is as necessary to a good speech as are excellent material and appealing subject matter.

An impromptu speaker has little time to consider a logical sequence of ideas. But if he is a straight thinker by nature, he will not stray far from a logical order when he presents his spontaneous ideas to his hearers. For a good story-teller must know better than to give his plot away before he is ready to do so, or he will lose all the value of suspense, and his audience is likely to miss the point entirely—especially if it is the point of a joke.

Suppose you have just three minutes in which to present your argument. You cannot deny that you will use your time most effectively by being logical, clear, and to the point. The same is true of a longer speech; the more logically developed it is, the better it will be.

It is well to begin a speech with an undisputed point. If you start in an argumentative manner, you antagonize your hearers instantly, and they do not listen in a mood to be persuaded. To illustrate, suppose we consider a speech in favor of a community playground. A good way to begin might be something like this: "Everyone will agree that a child likes to play and that to deny him the joy of play not only stunts his development —it is cruel." A logical development of the theme would be to cite instances of the cruelty of lack of play facilities for children, including perhaps one or two touching instances, and bringing in, at the same time, the practical factors, such as the proposed site, the initial cost, maintenance, etc. Other factors might well be the desirability of keeping children off the streets, away from automobiles; the advantages of supervised play in a clean, healthful place, under shade trees and on green grass; the physical exercise to be derived from play apparatus which can be supplied to a group, but can seldom be bought by each parent for his children; and so on. The logical sequence of these ideas could well lead up to a conclusion such as, "You have seen, my friends, what this project will mean to your children and to mine. Think back to your own childhood. You know how much you would have enjoyed such a playground. The means have been arranged for—surely the slight cost to you, over a period of years, is insignificant compared with the joy it will bring to your boys and girls. May I express your decision in words? You cannot do otherwise than support this worthy enterprise!"

The opening statement of the playground speech might even be preceded by a more general and more appealing statement, thus: "We all like to play—and go to the movies, or a ball game, or to a dance, or to the golf links. We have always liked to play. We liked to play when we were children. Perhaps, when we were kids, we went to the 'ole swimmin' hole,' or out to the barn, or over in the cow pasture. We had lots of room to play in and we had a lot of fun. But what about the child of today, in the city? Is he not being denied such play opportunities? Everyone will agree that a child likes to play and that to deny him the joy of play not only stunts his development—it is cruel."

There is our introduction. It meets the audience on common ground— it makes statements with which every listener must certainly agree. It appeals to the joy of play which all of us feel, and it creates sympathy with the subject. Now what? What comes next? Suppose you make an

outline of your speech, somewhat after the pattern of the following, which
is applied to the subject of the community playground.

    I.   Introduction.
        A. Possibly a humorous story about boyhood.
        B. Introductory remarks (as given above).
   II.   Body.
        A. Children want a playground.
           1. Concrete instances.
           2. Children's joy in other playgrounds.
           3. Denial of play unkind, even cruel.
        B. Children need a playground.
           1. As an aid in development.
           2. As a factor in health.
           3. As a safety-first precaution.
        C. The cost is slight.
           1. Cost of site and equipment.
           2. Cost of maintenance.
           3. Plan of payment.
           4. How much would your share buy *your* children?
        D. What are the disadvantages, if any?
  III.   Conclusion.

The preceding outline will serve as a basis for a logical development
of the idea. Local conditions and further research into the subject may
readily suggest further points that could be profitably brought in. Careful
consideration of the argument might show that a slight rearrangement
of the points would be more effective. You should approach any speech
in this way, considering it carefully from as many angles as possible, and
gradually working up an outline which seems to you the best presentation
of the subject.

It is possible to enhance the effect of the logical development by introducing suspense. The subject of the playground could be approached,
in a brief but probably effective speech, by painting a word-picture of
the drawbacks to children playing in the streets, ending each illustrative
incident with some such rhetorical question as, "What is the answer to
that? What easy solution will do away with that danger?" The possibilities
are numberless in this direction.

VOCABULARY AND STYLE

The speaker gives continual attention to mastery of the practical side
of good English. He should familiarize himself with the principles of
grammar, rhetoric, and effective use of words. It is very important, of

course, that the speaker watch his pronunciation; he should have a good dictionary so that he can verify any doubtful pronunciation.

Do not be too cocksure about your vocabulary. A moment's thought will show you that the fact that you know a word when you see it in your reading, or even when you hear someone else use it, does not mean necessarily that you can use the word properly yourself. For example, perhaps you know what the word *jejune* means—but can you use it properly? Check the meanings of all such words in your dictionary before using them. Probably over half the words you recognize belong in this class; they do not come readily to your tongue or pen, but they are in your mental vocabulary. A word is not truly yours until you use it.

The vocabulary of the public speaker is necessarily of a different order from that of the writer, for a very excellent reason. You must bear in mind that, as you speak, your audience has only one opportunity to hear your words and sentences. They cannot go back—as they can when reading an article or a book—and "read over" any sentence that is not clear; they cannot pause to look up a word in the dictionary. You must avoid words, therefore, that your audience is not likely to understand; your vocabulary for a given speech is definitely limited by the vocabulary of your audience. To overcome this difficulty, many speakers repeat important statements in various phrasings, using synonymous words or expressions, to be sure that such important statements "get across" to their hearers. To do this effectively, you must have a large working vocabulary and a comprehensive knowledge of synonyms. First of all, you should have a good handy dictionary. A good general encyclopedia will also prove very valuable. A book of synonyms or a thesaurus (book of words arranged according to meanings) is a useful reference work for any speaker's library. Later it will be a good idea for you to have a large, unabridged dictionary.

Hand in hand with words go figurative expressions. A study of figures of speech will well repay the prospective speaker. Eloquent orations are full of them, for they are highly expressive and appeal powerfully to the popular imagination. Notice the difference between saying, "at death life stops," and saying, "death is like the blowing out of a bright candle."

Sentence structure, too, is a subject in itself, and one that the speaker cannot ignore. In general, the beginner should avoid long sentences, especially if he is speaking without manuscript; further, long sentences are much more difficult for the audience to follow than shorter, pithier sentences. But some variation in sentence structure must be employed; otherwise the speech will sound jerky and broken. Study the sentences in famous speeches, and notice the different arrangement of clauses and phrases, the position of modifiers, the various ways of securing emphasis for important words by their position in the sentence. Notice that each paragraph has a key or topic sentence, stating or summarizing what the paragraph is about.

By all means steer clear of flowery language and "purple passages." The beginner is likely to slip into extravagant speech under the illusion that he is being eloquent. There is a difference between figurative expression and flowery language. The latter usually is ridiculous because of its exaggeration. Many orators verge dangerously on it, but they have learned by experience how much a particular audience can stand of such elaborate utterance. Steady reading of good literature will give you a sound background of judgment against which to test critically and choose between expressions which are absurdly showy and those which are sensibly fitting.

AIDS TO MEMORY

Do not belittle your memory; if you do, you may as well give up at once any hope you may have of being a public speaker. The person who goes around with the constant complaint that he has a poor memory will certainly never have a better one. Except when a speech may be read from manuscript (and those instances should be as rare as possible), the speaker cannot get along without a good memory. Audiences are sometimes irritated by a speaker's constant reference to notes. He must, therefore, train his memory as best he can, and improve it so far as he is able. He must have confidence in it, test it, and keep it in good working order. For, like any other human faculty, the memory can be improved through use.

In learning a speech by heart, bear in mind that it is easier to learn it as a whole rather than sentence by sentence. Read it through aloud, from beginning to end, stopping after each reading to repeat as much of it as you can. Note carefully the points at which you stumble, and keep a mental eye open for the parts you omit. Then read the speech aloud again, all of it, and follow with a repetition from memory. Do this three or four times each day until you have it by heart, and then repeat it, once or twice a day, to be sure that you do not forget it. Several repetitions daily, over a period of days, are much more effective than several hours spent on the speech in one day. For this reason, it is important to begin to learn your speech well ahead of the time when you are to give it.

Some people who memorize a speech word for word tend to deliver it without fire and enthusiasm. If you are such a speaker, it is better to try learning merely the substance of a speech. Ignore the exact words, but memorize the points you wish to make, in the order (the logical order, as you developed it in your outline) you wish to make them. Then try the speech, developing each point in your own words as you go along. You will, of course, have to learn verbatim any quotations you use for purposes of illustration, and you may choose to learn certain important sentences or figures of speech. The more practice you have at this kind of speech-learning, the more at ease you will become.

Memory courses make much of the value of association as an aid to memory. This is a sound psychological principle, capable of being used in various ways. You can associate each part of your speech with some key word or cue, and by remembering the order of the cues, you can give your speech in proper sequence of ideas. Or you can form a mental picture to associate with each part of your speech; this is a favorite method, and one that usually works well, for pictures are so vivid that they are not easily forgotten. Dates can be associated with events you know, or with other dates; or the numbers that compose the date can be associated with one another. A little experiment will show you how these associated ideas can be varied to suit your purpose.

The practicing speaker needs a room or a nook where he can be by himself. He should practice there, talking aloud, with the walls for an audience. If he can observe himself in a mirror, it may help him to develop appropriate gestures. Silly as this may sound to the novice, it is an essential method of practice that he cannot very well do without. Only actually speaking the words of a speech can give them their full value. Speaking aloud is of much more aid to the memory than silent reading or thinking the words.

ARGUMENTATION

Argumentation is the orderly and logical presentation of arguments. The subject is one to which many full-length books are devoted. It is closely linked with debating, which is the form of public speaking that school speakers first become acquainted with. Public debates in themselves are of great interest and importance. Many famous speakers may be heard in debates on vital questions of the hour. The more significant debates are often published afterward; the student of public speaking should secure and read as many of them as possible.

In any argument or debate it is necessary to observe the laws of reasoning. If you do not do so, your opponent or some one of your hearers may pick flaws in your talk, which will certainly not redound to your credit. Your case should never involve false conclusions, or start from false premises; sophistry is a dangerous and deceptive oratorical device, and should always be avoided lest it delude the speaker as well as the listener.

To present an argument, either in debate or in behalf of a project or enterprise, you must first analyze the issue to be proved. If the argument is to be part of a debate, you must forestall your opponent by analyzing his side of the question as well as your own. For every point you discover for his side, you can then prepare, if possible, an answer or refutation. If you are speaking alone on behalf of a question, remember that your audience contains opponents of the idea, who must be convinced. You must try to think of their objections and meet them one by one. Turn back to the discussion of the playground project and see how the outline was built up by an analysis of this kind. You must never forget the old saying that there are at least two sides to every question.

It is easy enough to make statements or assertions. But they are of little value without support. You must prove them if you can, but by all means support them with suitable argument if they are vital to your speech. You can support your assertions in various ways.

A fundamental way to support an assertion is to restate it. This does not mean repeating it. It does mean, to some extent, paraphrasing it, or putting it in other words. Indeed, you can preface your restatement with, "In other words." Suppose you assert that books increase the enjoyment of living. "In other words," you might say in restatement, "books widen the mental horizon, they open new vistas to the imagination, they show how others have enjoyed life, they quicken the perceptions, they sharpen the ability to discriminate, they provide a critical basis of judgment."

You can then pass to what is called general illustration of your assertion. This consists in taking the factors of your assertion and restatement and showing them in their individual aspects. You might proceed somewhat in this way: "Books record the thoughts and experiences of others. We can know comparatively few people intimately in real life. But we can become acquainted with scores of interesting people through books they have written or books that have been written about them. A poet tells us what he perceives through his highly developed senses. A dramatist gives us pictures of life as he sees it. A novelist makes a study of a group of people and reveals to us the inner motives of their lives."

The transition from general illustration to specific instances is natural enough—and it is the specific instance which is the most convincing to the average person. You can talk generalities all day long, and even if you strengthen your assertion, you may not convince your hearers. But if you can give them several definite, concrete examples, they will listen to you with a willingness "to be shown." Developing the same theme, that books increase the enjoyment of living, you might tell how they have done so for you—how a particular book or books have done so. "I never realized there was such beauty in the song of the skylark," you might say, "until

I read Shelley's 'Ode to a Skylark.' Let me quote a few lines to show you what I mean." Or you might say: "A friend of mine told me of his reading H. M. Tomlinson's *The Sea and the Jungle.* 'I had previously taken a similar trip,' he said, 'but I had not read Tomlinson's book at the time. I found the trip dull and monotonous. Yet, as I read that book, I remember several things that I might have enjoyed, had my eyes been opened. That book taught me how to enjoy such a journey. No matter how humdrum it seems at first thought, any journey may be vividly enjoyed if you know how to see and how to hear and how to notice. I tell you, that book is a masterpiece. I'll never forget it. I owe the author an everlasting debt.' "

Finally, you can call testimony to your aid. Testimony may sometimes take the form of the specific instance, as in the case of the reader just described. But what is meant by testimony is usually the quotation of authorities, of experts in their fields, who have made assertions which bear out the truth or validity of your assertion. Many famous authors have written about books, and have told of their value in human experience. You could quote statements from them, to support your own assertion that books increase the enjoyment of living. If your hearers doubt you, they may not so easily doubt Ralph Waldo Emerson, Henry David Thoreau, Arnold Bennett, Georg Brandes, and hundreds of others whose words you can summon to your support. But remember that testimony is merely corroborative—it never carries the weight and influence of the specific instance, no matter what the subject.

You can pile up each form of support in a cumulative series. By example after example, each as telling as, or more telling than, the last, you can build up a powerful argument.

In a debate, the rebuttal plays a particular part. In the rebuttal, each debater (or sometimes only one for each side) attacks the arguments previously advanced by his opponents, and attempts to destroy them by bringing forward arguments against them. New arguments are not introduced in the rebuttal, and according to the rules, should not be. Obviously, no matter how well prepared the main speeches of the debate may be, the rebuttals must be spoken on the spur of the moment, with only as much preparation as may be possible between speeches.

Wit and humor also enter prominently into all forms of argument, for the audience is particularly prone to be swayed by effective jests and comic sallies. If the argument of an opponent can be reduced to absurdity, or can be made into a joke, it is often an effective weapon to use humor— and even mild sarcasm—in this manner. Irony is a weapon of the same sort. No matter how reasonable the argument is, if the audience is made to laugh, the effect is to cancel out the powers of reason.

Laughter and sarcasm must be employed with discretion, however. Too heavy sarcasm, which bites with venom, is likely to be a boomerang, and swing back against the user of it. Even when making fun of your opponent, it is both good form and good sportsmanship to be courteous.

AFTER-DINNER SPEECHES AND TOASTS

The occasional speaker is most often called upon to speak "after dinner," which is to say, during or after a dinner or banquet, at which are assembled members of a club, members of the same profession, or persons united by some common cause or affiliation. The after-dinner speech can be quite serious, or it can be lightly humorous. A safe rule for length is, the shorter the better.

The after-dinner speech usually bears some relation to the purpose of the dinner or to the interests of the persons there assembled. It is often prepared in advance, for most persons know whether they are likely to be called upon for "a few words." But this is one occasion, at least, when the speech should be memorized, if not word for word, then in substance. For the use of manuscript is fatal, and the employment of notes is deadening—the after-dinner speech must appear to be spontaneous.

Unfortunately, many after-dinner speakers are insufferable bores. Their comrades, surfeited with a good meal, feel like falling asleep and wish heartily that the monotonous voice would cease its droning. A funny story or two, which must be apropos of the subject, will work wonders. A lively sense of humor, an ability to speak with enthusiasm, an air of good-fellowship, a good notion of when to sit down—these are essential to the successful after-dinner speaker.

The toast is a dinner speech of a special kind. A toast should be short. It should also be witty. It should have a definite application to the moment or to the occasion. It should have a clearly developed and *original* idea. And it should have an effective conclusion or climax. Poets have made rhymed toasts—Oliver Wendell Holmes was noted for his; humorists have made witty toasts—Mark Twain was celebrated for his. But what of the average speaker? He can merely take his cue from the masters and do the best he can.

Do not use a book of prepared toasts, except as a source of models. The toast must be original, if it is to be a true toast; it must, if possible, reflect your own sincere sentiments and be tinged with your own personality. Remember always that the toast is intimate and informal; it must not be spoken with too much solemnity, and it must not be proposed in an aloof and superior manner. Bear in mind that a toast rightly begins with such words as "Here's to——," or "I give you——," or "Let us drink to——." It must include your hearers with yourself—it is a spontaneous gesture of friendship, of an enthusiasm that is *mutual*.

DELIVERING THE SPEECH

Someone has said that a poet seldom knows how to read his own poems. Few playwrights have also been actors. The best professors, so far as their academic standing is concerned, are often the poor speakers in the classroom. The great scientists, the most learned men of the world, are seldom equipped to get upon a platform and expound their knowledge to an audience. These facts are no criticism of these men—they simply illustrate the truth that there is more to public speaking than simply having something to say. It is also necessary to know *how to say it*.

THE TELEVISION OR RADIO SPEAKER

The art of speaking before a television or radio microphone (without any audience) does not conform very well to the poetical description, by William E. Gladstone, of oratory as "that mysterious, intangible, indefinable something which first comes to the speaker from the audience as a mist, and which he returns to them as a flood." For the "microphone speaker" there can be no audience sense—there is no appreciative applause. Can there be any great oratory before the microphone, then? It used to be held that a musician, an actor, or a speaker could rise to the heights of his art only if he had the somewhat mystic presence of the audience to inspire him. It was held that a dress rehearsal before an empty house was after all only a rehearsal, and that the first-night performance, with the house packed, would give the actors that spontaneity and vivacity which they lacked up to that moment.

What, then, of the talking pictures? They are created and performed in soundproof studios, in a maze of wire and apparatus, where there is certainly no audience to inspire the actors or singers. Yet some rather wonderful performances have been recorded.

It appears that the television and movie artists of today need only the knowledge that there is an audience somewhere out in the world "listening in" or waiting to pack the theaters to watch and hear the motion picture. After all, in a large theater, the glare of the footlights conceals the audience—but the actors know that the audience is *there*. So it is with the television or radio speaker; as he talks into the microphone, he has a very vivid sense that his audience is *there,* even if the radio speaker is cut off the air and does not know it. The inspiration to be derived from an audience is thus shown to be within the speaker and not outside of him.

The radio speaker must be brief. He has just so many allotted minutes, and no more. When his time is up, he must stop to make way for the next feature on the program. Furthermore, the radio speaker must usually submit a written copy of his speech in advance, and he is required to stick to it substantially. He must therefore prepare his speech carefully.

The radio speaker should remember, too, that the microphone is a very sensitive instrument. He must not let himself fall into the notion that his audience is far away and that therefore he must speak louder than usual. The same tone used before a small audience (it is not even necessary to raise the voice, as is required in some auditoriums) is sufficient. Great care in enunciation and articulation is, of course, required.

The Art of Speaking Clearly

It is quite as important to strive always for *clear* and *careful* pronunciation. Carelessness in everyday conversation makes it very easy for us to fall into bad word-habits. The freedom of colloquial speech is very pleasant, but it can be harmful, and we must try continually not to let this influence detract from our clearness of utterance.

The finest speech can be ruined by mumbling, stuttering, hesitation, clipping of words (especially endings, like *-ing, -ed, -t*), slurring of syllables, and so on. Do you have to repeat what you say to your friends? Or, what is more significant, do you often have to repeat your words to strangers? If people cannot readily understand you the first time you say anything, there is probably something wrong with your manner of speaking. If people are continually saying "What?" to you, take the warning and try to speak more distinctly.

Articulation is sometimes synonymous with pronunciation, but it refers more exactly to the functioning of the tongue, lips, teeth, and jaw in making sounds. Tongue positions are usually taken naturally when you are speaking your native language, but if you have difficulty with your speech, it will do you no harm to spend a little time studying the various positions of the tongue for different English sounds. The lips help to form such sounds as *m, b,* and *p.* They should be held loosely enough to give these sounds clarity and force. The teeth and jaw are used in making many sounds. The teeth, of course, cannot be adjusted while speaking; but the jaw should not be held so tightly that your sounds are muffled.

A speaker—who is of necessity compelled to make everyone in his audience hear him distinctly—should give fullness and roundness to the vowel sounds (*a, e, i, o, u*). He should make the consonants distinct and clear. Notice whether you distinguish sharply between *p* and *b, f* and *v, d* and *t.* Do not slur the inner syllables of such words as *government, library, recognize, formerly,* and the like. Such conversational elisions as "let's," "I'll," and "don't" are permissible in informal speeches, but elisions must not be confused with careless slurring. In general, do not attempt to talk through your teeth—open your mouth so that the sounds may come out distinctly, and let the mouth act as a kind of sounding box to give that fullness and roundness which singers especially strive for. These factors making for clearness of speech are known as enunciation.

Whatever you do, do not speak in a monotone. Learn to vary your inflection or pitch to suit the sense of the statements you are making. Test yourself before a critical listener with the following:

I love her.

I love her!

I love her?

I love *her.*

I *love* her.

I love her.

Reading aloud is excellent practice. The "recitation" or "reading" so popular in earlier generations as a form of parlor entertainment is now largely a thing of the past; but, in its day, it was excellent training in voice culture. The next best thing is reading aloud to children, or to any assembled friends who may like to hear you—if you are proficient enough to keep up their interest. And you certainly cannot maintain interest in what you are reading unless you pronounce the words distinctly and correctly, and also lend a certain amount of feeling to the sentences or lines.

SOME PRINCIPLES OF DELIVERY

The inexperienced speaker may make the bad mistake of being pompous on the platform. Concerned too much with the dignity of his elevated position before an audience, he allows his speech to be stilted, unnatural, and decidedly trying to his hearers. The best speaker is he who can walk out on the stage with an easy, natural manner, which is the best approach to grace that most of us have; then to address the audience much as he would converse with friends, except that he may have to raise his voice and increase his vocal volume in a large auditorium.

One word of warning must be inserted here: bear in mind that to increase the volume of your voice does not mean to yell. You can secure emphasis and reach your listeners with full effect without having to shriek at the top of your voice. The speaker who thinks that the louder he shouts, the more convincing he is, shows how inexperienced he is. A good auditorium has acoustics which make your voice carry well to everyone in the audience, if you have good voice quality and strength.

Speaking in the open air is quite another matter. Unless the open-air audience is very small, or unless electric amplifiers are provided, the outdoor speaker must nearly always yell—or come very near to doing so—if he is to reach the outer circle of listeners.

Human thought is complex, and not all of its complexity can be conveyed in words on paper. The tone of the voice, the stress and pause on and between words all play their part. Try reading the first sentence of Lincoln's *Gettysburg Address* in a monotone, without emphasis or pause. Then try to put some expression into it, to render the sense of the words; your achievement should be something like this (as nearly as it can be suggested in type): "Fourscore and seven years ago—our fathers brought forth on this continent * a *new nation*—conceived in liberty * and dedicated to the proposition * that all men * are created * equal." The dashes (—) show longer pauses (indicated by commas in the usual form), the asterisks (*) shorter pauses (for emphasis); the word *new* should not be unduly stressed, but it should be given equal weight with *nation,* so that "new nation" is more like one word, or one idea, than a noun and a modifier.

The words to stress are those which are important, which is to say, those which carry the meaning. The intermediate or connecting words should be spoken distinctly, but lightly. If all the words are given equal weight, the result is not only monotonous, but probably almost meaningless. Take another sentence from Lincoln's speech: "But, in a larger sense, we cannot dedicate, we cannot consecrate, we cannot hallow, this ground." If the words to be stressed are capitalized, the sentence may look something like this: "But, in a larger sense, we canNOT DEDICATE, we canNOT CONSECRATE, we canNOT HALLOW, THIS GROUND." The words in small letters complete the sentence, but add less to the thought. Even the capitalized words should vary somewhat in emphasis or stress, and pauses should be inserted as explained in the preceding paragraph.

You can decide what to emphasize if you give a sentence careful consideration. It is clear that in the sentence just quoted the important idea is that *this ground* (these two words being given dignity and solemn significance because of the context) is *not* capable of being *dedicated* or *consecrated* or *hallowed* by the persons assembled there. Notice the difference in the following, which shows wrong emphasis: "BUT, in a LARGER sense, WE cannot dedicate, WE cannot consecrate, WE cannot hallow, THIS ground." Knowing that stresses should be used, many beginners put them in, but, unfortunately, put the stress on the wrong words. If this sentence is spoken as just written, it will have a semblance of oratory, perhaps, but it will lack real depth of meaning.

Inflection is a change in the pitch or tone of the voice—it may be either rising or falling. There is a rising inflection on the *not,* in "cannot dedicate," etc., in the preceding example. The inflection falls on the following verbs, as *dedicate, consecrate,* and *hallow.* Yet the inflection does not fall fully until the words *this ground* are reached. Nicety of inflection can be secured only with long practice. Listen closely to all the good speakers you have an opportunity to hear; experiment by modulating your own voice in reading or in delivering practice speeches; and pay attention always to the sense, to the thought that the words are meant to convey.

To come back to the use of the pause, it might be said that in the use of his pauses the master orator is revealed. Not only does he pause for emphasis, not only does he pause to lend expression and drama to his speech, but he also pauses to let a thought sink in, or to arouse suspense and interest in order to convey the full force of the thought that is to come. Consider this example: "What we have to face is murder. And murder, my friends, is no ordinary crime." Putting in a pause for suspense, we get: "What we have to face is—murder." The longer the breath is held on the verb *is,* the greater will be the suspense, provided that the pause is not so long as to be ridiculous. To let the full and dire significance of the word *murder* sink in, there should be a long dramatic pause at the end of that sentence—perhaps as long as four or five seconds, before the next sentence resumes the thought.

Although punctuation indicates pauses, the marks of punctuation are not inserted for the orator's benefit. Rather are they for the reader's benefit, to prevent misconstruction and to aid ready comprehension of the author's meaning. When the orator or speaker contributes drama to the written word, he finds it necessary to go farther than the marks of punctuation—he often inserts pauses or lessens them, regardless, apparently, of punctuation. Many marks of punctuation do not indicate true pauses at all: they are intended only to assist the reader's eye.

Even the force of utterance and the volume of the voice must be controlled by the sense. It should be clear at once that this sentence must be spoken gently: "It broke with the fragile sound of an eggshell." To speak such a sentence loudly would be absurd. But the following sentence may be given much greater volume: "The rumble of the guns rose to a boom and a roar!"

What of the speed with which the words should be spoken? This must follow the sense somewhat, of course. But, beyond that, it may be said that modern speakers let words fall from their tongues much more rapidly than did the speakers of a generation or more ago. The average modern speed, for the major portion of the speech, ranges between 150 and 200 words a minute. Each word must be spoken distinctly, nevertheless. The chief difference between this speed and the slower speeches of a bygone day is in the structure—the longer balanced and periodic sentences are not so much used today. The tempo of life has increased in all activities, and it is the same with public speaking.

When regulating the speed according to the sense, in certain passages, bear in mind the preceding injunction about force and volume. Do not describe a slow movement with a rapid rush of words, and *vice versa,* do not deliver the statement of a swift action in a funereal tone. Try reading the following stanza, which is a famous example of imitative poetry (onomatopoeia); the first two lines, obviously, should be read slowly, and the second two lines should be read much more rapidly:

> When Ajax strives some rock's vast weight to throw,
> The line, too, labors, and the words move slow.
> Not so when swift Camilla scours the plain,
> Flies o'er the unbending corn and skims along the main.

The delivery of the speech as a whole should be progressive, rising surely to the climax at the end. It may be likened to a man pulling on a rope—the rope representing the speaker's audience. He pulls steadily upward, then relaxes to take a new grip and pull again. In much the same way, the skillful speaker raises the audience toward his climax by gradual upward stages, letting them slip back a little between stages, but never all the way back, and increasing their interest and fervor with each successive stage. These progressive steps are secured by variation in the inflection or pitch of the speech as a whole, the use of major as well as minor pauses, and so on. The speaker himself shows growing enthusiasm, which, if he is convincing, is likely to find a sympathetic enthusiasm in his audience.

GESTURES

If you were to consult a book on reciting or elocution written about a half century ago, you would be amused to read the emphatic directions as to gesture. There must have been excessive swinging of arms and manipulation of hands in those days. But some gestures are undoubtedly very effective.

The posture for public speaking is simply the good standing posture of everyday life—upright, feet firmly on the floor, head up, shoulders back. You should not stand completely still—the statuesque posture is hardly desirable. Move about somewhat, stepping a little forward to emphasize a point, or a little backward during a pause. But do not *pace* the platform. Stand easily and step lightly, and you cannot go wrong.

Gestures are natural enough unless you have schooled yourself not to use them. The savage and the civilized child both gesture freely—and with good effect. Without being a human windmill, the public speaker can employ gestures with a modicum of common sense, remembering one or two fundamental physical requirements. All gestures should be made with the whole arm, from the shoulder, not merely from the elbow. The speed of movement should be in accord with the words then being spoken. In general, the gesture should begin a little before the words it is to illustrate, but it should end at the moment of the verbal climax.

Observe a good speaker closely, and you will notice that his gestures are differentiated appropriately. To mark his words with clear-cut definition, he extends the index finger. To show that he is explaining or revealing something, he extends his open hand. To lend force to the rejection of an idea, he makes a pushing movement with the back of the hand outward. If he is pointing a question, he holds his arm out, with the palm of the hand upward, as though weighing something. To emphasize an affirmative, he makes a forceful downward gesture, perhaps even going so far as to pound on the table with his fist, or to pound one fist into the other hand. These gestures are all graphic—they cannot be misunderstood—and they need not be used so often that they become gymnastics.

Your gestures will be most significant if they come largely from yourself, arising from your own feeling and your own interpretation of the words you speak. After all, gesture is not a ritual—it is a personal expression of your conviction. Every real public speaker finds at least a few gestures indispensable.

The question of gesture underscores the fact that there cannot be a great speech without a speaker capable of delivering it well. Public speaking at its best has three requirements—a speaker (the man), a speech (the thought), and the delivery (the interpretation). Facial expression can play its part too—solemnity when required, a pleasant smile at proper moments.

SINCERITY

The prospective public speaker should make a steadfast rule never to speak on any topic or to make any statement in which he does not sincerely believe. No matter how expert he may be in platform technique, the speaker is lost who does not believe what he is saying, and who does not believe it with a deep-seated conviction that only sound proof and indisputable evidence could ever shake. His sincerity will "get across" to his hearers.

Sincerity will give you *feeling,* the emotional background necessary to give convincing weight to your speech. Your feeling should never reach the point where you laugh aloud with a great guffaw or weep with racking sobs. But your feeling may very well bring a spontaneous smile to your lips, or very nearly if not quite bring tears to your eyes. It may make your voice vibrant with eagerness or husky with grief. It is the feeling of the speaker that gives vitality to his speech. His feeling is its blood, the source of any life it may have. The speaker who drones the words of another, or speaks by heart words which have no meaning for him, lacks not only the fire of oratory—he has not even a spark. How can he expect to kindle his audience if he has no warmth himself? The greatest speakers, far from being ashamed of feeling (in keeping with their speech), permit it to assist them in their art—but never allow it to hinder them, as by choking their utterance or obscuring their enunciation.

There is a great difference, however, between the actor and the speaker. The former may be called upon to give in to powerful emotions which render him well nigh speechless. The speaker must always *speak* (except for those pauses or silences which are a vital part of his speaking), and he must never allow himself to become so worked up that he cannot speak. Do not make the mistake of thinking that feeling is everything, and that if you feel deeply you can get up on a platform and sweep your listeners with you. Feeling is one thing, but controlled feeling, harnessed to an artistic purpose, is quite another.

Positive feelings, if they may be so called, are of more value to the orator than negative feelings. By positive feelings are meant those which are directed toward healthful, progressive, forward-looking action. Positive feelings by which the world's greatest orators have many times stirred their audiences include courage, piety, joy, affection, sympathy, patriotism, love, admiration, and happiness. Negative feelings usually make an audience distrustful and antagonistic. Such feelings include fear, grief, pain, mistrust, jealousy, envy, hate, melancholy, and disrespect. Now and then a negative feeling may be used with positive effect, as when hatred of a social evil is employed to arouse the audience to some action.

THE VOICE

To speak before an audience, you must have a well-developed voice, one that can give fullness and clearness to the language sounds, and one that does not fatigue easily. Unless you have some physical defect—and probably you have not—you can so train your voice that it will meet these requirements.

Training in singing is excellent for the speaking voice. Lacking that, the prospective public speaker will have to get along as best he can with the usual recommendations for voice culture.

So characteristic of a person is his voice that he is ordinarily easily recognized by its sound alone, even over the telephone. Some voices are pleasant, while others are harsh and strident and have nasal, grating, or other unpleasant qualities. It cannot be denied, then, that there are differences in voices. The kind of voice you have may make a great difference in your ability as a public speaker, unless you correct its faults and improve its good qualities.

Like the memory, the voice can be improved. Constant drill is a good tonic for the poorest voice, provided that the drill is of the right kind. Good speaking requires deep breathing and wide opening of the mouth (not so wide as in a yawn, naturally, but wide enough to give a full, round tone to the vowels); the basis of clear and prolonged speaking is the diaphragm, which separates the chest cavity from the viscera of the abdominal cavity. Speak from the depths of your chest (this does not mean that your voice should be pitched low). Learn the physiology of the voice, and you will find that it does not depend on any mechanical contrivance in the throat—it is produced by the vibration of the vocal cords, such vibration being set up by air pushed out from the lungs by the action of the diaphragm. Specific sounds are made by varying the shape of the mouth and the position of the tongue. Since your voice must depend on the air in your lungs, you cannot sing a long note or speak a long sentence unless you take sufficient breath.

If your "throat" tires from prolonged speaking, that fatigue is caused by an improper conception of the physiology of speaking. For the throat takes no part in speaking, except as a passageway. You tire your throat muscles when speaking publicly because you think that your voice depends on their contraction and relaxation. It depends, literally, on their relaxation! Your voice would not tire in an entire day of ordinary conversation, so why should it tire in a comparatively short public speech? Even if you have overcome stage fright, your self-consciousness has taken a grip about your throat. Breathe deeply, speak easily and fully with the exhaling breath, make no effort to contract your throat, but let your mouth open and allow the sound to gather volume in the back of the mouth. It will take practice—but the resulting improvement is worth many tedious hours of practice.

The Beginning and Ending of a Speech

Certain speeches require special forms of opening, or address to the audience. The general opening, of course, is simply, "Ladies and gentlemen," or "Fellow townspeople," or "Friends." If there is an organization, as at a political meeting, it is customary to address the presiding officer as "Mr. Chairman," or "Mr. Toastmaster," or "Mr. President," followed by an address to the others present; thus: "Mr. Chairman and fellow members," or "Mr. Chairman and friends," etc.

If the person directly addressed is a woman, it is customary to use "Miss" or "Mrs." before the masculine form of the title, as "Miss Toastmaster," or "Madam Chairman." The forms "Toastmistress" and "Chairwoman" are unacceptable.

Whatever you do, do not begin with an apology, such as, "Well, friends, I'm not much of a speaker, but I'm going to do my best and trust that you will bear with me." Nothing could be worse than such a plea. Always begin with cheerfulness and confidence. And, whatever you open your talk with, have it lead quickly into the introduction to the subject of your speech.

A warning also as to the ending of the speech. It should end sharply with the climax—a sentence of final summing up, a plea for action on the matter in hand, a last word of commendation if the speech is in the nature of verbal praise. *Never* say, "I thank you," at the end of a speech; that extravagant bit of platform courtesy is now completely out of date. Also, do not bow to the audience, either at the beginning or at the end of your speech. A slight nod of the head is sometimes permissible, but no more.

EXAMINATION QUESTIONS

1. What qualities should a good speaker have?
2. What is secondary in importance to personality and character in a public speaker?
3. What is the real cause of stage fright?
4. What is a good way to cure stage fright?
5. What is an *audience sense?*
6. What are the three important parts of a speech?
7. What is one of the easiest and most popular ways of getting the good will of an audience?
8. What is the *body* of the speech?
9. What is one of the first sources of speech material?
10. Where may a speaker look for humorous material?
11. How can a book of prepared speeches serve a useful purpose?
12. What are the primary interests that will appeal to any audience?
13. How must a speaker approach his audience?
14. How may the effect of a logically developed speech be enhanced?
15. In what respect is your vocabulary for a given speech limited?
16. Why should a speaker use short sentences?
17. What is the best way of learning a speech by heart?
18. What is the advantage of practicing a speech before a mirror?
19. State a fundamental way of supporting an assertion that you have made.
20. Which is the more convincing to the average person—general illustration or specific instances?

21. What is known as "testimony"?
22. What is the "rebuttal" in a debate?
23. What is a suitable length for the after-dinner speech?
24. What are the characteristics of the toast?
25. If there is no applause for the radio speaker, from where does his inspiration come?
26. What limitations are imposed on the radio speaker?
27. What is *articulation?*
28. What is *enunciation?*
29. How should inflection be varied?
30. What is the advantage in reading aloud?
31. What are the words to stress in the delivery of a speech?
32. How should the intermediate or connecting words be spoken?
33. What is meant by inflection?
34. What are the two properties of inflection?
35. How may inflection be developed?
36. Why does the master orator pause frequently?
37. What is the average modern speed at which a speech is given?
38. What is a good posture for a public speaker?
39. What gesture is used to emphasize an affirmative?
40. What facial expressions can play a part in public speaking?
41. What is the place of sincerity in a public speech?
42. What is one difference between the actor and the speaker?
43. What are meant by the positive feelings of an orator?
44. What do negative feelings include?
45. What kind of speaking voice should you have?
46. What does good speaking require?
47. Why does the throat get tired from prolonged speaking?
48. What are the general openings for a speech?
49. How should a speech end?
50. Should "I thank you" be said at the end of a speech?

For Further Study

Discussion Methods, by J. V. Garland and C. S. Phillips. (H. W. Wilson Co., New York.)

Handbook of Public Speaking, by John Dolman. (Harcourt, Brace & Co., New York.)

Hear! Hear!, by William Freeman. (Simon & Schuster, New York.)

How to Speak Effectively on All Occasions, by George W. Hibbitt. (New Home Library, Doubleday & Co., Garden City, N.Y.)

How to Speak in Public, by C. W. Wright. (Crown Publishers, New York.)

Speakers Notebook, by William G. Hoffman. (McGraw-Hill, New York.)

Speech Correction Manual, by J. Bender and V. Kleinfeld. (Rinehart & Co., New York.)

The World's Great Speeches, edited by Lewis Copeland, *New Edition.* (Dover Publications, Inc., New York.)

X

A Guide to Literature

AN INTRODUCTION TO LITERATURE

LITERATURE, the creative, imaginative, and durable writings of authors of the past and the present, is generally divided into two great categories, *prose* and *poetry*. Prose is the language that we speak in our daily lives, the language we read in newspapers, and hear in the streets and on the radio and television. Prose, when skillfully and artistically composed, is literature. Many great works have been written in prose: the Bible, the writings of great philosophers, and most novels. A character in a play by Molière was greatly surprised, as many of us are, when he was told that he had been speaking prose all his life. Poetry differs from prose in that it is more highly condensed, that it uses figures of speech more systematically, and that it is usually more rhythmic than prose. Any one of these characteristics could apply to prose as well, but taken as a group they define poetry generally. The appeal of poetry is directed strongly to the emotions. As a matter of fact, the English poet Wordsworth emphasized this point to the exclusion of all other elements. He said poetry is "the spontaneous overflow of powerful feelings; it takes its origin from emotion recollected in tranquillity." There is a close connection between poetry and music. Notice that we have not mentioned rhyme. Poetry need *not* rhyme.

Both poetry and prose may be further divided into certain *forms* which the two types of literature have assumed through the ages. These forms are not rigid classifications that were arbitrarily set up, but were developed as best fitting the ideas and feeling that writers wished to convey.

PROSE

Prose may be divided into two broad categories: *fiction* and *non-fiction*. Fiction is an imaginary invention, usually a tale conceived by the writer, although often with a basis in actuality; that is, a writer may make up a story out of whole cloth, or he may, out of some real incident or real set of characters, mold a story. Non-fiction does not tell an imagined story. It may relate the actual story of a man's life, in which case it is a *biography*. If an author tells the story of his own life, he is writing an *autobiography*. The other main form of non-fiction is the *essay*, which develops an opinion or describes a way of doing something, often with notable distinctions of style.

FICTION

The *novel* is the most popular form of writing today. A novel deals with a set of characters, in general presenting some segment of their lives together. The characters are related by the *action of the story,* or the plot; and the emphasis of the novel may be on the events of the plot, or on the main character, the hero or heroine of the story, or upon the society of people with which the novel treats. In reading a good novel, one is to some degree conscious of all of these elements, which combine to create the *development* and bring about the *denouement,* or conclusion, of the story. Accidental events, the workings of fate, the motives of characters, their emotions, their moral fibers, their passions and ambitions, and the special conditions (social, economic, and natural) of the particular background against which the story is developed—all these things are tools of the writer and contribute to the pleasure and understanding the good novel affords the reader. As in all forms of literature, the style of writing is appreciated not only for itself, but as it expresses, emphasizes, underplays, or renders vivid the particular characteristics of the story which make it unusual and interesting. The mood, or atmosphere, in which the author sets a novel, as well as the main theme, philosophy, or reflection on life which he may wish to develop along with his tale, is often expressed chiefly by his choice of words and manner of writing. The length of a novel may vary from perhaps two hundred pages, as in the case of *Ethan Frome,* to one thousand pages, as in the case of *War and Peace*. The form of the novel as we know it today is a relatively new form, having come into general use in the eighteenth century. The first great novelist in English was Daniel Defoe, author of *Robinson Crusoe*.

The *short story,* as its name implies, is short—perhaps two or three pages, sometimes fifty pages. The "shortness," however, is less a matter of absolute brevity than it is of being more limited in scope, and more compact in theme, than the novel. Its point of view is sharply focused either on one character or on a simple series of events, usually with less emphasis on background and detail. Edgar Allan Poe, a master of the short story, said that it should not contain a single word that was not absolutely necessary and appropriate to the whole. The whole, then, or unity of a short story, we may say, is in general more compact, more single-minded, than the vaster action of most novels. Present practice in the publication of short stories is usually to print them in magazines or other periodicals and then, if they have a permanent appeal, to collect them in an anthology of short stories or in a book of stories by one particular author. Great writers of short stories include Guy de Maupassant, Anton Chekhov, Edgar Allan Poe, Nathaniel Hawthorne, Ring Lardner, and Ernest Hemingway.

FORMS OF NON-FICTION

An *essay* is a more or less brief literary work dealing with one main topic. The essay may be an exposition of one's personal reaction to a person, event, or thing, in which case it is called a *personal* essay. Or it may be more objective in its approach to its subject matter, in which case it is a *formal* essay. The first essays in English were written by Francis Bacon. Among other famous English essayists are Addison, Steele, De Quincey, Lamb, Carlyle, Thomas Huxley. In America we have Emerson, Thoreau, James Russell Lowell, H. L. Mencken, Christopher Morley, Edmund Wilson. The essay as such is rapidly disappearing from our literature and its functions are being taken over by the magazine article, the signed newspaper column, and the newspaper editorial.

The word *biography* comes from two Greek words: *bios,* meaning life, and *graphein,* meaning to write. Literally, then, biography means "to write of life." Biographies are the life stories of people, usually famous people or people who have made some contribution to the world. A biography may be a mere recital of the bald facts of a person's life, or it may be an attempt to interpret a person's life from some point of view. Biography is an old form; one of the greatest of the ancient biographies is Plutarch's *Lives.* Probably the greatest English biography is Boswell's *Life of Samuel Johnson.* An outstanding American biography is Carl Sandburg's life of Lincoln. Outstanding autobiographies include those by St. Augustine, Cellini, Samuel Pepys, Benjamin Franklin, John Stuart Mill, Henry Adams, and Lincoln Steffens.

DRAMA

Drama, which may be written either in poetry or prose, is a literary form which is intended primarily for enactment on a stage. An individual dramatic work is known as a *play.* The great plays of the past have been partially or entirely in verse, but the tendency among modern dramatists has been to write in prose. A play is usually divided into a number of *acts;* each act may be divided into *scenes.* Classical plays are usually either *tragedies* or *comedies.* A tragedy is a play with a great, noble hero who possesses some major flaw of character. The plot often turns on an act committed by the hero against the gods or the moral order, for which he is duly punished. In tragedy the inevitability of this punishment is stressed. Among the greatest writers of tragedy are Aeschylus, Sophocles, Euripides, and Shakespeare, and in recent times Eugene O'Neill. Modern serious drama usually is not tragedy in the classical vein. Modern plays have eliminated the factor of the great and noble hero, preferring to deal with the fate of persons of more ordinary stature. In comedy the purpose is to arouse laughter and the ending or outcome is usually happy. Comedy may achieve its effect by exposing and poking fun at human weakness, by satirizing social customs, or simply by verbal dexterity and wit. Great writers of comedies include Aristophanes, Shakespeare, Molière, and among modern playwrights, George Bernard Shaw.

POETRY

Before discussing the forms of poetry, we shall describe some of the kinds of poetry.

Lyric poetry is probably the most familiar kind of poetry. It is closest to music, the ancient lyrics having been sung to the accompaniment of the lyre, whence its name. It is an expression of the poet's own feeling—about love, about nature, about a woman—in short, about almost any subject which may move him. The lyric is generally a short poem. Some of the great lyricists in English literature are Shakespeare, Burns, Blake, Wordsworth, Coleridge, Shelley, Keats, Tennyson, and, more recently, William Butler Yeats.

The *ode* is a special kind of lyric, written in a dignified and elevated style. In English outstanding odes are Wordsworth's "Ode on the Intimations of Immortality," Collins' "Ode to Evening," Keats' "Ode to a Nightingale," and Shelley's "Ode to the West Wind."

The *elegy* is a lament on the death of a person. The great elegies, however, go further than to mourn death. They often use the death of a person as a starting point from which they may proceed to a discussion of such matters as the meaning of death, life, and even the universe. Outstanding elegies in English are Gray's "Elegy in a Country Churchyard," Milton's "Lycidas," Shelley's "Adonais," Tennyson's "In Memoriam," Whitman's poem which begins "When lilacs last in the dooryard bloomed," and, among modern poems, W. H. Auden's "In Memory of W. B. Yeats."

Narrative poetry, like narrative prose, tells a story.

An *epic* is a long narrative, almost always in verse, dealing usually with the more or less fabulous adventures of a national or mythological hero. Great epics are: Homer's *Iliad* and *Odyssey,* the Scandinavian eddas, the Teutonic sagas, and the Anglo-Saxon *Beowulf.* The medieval romances, the stories of the knights and their ladies, such as Tristram and Iseult, are narrative poems. Chaucer's *Canterbury Tales* is a series of narrative poems.

The *ballad* is a short narrative poem, telling an actual folk story or a folk-like story in verse form. Popular folk ballads are "The Twa Corbies" and "The Wife of Usher's Well." Modern literary ballads include "The Ballad of Reading Gaol" by Oscar Wilde and Kipling's "A Ballad of East and West."

SOME ELEMENTS OF POETRY

We shall now consider three important elements of poetry: rhyme, meter and rhythm, and melody.

Rhyme refers to the correspondence of some of the sounds of words. The words *ate, rate,* and *late* rhyme, as do *grope, scope,* and *lope.* Note that in both groups of words the vowel sounds (*a* and *o*) are identical and the consonants following the vowels are the same. In most rhyming poetry, the rhyming words come at the ends of lines:

> How sleep the Brave who sink to *rest*
> By all their country's wishes *blest!*
> (*Collins*)

As we have already mentioned, and as we shall see shortly, all poetry does not and need not rhyme. When rhyme is used it is usually arranged in some definite pattern. We shall discuss these patterns in the section on stanza forms.

Rhythm and *meter* are closely allied characteristics of poetry. Rhythm refers to the flow of sounds, their rise and fall, their accents, and pauses. Meter is regularized, patterned rhythm. Notice how in this line of Wordsworth's,

> My heart leaps up when I behold,

it is possible to accent alternate syllables so that the line may be read (with some exaggeration, of course) as,

> My *HEART* leaps *UP* when *I* be*HOLD.*

Or, take this line of Ben Jonson's:

> Queen and huntress, chaste and fair.

This may be read as,

> QUEEN and HUNTress, CHASTE and FAIR.

In both lines given, the accented and unaccented syllables may be grouped into units containing at least one accented syllable:

> My *HEART*   leaps *UP*   when *I*   be*HOLD;*
> *QUEEN* and   *HUNT*ress   *CHASTE* and   *FAIR.*

Each of these groups is called a *foot.* A foot must contain at least one accented syllable. Our first example, with the accented syllable following the unaccented one, is called an *iambic* foot. The second, which has the accented syllable coming first, is called a *trochaic* foot. Note that these two types contain only two syllables to a foot. Other varieties of lines contain three syllables to a foot:

> I am *MON*   arch of *ALL*   I sur*VEY*
>   (*Cowper*)
> *WE* who have   *LOVED* him so;   *FOL*lowed him,   *HON*ored him
>   (*Browning*)

The first example has the accented syllable preceded by two unaccented syllables. This is called an *anapestic* foot. The second line, which has the accented syllable first, followed by two unaccented syllables, is a *dactylic* foot. These four patterns, iambic, trochaic, anapestic, and dactylic, are the most common in English.

We want now to consider the number of feet in lines of poetry. A line with but one foot is called *monometer:*

> Thus I
> Pass by
> And die,
> As one
> Unknown
> And gone.
> (*Herrick*)

Because the above lines have trochaic feet, we say that the lines are in *trochaic monometer.*

A line with two feet is called *dimeter:*

> He is gone on the mountain,
> He is lost to the forest.
> Like a summer-dried fountain,
> When our need was the sorest.
> (*Scott*)

Here the feet are anapestic, so the lines are in *anapestic dimeter*.

A line with three feet is called *trimeter:*

> Under the greenwood tree,
> Who loves to lie with me,
> And turn his merry note
> Unto the sweet bird's throat.
>
> (*Shakespeare*)

Here the feet are iambic, so the lines are *iambic trimeter*.

A line with four feet is called *tetrameter:*

> With blackest moss the flower-plots
> Were thickly crusted, one and all:
> The rusted nails fell from the knots
> That held the pear to the gable wall.
>
> (*Tennyson*)

Here the feet are iambic, so the lines are *iambic tetrameter*.

A line with five feet is called *pentameter:*

> Let me not to the marriage of true minds
> Admit impediments: love is not love
> Which alters when it alteration finds,
> Or bends with the remover to remove.
>
> (*Shakespeare*)

Here the feet are iambic, so the lines are *iambic pentameter*.

Lines may have more than five feet, but in English most poetry has no more than five. However, some poets have used *hexameter* (six feet) with great success—as Longfellow in *Evangeline:*

> This is the forest primeval. The murmuring pines
> and the hemlocks,
> Bearded with moss, and in garments green, indistinct
> in the twilight,

Part of the appeal of poetry lies in the *melody* of the lines. Rhyme provides some of the melody. Other factors making for melody are *alliteration, onomatopoeia,* and *assonance.* Alliteration means the repetition for effect of initial vowels or consonants. Here are some alliterative lines.

> The *f*urrow *f*ollowed *f*ree
> (*Coleridge*)
> *L*ap me in soft *L*ydian airs
> (*Milton*)

*Q*uips and *c*ranks and *w*anton *w*iles
(*Milton*)

Onomatopoeia is a long word that means simply the imitation in words of natural sounds. Many common words are onomatopoetic: *hiss* (for the sound of a snake), *buzz* (for the sound of a saw), *mew* (for the sound of a cat). Here are some onomatopoetic lines:

Dry clash'd his harness in the icy caves
And barren chasms, and all to left and right
The bare black cliffs clang'd round him, as he based
His feet on juts of slippery crag that rang
Sharp smitten with the dint of armed heels.
(*Tennyson*)

Note here how the hard *k* sounds, guttural *g*'s, and explosive *b*'s help paint a vivid picture of a man in armor moving clumsily about on rocky ground.

Assonance refers to the correspondence of vowel sounds. *Hate, dame,* and *lane* are in assonance because they all have the same vowel sound, the long *a*. Assonance differs from rhyme in that it does not have identical consonant sounds following the identical vowels. In the following selection the alternate lines are in assonance:

Maiden crowned with glossy blackness,
Lithe as panther forest-roaming,
Long armed naiad, when she dances
On a stream of ether floating
(*George Eliot*)

Stanza Forms

The unit into which most poetry may be divided is the *stanza*—poems may consist of one stanza or many stanzas. A stanza is really a thought unit that corresponds to a paragraph in prose. There are a number of standard stanza forms, composed of a certain number of lines of a definite number of feet, and a definite pattern of rhyme. The least complex unit is *blank verse*. It is not exactly a stanza form because it is based on the single line, any number of which may be used to make up a poem. The blank verse line is of iambic pentameter. Blank verse does not rhyme. This stanza form is usually used in long poems, like Milton's *Paradise Lost,* and in poetic drama. Some blank verse lines are:

It little profits that an idle king,
By this still hearth, among these barren crags,
Match'd with an agèd wife, I mete and dole

Unequal laws unto a savage race,
That hoard, and sleep, and feed, and know not me.

(Tennyson)

The *heroic couplet* consists of two rhyming lines of iambic pentameter. It was used by such poets as Chaucer, Dryden, and Pope. It is little used today.

Know then thyself, presume not God to scan,
The proper study of mankind is man.
Placed on this isthmus of a middle state,
A being darkly wise, and rudely great:
With too much knowledge for the sceptic side,
With too much weakness for the stoic's pride,
He hangs between; in doubt to act, or rest;
In doubt to deem himself a God, or beast;
In doubt his mind or body to prefer;
Born but to die, and reasoning but to err;

(Pope)

The *ballad stanza* is a stanza of four lines; the first and third are tetrameter, the second and fourth are trimeter. Extra unaccented syllables are frequent. The second and fourth lines rhyme, the first and third do not.

"Mak ready, mak ready, my merry men a'!
    Our gude ship sails the morn."
"Now, ever alack! my master dear,
    I fear a deadly storm!

"I saw the new moon yestreen,
    Wi' the auld moon in her arm;
And I fear, I fear, my master dear,
    That we sall come to harm!"

They hadna sailed a league, a league,
    A league but barely three,
When the lift grew dark, and the wind blew loud,
    And gurly grew the sea.

(Unknown)

Rhyme royal is a stanza of seven iambic pentameter lines with a definite rhyme scheme. In indicating rhyme scheme here and in other stanza forms we use this system: lines that rhyme with each other are given identical letters—all lines that rhyme with the first rhyming line are lettered *a*, with the second rhyming line, *b*, etc. The rhyme scheme of rhyme royal is *a b a b b c c*. Rhyme royal was a favorite form of Chaucer.

To you, my purse, and to non other wight
Compleyne I, for ye be my lady dere!
I am so sory, now that ye be light;
For certes, but ye make me hevy chere,
Me were as leef be leyd up-on my bere;
For whiche un-to your mercy thus I crye:
Beth hevy ageyn, or elles mot I dye!

(Chaucer)

Rhyme royal was used by Shakespeare in *The Rape of Lucrece.*

Ottava rima, used by the Italian Renaissance poets Ariosto and Tasso and in English by Wyatt and Byron, consists of eight iambic pentameter lines rhyming *a b a b a b c c.*

Milton's the prince of poets—so we say;
    A little heavy, but no less divine:
An independent being in his day—
    Learned, pious, temperate in love and wine;
But his life falling into Johnson's way,
    We're told this great high priest of all the Nine
Was whipt at college—a harsh sire-odd spouse,
For the first Mrs. Milton left his house.

(Byron)

The *Spenserian stanza,* an innovation of the English poet Edmund Spenser, is made up of nine lines—the first eight in iambic pentameter, the last of iambic hexameter (that is, of six iambic feet). This form was used extensively by the English romantic poets. Byron used it in *Childe Harold,* and Keats in *The Eve of Saint Agnes.*

A Gentle Knight was pricking on the plaine,
Ycladd in mightie armes and silver shielde,
Wherein old dints of deepe woundes did remaine.
The cruell markes of many a bloody fielde;
Yet armes till that time did he never wield:
His angry steede did chide his foming bitt,
As much disdayning to the curbe to yield:
Full iolly knight he seemed, and faire did sitt,
As one for knightly giusts and fierce encounters fitt.

(Spenser)

The *sonnet* is a lyric form that has been popular since it was perfected by the Italian poet Petrarch. Great poets have written in this form: Spenser, Shakespeare, Milton, Wordsworth, and many others. The recent American poet, Edna St. Vincent Millay, made skillful use of the sonnet. Sonnets have often been written in groups, called, naturally enough, *sonnet sequences.* Usually they revolve about a central idea, each separate sonnet developing one aspect of that idea. The sonnet is composed of fourteen iambic pentameter lines. There are two kinds of sonnets: the Italian or Miltonic and the Shakespearean. The Italian form may be divided into an *octet* (the first eight lines) and a *sestet* (the remaining six lines). The octet rhymes *a b b a, a b b a;* the sestet rhymes *c d e, c d e.* In the Shakespearean sonnet we have three four-line groups (*quatrains*) and a final couplet which is often an epigrammatic summary of the idea of the sonnet. The Shakespearean sonnet rhymes *a b a b, c d c d, e f e f, g g.*

> When I consider how my light is spent
> Ere half my days in this dark world and wide,
> And that one talent which is death to hide
> Lodged with me useless, though my soul more bent
> To serve therewith my Maker, and present
> My true account, lest he returning chide,
> "Doth God exact day-labor, light denied?"
> I fondly ask. But Patience, to prevent
> That murmur, soon replies, "God doth not need
> Either man's work or his own gifts. Who best
> Bear his mild yoke, they serve him best. His state
> Is kingly: thousands at his bidding speed,
> And post o'er land and ocean without rest;
> They also serve who only stand and wait."
>
> (*Milton*)

> When, in disgrace with Fortune and men's eyes,
> I all alone beweep my outcast state,
> And trouble deaf heaven with my bootless cries,
> And look upon myself, and curse my fate,
> Wishing me like to one more rich in hope,
> Featured like him, like him with friends possest,
> Desiring this man's art and that man's scope,
> With what I most enjoy contented least;
> Yet in these thoughts myself almost despising—
> Haply I think on thee: and then my state,
> Like to the Lark at break of day arising
> From sullen earth, sings hymns at Heaven's gate;
> For thy sweet love rememb'red such wealth brings
> That then I scorn to change my state with Kings.
>
> (*Shakespeare*)

Terza rima was first used by Dante in *The Divine Comedy*. In England two poets have made notable use of it: Chaucer and Shelley ("Ode to the West Wind"). Terza rima consists of stanzas of three iambic pentameter lines each (*tercets*). Each is linked to the next by the rhyme scheme, which is: *a b a, b c b, c d c, d e d*, etc. Shelley varied the form somewhat by adding a couplet after each four tercets.

> O wild West Wind, thou breath of Autumn's being,
> Thou, from whose unseen presence the leaves dead
> Are driven, like ghosts from an enchanter fleeing,
>
> Yellow, and black, and pale, and hectic red,
> Pestilence-stricken multitudes: O thou,
> Who chariotest to their dark wintry bed
>
> The wingèd seeds, where they lie cold and low,
> Each like a corpse within its grave, until
> Thine azure sister of the spring shall blow
>
> Her clarion o'er the dreaming earth, and fill
> (Driving sweet buds like flocks to feed in air)
> With living hues and odours plain and hill;
>
> Wild Spirit, which art moving everywhere;
> Destroyer and preserver; hear, Oh hear!
>
> *(Shelley)*

Free verse is different from any of the forms previously mentioned: it has no rhyme and it follows no regular meter. Its lines may be, and often are, of varying length. The free verse movement arose in France in the latter half of the nineteenth century as a reaction against what was considered the artificiality of rhyme and regular meter. In America free verse was used extensively by Walt Whitman. Though it lacks rhyme and meter, free verse must be written with as much care as other forms, for, if not controlled, it may turn into prose, or more likely, it will simply be formless and lack any literary distinction. Writers of free verse have striven to give their lines natural rhythms. Effective modern writers of free verse include Carl Sandburg, Amy Lowell, Edgar Lee Masters, and T. S. Eliot.

> When I heard the learn'd astronomer,
> When the proofs, the figures, were ranged in columns before me,
> When I was shown the charts and diagrams, to add, divide, and
>   measure them,
> When I sitting heard the astronomer where he lectured with much
>   applause in the lecture-room,

How soon unaccountable I became tired and sick,
Till rising and gliding out I wander'd off by myself,
In the mystical moist night-air, and from time to time,
Look'd up in perfect silence at the stars.

(Whitman)

ENGLISH LITERATURE

BEFORE SHAKESPEARE

Out of dim far ages came the several semi-barbaric tribes inhabiting what we know today as the British Isles (England, Scotland, Wales, and Ireland). The natives at the dawn of history were Celts, kin of a mixed racial group common to western and central Europe. In the year 55 B.C. these peoples' lands were invaded by the Romans, who left traces which still survive. The Romans withdrew in the year 410 A.D., never to return.

England received its name from the Angles, Germanic tribes who invaded the land and conquered the native Celts in the fifth century (about 449 A.D.). The Angles, accompanied by two other tribes, the Saxons and the Jutes, settled in what is now England, and effected a partial mixture of races, to be later mingled with the Danes and Normans, resulting in the English people of today. Until the Norman Conquest, in the year 1066, English literature was Anglo-Saxon; some learned works, which do not belong, strictly speaking, to English literature, were written in Latin.

Picture a rugged people, living close to the soil, fighting to secure what they wished. Victory in the hunt and in battle was their ideal and their chief goal in life. They were sailors, too, for they also fought the sea. Such literature as they had reflected the life they lived; it consisted of heroic songs, or long narratives in verse, telling of combat and courage, of daring and death.

THE BEGINNINGS

Beowulf, an epic poem that recounts the story of the hero Beowulf, is the best known of the ancient works of Anglo-Saxon literature; it was handed down for generations by word of mouth, often changed to suit the whims of those who chanted it. The poem was not recorded in writing until the year 1100. *Beowulf* represents a transition from the early pagan Anglo-Saxon literature to a Christian literature. Thus we recognize in the poem a glorification of the traditional pagan virtues: courage, physical strength, honor, and especially the desire for fame as a hero.

Fate, however, which the pagan mind conceived as impersonal and beyond even the control of the gods, becomes identified with the will and justice of God.

With the bringing of Christianity to England by the mission of St. Augustine at the end of the sixth century (the year 597), writers became for the most part dedicated to the Christian religion. These authors included Bede, who wrote an *Ecclesiastical History* in Latin, and Caedmon and Cynewulf, who wrote poetry—all in the seventh and eighth centuries. The monasteries of Northumbria were the centers of the learning of those times.

In another century England was again invaded, this time by the Danes. Alfred the Great gained power, and courageously drove back the invading tribes, saving some of the literature from the destroying hands of the barbarians. In literature, Alfred himself contributed translations from the Latin into Anglo-Saxon, an early form of what is now the English language, and he fostered the Anglo-Saxon Chronicle, a record of events continued until the year 1154.

In the eleventh century the Normans from France invaded and conquered England, and ultimately changed the language and literature of England profoundly. They brought to the language many French words which later became part of the everyday speech of the people. They also introduced new forms of literature.

The scattered kingdoms of England became united into one nation under the Norman conquerors. Brooding Anglo-Saxon literature was enlivened by the more cheerful and imaginative fancies of the Norman French, who had enriched their language with much of the Latin that came into France from the south. Conquered in war, the Anglo-Saxons triumphed finally in peace; they intermarried with their Norman masters, and the literature which spread throughout the land combined Anglo-Saxon and Norman influences. Out of Wales had come the legends of King Arthur and his knights; they were collected and written down. One of the simpler Anglo-Saxon dialects came into prominence, borrowing freely from the Norman French, so that today the English language is a composite of basic Anglo-Saxon common words, the more abstract and ornate French and Latin derivatives, and generous borrowings from all the tongues of the world.

Chivalry and religion dominated the life of the times. The nobles lived in rough castles of stone, fortresses from which they ruled the countryside, without anything like the comforts of modern life. Streets were running sewers. Life was rough, hearty, and often short. On the highways, which people of today would not dignify by calling them roads, one might meet nobility and clergy on horseback, bands of brigands, traveling performers, pack trains of commercial goods. Disease swept devastatingly through cities—in the fourteenth century, England was scourged with the Black Death—for hygiene and medical science were unknown.

CHAUCER

It is at about this time that the first great English poet lived. He was Geoffrey Chaucer (born about 1340; died 1400). His are the only works before the great plays of Shakespeare which are widely read today. Chaucer is often read in a modern version, really a translation, for the early English he used cannot be entirely understood without some study.

Chaucer lived to the full, busy with political and military affairs and some writing, observing his fellows and grasping the interplay of feelings that makes up what is called human nature. Then came his *Canterbury Tales,* a series of yarns supposedly spun by members of a band of pilgrims, riding their horses to Canterbury, put by Chaucer into vigorous verse. Pathos, humor, and drama intensify these tales; the characters are as human as our own neighbors, with the difference that Chaucer enables us to know his men and women as we never know our neighbors.

Here are the opening lines of the *Canterbury Tales* as they were originally written; although somewhat strange looking to the modern reader, they can be understood if read with a little care:

> Whan that Aprille with his shoures soote [sweet]
> The droghte of March hath perced to the roote,
> And bathed every vein in swich [such] licour [moisture]
> Of which vertu engendred is the flour [flower] . . .

OTHER EARLY WRITERS

Among others of the medieval period were Sir Thomas Malory, who collected (about 1470) the tales of the largely mythical King Arthur into his *Morte d'Arthur;* Langland (about 1330–1400), with his *Vision of Piers Plowman,* an allegorical poem which has a simple peasant as its central character; John Gower, whose *Confessio Amantis (The Confessions of a Lover)* is a long poem dealing with the dishonesty and vices to which lovers may fall prey; and John Wycliffe (died 1384), with a translation of the Bible, later completed by others.

Meanwhile, there had been the Hundred Years' War with France (1337–1453), preceded by the Crusades (1095–1272) on the Continent, the height of papal power in the thirteenth century, and the capture of Constantinople by the Turks in 1453. Oxford rose to a leading position in education.

In 1476 Caxton brought his printing press into England, and a new era opened. Caxton was more than a printer—he was an editor also. It was he who standardized English, eliminating many inconsistencies of spelling. He printed the *Canterbury Tales* and the *Morte d'Arthur,* in the so-called Midland dialect of Anglo-Saxon; this Midland dialect was to become the literary language. Modern English dates from this time.

Before the invention of printing, books were in manuscript form, copied by monks in the monasteries, or by whoever knew how to write and had the inclination to make copies. Education, including writing, was little sought, and the monks did most of such laborious work. After the invention of printing, books became more common, rudimentary trade in books began, and education increased. But many years would pass before what could be called a reading public would develop, providing a demand for literary works, and establishing authorship as a profession.

Living conditions improved but slowly. Preceding and during the time of Shakespeare, brutality rubbed elbows with beauty; this mingling is seen in Shakespeare's own plays. Harsh punishments were inflicted for petty crimes; torture was common. Public amusements took such forms as watching criminals being mutilated, and going to Bedlam Asylum (whence our word *bedlam*) to laugh at the antics of the insane. The gradual disappearance of feudalism and the decline of the trade guilds gave way to merchants, and laid the foundation of the modern economic system which is based on money, credit, and its exchange. Population increased, and London overflowed its historic walls—houses were built outside the narrow confines of the older city. Coaches appeared after a time, but on the better roads, which were few.

The influence of Greek, Latin, and the later Italian writers was strong, making itself felt in England after printed books were circulated. The revival of classicism at the end of the Middle Ages is usually called the Renaissance ("Rebirth"), which in northern Europe was most pronounced in the sixteenth century.

Adventure lured the bold, particularly after the discovery of America in 1492. Church domination had weakened: Protestantism began with Luther's antagonism to Rome (1517), England broke away from Rome, the monasteries were dissolved and their property confiscated. The rise of Protestantism is called in church history the Reformation; closely united with it was a pronounced strengthening of individualism and nationalism.

In England, one work stands out: Sir Thomas More's *Utopia* (whence our word *utopian*), a famous description of an ideal state, written in Latin, and translated into English after the author's death. William Tyndale (died 1536) translated the Bible, heralding the style of the later King James Version.

THE AGE OF ELIZABETH

The period when Elizabeth occupied the throne of England (1558–1603) saw England dominant as a world power. Her fleet ruled what was then known of the world, seizing final control of the seas in 1588, when Sir Francis Drake defeated the Spanish Armada. At home Elizabeth set herself up as a strong ruler and established Protestantism as the state religion. She encouraged industry and commerce. The middle class rose to new importance. Patriotism flamed. These conditions were clearly reflected in the literature of the day, not only in the works of Shakespeare but in that of many other brilliant figures whose output has made the Elizabethan Age one of the most vigorous and vital periods in the history of the literature of the world.

ELIZABETHAN DRAMA AND POETRY

The Elizabethan Age was an era of plays and of poetry. In ancient Greece the drama had its highest place of olden times, rising from the natural human tendency to "make believe" and to act the parts of others, into glorious literature. European interest in classical drama revived with the Renaissance, and the church had reawakened an interest in "play-acting." The early church pantomimes were called miracle plays; the Passion Play at Oberammergau, Germany, resembles these.

The miracle play presented religious scenes as examples of the accepted church doctrine. Soon characters were introduced who represented various vices and virtues: Charity, Righteousness, and the like. These brought about the morality play, which endeavored to teach right conduct by visual example. To entertain the crowd, short comic sketches or farces (called *interludes*) were introduced between scenes. Interludes developed a field of their own, somewhat like modern vaudeville acts.

Spoken parts began to appear in these presentations. When accompanied by poetry and music, the offering was called a masque, a form surviving as late as the *Comus* of John Milton. There soon began to be imitations of the classical dramas of Greece and Rome, and two schools of playwriting developed in England: (1) those who followed classical models, kept to the so-called "unities" of time, place, and action; (2) those who satisfied the popular demand for mixed farce and tragedy, and for chronicles, covering long periods of time, and who violated all the unities. Shakespeare belonged to the latter school.

Immediately preceding Shakespeare, Christopher Marlowe (1564–1593) wrote *Tamburlaine* and *Dr. Faustus;* from the latter play are these familiar lines: "Was this the face that launched a thousand ships, and burnt the topless towers of Ilium? Sweet Helen, make me immortal with a kiss!" Helen, here invoked, is Homer's fateful heroine, the beautiful Helen of Troy. Marlowe is often called the father of English tragedy. With his plays he brought to the stage a new vigor and new conception of character. His leading figures, Tamburlaine and Dr. Faustus, are titanic in their lust and unbridled in their expression.

Also just preceding Shakespeare was the great poet, Edmund Spenser (1552–1599), author of a long allegorical poem entitled *The Faerie Queene* which, although it is seldom read today by anyone except students of poetry, is important. Spenser was a leader in the Renaissance, or classical revival, and his high ideals of morality anticipated the doctrine of the Puritans, who were to rise to power in the next century. His marked appreciation of the physical universe, of natural beauty as an expression of universal goodness glorifying God, of personal beauty as a symbol of spiritual perfection, typifies Renaissance and not Puritan literature. In this feature and many others, the Renaissance recalls themes of the Greek classical world. Plato's insistence that goodness, truth, and beauty are essentially one is echoed in all the art and philosophy of the early Renaissance. One reason for this is the discovery of much Greek writing at this time, and its translation into Latin and modern languages. Spenser was an experimenter, and invented what has ever since been called the Spenserian stanza, a particular verse form that he developed for *The Faerie Queene*. His rich imagery makes him one of the most colorful of poets.

John Lyly, who died in 1606, had published his *Euphues* (whence our word *euphuism*) in 1579, setting the fashion of artificial language at court and in some of the literary works of the period, characterized by studied alliteration, extravagant figures of speech, and the like.

Holinshed (died about 1580) published his *Chronicles* of England, Scotland, and Ireland, to which Shakespeare was to turn for the material of some of his historical plays. Sir Thomas North (about 1535–1601) translated a French edition of Plutarch's *Lives* into English, which Shakespeare was to use as another source of dramatic material. Shakespeare did not invent his own plots; rather, he borrowed the plots, or skeleton stories, from others, and transmuted them into masterpieces of character delineation with the magic power of his genius.

SHAKESPEARE AND HIS CONTEMPORARIES

William Shakespeare (born at Stratford-on-Avon in 1564; died in 1616) contributed to English literature a group of plays whose richness and dramatic value have never been surpassed.

Of Shakespeare's life, little is known. He grew up in Stratford, probably much as any boy of the time. As a young man Shakespeare went off to London, presumably to seek his fortune. There, he sought the company of young actors. Between the ages of 26 and 30 he wrote his first plays, including the *Comedy of Errors, Henry VI,* and *Titus Andronicus,* and most of his famous *Sonnets.*

Shakespeare's greatest period was between the ages of 30 and 45, during the first seven years of which he wrote his famous comedies, including *A Midsummer Night's Dream, The Merchant of Venice, The Taming of the Shrew* (only partly Shakespeare's work), *The Merry Wives of Windsor, Much Ado About Nothing, As You Like It,* and *Twelfth Night.* Several histories (historical plays built about the kings Richard II, Henry IV, and Henry V) belong to this period, and two tragedies: *Romeo and Juliet* and *Julius Cæsar.* In the last eight years of his most productive period, Shakespeare wrote few comedies (*Measure for Measure* was one), but achieved his highest excellence with a group of supreme tragedies, including *Hamlet, Othello, Macbeth, King Lear, Antony and Cleopatra,* and *Coriolanus.* From the stormy period of his tragic expression, Shakespeare passed to an aftermath of calm, and once more to comedies: *Cymbeline, The Winter's Tale,* and *The Tempest,* all written after the age of 45. Shakespeare died at 52 and was buried in the church at Stratford.

Because Shakespeare's talents were so broad and so universal it is difficult to characterize his work briefly. He created a great gallery of characters, both comic and tragic—Falstaff, Bottom, Rosalind, Portia, Shylock, Macbeth, Lear, Hamlet—that theater-goers and readers have cherished as immortal creations. He displayed an understanding of human character unsurpassed in literature. His language, both in poetry and prose, is as versatile as it is memorable. Except for the Bible, his plays are the most frequently quoted works in literature.

Only because Shakespeare's genius is so great are his contemporaries overshadowed. The Elizabethan Age, in which he lived, was a time of extraordinary creativity in all fields of writing. Of the many men of this period who contributed greatly to English drama, Ben Jonson ranks second to Shakespeare.

Ben Jonson (born about 1573; died 1637) is remembered today for his lyrics, including "Drink to me only with thine eyes." His plays include the well-known *Every Man in His Humor* and his comic masterpiece, *Volpone,* which still delights audiences, inspiring laughter in the best tradition of comedy by astute satire on common human evils and weaknesses. Jonson followed the classical tradition.

The Authorized Version of the Bible, also called the King James

Version (for James I had ascended the throne in 1603, at the death of Elizabeth), was published in 1611, a model of English style.

THE BEGINNING OF MODERN THOUGHT

Sir Francis Bacon (1561–1626) made important contributions to the development of science through his philosophical treatises, but today his most widely read works are the essays which he himself scorned ("Of Truth," "Of Single Blessedness," etc.). His longer works include *The New Atlantis* (a fanciful romance about an ideal place of existence) and his important writings on logic and education, *Novum Organum* and *The Advancement of Learning*. Bacon's chief contribution to the age was his conviction that knowledge be sought by experimentation, instead of by relying solely on reasoning things out to logical conclusions which may not stand the test of trial.

Bacon's writings mark a break between the earlier approach to science and philosophy by abstract argumentation and dogma and the inquiring, scientific spirit of modern thinkers. The medieval method of investigation has been called *Scholasticism,* because medieval thinkers contrived to settle not only theological problems but also scientific questions by reference to Scripture and recognized scholarly works such as the treatises of Aristotle. From these works, they believed, the answer to *any* question could be deduced logically. Thus Galileo's discovery of spots on the sun was flatly denied because it could be deduced from established doctrines and various revered scholarly works that the sun was created perfect—hence spotless. The modern experimental scientists doubt all theories of pure logic, accepting as true only what has been scientifically demonstrated. This approach is called the *empirical* method.

Bacon's "new organ of logic" (*Novum Organum*) was the method of starting with the facts and drawing generalizations from them. Aristotle, long before the days of the scholastics, had proposed the original "organ of logic," the method of starting with a theory and deciding specific points to accord with it. Both of these methods of logic are, of course, necessary in science to establish useful themes and to draw feasible conclusions. In modern science, however, a theory is no more than tentative until it is proved. The medieval mind had considered a good theory, which accorded with the Bible and established doctrine, as necessarily correct.

Bacon's bold departure from the established methodology for philosophic and scientific inquiry was paralleled in a more religious vein by Sir Thomas Browne (1605–1682) in his famous *Religio Medici*. It has been said that Browne countered the scholastics within their own system of thought by offering a "second scripture" as an authority upon which to base modern thinking. This was, of course, *nature,* so long ignored (the Middle Ages had rather abandoned it to the Devil); it now became the object of careful study by philosophers and experimental scientists, just as it was the object of so much lyric poetry in the Renaissance.

The seventeenth and eighteenth centuries ushered in a flood of thinkers bent upon clearing away the confused dogma of the Middle Ages and establishing science upon a firm foundation of empirical investigation. Among these were the philosophers Thomas Hobbes, David Hume, and John Locke, and the famous scientist Isaac Newton.

Their writings had a profound effect, and a disturbing one, at first, upon the confidence of young men brought up to believe that all knowledge had been discovered and written in the books of the ancient philosophers, who needed only to be properly interpreted. This feeling is summed up by a famous line of the poet and preacher John Donne: "And new Philosophy calls all in doubt."

THE SEVENTEENTH CENTURY

The Puritans, the party of the middle class, were gaining power during and after the reign of Elizabeth. Charles I was crowned king of England in 1625. Growing dissension between the king and the Commons resulted in the emigration of many Puritans to New England and later in the execution of Charles I. From 1653 to 1658, Oliver Cromwell was Lord Protector of England.

The liberal spirit grew strong in those days. Englishmen had always been lovers of liberty, a trait of the national character which Americans have inherited and cherished. A steady rumble of discontent broke off, first, the dominance of Rome in religion, and second, the power of the absolute monarchy. The principle of the divine right of kings was overthrown when Charles I was beheaded for treason.

The unity of the Elizabethan Age gave way not only in the political life of the seventeenth century but in the field of letters as well. Aligned against the Puritans were the so-called Cavalier poets, Thomas Carew, Richard Lovelace, John Suckling, and Robert Herrick, whose lyric poetry carried on the tradition of chivalry. The spirit of these writers is exemplified by these lines of Herrick's:

> Gather ye rosebuds while ye may,
> Old Time is still a-flying;
> And this same flower that smiles today,
> Tomorrow will be dying.

Some of the sweetest songs in the language are works of these men.

John Donne

Far more profound than the Cavalier poets was another early seventeenth-century group of poets, of whom Donne was the greatest. John Donne (1573–1631) wrote lyric and religious poetry that is among the finest in the English language. It is a complex and witty poetry, making use often of puns and elaborate intellectual metaphors. The poetic metaphor, which is most often a simple comparison, was extended and complicated by Donne in an effort to unify the sacred and profane, the physical and the spiritual, and to thus deepen and widen the reader's understanding of the world and its relation to God. Seventeenth-century poets of this style have been called the "metaphysical poets." They also include George Herbert (1593–1633), Richard Crashaw (1612–1649), and Henry Vaughan (1622–1695). The following lines from Donne are typical of his wit and subtlety and his art of combining the light and the serious:

> Send home my harmless heart again,
> Which no unworthy thought could stain:
> But if it has been taught by thine
> To forfeit both
> Its word and oath
> Keep it, for then 'tis none of mine.

Donne became a clergyman; his sermons are noted for their depth and clarity and the beauty of his language.

Milton

The great poet of Puritanism, and one of the giants of English literature, is John Milton (1608–1674). In his poetry may be traced an almost constant conflict between the pleasures of life (the theme of the Cavaliers) and a more serious outlook on living. This is illustrated by the contrast between his two shorter poems, "L'Allegro" and "Il Penseroso." In his masterpiece, *Paradise Lost,* Milton shows his classical training, his scholarliness, and his noble-mindedness. An epic work in twelve books, *Paradise Lost* depicts the fall of Adam and Eve under the influence of the evil angel Lucifer. In the course of the poem scenes in Heaven and Hell are dramatized. Milton's powerful imagination is coupled with a deep insight into human nature. The plan of this great epic reveals Milton's profound religious convictions. The whole work is replete with splendid poetry written on a grand and noble scale. Here are the famous opening lines:

> Of man's first disobedience, and the fruit
> Of that forbidden tree whose mortal taste
> Brought death into the World, and all our woe,
> With loss of Eden, till one greater Man
> Restore us, and regain the blissful seat,
> Sing, Heavenly Muse . . .

Other writers of Milton's time were John Bunyan, who wrote the famous parable, *Pilgrim's Progress;* Andrew Marvell, lyric poet; and Sir Thomas Browne, prose writer of a sonorous style, author of *Hydriotaphia, or Urn Burial,* and already mentioned for his *Religio Medici.*

THE RESTORATION

Following quickly after the death of Cromwell, when no one else among the commoners was strong enough to seize the reins of government, Charles II was crowned in 1660, restoring the Stuarts to power. He ruled for a quarter of a century. The theaters, which had been closed by the Puritans, were reopened. In 1666, a year after London was swept by the Great Plague, the city was gutted by the famous fire, to be largely rebuilt a few years later by the architect Sir Christopher Wren. The spirit of the times is clearly seen in the *Diary* of Samuel Pepys.

The reopening of the theaters saw a revival in dramatic writing. The serious side of the theater was represented by John Dryden (1631–1700), whose plays were popular but are little read today. Dryden was also an effective satirist (*Absalom and Achitophel*), a critic (*Essay on Dramatic Poetry*), and a lyric poet ("Alexander's Feast"). Comedy in the theater was represented by William Wycherly and William Congreve, whose witty plays mirror some of the moral looseness of the times.

THE EIGHTEENTH CENTURY

The eighteenth century in English literature is usually called an age of classicism. This implies both a following of classical models, as in the Renaissance, and a striving for perfection of form and style. Reason dominated feeling, and a carefully phrased English prose resulted. The English novel was born, and toward the end of the eighteenth century there was a breaking away from classicism in both prose and poetry toward a new romanticism, and an approach to the liberalism of letters which characterizes the twentieth century in which we live.

Authorship, so far, had never been very rewarding as a profession. Playwrights had profited from their dramas, but what profit there had been in literature was due to the generosity of so-called patrons. In the eighteenth century, with Parliament taking the lead in government, political parties developed (Whigs and Tories), and the partisans employed the best pens to urge their cause, so that authorship received, in addition to continued patronage by the nobility and men of wealth, some political encouragement and reward.

The eighteenth century was an age of literary domination and imitation. John Dryden, in the latter part of the preceding century, had set the fashion in letters; now Alexander Pope and Samuel Johnson in turn took their places as literary dictators.

Life remained much the same. Artificiality in manners and dress was associated with many brutalities and vulgarities. Coffee houses came into vogue as the meeting places of merchants and of authors, and of others who wished to gather in common interest to discuss topics of the hour. This gossipy interchange of ideas was inevitably reflected in much of the literature of the time. Humanitarian ideals became stronger, and industrial evils were gradually corrected. The invention of machinery later concentrated population in towns, impoverished the craftsmen, and created an often oppressed working class. Gambling was a respectable amusement. Dress was at first dandyish among the upper classes, but later turned more toward the sober styles that have come down to our own day. Though superstition was still strong, science began to come into its own; at the beginning of the century, Newton observed and put into words the phenomenon of gravitation.

Daniel Defoe (born about 1659; died 1731) established the realistic novel with his use of amazingly convincing detail. *Robinson Crusoe,* best known of his works, is a household classic. More strictly realistic is *Moll Flanders.* Defoe also wrote, like many of his contemporaries, numerous political pamphlets, and his *Journal of the Plague Year* is still read.

Joseph Addison (1672–1719) and Richard Steele (1672–1729) wrote periodical papers known as the *Tatler* and *Spectator*—harbingers of the modern newspaper. Their essays were highly polished, particularly those of Addison, and won a host of readers. The *Spectator* papers, which deal with the imaginary Sir Roger de Coverley, a country gentleman of the time, are still read with interest. Both Addison and Steele looked upon themselves as teachers charged with the duty of instructing their readers in matters of taste, conduct, and morals. This didactic aim runs through much of the literature of the age of classicism.

Jonathan Swift (1667–1745) wrote satire, which was much in fashion. His chief work, a masterly satire, has not been read as such by most of his readers: *Gulliver's Travels* was supposed to make mankind wither in shame and humility at its cruel exposure, but the imaginary elements of the narrative are so intensely interesting in themselves that the effect of the satire is blunted. Swift's satire, often bitter and unreasonable, springs from his vexation over man's failure to capitalize on his resources and talents.

Alexander Pope (1688–1744) was a leading figure of the eighteenth century. Of his works, the best known are *An Essay on Man,* which contains many oft-quoted lines, *The Rape of the Lock, The Dunciad,* and his translations of Homer's *Iliad* and *Odyssey.* Pope cultivated the heroic couplet.

The last half of the century is crowded with names and events—dominated, in history, by the American Revolution and the French Revolution. George III sat on England's throne, soon after India and Canada had been added to the Empire's foreign possessions. Frederick the Great brought Prussia into prominence; Catherine the Great kept Russia in the foreground.

Samuel Johnson (1709–1784) dominated the literary scene, not so much for what he wrote as for the manner of man he was. His works are seldom read today, but he is a familiar figure through James Boswell's amazingly intimate biography of him. Boswell dogged the great man's footsteps, took notes, and later wrote everything down, without choice or favor. Johnson did a great work with his English Dictionary, long since out of date, but on which he lavished his best efforts. One of the ironies of fate is that the letter in which Johnson refused to dedicate his Dictionary to Lord Chesterfield is today perhaps the most famous piece of writing that he ever penned. It marked the end of the influence of the patron of letters.

Oliver Goldsmith (1728–1774) won fame and the love of posterity. His many works can for the most part be read with great enjoyment today. His one novel, *The Vicar of Wakefield,* a sentimental tale of the trials and tribulations of a country parson and his family, stands in popularity beside his dramatic comedy, *She Stoops to Conquer,* and alongside his *Deserted Village,* a fairly long poem dealing with the effects of the enclosure movement on the lives of the peasantry.

Richard Brinsley Sheridan (1751–1816) is famous for two plays, still favorites, *The Rivals* and *The School for Scandal.*

Robert Burns (1759–1796), who wrote many poems in the Scottish dialect, sang his way into the hearts of his readers. "The Cotter's Saturday Night" is probably his best-known single poem; there are unforgettable lines in such lyrics as "Auld Lang Syne," "Flow Gently, Sweet Afton," and "To a Mouse." There is a sweet tenderness in Burns' poetry unmatched in English literature.

Other noted poets of the period were Thomas Gray (1716–1771), beloved for his *Elegy Written in a Country Churchyard,* which begins with the famous line, "The curfew tolls the knell of parting day"; William Cowper (1731–1800), admired in his day for the long poem *The Task,* but today appreciated for his moving short poems and hymns and for his delightful comic poem, "The Ride of John Gilpin"; and William Blake (1757–1827), recognized today as one of the greatest English poets, whose strongly original poems have a mystical quality which is also found in his remarkable engravings.

This was also an important period in the development of the novel. Major novelists were: Samuel Richardson (1689–1761), who began a novel by accident, intending to turn out a guide to letter-writing and achieving *Pamela,* to be followed by *Clarissa Harlowe,* both novels in the form of letters written by young women in sore straits; Henry Fielding (1707–1754), novelist, whose *History of Tom Jones* is one of the outstanding prose works of the century; Tobias Smollett (1721–1771), author of *Adventures of Peregrine Pickle* and *Humphrey Clinker;* and Laurence Sterne (1713–1768) and his *Sentimental Journey* and oddly amusing *Tristram Shandy.* Thrillers of the period were written by Matthew Gregory Lewis (1775–1818), later known as Monk Lewis, author of *The Monk,* a wildly supernatural novel, and by Ann Radcliffe (1764–1823), author of *The Mysteries of Udolpho.* Both these latter novelists break over into the romanticism of the nineteenth century, as do many of the later writers of the eighteenth century.

Significant among writers of prose were Edmund Burke (1729–1797), political philosopher and orator, whose "Speech on Conciliation with the Colonies" is still studied in schools; Edward Gibbon (1737–1794), historian, important both for accuracy and literary gift in his *Decline and Fall of the Roman Empire;* and Lord Chesterfield (1694–1773), known for his delightful letters on the ways of the world, written to his natural son.

THE ROMANTIC ERA

The first third of the nineteenth century saw the dominance of a literature which we characterize as romantic. Romantic literature may be considered as expressing, in general, a spirit opposed to classicism. It is far less restrained and is much more personal, expressing often the turmoil in the heart of the poet rather than the sentiments of the world about him. Other characteristics of romantic poetry are: a tendency towards mysticism; high, almost revolutionary idealism stemming from the liberal movements of the day; a tendency to dwell on the beauties of nature; a fondness for the foreign and strange.

Life began now to change in earnest. Harsh punishments were slowly abolished. Labor conditions, abominable in the first part of the century, were later much improved. Men began to dress more somberly; women's fashions went through a galaxy of styles.

Two poets came on the scene by publishing some of their poems together: William Wordsworth (1770–1850), identified mainly with his great nature poems, and Samuel Coleridge. Among the lyrics of Wordsworth that are high in poetic excellence are: "Tintern Abbey," "Ode to Duty," "Ode on the Intimations of Immortality," "Michael" (a dramatic poem of simple tragedy), "I Wandered Lonely as a Cloud," "The Highland Reaper," "The Happy Warrior," "She Dwelt among the Untrodden Ways," and "She Was a Phantom of Delight."

Wordsworth's friend, Samuel Taylor Coleridge (1772–1834), was as great a literary critic as he was a poet. The best known of his works is the narrative poem, written in a weirdly haunting style, *The Rime of the Ancient Mariner*. Two fragments, incomplete though they are, illustrate his genius, which a natural lethargy (increased by opium, in which he indulged) did not enable him to realize to the full; they are *Kubla Khan* and *Christabel*. His literary criticism is concentrated in *Biographia Literaria*. Coleridge's verse is highly melodic. He weaves a spell of subtle magic, investing his poetry with mystery and wonder.

Lord Byron (1788–1824) returned to England from a Continental tour and published the first two cantos of *Childe Harold's Pilgrimage*. He was famous overnight, and became the literary lion of London. Best known of his shorter poems is "The Prisoner of Chillon." Two of his poetic dramas still find readers: *Manfred* and *Cain*. His *Don Juan,* a narrative poem, woven somewhat freely on the legendary character of the same name, is a witty satire on English society.

John Keats (1795–1821), though he died of tuberculosis at the age of 26, won enduring fame as a poet. Compared with the tranquillity of Wordsworth's style, Keats' poetry is more impassioned. Keats could read literature of the past with sincere admiration and write poetry about it. Keats' lines are filled with exquisite wonder. His senses are alive: it is clear that he felt, saw, heard, and even tasted and smelled keenly. Best of his short poems are: "On First Looking into Chapman's Homer," "La Belle Dame Sans Merci," "Ode to a Nightingale," "Ode on a Grecian Urn," "To Autumn," "Ode on Melancholy," and "Bright Star, Would I Were Steadfast as Thou Art." This same beauty is also found in his longer poem, *The Eve of St. Agnes*. His epic, *Endymion,* and the fragment, *Hyperion,* should be read for their verbal magic.

Associated with Keats in many ways, Percy Bysshe Shelley (1792–1822) was more ethereal, far more impetuous in character and imprudent in his activities. He, too, died young. Shelley was a violent rebel in his early youth: he wrote a carefully reasoned pamphlet on atheism, for which he was expelled from Oxford. He was an anarchist in his beliefs. Shelley was deeply influenced by the radical William Godwin (1756–1836) and took over many of his ideas. With Godwin's daughter Mary, Shelley roamed the Continent; after the death of his first wife he married Mary Godwin. Mary became known in her own right, under the name of Mary Wollstonecraft Shelley (1797–1851), as the author of *Frankenstein,* a novel about a gruesome mechanical monster, created by Frankenstein, the principal character.

Dubbed "mad Shelley," in his early years the poet produced *Queen Mab,* to be followed in a few years by *Alastor* and *The Revolt of Islam.* Still under the influence of the revolutionary trend of the times, Shelley created his magnificent poetic drama, *Prometheus Unbound,* in which Shelley the singer triumphs over Shelley the rebel. Then came his tragedy, *The Cenci.* After that he penned the superb "Ode to the West Wind," followed by "The Cloud," the enchanting music of "To a Skylark," and the wondrous elegy to Keats, *Adonais.*

Sir Walter Scott (1771–1832) wrote many historical novels and several narrative poems and ballads. His longer poems are *The Lay of the Last Minstrel, Marmion,* and *The Lady of the Lake.* Best among his novels are the following: *Waverley* (from which the group called Waverly Novels took its name), *Guy Mannering, The Heart of Midlothian, The Bride of Lammermoor, Ivanhoe, Kenilworth, Quentin Durward,* and *The Talisman.* Scott was spurred to great literary activity by his honorable desire to pay off a tremendous debt which he might have escaped, legally, under the English bankruptcy law.

Charles Lamb (1775–1834) was lovably humorous in his quaint essays. He wrote under the pen name of Elia, whence the title of his collected pieces, *Essays of Elia.* One of his most popular essays is "Dissertation on a Roast Pig." In collaboration with his sister Mary, he wrote *Tales from Shakespeare,* prose versions of Shakespeare's plays, retold for children.

Other famous writers of the early nineteenth century were Jane Austen (1775–1817), one of the first women to win literary fame, author of such excellent novels as *Pride and Prejudice* and *Sense and Sensibility;* Thomas De Quincey (1785–1859), a strange genius producing such eccentric works as *Confessions of an English Opium-Eater* and *Murder as a Fine Art,* remarkable alike for their subject matter and their unique style.

THE VICTORIAN AGE

Science now gained power and influence. Transportation and communication were notably increased, especially by the railroad, to be later augmented by the telegraph, telephone, and finally the modern radio and automobile (in the twentieth century). Social unrest—indeed, unrest all through the social and industrial order—awakened new interests, fostered new lines of thought. The reading public grew by thousands, until in our own day the publishing of books is a large industry. New and better methods of printing were constantly developed. Wider circulation of literary works, and commerce and communication between countries, have spread the world's literature in all directions. From 1837 to 1901, Victoria reigned on the throne of England. Works of the period are frequently grouped together as Victorian.

Alfred Tennyson (1809–1892) was a quiet poet; his emotions are always restrained, though his music is often enthralling. Tennyson's art is best seen in such short lyrics as "Break, Break, Break" and in the songs from *The Princess*. His faith in life was severely shaken by the death of his friend, Arthur Hallam, in 1833; the grief and mental turmoil through the years following resulted in the metrical masterpiece *In Memoriam*. Preceding this were such skillfully wrought poems as "The Lotos-Eaters," "Ulysses," and "Locksley Hall." In 1854 he wrote his most popular short poem, "The Charge of the Light Brigade." Five years later came the first of his *Idylls of the King,* a series of poetical narratives retelling, in his own Victorian way, the legends of King Arthur, Lancelot, Elaine, Guinevere, and the rest. *Enoch Arden* is the simplest human story among Tennyson's poems. Many poems emerged in his later years, among them *Rizpah* and the brief "Crossing the Bar," a somewhat mystical interpretation of death which the poet wished might close all collections of his works.

In Robert Browning (1812–1889), another outstanding poet of the period, are found the most vivid portrayals of varied human characters since Shakespeare. Although Browning has been thought obscure by some readers, this criticism is not wholly sound; it may be justified, however, because Browning is indeed frequently subtle, indirect, and allusive beyond the capacity of many readers to follow. The work of Tennyson and that of Browning are sharply contrasted. A gallery of characters appears in Browning's dramatic monologues; the dramatic monologue is a poem, supposed to be spoken by one person at some important moment in his life, in which the delineation of the character of the person speaking is accomplished through the medium of his own words. Best among these are "My Last Duchess," "The Bishop Orders His Tomb at St. Praxed's Church," "Andrea del Sarto," "Fra Lippo Lippi," and "Abt Vogler." Of his other shorter poems, some of the best known include "The Pied Piper of Hamelin," "The Last Ride Together," "How They Brought the Good News from Ghent to Aix," and "An Incident of the

French Camp." His longer works include *A Blot in the 'Scutcheon,* a play; *Pippa Passes;* and *The Ring and the Book.*

Elizabeth Barrett Browning (1806–1861), the wife of Robert Browning, won fame in her own right with her *Sonnets from the Portuguese,* a series of love poems addressed to her husband.

Another important poet of the period was Matthew Arnold (1822–1888), who was also a critic and essayist. His best-known poems are "Dover Beach," and the longer *Sohrab and Rustum.* Of his prose, notable titles are *Essays in Criticism, Literature and Dogma,* and *Culture and Anarchy.* Arnold, a classicist in an age of waning romanticism, sought to establish absolute standards of criticism.

Thomas Babington Macaulay (1800–1859) wrote staid prose, exemplary in its phrasing, but characterized by a satisfaction with life which few of his contemporaries felt. His essays are his best-known works; some of them—those on John Bunyan, Samuel Johnson, and Oliver Goldsmith —were written for, and first appeared in, the *Encyclopædia Britannica.* One volume of verse, *The Lays of Ancient Rome* (including the popular "Horatius at the Bridge"), is famous.

Thomas Carlyle (1795–1881) was not satisfied with life as was Macaulay. Bitter, stern, harsh, Carlyle flung his harshly phrased sentences at the evils of his day, and flayed, too, the fundamental shortcomings of humanity. Reacting against the materialism of the industrial era, Carlyle set forth the idea of salvation by work as exemplified in the life of the Middle Ages. His belief in the sanctity of the individual was broadened so that he placed great faith in the person of a hero to lead those less highly endowed. He wrote in an odd style, somewhat imitative of German, often quite unlike English, and yet strong, convincing, and effective. His style has been distinguished by calling it "Carlylese." Perhaps the most eccentric and most essentially individualistic work in the English language is Carlyle's *Sartor Resartus,* which might be subtitled "The Philosophy of Clothes." Disguised partly as a hoax, built around clothing as a universal symbol, this extraordinary book powerfully embodies Carlyle's peculiar genius; it is a book that repays rereadings. Carlyle's other works include the following: *The French Revolution, Heroes and Hero-Worship, Past and Present, Life of Schiller,* and many translations from the German.

John Ruskin (1819–1900) also was not satisfied with his age. Neither so bitter nor of such stature as Carlyle, Ruskin nevertheless profoundly influenced his day. He is best remembered for his art criticisms; Ruskin, like Browning, was intensely interested in painting. Ruskin believed that no art was possible under the social and economic conditions of his day, so he attempted to bring about a reform of these conditions. *Modern*

Painters is Ruskin's famous work about art. Ruskin's other works are *Seven Lamps of Architecture; The King of the Golden River; Unto This Last* (political economy); *Sesame and Lilies* (popular lectures).

Meanwhile an interesting phenomenon was taking place in literature: poetry, which had heretofore been the most important and influential of literary forms, began yielding place to the novel. Possibly the reason for this was that a new reading public, composed mostly of the middle class, was interested in reading of its own life in literature. Novels catered to this need. The Victorian age saw the rise of a group of brilliant novelists who were concerned with the meaning and portrayal of everyday life.

Charles Dickens (1812–1870) was one of the most prolific as well as one of the greatest novelists in English literature. In his novels he attacked social evils of his day, especially child labor and the injustice of the debtors' prisons common in his time. Though some of his characters are grotesque, most of them are wonderfully human; many of his pages are enlivened with great humor, and there is a consistent faith in human nature; his stories have remained popular. *Pickwick Papers,* a book which made him famous when he was about 25, is a humorous story in a class by itself. Also in a separate group are his Christmas stories, chief among them "A Christmas Carol." One historical novel deals romantically with the French Revolution: *A Tale of Two Cities.* Best known of his many other novels are: *David Copperfield, Great Expectations, Oliver Twist,* and *The Old Curiosity Shop.*

William Makepeace Thackeray (1811–1863) was a novelist-rival of Dickens. Though he handled pathos more convincingly than Dickens, and was in many ways a more charming humorist, Thackeray was never so popular as the author of *Pickwick Papers.* Thackeray was also an artist, and illustrated much of his own work. His finest and most popular novel is *Vanity Fair;* others are *Pendennis, Henry Esmond, The Newcomes,* and *The Virginians.* He also wrote humorous essays, gathered in *The Book of Snobs* and *The Roundabout Papers;* in literary criticism, he produced *The English Humorists.*

George Eliot was the pen name of Mary Ann Evans (1819–1880), whose novels are profound character studies, heralding the modern psychological novel. *Silas Marner* is probably her most widely read novel. Others, all of extraordinary excellence and power, are *Adam Bede, The Mill on the Floss, Romola, Middlemarch,* and *Daniel Deronda.*

Wilkie Collins (1824–1889) does not stand so high in literature as his contemporary novelists, but he excelled in one aspect of story-writing —the complexity and excellence of his plots. *The Moonstone* is among the greatest mystery yarns in the language, closely seconded by his *Woman in White.*

Edward Bulwer-Lytton (1803–1873) was a popular novelist in his day, but only two of his works have survived the ordeal of time. The first is his historical romance, *The Last Days of Pompeii,* and the second is his historical drama, *Richelieu.*

Anthony Trollope (1815–1882) wrote *Barchester Towers,* a realistic and satirical depiction of life in an English cathedral town, and *The Warden.*

Charlotte Brontë (1816–1855) will not be forgotten, for she wrote *Jane Eyre.* Her work is rather cloistered, but she made up with imagination what she lacked in experience. Her sister, Emily Brontë (1818–1848), won fame with *Wuthering Heights,* a novel of terrible vengeance.

Lewis Carroll was the pen name of Charles L. Dodgson (1832–1898), who expected to be remembered for his contributions to mathematics, but is endeared to the world, instead, by his half-juvenile, half-adult story, *Alice in Wonderland,* the most delicious nonsense ever penned. Allusions to *Alice* are astonishingly frequent in present-day writing.

Lesser names of the period are legion. Chief among them are Richard Doddridge Blackmore (1825–1900), author of the romantic novel, *Lorna Doone;* Charles Reade (1814–1884), author of *The Cloister and the Hearth;* Charles Kingsley (1819–1875), author of the robust adventure tale, *Westward Ho,* and of the juvenile classic, *Water Babies;* Thomas Hughes (1823–1896), author of *Tom Brown's School Days.*

Edward FitzGerald (1809–1883) deserves a paragraph by himself because of his metrical translation of a Persian poem—an English version that has won its niche in English literature, and has been increasingly popular in the twentieth century. That poem is the opulent *Rubaiyat of Omar Khayyam,* which sings of the joys of wine, poetry, and love.

After the middle of the century, a group of poets and painters joined in favoring a revival of medieval themes. They called themselves the Pre-Raphaelites, referring to the period before the Renaissance paintings of Raphael in Italy. Dante Gabriel Rossetti (1828–1882) was prominent in this group both as a poet and a painter. Of his poems, the best known are *The Blessed Damozel* and some fine sonnets. William Morris (1834–1896) was a poet and also greatly interested in handicrafts and the satisfaction which comes from making things by hand. Among his poetical works are *The Defence of Guenevere* and *The Earthly Paradise.* Of the Pre-Raphaelite painters, the best known is Burne-Jones.

Algernon Charles Swinburne (1837–1909) was a poet given to voluptuous and sensuous imagery—a radical, an extravagant, and a prodigal user of rhyme and alliteration. Yet there is no more captivating music than that found in his "Deserted Garden," "Garden of Proserpine," "Atalanta in Calydon," and many other fine poems.

TRANSITIONAL WRITERS

A few prominent names toward the end of the century carry us over into the first decade of the twentieth century.

George Meredith (1828–1909), who anticipated the modern psychological presentation of character in his novels, was little appreciated in his lifetime; his recognition has been slow. *The Ordeal of Richard Feverel* deserves more popularity. *The Egoist* and *Diana of the Crossways* are also outstanding.

Thomas Hardy (1840–1928) won greatest fame as a novelist with *The Return of the Native;* among his other great novels are *Far From the Madding Crowd, The Mayor of Casterbridge,* and *Tess of the D'Urbervilles.* A deep and understanding sense of the tragic in life characterizes Hardy's work. In his later years, he devoted himself to writing poetry and composed some charming lyrics as well as a number of philosophical and rather skeptical poems. Like his novels, these stress the inscrutable and often cruel workings of chance. He also wrote a mighty epic drama, *The Dynasts.*

Gerard Manley Hopkins (1844–1899), an intensely dedicated priest, wrote little poetry, wrote it perfectly, and had no public during his lifetime. Today his vigorously packed, powerful, rich-sounding, deeply sincere poems are highly admired. He anticipated the style and technique of much twentieth-century poetry.

Robert Louis Stevenson (1850–1894), incurably romantic, lifted adventure to a lofty pinnacle and endeared himself to boys with his *Treasure Island.* Children everywhere delight in his *A Child's Garden of Verses.* Probably his most famous tale is *Dr. Jekyll and Mr. Hyde,* a curious study of double personality. Of his essays, the best are in *Virginibus Puerisque* ("For Boys and Girls"), *Inland Voyage,* and *Travels with a Donkey.* Among other novels are *Kidnapped* and *The Master of Ballantrae.*

W. S. Gilbert (1836–1911) wrote the spoken or sung words (librettos) for the enjoyable comic operas of Sir Arthur Sullivan, who composed the music. Best among them are *The Mikado, H.M.S. Pinafore,* and *The Pirates of Penzance.* Gilbert also wrote *Bab Ballads.*

Oscar Wilde (1856–1900) had a strangely notorious career. His public disgrace cast a shadow over his deserved fame as a poet and wit. Following his trial for misconduct, the name of Wilde was anathema to many; in late years his works have regained an appreciative audience.

His best plays are his smart comedies, *Lady Windermere's Fan* and *The Importance of Being Earnest*. His weirdly haunting tragedy, *Salome*, was written in French, and translated into English by another writer. *The Picture of Dorian Gray* is a novel which explores the psychology of decadence in extravagant dramatic terms. Of his poetry, *The Ballad of Reading Gaol* is the best known; "The Sphinx" is perhaps the oddest. *De Profundis* ("From the Depths") is an autobiographical essay, written in prison. Most joyously charming are his fairy tales, even when they deal with tragedy, including "The Happy Prince," "The Birthday of the Infanta," and several others.

Three interesting poets of the end of the century are: Ernest Dowson (1867–1900), whose short lyric, "Cynara," is often quoted; John Davidson (Scottish, 1857–1909), perhaps best known for his *Ballads and Songs;* and Francis Thompson (1859–1907), a mystical poet with an amazing gift of expression, as in his finest poem, "The Hound of Heaven."

Among noted prose writers of the period there are several important novelists, essayists, and dramatists: Samuel Butler (1835–1902), author of *The Way of All Flesh* and of the satire *Erewhon;* Walter Pater (1839–1894), a literary connoisseur and essayist, author of *Marius the Epicurean;* George Gissing (1857–1903), author of *New Grub Street;* George Moore (1852–1933), beginning as a realistic novelist (*Esther Waters*), ended his career with great emphasis on literary style (*The Brook Kerith*); John Millington Synge (1871–1909), Irish dramatist, author of *Riders to the Sea* and *The Playboy of the Western World*.

THE TWENTIETH CENTURY

The twentieth century is an era of scientific advancement and of amazing progress in technology. The fact that, despite his great material advances, man is still not fully realizing his potentialities, the fact that thousands of people are still ill-housed and ill-fed, the fact that hypocrisy and sham are still rampant has given pause to many writers. Some have tried to find solutions in socialism or in mysticism; some have been content merely to describe conditions as they saw them. At any rate, the major writers of this century have in their own ways dealt with these problems in their works. As in the late Victorian era, the novel has been the dominant literary form.

WRITERS BEFORE THE FIRST WORLD WAR

Rudyard Kipling (1865–1936) lived in India and wrote most of his early works there. Quite a number of these early stories, as in *Plain Tales from the Hills,* deal with British soldiers in India. *Kim,* a novel steeped in the lore of India, is probably his best book. His poems—"The Vampire," "Gunga Din," and "Mandalay" (which has been set to music)—are extremely popular. Notable also are his books for children, *The Just So Stories* and *The Jungle Books*.

George Bernard Shaw (1856–1950) was strongly individualistic in the field of letters and a man of striking personality. His plays, most of them comedies, constitute his powerful literary work, together with his long prefaces which explain his purpose and enfold his ideas. Although his characters tend to lack emotional content and his themes are fundamentally intellectual, Shaw's extraordinary wit, his perfect understanding of all classes of society, and his strong sense of drama have made his plays outstanding. Well known among the long list are *Candida, Man and Superman, Major Barbara, Androcles and the Lion, Caesar and Cleopatra, Saint Joan,* and *Back to Methuselah. Pygmalion* provided the story and much of the dialogue and lyrics for the musical, "My Fair Lady."

Sir James Matthew Barrie (1860–1937), novelist and dramatist, is noted for his charming style, apt characterization, and appealing whimsy and sentiment. His novel, *Sentimental Tommy,* is no less popular than such plays as *Peter Pan, What Every Woman Knows, The Admirable Crichton,* and *A Kiss for Cinderella.*

Joseph Conrad (1857–1924), born in Poland, decided upon English as the language in which he would write, and became a master in its use. Among his greatest novels are: *Almayer's Folly, Lord Jim, The Nigger of the Narcissus, Chance, Victory,* and *The Rescue.* Outstanding among his shorter stories are *Heart of Darkness* and *Youth.*

W. H. Hudson (1841–1922) is best known for his novel, *Green Mansions,* a poetic fantasy set in the South American jungle. Other novels of Hudson are *The Purple Land* and *A Crystal Age.* Hudson, who described himself as a naturalist, wrote a number of books dealing with birds and other animals and plant life in their natural settings, some in South America and some in England. Though most of his life he was an English citizen, he was born in the United States and grew up in Argentina.

Arnold Bennett (1867–1931) was the author of several highly realistic novels, of which *The Old Wives' Tale* is the best known. Bennett was more interested in the interplay of his characters than in social criticism to which many of his contemporaries were devoted.

John Galsworthy (1867–1933), prominent both as novelist and dramatist, is chiefly known for the group of novels centering on one family, *The Forsyte Saga.* Galsworthy was concerned in his writings with social problems and complications rising out of class distinction. This is very marked in his plays, among which *Strife* and *Justice* are notable.

H. G. Wells (1866–1946) won wide American fame with his *Outline of History,* which had been preceded by many short stories and novels. His varied work is evident in *Tono Bungay, Mr. Britling Sees It Through,* and *Men Like Gods.* Wells is the scientist in literature, applying the rule of reason to life. He wrote many works of social criticism, among them "A Modern Utopia." He is also identified with his creation of the modern "science fiction" novel. Written with a fine feeling for the flavor of English life, his best novels make interesting and amusing reading.

Sir Arthur Conan Doyle (1859–1930) created Sherlock Holmes and made his name a household synonym for "detective." "The Red-headed League" and "A Scandal in Bohemia" are two of his best-known yarns.

The poetry of A. E. Housman (1859–1936), a classical scholar and author of *A Shropshire Lad,* marks clearly an end to the romantic period. In a simple, direct style these poems describe the English countryside, portraying—often with sharp pessimism—run-of-the-mill characters, their brief passions, their perfidies, their vanities, and their callousness. His "Loveliest of Trees" and "To an Athlete Dying Young" are famous.

John Masefield (born 1874) is a skillful craftsman in narrative poetry, and has written much prose of merit, including plays. Probably his best-known short poem is "Sea Fever." He was named poet laureate in 1930. Longer poems of dramatic narrative are *The Daffodil Fields, The Everlasting Mercy,* and *Dauber.*

Two other noted poets are Alfred Noyes (1880–1958), author of such popular short poems as "The Barrel Organ" and "The Highwayman," and Walter de la Mare (1873–1956), greatly gifted as a lyric poet primarily interested in fantasy, which also characterizes his short stories and the longer *Memoirs of a Midget.*

The outstanding poet of this period was the Irish-born William Butler Yeats (1865–1939), a leader of the Irish national and literary renaissance and one of the great poets of English literature. In Yeats were joined unusual lyrical gifts with a profound understanding of the meaning of mythology and an impassioned vision of life. The technical excellence of his poetry is remarkable. He wrote several volumes of short poems and a number of poetical dramas (*The Countess Kathleen* and *The Land of Heart's Desire*). Yeats created an elaborate intellectual scheme of history and a rich symbolism out of a strange mixture of magic and philosophy.

WRITERS AFTER THE FIRST WORLD WAR

Whereas the writers of the first part of the century were for the most part active in their criticism of life as they saw it, many of the writers who came into prominence after the first great war took refuge in cynicism, despair, and a bitter brand of satire.

The dominant literary figure of the 1920s and 1930s was the Irish-born cosmopolite, James Joyce (1882–1941). Joyce saw modern man as a weak counterpart of the Greeks' heroic figures. This contrast provides the theme of his unusual novel, *Ulysses.* The language of this work is extremely complicated, for Joyce's references are highly recondite and personal. Added to this are his "stream of consciousness" passages, where he tries to present the thoughts of his characters in the disorganized, illusive manner in which they occur.

D. H. Lawrence (1885–1930) chose as his theme the difficulty of overcoming the man-made barriers between people, and particularly between men and women. The best of his works are *Sons and Lovers* and *The Rainbow.*

Virginia Woolf (1882–1941) is the outstanding woman novelist of the day. Highly sensitive and written in a personal, introspective style are her novels, *Mrs. Dalloway* and *To the Lighthouse.* Quite unlike her other works is *Orlando,* the story of a hero who lives throughout the various ages of English history, changing his ways, clothes, passions, ambitions, and beliefs along with the changes of fashion and thought.

In biography Lytton Strachey (1880–1932) is outstanding. His biographies of public figures (*Eminent Victorians* and *Queen Victoria*) take them off the pedestals on which they were set by more conventional biographers and describe them as ordinary human beings.

Alfred North Whitehead (1861–1942), a noted philosopher, developed the implications of Einsteinian science to a new view of the universe and history. His most widely read work is *Science and the Modern World.*

Aldous Huxley (born 1894) is a descendant of two great Victorian figures, Thomas Huxley and Matthew Arnold. He has lent the novel a satirical brilliance. His best work is *Point Counter Point,* which examines the claims of art, science, and one type of politics as ways of life; he rejects them all. In his most recent books (*After Many a Summer Dies the Swan* and *Eyeless in Gaza*) he has shown signs of accepting a sort of scientific mysticism.

W. Somerset Maugham (born 1874) is best known for his novels, *Of Human Bondage* and *The Moon and Sixpence,* although his writings also include a number of notable short stories, several plays, and interesting reminiscences.

Other outstanding writers include George Orwell (1903–1950), author of the prophetic satire *1984;* and Frank O'Connor (born 1903; Irish), a master of short stories. Distinctive in their style and in their strangely fascinating mood are the short stories of Isak Dinesen (born

1883; real name, Baroness Blixen), a Danish woman who writes in English. Her *Seven Gothic Tales* and *Out of Africa* are exceptional books.

RECENT AUTHORS

The recent period saw the emergence of three interesting poets: Stephen Spender (born 1909), Cecil Day Lewis (born 1904), and Wystan Hugh Auden (born 1907). Their styles are difficult, but they are interesting as poets who try to incorporate the details and symbols of the modern urban world in their poetry. Outstanding among the poets of the period was a Welshman, Dylan Thomas (1915–1954), who died young and doubtless before he had realized his full potential. His poetry was rich, vivid, lusty, and very powerful. His language evoked with a great force the deep meaning and drama of nature, in which he saw humanity as intimately participating. Among Thomas' best-known poems are "October Morning," "In My Dark and Sullen Art," "In the Park," and the poetic play, *Under Milk Wood.*

Among recent English playwrights, Christopher Fry (born 1907) has won a special place through the distinctive and imaginative atmosphere of his plays in verse, notably *The Lady's Not for Burning, Venus Observed,* and *The Dark is Light Enough.*

Sean O'Casey (born 1884) is an Irish dramatist who, like many Irish authors, is closely related to his English contemporaries and to English literature. He is discussed in the section on Irish literature, which follows.

IRISH LITERATURE

Although writers who were born in Ireland, but who write in English, are usually included among the contributors to English literature, Irish literature has a distinct place in the literature of the world, and its early works are written in the native language, Gaelic.

Ireland has a large heritage of saga romances, recounting the traditional legends of the early tribes. The mythological cycle of these contains stories of conflicts among the pagan gods. One great heroic cycle deals with the hero Cuchulain and dates from about the first century. Cuchulain is the chief champion of the king of Ulster, and single-handed he defends his royal master against the united forces of Ireland. Another great legend tells the tragic story of Deirdre, whose beauty is as famous as that of Helen of Troy.

There is also the Fenian or Ossianic cycle. This tells of Finn and his band of warriors, including his two sons, Fergus and Ossian. Many popular tales of Finn and his Fenians exist in Ireland, not all of them yet reduced to writing. It is curious to note here that in 1762, or thereabouts, one James Macpherson perpetrated a famous literary hoax. Basing his work largely on Celtic legend, he succeeded in temporarily fooling eminent scholars with a supposed translation of some newly found ancient manuscripts dealing with the Ossianic cycle. These make rather good reading still, but they are mostly Macpherson's own work.

The Danish period of conquest and influence (795–1014) in Ireland saw the destruction of schools and monasteries, but literature went on. Gormly and MacLaig were important bards. In the eleventh and twelfth centuries most of the saga romances were collected and written down. But after the Norman conquest of England, the thirteenth, fourteenth, and fifteenth centuries had little to offer in new contributions to literature. The Irish language began to decline as a literary medium of expression. Some thousands of lines of Ossianic poems were recorded in this period, apart from the Ossianic or Fenian cycle already mentioned. In the early eighteenth century, poetry became freer and adopted rhyme.

By the nineteenth century, the native Irish tongue was practically extinct as a literary language. Many Irish-born writers contributed more truly to English literature than to Irish, among them Oliver Goldsmith, Edmund Burke, Richard B. Sheridan, Oscar Wilde, and William E. H. Lecky. More definitely associated with Ireland is the poet and wit, Thomas Moore (1779–1852). James Clarence Mangan (1803–1849) might be described as an Irish Poe.

Though Maria Edgeworth (1767–1849) was English, she wrote some novels of Irish life, among them *Castle Rackrent*. Charles Lever (1806–1872), Irish novelist, pictured youthful Irish swagger in his *Charles O'Malley*. Samuel Lover (1797–1868) gave us *Handy Andy* and *Rory O'More*. John Banim (1798–1842) and his brother Michael contributed *Tales of the O'Hara Family*. William Carleton (1794–1869) is well known for his *Traits and Stories of the Irish Peasantry*.

Irish literature came to the fore of world attention with the Celtic revival, at the beginning of the twentieth century. The work of new writers was encouraged and the treasures of the national literature revived. At the same time there was a revival of the Gaelic tongue as the national language, and Ireland now recognizes both Gaelic and English as official.

William Butler Yeats (1865–1939), winner of the Nobel prize for literature in 1923, was among the most influential writers of the revival. He is the chief poet of modern Ireland. We have discussed his work in the section on English literature. George William Russell (1867–1935) is known in England and America by his literary signature "AE"; he is both Irish poet and painter. John Millington Synge (1871–1909), mentioned under English literature, led the revival in the drama, and stands out as a great Irish playwright. Of his plays, two are very well known indeed, namely, *The Playboy of the Western World* and *Riders to the Sea.* Lady Gregory (1859–1932; her real name was Augusta Persse) was an important dramatist and poet and one of the leaders of the Celtic revival. Padraic Colum (born 1881), another noted Irish writer, spent his later years in the United States. George Moore, a novelist, we have considered under English literature.

Lord Dunsany (born 1878) was an author, soldier, and playwright, chief among his books being typically Celtic wonder tales such as *A Dreamer's Tales* and the drama, *The Laughter of the Gods.* James Stephens (born 1892) is characteristically Irish, his most famous book being the delightful philosophical-whimsical story, *The Crock of Gold;* this same quality is found in his poetry. James Joyce (1882–1941), Irish born, was an experimenter in new modes of expression whom we have already considered in English literature.

Sean O'Casey (born 1884) wrote many fine realistic plays for the Abbey Theater, a famous Irish experimental theatrical group. These include *Juno and the Paycock* and *The Plough and the Stars.* His volumes of reminiscences are works of exceptional interest and distinction.

Samuel Beckett (born 1906), an Irishman who lives in France and writes in French as well as in English, has won recent fame as a playwright. In his *Waiting for Godot,* he elaborates on the antics and the patter associated with clowns to produce a strangely fanciful play, which in wit and pathos is deeply moving in its implications of the basic loneliness, cruelty, and desperation which is man's lot.

AMERICAN LITERATURE

American literature developed in the English tradition, for it was written in the English language, at first by emigrants from England or their descendants. Later, as other races and nationalities mingled their blood with that of the English colonists, foreign elements contributed their part to the growing literature of the new nation. Today American literature is diverse, owing to the great expanse of the country and to the great differences in climate, industries, and other phases of life.

COLONIAL LITERATURE

The colonial period of American literature is meager in imaginative works. Intensely occupied with making homes in a rugged land, the people had little time either for writing books or for reading them. Some English works, naturally, were imported. But, as the years passed, crowding thoughts demanded expression, and gradually an American literature emerged. It was never centered in one place, as English literature has been largely centered in London.

It was a struggle for the leaders of the American Revolution to unite the various colonies into one nation. The colonies differed in local interests as well as in their heritage. Through the early history of the United States, internal strife was rampant, culminating finally in the great Civil War, when the question of union was decided definitely. Out of such diversity a diversified literature arose.

Cotton Mather (1663–1728), stern theologian, figured more memorably in the trials of "witches" than in literature. Jonathan Edwards (1703–1758) expounded religion and philosophized in *The Freedom of the Will. The Day of Doom,* by Michael Wigglesworth (1631–1705), was a theological poem that was read throughout New England.

The first name of importance is that of Benjamin Franklin (1706–1790), who preached common sense and worldly wisdom. He was a printer, a statesman, a man of the world. Translated into a dozen languages, his *Poor Richard's Almanack* is crammed with pithy utterances, some original, others copied. Almanacs were, with the Bible, the chief literary fare of the period. Some of Franklin's shorter sketches are widely reprinted even now, among them "The Whistle." His *Autobiography* is noted for its simple, clear style.

The period of the American Revolution saw a great outburst of literary effort, both on the side of the revolutionaries and on the side of the Tories. Little of this work survives, but the impetus thus given to literature lasted into the nineteenth century, giving rise to the first body of genuinely American literature.

Thomas Jefferson (1743–1826) wrote the political prose of the nation, including the Declaration of Independence. He was a dominant figure, strong in his liberal beliefs, a thorough democrat. He founded the University of Virginia.

Thomas Paine (1737–1809) gave the skill of his pen to the cause of independence, writing persuasive pamphlets to aid the American cause, among them *Common Sense*. His views, too, were liberal; he is remembered today as a rationalist. He criticized the Bible in his *Age of Reason*.

Philip Freneau (1752–1832) was the first significant American poet, but today only a few of his poems are read.

THE NINETEENTH CENTURY

The late eighteenth and early nineteenth centuries ushered in a host of writers and works of varying merit. These were the days of nationalism. The country was greatly enlarged by the Louisiana Purchase, the western and southern area bought from France. In 1812 there was war with

England. The Monroe Doctrine was promulgated (1823). Slavery was becoming a national issue. Fulton invented his steamboat in 1807. Railroads drew the country closer together. McCormick invented his reaper in 1831. For almost the first time, writers began to explore the American scene in literature.

Washington Irving (1783–1859) was the first successful professional author in America. He was certainly the first American writer to be acknowledged in England. He is at his best in such tales as "Rip Van Winkle" and "The Legend of Sleepy Hollow," to be found in *The Sketch Book,* and *Tales of a Traveler. Knickerbocker's History of New York* is an ambitious humorous work, still entertaining. Having served as attaché of the American legation in Madrid, he recalls his Spanish sojourn in *The Alhambra* and *The Conquest of Granada.*

James Fenimore Cooper (1789–1851) wrote long romantic novels, relating extraordinary adventures, with the frontier as his background. The style is seldom all that can be desired, and his "females" are impossible "creatures" (as he called them), but the stories are always told with vigor. His best novels are *The Spy, The Pilot,* and the Leatherstocking Tales which revolve around the hero Natty Bumpo—*The Deerslayer, The Last of the Mohicans, The Pathfinder, The Pioneers,* and *The Prairie* (to be read in the order named).

William Cullen Bryant (1794–1878) was the earliest American poet whose fame has endured. His best poem is undoubtedly "Thanatopsis," a poetical view of death; other familiar titles are "To a Waterfowl" and "To the Fringed Gentian."

We pass now into the busy midst of the nineteenth century, when American writers looked far afield for their thoughts and subjects. The Unitarian movement was strong in religion. Slavery became a dominant issue, both political and humanitarian. Oratory leaped into the foreground. Some of the finest poetry of American literature was produced. The short story—under the guidance of Poe and Hawthorne—became a national literary form. It is this period that is often called the American Renaissance.

About 1836 what was called the Transcendental movement was at its height in Boston. In American literature, *transcendentalism* has a restricted meaning, distinct from its meaning in Kant's philosophy. A group of the writers of this period held that within man were instincts or intuitions which were stronger and more reliable than the results of experience. They held, in short, that man had within himself powers which did not depend on the material world—powers which *transcended* the evidence of the senses and of knowledge that could be gleaned from books. This aspect of transcendentalism accounts for the element of individualism in the literature of this period. Leading transcendentalists were Ralph Waldo Emerson, Henry David Thoreau, Nathaniel Hawthorne, Amos Bronson Alcott, Margaret Fuller, and Theodore Parker.

Ralph Waldo Emerson (1803–1882), a friend of Thomas Carlyle, was deeply influenced by Carlyle's works. He was the first American philosopher of note. He advocated practical ideals. Emerson wrote poetry, but his fame rests on his lectures and essays—where the sentence is ever mightier than the paragraph, where the part is stronger often than the whole, for Emerson wrote some of the most highly concentrated sentences in English. His lecture entitled "The American Scholar," delivered at Harvard in 1837, should be on the required reading list of every educated person. Perhaps the cream of his essays is to be found in those entitled "Self-Reliance," "Character," "Manners," "The Over-Soul," "Spiritual Laws," "Compensation," "Beauty," and "Love," and in *Representative Men*.

Henry David Thoreau (1817–1862) was a recluse and a radical thinker. He observed nature conscientiously, and commented on human life sagely. *Walden,* an account of a stay in the woods, is his chief work.

Henry Wadsworth Longfellow (1807–1882) was—and still is, to some extent—the people's poet. His work has plodded a hard road up and down in the estimation of critics. Longfellow has been both over-praised and over-condemned. Of his shorter poems, the most popular are: "The Village Blacksmith," "A Psalm of Life," "The Wreck of the Hesperus," "The Skeleton in Armor," and "The Day is Done." *Evangeline* is his most ambitious work, as a single narrative; *Tales of a Wayside Inn* is the most ambitious as a series (containing the famous "Paul Revere's Ride"). Two other titles are well known: *Hiawatha,* based on Indian legend, and *The Courtship of Miles Standish*. Of great skill is his translation of Dante's *The Divine Comedy*.

James Russell Lowell (1819–1891) was another leader in the strong New England literary movement, which was centered in Boston. *The Vision of Sir Launfal* is a long poem, reminiscent of the Arthurian tales of knighthood and the Holy Grail. Numerous short poems came from his pen, many paying tribute to the charms of nature. Of his prose, *Among My Books* and *My Study Windows* are the best collections; probably the most familiar single title is "On a Certain Condescension in Foreigners."

A poet of more simple virtues was John Greenleaf Whittier (1807–1892). *Voices of Freedom* is a collection of lyrics written against slavery. *Snow-Bound,* an idyllic picture of rural life in New England, seems likely to stand as Whittier's masterpiece. Other titles are "Maud Muller," "The Barefoot Boy," "Skipper Ireson's Ride," and "Barbara Frietchie."

Oliver Wendell Holmes (1809–1894) was a physician and a professor before he was a poet, but he was always a wit. "The Chambered Nautilus" is a worthy serious poem, didactic though it is. "Old Ironsides" rang its patriotic phrases nation-wide to save the frigate *Constitution* from destruction. His "The Deacon's Masterpiece; or, The Wonderful One-Hoss Shay," with its rollicking humor, will probably survive, as did the shay, its hundred years and a day. His novels—even the best, *Elsie Venner*—are no longer considered important. Of his prose, *The Autocrat of the Breakfast Table* is a conglomerate of everything under the sun, united in the loose superstructure of a boarding-house table dominated by the Autocrat.

The most colorful literary figure of the period was Edgar Allan Poe (1809–1849), noted for his striking originality in both prose and poetry. If Poe's poetry were lost to the world, he would be famous for his stories; if his stories were also somehow lost, he would be famous for his criticism. The remarkable aspects of his stories are their eerie scenes, their impressions of gloom, their somber tragedy—in short, Poe's skill in creating strange but convincing atmosphere. Poe's poetry is remarkable for its metrical perfection. As a literary critic he had much that is sound to say on the topics of poetry and the short story. "The Raven" is Poe's most popular single poem; others of note are: "The Bells," "Ulalume" (an almost meaningless poem, depending for its effect on the sound of the words alone), "Annabel Lee," and "To Helen." His *Tales of the Grotesque and Arabesque* include his best stories; some of the more familiar titles are "The Fall of the House of Usher," "The Black Cat," "The Cask of Amontillado," "The Masque of the Red Death," "William Wilson" (a tale of double personality), and "The Murders in the Rue Morgue" (the first true detective story, the ancestor of the Sherlock Holmes tales and their like). "The Gold Bug" is an adventurous "novelette" of mystery and treasure-hunting. Poe wrote, too, many pseudo-scientific stories, such as "Hans Pfall" and "The Descent into the Maelstrom."

Of equally impressive stature, and far more interested than Poe in the subtle significances of human conduct, was Nathaniel Hawthorne (1804–1864), a master of sketches, stories, and novels. His work is also extremely varied.

His *Twice-Told Tales* and *Mosses from an Old Manse* contain the finest of his shorter sketches and stories, among them "Mr. Higginbotham's Catastrophe," "The Minister's Black Veil," "The Ambitious Guest," and "Dr. Heidegger's Experiment." His short-story masterpiece is "The Great Stone Face." Of his novels, *The Scarlet Letter* made him famous for all time; in this book are concentrated Hawthorne's puritan attitude, his tendency toward unreality, and his subtle charm. The plot is built around the sin of adultery, with the emphasis on the magnitude of the sin. *The House of the Seven Gables* is a less severe narrative, but the effects of sin also dominate that story. Children delight in his *Grandfather's Chair,* a series of colonial legends retold expressly for them. His *Wonder-Book* and *Tanglewood Tales,* modern versions of the classic myths of ancient times, are also childhood delights.

Herman Melville (1819–1891), author of the novels *Moby Dick* and *Typee,* is a writer who has come into prominence only in recent decades. Little read in his own lifetime, he is regarded today as a romantic who wrote in terms of symbols. *Moby Dick* may be read simply as an adventure story of a sea captain seeking vengeance on a whale that had ripped off his leg, or it may be considered as a kind of allegory of man's unsuccessful search for vengeance on a blind fate.

Walt Whitman (1819–1892) lived and wrote his poems in this period, although his work places him among the moderns. He broke courageously away from the traditions of poetry, and wrote with a large vision, with a generous and kindly and lovably democratic spirit, of everything, for everything seemed to him to be interesting, good, and worthy. Called immoral, he was unmoral; Whitman saw no evil in what is natural. *Leaves of Grass,* his collected verses, has been the stormy battlefield of critics ever since its recognition. Its contents are of unequal merit, but even the best poems had to wait for this century to win any large group of admirers. In his poetry Whitman is the free, almost unrestrained voice of individualism. Many of his poems are in the first person—"I"—yet it is clear that he speaks not for himself alone but for all mankind. He is broad in his sympathies for suffering mankind; many of his most touching poems deal with the Civil War. Whitman is the great democrat in poetry, the champion of the common man's right to participate in life to the full. Whitman is important too for the influence he had on writers after him, both on their form (he showed the possibilities of free verse) and on their content.

Other noted writers of the period were Edward Everett Hale (1822–1909), clergyman, author of many short stories, the most widely read being "The Man Without a Country"; Harriet Beecher Stowe (1811–1896), author of the anti-slavery novel, *Uncle Tom's Cabin;* Richard Henry Dana (1815–1882), author of *Two Years Before the Mast;* Louisa May Alcott (1833–1888), author of *Little Women;* Daniel Webster (1782–1852), statesman and orator, whose "Bunker Hill Orations" are school classics, and whose "Reply to Hayne" is an oratorical masterpiece. Daniel Webster should not be confused with Noah Webster (1758–1843), the first great American lexicographer, whence "Webster's" dictionaries.

THE BEGINNING OF REALISM

Toward the close of the nineteenth century America was definitely becoming an industrial nation. Large cities sprang up and the great West began gradually to be settled. These two facts had a great influence on literature. Heretofore, the unsettled West had served as a kind of escape area for persons dissatisfied with the more cultivated East. Now, with the whole country settled, there was no "ideal" land to turn to. At the same time the rise of industrialism and its many attendant evils caused men to turn to the realities of life—often of everyday, humdrum life. To the concern with the individual that was characteristic of the transcendentalists was now added concern with the individual in a real environment. In literature this change was known as *realism*. Realism in literature means the attempt to depict life as it actually exists. Realism has been the dominant method in American literature up to our day.

Mark Twain, whose real name was Samuel Langhorne Clemens (1835–1910), was the greatest American humorist, who would have scorned life if he had not been able to laugh at it. He pointed a steady finger of fun at shams of all kinds. Great novels of American boyhood are his *Tom Sawyer* and *Huckleberry Finn*. His first, and perhaps best, short humorous story was "The Celebrated Jumping Frog of Calaveras County." In *The Innocents Abroad*, he twitted the solemn sightseeing of tourists. *Roughing It* depicts early mining life. *The Prince and the Pauper* is a romantic children's story. In *Life on the Mississippi*, Mark Twain gave us an autobiographical record of the period and section he describes. Of his longer works, *A Connecticut Yankee in King Arthur's Court* is the most hilarious. A more serious tone is revealed in *Joan of Arc*. Two short stories, "The Man That Corrupted Hadleyburg" and "The Mysterious Stranger," published posthumously, reveal the deep pessimism that underlay all of Mark Twain's fun-making. Among his remaining works are *The Gilded Age, Adam's Diary, A Tramp Abroad, Pudd'nhead Wilson, Following the Equator, Captain Stormfield's Visit to Heaven,* and dozens of short tales and sketches.

William Dean Howells (1837–1920) is little read today but he was influential through his introduction of his conception of realism. His best novels, *The Rise of Silas Lapham* and *A Hazard of New Fortunes,* are sincere but hardly inspired.

Henry James (1843–1916), brother of William James (philosopher), is claimed by American literature though he lived and wrote for most of his later life in Europe. *Daisy Miller* and *The Portrait of a Lady* are the best known of his early characteristic novels; *Washington Square* is also exceptional. *The Ambassadors,* an example of his later more studied and carefully wrought stories, is one of his best works. James wrote with great subtlety, in a fine though somewhat complicated style. His novels are difficult but rewarding reading; he is one of the great novelists. He occasionally wrote intellectual "thrillers," of which *The Turn of the Screw* is a notable example.

Stephen Crane (1871–1900) is the author of a few poems and stories and one well-known work, *The Red Badge of Courage.* This realistic novel relates the story of a young man in the Civil War caught between the impersonal war machine and the desire for self-preservation. Although Crane never participated in a battle, it has been considered a masterpiece of war literature.

O. Henry, whose real name was W. Sydney Porter (1862–1910), wrote short stories which often depend for their effect on a "surprise twist" at the end. His influence on contemporary short-story writing is still strong, especially in so-called "short short stories." His life was as chaotically varied as the subjects of his tales. Typical of his stories are "Mammon and the Archer," "An Unfinished Story," and "A Municipal Report." Though condemned by some as a mere trickster, O. Henry has been not undeservedly popular; much of his work, even when hasty composition is obvious, has vivacity and genuine human sympathy. His collected stories are grouped under such book titles as *The Four Million, Cabbages and Kings,* and *The Roads of Destiny.*

Frank Norris (1870–1902) struggled valiantly with industrial and financial turmoil in his novels. *McTeague,* a realistic character study, stands among his best, though *The Octopus* and *The Pit* are fully as well known.

Jack London (1876–1916) wrote of socialism and of life in the rough. Such a well-told yarn as *The Call of the Wild* entitles him to some enduring popularity. *The Iron Heel* depicts social strife and is a remarkable prophecy of fascism. Familiar titles of London's novels are *White Fang, Martin Eden,* and *The Sea Wolf.*

Transitional to the twentieth century are also the following: Frank R. Stockton (1834–1902), humorist, author of the unique tale, "The Lady or the Tiger?"; Lew Wallace (1827–1905), army general, author of *Ben-Hur;* Joel Chandler Harris (1848–1908), folk-writer, author of *Nights with Uncle Remus;* Francis Bret Harte (1839–1902), author of "The Luck of Roaring Camp" and "The Outcasts of Poker Flat"; Ambrose Bierce (1842–1914), author of such horror stories as "The Damned Thing" and such war stories as "The Horseman in the Sky," and of the cynical *Devil's Dictionary,* composed of alphabetical antipathies; Eugene Field (1850–1895), journalist, author of many children's poems;

Emily Dickinson (1830–1886), recluse and remarkable poet, whose work has only recently been recognized for its originality and depth; William Vaughn Moody (1869–1910), poet and playwright, author of *The Great Divide;* James Whitcomb Riley (1849–1916), popular poet, author of *The Old Swimmin' Hole;* Clyde Fitch (1865–1909), playwright, author of *The Truth;* Robert G. Ingersoll (1833–1899), freethinker, author of many noteworthy speeches.

THE TWENTIETH CENTURY

The writers of the twentieth century carry on for the most part the realistic tradition of the late nineteenth century. Theodore Dreiser (1871–1945), an outspoken novelist, is highly praised for his realism, often condemned for his style. Dreiser wrote in a somber vein not at all relieved by humor, but with deep sincerity. *Sister Carrie* and *Jennie Gerhardt* are studies of women; *The Financier* and *The Titan* present Frank Cowperwood, buccaneer of business. Dreiser's most ambitious work is *An American Tragedy,* a murder trial elaborated into a comprehensive novel. His aim in this work is to show the tragic influence of modern society on a young man.

Edith Wharton (1862–1937) achieved great power in her novel, *Ethan Frome,* a tragic study of rural New England, and the protagonist's groping for happiness amidst incomprehension and poverty—and finding frustration and misery. In *Ethan Frome,* especially, is seen the psychological probing of character, of the inner springs of human emotions and actions, that is the motivating force behind scores of modern novels. Edith Wharton depicts New York society life vividly in *The House of Mirth, The Age of Innocence,* and other novels.

Booth Tarkington (1869–1946) wrote of boyhood in *Penrod.* He won popularity with such pleasing novels as *Monsieur Beaucaire, The Magnificent Ambersons,* and *Alice Adams.*

Sherwood Anderson (1876–1941) wrote in a mood and manner quite different from his contemporaries; his work is, to many readers, depressing and obscure. Certainly he writes subjectively—which is to say, in his own way, giving his intimately personal reactions instead of what he might observe impersonally and objectively. The dominant feeling in his work is one of skepticism. *Winesburg, Ohio* and *The Triumph of the Egg* are his two best-known books.

Sinclair Lewis (1885–1951) rose to fame on the popularity of his novel, *Main Street,* which is an almost photographic study of life in a typical small town. Later books were *Babbitt,* a satiric but not unsympathetic study of an American businessman in a quixotic quest for beauty; *Arrowsmith,* the life of an idealistic doctor; and *Elmer Gantry,* a scathing picture of an immoral preacher. Lewis was awarded the Nobel prize for literature in 1930; he was the first American writer to be so honored.

Joseph Hergesheimer (1880–1954) wrote colorful historical novels, including *The Three Black Pennys, Java Head,* and *The Lay Anthony,* which won him not only popularity but credit for a commendable style.

Upton Sinclair (born 1878) was a socialist and a propagandist. *The Jungle* depicts realistically conditions in slaughterhouses; it made not a little stir when it first appeared. Upton Sinclair presented data in opposition to capitalistic influence and control of the masses of the people. In *Oil!* Sinclair reached national popularity.

James Branch Cabell (1879–1953) was a writer of odd fantasies and romances. *Jurgen*—which became a "best seller" because it was suppressed for supposed obscenity, and later released—is good allegorical fun for those who can follow its somewhat mystifying construction.

Edgar Lee Masters (1868–1950) belongs in the group of significant poets of the early part of the century. His fame rests on his *Spoon River Anthology,* a gallery of portraits in free verse told by the fascinating means of having people speak their own epitaphs. His scene is an American small town, whose manners and morals are sharply but subtly criticized.

Edwin Arlington Robinson (1869–1935), a portrayer of human character in a cerebral verse, gives us such figures as "Flammonde," "Miniver Cheevy," "Richard Cory," and "Aaron Stark," and revives Browning's dramatic monologue in such a poem as "Ben Jonson Entertains a Man from Stratford." He reached an amazing popularity with his Arthurian legend *Tristram,* a long narrative poem belonging with the preceding *Merlin* and *Lancelot.* The title poem of the volume called *The Man Against the Sky* is an enviable contribution to American poetry.

Amy Lowell (1874–1925) startled modern poets with her ultramodernism. Technically she was an imagist. Though a lesser poet herself, she propagandized the imagist movement, which took its roots in the French "art for art's sake" of the late nineteenth century. Emphasis was on the plastic beauty and detailed perfection of the physical image.

Greatest of the imagists, though he has since experimented with many styles, is Ezra Pound (born 1885), who won a large public with his early musical and rich lyrics, reminiscent of ballads of the old Provençal troubadours; later he developed the complicated, obscure, intellectual style of *The Cantos,* written in numerous languages and understood by a minimum number of scholars. In 1945 he was arrested for treason in Italy, where he had aided the Fascist cause; he was judged insane and put in a mental hospital. Despite unanimous condemnation of his politics, his talent is still admired in the poems of *Provença* and *Cathay*, in such popular poems as his "Ballad of the Goodly Frere," in his expert translations from Chinese and Japanese, and in such mature critical works as *The ABC of Reading*.

Carl Sandburg (born 1878), poet and follower of Walt Whitman, saw great vigor and beauty in the raw American scene. His six-volume biography of Abraham Lincoln is a major work of our day.

Robert Frost (born 1875) is a New England poet in subject matter, but universal in the quiet appeal of his natural philosophy, if such his verse may be called. His verse moves smoothly, as though the lines were spoken, without haste, by a thoughtful farmer. *North of Boston* is the best-known collection of Frost's poems; single titles are: "Mending Wall," "Apple Picking," "Birches," "The Road Not Taken."

Eugene O'Neill (1888–1953) is generally recognized as the greatest of American dramatists. His first play, *Beyond the Horizon,* immediately revealed his powerful understanding of and ability to reveal the conflicts which make life difficult for many people. In *The Emperor Jones* he probes the soul of a Negro who reverts to savagery. *The Hairy Ape* and *The Great God Brown* are examples of his interesting experiments in new forms of dramatic expression. His experimental tendency reached a climax in *Strange Interlude,* which studies human motives by causing characters to speak not only what they would naturally say, but what they think almost at the same time. *Anna Christie, Desire Under the Elms,* and *Mourning Becomes Electra* are among other notable plays by O'Neill. *Long Day's Journey into Night,* one of O'Neill's last plays, and produced after his death, was a very personal play written with all his great dramatic power.

T. S. Eliot (born 1888; living chiefly in England) is the author of *The Waste Land,* a long and difficult poem aiming to show the aridity of modern life as compared with the life of other days. He has had a great influence on the younger poets of today. Other well-known works by Eliot are *The Four Quartets* and two plays, *Murder in the Cathedral* (in verse) and *The Cocktail Party*.

A major poet who achieved wide recognition very late in his career was Wallace Stevens (1879–1956). His verse is a subtle complex of nuance, perfect imagery, and very precise if often elusive ideas. Of the same generation as Stevens is William Carlos Williams (born 1883). He is the author of *In the American Grain* and *Paterson,* enjoyed for the simplicity of his tone and the beauty of the poetry.

E. E. Cummings (born 1894), who drops the capital letters from his name as from the first lines of his verse, is an unusual poet, equally proficient in two styles: subtle, fragile lyricism; and merciless, keen satire. His best work, however, is a novel, *The Enormous Room,* a modern war-time version of *Pilgrim's Progress.*

Clarence Day (1874–1935), best known for his book of entertaining recollections, *Life with Father* (later made into a play), is a source of delight not only for his humor but for pithy satire, as seen in his *This Simian World.*

Stephen Vincent Benét (1898–1943), noted both as a short-story writer and as a poet, is best known for his story *The Devil and Daniel Webster.* Among his poems, the moving Civil War narrative *John Brown's Body* is outstanding.

Ogden Nash (born 1902) is a unique poet; his verse reveals an ex-traordinary gift for satire and comedy.

A number of novelists achieved fame after the First World War.

Ernest Hemingway (born 1898) writes in a terse, close-lipped style of men and women searching for fulfilment in a torn world. *The Sun Also Rises* deals with intellectuals in postwar Paris. *A Farewell to Arms* is a tenderly written love story set in Italy during the First World War. His scene in *For Whom the Bell Tolls* is Spain during the Spanish Civil War.

John Dos Passos (born 1896), whose scene is industrial America, is concerned with good people who are twisted and thwarted. His trilogy, *U.S.A.,* takes a wide variety of characters and shows how they never realize their own capabilities and talents.

Willa Cather (1876–1947), who wrote excellent stories and novels, is best known perhaps for *Death Comes for the Archbishop.*

Thomas Wolfe (1900–1938) described the American scene through his personal experience of it, writing with great vigor and in a rich, some-what poetic style. Most important of his works are the four novels, *Look Homeward, Angel, Of Time and the River, The Web and the Rock,* and *You Can't Go Home Again.*

John Steinbeck (born 1902) shows sympathy and understanding for and a great ability to dramatize the lives of people who have fared badly in economic and personal struggles. At times sentimental, his novels are nevertheless graphic and moving. His most famous work is *The Grapes of Wrath.* Other major works are *East of Eden, The Red Pony, Tortilla Flat,* and *Of Mice and Men.*

Outstanding among modern authors is William Faulkner (born 1897), whose best novels are *Sanctuary, The Sound and the Fury,* and *Light in August.* Most of his works deal with an imaginary county in Mississippi (Yoknapatawpha County), whose wide panorama of characters is por-trayed in a style that is rich and complicated, but intensely dramatic. He has plumbed the depths of man's struggle with fate and evil more deeply than any other modern American writer. He was awarded the Nobel prize in 1949.

Other significant fiction writers include Nathaniel West (1906–1940), who combined his satirical gift with a strange brand of mysticism to produce a vivid caricature of life in his novels *Miss Lonelyhearts* and *The Locusts;* James T. Farrell (born 1904), whose novel *Studs Lonigan* is a powerful story of the wasted life of a young man brought up in the slums of Chicago; Richard Wright (born 1908), outstanding Negro novelist, who achieved renown with *Native Son,* a story that depicts the bitterness in the heart of a young Negro; Truman Capote (born 1924), whose *The Grass Harp* stands out among his rather effete, flowery prose; James Thurber (born 1894), unparalleled humorist, who wrote *Men, Women and Dogs* and *My Life and Hard Times;* Robert Penn Warren (born 1905), author of *All the King's Men;* Norman Mailer (born 1923), author of *The Naked and the Dead;* John O'Hara (born 1905), who wrote vivid realistic sketches (*Pal Joey*) and a penetrating sociological novel, *Appointment in Samarra;* Irwin Shaw (born 1913), whose *The Young Lions* is a war novel; Eudora Welty (born 1909), leading among short-story writers of the South; and Saul Bellow (born 1915), author of *The Adventures of Augie March,* a novel rich in humor and vivid characterization.

In the drama some outstanding writers in addition to O'Neill are: Thornton Wilder (born 1897), known for his *Our Town,* written to be staged without scenery, and *The Skin of Our Teeth,* as well as his novel, *The Bridge of San Luis Rey,* which, like his plays, is at once very moving and symbolic; Maxwell Anderson (born 1888), who is a leading writer of poetic drama (*Elizabeth the Queen* and *Winterset*); Robert E. Sherwood (1896–1956), who wrote a number of fine plays, is probably best remembered for *The Petrified Forest,* although *Abe Lincoln in Illinois* and *There Shall be No Night* are also examples of his worth; Clifford Odets (born 1906), who writes sympathetically of the tragedies of ordinary people (*Waiting for Lefty, Awake and Sing*); and Lillian Hellman (born 1905), whose better plays (*The Children's Hour, The Little Foxes*) show mastery of plot construction and an ability to portray a wide variety of characters.

More recently, Tennessee Williams (born 1914) has provided the theater with a number of its best plays, notably, *The Glass Menagerie* and *A Streetcar Named Desire.* He writes usually of desperate people pitted against one or two poetic characters in an intense drama. Also showing exceptional gifts in dramatic writing are: Arthur Miller (born 1915), who won wide recognition with his plays *Death of a Salesman*

and *The Crucible;* and William Inge (born 1913), who has shown notable ability to convey the impact of people in a small group upon one
another in such plays as *Picnic.*

ORIENTAL LITERATURE

Most ancient in the literature of the world are the classics of the Orient,
the area considered the cradle of civilization. Great works have come
down to us from the Babylonians, the Assyrians, the Egyptians, the Hebrews, the Persians, the Arabs, and, farther east, the Hindus (in India),
the Chinese, and the Japanese. Most of the literature of these ancient peoples is remote from the Western world; it remained unknown, in a large
measure, until recent years. It goes back to at least 5000 years B.C. In
earlier centuries it was not written down, but was preserved in the memories of men and passed on by word of mouth from generation to generation. Much of it was later written on stone or clay tablets, the Egyptian
in hieroglyphics and the Babylonian and related civilizations in cuneiform
characters. Parchment made from the skin of animals was used, as was
also papyrus, and later paper, which was invented by the Chinese, adopted
by the Arabs, and brought into Europe.

Very ancient is the Babylonian *Epic of Gilgamesh,* a legendary account of the hero Gilgamesh, containing a story of a Babylonian deluge.

Among the Persian classics are notably the *Zend-Avesta,* religious
book of Zoroastrianism, and the *Shah Namah* (Book of Kings) of Fir-
dausi (Abul Kasim Mansur, who lived about 1000 A.D.), in which is
found the episode of Sohrab and Rustum used by Matthew Arnold in
his famous poem. Best known of all Persian works is the colorful *Rubaiyat of Omar Khayyam,* familiar in English in the splendid metrical translation by Edward FitzGerald.

The ancient Egyptians left one classic work, known as *The Book of
the Dead,* which through prose and a form of verse gives the instructions
thought necessary to the soul on its last journey.

The Arabian religious classic is the *Koran,* containing the tenets of
Mohammedanism. The great Arabian literary classic known and loved
by modern English readers is the *Thousand and One Nights* or *Arabian
Nights' Entertainment,* beautifully translated by Sir Richard Burton and
others, consisting of long historical romances, fairy tales, and fables of
beasts, by an unknown author or authors, dating from sometime in the
thirteenth or fourteenth century. The device of the collection is familiar:
a sultan of the Indias becomes vindictive because of the infidelity of his
wife, and, to punish all women, he vows to take a new sultana each night
and have her killed the next morning. But Scheherazade, chosen to be

one of the sultanas, began each morning a new tale designed to excite the sultan's curiosity, and so clever was she that she regaled him for more than a thousand nights and remained his sultana thereafter. Famous among these yarns are the adventures of Sinbad the Sailor, Ali Baba and the forty thieves, and Aladdin.

The literature of India is recorded in Sanskrit, now a dead language. Most ancient is the sacred *Veda,* source of Brahmanism. The writings of Buddha (Gautama Siddhartha), who lived probably about the sixth century B.C., are in Pali, a Sanskrit dialect; they are the foundation of Buddhism, a system of moral teachings forming an Oriental religion. The *Mahabharata* is a great Hindu epic, eight times as long as the *Iliad* and the *Odyssey* combined. Written a little later, the other great Hindu epic is the *Ramayana.* The *Sakuntala* is a fascinating Sanskrit drama by Kalidasa, often called the "Shakespeare of India," who lived about 550 A.D. The best-known name in the modern literature of India is Rabindranath Tagore, poet of Bengal (1861–1941), winner of the Nobel prize for literature in 1913.

Among Chinese classics, Confucius (Kung Fu-tse, "Reverend Master Kung"), 551–478 B.C., philosopher and sage, is the great fountainhead of his country's literature. Lao-tse was another outstanding Chinese philosopher of the time.

Japanese literature was greatly influenced by the Chinese, and, in modern times, by Western writings. Most Japanese in character is the *no,* the native drama, which is almost incomprehensible to those not familiar with its traditions.

The ancient Hebrews gave to the world the books which are now the Old Testament of the Bible. (The New Testament is a translation from Greek manuscripts.) The *Talmud* is the name given to the body of Jewish canonical and civil law, illustrated with many tales and parables, made up of the Mishna (text) and the Gemara (commentary).

ANCIENT GREEK LITERATURE

English literature owes much to that of ancient Greece, not only in style and inspiration, but in subject matter. Many a poet and dramatist has borrowed freely from the Homeric epics, or from the legends of the gods or demigods and heroes of classical lore.

THE HOMERIC EPICS

Earliest of the Greek classics are the *Iliad* and the *Odyssey* of the greatest poet of classical times, Homer. Homer probably lived about 900 B.C., and little is known of his personal life. It is said that he was blind. His two great epic poems are doubtless based partially on songs and legends handed down from early times by word of mouth. Although Homer was revered in ancient Greece as the author of the *Iliad* and the *Odyssey,* some scholars hold that they are the work of several writers, whose names have not survived. Wandering bards recited them to music throughout Greece; and seven Greek cities claimed Homer as a native.

The *Iliad* is the epic of the Greek expedition against Troy (Ilium), an ancient city of the Hittite empire in Asia Minor, which is known to have really existed. The material of the long poem, however, is largely legendary. It tells how the Greeks, led by Achilles, Agamemnon, and his brother Menelaus, sailed to Troy and laid siege to the city, finally conquering it. They sought to rescue Helen, the wife of Menelaus, who had run off with Paris, son of the king of Troy. Paris was aided in his venture by Aphrodite because in his famous Judgement between the goddesses, Aphrodite, Athena, and Hera, he gave the golden apple marked by the goddess of discord "for the fairest" to the goddess of love, who promised him Helen in return. Although the god Zeus remained neutral in the Trojan War, other Greek deities took part in the struggle and lent supernatural aid to both Greeks and Trojans. The happenings of the *Iliad* are in the tenth and last year of the Greek siege of Troy, in which the Greeks were victorious. Achilles is roused to wrath by Agamemnon's theft of Briseis, his concubine (part of the spoils of war), and temporarily deserts the Greeks. Then, because his closest friend is killed by the Trojan hero Hector, he re-enters the battle and pursues Hector around the walls of Troy, finally, with the aid of the gods, killing him. Hector's body is dragged in the dust, and finally buried. The beautiful Helen is reclaimed by her husband Menelaus and taken back to Sparta.

The *Odyssey* relates the amazing adventures of Odysseus (Ulysses), who was one of the Greek chieftains fighting before Troy in the *Iliad.* Odysseus is the king of Ithaca, and Homer describes his roundabout and dallying return home after the fall of Troy. He kills the Cyclops, a one-eyed giant named Polyphemus, after blinding him. He goes to Ogygia, the island home of a beautiful sea nymph, Calypso, and is detained by her charms seven years. Led by the lovely princess Nausicaä, he goes to the court of her father, King Alcinous, and tells many a tale, including an account of his visit to the enchantress Circe, who changes men into beasts, but Odysseus, aided by a god, had escaped her wiles and freed some of his companions from her spell. He also tells of his visit to the Lotophagi, or Lotus-Eaters, who from chewing lotus plants have wonderful dreams and live in indolence and pleasure. He relates the terrors of Scylla and Charybdis, two monsters who lie in wait for vessels. He describes the Sirens, beautiful maidens who seek to lure mariners on dangerous rocks, and how he plugged his ears (so as not to hear their singing) and steered his ship past them in safety. Returning finally to Ithaca, Odysseus finds his faithful wife, Penelope, beset by many suitors: these wooers he slays, with the aid of his son, Telemachus.

A little later than Homer lived Hesiod (about 776 B.C.), author of *Theogony* and his main poetical work, *Works and Days*.

THE LYRIC POETS

The names of nine Greek lyric poets are known; fragments of the work of seven of them have survived. Sappho, who probably lived about 600 B.C., was the first of the Greek lyric poets. She sang, on the island of Lesbos, of love among women, whence "Lesbian love." Only a few fragments of her work have survived. The odes of Pindar, who lived from 522 to about 448 B.C., are next most famous among the Greek lyrics; his style is noted for its splendor.

DRAMA

Athenian genius flowered into an apex of literary expression, especially in drama, between 480 and 300 B.C. Greek drama was founded by Thespis, whence comes the familiar adjective "Thespian."

Aeschylus (525–456 B.C.) probably created the form of classical tragedy. He initiated the use of two actors (before him there had been only one), who—with the aid of the chorus—performed all the parts. The Greek dramas were written in poetry, the actors wore masks, and the chorus, individually performing the roles of anonymous townspeople, as a unit commented on the action and events. This form of presentation, along with the fact that the plots were well known and belonged to the racial mythology, gave the tragedies a universal, often a religious, quality. The theme of all Greek tragedy is man's conflict with fate and with the weakness or evil within himself. Aeschylus' most famous plays are *Agamemnon,* the *Choephoroe,* and the *Eumenides,* a related trilogy about the murder of a king, vengeance by his son involving matricide, and the expiation by him of that sin; and *Prometheus Bound,* which deals with the legend of Prometheus, a Titan, who stole fire from Olympus and was condemned by Zeus to eternal torment. This play allegorizes a conflict between supreme knowledge (and goodness) and supreme power; it hints at very profound theological themes, but as the two following plays of the Prometheus trilogy are lost, we can only guess at the resolution.

Sophocles (about 496–406 B.C.) was the second and perhaps the greatest of Greek tragic poets. Only seven of his plays have survived in their complete form. Best known is *Oedipus the King,* which tells the tragedy of Oedipus, who unwittingly married his mother, committing the dread crime of incest. The king's fate is further related in *Oedipus at Colonus*. Oedipus' daughter is the central character of *Antigone,* a drama of a young woman's individual righteousness and nobility according to the Greek ideal. Sophocles' *Electra,* another magnificent drama, tells the tragic story of Agamemnon. Sophocles added a third actor to the dramatic performance and wrote each play as an independent unit, thus breaking away from the traditional related trilogy.

Euripides (480–406 B.C.) was the third of the great tragic poets, although he often combined tragedy and comedy in a way that is characteristic of later European playwrights. Eighteen of his plays have come down to us. Among them are *Medea,* the tragedy dealing with the treacherous actions of the enchantress-wife of Jason; *Iphigenia in Aulis* and *Iphigenia in Taurus,* the story of the maiden who was saved from an unwilling sacrifice; *The Bacchae,* dealing with the cult of Dionysus (Bacchus), and *Alcestis,* a tragicomedy about a woman who sacrifices her life for an egotistical husband and is rescued from the underworld by Hercules and reunited with her husband. *The Trojan Women* is a powerful commentary on the tragedy of war and a plea for peace.

Aristophanes, who lived from 450 to about 380 B.C., was a comic playwright. He used comedy to satirize the life of his day. Eleven of his masterly dramas have survived. In *The Clouds* the philosophers of the day are caricatured, chief among them Socrates. *The Birds* ridicules, through an allegory in which birds represent human beings, the belligerent ambition of the Athenians to proceed against Syracuse. *The Frogs* finds fun in a search in the underworld for a poet whom Athens needs, the three famous tragic poets having died.

HISTORY

Herodotus (about 484 to about 425 B.C.) is called the "Father of History." He traveled far and wide in the world of his day, observing and recording what he saw. His history, written vividly, though not always accurately, deals with the early story of Greece and the later Persian wars.

Thucydides (about 471 to about 400 B.C.) wrote a fine history of the Peloponnesian War in Greece. He was a participant in the war and describes it from the point of view of an eyewitness.

Xenophon (about 430 to about 357 B.C.) in his *Anabasis* tells of the retreat of the Ten Thousand from Persia, a thrilling military narrative. His *Memorabilia* gives an intimate picture of the philosopher Socrates, whom he knew in his youth.

Demosthenes (about 384 to 322 B.C.) was an orator. His tongue was as persuasive as many a sword. Famous indeed are his *Philippics,* stirring speeches against King Philip of Macedon, denouncing him to the Athenians and calling upon the Greeks (in vain) to oppose Philip's conquest of their country.

PHILOSOPHY

Plato (about 429–347 B.C.) is the best known of the world's philosophers; he has had a profound influence on all Western philosophy. His famous *Dialogues,* recounting the question-and-answer discourses of Socrates, have given us the now familiar form of the "Socratic dialogue." Among the best known of the dialogues are the *Crito,* the *Phaedro,* the *Apology,* and the *Symposium.* In the *Republic,* Plato gives his conception of an ideal state.

Aristotle (384–322 B.C.) was the pupil of Plato. His influence has been greater in many ways. During the Middle Ages his name was dominant. His studies in logic and his groundwork in the sciences were fundamental. Also notable among his writings are the *Politics* and the *Nicomachean Ethics;* his short treatise on *Poetics* is a basic work of literary criticism.

LATER WRITERS

Epicurus (about 342–270 B.C.) was a philosopher who stressed pleasure as the supreme good—pleasure obtained by counteracting animal desires. Epictetus (about 60 to about 120 A.D.) was a Greek slave known by his Latin pseudonym. The *Moral Discourses* give his philosophy of Stoicism, which is opposed to Epicureanism. The discourses were set down by one of his pupils, though they bear the name of the master.

Plutarch (46–120 A.D.), though he lived in Rome and came after the great period of Greek literature, was a Greek and wrote in Greek. "Plutarch's Lives," as his biographical work is usually designated, recounts the lives of famous men—23 Greeks and 23 Romans. Shakespeare used Plutarch as the source of some of his historical plays.

In the tenth and, later, in the fourteenth centuries, a great collection of Greek poetry was made at Constantinople; this is known as the *Greek Anthology.* The selections run from 700 B.C. to about 1000 A.D., some 4,000 items in all, including poems, epitaphs and epigrams; the original epigram was a short verse with a witty or satirical turn to it.

ROMAN LITERATURE

Roman classics were written in Latin, a language which, though it is now dead, had a deep influence on western European tongues—especially on Italian, French, Spanish, Portuguese, and Rumanian (which are called the *Romance* languages, because of this Roman influence), and also on English. The study of Latin, both as literature and as a language, therefore, is an excellent basis for a full understanding of these modern languages. Roman literature was more or less influenced by Greek culture, after Rome had come into contact with Greece. Although the sway of the Roman Empire was extended over Greece, the native character of Greek thought and writing was never lost—it was merely absorbed. Part of the great heritage of ancient Greece has been passed on to us through the Romans.

DRAMA

Plautus (about 254 to 184 B.C.) was an imitator of Menander, a later Greek writer of comedies, who was less gifted than Aristophanes, being primarily interested in plot and situation. Shakespeare's *Comedy of Errors* is a re-creation of *The Menaechmi,* one of the comedies of Plautus. Best known of the twenty plays that have come down to us are probably *The Captives* and *Trinummus.*

Terence (about 190 to 159 B.C.), another writer of comedies, also influenced by Menander, died young, but left six plays to posterity, best known of which is the *Adelphi* ("The Brothers").

Seneca, noted as a prose writer, wrote several tragedies, mostly dealing with Greek legends.

POETRY

Lucretius (96–55 B.C.) was a philosopher as well as a poet. His *De Rerum Natura* ("The Nature of Things") is a fascinating philosophical argument in verse. It has been remarked that "Lucretius has drunk deeper of the scientific spirit than any other poet of ancient or modern times except Goethe."

Catullus (about 87 to about 54 B.C.) was described as the "tenderest of Roman poets" by Lord Tennyson. He wrote many appealing love lyrics.

Virgil (70–19 B.C.), or Vergil, was a poet of the Augustan Age of Roman literature. He was acclaimed as the Roman Homer when he wrote the legendary epic of Aeneas, called the *Aeneid*. Preceded by the *Eclogues* and the *Georgics,* collections of shorter poems, the *Aeneid* is the best known of Virgil's works. It recounts the adventures of Aeneas, who rescues his father from the burning walls of fallen Troy (at the close of the *Iliad*) and sets out to fulfill his destiny, which is to lead the Trojans to Italy, where they are to found Rome. He voyages for seven years, visiting Thrace, Crete, Epirus, and Carthage. In Carthage he dallies with Queen Dido, telling her all that has happened, including the story of the Wooden Horse with which the Greeks fooled the Trojans and thereby gained entrance to the doomed city. At last he resigns himself to his destiny and leaves the fair Dido, who, broken-hearted, kills herself.

Horace (65–8 B.C.) addressed many of his odes to his benefactor, Maecenas, a great patron of Roman letters. The *Odes* of Horace are among the most magnificent heritages of Roman literature.

Ovid (43 B.C. to 17 A.D.) wrote elegiac poetry. Elegiac verse, aside from its peculiar meter, is distinguished by its plaintive tone, its mournfulness. The most famous work, however, is the *Metamorphoses,* which relate in verse the early Roman myths.

Juvenal (about 60 to 140 A.D.) was a satirical poet who castigated the decadent society of his time.

PROSE

Julius Caesar (100–44 B.C.), famous as a general and statesman, gave to Latin literature his "Commentaries on the Gallic War," which, with Cicero and Virgil, is generally used as a text in the study of Latin.

Marcus Tullius Cicero (106–43 B.C.) was a great orator. Among his orations which are most widely known are especially his tirades against Catiline, a political conspirator. Cicero's letters are also notable.

Livy (59 B.C. to 17 A.D.) was a Roman historian. He wrote a comprehensive history of Rome in 142 books, from the time of Aeneas to 9 B.C. Only 35 of these books have survived; like so much Greek and Latin literature, the manuscripts of the others were lost or destroyed before later readers could take pains to preserve them. We know of these lost books because of references to them in the writings of other authors.

Seneca (about 4 B.C. to 65 A.D.) wrote his *Moral Discourses.* Martial (43–104 A.D.) wrote brief poetic epigrams, of which he left several hundred, in 14 books. Tacitus (55–117 A.D.) wrote *Germania,* a study of the Teutonic tribes to the north, and other histories.

Apuleius (born about 114 A.D.) left the classic *The Golden Ass,* an early form of a novel, containing a famous telling of the legend of Cupid and Psyche, a translation of which Walter Pater included in his classic, *Marius the Epicurian.*

Marcus Aurelius Antoninus (121–180 A.D.), Roman emperor, is known for his *Meditations,* sometimes called his "Golden Sayings," brief and pithy observations on life and morals.

Aesop's Fables were credited to Aesop, who was a Greek slave living from about 620 to 560 B.C., but he did not write his own tales. They were written down much later by Latin writers, in the third century A.D. or thereabouts. Some authorities dispute the existence of Aesop. But the fables remain, and are generally known by his name. They deal with animals who talk and act like human beings; incidents of the fox and the grapes, the tortoise and the hare, have entertained readers to this day and are remembered with their appended morals.

Later writers in Latin were mostly theologians, known as the church fathers, among them St. Augustine (354–430 A.D.), who penned his *Confessions,* an intimate biography of religious conversion and faith.

St. Thomas Aquinas (around 1225–1274), the most famous scholastic and Catholic theologian, was greatly influenced by Aristotle.

ITALIAN LITERATURE

During the interval between the fall of Rome and the later Middle Ages is the period known as the Dark Ages, in which cultural activities were at a low ebb and the literature of Europe received no outstanding additions. In the later Middle Ages the creative spark was struck again, to revive to new life with the Renaissance (the revival of learning).

DANTE

Dante is one of the greatest figures in the world's literature. Dante Alighieri was born in Florence in 1265 A.D. and died in 1321. He fell in love in his youth with Beatrice, whom he never was able to woo in person, but whom he kept in his memory, even after her death at the age of 24. He married two years later, but, owing to political strife, he was banished from Florence in 1302 and never returned to that city. He wandered alone the remaining years of his life, and died and was buried in Ravenna, where his tomb, a splendid monument, still stands.

Dante's name is associated almost exclusively with his great masterpiece, *The Divine Comedy*—a comedy because it ends happily, divine because of its supernatural theme. It tells of a wonderful journey made by Dante (in imagination), starting on the night before Good Friday in the year 1300, through the Inferno (Hell), Purgatory, and Paradise (Heaven). The journey takes five days.

Stupendous indeed is Dante's conception of Hell—an inverted cone, with its apex at the center of the earth, and Lucifer, the fallen angel, pinioned there. Dante makes his Hell a very real place, full of suffering so vivid that great pity is evoked for its victims. The variety of punishment presented is a feat of the author's imagination. Mounting to Purgatory, which is placed in the southern hemisphere of the earth, one sees various temporary forms of punishment. Virgil, author of the *Aeneid,* is Dante's guide through Hell and Purgatory. Beatrice is his guide to Paradise, and we are told of the heavens revolving around the earth: the Moon, Mercury, Venus, the Sun, Mars, Jupiter, Saturn, the Fixed Stars, and the Crystalline Heaven. Beyond all is the immovable Empyrean, the Heaven of Pure Light, where is the residence of God, the Eternal One, who moves the Universe. In Paradise joy and love prevail.

Through all of Dante runs the spirit of the Middle Ages, extravagant fancies, somber brooding, and faith in the supernatural. The intensity of Dante's vision, the fascination of his characterizations, and above all the superb beauty of the poetry make *The Divine Comedy* one of the world's masterpieces.

THE RENAISSANCE

Dante represents in Italian literature a transition from the late Middle Ages to the Renaissance. The period witnessed the invention of printing, the revival of learning, and the birth of humanism; people turned again to the classics of the past and to new interest in human life for its own sake.

Petrarch (1304–1374) was the first and perhaps the most important of the Humanists, as the scholars were called who helped to bring the classics of antiquity back into popular favor during the Renaissance. He wrote mostly in Latin: letters, literary criticism, history, biography. His *Canzoniere* were written in Italian; they were love verses addressed to Laura (already married to someone else), who did not return Petrarch's deep love.

Giovanni Boccaccio (1313–1375), called the "Father of Italian Prose," was a great teller of tales. His *Decameron* is world famous. It is a collection of 100 tales, told by ten people (seven men and three women), to pass the time while they were isolated to escape the plague then raging in Florence (in the year 1348). The tales are written with great vigor and gusto and make capital of the weaknesses of society in Boccaccio's day. Some of the stories are considered immoral; all are entertaining. Boccaccio in this work foreshadowed the development of the modern short story.

During the century and a half following the death of Boccaccio, Italy had a great surge of creative genius in fields other than literature, especially in sculpture and painting. Michelangelo (1475–1564) also contributed his sonnets to literature. Ariosto (1474–1533) was the great poet of the period. His *Orlando Furioso (Mad Roland)* is a famous metrical romance, telling of the wars of the Saracens and Charlemagne, concluding with the overthrow and death of the Saracen leader. The same character, Roland, appears in all the romances of Charlemagne's exploits, notably in the "Song of Roland" and many French romances. Torquato Tasso (1544–1595) won immortality with his *Jerusalem Delivered,* a long heroic poem, telling of the liberation of Jerusalem by Godfrey of Bouillon in the Crusade of the eleventh century. Machiavelli (1469–1527) was a statesman and political writer. *The Prince* is his outstanding work. It gives worldly counsel to statesmen on the most advantageous measures for maintaining absolute government; the adjective "Machiavellian" means, even today, pertaining to the doctrine "that any means, however lawless or unscrupulous, may be justifiably employed by a ruler in order to establish and maintain a strong central government." Vasari (1511–1574), a painter and architect, gave the world his *Lives of the Painters,* important biographies of the artistic geniuses of Italy. Benvenuto Cellini (1500–1571), a sculptor of lasting fame, wrote one of the world's frankest autobiographies, telling boastfully of his art, his quarrels, his love affairs.

LATER WRITERS

The Renaissance saw Italian literature reach its peak. Only a few Italian authors since that day have achieved world-wide renown.

Goldoni (1707–1793), called the "Italian Molière," wrote many comedies and a frank series of memoirs. Alfieri (1749–1803) was a tragic poet, but also the author of comedies and an autobiography. Manzoni (1785–1873) was a novelist, the best known of his works being *I Promessi Sposi (The Betrothed),* often referred to among the great novels of the world. Giacomo Leopardi (1798–1837) wrote many lyric poems. Best known, perhaps, because of his vivid realism and amorous exploits, is Casanova de Seingalt (1725–1798), an adventurer in every sense of the word, who left us his *Memoirs* in several volumes. Giuseppe Mazzini (1805–1872) brings us down to modern times. He wrote several political works and was an important figure in Italy's history.

Modern Italian writers include, among the novelists, Giovanni Verga (1840–1922) and Ignazio Silone (born 1900). Italo Svevo (1864–1928) wrote psychological novels, including *Zeno's Conscience.* Giovanni Papini (1881–1956) wrote fiction and verse, but was known principally as a philosopher. Alberto Moravia (born 1907) is a novelist and short-story writer who has been compared to the great Chekhov.

Among the poets were Giosuè Carducci (1835–1907), winner of the Nobel prize for literature in 1906; and Gabriele D'Annunzio (1863–1938), a striking romantic both in his writings and in his life.

Benedetto Croce (1866–1952) was an outstanding philosopher and critic, particularly a philosopher of history. Guglielmo Ferrero (1871–1942) was a prominent historian.

The great modern Italian playwright was Luigi Pirandello (1867–1936), the author of such exceptional plays as *Six Characters in Search of an Author, Right You Are If You Think You Are, As You Desire Me,* and many brilliant one-act plays.

SPANISH LITERATURE

The literature of Spain has ebbed and flowed, at times occupying a leading place in the literature of the world, at other times producing works of little interest to the world at large.

THE EARLY PERIOD

The Cid is the Spanish national epic. It recounts the exploits of the hero, Ruy Diaz de Bivar, an eleventh-century champion of Christianity and Spanish royalty. Historically, the Cid was pretty much of a rogue. Several other chronicles tell of him, giving him an undeserved halo or two and glorifying him in the manner of heroic legend. *The Cid* was written in the twelfth century; its author is unknown. What we have is only a fragment. Many of the episodes concerning the Cid are contained in a wonderful group of ballads, often called *The Cid Ballads.*

Many Spanish ballads accumulated during the centuries, lengthy collections of them having been compiled in the sixteenth and seventeenth centuries. These tell in song many of the old legends of the country and have been many times translated into English.

Famous for its roguish plot is *Lazarillo de Tormes,* which appeared in 1553; its author is unknown. The plot is taken up with the adventures and deeds of Lazarillo, who is various kinds of a rascal. This is the first of the picaresque novels, so called because the central character, or "hero," is some sort of *picaro,* or rogue.

Greatest and most popular Spanish work throughout the world is the *Don Quixote* of Miguel de Cervantes Saavedra (1547–1616), who was living and writing while Shakespeare was penning his masterpieces in Elizabethan England. Lord Macaulay called *Don Quixote* "the best novel in the world beyond all comparison" and this view is shared by many in every generation. Its central figure is Don Quixote, a tall, ungainly knight-errant, self-appointed to roam the land correcting wrongs. He is accompanied by his squire, Sancho Panza, who, with down-to-earth realism, sees through his master's uncontrolled tendency toward idealization. Don Quixote reads too many books of romantic chivalry and becomes obsessed with the desire to go forth and do likewise—which gives the book its plot, and provides both humor and pathos. The episode in which the ludicrous knight charges the windmills, believing them to be monsters, is well known. Don Quixote is mad—in only one particular; otherwise, he is lovable and often pathetic.

Spanish drama began with Lope de Vega (1562–1635). He wrote some 1,800 plays, of which about 300 have survived. He was versatile and prolific almost beyond belief, and no single play stands out as his masterpiece. Calderón de la Barca (1600–1681) wrote several plays, putting more poetry in them than Lope de Vega did in his; he also wrote lyric poetry. Most famous of Calderón's plays is *La Vida Es Sueño* (*Life Is a Dream*). His *Magico Prodigioso* is known to us in Shelley's translation. Edward FitzGerald, of *Omar Khayyam* fame, translated several of the other plays.

The poet Fray Luis de León (1527–1591) wrote notable religious poems and mystical writings; he was professor of theology at the University of Salamanca.

LATER WRITERS

There were a number of important Spanish novelists in the latter part of the nineteenth century. Don Pedro Antonio de Alarcón (1833–1891) contributed a notable picaresque novel, *El Sombrero des Tres Picos* (*The Three-Cornered Hat*). Juan Valera (1824–1905) wrote *Pepita Jimenez,* a novel of a priest's temptation. José Maria de Pereda (1833–1906) gave us *Pedro Sanchez.* Other writers are: Benito Pérez Galdós (1843–1920), author of *Doña Perfecta;* Armando Palacio Valdés; Emilia Pardo Bazán; and Fernan Caballero (1796–1877; real name Cecilia Bohl von Faber), whose best-known book is *La Gaviota* (*The Sea Gull*). More recent are Vicente Blasco Ibáñez (1867–1928), author of the popular novel *The Four Horsemen of the Apocalypse,* dealing with the First World War, and Pío Baroja (1872–1956), among whose powerful books is *The Tree of Knowledge.*

Spanish drama came into prominence again with José Echegaray (1833–1916), winner of the Nobel prize for literature in 1904, whose *El Gran Galeoto* has a place among important modern European plays. Most important of recent Spanish dramatists is Jacinto Benavente (1866–1954), also a Nobel prize winner. Among his plays are *The Bonds of Interest, The Passion Flower, Saturday Night,* and *The Prince Who Learned Everything from Books.* Martínez Sierra (1881–1947) is well known for his *Cradle Song.*

The great modern Spanish poet and playwright is Frederico García Lorca (1899–1936), whose plays recapture the simplicity and force of classical tragedy. He studied the traditions, literature, and myths of the Spanish people, particularly the Andalusian Gypsies, catching their gaiety and their somber melancholy, which combine in a deep, reverent, almost religious love of life. He was a truly national poet. Translations of his poetry have been universally admired.

Among modern Spanish philosophic writers, especially important are: Miguel de Unamuno (1864–1936), one of whose characteristic works is *The Tragic Sense of Life,* and José Gasset y Ortega (1883–1955), author of *The Revolt of the Masses.*

Luis de Camoëns (1524–1579) wrote the *Lusiad,* the national epic of Portugal; it takes its name from Lusitania, the Roman name of the region almost identical with modern Portugal. This is the only Portuguese work to have received world renown.

FRENCH LITERATURE

THE BEGINNINGS

Before France was conquered by the Romans under Julius Caesar (58–50 B.C.), it was populated by barbarous tribes. After the dominance of the Roman Empire, the Franks, a Teutonic people, overran the land and gradually developed a modified form of Latin which became modern French.

The *Chanson de Roland* (*Song of Roland*) is built around the epic deeds of Charlemagne and his hosts. In particular, it tells of Roland, a nephew of the emperor, and his bloody defense of Christianity against the Saracens. The battle scenes are gory, but the combatants are heroic. This epic was composed toward the end of the eleventh century.

About the same time, there grew up a body of French versions of the legends of King Arthur and his knights, borrowed from the Celts and fused with French lore. The period was also full of French versions of the romances of antiquity. Along with these were many lyric poems and ballads, singing of love and brave deeds—but particularly of love. The singers of southern France (Provence) were called troubadours. Allegorical poems were also in vogue, the best known of these being *The Romance of the Rose.* The *fabliau,* or short verse tale, typified another large group. Among the beast epics or animal fables in verse was the famous *Romance of Reynard.*

THE RENAISSANCE

The Renaissance marked a new zest for life and literature in France. Individual effort became strong and important. François Villon (born 1431, died sometime after 1463) was the first important French writer of the Renaissance. He was a rollicking poet, but also a vagabond, thief, and rogue. He wrote many ballades and rondeaux. His works are marked by gaiety, tenderness, and a concern with death.

François Rabelais (1495–1553) is perhaps the greatest figure of the period. His *Gargantua* and *Pantagruel,* named for their chief characters, are huge, sprawling narratives, filled with animal hilarity; his work gave us the adjective "gargantuan." Buffoonery, jocularity, and comic vulgarity are mixed well into the two massive yarns to shock the sensibilities of the timid and to delight the risibilities of the hearty. Hence the adjective "Rabelaisian."

Michel de Montaigne (1533–1592) wrote many short essays, picturing an enlightened amusement at and a skeptical tolerance of life that are very modern in tone.

The *Heptameron* of Margaret, Queen of Navarre (1492–1549), is a collection of tales patterned somewhat after Boccaccio's *Decameron.*

THE SEVENTEENTH CENTURY

The seventeenth century is called *le grand siècle* ("the great age"), with King Louis XIV and Cardinals Richelieu and Mazarin; the day of the palaces of Versailles and the Louvre, with France leading Europe, and a new classicism in vogue.

Pierre Corneille (1606–1684) is famous for his great tragedies, of which the best known are *The Cid,* based on the Spanish epic, and *Polyeucte,* a tragedy of Christian martyrdom. His comedies are less known, except for *Le Menteur* (*The Liar*).

Jean Racine (1639–1699), like Corneille, is a strict classicist. He wrote almost exclusively tragedies, in which the main character is confronted with a conflict between his passion and his honor. His psychology is more complicated and realistic than that of Corneille. Typical plays of Racine are *Andromaque* and *Phèdre;* both are based on classical Greek plays. To a degree, Racine may be said to hold somewhat the place in French literature that Shakespeare does in English literature. However, he lacks the richness, variety, boldness, and especially the humor of Shakespeare. It is interesting to note that until modern times the French considered Shakespeare's drama to be crude and unclassical.

Molière (1622–1673), one of the world's greatest masters of comedy, stands head and shoulders above all other dramatists and writers of the period. Best known among his splendid comedies are *Le Misanthrope;* *Les Précieuses Ridicules,* a satire on society women; *Tartuffe,* a severe indictment of religious hypocrisy; and *Le Bourgeois Gentilhomme (The Middle-Class Gentleman).*

Jean de la Fontaine (1621–1695) wrote his *Fables,* delightful short tales or fables, somewhat in the Aesop manner.

Blaise Pascal's (1623–1662) *Pensées (Thoughts)* are still widely read and his influence has been extremely important. Pascal, whose early life was that of a libertine, became an outstanding scientist and mathematician, and later turned to writing philosophy. He was one of the earliest thinkers to argue the truth of Christianity from psychological and even mathematical grounds, rather than purely Scripture and revelation. His famous "bet," in which he compares mathematically the odds of the unbeliever's "gamble" for the *finite* pleasures of life against those of the faithful believer who "risks" these dubious and temporary pleasures for the rewards of *infinity,* is typical of his intellect. It reminds us somewhat of the use of wit and ingenious logic in the religious "metaphysical poets" of England in the same period. The seventeenth century, as a meeting point between the firm traditions of the past and the flood of new learning in science and mathematics, was a particularly rich period of culture.

The Moral Maxims of the Duc de la Rochefoucauld (1613–1680) are concise and witty.

THE EIGHTEENTH CENTURY

The *Gil Blas* of René le Sage (1668–1747) is an outstanding picaresque novel of the eighteenth century. Engaged in many occupations, the hero, Gil Blas, a not altogether admirable Spaniard, tells his life story, with egotistic emphasis on his adventures. The Abbé Prévost (1697–1763) left to the world the remarkable love romance of *Manon Lescaut,* a penetrating study of the psychology of a woman's heart. Pierre Augustin Caron (1732–1799), known by his pseudonym, Beaumarchais, wrote several comedies, among them *The Barber of Seville* and *The Marriage of Figaro,* both of which make fun of the nobility.

François Marie Arouet (1694–1778), always known by his pseudonym, Voltaire, was a leader in the radical philosophic movement in France. Of his romances and skeptical writings, probably the most popular is *Candide,* a satire on the notion that this is the best of all possible worlds. *Zadig* is quite as delightful, in a similar vein. Voltaire attacked dogma and church ritual vigorously.

Baron de Montesquieu (1689–1755) was a French jurist and philosopher. His outstanding work is *L'Esprit des Lois* (*The Spirit of the Laws*). Prominent among those who hastened the French Revolution was Denis Diderot (1713–1784), one of the group known as the Encyclopedists, who wrote the great French Encyclopedia: *Encyclopédie ou Diction-naire raisonné des Sciences, des Arts, et des Métiers* (1751–1772), with a supplement and index in 1776–1780. This vast compendium is a monument of the scholarship of the time; its general tone is rationalistic.

Jean Jacques Rousseau (1712–1778) forecast the later Romantic movement. His autobiographical (though probably not always truthful) *Confessions* is a strange, introspective classic. His *Le Contrat Social* (*The Social Contract*) is a remarkable contribution to political theory. Rousseau was a strong advocate of democracy.

François René de Chateaubriand (1768–1848) bridges the gap into the following Romantic period. He was a dreamer and mystic. Worthy of note is his *Mémoires d'Outre-Tombe* (*Memoirs from Beyond the Tomb*). His two romantic novels, *Atala* and *René,* are stories in which American Indians are leading characters; and it is from these that the phrase "noble savage" comes.

THE ROMANTICISTS

The French Revolution at the end of the eighteenth century marked a sharp division between the earlier classicism and the later romanticism of the nineteenth century. There was a reaction from the formality of classic tradition, with a new emphasis on imagination and sentiment.

Victor Hugo (1802–1885) was the literary giant of the period. He wrote a great deal of lyric poetry. Four of his novels stand out: *Notre-Dame de Paris* (*The Hunchback of Notre Dame*), a backward glance at medieval life, centered around the cathedral of Notre Dame in Paris; *Les Misérables,* telling of the misfortunes of Jean Valjean and his adopted daughter Cosette; *Travailleurs de la Mer* (*Toilers of the Sea*); and *Quatre-Vingt-Treize* (*Ninety-three*). Of his plays, *Hernani* and *Le Roi s'Amuse* (*The King Enjoys Himself*) are the most widely read today.

Hugo was a leader of the Romantic movement, which included many notable writers. Among them was Alfred de Musset (1810–1857), poet and dramatist. Of his plays, *On ne Badine pas avec l'Amour,* an ironic and sensitive comedy reflecting the author's love affair with George Sand, is notable. Théophile Gautier (1811–1872) is well known for his poetry and for his short stories, of which "The Mummy's Foot" is representative. Gautier's novel *Mademoiselle de Maupin* contains many poetic descriptions of the beauty of nature and of passionate love. His poetry, typified by delicateness and perfection of detail and an effort to render images plastic and visible to the reader, initiated the "art for art's sake" movement.

Alexandre Dumas, the elder, (1802–1870) is a towering figure who wrote prodigiously. The romantic fascination of his novels still holds thousands of readers enthralled, especially *The Three Musketeers,* with D'Artagnan, the scintillating swordsman, and the one-for-all and all-for-one trio, Aramis, Athos, and Porthos; and, of course, *The Count of Monte Cristo,* a historical adventure story. The character of D'Artagnan also figures in *Vingt ans après* (*Twenty Years After*) and *Le Vicomte de Bragelonne.*

Honoré de Balzac (1799–1850), more realist than romanticist, was perhaps the greatest French novelist. Almost a hundred novels and tales came from his pen, comprising the series which he called *The Human Comedy.* This series presents in great detail the society of the day, picturing realistically persons from all classes and professions. The major novels in this series are: *Le Père Goriot, Cousine Bette, Eugénie Grandet,* and *La Peau de Chagrin* (*The Wild Ass's Skin*).

George Sand is the pseudonym of Lucile Aurore Dupin (1804–1876), who won enviable fame with novels presenting the woman's side of the right to love. Prosper Mérimée (1803–1870) contributed to French literature several short stories and short novels, including *Carmen.* The dramatists of the period are little read today; the most prominent names are Eugène Scribe (1791–1861), Alexandre Dumas, the younger, (1824–1895), and Victorien Sardou (1831–1908), who wrote for the great actress, Sarah Bernhardt.

Charles Baudelaire (1821–1867), poet, was not, properly speaking, of the Romantic school. His poetry is second, if to any, only to that of Victor Hugo. His *Les Fleurs du Mal* (*The Flowers of Evil*) is unique. Baudelaire led the group called the Parnassians, who were prominent in the Second Empire (1852–1870); they preached art for art's sake, and stressed form rather than content. Baudelaire took the first bold departure from the romantic ideals, causing considerable scandal and initiating a new trend in modern poetry. He chose to discover beauty and meaning in aspects of life and objects which heretofore were considered unfit not only for verse but even discussion. His "La Charogne" ("The Corpse") is a typical poem of *The Flowers of Evil;* it follows a brief preface in which the poet addresses his reader as a brother, a similar person, and a hypocrite. The volume stresses equally humanity's striving for a lost spiritual paradise and its deep lust for inebriation of the senses, for new beauty wherever it may be found. Baudelaire discovered new possibilities in language, particularly the use of words and images as symbols of ideas too elusive to be described.

An unusual genius took the limelight just following Baudelaire and has influenced a majority of modern poets, both French and American. He was Arthur Rimbaud (1854–1891), who wrote a number of poems and the celebrated *Une Saison en Enfer* (*A Season in Hell*) before he was 19; whereupon he renounced literature, went to Africa to take up odd, obscure, and disreputable businesses, and returned to France to die of innumerable diseases at the age of 37. His poetry broke with all classical and romantic tradition, which he despised. It had these characteristics which have passed into so much modern literature: revolt against all social and literary convention; a mystic concept of the poet as prophet; an effort to distort language in order to achieve new and unconventional meaning; the use of apparently disconnected words to invoke (as in old magical formulae) a mystic, unearthly vision; harsh and disharmonious sound and style to shock the reader into a sharper perception of the meaning; and a structure of meaning that lacks logical sequence but can be understood symbolically.

Rimbaud's attempt was to re-create paradise by an intense revolt and destruction of all that is human; when he failed, he gave up literature.

A close associate, alternately friend and bitter enemy of Rimbaud, was Paul Verlaine (1844–1896). In his early poetry he sought the same goals as Rimbaud, with whom he debauched on absinthe; but he later turned his technique to writing beautiful and profound religious poetry.

The poets of the post-Romantic period are usually referred to as the "Symbolists." One of the most interesting and characteristic of this group was Stéphane Mallarmé (1842–1898). His poetry is at best beautiful, deep, intellectual, and technically perfect. At times, however, it is evocative but meaninglessly obscure. Mallarmé was the author of "L'Après-midi d'un Faune" ("The Afternoon of a Faun"), which became the motif of Debussy's famous orchestral work.

THE REALISTS

Opposed to the romanticists were the realists, or naturalists, who strove to hold the mirror up to Nature and present her unsoftened and unadorned by imagination and sentiment. They were often harsh, and, at times, noticeably coarse, but their work has a vitality that the romanticists lacked.

Gustave Flaubert (1821–1880), sometimes acclaimed one of the greatest novelists in world's literature, was a realist when he wrote *Madame Bovary,* an almost surgical probing of a woman's character and her life in a small French village as the wife of an unimaginative doctor.

Flaubert was something of both romanticist and realist when he wrote *Salammbô,* a superb historical novel of ancient Carthage.

Alphonse Daudet (1840–1897) delves somewhat into the labyrinth of the mind, and just escapes being a true realist. His *Sapho* stands out among the world's imaginative conceptions of passionate women. Three of his novels deal ironically with the fanciful character, Tartarin of Tarascon, a boastful adventurer.

The naturalist in literature took a slight departure from the strict code of the realist; although he remained a realist, as distinguished from a romanticist, the naturalist placed a great deal of emphasis on character analysis, particularly in relation to environment. Émile Zola (1840–1902) is the chief exponent of this school. *L'Assommoir* deals with working people, depicting with forceful realism their sorrows and misfortunes. *Nana* is a vivid novel with a self-centered courtesan for its heroine. *Germinal* is a story of industrial strife.

Guy de Maupassant (1850–1893), who took Flaubert for his master, wrote few novels, achieving his greatest mastery in the short story. Of his short stories, there are two hundred or more, each brief, vivid, and with an almost epigrammatic quality; some of the most famous are "The Necklace," "The Piece of String," "The Coward," "Moonlight," and "Mademoiselle Fifi."

Pierre Loti is the pseudonym of Louis Marie Julien Viaud (1850–1923), who broke away from naturalistic conventions in his *Madame Chrysanthème,* a curiously appealing picture of Japanese life, and his powerful *Le Pêcheur d'Islande (The Iceland Fisherman).*

Charles Augustin Sainte-Beuve (1804–1869) is famous for his critical studies, which reveal his extraordinary gift for brief biography. Along with him may be named Hippolyte Taine (1828–1893), who wrote an excellent *History of English Literature.*

Eugène Sue (Marie Joseph), who was born in 1804 and died in 1857, was a popular novelist. Best known in English-speaking countries are his *Les Mystères de Paris (The Mysteries of Paris),* in ten volumes, and, quite as long, his *Le Juif Errant (The Wandering Jew),* both works strongly socialistic in tone.

MODERN WRITERS

Turning against the realists, naturalists, and Parnassians were the "symbolists," whose chief French representative, Mallarmé, we have already discussed. Edmond Rostand (1868–1918) represented this style in his dramas; his most famous play beyond a doubt is *Cyrano de Bergerac,* and next may be mentioned his *Chantecler.*

In contrast to Rostand is the completely realistic Eugène Brieux (1858–1932), with his *La Robe Rouge* (*The Red Robe*) and *Les Avariés* (*Damaged Goods*). The names of three novelists of this period should be mentioned: Paul Bourget, Maurice Barrès, and Marcel Prévost.

We now come to the powerful literary figure of Anatole France (1844–1924), whose real name was Jacques Thibault. His early *The Crime of Sylvester Bonnard* has been lastingly popular. *Penguin Island* satirizes humanity in the guise of a colony of penguins. *The Revolt of the Angels* reveals his somewhat cynical philosophy. Other outstanding works are *Thaïs, La Rôtisserie de la Reine Pédauque,* and *The Red Lily*. He won the Nobel prize for literature in 1921.

Romain Rolland (1866–1945), winner of the Nobel prize for literature in 1915, wrote *Jean-Christophe,* a novel of an extraordinary musician who is Beethoven-like in his passions.

Marcel Proust (1871–1922) is the author of a long novel called *The Remembrance of Things Past*. It is one of the most significant of modern works. Proust follows the stream-of-consciousness method in trying to recapture the essential meaning of his past, peopled with men and women of fashionable society. *Swann's Way,* the first section of this work, has a unity of its own and may be enjoyed apart from the complete work.

Charles Péguy (1873–1914) was known especially for his *Le Mystère de la Charité de Jeanne d'Arc,* a long melodious work in free verse. Péguy had a great admiration and feeling for the French peasantry. Guillaume Apollinaire (1880–1918) was the chief poet of the surrealists, a group who exalted the irrational mind and took their themes from unconscious thoughts and dreams. Henri Barbusse (1873–1935) won considerable fame with his war novel, *Under Fire*.

An extremely important dramatist and poet is Paul Claudel (born 1868), who is a direct literary descendant of the symbolists. His writing is religious, and he has tried to give new symbolic meaning to the theology of sacrifice, purification, redemption, and faith. His masterpiece is *L'Annonce Faite à Marie* (*The Tidings Brought to Mary*), a drama based on the medieval form of the miracle play.

Albert Schweitzer (born 1875), in Alsace, has won world-wide recognition for his humanitarian work (particularly for his hospital at Lambaréné in central Africa) and for his philosophic and theological interests. His views are recorded in his book *Out of My Life and Thought*. A phrase especially associated with Schweitzer is "reverence for life."

Jules Romains (born 1885) was the author of the many-volumed novel, *Men of Good Will,* which presents a broad panorama of the life of Frenchmen in Paris and in the First World War. Roger Martin du Gard (born 1881) was a Nobel prize winner, author of the novels *The Thibaults* and *Summer 1914,* which are studies of French society before the war. Louis Aragon (born 1895) achieved recognition in this period as a lyric poet and novelist.

Following the First World War a number of new, experimental writers achieved literary fame. André Gide (1869–1951) was author of the psychological novels *The Counterfeiters* and *Strait Is the Gate;* he also wrote *The Immoralist* and *Fruits of the Earth,* in which he preached an intellectual system of license, freedom from rationality and principle, and indulgence in bodily pleasure.

Antoine de St. Exupéry (1900–1944) wrote *Night Flight* and *Wind, Sand, and Stars,* in which he exalted the drama of the early one-man flights over the deserts and unexplored territories. He was also author of the classic children's tale, which adults read with deep enjoyment, called *The Little Prince.* St. Exupéry did not feel the need for developing a new intellectual scheme as so many of his contemporaries did.

Jean Giraudoux (1882–1944) is best known for his plays. His remarkable gift for satire and his ability to express deep, evocative themes with unusual grace and lightness have produced a number of outstanding works. Among them are *The Mad Woman of Chaillot, Ondine,* and *Tiger at the Gates.*

An unusual playwright and novelist was Jean Cocteau (born 1891), whose writings are often highly surrealistic. His fanciful intellect and very individualistic sense of humor contribute to the success of such well-known plays as *The Infernal Machine,* based on the Oedipus legend, and *The Typewriter.*

Jean Paul Sartre (born 1905) is the accredited leader of the French "existentialist" movement, which finds its roots in the philosophers Kierkegaard, Heidegger, and Jaspers. It postulates essentially a new freedom and a new responsibility of the individual to define himself personally by his chosen actions within the world. A man's actions are, according to this philosophy, his only definition, his only purpose, and his only reward. Roughly, then, truth is defined as *existence* rather than beliefs, ideals, or ideas. Sartre gave expression to his concepts in a number of philosophic plays, notably *La Chambre (No Exit)* and *Les Mains Sales (The Red Gloves),* and a treatise called *Being and Non-Being,* and his fascinating novel, *Nausea.*

Jean Anouilh (born 1910) shows a somewhat similar intellect in his plays, but he is less philosophical. His plays are far superior dramatically. Outstanding among them is *Antigone* (based on the play by Sophocles), a fascinating display of an individual's power to deny conventions, bad laws, and a corrupt happiness, and passively affirm truth and right for its own sake. Other plays by Anouilh include *Medea* and *Le Voyageur Sans Bagages* (*The Traveler without Luggage*).

Presenting an individual brand of existentialism is Albert Camus (born 1913), who stresses the absurdity of life when men try to see it as ordered and significant, and the necessity to appreciate it for its own sake. His best known works are *The Plague, The Stranger, The Myth of Sisyphus*, and *The Fall*.

The two best known Belgian writers wrote in French. Maurice Maeterlinck (1862–1949), a world literary figure, was a symbolist. His leading plays are *Pelléas and Mélisande*, which shows his almost metaphysical tendencies; *The Blue Bird*, a fantasy dealing with two children in their search for happiness; and *Monna Vanna*, with a more melodramatic plot. He won the Nobel prize for literature in 1911. Émile Verhaeren (1855–1916) is the greatest Belgian poet; he lived to give voice to the agony of Belgium desolated by the First World War.

GERMAN LITERATURE

THE BEGINNINGS

We pass now to Northern peoples and to the Teutonic languages, which include German, Scandinavian, and Dutch. The original Franks who settled in Gaul (France) were Teutonic, but they adopted the elements of the Latin language from the south, giving birth to modern French. The Teutons of Germany retained their guttural and sterner speech, which developed into High and Low German and many dialects, spoken today as German not only in Germany but also in Austria and Switzerland.

The early German epic was the *Nibelungenlied* (*Song of the Nibelungs*), the Nibelungs being children of the mist, a race of dwarfs in Teutonic mythology, who had gained control of the consecrated gold (the Rheingold) of the Rhine River. The *Nibelungenlied* tells the story of Siegfried, Brünhild, Kriemhild, and the royal house of Burgundy. Nibelungs were the original possessors of the ring worn by Siegfried. The story of this ring, fashioned by the dwarf Alberich from the Rheingold, forms the theme of Wagner's operatic tetralogy which is based on the Norse *Volsunga Saga* instead of the German epic; the gods of Northern myths are important characters in the Wagnerian dramas.

German literature of the later Middle Ages consists of numerous court epics, medieval romances (including versions of the King Arthur legends), the "love songs" of the minnesingers (twelfth to fourteenth centuries), the poetry and music of the meistersingers ("mastersingers" of the guilds, from 1300 to 1500), and folk songs of the people.

FROM THE RENAISSANCE TO THE EIGHTEENTH CENTURY

Both the Reformation, within the church, and the Renaissance, in the area of culture, influenced the birth of a modern tone in German literature. Martin Luther (1483–1546) led the Reformation, writing various tracts on Protestantism and translating the Bible anew. This translation established popular German as a literary language. Luther's hymns are also famous.

Since many writings of this period were in Latin, they are not truly German literature, although they were written by Germans. The holocaust of the Thirty Years' War (1618–1648) made the seventeenth century a desert so far as literary creation is concerned.

The eighteenth century was given vigor by Frederick the Great, who ruled from 1740 to 1786. Toward the end of the century, the Storm and Stress (*Sturm und Drang*) period was a kind of literary convulsion, strengthening nationalism and opposing foreign influence, especially French. Classicism came in at the close of the century, to be followed, as in other countries, by romanticism in the early nineteenth century.

Friedrich Gottlieb Klopstock (1724–1803) gave impetus to the new movement with his *Der Messias* (*The Messiah*), an epic poem. He owed much to John Milton's *Paradise Lost*. Christoph Martin Wieland (1733–1813) made early translations of Shakespeare into German; his *Oberon*, an original work, is his masterpiece. (The most notable translations of Shakespeare into German are, however, by August von Schlegel.)

Gotthold Ephraim Lessing (1729–1781) was an exponent of the rationalistic movement. His *Laokoön* is a masterly piece of literary and art criticism; of his plays, *Nathan the Wise,* a philosophical study, is the most famous.

Immanuel Kant (1724–1804) is of world importance in philosophy. His *Critique of Pure Reason* is speculative and thought-provoking, as are also his critiques of practical reason and of judgment. His work laid the foundation of modern metaphysics, and founded the tradition of modern idealism.

Other influential writers of the period were Johann Gottfried von Herder (1744–1803), author of essays and poems; Jean Paul Friedrich Richter, popularly known as "Jean Paul" (1763–1825), author of stories and novels; Friedrich von Hardenberg (1772–1801), romantic novelist who wrote under the name "Novalis"; and E. T. A. Hoffman (1776–1822), author of many weird tales.

GOETHE AND SCHILLER

Goethe and Schiller are among the world's literary immortals, and their names are often linked because they were not only contemporaries but were friends.

Friedrich von Schiller (1759–1805) became known to English readers through the writings of Thomas Carlyle interpreting German thoughts and culture. Carlyle said: "Schiller may or may not be called a man of genius by his critics; but his mind in either case will remain one of the most enviable which can fall to the share of a mortal." Schiller's *Die Räuber* (*The Robbers*) bowed him into his country's literature. *Don Carlos* was his first play in verse; it deals with the tragedy of Don Carlos of Spain. As a historian, he produced masterpieces in his *History of the Netherlands* and the *History of the Thirty Years' War*. Of his poems, especially noted is his *Das Lied von der Glocke* (*The Song of the Bell*). Among his later historical dramas, *Maria Stuart* (*Mary Stuart*), based on English history, and *Die Jungfrau von Orleans* (*The Maid of Orleans*), with Joan of Arc as the central figure, are the best. Of all his work, however, his *Wilhelm Tell* is the best known and the most widely read drama he ever wrote.

Johann Wolfgang von Goethe (1749–1832) is the most universal of German geniuses. Goethe's *Faust* may be placed alongside the *Iliad*, *The Divine Comedy* of Dante, the *Don Quixote* of Cervantes, and Shakespeare's plays, among world masterpieces.

Faust is a stupendous mixture of medieval magic and alchemy, of the Storm and Stress, classical and romantic movements, of philosophy and science, of intellectual and moral liberalism. It is based on the legend of Faust, a medieval doctor of magic, in league with the devil, to whom he has sold his soul. The devil appears as Mephistopheles, typifying the opposite pole of Faust's character, in a kind of dualism, comparable to a Dr. Jekyll and Mr. Hyde conception. The general theme is the attempt of Mephistopheles to give Faust one moment of complete satisfaction, free from striving and ambition; if he can do this, Mephistopheles is to receive, in payment, Faust's soul. Starting with a prologue in Heaven, the drama proceeds through many episodes—extravagant orgies and revelries, infatuation for Gretchen, and consequent tragedy. The culmination comes with Faust's realization that his satisfaction lies in eternal effort or striving to secure the welfare of humanity. For this the devil claims his reward, according to the bargain, but in the process Faust—whose nature was of depths that the devil could not fathom—has reached spiritual redemption. By this regeneration Faust is saved.

Second to *Faust,* but in prose, is Goethe's *Wilhelm Meister,* available in a fine translation by Thomas Carlyle. It is in reality a kind of novel, semiautobiographical, containing much of Goethe's philosophy. *Egmont* is a historical tragedy, dealing with the Dutch struggle for liberty. *The Sorrows of Werther,* largely autobiographical, telling of the hopeless love of Goethe himself for the betrothed of his friend, was to become a symbol of youthful grief. *Hermann und Dorothea* is a narrative poem of middle-class life. Many of Goethe's shorter poems are exquisite.

THE NINETEENTH CENTURY

The early nineteenth century saw the growth of romanticism in German literature, typified in the writings of Heinrich Heine (1797–1856). His fame rests principally on his lovely lyric poems.

Jacob Ludwig Karl Grimm (1785–1863) and his brother Wilhelm Karl Grimm (1786–1859), philologists, won literary fame with their collection known as *Grimm's Fairy Tales.* Other writers of the period were August Wilhelm von Schlegel (1767–1845) and Friedrich von Schlegel (1772–1829), brothers and collaborators; Clemens Brentano (1778–1842), novelist and dramatist; Bettina von Arnim (1785–1859), collector of folk songs; Adelbert von Chamisso (1781–1838), poet, wrote the fanciful story of *Peter Schlemihl,* "the man who sold his shadow."

An outstanding dramatist of the early nineteenth century was Heinrich von Kleist (1777–1811), whose most famous play is *Prinz Friedrich von Homburg.* A little later are the poetic plays of Franz Grillparzer (1791–1872), an Austrian, perhaps best known for his trilogy, *The Golden Fleece,* and for *Des Meeres und der Liebe Wellen (Waves of the Sea and of Love),* dealing with the tragic love of Hero and Leander. Toward the middle of the century, Christian Friedrich Hebbel (1813–1863) wrote a number of very individual and powerful tragic dramas, including *Gyges and his Ring, Herod and Mariamne,* and *Agnes Bernauer.*

A memorable lyric poet of this period was Eduard Mörike (1804–1875).

Among important philosophers were Georg Wilhelm Hegel (1770–1831), who followed somewhat in the tradition of Kant's idealism, and Arthur Schopenhauer (1788–1831), often referred to as a pessimist. Later came Friedrich Nietzsche (1844–1900), whose *Thus Spake Zarathustra* is a classic of philosophy, as is his *Beyond Good and Evil;* Nietzsche preached the doctrine of a superman and the will-to-power.

MODERN WRITERS

During the early part of the twentieth century the two most familiar German names were Gerhart Hauptmann (1862–1946), winner of the Nobel prize for literature in 1912, and Hermann Sudermann (1857–1928), both dramatists of the naturalistic school. Sudermann has one significant novel to his credit, *Frau Sorge* (*Dame Care*); but he was famous chiefly for his plays, among them *Magda* (*Heimat* is the German title). Hauptmann's name is most often associated with his fine drama, *The Weavers,* and with his poetic play, *Die Versunkene Glocke* (*The Sunken Bell*).

Arthur Schnitzler (1862–1931), writing in German, was an Austrian physician and dramatist whose work has been widely translated.

Jakob Wassermann (1873–1934) was one of the first major novelists to draw upon the findings of Freudian psychology in creating his characters and the action of his stories. Most famous of his many excellent novels is *Christian Wahnschaffe* (known in English as *The World's Illusion*).

Thomas Mann (1875–1955) is widely known. He was a novelist and short-story writer of great distinction. His *Buddenbrooks* is a story of a middle-class German family. *The Magic Mountain* is one of the great works of modern literature: it is a philosophical novel laid in a Swiss sanatorium. His *Joseph* series is a retelling with modern overtones of the story of the Biblical character. Mann won the Nobel prize in 1929.

Rainer Maria Rilke (1875–1926), an Austrian who lived in Prague, holds an eminent position among the finest modern poets. His best-known poems, *Sonnets to Orpheus, Requiem and Other Poems, Duino Elegies,* and his admirable *Letters to a Young Poet* represent a deeply spiritual attempt to define mankind in terms of its historical and mythological past and its destined future. He saw the human race as a slowly developing accomplishment in the realm of the spirit.

Franz Kafka (1883–1924), who also lived in Prague when Bohemia was part of Austria, wrote in German. Under the influence of early existentialist philosophy, he was tortured by the problem of man's position in the universe, the vagueness of his duty, and the absurdity of his ideals and actions. Kafka's novels and stories often resemble the world of dreams—composed of vague unexpressed fears, a strange illogical chronology, the sense of frustration, unknown desires and impotence, and especially the feeling of being dealt with arbitrarily. His best-known works are *The Trial, The Castle,* and the short stories in *The Penal Colony*. Kafka has had a great influence on many modern writers, especially the surrealists.

Swiss literature in German is well represented by Gottfried Keller (1819–1890), author of a number of exceptionally fine novels and short stories. More recent is Carl Spitteler (1845–1924), a Swiss poet, author of the epic *The Olympian Spring* and winner of the Nobel prize in 1919.

Among Hungarian writers, the best known to Americans is the dramatist Ferenc Molnár (born 1878), author of *Liliom* and other outstanding plays.

Dutch literature, such of it as has been written in the Dutch language, has not achieved world-wide attention. The Dutchmen who contributed outstanding works wrote in Latin: the great humanist, Desiderius Erasmus (1466?–1536), who wrote *Praise of Folly;* and Baruch Spinoza (1632–1677), whose great contribution to philosophy is contained in his *Ethics.*

SCANDINAVIAN LITERATURE

Scandinavia, which includes Sweden, Norway, Denmark, and Iceland, is inhabited by Teutonic peoples. Gradually the countries have become separated, in language and in government, but they have the same literary inheritance, handed down to them from the bards of the Viking days.

THE BEGINNINGS

The *Eddas,* originally in Old Norse or Icelandic, are the Scandinavian epics. The *Elder Edda* is a poetic narrative, made up of some 33 heroic and mythological songs, which were probably composed between the tenth and thirteenth centuries and whose authorship is unknown. The *Younger Edda* is in prose, and was compiled and perhaps partly composed by Snorri Sturluson (1179–1241); it contains the elements of northern Teutonic mythology.

Sigurd, the Norse Siegfried (compare the *Nibelungenlied* of German literature), is a hero of the *Elder Edda.* Here also appear the gods Odin and Thor and Balder, the goddesses Frigga and Freya, the Valkyries, the dwarfs and giants, and Asgard and Valhalla.

The saga was in Norse or Icelandic form, and was a kind of prose tale, telling traditional history of a family or hero. The story of Eric the Red forms the theme of one saga. Snorri Sturluson's *Heimskringla* (*Circuit of the World*) is an important historical saga. The *Njalssaga* (*The Story of Burnt Njal*) is available in an excellent translation. Best known of the sagas is the *Volsunga Saga,* which gives the Norse version of the

Sigurd (Siegfried) and Brynhild (Brünhild) legends, used by Wagner in his famous operas.

DANISH LITERATURE

The first name of importance in Danish literature is that of Ludvig Holberg (1684–1754), satirist and humorist. His *Niels Klim's Underground Journey* is fairly well known. He was called the "Danish Molière." Also worthy of particular mention is Johannes Evald (1743–1781), whose poetic drama, *The Fishermen,* contains the Danish national anthem, "King Christian Stood by the Lofty Mast." Adam G. Oehlenschläger (1799–1850) represented the early Romantic movement in Denmark. He is still the chief poet of the country. His *Aladdin,* a poetical version of the Arabian Nights tale, is representative of his work.

Hans Christian Andersen (1805–1875) is internationally known for his delightful fairy tales, although he also wrote romances, poems, and dramas. Andersen's fairy tales are his original creations, not versions of older legends. "The Mermaid," "The Brave Tin Soldier," and "The Little Match Girl" are familiar.

Jens Peter Jacobsen (1847–1885) is known especially for his novel, *Nils Lyhne,* written with a sensitive feeling for words which influenced the style of a number of Danish and Continental writers. Martin Andersen Nexö (born 1869) wrote a powerful novel in *Pelle the Conqueror,* a long, autobiographical story with the Danish labor movement as the background.

Among Danish writers, Sören Kierkegaard (1813–1855) is outstanding. His philosophical works have had extraordinarily wide influence. As a Christian existentialist, he turned the tide of theology to a radically personal, individualistic, and subjective basis. He rejected the value of moral improvement and placed spiritual faith on a pinnacle, as the only human endeavor of value. He was a profound psychologist and a writer of great satiric and poetic talents. His view of life as a total absurdity, resolved only by absolute love and absolute faith, has penetrated the thought of almost all modern philosophy and much literature.

Isak Dinesen is a Danish woman who wrote superb stories in English; we have already discussed her in the section on English literature.

NORWEGIAN LITERATURE

Norwegian national literature may be said to have begun with Henrik Wergeland (1808–1845) and Sebastian C. Welhaven (1807–1873), authors of plays, poems, and criticisms.

Björnstjerne Björnson (1832–1910), winner of the Nobel prize for literature in 1903, was a novelist, poet, and especially known as a playwright, whose outlook was optimistic. Of his novels, *The Fisher Maiden* is representative of his early work, and *In God's Way* typifies his later realism. His best-known play is *Beyond Human Power*.

Henrik Ibsen (1828–1906) takes his place among world figures, jostling elbows with the great immortals, beyond a doubt the greatest of all Scandinavian writers. He is gloomy and brooding compared with his contemporary, Björnson. But his problem plays are penetrating analyses of human motives and character. His first play of importance was *Brand*, which was followed in 1867 by the unique *Peer Gynt*, a semi-mythical poetic drama. *Pillars of Society* was the first of his social problem plays. *A Doll's House*, with awakening feminism as its theme, is the most famous of this group. The slamming of the door by the heroine of that play was heard throughout the world. *Ghosts* is an unforgettable study of hereditary disease and insanity. *An Enemy of the People* followed. Then came *The Wild Duck, Rosmersholm, Hedda Gabler, The Master Builder,* and several others.

Jonas Lie (1833–1908) was a popular novelist, intimate friend of both Björnson and Ibsen. Johan Bojer (born 1872) won fame in the English-speaking world with his novels, but is not ranked very high by Norwegian critics. Knut Hamsun (1859–1952), winner of the Nobel prize for literature in 1920, is known for his *Growth of the Soil*. Sigrid Undset (1882–1949), winner of the Nobel prize for literature in 1928, wrote novels, her masterpiece being *Kristin Lavransdatter*.

SWEDISH LITERATURE

Esaias Tegnér (1783–1846) was an outstanding poet of the first Swedish national literary movement. His *Svea* won the Swedish Academy prize, but his *The Children of the Lord's Supper* is his best work. Johan Ludvig Runeberg (1804–1877) was another poet of the first rank; he was born in Finland. *The Grave in Perrho* won the Swedish Academy prize. Verner von Heidenstam (1859–1940), Swedish poet laureate, won the Nobel prize for literature in 1916. Ludvig Almqvist (1793–1866) wrote popular romances. The novels of Fredrika Bremer (1801–1865) were widely read; she traveled in the United States in the middle of the nineteenth century and wrote a book of her impressions.

Emanuel Swedenborg (1688–1772), a widely influential Swedish religious leader, presented his concepts in such a book as *Heaven and Hell*.

August Strindberg (1849–1912) is outstanding among Swedish writers and one of the greatest modern dramatists. His earlier plays, such as *Miss Julia* and *The Father,* deal powerfully with realistically sordid, oppressive themes. In his later plays, such as *Easter* and *A Dream Play,* Strindberg expressed himself in symbolic and often morbid fantasy.

Selma Lagerlöf (1858–1940), winner of the Nobel prize for literature in 1909, has been widely popular. Her novels include *The Story of Gösta Berling* and *The Emperor of Portugallia.*

The Swedish scientist Alfred B. Nobel (1833–1896) established the annual Nobel prizes (each worth about $40,000), among them one for literature. The awards are granted on a world-wide basis for outstanding achievement, and individuals in all countries are considered for each choice. Other Nobel prizes are awarded in physics, chemistry, medicine, and for the greatest contribution to world peace.

FINNISH LITERATURE

Geographically, Finland is grouped with the Scandinavian countries, and this association has been increasingly important in recent years.

The legends and cultural traditions of Finland are quite distinct, however, from those of the other northern European countries. The myths and legends of the Finnish are recorded in the great Finnish epic, *The Kalevala.* The characters and episodes are often referred to in the works of modern Finnish poets and are also reflected in music by the great modern Finnish composer, Jean Sibelius.

RUSSIAN LITERATURE

Russia has been for centuries a sprawling geographical giant in eastern Europe and in northern Asia: the land of steppes, Cossacks, and peasants, czardom, Slavs and Tatars and Scandinavian invaders; influenced by both the Orient and the Occident, now the scene of the most powerful modern Communist government.

As with other nations, Russian literature has its foundation in accumulated folk songs and folk tales. The Russian language was given literary standing during the reign of Peter the Great (1672–1725). Genuine Russian literature, of world importance, did not appear until the early years of the nineteenth century; during the interval between 1800 and our own day, several literary giants have wielded their pens in Russian.

Alexander Pushkin (1799–1837) gave the first impetus to Russian national literature and is Russia's most famous poet. *Boris Godunov,* his historical drama, is the basis for the great opera by Moussorgsky. Of his prose writings, the long story, *The Captain's Daughter,* is the best known.

Nikolai Gogol (1809–1852) was the first great Russian novelist, and in some of his works is one of the best Russian humorists. Of his shorter pieces, *The Cloak* is the most masterly. In *Dead Souls* he satirically depicts Russian society. *Taras Bulba* is a realistic war novel. *The Inspector-General* is an excellent comedy. Among his weird pieces is the *Memoirs of a Madman.*

Ivan Turgenev (1818–1883) belongs to the great trio of Russian literature; the other two are Dostoevski and Tolstoy. Turgenev deals sympathetically with passionate love, although the general mood of his work is melancholy. Nearly all his work is available in English translation. His *Fathers and Sons* is probably his best-known novel.

Fëdor Dostoevski (1821–1881) wrote *Poor Folk* when he was 24 years old, "with passion and almost with tears." *Crime and Punishment* is the masterpiece which followed his terrible experiences as a prisoner at hard labor in Siberia. *The Brothers Karamazov* is another of his great novels. Dostoevski's concern is with the psychology of tormented, passionate individuals and with the deep, eternal problems of life.

Leo Tolstoy (1828–1910) is probably the best-known Russian writer. Of him Henry James wrote: "The perusal of Tolstoy—a wonderful mass of life—is an immense event, a kind of splendid accident, for each of us." His is a commanding, creative genius. His *War and Peace* is a long, panoramic novel, revealing his grand conception of war and history. *Anna Karenina* is also a masterwork, dealing with the tragedy of the heroine, her marriage and illicit love. In *The Kreutzer Sonata,* Tolstoy discloses his ideas of love and marriage. *Resurrection* is a powerful piece of social criticism in fiction form.

Prince Kropotkin (1842–1921) wrote criticism and revolutionary propaganda. Griboyedov (1795–1829) was a dramatist, as was also Ostrovski (1823–1886), who wrote *The Storm;* Mikhail Artsibashev (1878–1927), novelist and dramatist, wrote *Sanin;* Feodor Sologub (1863–1927) belongs to the same period and is famous for his short stories. Dmitri Merezhkovski (1865–1941), novelist and critic, was the author of *The Romance of Leonardo da Vinci.*

Anton Chekhov (1860–1904) will always be remembered for his masterly short stories, of which there are about 300, and for his famous plays, *The Cherry Orchard, The Sea Gull, Uncle Vanya.* Leonid Andreyev (1871–1919) castigated war in his *The Red Laugh;* he is also widely known for his play, *He Who Gets Slapped.*

Maxim Gorki (1868–1936), whose real name was Alexei M. Pyeshkov, was a novelist and playwright. *The Lower Depths* is a powerful, realistic drama. Of his short stories, "Her Lover" is characteristic and an admirable piece of work. His autobiography is contained in *My Childhood* and *In the World.*

Of the writers who have developed since the Russian Revolution, Mikhail Sholokhov (born 1905) should be mentioned. His broad panoramic novel, *The Silent Don,* deals with the indecision of a Cossack youth in the face of the turbulent events of the war and revolutionary period.

Polish literature is related to Russian, the Poles also being a Slavic people. Nicolaus Copernicus (Kopernicki), who lived from 1473 to 1543, was a great Polish astronomer who described his scientific findings in Latin. The most famous Polish man of letters was Henryk Sienkiewicz (1846–1916), winner of the Nobel prize for literature in 1905, and author of the novel of Roman life, *Quo Vadis?* A later Nobel winner (1924) was Wladyslaw Stanislaw Reymont (1868–1925), novelist.

SOUTH AMERICAN LITERATURE

The earliest literary works of South America were accounts of explorations and conquests, by such men as Gonzalo Fernández de Oviedo y Valdés (1478–1557) and Francisco López de Gomara (1511 to about 1577). The first true native writer was an Inca Indian, Garcilaso de la Vega (1540–1616), followed by Fernando de Alva Ixtlilxochitl (1568–1648).

Among Latin American epics should be mentioned the *Hernandia* by the Mexican Francisco Ruíz de León (published 1755) and the *Uruguay* (published 1768) by the Brazilian José Basilio da Gama.

In the nineteenth century a number of noted figures appeared. Domingo José Gonçalves de Magalhães (1811–1882), of Brazil, was a distinguished poet and philosopher. José Mármol (1818–1881) wrote the famous political novel, *Amalia.* José María Heredia (1803–1839) was a noted Cuban poet and patriot who for a time lived in the United States. (A cousin of the same name lived in Paris and wrote poetry in French.) Miguel Antonio Caro (1843–1909) was a Colombian author of note. Domingo Faustino Sarmiento (1811–1888), president of Argentina (1868–1874), was a writer of so-called "Gaucho poetry," dealing with the Indian cattle breeders of the pampas and their life. Ricardo Palmo of Peru (1833–1919) made an art out of carefully told historical anecdotes.

Notable among South American writers was Rubén Darío (1867–1916), of Nicaragua and of South America as a whole, who led a modernist movement in Spanish American literature. Other writers advocated national and racial solidarity, among them the "Latin Emerson," José Enrique Rodó (1872–1917) of Uruguay. Gabriela Mistral (born in 1889), Chilean poet, won the Nobel prize in 1945.

EXAMINATION QUESTIONS

1. What is the best known of the ancient poems of Anglo-Saxon literature?
2. Where did the legend of King Arthur and his knights originate?
3. What great English poet was born in 1340?
4. How were books produced before the invention of printing?
5. Who wrote *Utopia?*
6. What were the early church pantomimes called?
7. Who was the leading literary light of the Elizabethan Age?
8. Who was the author of *The Faerie Queene?*
9. What was the span of William Shakespeare's life?
10. Were Shakespeare's plays written in prose or poetry?
11. Is Shakespeare's *Hamlet* a tragedy or comedy?
12. Who wrote "Drink to me only with thine eyes"?
13. Who was the greatest of the metaphysical poets?
14. What was John Milton's greatest work?
15. Who is the author of *Pilgrim's Progress?*
16. What novel by Daniel Defoe is still a household classic?
17. Who was Sir Roger de Coverley?
18. As what form of literature was *Gulliver's Travels* intended?
19. With which two works is Samuel Johnson mainly associated?
20. What was Oliver Goldsmith's one novel?
21. Who wrote "Tintern Abbey"?
22. Why was Shelley expelled from Oxford?
23. Who wrote *Frankenstein?*
24. What essayist wrote under the pen name of Elia?
25. What prompted Tennyson to write *In Memoriam?*
26. Who was Elizabeth Barrett Browning?
27. What is the name of Charles Dickens' famous novel dealing with the French Revolution?
28. Who wrote *Vanity Fair?*
29. What was the real name of the author of *Alice in Wonderland?*
30. Who wrote the libretto for *The Pirates of Penzance?*
31. In what country did Rudyard Kipling write many of his early works?
32. In what field of literature is George Bernard Shaw outstanding?
33. What English novelist and dramatist was particularly concerned with social problems and complications rising out of class distinction?
34. Whose poetry marks clearly an end to the Romantic period?
35. Who wrote the novel *Ulysses?*
36. What Welshman was outstanding among the poets of the recent period?
37. Who is the chief poet of modern Ireland?
38. Who wrote the Declaration of

Independence for the American Colonies?

39. What kind of novels did James Fenimore Cooper write?

40. Name three leading transcendentalists.

41. Who wrote "Old Ironsides," and for what occasion?

42. What are some remarkable aspects of Poe's stories?

43. Who was the author of *The Scarlet Letter?*

44. What two great novels of American boyhood did Mark Twain write?

45. Who was the famous brother of Henry James, the novelist?

46. What sort of novel is Sinclair Lewis' *Main Street?*

47. Who wrote a famous novel dealing with conditions in slaughterhouses?

48. Who was the greatest of the imagists?

49. Who is the central character in Eugene O'Neill's play *The Emperor Jones?*

50. Who is the author of *The Enormous Room?*

51. What outstanding modern author's works deal with an imaginary county in Mississippi?

52. Who is the author of *The Grapes of Wrath?*

53. Where did the most ancient classics originate?

54. Identify the *Epic of Gilgamesh.*

55. What Persian poem was translated into English by Edward FitzGerald?

56. What is the Egyptian *Book of the Dead?*

57. In what classic occurs the story of *Ali Baba and the Forty Thieves?*

58. What religious classic contains the tenets of Mohammedanism?

59. In what language is the literature of India recorded?

60. When did Confucius live?

61. What is the *Iliad?*

62. Who were the Sirens?

63. Who was Sappho and when did she live?

64. By whom was the form of classical tragedy probably created?

65. What Greek tragic poet often combined tragedy and comedy in a way characteristic of later European playwrights?

66. Who was called the "Father of History"?

67. Who is the central character in Plato's dialogues?

68. What Greek writer was the source of some of Shakespeare's historical plays?

69. In what language were the Roman classics written?

70. How was Catullus described by Lord Tennyson?

71. How is elegiac verse distinguished?

72. Who was Aesop?

73. Who was the most famous scholastic and Catholic theologian?

74. What is considered Dante's masterpiece?

75. What is Boccaccio's *Decameron?*

76. With which Italian work is the adjective "Machiavellian" associated?

77. Who is the great modern Italian playwright?

78. What did Lord Macaulay call *Don Quixote?*

79. How many plays did Lope de Vega write?

80. Characterize the plays of Lorca.
81. Who was François Villon?
82. Where do we get the adjective "gargantuan"?
83. What writer may be said to hold somewhat the place in French literature that Shakespeare does in English literature?
84. Name a satire by Voltaire.
85. Name one of Victor Hugo's best-known novels.
86. What French poet, taking a bold departure from romantic ideals, initiated a new trend in modern poetry?
87. For what form of writing was Guy de Maupassant famous?
88. Name the famous long novel by Marcel Proust.
89. Who is the accredited leader of the French existentialist movement?

90. Of what nationality is Maurice Maeterlinck?
91. Who was Immanuel Kant?
92. Who was the Faust of German legend?
93. What philosophy did Nietzsche preach?
94. Name two works of Franz Kafka.
95. For what is Hans Christian Andersen principally noted?
96. What is the theme of Ibsen's *A Doll's House?*
97. How did the later plays of August Strindberg differ from his earlier plays?
98. Who composed the great trio of Russian literature?
99. Who wrote *War and Peace?*
100. Name a Russian writer of masterly short stories and plays.

FOR FURTHER STUDY

AMERICAN LITERATURE, by Russell Blankenship. (Henry Holt & Co., New York.)

THE AMERICAN MIND, edited by H. W. Warfel, R. H. Gabriel, S. T. William. (American Book Co., New York.)

ANTHOLOGY OF ENGLISH LITERATURE, edited by R. P. McCutcheon and W. H. Vann. (Henry Holt & Co., New York.)

ANTHOLOGY OF WORLD PROSE, edited by Carl Van Doren. (Reynal & Hitchcock, New York.)

A HISTORY OF ENGLISH LITERATURE, by E. Legouis and L. Cazamian.

(The Macmillan Co., New York.)

MAIN CURRENTS OF AMERICAN THOUGHT, by Vernon L. Parrington. (Harcourt, Brace & Company, New York.)

MODERN BRITISH AND AMERICAN POETRY, edited by Louis Untermeyer. (Harcourt, Brace & Company, New York.)

TELLERS OF TALES, edited by W. Somerset Maugham. (Doubleday & Co., New York.)

WORLD LITERATURE, edited by E. A. Cross. (American Book Co., New York.)

XI

A Guide to the Arts

THE NATURE AND USES OF ART

THOSE THINGS MADE by man which affect or move us so that we see or feel beauty in them come under the heading of art. In appreciating art, in developing judgment as to what is good and what is inferior in art, there are certain guides or principles that apply to all art forms. These are the principles of *rhythmic repetition, dominance* and *subordination,* and *proportion* and *symmetry*. The elements of design with which these are achieved are *line, light* and *shade,* and *color*. Rhythmic repetition is the repetition of one design motif in an organized arrangement so that it forms a pattern and gives a sense of movement to a design; this effect may be achieved by repeating a line, a form, or a color. Dominance and subordination are used to bring order into what might otherwise be disorder by having one motif stand out as the center of interest, and by balancing this by smaller motifs which complement the central motif. Proportion and symmetry are the means by which balance is achieved; when a design is symmetrical it gives the impression that all the elements are evenly distributed. This effect may be achieved by arranging a motif on one side of the design, and by balancing it with the same motif on the other side, or by placing the main motif in the center of the design. These are examples of *bi-symmetrical* arrangement. It may also be done by having a dominant motif balanced by two or more smaller units so arranged that they seem of equal weight with the larger motif. This is an example of *asymmetrical* arrangement.

The elements of design which we have just described should be present in all forms of art. Art need not be something known to us only in a museum or an art gallery, but should be, and in reality frequently is, part of our daily lives. We experience beauty in the way our parks are planned or our communities are laid out, in the way the building that we work or live in is designed, in our furniture, our clothes, and in the utensils and implements that we use around the house. The degree of beauty that is present in each of these areas of our daily living depends on the amount of imagination and care that goes into their designing and building. Communities should be planned, for example, according to the principles of

Bi-symmetrical arrangement.

Asymmetrical arrangement.

design, and at the same time should meet the needs of the people who live in them. They should take advantage of the natural sites and should give the impression of unity rather than a helter-skelter effect which will eventually lead to congestion, overcrowding, and ugliness.

In planning a community the first consideration is to allow enough room for the needs of the population that will use it. There should be enough roadways to permit speedy travel from one part of the com-

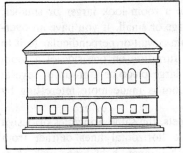

Rhythmic repetition.

Dominance and subordination.

munity to another. Parks should be plentiful and playgrounds should be provided for children. The planning of the individual buildings is also important for the utmost in beauty. Even though the buildings are individual units, they should conform in feeling and design to an over-all, consistent pattern.

In planning a home the needs of the family must be considered—the number of persons in the family, their interests, and their general taste. The decoration and arrangement should be based on these factors. The principles of design ought to be applied to make the most of the physical nature of the house or apartment. For example, if a room is dark and doesn't get enough sunlight, you might use bright, warm colors such as pink, yellow, or peach to help make it more cheerful. But if a room gets more than enough sunlight, blue, green, or light violet walls will make it appear cooler and more pleasing. Harmony can be achieved by wise contrasts or by use of related colors. In a small room it is better to use colors that are close in value, such as lighter and darker shades of the same color. In a large room, bolder contrasts may be employed. Furniture should be selected to fit in with the general plan of decoration. If the house is done in American colonial style, for example, the furniture should harmonize with that style in general feeling; it should not be over-elaborate or too sophisticated. In selecting furniture it is wise to plan a room around an object that is particularly significant for you. Sometimes this will be a painting, which will give you the key for your color scheme. Or it may be a piece of furniture of a particular period. The lines and general design feeling of this piece should determine to a large extent the character of the other pieces. In addition, of course, furniture should be selected for its usefulness, comfort, and durability. As in many other forms of art, there are fads in furniture; since you buy furniture comparatively infrequently, be sure that what you buy will not become ugly to you as your taste changes. Avoid unnecessary decoration in furniture; this increases the cost of the pieces without adding to their beauty. Skillful arrangement of furniture can make a room look larger or smaller, depending on whether the pieces are large or small. If you have an oversized room, try placing pieces away from a wall or perpendicular to it to cut down the space. A heavy piece of furniture on one side of a room should be counterbalanced by another large piece or a group of several smaller pieces on the other side. A room is made more interesting by having in it furniture of varying height.

In clothing, as in other everyday objects, the same principles of design apply. Vertical lines add height, while horizontal lines detract from height. Dark colors make a person look thinner, light tones make him look heavier. Smooth textures are more formal than rough textures. In planning a costume always consider your own personality, the attractive features of your physical being, and the occasion for which you are dressing.

These are some of the everyday applications of the principles of art. They apply as well, of course, to the fine arts—that is, those arts which in the main are created for no utilitarian purpose, but rather for the display of an artist's conception of the beauty of the world about him. We shall take up painting, architecture, sculpture, and music.

STYLES IN ART

Before we discuss the art of various countries throughout history, a brief discussion of style will be useful. Style is a word used to indicate the manner in which subject matter is treated by an artist. The style of a painting is analogous to the style of a poem or a story. Thus a painting which would depict in detail, for example, a shipwreck with a frank representation of drowning and wounded people would be a painting in the realistic style. The more objectively it was done, the closer the style would approach naturalism. If, on the other hand, the representations were exaggerated, perhaps sentimental and heart-rending, and stressed the heroic courage of the people, the style would be romantic.

Style, in painting, depends upon the individual painter. It is also very much dictated by the time in which the painter lives and the country where he works. The time and place a painter belongs to will place him in one or another tradition. These historical traditions are termed "styles." They develop one from another, by experiment and criticism, much as the styles in literature develop.

The main European styles are the Greek Classical Style; the Medieval Style, also called Gothic; the Renaissance Style; the Baroque Style (approximately seventeenth century), sometimes considered late Renaissance; the Neo-Classical, Romantic, and Realist Styles of the eighteenth and nineteenth centuries; Symbolist and other modern styles, up to Abstract art. There are many other known styles; the ones we have mentioned—which apply to painting, sculpture, and architecture—differ in the various countries where they are found.

Historians of art have remarked that each important style may be divided into three periods: the early or archaic; the middle, high or classical; and the late, which is sometimes a flourishing and sometimes a decadence. The early or archaic period is the one in which a style is initiated. It is always simple, often crude, never elaborate; in architecture the design is usually simple and symmetrical. The classical period of any style is usually considered the height of perfection in that style. There is a balance between detail and structure, between artificial design and naturalism, and between the traditional form and individual innovation. The late period is often beautifully elaborate, decorative, but too full of detail and individual flourishes as compared to the main structure or design.

These three periods are seen clearly in the Greek Classical Style, in the Medieval or Gothic Style, and in the Renaissance Style; they are not so clearly seen in modern styles.

PAINTING

PREHISTORIC

Countless ages ago in Europe primitive man lacked all the comforts of life except fire, pottery, and crude stone implements; yet, in spite of his savage state, he drew and painted pictures. His weapons and pottery were decorated with rude lines, and on the walls of his caves were rough pictures, simple outline drawings scratched on soft stone by a harder stone chisel, of the giant elephants and other animals he killed in the hunt. Two motives may have prompted these crude artists: the desire to record facts in a more or less permanent form, and the desire to insure success in the hunt through the "magic" of these drawings.

EGYPTIAN

Although at first painting as distinct from colored stone carving was rare, in the later history of Egypt painting with colors and brush was a much more common occurrence. The subject matter of the wall paintings (murals) consisted of the history of each king's rule: a band of writing accompanied an illustrative series of pictures, either painted flat or chiseled in shallow relief. The outlines were filled in with simple colors from the earth and from metals. Later, the greater ease and freedom of the brush replaced the chisel. The formal Egyptian style of drawing depicted processions of stiff-limbed men strung out in measured bands or friezes around the walls. Both men and women were drawn with square shoulders, small waists and hips, long legs and arms, and flat hands and feet. The heads, legs, and arms were drawn in profile, while the chest and eye were twisted to show the flat front view. Because they knew nothing about light and shadow or perspective, or composition designed to attract the eye to a specific spot, Egyptian artists called attention to the chief character in their picture by making him much larger than his neighbor. Thus kings and gods appear as giants.

The Egyptians painted to decorate sacred tombs of rulers with the comforts of his everyday life to help him towards a more comfortable afterlife, and to tell a story.

MESOPOTAMIAN

Fertility and a favorable climate like that of Egypt caused the growth of an early civilization in the valley of the Tigris and Euphrates rivers. Babylonian and Assyrian temples and tombs were comparatively without painted decoration, but the Babylonians glorified their king by decorating his palace with colored bas-reliefs, cut in alabaster slabs, telling of his deeds.

Painting was usually done on tiles with mineral colors, afterward glazed by baking. When affixed to the walls, the tiles fitted into decorative scenes or conventional border designs. These are the earliest examples of mosaic work. The Babylonians also made crude frescoes; that is, they painted on wet plaster with tempera (colors mixed with egg yolk instead of oil) and on pottery.

Two types of male figures were repeated: the bearded and the beardless. They represented heavy-featured, muscular Semitic warriors. As in Egypt, the figure was in profile with eye and chest twisted to show the front view. Long, straight robes hid the anatomy completely. While these garments eliminated graceful limbs, they contributed sumptuous decoration, since every detail of their design was brilliantly colored, sometimes with gold or bronze.

The conquering Persians contributed nothing new; they copied what they found. The end of Mesopotamian art followed Alexander's conquest. National characteristics disappeared under Greek influences.

ANCIENT GREEK

The imaginative Greeks dedicated their lives to the achievement of intellectual, ethical, and physical ideals. Their deities, created in the image of Hellenic men and women, each representing a Greek ideal, formed the subject matter of their art, together with legendary heroes like Hercules, whose feats were god-like. Since Greek painting was to honor the gods, and the gods were fashioned in the likeness of the perfect Greek man, the motive inspiring Greek art was really praise of Greek character and way of life. The desire to decorate had its influence also.

Greek vase-painting is famous. The earliest examples show simple designs of crude black horizontal bands. Later vases (900–700 B.C.) had more intricate geometric designs, including the famous narrative Greek borders. Black designs on red pottery (700–480 B.C.) showed Oriental influences in lotus-leaf patterns and winged animals. After this, the human figure became the chief interest of Greek painters. Landscape was ignored except when a tree was inserted for symmetry, but in spite of their beautiful drawing and knowledge of anatomy, the vase-painters knew very little about perspective. Red-figured ware with black backgrounds (525–300 B.C.) show the most exquisitely drawn figures assembled in charming compositions. The development in vase decoration from simple geometric designs, to a geometric, unrealistic representation of people and gods, toward a more naturalistic design (the faces beginning to show expression), and finally to less disciplined, more ornate embellishments is an example of the progress of Greek art through the three fundamental periods of style. This development is paralleled, of course, in the more important Greek art of sculpture. The middle or strictly classical period of Greek art is about 480–420 B.C., and is followed by the post-classical but very fine fourth-century (B.C.) style, which leads into the later decadence.

Unlike Egyptian and Babylonian paintings, Greek frescoes were associated with individual artists, Polygnotus (about 465 B.C.) being the best known. Portraiture was attempted, but imperfectly—so that there might be no mistake, the name of the subject was inscribed beneath each picture. Apollodorus (about 440 B.C.) was nicknamed "shadow-painter," or the Shadower, because of his achievements in natural perspective—as in his rounding of human figures. Zeuxis of Ionia (about 430 B.C.) tried to give the illusion of reality to his work. It was reported that a bunch of his painted grapes was pecked at by birds. Parrhasius (about 400 B.C.) is said to have fooled Zeuxis with a painted curtain. Both men must have known color, modeling, and relief in order to imitate nature so well.

With Philip and Alexander came the Hellenistic period (about 323 B.C.), when Apelles painted many graceful allegorical figures. "Aphrodite," carried to Rome by Augustus, and "Alexander with the Thunderbolt" are the most famous of his works. After the time of Alexander, painting deteriorated and the artists tended to concentrate on reproducing faithfully numerous details. This produced confused pictures without distinction. This is the late period of Greek art called the Hellenistic period.

ANCIENT ROMAN

When the Romans conquered the Greeks, they adopted Greek art forms. Unfortunately, painting had already declined, and the examples followed by the Romans belonged to the decadent Hellenistic period. The walls at Pompeii, buried by an eruption of Vesuvius and preserved for centuries in the volcanic ash, were uncovered by archaeologists, and they enable us to study Roman mural decoration. Down to 80 B.C., such wall decorations were divided into panels with painted bands of color or geometric patterns. After that date, down to the Christian era, the architectural style was popularized. Pictures in the center of panels were framed by painted columns, pediments, cornices and the like, with careful perspective to give the illusion of reality. This fashion degenerated into an ornate style, lasting till 50 A.D., that covered the walls with architectural motifs in involved confusion. The painting of architecture became fantastic in detail. Walls were crowded with painted panels, balconies, steps, etc., receding into the distance, which were as maddening to look at as a drawing of a person's reflection shown innumerable times in mirrors.

Because of the republican Roman government, political personalities became more important than religious subjects, which, when used, were borrowed from the Greek. Thus portrait-painting was encouraged. It was realistic, but showed the Roman lack of imagination. Heads were characterized by uniform oval faces, enormous black eyes heavily lashed, long straight noses with lifted nostrils, and full, generous mouths.

ITALIAN

Although the Roman Empire did not fall until 476 A.D., influences of the early Christians in Rome and in Byzantium and of the barbaric tribes of the north were seen in painting and decoration more than one hundred years before the fall of Rome, and continued till about 1250 A.D. These groups produced works that were characterized by a lack of naturalistic drawing, a marked interest in symbolism, rich ornamentation based on floral and geometric patterns, and very effective use of rich color and texture. Because the early Christians opposed idolatry, the use of the human figure was not permitted in painting at first, but this concept changed later. The artists then had little knowledge of anatomy, and stiff, ungainly figures resulted. The designs, however, were unusually perfect in their balance of simple forms and elaborate marginal decoration.

The function of painters in this period was to decorate walls of the churches with mosaics (tiny pieces of colored glass or stone put side by side in cement to form a picture or design) and frescoes, and to do miniatures with which to illustrate books. These painters borrowed their models from Roman frescoes and Hellenic art, but produced squat, ungainly figures because of their lack of skill. Backgrounds and perspective vanished and gave way to richly colored and decorative jewels and embroideries on the gowns of the figures shown. Actually the form of the human body remained more symbolic than life-like.

With the growing interest in study of Greek culture and philosophy in the thirteenth century, painting tended to become less stiff and drawing technique showed more awareness of nature. The influence of Greek culture at this time is one of the characteristics of the movement which we call the Renaissance.

Just prior to the Italian Renaissance and considerably overlapping it in time, a number of painters, mostly unknown by name, produced the paintings which we call Medieval. They derive from the Byzantine mosaics, but they show far greater skill in drawing. Lacking perspective, they represent figures symbolically as larger or smaller according to their importance. Formal design and structure predominate over naturalistic details. Most of these Medieval Italian painters were centered in Siena, where the Renaissance Style did not appear until long after it had developed in Florence.

The Florentine school was intent on innovations; the Sienese, on traditional decoration. Cimabue (1240?–1302?), of Florence, was one of many artists who loosened drapery folds, gave a new tilt to heads, and injected life into conventional figures. He is noted also as the teacher of Giotto. Giotto (1276?–1337?) is considered the first Renaissance painter. His works show an appreciation of perspective and bodily motion. He worked in Florence and in Assisi, where he did famous frescoes in the Church of St. Francis.

The study of the body was subordinated in Siena to beauty of expression and ornate costumes. Duccio (1260?–1339?) retained the Byzantine model but perfected such details as hands and feet, and added rich coloring. Lacking Giotto's dramatic force, Duccio is noted for his poetic inspiration. The Lorenzetti brothers (fourteenth century), like Giotto, painted decorative frescoes in narrative style. Ambrogio Lorenzetti stands with Giotto and Duccio as one of the great painters of the early Renaissance. His painting was perhaps the most delicate and fine. Another major Sienese painter was Simone Martini (1283–1344).

The Renaissance brought a rebirth of interest in classical learning and the study of nature at first hand. Greek statuary was studied, and thoughtful inquiries into the sciences were begun. Paintings produced at this time show nature and character study and a considerable advance in technique and naturalism. The early Renaissance is marked by simplicity, strong stylization, and a tendency toward strictly symmetrical design; also depiction of nature and people remained conventional and primitive. These are characteristic of the beginnings of most great movements in the arts.

In spite of awakened worldly interests, the church was still the greatest patron of the arts, sponsoring about three-fourths of the paintings of the century, which were done in fresco on the wall spaces of chapels, churches, and cloisters.

The city of Florence was the greatest art center of the times. The nude figure was studied by Masolino (1383?–1447?), as his "Baptism" testifies, while his pupil Masaccio (1401–1428) was the first great student of nature who mastered form and drapery. His "Peter Giving the Tribute Money" is very famous; the figures are for the first time full-bodied, massive, and suggestive of motion, whereas earlier painting appears flat and one-dimensional. Masaccio evidences a new interest in the psychology and the emotional drama of the moment he depicts.

Fra Angelico (1387–1455), one of the most outstanding early Renaissance painters, applied his brush in a more delicate and ethereal style. His pictures are usually panoramic, renowned for the beauty of his color tones and the perfection of his angel figures. The paintings of Fra Filippo Lippi (1406–1469), who was much influenced by Angelico, begin to approach the style of the high or classical Renaissance, with their sharply linear figures, their magnificent colors, the perfection of design, and the deeply revealing portraiture.

Botticelli (1447?–1510), outstanding in this period, combined classic form and subjects with an appreciation for nature. Botticelli's women, in their floating draperies, breathe a graceful, melancholy charm. His decorative sense and feeling for color composition were perfect, as is shown by his "Primavera."

Piero della Francesca (1420?–1492), of Umbria, was a master technician, grasping elusive atmosphere. Signorelli (1441–1523) succeeded with complicated foreshortening, though his colors and textures were coarse. Perugino (1446–1523?) carried out the Gothic devotional fervor in oils; he was the first Italian to employ them. The gigantic and inventive landscape backgrounds of Pinturicchio (1454–1513) graced Sienese walls and the Borgia apartments in the Vatican.

Padua was the center of classical influence. This was best reflected by Andrea Mantegna (1431–1506), who was a student of ancient sculpture. Mantegna made figures that looked like human beings turned into bronze. His paintings also showed a strong sense of drama.

Neither piety nor classicism strongly interested the Venetians, who were for the most part rich merchant princes eager to beautify their city. They fostered a rich decorative art. Color, most sensuous in its appeal, was, and continued to be, their distinctive achievement. In color harmony and technical perfection, Giovanni Bellini (1426?–1516) excelled.

Leonardo da Vinci (1452–1519), born in Florence, represents the pinnacle of classic or high Renaissance painting. He was a man with an extraordinary range of interests, a pioneer in the sciences as well as a consummate artist. His studies in anatomy and in drawing perspective (he studied also the use of color for perspective) contributed greatly to the technique of this period's painting. His famous "Mona Lisa" testifies to his interest in the mysterious, elusive quality of the human face. His use of symbolism is secondary to his study of humanity and nature.

Michelangelo (1475–1564), like da Vinci one of the world's supreme artists, was a creator of forms and ideas. His paintings in the Sistine Chapel have power, strength, and grace. His interest in sculpture is reflected in his painted single figures, which are round and massive as if in relief. His drawing was magnificent; he gave less thought to color and perspective. Michelangelo will always be revered as the representative of individualism in art.

Raphael (1483–1520) was a master of rhythmical proportion and composition. His interest was in technical perfection. In his texture-painting, graceful modeling, and serenity, he easily excelled.

The sixteenth century accomplished the classic point of Renaissance, when the Italians glorified humanity and nature at the expense of religious zeal. The medium was oil-painting on canvas or wood inserted into walls and ceilings. An aspect of this period of painting is the concern for "ideal" beauty in the Classical (Greek) sense and a poetic preoccupation over melancholy and nobility of sentiment. This trend is noticeable in the fine portraits of Bronzino (1502–1572).

At Parma, Correggio (1494?–1534) was inspired by the charm of worldly things. Because of his love for delicate subjects, he is known as the "Faun of the Renaissance." At Ferrara, Dosso Dossi (1479?–1542) contributed splendid light and shade values. Andrea del Sarto (1486–1531), the "faultless painter," lacked nobility of feeling, but he populated his canvases with figures that were beautifully molded.

The Venetians of the sixteenth century sought primarily decorative effects gratifying to the senses. Color was so skillfully handled that it resulted in power and beauty. Giorgione (1478?–1510) painted *fêtes* and fables in landscape settings with technical perfection. By glazing his oil paints, he secured deep, brilliant color tones. His drawing was not stressed, the Venetians preferring to model with masses of light, shade, and color. Because Titian (1477–1576) combines so many of the virtues of Italian art, the perfection of his paintings is difficult to describe; he has exquisite imaginative power, knowledge of nature, and mastery of technique. His men and women are saturated with glowing life. Veronese (1528–1588) was an outstanding draftsman and colorist. Jacopo Tintoretto (1518–1594) was another Venetian master of this period. His pictures are dramatic in action and color contrast; they announce the coming Baroque Style.

The seventeenth-century Baroque Style is better seen in Italian architecture (which will be discussed later) than in the painting. In painting it is both naturalistic and ornate, featuring sharp contrasts of light and shade, dramatic action or dramatically painted nature scenes. Thus it is a flowering of the late Renaissance and sometimes considered to be a part of that style. The most characteristic Italian representative of this period is Caravaggio (1565–1609). The paintings of Tiepolo (1696–1770) are typical of the Italian late Baroque or eighteenth-century style.

Interesting as these later painters are, it may be said that the great national genius in Italian painting came to an end in the late sixteenth century.

FRENCH

Early French painting was too greatly influenced by foreign art to be distinctive. Roman frescoes were copied, followed by melancholy Byzantine types painted in miniature on ivory, on illuminated manuscripts, walls, and, in the thirteenth century, on church windows. By the fifteenth century the influence of naturalism became apparent in landscape backgrounds, with blue skies replacing the gold leaf. This change of emphasis was due to the situation of the French court, halfway between Italian and Flemish art centers. Artists *en route* between countries left their influence on French art.

Because of his interest in art, Francis I invited Leonardo da Vinci, Andrea del Sarto, and other Italians to his châteaux in the Touraine, where they completely overshadowed local artists and by their influence created an Italianized school of French painting. Through the seventeenth century French art continued to be steeped in Italian tradition. Nicolas Poussin (1594–1665) borrowed from the Italian classical period, founding the classical school in France. Claude Lorrain (1600–1682) painted classic panoramic scenes: wooded hills, streams, Greek temples, and heavenly groves, like theatrical backdrops. He was the first artist to paint golden sunlight.

Georges de la Tour (1593–1652) was a typically Baroque painter; exemplary are his candlelit scenes, variously light and deeply shaded, very dramatic.

In the eighteenth century, under Louis XV, art cast off its Italian-classic yoke and became frivolous. Shepherds in satin, immaculate sheep nibbling Arcadian foliage, and romancing court lovers were the pretty subjects then popular. Watteau (1684–1721) was the master of this school; by varying the thickness of his pigment, he achieved brilliant versatility with his brush.

François Boucher (1703–1770), applying a similar style to the treatment of his court scenes, produced rather conventional and insipid paintings. Fragonard (1732–1806) painted with vivacity, using delicate color harmonies. His charcoal drawings also are exquisite. Modern feeling for color in atmosphere may be found in the paintings of Chardin (1699–1779), who realistically portrayed the effect of light on color and surfaces in his scenes of family life.

The early nineteenth century saw a return to classic models painted with great severity. Jacques Louis David (1748–1825) painted heroic themes in a Neo-Classic Style. Prud'hon (1758–1823) used shadows which created graceful, phantom-like figures. Ingres (1780–1867) is noted for his exquisite linear style and for his sensitivity to form and to color, especially in his flesh tones. He introduced the style of the single figure into French art, as, for example, his "Odalisque."

The self-conscious mood of individualism found expression in the Romantic movement, beginning about 1822, with Géricault (1791–1824) and Delacroix (1799–1863) as its leaders. Color, light, and atmosphere suggested tragic-romantic moods. Details were slurred to give a general effect. Subject matter was often exotic, with extravagant oriental scenery. Narrative motifs were intensely emotional or savagely violent.

By 1830, romantic painters began a close study of nature. The Barbizon school treated nature with poetic atmosphere and color, resulting in the charming landscapes of Corot (1796–1875), whose silvery grays and greens faithfully portrayed the half-lights of early morning and twilight. Théodore Rousseau (1812–1867) contributed golden-brown tones and broad brush strokes to landscape, while Diaz (1807–1876), of Spanish origin, created variety with brilliant colors. Daubigny (1817–1878) painted light as seen along river banks at twilight, achieving his effects with simple mass treatment which bridged the way from Corot's fastidious brushwork to the Impressionists.

Jean François Millet (1814–1875) revealed peasant life with, at his best, poetic force and simplicity. A precursor of the Realist school, his work often degenerates into sentimentality. "The Sower" and "The Gleaners" exemplify beauty in light, color, and motion. Meissonier (1815–1891) painted Napoleonic battle scenes down to the minutest details. Puvis de Chavannes (1824–1898) was a mural painter who used simple but graceful designs and charming color.

Courbet (1819–1877) heralded the moderns by depicting both the beauty and ugliness of nature. In this he parallels the style of the French poets of this period. Courbet founded the School of Realism. His "Burial at Ornans" is a famous picture, depicting a commonplace provincial funeral, objectively, without stress of sentiment, lacking the slightest note of the tragic or the heroic—there is even a dog in the picture. At first it caused a scandal in Paris, although from 1850 Courbet and the Realists achieved increasing acclaim. In technique they were concerned, not with details, but with great truths expressed in vivid colors and light and shade patterns. Courbet's brushwork was masterful.

Édouard Manet (1832–1883) introduced the theories of Impressionism. To paint nature not as it actually is, but as it impressed him, was his object. It must be stressed that the attempt was not romantic, but rather it was an effort to achieve a more exact reality. In particular, Manet wished to catch the vividness and drama of whatever moment he was painting. His technical discoveries include the individual relations of light and shadow, flat surfaces, and exact values of color tones. His early pictures, which are his best, are characterized by a perfect harmony of colors, particularly grays and blacks. Later on he became more truly "impressionistic," adapting the method of his contemporary, Claude Monet.

Claude Monet (1840–1926) used little multicolored brush strokes side by side to give his landscapes and seascapes the effect of a vivid, transient instant. In divorcing light from the object and using pure colors placed side by side, he succeeded in recomposing light on his canvas. The method is best exemplified by his famous studies of the Rouen Cathedral. There are twenty-four of them, each done at a different time of day; they show the effect of the varying daylight and intensity and color of the sun. Sisley (1830–1899), Pissarro (1831–1903), and Renoir (1841–1919) modified this technique.

Renoir, picturing middle-class life, was a sensuous, brilliant colorist of the Impressionist school. Georges Seurat (1859–1891) carried the Impressionist method to an extreme by his use of dots of paint on the canvas, which, seen from a distance, merge into natural shades. His sense of design and form was greater than that of the early Impressionists. Henri Rousseau (1844–1910) painted naïve, primitive pictures; best known are his jungle canvases.

Edgar Degas (1834–1917), famous for his ballet pictures, was the most individual and talented of the Impressionists. His compositions show great imagination in design and unusually skillful drawing, movement, and coloring.

A very important painter, now extremely popular, was Henri de Toulouse-Lautrec (1864–1901), whose lithograph posters have become famous. His use of color was bold and fascinating. His oils show a sense of satire that far transcends caricature. Oddly, in his representations of the famous dance hall, the Moulin Rouge, he has combined in his figures a realistic sense of their boredom with a vital, catching *joie de vivre*. Very popular also are the Montmartre scenes so refreshingly painted by Maurice Utrillo (1883–1955).

Vincent van Gogh (1853–1890), although classed as a post-Impressionist, was a colorist too, having a liking for pure color in broad surfaces. Van Gogh was born in Holland, and his very fine early paintings were done in his native country; however, since all his later work was done in France and was so much a part of the French modern tradition, he is classed here with the French painters. His vivid, violent paintings of hayfields and sunflowers seem to express the great energy and tragedy of humanity. He was able to sell only one picture during his lifetime and died heartbroken and insane. Gauguin (1848–1903) created superb designs in a primitive, symbolistic style inspired by the South Sea Islanders, among whom he lived for a considerable time. He is considered a Symbolist.

Paul Cézanne (1838–1906) was an outstanding innovator. His feeling for atmosphere changes in landscape reveals itself in classic compositions which also show an unusual mastery of color. His development away from naturalistic depiction, or even symbolic depiction, toward plastic form and a three-dimensional geometric style greatly impressed the younger artists. Also Cézanne developed a perspective of several intersplicing planes.

MODERN ART IN FRANCE

France has been in our times the art center of the western world. For a better understanding of the various trends in modern art, a few of the artists we will discuss will be treated in considerable detail.

Following Cézanne, a group of post-Impressionists claimed the world's attention. Chief representatives were Derain (1880–1954), Rouault (1871–1958), Matisse (1869–1954), and Modigliani (1884–1920; born in Italy). Derain was notable among the revolutionary group who painted "Fauve" ("untamed beast") canvases, typified by large, simple shapes and figures in savage, violent, unnaturalistic colors. Matisse also employed a great variety of colors and showed an interest in abstract design. In his later years he designed and did all the art work for the Chapel of St. Domenique in Vence near the French Riviera. Modigliani's nudes show a tendency toward caricature and a beautiful rich tone of flesh color. Rouault was a master portraitist, whose models came from the circus and the Bible. His dark, heavy applications of paint—pressed onto the canvas with a palette knife—express a somber, tragic quality that is deeply moving. The works of Raoul Dufy (1878–1953) are immediately recognizable from his very unique and exquisite colors. He experimented also with the representation, by multiple figuring, of motion in painting. This was an innovation of a group of Italian artists (Futurists), otherwise unworthy, of the First World War period.

Experiment and drastic originality in colors were closely paralleled by very significant innovations in form. Pablo Picasso (born 1881) and Georges Braque (born 1881) "discovered" simultaneously the technique called Cubism. Much has been written and thought about this style. It has been suggested that it represents in visual art the science and philosophy of the fourth dimension. Forms in Cubistic paintings are often repeated, with variations and overlapping each other, as if one shape were being seen simultaneously from various viewpoints. In Picasso's celebrated "Girl Before Mirror" it is possible to understand that the model is represented simultaneously in her youth and her age. The more important aspects of Cubism are its accent on geometric shape, its use of various flat, interspicing planes which distort the perspective, and frequently a rather sophisticated sense of humor. Braque's Cubism is remarkable for his sensitivity of color harmony, particularly of his greens and browns. Juan Gris (1887–1927) was another significant Cubist.

Picasso originated a great number of trends and participated in almost all the modern movements. He stands out as the genius of modern art. Although born in Spain, he has done most of his work in Paris and the south of France. His very early pictures, imitating Lautrec, were quickly followed by a number of rather grotesque but moving canvases usually cast in an atmosphere of blue. This "blue" period is contrasted with his later "rose" period, dealing almost entirely with circus characters. He catches vividly their feeling of loneliness and quiet, resigned sensitivity —in a nostalgic, mysterious atmosphere of rose light. Picasso's "Young Ladies of Avignon" is an important representative of his African period, resulting from a study of the masks of that country. His bullfighting pictures are often extremely moving, despite the abstract treatment. The bull takes on for the artist a symbolic value, possibly of the tragic, proud, sacrificed hero. The "Guernica," painted in 1935, was inspired by the destruction of the town of Guernica in Basque Spain by the Fascists. In the stark black-and-white enormous mural Picasso has depicted the horror and commotion of war, the cowardliness of cruelty, and the heroism of the sufferers through which a new world is destined to be born. There is much symbolism: an obvious example is in the use of newspaper covering the body of the treacherous, dying horse. The horse represents weakness and cruelty, avenged by the bull (which in ancient mythology represents godhead). The newspapering suggests propaganda. Knowledge of these symbols is wholly unnecessary to appreciate the bold tones and structure of the impressive panorama of destruction.

The recent years have witnessed a great number of modern styles, many of them short-lived. Paris, as a center of artistic innovation, has attracted many foreigners and influenced others who will be mentioned here. The Surrealist movement of the twenties produced many remarkable pictures. Salvador Dali (born 1904 in Spain) was a leader in painting irrational, almost automatic, and often symbolic scenes. The necessity to calculate a meaning, as if one were reading a poem—when the meaning does not impress the spectator visually—is a serious failing of the Surrealists, especially Dali. Moreover, his paintings are done in an academic, unoriginal technique which does not harmonize with his usual subject matter. De Chirico (born 1888 in Italy) paints in a stark, classical style; his pictures of deserted buildings haunt one with a sense of a lost, undirected humanity. Joan Miró (born 1893 in Spain) created beautiful and whimsical fantasies which are particularly delightful. Max Ernst (born 1891 in Germany) produced a Surrealist brand of photography.

Paul Klee (1879–1940) belonged to the German Expressionist group; we mention him here because of his close tie to French art and especially Surrealism. His richly colored abstractions recall primitive design; they are an attempt to *express* the profound subconscious in art forms. His designs are whimsical and show a very rich imagination and sense of humor. Kandinsky (1866–1944), a Russian, studied in Germany with Klee. His canvases, featuring bar-like shapes and sheets of color, sometimes successfully pictorialize a rhythm of music.

Fernard Léger (born 1881) and Piet Mondrian (1872–1945; born in Holland) each developed unique styles. Léger painted people and buildings in crude geometric form, rather as if they were machinery. Mondrian developed a style of pure design—consisting eventually of only lines and blocks of color. They evoke successfully certain moods and reactions, but they tend to degenerate into decoration.

The tendency of contemporary art is to simplify forms and avoid any humanistic, narrative, or natural representation.

SPANISH

Early Spanish painting, like the French, borrowed from other cultures, and it particularly reflected Byzantine influence. The Church motivated art in Spain until portraiture developed. Miniatures and frescoes, religious in nature, were done in tempera. Gold leaf was used lavishly, and frequently details were molded in relief in gesso (a type of plaster of Paris). They were dramatic and grimly realistic.

In the sixteenth century a Castilian school was developed, of whose members Fernández Navarrete (1526–1579), a disciple of Titian's, was one of the first to add warmth of color to the traditionally somber gray Spanish canvases.

Theotocópuli (1548–1625), called El Greco, influenced by Venice, was an outstanding genius. His monks and madonnas have elongated bodies, sorrowful eyes, and magnificent form dependent on color and shadow. His canvases are dramatic in movement and texture; they often have a "gothic" mystic quality.

Velásquez (1599–1660) was the greatest Spanish painter. His portraits are in the courtly, aristocratic style. In narrative painting—an episode set in landscape or interior—his genius is completely rounded, intensely individual, and yet gives us a broad characterization of Spanish life in his time. There is a sense of order and triumph in the dramatic harmonies of light and color and the simple solidity of Velásquez' compositions. His technique is varied and faultless.

Murillo (1618–1682) headed the Andalusian school, painting large canvases of religious inspiration. His outlines were graceful, and his textures had a classic, sensual quality. There is a warm, intense, almost dramatic richness to his color schemes.

Francisco Goya (1746–1828), in typically Spanish style, gave bloody and brutal subjects a profound tragi-comical turn, often coloring the most wretched of subject matter with caricature and ridicule. His painting was truly great; his contrasting tone of light and shade is particularly effective. In his portraits we see his technical skill and shrewd characterization.

FLEMISH

With Hubert van Eyck (1370?–1426) and Jan van Eyck (1390?–1440), Flemish painting (which is often thought to be characterized primarily by its naïve realism and *genre* qualities) became important. The Van Eycks' St. Bavon altarpiece at Ghent excels all other painting of the period in its jewel-like perfection of detail and in its pathos and sentiment. Pathos was also the charm of the ingeniously fine figures of Van der Weyden (1400?–1464), while those of Hans Memling (1430–1495) are quiet and dignified. The technical qualities of Flemish painting of this period have been admired up to the present day. The fineness and perfection of detail is so great that examination of canvases under magnifying lens reveals the exact service of each brush stroke. The Flemish were masters of lacework and textiles, which are represented with exquisite and subtle technique in their paintings. Richness of design and color in the clothing and other clothwork represented in Flemish painting has never been excelled. "The Entombment at Antwerp" of Quinten Matsys (1460?–1530) inspired a new trend in Flemish art by introducing variety into modeling, color, and facial expression, and by increasing the figures almost to life size. Bueckelaer (1530–1573) painted kitchens and vegetable stalls to exhibit the perfection of his still-life technique. Realism breathed in the Flemish people painted by Pieter Breughel (1525?–1569). His four paintings which depict the seasons are among the great realistic masterpieces in the medium. A strange painter, whose grotesque, symbolic creations have received much attention today, is Hieronymus

Bosch (1462?–1516), considered by the modern Surrealists as the first Surrealist.

Owing to the Italian influence, there was no national art in the sixteenth century. The seventeenth century marked the climax of great painting in Flanders. Peter Paul Rubens (1577–1640), a great genius, painted all subjects, but chiefly religious ones because of popular demand. Sensuous rather than spiritual, his line and color were more inspiring than any tenderness of expression. His conceptions are huge and brilliantly painted with an eye to decorative possibilities. As a technician in the use of the brush, Rubens stands with Titian and Velásquez. Van Dyck (1599–1641) followed his manner with more restraint and a warm flesh tone which characterizes his famous portraits. The eighteenth century was marked by a decline, and the nineteenth and twentieth centuries in Belgium became strongly allied with French art.

DUTCH

Dutch painting has much in common with the Flemish. Realism was the dominant tone of Dutch art and the everyday Dutch scene was its subject matter. The portraits of Frans Hals (1581?–1666) give a perfect illusion of his subjects' actual physical presence.

Rembrandt (1606–1669), a portraitist with a strong sense of drama, is the greatest of Dutch painters and one of the world's most famous masters of art. He accentuated important features by lighting them strongly and sinking the others into dark colorless shadows which were nevertheless luminous. His success in portraiture was due to his deep sympathy with humanity: in the gesture of a single hand, he could portray a universal emotion.

Ter Borch (1617–1681) painted interiors and portraits on a small scale with much technical skill. Steen (1626–1679) was his opposite, painting debaucheries with a divine brush stroke ill-suited to his unpleasant subjects. Pieter de Hooch (1629–1677?) delighted in clever interior compositions with sunlight pouring through windows on people standing on checkered floors, and illuminating garnet and deep yellow objects. Vermeer (1632–1675) chose subjects similar to these three Dutch painters, but he excelled them in technique and in characterization of the figures in his scenes.

In the eighteenth century in Holland, painting was smothered under mountains of minute details: realism was carried to photographic extremes. In the nineteenth century artists depicted peasant subjects, painted canals and skies dark with drifting clouds, and did landscapes and cattle in a silver atmosphere suggestive of Corot. Van Gogh, the most important modern Dutch painter, has been discussed in the section on Modern Art in France.

GERMAN

Illuminated manuscripts and inferior wall paintings were the chief mediums of German art up to the thirteenth century. They were better drawn than contemporary Italian frescoes, but lacked modeling. The walls and ceilings of German churches were painted blue; the figures were drawn over this, and surrounded by architectural ornaments. Eventually stained glass and inset panels replaced the wall paintings. Altar decorations were painted on golden grounds with light figures.

In the fourteenth century northern sentiment started to be manifest in the flowing draperies, willowy figures, and sentimental head poses. There was a school at Cologne in the fifteenth century which delighted in rich detailed ornamentation. At Nuremberg the altarpieces of Wohlgemuth (1434–1519) had sharp outlines due to the influence of wood engravers.

The greatest of German painters was Albrecht Dürer (1471–1528), whose work is marked by an extraordinary skill in the handling of even the most minute details of his many notable paintings, which include both religious subjects and portraits. His superb engravings reveal this same skill.

Second only to Dürer among German painters was Hans Holbein the Younger (1497–1543), who lived for a time in England and is best known for his penetrating and beautifully designed portraits of British royalty at the court of Henry VIII.

Lucas Cranach the Elder (1472–1553) was one of the great German painters. His linear, simplified style, verging often on caricature, expressed an ingeniously naïve, humorous, and often pathetic quality.

The imitation of Italian art stifled German creative art in the seventeenth and eighteenth centuries, followed for a time by an attempt to revive the Italian Pre-Raphaelite Style.

The most distinctive German painting of the nineteenth century is the work of the Swiss painter Arnold Böcklin (1827–1901), who created his own world of mythical landscapes peopled with mythical figures. Although critics point to certain technical limitations, there is unquestioned fascination in his fine composition, skillful use of color, and originality of subject matter. Among the best known of his paintings are "The Island of the Dead" and "The Sacred Grove."

With the twentieth century came the French influence toward individualism: new themes and fresher paint. Important also was the influence of the great Norwegian painter Edvard Munch (1863–1944), whose work, often morbid in feeling, is very distinctive and powerful.

Paul Klee has been discussed in the section on Modern Art in France. George Grosz (born 1893) is known for his perceptive, very moving caricatures—especially those of war cruelties.

BRITISH

The English seem seldom to have felt the decorative qualities of plastic beauty. When their art did thrive, it was more to illustrate stories than to create art for its own sake. Because of fidelity to the model, their best work has been done in portraiture and landscape.

Illuminated manuscripts were made in Ireland and England in the thirteenth century. They show Byzantine influence. Any wall paintings must have been destroyed in their countless civil wars. From the fifteenth to the eighteenth century the English contented themselves with imported portrait painters: Holbein and Van Dyck among others.

Hogarth (1697–1764) was the first truly original English artist. He caricatured in paint, on small canvases, the fashions and vices of his time.

Sir Joshua Reynolds (1723–1792) made his fame as a portrait painter—especially of handsome women and noted men of the period. Thomas Gainsborough (1727–1788) was more the individualist who consciously attempted to break academic rules. His "Blue Boy" was painted as a revolt against Reynolds' idea that warm color and light are essentials of good painting. His numerous portraits of aristocratic women are highly decorative though superficial. The portraits of Romney (1734–1802) against plain backgrounds were much livelier than those of his predecessors. The one purely imaginative artist was William Blake (1757–1827), whose illustrations for the Book of Job show graceful grandeur in the lithe bodies and floating draperies of angel hosts.

John Constable (1776–1837), influenced by the Dutch, was somber in color, but his pleasure in rural life is admirably portrayed on his canvases. He dappled sunlight over his scenes, and helped eliminate brown from landscapes by introducing greens and blues. Joseph William Turner (1775–1851) was England's renowned romantic painter. He delighted in sunsets as seen on mountains, seashores, and marble buildings. His vivacious palette dazzled his public and at times verged on the theatrical. Burne-Jones (1833–1898), best of the Pre-Raphaelite school, attempted to reach the truth through a melancholy and poetic simplicity. His wan colors and willowy ladies, nevertheless, have an interesting decorative effect in their grace of line.

In the twentieth century, English painters have been greatly influenced by French movements.

Very distinctive are the paintings of village streets by Jack Butler Yeats (1871–1957), Irish artist, brother of the poet William Butler Yeats.

AMERICAN

Early America was too busy with pioneering to have the leisure requisite for art. The earlier artists spent most of their time in England, and they often copied English paintings. Dry and mechanical as the others, Peale (1741–1827) was more fortunate in having Washington as a sitter, as did Gilbert Stuart (1755–1828), the best American portrait painter in his period. These early painters may seem staid to the modern observer.

By 1825 landscape painting developed under the brushes of Doughty (1793–1856) and Cole (1801–1848). Kensett (1818–1872) added a hazy atmosphere suggestive of poetic autumnal days. A German by birth, but an American by adoption, Leutze (1816–1868) painted large historical scenes such as "Washington Crossing the Delaware," pictorially decorative, but lacking emotional expression. Hunt (1824–1879) studied under Millet and came back to America to teach that art was in the painter, not in the subject. After the Centennial Exhibition in 1876, art received an impetus, and by 1878 the Art Students' League and the Society of American Artists were incorporated. Young artists went to Europe for instruction, and though American art has followed French methods ever since, in subjects and motifs the Americans are distinctive.

The seascapes of Winslow Homer (1836–1910) show deep feeling for color, and originality, and energy in execution. Albert Ryder (1847–1917) rendered reality in a mystic manner. John Singer Sargent (1856–1925) brought skilled technique to portraiture; his effects were brilliant and spectacular. William Merritt Chase (1849–1916) painted *genre* and still life with a vivid palette and sure technique. James Abbot McNeill Whistler (1834–1903), who lived in England, was a forerunner of the moderns. Light, air, and space give a mysterious atmosphere to his canvases. The landscapes of George Inness (1825–1894) and Alexander Wyant (1836–1892) portrayed the Hudson River Valley.

Grant Wood (1892–1942), Thomas Hart Benton (born 1889), and John Steuart Curry (1897–1946), associated with the Midwest, and Paul Sample (born 1896), in New England, are widely recognized as artists of originality, distinctively American in subject matter and treatment.

Edward Hopper (born 1882), Charles Burchfield (born 1893), and Charles Sheeler (born 1883) are other noted painters of the period. Of a more experimental tendency have been Max Weber (born 1881) and Yasuo Kuniyoshi (born 1893). John Marin (1872–1953) is outstanding in this group for his vibrant, fresh, active canvases, particularly his seascapes, which borrow much from French Impressionism. He worked, however, principally in water color, achieving a maximum of vivid realism with only a few elementary hues.

Outstanding in the modern Abstract school in America are Alexander Calder (born 1898) and Joseph Albers (born 1888). Calder, recognized as a highly individual artist, has created the *mobile,* a system of balanced shapes hung from branches of wire and string and allowed to move freely. Albers has experimented with pure design in a way that resembles the works of Mondrian but is less formal. For the most part, however, American abstract art, though highly decorative, has thus far shown little originality.

ARCHITECTURE

PRIMITIVE

One of the first desires of primitive man was to shield himself from the elements in caves or in holes scooped out of hillsides. Others found it advisable to weave tree boughs together, like the South Sea Islanders, or to overlay poles with animal skins, like the American Indians, or to build with blocks of ice, like the Eskimos. The materials used were those that were common where the tribes lived. Since these structures were evolved merely for protection, we do not speak of them as forms of architecture. Not necessity alone, but a desire for beauty, is essential to dwellings with esthetic qualities. This artistic consciousness did not awake until the dawn of civilization.

EGYPTIAN

The Egyptians' knowledge of geometry and other mechanical sciences enabled them to build the Pyramids, during the Ancient Empire, from 5000 B.C. to 3000 B.C. The Middle Empire, from 3000 B.C. to 1700 B.C., saw the production of rock-cut tombs. The New Empire, 1700 B.C. to 35 B.C., was the golden era during which arose the great temples, Karnak, Memphis, and Luxor.

The Pyramids (built as tombs for deceased Pharaohs) are the most ancient monuments with architectural characteristics. Their massive construction is a marvel of mechanical ingenuity, with symmetry and simplicity which give them some claim to esthetic beauty. The later rock tombs are of little architectural interest, since they are hidden in hillsides.

The plan of the Egyptian temple included a plain wall, from the doorway of which a row of sphinxes led to a forecourt surrounded by columns. From this a dark, columned hall led to an inner sanctuary. The enormous circular columns were painted with brilliant hues. Picture writing covered the sloping walls from the floor to the flat roof. The beautiful columns were used to support the roof and not only as decorative additions. One strictly Egyptian architectural form is the obelisk—a tapering stone needle tipped with bronze, symbolizing a ray of the sun, erected to glorify kings.

The entrances to some of these tombs were lintels supported by sturdy columns, the predecessors of the Greek Doric style.

ANCIENT GREEK

The Greeks' passion was for ideal beauty; and their religion, which inspired their architecture, looked toward the perfection of Hellenic man. Because of their maritime pursuits, they were able to study architecture both in Egypt and the Orient, and to re-create what they saw into a typically Greek form which is one of the most perfect expressions of architectural beauty the world has ever known.

The Lion Gateway at Mycenae shows that there was an early period of Greek architecture, from about 1500 B.C. to 1100 B.C., when tombs and city gateways were built which employed the keystone principle. Many unproductive centuries intervened, when Greece was too much occupied with civil and the Persian wars to cultivate the arts. Under Pericles, from 460 B.C. to 429 B.C., there was a marvelous rebirth of art, and in place of the earlier buildings on the Acropolis at Athens the great temples which we know were built. Phidias, the sculptor, directed the building of Pericles' Athens and succeeded in making it the most beautiful city in the world.

The temples are the Greeks' best-known architectural expression. They were built with columns supporting the roof beam, as were the Egyptian temples, with one great difference: the Greek columns were on the outside, the Egyptian on the inside. This was due to a difference in conception. The Egyptians used their temples for worship, while the Greeks built theirs as shrines to house the images of the gods. It was the Greek custom to worship outside the temple. The usual plan of a Greek temple showed a rectangular building open at both ends, without windows, and surrounded by either a single or a double row of columns.

An "order," in classical architecture, refers to an entire column, including its base, shaft, and capital (top), with the structure which rests on it, called the *entablature*. This consists of a horizontal undecorated beam, resting on the columns, a frieze divided into square panels usually sculptured, called *metopes,* separated by projecting blocks, called *triglyphs*. On this rested the triangular gable containing sculpture. In Greece there were three "orders": Doric, the simplest; Ionic, the most graceful; and Corinthian, the most ornate. The Doric column had no base, resting directly on the stone platform, and was thicker at the bottom, swelling gently into a smaller top section. The Doric column was fluted: 16 to 20 channels ran vertically its entire length, separated by sharp edges. The Doric capital was a plain square stone block with right-angled edges. This simplicity contributes to the impression of strength and reticent beauty.

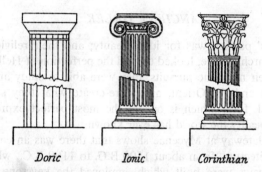

Doric   *Ionic*   *Corinthian*

The Greek Orders: Doric, Ionic, Corinthian

The Parthenon is the best example of the Doric order. Built by Ictinus of Pentelic marble, this temple of Athena had 8 Doric columns in front and 17 on each side, 34 feet high and over 6 feet in diameter. The internal plan included a rectangular chamber with a sacred cell at one end, in which stood the ivory and gold statue of Athena. Other sculpture by Phidias fitted into the triangular gable ends, and the bas-relief represented the Athenians honoring the virgin goddess.

The Ionic order originated in Asia Minor, its distinguishing mark being its capital, which consists of two spiral ornaments or volutes similar to curled ram's-horns. The Erechtheum and the Temple of Wingless Victory are Ionic. The former housed many shrines, and was therefore irregular in design as compared with Doric temples.

Corinthian columns had capitals decorated with rows of acanthus leaves, while the shafts were particularly slender. The monument of Lysicrates illustrates the Corinthian style.

The orders were the basic design of the Greek temples, enhanced by moldings, the shadows of which added a whole system of decoration to the building. Sculpture always complemented Greek architecture, which was characterized by repose and harmonious proportion, owing to a perfect balance between vertical and horizontal lines, masses of light and shade, and subtle curves which appear straight in the dazzling Mediterranean sunshine.

ROMAN

Roman architecture was a development of the Greek, gaining in richness but losing in refinement. The Romans, by one architectural innovation, changed the whole appearance of their buildings. This was the arch, which instituted curved lines and made possible great interiors uninterrupted by columns. With the arch came the invention of concrete, making possible the creation of curved surfaces, such as the dome of the Pantheon. Temples were not the Romans' chief form of expression. Their worldliness fostered the erection of theaters, aqueducts, circuses, baths, and triumphal arches, a type of architecture peculiar to a martial people. There were five Roman orders, all modifications of the three Greek orders.

The elliptical amphitheaters were among the greatest architectural creations of the Roman Empire; the largest is the Colosseum in Rome, opened in 80 A.D. It was possible for 40,000 spectators to be seated, and there was room for 40,000 more. Its size was not its only impressive feature; the sweeping lines of the entablature, and the reduplication of parts, added to its beauty.

The Pantheon, in use for nearly 1,800 years, still retains its original walls and vaultings; even the big bronze doors are the old ones. All the light enters from an aperture in the ceiling, and is evenly distributed, giving a wonderful effect. The Pantheon is in two parts: the rotunda and the portico, supported by twelve granite Corinthian columns 50 feet high. The interior is rendered magnificent by the great dome 140 feet high and the seven niches, alternately rectangular and semicircular, which break up the rotunda. The weight of the concrete dome is supported by walls 20 feet thick.

The Arch of Constantine, dedicated in 315 A.D., has three archways, each ornamented with four Corinthian columns on pedestals. A high attic rests on the entablature, the central part of which bears inscriptions. Medallions and sculptural relief ornament all available space. The Arch of Titus is simple and consists of a single archway.

EARLY CHRISTIAN

Constantine, the first Christian emperor, founded three large basilicas (churches) at Rome, inaugurating a new structural principle: the truss in roofing. This is a frame of beams and rods so fastened as to make a continuous bridge across an open space. The basilicas were built with one large hall with a portico attached, while galleries encircled the whole. The central aisle was separated from the side aisles by columns. The semicircular sanctuary at the far end held the altar. The exteriors were extremely plain, while the interiors were gorgeously decorated with marbles and mosaics. Early Christian basilicas were lighted from windows in the walls of a story rising above the columns (clerestory). Both the Romanesque and Gothic styles were outgrowths of this style.

Constantine's Eastern Empire was the seat of Byzantine architecture, which was greatly influenced by Oriental styles. Justinian's church of St. Sophia, at Constantinople, dedicated in 537 A.D., was the first of this school; St. Mark's, built at Venice in 1100, was the last. The distinguishing feature of all Byzantine architecture is the large central dome surrounded by smaller domes. Each dome in itself comprised two: the lower semicircular dome, being cut off at a certain point, was capped with a smaller dome. Small windows in these domes let in the light. The ground plan was in the shape of a cross, the four terminations and point of crossing each being crowned with a dome. Mosaic and stone fretwork, applied after the construction was completed, made lavish interiors.

MOORISH

The Moors in Spain, with their stronghold called the Alhambra, created a characteristic architectural form, replete with luxurious details, embodied in temples and mosques. Its chief characteristics are the horseshoe arch, pointed domes and minarets, and the brilliant coloring applied in geometric designs to surfaces of all structures, sculptures, and pictures.

The citadel-palace of the Alhambra in Granada, built from 1248 to 1306, is considered the finest example of Spanish-Moslem art. The inner gardens, fountains, balconies, and double-arched, richly ornamented gateways, all make for a peculiarly delicate and brittle sort of impressiveness. Many buildings of Saracenic style were built in India from the eleventh to the fourteenth centuries, chiefly mosques. The Taj Mahal, entirely of white marble, at Agra, is the "pearl" of Indian architecture; it is the tomb of a former ruler's favorite wife.

ROMANESQUE

The term Romanesque is used to describe the style of Christian architecture founded on the Roman. Like early basilicas, it had round arches for all openings, and small windows which did not weaken the strong walls necessary to support the outward pressure of the wooden or vaulted stone roof. The ground plans of the churches also followed the cross transept. A great variety of columns appeared, including short, slender shafts carrying braided motifs cut in relief.

Instead of depending on flat colorful mosaics, the Romanesque building introduced moldings and ornamental carving. Frescoes contributed the color. The circular baptistries were also an integral part of the whole, as was the wheel or rose window above the altar. Unlike the graceful Byzantine skylines and the barn-like basilica contours, the Romanesque was relieved by towers, but, compared with the Gothic which followed, it was very heavy, owing to the necessity for supporting its great stone vaulted roofs.

Cloisters, suiting the devotional spirit, were covered walks running around one or more sides of a monastery or church garden court; the early ones had round Romanesque arches, the later had Gothic.

The group of buildings at Pisa, which include the cathedral and baptistry and leaning tower, are the best examples of the Romanesque style. The form of the basilica was followed, with the addition of arm-like transepts making a Latin cross. The nave was separated from the side aisles by two rows of twelve huge red granite columns that once stood in Greek or Roman temples. On these columns rest upper walls of dark and light marble in strips pierced with windows. On these walls rest the trusses that support the main lead-coated roof. The crossing of the nave and transepts is topped with a dome of later date.

In 1174 the neighboring bell tower or campanile of white marble was built. This is the leaning tower of Pisa, and it is still a question whether it was erected purposely to lean as a wonder for spectators, or whether it was due to the sinking foundation that Benenato in 1234 undertook to continue, and Pisano to complete, the tower which could be kept in equilibrium only by adding successively smaller stories.

Romanesque architecture did not flourish in Italy alone. The church at Vézelay in France is a fine example, as is the Church of the Apostles at Cologne. This was called in Germany Rhenish architecture, because churches on the Rhine show similar characteristics, though some are completely circular in shape. In England this form was called Norman. Durham Cathedral is a splendid example, as are also the porch and stairway of Canterbury Cathedral. Romanesque architecture predominated in Europe from about 1000 to 1150, and continued beyond that in many regions.

GOTHIC

From approximately 1150 through the sixteenth century, cathedrals rose in France, Germany, Italy, and England, all showing similar characteristics, to which we give the name Gothic. The thirteenth century was the classical period of the Gothic style, with lines rising vertically to the heavens, expressing in their soaring spires and steeples the spiritual yearning of the early Church. Yet every change from Romanesque to Gothic marked the solution of a structural problem. Because the height of the rounded arch was fixed by its width, the new designers evolved the pointed arch, whose span and height were unrelated. The ugly thick walls necessary to support the weight of a vaulted stone roof were abandoned for thin walls, and the problem of support was solved by flying buttresses, piers, and arches whose weights leaned toward one another, creating a perfect balance. Since the framework, and not the walls, was the strength of Gothic cathedrals, many windows could be cut in without weakening the roof.

Ribbed vaulting, rich carving, high narrow moldings, and stone tracery framing windows of magnificent stained glass contributed to the elegance of the Gothic style. Light rays streaming through the jeweled windows filled the interior with glowing color. The floor plan followed the Romanesque, with tapering steeples where domes had been, and a series of small chapels around the semicircular choral apse. Doorways were elaborately sculptured, and waterspouts ended in fantastic winged animal heads known as *gargoyles*.

Notre Dame de Paris, the most famous example of early French Gothic cathedrals, has both grandeur and simplicity, its supporting buttresses being graceful and strong. The front of the church is almost exactly symmetrical, with its three great doorways richly ornamented with sculptured figures and gargoyles. The horizontal and vertical lines of Notre Dame, which was built in the twelfth century, are equalized, giving an over-all square design to the structure.

The cathedral of Chartres, built in the thirteenth century, exemplifies the vertical thrust of Gothic architecture at its height. The ornamental sculptures of this period show a greater naturalism, and the art of stained glass is at its peak.

An example of the late Gothic style (called Flamboyant) is the French church of Bourg (fifteenth century), renowned for the beauty of its sculptures, which are florid, excessively detailed, and predominate over the structural design. The fundamental simplicity of the Gothic style is lost, giving a sense of confusion and exaggerated individuality.

The Gothic style, most beautifully developed in France, was practiced throughout Europe.

In England, Gothic grew out of Norman, which already used buttresses—though flat, plain ones—and some pointed arches; but isolated features do not make a unified style. From the eleventh to the sixteenth century there was a constant evolution toward pure Gothic, the Tower of London exemplifying the Norman, Westminster Abbey the Early English (1200–1306), Warwick Castle the Decorated, and Canterbury nave and tower the Tudor (1400–1550) style, which featured enormous windows, lower roofs, perpendicular lines, and the roses of the house of Tudor. Westminster Abbey is perhaps the most graceful and magnificent development of the Gothic style in England, its unity of design being second only to Salisbury. Impressive in size, it is built of gray stone shading from white to black; the bold buttresses have a simple beauty.

Very few true Gothic churches were built in Italy. This is because the Renaissance came so early to Italy that the Gothic style never grew to any importance in that country except for the famous cathedral of Milan. The Florence Cathedral, in its original structure approaching the Gothic style, was built by Cambio, one of the great architects of the Middle Ages. This cathedral shows, however, characteristics of the early Renaissance; and this is particularly true of the famous bell tower designed by Giotto.

Other notable Gothic cathedrals include the one at Cologne, which dominates the city, and the cathedrals of Amiens, Reims, and Bourges in France.

RENAISSANCE

The revival of learning from the fourteenth to the sixteenth century encouraged a new freedom of thought which inspired artists with individual genius to create the architectural forms of the Renaissance, embodying the characteristics of Greece and Rome applied to secular rather than religious buildings. The one original feature of this period was the dome set on a pillared drum, crowned with a lantern which topped the church structure. The Florence Duomo, St. Peter's, and St. Paul's illustrate this type.

The Renaissance style in architecture, as in painting, developed in Italy long before it arrived in other countries. It was latest in England. In Florence, Giotto's bell tower announced a new conception of design, stressing geometrical symmetry with the square and circle replacing the pointed arch as motif. Alberti (1404–1472) was the most famous of the Italian architects of the early Renaissance.

The classic influence is apparent in the fronts or façades of Roman and Florentine palaces and French châteaux. The columns are not integral parts of the structure but are exterior ornaments, while the Roman semicircular arch graces every doorway. Architects of the Renaissance borrowed the details of their buildings from the ancient world. This overlaying of detail, when it was taken to excess in the sixteenth century, made even the best architecture of that period seem unnatural and disharmonious—or, more exactly, affected. This late Renaissance style has been classed Mannerist.

Renaissance architecture can be divided into four periods, with the dates varying enormously in each country, as follows:

(1) 1420–1490—Original, graceful, and free decorative detail from Rome.
(2) 1490–1550—Classic, characterized by use of the ancient orders as motifs.
(3) 1550–1600—Late Renaissance, including Mannerist and early Baroque styles.
(4) 1600–1700—The Baroque, at best grand and magnificent, though often marked by a decline of Renaissance style, with exaggerated orders, excessive decorations, and bulbous forms. The latter half of the century introduces the Rococo, marked by lighter but overintricate decorative display, such as scrollwork.

On the Gothic cathedral proper at Florence, Brunelleschi undertook to build a Renaissance dome, octagonal and pointed, topped by a lantern. Michelangelo declared that he could not have created anything more beautiful. The palaces of the Medici were also erected during this time, including the Pitti Palace, the Uffizi Palace, and the Ricardi, designed by Michelozzi, the Doge's Palace in Venice, and those erected by Palladio. Brunelleschi designed the Pitti Palace, leaving the enormous blocks of stone rough on the outside.

St. Peter's in Rome was begun by Alberti and Rossellino according to the design of Bramante, enhanced by the dome of Michelangelo and his details of the orders. Maderno was later responsible for the façade, and Bernini for the columnar approach. Seen from the Pincian Hill, the magnificent ensemble of St. Peter's shows to its best advantage, but, when gazed at near at hand, the façade almost hides the beautiful dome.

Bernini (1598–1680), noted also as a sculptor, was the greatest architect of the Baroque style, which in Italy almost always avoided the more decadent aspects of the late Renaissance. The Italian Baroque is typified by a grand, dramatic rhythm of diverse structures and both round and square design. The use of violent relief to produce light and shade is a Baroque technique. Typical of this style is an undulating façade of a system of columns such as the ones surrounding the court-yard of St. Peter's.

In France, Renaissance style was followed in erecting palaces, of which the two most famous are at Fontainebleau and Versailles, which borrow much from the Italian style, giving it a more graceful and courtly appearance. One of the most beautiful pavilions of the Louvre palace was designed (1665–1670) by Claude Perrault. Jacques de Gabriel built the Petit Trianon at Versailles, and he designed the Place de la Concorde, in Paris, in 1753.

Sir Christopher Wren did the most notable work of the English Renaissance in designing St. Paul's Cathedral (1675–1710), the dome of which is the crowning feature of two stories, the first Corinthian, the second Composite. Inigo Jones, in the sixteenth century, designed the palace of Whitehall in London.

MODERN

Degenerate showiness followed the Renaissance, and a Greek revival followed in England and Germany in 1800; during the century the British Museum, the University of London, the museums in Berlin, and the Dresden Theater were erected. By 1850 a Gothic revival was inaugurated, but it was unproductive.

In America the Colonial or Georgian style is a modified and simplified Renaissance, keeping the columns—but squaring them at times, as they are at Mount Vernon—and tending toward low, horizontal lines.

The classic revival in America is exemplified by the Capitol in Washington, which is in the Neo-Roman style. Columns in porticos and façades are employed with greater simplicity than usual. But none of these early types was as strictly American as is the modern steel skyscraper which evolved from the necessity for providing working space for millions of people on limited ground space. The Woolworth Building was the first beautiful example, soaring and graceful. It has been followed by many others, with vertical lines and towering pinnacles combining Greek simplicity with Gothic movement, and evolving a modern tempo in architectural expression, culminating in the Empire State Building in New York City, the tallest structure in the world, the group of modern buildings known as Rockefeller Center, and the United Nations buildings in New York.

An important characteristic of much of modern architecture should be noted. That is the unity of function and design. Modern architects, such as Frank Lloyd Wright (born 1869), Le Corbusier (born 1887), and the group stemming from the Bauhaus in Germany, notably Gropius (born 1883), believe that the appearance of a building should be determined by the use to which it is to be put; that it should contain no unnecessary ornament; and that it should harmonize with its physical surroundings. These men are representative of the architects who have been responsible for many modern buildings that are remarkable for their simple beauty.

SCULPTURE

Sculpture is the representation of a figure, person, or object in some solid medium such as stone, clay, metal, or wood. As in painting and architecture, standards of beauty and effectiveness in sculpture have changed with the times. One age has preferred a naturalistic rendering of an object; another has preferred a stylized, conventionalized representation. Whatever the dominant standard of a particular era, all good sculpture makes its effect by the beauty of its texture, the unity of its design, and by the emotional quality it conveys to the spectator.

EGYPTIAN

Many examples of Egyptian sculpture are still in existence: statues executed in stone, terra-cotta (red clay), bronze, and bas-reliefs from tombs, the latter depicting scenes from daily life and religious processions. The main features of most of Egypt's sculpture, like her architecture, were huge size and indestructibility. The Sphinx will present her inscrutable face to countless more generations of men.

Individual figures were stiff, either sitting with their knees pressed tightly together and having a rigid look about the head, body, and lower limbs, or standing with the right foot forward, head erect, and an immovable stare. These formal conventions make all the statues look more or less alike, but they were meant to be portraits of individual civic officials, Pharaohs, and gods. In images of deities, human bodies are often given symbolic heads of animals, such as jackals, hawks, rams, and cats. The Egyptians had no knowledge of grouping in sculpture; when more than one figure was required, they placed them side by side, like the statues which lead up to their temples. All Egyptian sculpture was brilliantly painted.

ASSYRIAN AND BABYLONIAN

The Chaldean reliefs found at Susa and Tello, and those at Nineveh, are of alabaster, and, like the paintings, chiefly commemorate the victories of kings. Unlike the rigid, straight-lined Egyptian sculpture, the Babylonian reliefs portrayed round, muscular figures. The hunting scene from Nineveh—showing horses, dogs, lions, and men in bas-relief—is a wonderful example of decorative sculpture, the animals being particularly natural. Winged bulls with human heads, and monsters with eagles' beaks, were drawn with a fine regard for ornamental design. Action and brutality were reflected in the sculpture of this region, as contrasted with the philosophic repose of the dwellers on the Nile.

GREEK

Greek sculpture developed with the aid of Hellenic philosophy, ceremonial and theatrical dancing, and athletic competitions. Myron's "Discobolus" illustrates the perfectly balanced Greek athletic ideal. The Greeks aspired to produce an ideal conception of a natural form. Even the earliest Hellenic sculpture, rough-hewn from wooden blocks, had a hint of that proportion which made later works immortal. When stone began to be used (the mountains of Greece contain large quantities of marble) the same simple block-like figures were copied in the new medium.

By the sixth century B.C., all over the Greek-speaking world stood temples decorated with pediments, friezes, etc., of group sculptures and reliefs in marble. Still stiff in form, these were more relaxed than the archaic style, and the more accustomed to handling marble the sculptors became, the more naturalistic was their art, until, finally, by the fifth century B.C., they attempted portraiture, and memorials of heroes and athletes were produced in great numbers.

No originals of Myron's work exist, but there are some excellent marble copies, notably of the "Discobolus" (Discus-Thrower) and "Penthali." The motion of Myron's figures was a new and successful departure from the old forms, and he excelled in depicting muscular action. The faces of his statues are unemotional and severe.

Phidias (500?–432 B.C.) is considered the greatest of the Greek sculptors because of his magnificent decorations for the Parthenon. The groups in the triangular pediments illustrate Athena's birth and her protection of Athens, while the frieze, 524 feet long, represents a processional rejoicing. These masterpieces are created with artistic perfection, being both beautiful and sublime. Phidias had a majestic conception of the human form, and compositional harmony. He also possessed a talent for delicate modeling, particularly rich and various in the treatment of broad and flowing draperies, which were immediately related to the body beneath. Ivory, gold, precious stones, and bright coloring ornamented his figures. Ancient writers tell us that his finest statues were the Athena (30 feet high), in the Parthenon, and the seated Zeus in the temple of Olympia.

Polyclitus invented and published rules for the proportions of the human body. His "Doryphorus" became a standard of measurement for many years. He is known particularly for his harmoniously proportioned athletes balanced on one foot, a position imbuing them with an easy grace, and for his conception of the Amazon (warrior woman) type.

The later Attic school, in the middle of the fourth century B.C., was led by Praxiteles and Scopas. Not so harmonious as the sculpture produced by Phidias, their work reflected a change in Greek thought: it was more emotional and less reposeful. Scopas was the architect hired for the rebuilding of the temple of Athena at Tegea. Passion and character were displayed in the expressions of his figures, marking the beginning of dramatic sculpture. Lysippus, in the latter half of the fourth century B.C., replaced the graceful, somewhat sensuous art of Praxiteles with bronze statues suggestive of manly strength. They were life-like characterizations accurately executed, particularly in the treatment of the hair. He changed the proportions set by Polyclitus, making the head smaller and the body more slender and elegant.

After the time of Alexander the Great, sculpture declined in Greece. The islands and Asia Minor took the leadership, accentuating emotion until it became mere theatrical agitation. The "Colossus of Rhodes" and "Laocoön," the man and youths struggling with pythons, had admirable technique marred by an emotional overemphasis typical of this late period called "Hellenistic."

ROMAN

The Roman conquest in the second century absorbed Greek art, although Greco-Roman works are merely copies of old Greek models. Pasiteles, an Italian Greek, by attempting nature study, tried to revive sculptural art, without much success—though realistic flower, fruit, and leaf forms were introduced into sculptured decoration. But after Trajan's death in 117 A.D., Hadrian tried to encourage a Greek revival which resulted only in producing pretty images of young men, all of them of one type.

However, Rome excelled in sculptural portraiture. In contrast to the abstract intellectual forces in Greece, the Romans were materialistic, and their busts were the realistic images of living men. Rome's power depended on the strength of her leaders, whose portraits in the round are exceptionally life-like and are among the finest the world has ever produced.

EARLY CHRISTIAN AND BYZANTINE

Because sculpture could not be used to teach Bible stories without suggesting heathen idols, the early Christian Church frowned on figures in the round and succeeded in suppressing this art form. Finally the Oriental luxury associated with Constantine's Byzantine court demanded some solid expression, and sculptors started to carve reliefs on the elaborate coffins of the deceased. The coffins were large enough to hold two bodies, and often simple-plane portrait busts were set in hollowed niches in the covers.

From the eighth to the eleventh century, metalwork often took the place of marble; the high altars and confessionals were decorated with ornamental and symbolic designs. Stone sculpture tended to be limited to two dimensions and to follow closely the shape of the architectural form. There was little attempt to portray subjects naturalistically, the emphasis being on symmetry of design and symbolic meaning. From this period through the early Middle Ages, artists made use of a large store of traditional church symbolism. The dove, for instance, represented the soul or the Holy Ghost; a flock of sheep stood for the disciples; the phoenix (the bird that burns to death, a new bird rising from the ashes) was a symbol of immortality. Decorative figures were borrowed from pagan sculpture; the Greek legends, such as the story of Cupid and Psyche, held a fascination and meaning for the Christian artists.

ROMANESQUE AND GOTHIC

The fact that Romanesque architecture was horizontal and without motion and that the Gothic was vertical and soaring had a like effect on the sculpture of the two periods. The Church had the exclusive direction of Romanesque sculpture, and the Gothic was executed by lay craftsmen whose imaginations were able to expand and elaborate upon the ecclesiastical traditions. The Roman influence was strong in the early period, the monks preferring to study old statues rather than living models. However, Byzantine influence was also felt in the use of elaborate conventional designs. Figures of this cloister period were stiff and elongated.

In Italy during the Romanesque period little was produced in the round. Carving and modeling were confined to church portals and pulpits, baptismal fonts, and the like. Such secondary ornamentation cannot have that internal harmony which makes for great art. The French, however, had a stronger feeling for the relation of sculpture to architecture. They crowded the recesses of their church porches with life-sized and colossal (larger-than-life) statues.

This period in Germany was distinguished by more naturalism and energy of movement. At Hildesheim, columns reminiscent of Trajan's were erected, with spiral bands of relief sculpture. The figures were naïve, and their draperies pretended to classic folds. But in miniature work the artists of the Rhine were unsurpassed. They executed tiny ivory carvings with enamel, which were as delicate, graceful, and intricate as anything that has since been produced on a similar minute scale. Wood-carving was also a Northern achievement, exemplified both in church doors and in the colossal crucifixes of Saxony and Bavaria.

The Gothic period in Italy is typified by the works of Nicola Pisano (1225?–1278). They were not truly sculpturesque because of overelaboration: they were sculpture degenerated into a glorified form of architecture. His first works were loaded with details, but, after studying the classics, he caught a certain beauty of conception. Lacking this beauty, his son Giovanni Pisano (1245–1320?) was sincere and virile. Love of nature, as taught by St. Francis in the thirteenth century, inspired the work of Giotto and Andrea Pisano in Florence, where a humanistic and naturalistic art arose, leading into the style of the Renaissance.

French Gothic sculpture can be best illustrated by the western portals of Notre Dame Cathedral in Paris, built in 1225, and by the statuary and reliefs carved for cathedrals at Chartres, Reims, and Amiens, each of which was adorned with several thousand figures. The subject matter was religious.

German Gothic sculpture reached its culmination in the cathedrals of Naumburg and Bamberg (1250–1300), where statue portraits of their princely founders stood against the pillars. These statues were simple and realistic, and the treatment of their draperies was highly original and successful.

RENAISSANCE

In Italy, from 1300 to 1450, there was a great surging of emotional and intellectual energy which interested man in himself and in the universe in relation to himself—a movement called Humanism.

In 1403, Ghiberti (1378?–1455) went to Florence to complete the Baptistery doors, for his design won in a competition with the architect Brunelleschi. Later he replaced these with another pair referred to as the

"Gates of Paradise," unveiled in 1452. Each of the 20 panels represents a Bible scene from the story of the creation to Solomon. The illustrations are masterful.

Donatello (1386–1466), a pupil of Ghiberti, was the great transitional sculptor between the Pisani and Michelangelo. He began working in the round while rebuilding the church of Or San Michele in Florence, filling in the ornamental niches with statuary. Della Quercia (1371?–1438) portrayed natural beauties, while Della Robbia (1399?–1482) created a poetry of rhythmic motion in his panels of children placed in the singing gallery of Florence's cathedral. His art was affectionate and peaceful as compared with Donatello's restless searching for new forms of expression. Verrocchio (1435–1488) used plaster of Paris for his molds, reviving the ancient method, which had been replaced by burnt gypsum.

Michelangelo (1475–1564) in many ways exemplifies the flowering of Renaissance sculpture in Italy. He was a poet-artist of mighty energy and genius, forever striving to express the emotions and intellectual activities of his time. Of the three arts in which he was skilled, he preferred sculpture. His "David" is a fine, loose-limbed figure 13 feet high, modeled when the sculptor was 26 years old. His "Pietà" was truly an expression of many of his figures, suggesting both human sorrow and a stoic indomitable spirit. The four reclining figures on the Tomb of the Medici are very famous; they represent: "Twilight," "Dawn," "Day," and "Night." His women, like those of the Greeks, were slightly masculine in their proportions; he would often distort or idealize certain features of the body to express an idea.

A genius among craftsmen, Benvenuto Cellini (1500–1571) created small bronzes exquisitely. His work in metals was like enlarged jewelry. His cup at the Metropolitan Museum in New York City and his saltcellar in Venice are brilliant examples of the fastidiousness of his workmanship in gold and enamels. His statue of Perseus in Florence is full of the fire of life.

Renaissance sculpture in France during the fifteenth century was still under the influence of the Italian school. Jean Goujon (1510?–1566?) developed a typical Renaissance style. His sculpture combined Flemish pictorial naturalism with Italian grace. His reliefs on the choir screen of St. Germain l'Auxerrois are harmonious and elegant.

Under Louis XIV, in the seventeenth century, French sculpture developed a dramatic, regal style with an emphasis on sharp relief; it was at times pompous and sacrificed the tranquil harmony of the earlier period. The eighteenth century delighted in graceful, aristocratic forms and sentiments. Houdon (1741–1828) worked for naturalism and the exact reproduction of his sitters' likenesses, and found the spirit within the man in his seated statues of Voltaire and Rousseau and his busts of Molière, Diderot, Franklin, Washington, and others.

The Renaissance in Germany dawned slowly, and when it did come, sentiment triumphed over form. The sixteenth century was overrun by foreign styles, chiefly Italian, while French influence permeated the seventeenth and eighteenth centuries. The equestrian statue of the Great Elector, Frederick III, by Andreas Schlüter (1664–1714), is noteworthy.

MODERN

The modern movement in sculpture begins with the spectacular genius of Auguste Rodin (1840–1917) in France at the end of the nineteenth century. It was a period of vigorous individualists, all of whom strove to be interpretative about homely subjects. Rodin's works are vigorous and sensuous. His was the practice of making the figure or group look as though it had emerged from an untrimmed mass, a method which tended to simplify form. Although he worshiped the Greeks, he himself was more romantic than classic, and more the realist than the idealist. He cared more for the appearance of masses than he did for the abstract beauties of proportion. He was really an impressionistic sculptor; he transferred the interest from the objects to the light that falls upon them. In other words, he originated atmosphere in the carving of marble, not caring so much for the actual body form as for its luminosity. Often he thickened forms and exaggerated lines to obtain glowing masses.

Other modern sculptors who have achieved renown are Aristide Maillol (1861–1944), Charles Despiau (1874–1946), and Gaston Lachaise (1882–1935), French; Ernst Barlach (1870–1938), Georg Kolbe (born 1877), Wilhelm Lehmbruck (1881–1919), and Hans Arp (born 1888), German; Jacob Epstein (born 1880 in the U.S.), Henry Moore (born 1898), English; Ivan Mestrovic (born 1883), Yugoslav; Aleksandr Archipenko (born 1887), Russian; Carl Milles (1875–1955), Swedish; Augustus Saint-Gaudens (1848–1907), Daniel Chester French (1850–1931), George Grey Barnard (1863–1938), Lorado Taft (1860–1936), and William Zorach (born 1887), American.

MUSIC

Music has served man in many ways. It has figured in his religious ceremonies, either as an expression of his feelings or as a medium of supplicating or placating a deity. It has served as a means for the expression of an individual composer's deepest emotions. It has accompanied dances.

It has served purely as entertainment, to lighten one's spirits. All these are legitimate functions of music, the particular function determining to a large extent the forms of music. To trace the history of music is to indicate the different forms through which music has evolved. Prehistoric man must have known that he could produce sound by blowing tube-shaped instruments, striking resonant surfaces, or even plucking strings, for the twang of the arrow echoed pleasantly in his ear. We know that the ancient world had its music, but the Aeolian harps of Greece and Egypt are lost to us. Their scales differed from ours, and we have no way of learning how their music sounded, because they did not write it down, and even if they had done so, we should not know how they wished it to be played. We do know something about historical sources of the music which we call "ours," that which is known as Western European music. The string instrument, particularly the bow, came from the seventh- and eighth-century Arabian culture; the Egyptians had a harp, though of an odd shape; the Hebrews sang in chorus and used horns in their temple worship. The Greeks played on the lyre to accompany song and dance; and under Nero's rule (54–68 A.D.) in Rome came the birth of musical theorists who paved the way for written music.

EVOLUTION OF THE SONG

The simplest musical form was the song. The folk songs of European nations are the heartfelt expression of the people, handed down from generation to generation by tonal memory. Many of them are recognized as great music today. These early songs were both sad and merry. The Volga boatman's song, which the slaves chanted as they pulled on the heavy barge ropes, expressed all the misery of their servitude and physical exhaustion. Its harmonies and soul-stirring cadences put us in somewhat the same despairing mood as the men who originally sang it. In contrast, we have the joyful Hungarian folk dances which move us to abandon by the rapid swing of their exciting rhythms.

As the knowledge of musical forms advanced, these tuneful outpourings of the people gave rise to "art songs," the productions of individual men who wrote melodies suggested by poems or situations. Franz Schubert (1797–1828) was one of the greatest of these composers because of his skill in characterization. In *Hark! Hark! The Lark,* the phrase "Arise, arise, arise" soars in melody, while in *Gretchen at the Spinning Wheel* there is the very rhythm of the revolving wheel. Robert Schumann (1810–1856), Robert Franz (1815–1892), and Edvard Grieg (1843–1907) all wrote lyric songs which idealized emotion. The art song achieved a balance between lyric and dramatic qualities in the songs of

Johannes Brahms (1833–1897) and Franz Liszt (1811–1866). Hugo Wolf (1860–1903) and Richard Strauss (1864–1949) wrote dramatic songs, discarding formal plans and introducing descriptive music whenever the words suggested it.

CHURCH MUSIC

Early musical art enjoyed the patronage of the Church, as did painting and architecture; and the early Christian dogmas, which placed purity of soul above all material things, are clearly reflected in the choral music which gave an effect of purity and repose far removed from all profane passion. Palestrina (1528?–1594) and Orlando de Lasso (1532–1594) created polyphonic choruses which are still used in church services. "Polyphonic" means "many-toned," and the chants were so called because each melody was sung by a different group of voices, low and high, coming together on one note at certain moments, a harmonious sounding together that absorbs each melody and leaves an impression of remoteness so unearthly that it has often been called "angels' voices." The soaring quality of these chants was accentuated by their even flow. There was no natural resting place such as is provided by the modern major and minor scale. This lack of dissonance, or struggle, of rhythmic meters and tonality expresses a very pure musical quality, almost abstract.

OPERA

In 1600 the "Camerata," a group of musical innovaters inspired by the spirit of the Renaissance, met at Florence, and their new music was the beginning of *opera,* an expression of human emotions in dramatic form, in contrast to polyphony, which had succeeded in expressing divine aspirations. To express passion the individual voice was required, and choral polyphony was suppressed. Their first form was called a "recitative," and comprised a single voice moving up and down, merely exaggerating the cadences of natural speech. Claudio Monteverde (1567–1643), a Venetian, in his *Lament of Arianne,* further individuated his singer's voice by widening its range and introducing dramatic dissonances. He also invented the *tremolo* of the bow and the *pizzicato* (plucking of strings) for effects.

Early Italian opera was really a concert in costume. Vulgarity of technique was indulged in to gain the plaudits of the audience. The orchestra lacked instrumental variety and was used only to accompany solos. Conventions dominated Italian opera, the subject matter of which was usually selected from classical mythology, and there were three male and three female singers. The first major departure from these conventions was in the operas of the German composer Christoph Gluck (1714–1787), who improved its dramatic effectiveness. Gluck changed the *overture*—which heretofore had been incidental music played while the audience chatted—to a characteristic piece of music which would give a suggestion of the opera which was to follow. Gluck also did much to bring life to opera. Although his stories were traditional in that they were taken from mythology, he made his characters live and through them heightened the emotion of his scenes. He did away with much of the artificiality of the use of the voice. Gluck's operas *Orfeo ed Euridice* and *Alceste* are quite often performed today. His theory of dramatic opera was later more fully developed by Wagner.

Almost contemporary with Gluck, but far different in style, was Wolfgang Amadeus Mozart (1756–1791). His operas dealt with literary rather than mythological figures. His music has tremendous charm and a lightheartedness as well as seriousness. His operas which are most popular today are *Don Giovanni, The Marriage of Figaro,* and *The Magic Flute.*

Carl Maria von Weber (1786–1826) was the first to discover that different instruments, by their varying timbres, or sound qualities, could suggest both objects and situations. This was the birth of musical *motifs.* A motif, as used in opera, is a short musical theme recurring with variations and associated with a character, an event, or a scene.

Richard Wagner (1813–1883) was one of the greatest of all composers of opera. The fact that he wrote both the music and the libretto (the book or play of the opera) gave a unity to his operatic conceptions which did much to accentuate their power. Outstanding among Wagner's works are *Lohengrin,* Tannhäuser, the *Ring of the Nibelungen* (in four parts), *Die Meistersinger, Tristan und Isolde,* and *Parsifal.* Rather than call them *operas,* Wagner spoke of his works as *music-dramas,* whose soul was action. Taking Germanic legends for themes, he imbued opera with a new life, giving it greater dramatic qualities. In order to break down other conventions and give himself free rein for expression, he discarded the set arias and substituted what he called infinite melody, with its *leitmotifs* suggesting plot developments through the medium of the orchestra. By all these means, Wagner managed to put together a subtle and expressive sound fabric, really a kind of musical architecture in which each part had its reason for being.

Giuseppe Verdi (1813–1901) was as important a figure in Italian opera as Wagner was in German opera. Vastly different in style and temperament from the German master, Verdi was less of an innovator, although his works are highly dramatic. He preserved the set aria and the recitative, depending upon an extraordinary gift of melody for effect. Verdi wrote more than a score of operas, of which the most popular today are: *Rigoletto, La Traviata, Il Trovatore, Aïda, Otello,* and *Falstaff.*

In Russian opera, *Boris Godounov* by Modest Moussorgsky (1835?–1881) is an outstanding, powerful masterpiece.

Two of the most popular of all operas are *Carmen,* by Georges Bizet (1838–1875), and *Faust,* by Charles Gounod (1818–1893), both French.

Of the late nineteenth and early twentieth centuries, a few composers may be mentioned as characteristic and as individually important. Giacomo Puccini's (1858–1924) great melodic works include *La Bohème, La Tosca,* and *Madame Butterfly.* Richard Strauss (1864–1949) created *Salome, Elektra,* and *Der Rosenkavalier,* powerful works deriving from the tradition of Wagner. *Pelléas et Mélisande,* by Claude Debussy (1862–1918), the French Impressionist, is a mystical work which is remarkable, maintaining its gossamer unreal quality throughout.

More recent operas are *The Love for Three Oranges,* by Prokofiev (1891–1953), and *Wozzeck* (very modern in its tonal effects), by Alban Berg (1885–1935). Special mention should be made of *Porgy and Bess,* by George Gershwin (1898–1937), and *The Medium,* by Gian-Carlo Menotti (born 1911).

THE ORATORIO

Closely allied to opera is the *oratorio,* a dramatic poem in a musical setting, with recitatives, arias, and choruses sung without action or costumes on the concert stage. Its great eighteenth-century progenitors were George Frederick Handel (1685–1759) and Johann Sebastian Bach (1685–1750). Handel, a German who wrote many of his works in England, used pleasing Italian melodies which have great popular appeal. He wrote *The Messiah,* containing the stirring "Hallelujah Chorus," in 24 days. Bach's vocal works, more exactly called cantatas, were more profound: they made their effects through harmony and polyphony, and were both earnest and devout. The *Mass in B Minor* reaches the sublime. Just as devout, but more delicate in conception, *The Creation* and *The Seasons* of Joseph Haydn (1732–1809) are similar to the oratorios which Felix Mendelssohn (1809–1847) wrote later in his *St. Paul* and *Elijah.* In the latter part of the nineteenth century César Franck (1822–1890) wrote his *Beatitudes.*

DEVELOPMENT OF THE PIANOFORTE STYLE

The history of instrumental music begins with the first keyboard instrument, the harpsichord. Instead of horizontal "voices," as were used in polyphonic singing, the harpsichord made easier the formation of vertical chords; and this resulted in greater accent and in rhythm more natural to the dance than to the song. That is the reason for so many dance rhythms in later sonata and symphony compositions.

Domenico Scarlatti (1683–1757) was the first to discontinue composition in voices and to start striking eight or nine notes simultaneously, followed perhaps by only one. The tone of the harpsichord was not sustained: loudest when first struck, it rapidly dwindled. Because of this defect, rapid, highly accentuated pieces were popular, which showed the skill of the performer and composer by unusual rhythms and brief themes, rather than by slow, sentimental melodies. Handel and Bach therefore wrote in dance rhythms, such as minuets, gavottes, sarabands, and *gigues.* The result was not cold or metallic, for the harpsichord had tone color, which means that the plucking of the strings could produce both clear tones and softly muted ones, providing contrast. Harmony was sustained by dividing a tone into the notes which produced it; and, by repeating these rapidly, an illusion of continuity was successfully attained.

Next came the clavichord, which was Bach's favorite instrument, as is shown by his collection of 48 fugues and preludes called the "Well-tempered Clavichord." By varying the pressure on the keys of the clavichord, the player could make the sound tremble or whisper, and this intimate personality gave the clavichord great light and shade possibilities. Naturally pieces composed on so delicate an instrument would be poetic and suggestive. Instead of telling the whole story, Bach's preludes sketch the outline and demand sympathetic and intelligent listeners to create the full moods which he skillfully suggested.

Finally, with Mozart, the pianoforte came into its own. His skill in playing was equaled only by his love of pure beauty and noble expression. The pedal of the piano made possible sustained harmonies and soft and loud tonal contrasts with sharper accents. Because tone could be indefinitely carried, the left hand was freed and variety was added, as in *Fantasia in C Minor.* Mozart's whole style was refined and delicate, beginning with his first minuet, written when he was six years of age.

After Mozart, Beethoven, Schumann, Brahms, and César Franck used pianistic rhythmic patterns and introduced dissonances and changing harmonies fused by the pedal. Brahms and Schumann were fond of rhythmic syncopations, in which one scheme of accents conflicts with another in the notes of the melody.

Frédéric Chopin (1809–1849) was notably sensitive, creating a pedal atmosphere—a vibration or fringe of softer sound around the original chord, making an elusive tone in which the note floats. Chopin's waltzes, mazurkas, and études are almost pure pianistic music. He was one of the group of artists patronized by Louis Philippe, as was Franz Liszt, the Hungarian pianist-composer, who in seeking sensation demanded that his instrument provide climactic effects. Anton Rubinstein (1830–1894) had a great vogue because of his dramatic virtuosity. Russian-born Sergei Rachmaninoff (1873–1943) is also a famous composer for the piano, as in his *Prelude in C Minor.*

Among later great composers for the piano, Claude Debussy is outstanding. His *Clair de Lune* is widely known. Like Debussy, Maurice Ravel (1875–1937) and Scriabin (1872–1915) were Impressionists, content to relax classical tradition to convey potent moods.

FURTHER EVOLUTION OF MUSICAL FORMS

After the development of the keyboard style, musicians realized that they would have to evolve more complex forms than the short dance suites to express fully the harmonic range of the new instrument, the pianoforte. Scarlatti and Bach, in the eighteenth century, contented themselves with simple two-beat and three-beat dances, and when they required something more profound, they renewed polyphonic harmonies. From their pioneering to the apex of developmental form in the sonatas of Beethoven (1770–1827), the evolution can be divided into three phases as follows:

(1) Scarlatti used a two-part form, starting at times in a minor key, swinging away to a contrasting major key with a falling cadence. The second half is the exact reverse, beginning with the theme in the major key and ending with a final cadence in the original minor. Two such well-marked halves were bound to become monotonous, however.

(2) This mechanical impression was somewhat helped in the three-part form used by Bach and Scarlatti also. The first was a statement of themes in one key, the second was like a discussion of the same themes in a variety of keys, and the third was like a summary in the original key with a decisive climax. Minuets, quartets, and eighteenth-century symphonies employed this form.

(3) The next period consisted of a further amplifying of the three-part composition. In Beethoven's first sonata the first theme lasts for 20 measures, and there are three themes in all—the first in one key and the next two in a different key. The statement of these themes came to be called the *exposition.* The *development* was the name applied to the second part, which included an expansion or variation on the original themes played in many different keys. The third section, named the *recapitulation,* contained all the elements introduced in the exposition, and all were keyed the same.

Beethoven's marvelous success with the fully developed sonata form was due to the unity of his themes, which nevertheless gave infinite variety.

His sonatas may be described as continuous musical thoughts. A different conception is found in the compositions of Chopin, Schumann, Grieg, and the American, MacDowell, all of whose piano sonatas give the impression of brightly colored beads strung on the slenderest imaginable thread.

The concert form sonata for a solo instrument accompanied by the orchestra was perfected by Mozart and is known as the *concerto*. It consists of three movements: (1) an *allegro* in sonata form; (2) an *andante,* a short slow movement; (3) a lively *rondo finale*. Near the end of each movement there is usually a *cadenza* which allows the soloist to play alone and brilliantly. The exact form of each movement varies with the composer.

CHAMBER MUSIC

Chamber music has been compared to a literary essay because of the purity of its form and its appeal to the intellect. In a marvelous *ensemble* of two violins, viola, and violoncello, no one instrument takes precedence over the others. There is a delightful musical courtesy in the way each instrument allows the others to speak. Not volume, but rather understatement, a concentration of necessary material, is characteristic. One might say that chamber music is well edited, with everything irrelevant discarded.

Music of this refinement evolved in the eighteenth century under aristocratic patronage in Germany and Austria. Haydn wrote 77 string quartets, formal and precise. However, Beethoven's 17 works are the outstanding achievements of chamber music. His later quartets point to modernism by their increasing use of tone color. Schubert, Schumann, Brahms, Franck, Dvořák, and Smetana all lent their talents to this type of composing. More recent composers who have added variety to chamber music are Debussy, Ravel, and Stravinsky.

SYMPHONIC MUSIC

The *symphony* is today the most popular form of serious musical expression. A symphony is a composition for orchestra consisting of three or four distinct *movements*. Each movement usually has its own melodies or *themes* which are developed in characteristic ways. The movements of a symphony are played in different *tempi* (speeds), with pauses generally following each movement. The unity of a symphony derives from the over-all emotional quality and from the tonal relationships of the movements. The first movement of a classical symphony is generally in the so-called *sonata* form, where two main themes are presented and developed in juxtaposition to each other. The second movement is slower than the first and follows no set form. The third movement may be in *minuet* or *scherzo* form; the minuet is courtly, the scherzo playful. The final movement is generally rapid and in *rondo* form, with one main theme and several others played alternately. Most symphonies have no names. We refer to them by number or key, as, for example, Mozart's G Minor, Beethoven's Fifth, or Prokofiev's Third. The reason for this is that symphonies are for the most part *absolute music;* that is, the composer expects the music to stand for itself without reference to any literary story or scene. He wants us to concentrate on the musical ideas and emotions he is trying to convey. Some symphonies, it is true, do bear specific names (Haydn's *Farewell,* Beethoven's *Pastoral,* Tschaikowsky's *Pathétique*). These arise frequently from the circumstances of their composition or are descriptive of the mood the composer wishes to present, in which case the symphony approaches the category of *program music.*

Before proceeding with the symphony, we should know something about the symphony orchestra. The instruments which comprise our symphony orchestra are of four types: string choir, percussion, wood-wind, and brass-wind. The string choir includes the instruments played with bows—violins, violas, violoncellos, and bass viols. The wood-winds are of two types—the reeds, which include the clarinet, oboe, English horn, bassoon, and saxophone, and the non-reed, notably the high-pitched flute, of which the tone is clearer than that of the slightly nasal reed instruments. A quintet of horns forms the brass-wind group—trumpet and cornet, the mellow-sounding French horn, trombone, and deep-throated tuba. Percussion instruments are struck to produce sound, and also include two types—the rhythmical drums (bass, square, kettle) and tympani, and the melodious xylophone.

These instruments can produce a tone color impossible for the human voice to achieve. In the orchestra's first stage under Bach and Handel, the value of the instrumental timbres was recognized, and polyphony, discouraging, as always, to individual voices, forced the division by pitch. Violins, flutes, oboes, and trumpets carried the soprano parts, while cellos and bassoons contributed the alto. In this way there was no tonal contrast, the horn being the only instrument allowed to play alone, principally because it did not fit in very well with its neighbors. The harpsichord was played, moreover, to "fill in" whatever changes in harmony there were, thus eliminating by fusion the one chance of a tonal variety. Neither Bach nor Handel wrote what we consider as symphonies today.

The first composer to write in modern symphonic form was Franz Joseph Haydn, who wrote 125 symphonies. With Haydn came the definite separation of the instrumental voices. He threw out the harpsichord and instituted bassoon solos in his later symphonies.

Very nearly contemporary with Haydn was Mozart, who wrote 49 symphonies. Like Haydn, Mozart was a master melodist, but there is evident in the best of Mozart's symphonies a seriousness and nobility not too frequently present in Haydn's work. Mozart used the resources of his orchestra skillfully and with full attention to the tonal possibilities of the choirs.

The symphonies written by Mozart and Haydn are *classical* in form and feeling; that is, they follow certain definite patterns and are more or less restrained. With Ludwig van Beethoven we come to a composer who, while utilizing the classical form, invested it with greater freedom and variety and eventually burst the limits of the classical form. Beethoven was the consummate genius of the symphonic form. He was blessed with an advanced state in the development of instruments, with the foundations laid by Haydn and Mozart, and, with magnificent intellectual and emotional powers, contributed a perfectly unified variety and richness of expression to symphonic form. Even in his earliest symphonies Beethoven gave solos to the least obvious instruments in the orchestra, often achieving unconventional and whimsical effects. Further, he courted lively, erratic tonal contrasts that gave great power to his works, and he used suspense, giving recurring glimpses of great themes before they burst on the ear in all their glory. He combined soaring poetry with logical feeling in the development of his themes. Beethoven wrote nine symphonies which are landmarks in musical history. The First, Second, and Fourth are restrained in feeling, while the Third is heroic in scope (it is called the *Eroica*). The Fifth is again on a grand scale. His Sixth or *Pastoral* is descriptive of the moods of nature. The Seventh and Eighth are both vigorous and full of spirit. In his Ninth, Beethoven wrote his longest symphony. Not satisfied with the resources of the orchestra, he called upon a chorus and four soloists in the last movement, which is a musical setting of Schiller's "Ode to Joy." Here Beethoven sings out his belief in the brotherhood of man.

After Beethoven there came more variety in form, coupled with the modern tendency to diffuse design. Later composers of the nineteenth century tended to be more restrictive in their symphonic output. Of Schubert's symphonies two are most notable; also two of Mendelssohn's and three of Tschaikowsky's. Schumann contributed four, Brahms also four, and César Franck wrote only one.

Of all these, Brahms combined most successfully a classic unity with the modern or romantic variety of tonal color and intense emotion. His music was pure and refined, and part of its nobility is due to the fact that it was unadorned. His was an unusual balance of imaginative eloquence combined with a surprising knowledge of old forms. His Fourth Symphony, like medieval modes, is composed half in the major and half in the minor scale, while the splendid finale is in the old polyphonic, contrapuntal style of the *passacaglia*. Whenever he borrowed these traditional devices he employed them with a reanimated spirit.

Tschaikowsky (1840–1893) expressed sincere, vivid moods and passionate feeling in warm colors through his favorite mediums: harmony, rhythm, and orchestral timbres.

PROGRAM MUSIC

Even with Beethoven we find the beginnings of the romantic type of realism which makes music depict scenes or characterizations. The chief exponents of this school of program music were Berlioz (1803–1869), Liszt, and Richard Strauss. Berlioz may be said to have created program music, from which came the *symphonic poem* or *tone poem*. A symphonic poem is an orchestral telling of a story with the successive incidents presented in musical terms based on themes, but with no formal arrangement as in a symphony. Liszt used germinal motives in all the parts, re-created to suit the emotional needs of the story, thus giving a feeling of interrelationship between the parts. He was prone to exaggerate in order to obtain theatrical effects, which were more luxurious than distinctive. Strauss introduced humor in some of his tone poems (as *Till Eulenspiegel*) and employed the full modern orchestra to portray new feelings, attitudes, moods, and atmospheres.

CONTEMPORARY MUSIC

Like most new works of art, new musical compositions at first sound strange and are often incomprehensible. But in time the best of these new compositions will doubtless themselves become classics. We can only mention here a few of the more outstanding contemporary composers.

Igor Stravinsky (born 1882), Russian expatriate, first achieved fame with *The Firebird* and *The Rites of Spring,* both written originally as ballet music. Jan Sibelius (1865–1957), the great Finnish composer, contributed seven symphonies and several tone poems. A kind of gray melancholy pervades his work. Arnold Schönberg (1875–1951), an Austrian, began as a Wagnerian romantic (as in *Transfigured Night*) but later developed a difficult, atonal style. Among modern French composers Maurice Ravel, Darius Milhaud (born 1892), and Arthur Honegger (1892–1955) are outstanding. Paul Hindemith (born 1895), German, composes in a distinctive style that is frequently more rewarding than the work of many other modern pioneers in music. Ernest Bloch (1880–), born in Switzerland, an American by adoption, is among the very gifted modern composers, his *Schelomo* being especially noted. Two modern Russian composers are among the ablest in the symphonic form: Sergei Prokofiev wrote five symphonies, many sonatas and concertos, and a musical story for children, *Peter and the Wolf,* demonstrating his wide range of expression and great technical ability; Dmitri Shostakovitch (born 1906) has written nine symphonies—the best of these, the First and Fifth, show a great gift of invention. Benjamin Britten (born 1913) and Ralph Vaughan Williams (born 1872) are the best-known modern British composers. The music of Manuel de Falla (1876–1946) is at once very Spanish and very individual. One of the most strikingly original among modern composers is Béla Bartók (1881–1945), Hungarian.

American composers include Charles Martin Loeffler (1861–1935), Charles Ives (born 1874), Charles Tomlinson Griffes (1884–1920), George Gershwin, Roy Harris (born 1898), Aaron Copland (born 1900), and many other gifted men who write brilliantly and skillfully. American serious music has not yet, however, reached full maturity.

EXAMINATION QUESTIONS

1. What may have been two motives of primitive man in drawing and painting pictures?
2. What was the first great civilization to develop pictorial art?
3. What subject became the chief interest of Greek painters?
4. What ancient city, preserved for centuries in ashes, enables us to study Roman mural decoration?
5. What encouraged portrait painting in Rome?
6. Who was the teacher of Giotto?
7. What painter is said to represent the pinnacle of high Renaissance painting?
8. When did Michelangelo live?
9. Who is the most characteristic Italian representative of the Baroque style in painting?
10. Name typical subjects characteristic of eighteenth-century French art.
11. Who founded the School of Realism?
12. What series of paintings best exemplify the impressionistic method?
13. What works of Toulouse-Lautrec have become particularly famous?
14. What two painters simultaneously "discovered" Cubism?
15. What style did Piet Mondrian develop?
16. Of what nationality was Velásquez?
17. Who were the first important Flemish painters?
18. What Dutch artist accentuated important features by lighting

them strongly and sinking the others into dark colorless shadows?

19. What were the chief mediums of German art up to the thirteenth century?
20. What did Hogarth caricature?
21. Where did Whistler live?
22. Who is the creator of the mobile?
23. What is one strictly Egyptian architectural form?
24. What were the Greeks' medium of architectural expression?
25. What was the capacity of the Roman Colosseum?
26. What is the Taj Mahal?
27. What architectural style does the term Romanesque describe?
28. In what form of architecture was the flying buttress used?
29. Where did the Renaissance style begin?
30. Of what style is the ensemble of columns at St. Peter's in Rome?
31. Name the two most famous Renaissance palaces in France.
32. In what style is the Capitol at Washington, D.C.?
33. What were the main features of most of Egypt's sculpture?
34. What Greek sculptor made the decorations for the Parthenon?

35. Why did the early Christian Church frown on sculpture?
36. Who was Benvenuto Cellini?
37. What French modern sculptor made the figure look as though it had emerged from an untrimmed mass?
38. What is the simplest musical form?
39. Where did musical art get its first patronage?
40. What does "polyphonic" mean?
41. What is the plucking of strings on a musical instrument called?
42. Whose operas were based on the *Ring of the Nibelungen?*
43. What is an oratorio?
44. In what oratorio does the "Hallelujah Chorus" occur?
45. What two instruments preceded the development of the pianoforte?
46. How do we designate music that tells a story?
47. How do we classify the symphonies of Haydn and Mozart?
48. Who is the composer of the *Eroica* Symphony?
49. How many symphonies did Brahms compose?
50. Who is the composer of *The Firebird* and *The Rites of Spring?*

FOR FURTHER STUDY

ART THROUGH THE AGES, by Helen Gardner. (Harcourt, Brace & Co., New York.)

THE ART OF ENJOYING MUSIC, by Sigmund Spaeth. (Whittlesey House, New York.)

MEN OF ART, by Thomas Craven. (Simon & Schuster, New York.)

MODERN ART, by Thomas Craven. (Simon & Schuster, New York.)

MUSIC LOVERS HANDBOOK, edited by Elie Siegmeister. (Wm. Morrow, New York.)

XII

French Self Taught

HOW TO STUDY FRENCH

THE study of most languages is best begun from the outside in—that is, the student acquires a better foundation in a language if he is not confronted at the start with the intricacies of grammar, but learns a few everyday words and phrases and how to express a few simple ideas. This is the natural way of learning a language, for it is the way a child learns to speak. Later he discovers structure. He learns that, if words are bricks to be built into sentences, grammar is the mortar with which they are held together. The following pages endeavor to follow this natural order: first the rudiments of conversation, then a breaking down of the language into its component parts, which the student, as he grows more skillful, will be able to use to express his own ideas.

We begin our study of French with some fundamental rules of pronunciation. Progress in any language is hastened if meaning and sound are memorized together. In the lessons which follow, whether listed as "oral" or "written," do not fail to pronounce aloud the words which you are studying. Thus sound and meaning will work together to help the memory. Go over each exercise until you are thoroughly familiar with it, and try, between lessons, to repeat the words, phrases, and idioms that you have learned. Your object must be to learn to *think* in French. Try at first to confine your French conversation to objects and experiences you are likely to encounter daily, so that the words which describe them will become fixed in your mind by a process of association.

PRONUNCIATION

ACCENTS

The acute accent (´) is written over the vowel *e* only. It indicates that the *e* is to be pronounced somewhat like the English *a* in *gale,* but without the drawl.

The grave accent (`) is written over three vowels: *a, e,* and *u.* It does not alter the pronunciation of either *a* or *u,* affecting them simply in the spelling of certain words. But when written over *e,* the grave accent gives this letter the sound of the English *ai* in *hair.*

The circumflex accent (^) indicates that the vowel or diphthong which it affects is long (slightly drawled in speaking).

In giving equivalent sounds where symbols are needed, we follow the key in the section on "Good English Self Taught" (page 388).

THE CEDILLA

When *a* or *o* or *u* follows *c,* the sound of *c* is hard (like *k*) unless it is written with a cedilla (*ç*). The cedilla gives *c* the soft sound of *s* (ça, ço, çu = sa, so, su).

VOWEL SOUNDS

The A (English: halfway between *pAnt* and *pArt*)
Examples: âtre, âne, part, tas.

The Open E and AI (English: *hAIr*)
Examples: frère, conquête, souhait, aise, naître.

The Closed E (English: *mAle*)
Examples: manger, ciré.

The Mute E (not pronounced)
(*The Mute E simply gives more force to the preceding letter*)
Examples: flute, poule, amie, ferme.

The Sourd E (English: *fUn*)
Examples: que, se, me, le, te, de, regarde.

The Open EU and ŒU (English: *hEr*)
Examples: bœuf, sœur, meurs.

The Closed EU and ŒU (English: kIrk)

Examples: peu, nœud.

The Simple I (English: sardIne)

Examples: fine, gilet, cil.

The U (English: a sound between the *ee* in *swEEt* and the *u* in *stUpid*, lips being pursed as if you are trying to whistle. There is no exact English equivalent.

Examples: cru, su, plus, du.

The Open O (English: bUt)

Examples: poli, romain, noblesse, tort.

The Closed O, AU, EAU (English: hOle)

Examples: Rhône, rôle, drôle, eau, landau.

The OU (English: spOOn)

Examples: mouvoir, soupe, nouvel.

The Simple Y (English: sardIne)

Examples: pays, crayon, essuyant.

FRENCH NASAL SOUNDS

Perhaps the French nasal may best be described as a "grunt," since there is no similar sound in English. The breath is expelled suddenly, as in the exclamation: "Humph!"; but throat and mouth remain open. Thus, in pronouncing, *on, an, in,* and *en,* the mouth shapes the vowel sound and the vocal cords produce the grunt; but the consonant *n* is not pronounced with the tongue, since it merely indicates the nasal quality of the vowel. When pronunciation is given in these lessons, *nh* indicates a nasal sound; thus, long (pronounced *lōnh*); bon (pronounced *bōnh*); fin (pronounced *fănh*); en (pronounced *awnh*); jambe (pronounced *zhamhb*). Note that the nasal *an* and *am* are usually spoken practically alike (*anh = amh*).

The Nasal A (Pronounced änh)

Examples: grand, plan, rampe, France, en, temps. (I want to say: *an, en, am, em.*)

The Nasal Open E (Pronounced *ănh*)

Examples: sein, peintre, main, impure, lin, loin, tien, bien, sympathie. (I c*an* say: *ein, ain, in, eim, aim, im.*)

The Nasal Open O (Pronounced *ōnh*)

Examples: mont, bon, comte. (It won't take l*on*g to say: *on, om.*)

The Nasal Open U (Pronounced *unh*)

Examples: un, Lebrun. (Your *un*cle can say: *un, um.*)

TRUE DIPHTHONGS

A true diphthong is formed when two vowel sounds have no consonant between them and are pronounced together, as in *Di-eu, bi-en, pa-y-san, cu-ir, lo-in, lu-i, Lou-is.*

The diphthong *oi* gives the sound of *wa* in *water*.

In other combinations (except nasal), and when standing alone, the letter *i* is pronounced like *ee* in the English word *meet;* the same is true of the letter *y*.

THE DIERESIS

When it is necessary to indicate that a certain one of two or more vowels has a separate sound, the dieresis (¨) is used; e.g., je *haïs* (*ah-ee*).

CONSONANTS

Consonants have very much the same sounds in French as in English, except certain combinations with other letters; for example, the consonant *n*, when it is a part of the nasal *en*, or *on*, is pronounced differently from *n* at the beginning of a syllable. The French word *non* illustrates the two different values of the consonant, being pronounced *nōnh*.

When *c* is followed by *e, i,* or *y*, it is pronounced like a soft *s*, as in *ce*, and *ci*. When *c* is followed by any other letter it is pronounced like *k*, unless the soft sound is indicated by a cedilla (*ça*): ce, ci, ça, ço, çu (soft *c*).

When *ch* is followed by a vowel it is pronounced like *sh*, as in *chien*, except where it occurs in words of Greek derivation, like *Chloé, écho, Christ,* etc. In such words *ch* is pronounced like *k*.

When *g* is followed by *e, i,* or *y,* it is pronounced *zh,* or like the *s* in the English word *measure;* for instance, *gérant* (pronounced *zhayranh*). When *g* is followed by any other letter it is pronounced like *g* in the English word *good;* for instance, *Gaul, gris* (pronounced *Gole, gree*).

The letter *h* is never sounded by itself. It has a definite value in certain combinations like *ch* and *ph;* and in certain words it has a value called "aspirate." The word *haut* illustrates the aspirate *h,* which means simply this: one must say, "Le haut (the top)" or "Du haut (from the top)"; but in the case of the word *homme,* which does not begin with an aspirate *h,* one may leave out or *elide* the preceding vowel, thus: "L'homme (the man)" or "De l'homme (from the man)." But in neither word does *h* have a sound. *Haut* is pronounced *oh* and *homme* is pronounced *umm.*

S, at the beginning of a word, and *ss* wherever found have the sound of *s* in the English word *sing.* But a single *s* coming between two vowels is pronounced like *z* in the English word *zebra;* for instance, *cousin* (pronounced *koo-zănh*).

T is ordinarily pronounced like *t* in the English word *tell,* except that in speaking the letter the French place the tongue at the roots of the front teeth, giving *t* a softer, duller sound than English-speaking people do. When *t* is followed by *ion, ial,* or *iel* (and is not preceded by *s,* as in *bestial*) it is pronounced like a soft *s;* for instance, *motion* (pronounced *mo-see-onh*). In words which end in *atie,* and in a very few other words which end in *tie,* the *t* is pronounced like a soft *s.*

Wherever *th* is found it is pronounced like a simple *t.* Thus, *Thor* is pronounced in French, *Tor.*

When *x* begins a word (as in *Xavier*), and whenever at the beginning of a word it stands between *e* and another vowel (as in *exiger*), it is pronounced like *gz;* thus, *Xavier* is pronounced *Gza-vee-ay,* and *exiger* is pronounced *egg-zee-zhay.* Elsewhere *x* is usually pronounced like *ks,* as in English, except in the case of numerals (*deuxième, sixième,* etc.), where it has the sound of *z,* as in the English word *Ezra.*

In certain combinations, *g* and *l* are said to have a *liquid* value. This means that *g* followed by *n* (*gn*) makes a combination which is pronounced like the *ny* in the English word *canyon.* Thus, *Guignol* is pronounced *Geen-yoll, gagne* is pronounced *gan-yh,* etc. *L* or *ll* following *i* is in most words pronounced like another *i.* Thus, *taille* is pronounced *ta-ee-ee,* the final *e* in this word being mute or soundless. But there are certain exceptions, where *l* and *ll* preceded by *i* have the usual (non-liquid) sound; for instance, *ville, village, fil, tranquille, mille, civiliser,* pronounced *veel, veelazh, feel, tranh-keel, meel, cee-vee-lee-zay.*

When the French wish to give *g* a hard sound (as in *get*) before the letter *e* or the letter *i,* they write a letter *u* betwen *g* and the vowel; in such combinations the *u* is naturally silent. Thus *Guignol* is pronounced *Geen-yoll,* and *guerre* is pronounced *gair.*

A consonant at the end of a word is usually silent unless it is followed by a word which begins with a vowel. Thus, *plus* alone is pronounced without any *s* sound; but in *plus ou moins* the *s* sound is carried over from *plus* to *ou* and has a *z* sound. There are frequent exceptions to this rule, however. *L* is always pronounced when it comes at the end of a word. *R* is always pronounced when a word ends in *oir* or in *ir* or in *ur* or in *or.* *M* and *n* following a vowel at the end of a word are either nasal or pronounced as in English.

OTHER PRIMARY RULES

French and English differ very little in their use of capital letters. The French do not use capitals in spelling adjectives made from proper names (*français, américain,* etc.), days of the week, months of the year, and the pronoun *je,* meaning *I*—unless the word happens to begin a sentence.

Articles, adjectives and pronouns must agree in gender and number with the words which they modify or stand for. That is, a feminine noun or pronoun is modified by feminine articles and adjectives, and a masculine noun or pronoun is modified by masculine articles and adjectives; likewise a masculine pronoun can refer only to a masculine noun, a feminine only to a feminine.

Nouns form their plurals, in general, by adding *s* to the singular form; or, when the singular ends in *au* or *eu,* by adding *x;* or, when the singular ends in *al,* usually by changing *al* to *aux. Exceptions:* When the singular form ends in *s, x,* or *z,* the plural form is the same as the singular. *Bijou, chou, genou, joujou,* and others which end in *ou* form the plural by adding *x* to the singular.

Adjectives form their plurals as do nouns, except adjectives ending in *eu.* They add *s* to form the plural: *bleu, bleus.* Note that the singular feminine always ends in *e;* hence the feminine plural is always formed by adding *s* to the singular.

French-to-English and English-to-French translations of all written exercises in the following lessons will be found beginning on page 601. Use the translations only to correct the exercise after it has been written. If you are not familiar with a word used in these exercises consult the vocabulary at the end of this section.

LESSON I

In the next few pages a rough-and-ready phonetic spelling has been employed to illustrate the pronunciation of French words, wherever the

French sounds may be thus suggested. Where the French sounds are so different from English ones that they cannot easily be suggested by this means, italics indicate that the reader should consult the instructions on the preceding pages.

Memorize the following and their pronunciation:

MASCULINE SINGULAR

French:	Le,	un,	mon,	ton,	son,	notre, votre, leur.
Pronounced:	Luh,	unh,	monh,	tonh,	sonh,	not-r, vot-r, *leur.*
					his,	
English:	The,	a,	my,	thy,	her,	our, your, their.
					its,	

FEMININE SINGULAR

French:	La,	une,	ma,	ta,	sa,	notre, votre, leur.
Pronounced:	La,	*une*,	ma,	ta,	sa,	not-r, vot-r, *leur.*
					his,	
English:	The,	a,	my,	thy,	her,	our, your, their.
					its,	

MASCULINE AND FEMININE PLURAL

French:	Les,	des,	mes,	tes,	ses,	nos, vos, leurs.
Pronounced:	Lay,	day,	may,	tay,	say,	noh, voh, *leur.*
					his,	
English:	The,	some, my,	thy,	her,	our, your, their.
					its,	

Note that the final *e* of a word, for instance *rue*, is silent unless it bears a written accent above it.

Fr.	Par	la	rue.
Pron:	Par	la	r*u*.
Eng:	Through	the	street.

Fr:	A la maison.	Dans	la cour.	A la porte.
Pron:	Ah la may-zonh.	Dawnh	la coor.	Ah la port.
Eng:	To the house.	In	the yard.	At the door.

Fr:	Sur le seuil.	Dans	le vestibule.	Dedans (adv.).
Pron:	S*ur* luh s*eu*-ee.	Dawnh	luh ves-tee-b*ul*.	Duh-dawnh.
Eng:	On the threshold.	In	the vestibule.	Within.

Fr.	Du	salon.	Au	rez-de-chaussée.
Pron:	Du	sa-lonh.	O	ray-dshoh-say.
Eng:	From the parlor.		On the ground floor.	

Fr:	Du	plancher	jusqu'au	plafond.
Pron:	Du	planh-shay	zh*u*s-ko	pla-fonh.
Eng:	From the floor		to the	ceiling.

NOTE: *Du* is a shortened form of *de le*; *au* is a shortened form of *à le*. *Du* and *au* are the forms used before words beginning with a consonant or *h* aspirate. *De l'* and *à l'* are the forms used before words beginning with a vowel or silent *h*. *De la* (of the, from the, *feminine*) and *à la* (to the, at the, on the, etc., *feminine*) are never shortened except before words beginning with a vowel or silent *h*, when they become *de l'* and *à l'*.

+	le
de	du
à	au

Fr:	Entre	la	cuisine	et	la	salle à manger.
Pron:	Awnh-tr	la	c*u*-ee-zeen	eh	la	sal ah manh-zhay.
Eng:	Between	the kitchen		and the dining room.		

Fr:	Au	mur de	ma chambre	au deuxième	étage.
Pron:	O	m*u*r duh	ma shamh-br	o de*u*z-ee-em	ay-tazh.
Eng:	On the wall of		my bedroom	on the third	floor.

NOTE: *Deuxième* means *second* in English. Therefore *deuxième êtage* means literally *second landing*, which corresponds to the *third floor*.

Fr:	Sous	l'	escalier.	Au delà de la	fenêtre.
Pron:	Soo	l	ess-cal-yay.	O duh-la dla	fne-tr.
Eng:	Beneath	the staircase.		Beyond	the window.

Fr:	Avec	les	meubles (*masculine*).	Sur une	chaise.
Pron:	A-vek	lay	m*eu*b-l.	S*u*r *u*n	shehz.
Eng:	With	the (pieces of) furniture.		Upon a	chair.

Fr:	Devant	la	table.	Derrière	le	fauteuil.
Pron:	Duh-vanh	la	tah-bl.	Der-ree-air	luh	foh-t*eu*-ee.
Eng:	Before	the table.		Behind	the armchair.	

Fr:	Au-dessus de la	bibliothèque.
Pron:	O-d-s*u*	dla	beeb-lee-o-tek.
Eng:	Above	the	bookcase.

Fr: Autour de la cheminée.   Au-dessous du sofa.
Pron: O-toor dla shuh-mee-nay. O-dsoo   du sofa.
Eng: Around the   fireplace.   Underneath the sofa.

Fr: Pour mon bureau. Près de   son lit.
Pron: Poor monh bu-ro. Pray dsonh lee.
Eng: For my   desk.   Near (her) his bed.

Fr: A travers le tapis après   la souris.
Pron: Ah tra-vair luh ta-pee ah-pray la soo-ree.
Eng: Across   the rug   after   the mouse.

Repeat the above expressions several times until they lose their unfamiliar sound. Learn the pronunciation as carefully as possible. It is well to mention at this point that the emphasis or stress upon words and syllables varies much less in French than it does in English. The French tend to put a *very* slight emphasis upon the last syllable of most words.

LESSON II

Memorize the following together with their pronunciation:

Fr: Je   suis, vous êtes, il   est, elle   est.
Pron: Zhuh swee, vooz eht, eel   eh, el   eh.
Eng: I   am, you are, he (it) is, she (it) is.

Fr: Nous sommes, vous êtes, ils sont, elles sont.
Pron: Noo sum,   vooz eht, eel sonh, el sonh.
Eng: We are,   you are, they are, they are.

Notice the pronunciation of *vous êtes*, above. The *s* of *vous* is sounded because "vooz eht" is easier to say than "voo eht". When *vous* stands alone or before a consonant, of course the *s* is silent.

Fr: J'ai, vous avez, il a, elle a.
Pron: Zhay, vooz avay, eel ah, el ah.
Eng: I have, you have, he has, she has.

Fr: Nous avons, vous avez, ils ont, elles ont.
Pron: Nooz avonh, vooz avay, eelz onh, elz onh.
Eng: We have, you have, they have, they have.

There being no neuter gender in French, *il, ils, elle, elles,* are used to refer to things as well as to people and animals.

Fr: Je   suis content. J'ai soif. J'ai faim.
Pron: Zhuh swee conh-tawnh. Zhay swaf. Zhay fănh.
Eng: I   am glad.   I am thirsty. I am hungry.
               (I have thirst) (I have hunger)

If the speaker is feminine, one must say: "Je suis contente," since the adjective *content* (glad) refers to a feminine person. The addition of the final *e* causes the last *t* to be sounded: *conh-tawnt*.

Fr: Je   suis fâché.   J'ai   chaud. J'ai   froid.
Pron: Zhuh swee fa-shay. Zhay show.   Zhay frwah.
Eng: I   am   angry.   I am hot.   I am cold.
                        (I have heat) (I have cold)

NOTE: If the speaker is feminine, *fâché* would be changed to *fâchée*.

Fr: Je   suis malade. J'ai   peur. J'ai   sommeil.
Pron: Zhuh swee ma-lad. Zhay pe*ur*. Zhay sum-may.
Eng: I   am   ill.   I am afraid. I am sleepy.
                        (I have fear) (I have sleep)

NOTE: *Malade* is spelled and pronounced alike in masculine and feminine. Further study will show many adjectives of this sort.

Fr: Je   suis fâché   que vous ayez sommeil.
Pron: Zhuh swee fa-shay   kuh vooz a-yay sum-may.
Eng: I   am   distressed that you   are   sleepy.
                                        (have sleep)

Fr: Je n'ai pas peur,   mais je   suis très malade.
Pron: Zhnay pah pe*ur*,   may zhuh swee tray ma-lad.
Eng: I am   not afraid, but I   am   very ill.
        (have not fear)

NOTE: *Ne . . . pas* is the separated negative, meaning *not*. Its usual position in a sentence is illustrated above. The *ne* becomes *n'* before a word beginning with a vowel or silent *h*.

Fr: Qu'avez-vous? Qu'a-t-elle? Etes-vous fâchés?
Pron: Ka-vay voo?   Ka-tel?   Eht voo fa-shay?
Eng: What have you? What has she? Are you angry?
        (What's the matter with you?—with her?)

In asking a question, the French reverse the position of the verb and subject, as we do in English; e.g., *Qu'* (what) *avez* (have) *vous* (you)? But this reversal of position makes necessary a hyphen between verb and subject (*avez-vous*). In *a-t-il* or *a-t-elle*, a *t* is inserted between verb and subject for the sake of easy pronunciation.

Write the following sentences in French: 1. He is in the yard. 2. She is at the door. 3. They are at home (in the house). 4. We are in the street. 5. The chair is in the vestibule. 6. I have a bed and a sofa. 7. You are not afraid. 8. My bedroom is on the ground floor. 9. They have a window between the dining room and the kitchen. 10. He has a bedroom beyond the parlor. 11. Our chairs are on the second floor. 12. His bookcases are under the staircase. 13. Your rug is on her floor. 14. The mouse is underneath my armchair. 15. Their table is near his bed. 16. I have a chair for my desk. 17. It is above the fireplace. 18. I am glad that they are not in (use *dans*) the street. 19. She is sleepy but she is not ill. 20. What's the matter with him? He is not on (use *sur*) the chair.

NOTE: Remember that possessive adjectives (*mon, ma, son, sa,* etc.) agree in number and gender with the nouns they modify, *not* with the personal possessor. For instance, *sa chaise* may mean either *his* or *her chair; ses maisons* may mean *his houses* or *her houses,* but it could not mean *their houses,* since the word for *their* is *leur. Their houses* in French would be *leurs maisons.*

LESSON III

Memorize the following together with their pronunciation:

Fr:	Qui est ce	monsieur?	C'est	Monsieur	Lebon.
Pron:	Kee eh suh	m'syuh?	Say	M'syuh	Luh-bonh.
Eng:	Who is this (that)	gentleman?	That is	Mr.	Lebon.

NOTE: *C'est* (a contraction of *ce est*) means *that is* or *this is* or *it is.* Notice how rapidly *Monsieur* is pronounced, so that it sounds like M'syuh.

Fr:	Il	est mon	professeur	et	l'ami	de mon	père.
Pron:	Eel	eh monh	pro-fes-*seur*	eh	la-mee	dmonh	pair.
Eng:	He	is my	professor	and	the friend	of my	father.

NOTE: The only way to say "my father's friend" is shown above.

Fr:	Je n'ai pas de père;	je	n'ai qu'une mère.
Pron:	Zhnay pah dpair;	zhnay	kun mair.
Eng:	I have not any father;	I have not except	a mother.
	(no father)		(only a mother)

NOTE: *Je n'ai pas de*—is the correct way to say, "I have no." *Je n'ai que*—; *ils n'ont que*—(I have not except—; they have not except—) is the correct way to say, "I have only—; they have only—." Notice that in the last two instances the second half of the negative, *pas,* is omitted.

Fr:	J'ai	quelque chose	à vous dire,	Mademoiselle.
Pron:	Zhay	kel-k	shows ah voo dee-r,	Mad-mw-zel.
Eng:	I have something		to you to say,	Miss.
			(say to you)	

Fr: Nous n'avons rien   à manger   aujourd'hui.
Pron: Noo na-vonh ree-anh ah manh-zhay o-zhoor-dwee.
Eng: We   have not anything   to eat   today.
                (nothing)

NOTE: When *ne . . . rien* (not anything, nothing) is used, the second half of the negative, *pas*, is omitted. *Aujourd'hui* is considered one word, meaning simply *today*.

Fr: Vous avez des pêches, du sucre,   et de la crème.
Pron: Vooz a-vay day pesh,   du suk-r,   eh dla   krem.
Eng: You have of the peaches, of the sugar, and of the cream.
                (some)   (some)   (some)

NOTE: *Des* is the contraction of *de les*. Observe how to say "some." Contractions of *a, de,* and the definite article:

+	le	les
de	du	des
à	au	aux

Fr: Ils   ont plus d'argent   que moi.
Pron: Eelz onh plu   dar-zhawnh kuh mwa.
Eng: They have more (of) money than I.

NOTE: In English one would say, "—more money than *I* (have)"; but "plus d'argent que *je*" would not be correct French.

Fr: J'ai   envie   de manger   une pêche.
Pron: Zhay awnh-vee dmanh-zhay un pesh.
Eng: I have desire   of to eat   a   peach.
                (a mind to)
        I feel like eating a peach.

Fr: J'ai   tant   d'amis; je suis très heureuse.
Pron: Zhay tawnh   da-mee; zhuh swee trayz *eu-reuz*.
Eng: I have so many friends; I   am   very fortunate (happy).

NOTE: *Tant* (so many, so much) is always followed by *de* (of) before a noun. Notice that *heureuse* is feminine (the masculine is *heureux*). Hence in the above sentence the speaker is feminine, while her friends (*amis*) are masculine. She is certainly happier than if all her friends were *amies!*

Fr: Mes amies sont toutes belles et leurs enfants   tous beaux.
Pron: Mayz a-mee sonh toot   bel   eh leurz awnh-fawnh tooss bo.
Eng: My friends are all beautiful and their children all handsome.

NOTE: Observe that the adjectives *toutes* and *belles* are the feminine plural forms, agreeing with the feminine plural noun *amies*. Likewise *tous* and *beaux* are masculine plural forms in agreement with *enfants*, which is masculine or common gender and plural. The masculine and feminine singular would of course be: *tout, toute* (all), and *beau, belle* (beautiful, handsome, fine). Before a word beginning with a vowel or silent *h, beau* becomes *bel.*

Write the following sentences in French: 1. Who is in the parlor? Mr. Lenoir. 2. Has Mr. Leblanc a beautiful house? (French style is: Mr. Leblanc, has he a beautiful house?) 3. No (*Non*), but he is a very fine man. 4. Those are (*ce sont*) your friends (masculine) who are at the door. 5. Haven't you (*n'avez-vous pas*) something to say (*à dire*)? 6. Yes (*Oui*), I have something to say to you, but you have nothing (not have anything) to say to me. 7. She has no mother; she has only a friend (feminine). 8. Is your father a friend (Your father, is he a friend) of my professor? 9. I have peaches and cream to eat today. 10. Miss Lebon is with his mother in the kitchen. 11. I have a mind to say (I feel like saying) something to (*à*) your professor. 12. The sugar is not in the dining room. 13. I am not your father, but I am your friend. 14. Is he not (*n'est-il pas*) her father? 15. My mother's friend is very ill. 16. Some mice are under the staircase, and a peach is on the floor. 17. I have no money, but I have so many children that I am very happy. 18. The mothers are all beautiful. 19. She has a beautiful rug on the wall, from the ceiling to the floor. 20. I have so many peaches that I have no desire to eat.

LESSON IV

Turn to the Conjugation Lists following these lessons and study the whole of the First Regular Conjugation, also the irregular verbs AVOIR *and* ETRE. In the lessons that follow, pronunciation and English meaning will not always be indicated on the lesson page; wherever they are not so indicated, reference must be made to the previous instructions in pronunciation and to the vocabulary and conjugation lists at the end of this section.

LESSON V

Study and review the Second and Third Regular Conjugations on pages 588 and 589 until you have thoroughly memorized them.

Translate into English: 1. J'ai mangé de la viande. 2. Ma mère a rôti le poulet. 3. Il a vendu la vache. 4. La vache qu'il a vendue mangeait les choux. 5. Avant de manger un poulet on le rôtit. 6. Nous ne vendons pas nos enfants. 7. La cuisinière rôtira la viande avant que nous mangions le dîner. 8. Si je n'avais pas vendu la vache, nous n'aurions rien à manger aujourd'hui. 9. Pendant que je rôtissais la viande mes amis mangeaient des bonbons. 10. Ils ne vendront pas les poulets avant de les rôtir.

Notes

In the word *mangeait* the student will have noticed that *e* is retained after the *g,* whereas in *mangions* no *e* appears. The reason for this is that *g* followed by *a, o,* or *u* is hard (as in *good*) and an *e* must be inserted to preserve the soft sound (*mangeait; i.e.,* manh-zhay). In the case of *mangions,* however, the *g* followed by *i* is soft anyway, and no softening *e* is needed.

In the 10th sentence (*—les rôtir*), observe the use of *les* to mean *them.* Similarly in the 5th sentence (*—le rôtit*), *le* means *it.*

Most French verbs follow the three regular conjugations in all their forms, but many other French verbs are irregular in certain of their forms. Some, like AVOIR and ETRE, are extremely irregular; others are less so. Following the Three Regular Conjugations at the end of the section, the irregular verbs used in these lessons (or verbs with exactly similar irregularities) are conjugated. Only the *irregular forms* of such verbs are given in most cases, it being understood that *the forms omitted are regular.* Each sample verb is numbered, and every verb in the lesson text which bears the same number is conjugated like the sample.

LESSON VI

Memorize the following expressions and their meanings:

Il y a: *There is; there are; ago* (a certain time). En retard: *Late* (of persons). Il y a huit jours: *A week ago.* Verser: *To upset, overturn.* S'approche de—: *Approaches* (literally: *approaches itself to—*). Vous rappelez-vous: *Do you recall* (*to yourself*)? Se rendre compte de—: *To realize.* En route: *On the way.* Le peu d'espace dont nous disposions: *The small amount of space which we had at our disposal* (literally:— *of which we were disposing*). Nous venions de recevoir: *We had just received* (or *secured*). Billets de bagages: *Baggage checks.* Chef de train: *Railway guard.* Nous montions dans: *We were climbing into.* En voiture: *All aboard!* A bord de: *On board.* Le soir même: *That very*

evening. S'arrêter: *To stop moving.* Mouiller l'ancre: *To drop anchor.*
Nous nous trouverons: *We shall find ourselves; we shall be.*

Notes for the Following Exercise—

The city of *Havre* is always preceded in French by the definite article
(*le*), the Engish translation of Le Havre being *The Harbor.*

Nous nous sommes trouvés: The Past Indefinite Tense of a reflexive
verb is always conjugated with appropriate forms of the verb *Etre* (to
be), not with *Avoir* (to have). In English we say: "We have found (or
found) ourselves"; but in French we say: "We ourselves are found"
(*nous nous sommes trouvés*). The same is true of the Pluperfect and the
Anterior tenses.

Nous sommes arrivés: Certain verbs like *Arriver* (to arrive), *Venir*
(to come), *Aller* (to go), *Sortir* (to go out), *Partir* (to go away), *Monter*
(to go up), *Descendre* (to go down), *Revenir* (to come back), *Retourner*
(to go back), *Entrer* (to go in), *Naître* (to be born), *Mourir* (to die),
Tomber (to fall), and *Rester* (to remain) are conjugated in Past Indefinite Pluperfect, and the Anterior tenses with forms of the verb
Etre, not with *Avoir.* See the Conjugation Lists. The past participle in
these conjugations always agrees in number and gender with the subject
of the verb; hence *arrivés,* masculine plural, to agree with *nous.* If the
subject were feminine singular it would require *arrivée;* if feminine
plural, *arrivées.*

Translate into English. (The numbers in parentheses refer to the
conjugations of verbs on pages 585–600):

En Voyage

—Nous avons quitté (1) la maison dans le petit village où nous demeurions (1), il y a huit jours. Maintenant le vaisseau s'approche (1) de
la côte de la France. Demain matin nous débarquerons (1) dans le
Havre.

—Vous rappelez-vous (1) les heures de préparation pour ce voyage?
—la confusion des derniers moments quand nous voulions (were wishing) jeter (1) dans les malles toutes nos possessions, sans nous rendre
(3) compte du peu d'espace dont nous disposions (1), —la grande
hâte due départ dans le taxi, qui, après être arrivé (1) une demi-heure
en retard, a presque versé (1) cinq fois en route à la station, —la peur
d'avoir manqué (1) le train?

—Oui, mais enfin nous nous sommes trouvés (1) dans le wagon du
chemin de fer. Nous venions (10) de recevoir nos billets de bagages, et

nous montions (1) dans le wagon au moment que le chef de train a crié (1), "En voiture!"

—Oui, je m'en souviens (remember). Et à bord du vaisseau lorsque nous quittons le port de New York je ne pouvais (could) pas trouver (1) mon passeport!

—Quelle horreur! Et le soir même vous l'avez découvert (8) dans votre valise, dans laquelle vous l'aviez mis.

—Mais voilà que le vaisseau s'arrête! Nous allons mouiller (1) l'ancre. Bientôt les officiers du port viendront (10) à bord, et demain nous nous trouverons dans la ville du Havre. Nous sommes arrivés.

LESSON VII

Memorize the following expressions and their meanings: Cela vaut bien le prix: *That is well worth the price.* Aussitôt que le garçon s'en va: *As soon as the boy (bellboy) goes away.* A demi: *Halfway.* L'envie . . . nous saisit: *The desire seizes us.* Quand vous aurez fini—: *When you have finished—.* De vous laver, de vous raser, de vous nettoyer les dents: *With washing yourself, with shaving yourself, with cleaning your teeth.* Les deux: *Both.* Quand vous vous serez brossé les cheveux: *When you have brushed your hair.* Prêt à: *Ready to.* C'en est assez: *That's enough; that'll do.* Moi, je meurs de faim: *Myself, I am dying of hunger.* Quand vous vous livrez à l'ironie: *When you indulge in irony (sarcasm).* Vous avez l'esprit aux talons: *Slang—"Your brains are in your feet."* Allons donc: *Come! Come, then! Come, now!* Un tel; une telle: *Such a—.* Si vous faites un meilleur dîner que moi: *If you make a better dinner than I.* En effet: *In short; in effect.* Bien qu'il soit l'heure de déjeuner: *Although it may be lunch time.* Je vais commander: *I am going to order.* Tout le monde: *Everybody.* Tout ce qu'il faudra: *Everything that will be necessary.* Pour me faire gourmand: *In order to make myself a glutton (a "pig").* Ça m'est égal: *It's all the same to me.* Peut-être: *Perhaps; maybe.*

Notes for the Following Exercise—

Le garçon nous précède: The present tense here used is called *the historical present,* a narrative style referring to past time. It is frequently employed in French to give vividness to the narrative.

On n'oserait jamais:—With *jamais* only the first part of the negative *ne . . . pas* is used.

Américains: The word is here used as an adjective modifying *nous.* The translation is: *They take us for American.* "They take us for Americans" would be in French: *On nous prend pour DES américains.*

Quand vous vous serez brossé—: The second *vous* is called *dative of reference,* and may be translated *for yourself.* In English one says: "When you have brushed your hair"; the literal translation of the French is: "When you for yourself will have brushed the hairs."

Les cheveux: The French do not use *cheveu* (hair) in a collective sense, as we do in English. Referring to all the hairs of the head, they employ the plural, *cheveux* (hairs).

Vous vous imaginerez: Here the second *vous* is not a dative of reference, but is the object of *imaginerez.* The translation is: "—you will imagine yourself."

A l'Hôtel

Après avoir quitté le vaisseau nous sommes montés (1) dans un taxi qui se trouvait près du quai. Nous avons donné (1) au chauffeur le nom d'un bon hôtel, et après dix minutes de zigzaguer (zigzagging) par la foule de bicyclistes, d'automobiles et de gens à pied, nous y sommes arrivés (1) sain et sauf. Nous descendions (3) du taxi lorsqu'un garçon a saisi (2) nos valises et a disparu dans le foyer de l'hôtel. Nous l'avons suivi au bureau, où un autre employé nous a accueillis (7).

—Messieurs désirent (1)?

—Deux chambres avec salle de bain.

—Bien, messieurs, nous avons un bel appartement exposé (1) au soleil, les deux pièces bien larges et admirablement meublées (1). Voulez-vous (do you wish) les voir tout de suite?

—Combien faut-il (is it necessary) payer (1) par semaine?

—Trois cents francs par semaine, messieurs, ou cinquante francs par jour. Et je vous assure que l'appartement vaut (is worth) bieu le prix. Le garçon vous le montrera (1). Voulez-vous monter immédiatement?

Le garçon nous précède (1) à l'ascenseur. Il est évident que tout le monde nous prend pour des américains, autrement on n'oserait (1) jamais nous demander (1) un tel prix pour deux chambres. L'ascenseur s'arrête (1) au troisième étage et le garçon nous amène (1) jusqu'au numéro trente-sept. Les pièces sont vraiment belles, avec de grandes fenêtres qui laissent (1) entrer (1) le soleil par des rideaux blancs et roses. Du tapis sur le plancher jusqu'au couvre-lit, tout est sans tache et charmant après la fatigue du voyage. Il y a même un téléphone sur une petite table dans un coin. Malgré les trois cents francs par semaine, nous sommes bien contents de nos chambres.

Aussitôt que le garçon s'en va (6) avec un pourboire magnifique, nous commençons (1) à disposer (1) nos biens; mais lorsqu'ils sont à demi déballés, l'envie de nous plonger dans l'eau froide nous saisit (2) et nous cherchons (1) le bain pour effacer la souillure du voyage.

—Quand vous aurez fini (2) de vous laver (1), de vous raser (1), de vous nettoyer (1) les dents et de vous vêtir—en effet, quand vous vous serez brossé (1) les cheveux, poli (2) les ongles et frisé (1) les sourcils, peut-être vous vous imaginerez (1) prêt à descendre (3). Moi, je meurs (9) de faim!

LESSON VIII

Memorize the following expressions and their meanings: Eh bien: *Well,—.* Nous voici: *Here we are.* Mon vieux: *Old fellow.* Depuis un quart d'heure: *Since a quarter of an hour ago, for a quarter of an hour.* Le voici qui vient: *Here he comes now.* Allez-vous faire apporter: *Are you going to have brought—?* Tout ce qu'il y a écrit: *Everything that is written.* En goûter: *To taste (of) it; to taste (of) them.* Je ne sais que faire: *I don't know what to do.* Je ne veux plus attendre: *I don't want to wait any longer.* Pour commencer: *To begin with.* Au jus: *Juicy; with juice; medium.* C'est bien: *It is well; very well.* Me refuser: *To deny myself.* Il m'épargne la peine: *He saves me the trouble.* A l'instant: *At once; immediately; as quickly as possible.* J'en suis bien content: *I am very glad of it.* Vous avez bien fait: *You have done well.* Ris de veau: *Sweetbread.* Ils nous attendent: *They are waiting for us.* Au lieu de: *In place of.* Cela nous va mieux: *That suits us better.* Bon marché: *Cheap.* De toutes les choses qui vous frapperont les yeux: *Of all the things which will strike your eyes; which will catch your eye.* Ils coûtent cher: *They are expensive* (literally—*They cost dear*). Sans satisfaire à aucun besoin véritable: *Without filling any real need.* En voyant s'approcher des américains: *Seeing Americans approach.* Hausser le prix: *To raise the price.* Mon Dieu: *Heavens! My Lord!* Il nous faut nous tenir sur nos gardes: *We must be on our guard.* En méditant sur le menu: *In poring over the menu.* Pendant que: *Whilst.* Allez toujours: *Keep right on; go on!* De plus: *Furthermore; besides.* Un dessert qui cadre avec ce vin blanc: *A dessert which goes with this white wine.* A la vôtre: *To yours (your health)!* Bon appétit: *Have a good appetite!* Vous souhaiter un bon appétit: *To wish you a good appetite.* Vous ne vous permettez pas: *You don't allow yourself.*

Notes for the Following Exercise—

Le voici qui vient; qui apporte le consommé: The French use a clause introduced by *qui* in place of the English *participle.* Thus, "coming" is *qui vient* (who comes), and "bringing" is *qui apporte* (who brings).

Un dîner simple et bien préparé: The student will already have observed that many adjectives in French *follow* the substantives they modify.

En méditant sur le menu: The present participle in French is invariable and is generally introduced by the preposition *en,* which may be translated *while, in, by, upon.*

J'ai trois amies charmantes: I have three charming friends. When used as an adjective the particple agrees with the noun it modifies.

A la Table

—Eh bien, nous voici assis (sitting) depuis un quart d'heure, et je ne vois (see) pas le garçon.

—Calmez-vous (1), mon vieux! Nous venons de nous asseoir (we have just sat down), il y a deux minutes au plus. Quant au garçon, le voici qui vient (10). Allez-vous (6) faire (to have) apporter (1) tout ce qu'il y a écrit (written) sur le menu?

—Mais non! J'y trouve (1) tant de plats que je n'ai jamais rencontré (1) dans mes livres de classe que je ne sais que faire ni quoi choisir.

—Bien. Choisissez (2) à votre convenance. Moi, je ne veux (wish) plus attendre. —Garçon! Le consommé pour commencer (1); puis du rosbif au jus avec des pommes frites et des haricots verts.

—C'est bien! Et vous, monsieur? Vous désirez—?

—Oh, moi aussi, je ne puis (can) pas me refuser (1) ni le rosbig avec des pommes frites ni les haricots verts. Mon ami m'épargne (1) la peine de choisir, et j'en suis bien content.

—Bien, messieurs, je reviens à l'instant.

—Vous avez bien fait (You did well), mon ami. Les ris de veau, les soufflés, et une infinité de mets rares et délicats nous attendent (1) dans tous les restaurants de la France; mais à présent un dîner simple et bien préparé nous va (6) mieux. Pour continuer (1) la même idée, vous trouverez (1) que de toutes les choses qui vous frapperont (1) les yeux dans les magasins français, le plus utiles sont bon marché, et les bizarres et les éclatantes coûtent (1) cher, sans satisfaire (satisfying) à aucun besoin véritable. Cependant, je crains (fear) que tous les commis français, en voyant (seeing) s'approcher des américains, haussent (1) les prix de toutes leurs marchandises. Il nous faut nous tenir (10) sur nos gardes, même en achetant (1) une épingle!

—Mais voici le garçon qui apporte le consommé. Pour le dessert—

—Mon Dieu! Vous commencez (1) déjà à parler (1) du dessert, et nous n'avons pas encore commandé le vin.

—(Au garçon) Du vin blanc, s'il vous plaît. Je n'aime (1) pas le vin rouge—le vin ordinaire que beaucoup de français boivent (drink) au lieu d'eau.

—Comme je disais (was saying), mon ami, vous pouvez (may) passer (1) le temps en méditant (1) sur le menu pendant que je mange le dîner. J'ai déjà choisi mon dessert. J'aurai (4) des fraises avec de la crème, des petits gâteaux, et naturellement du café noir avec un petit verre de cognac. Voilà!

—Allez toujours, bavard! Vous ne vous permettez (allow) pas le plaisir de méditer sur des choses délicieuses. Moi, je préfère (1) en goûter (1) d'avance. De plus, je dois (must) choisir un dessert qui cadre (1) avec ce vin blanc que je bois (drink) à votre santé!

—A la vôtre! Il est inutile de vous souhaiter (1) un bon appétit.

LESSON IX

Translate into French: 1. We were living in a small village near Le Havre. 2. Do you recall where you put my passport? 3. I fear that your friends were in the taxi which (use *qui*) overturned on the way to the village. 4. I threw my valise into the taxi and called out (use *j'ai crié*) the name of my hotel. 5. Finally I found the station and climbed into the coach just as (*au moment où*) the train was stopping. 6. He doesn't want to wait on board the vessel. 7. They have just disembarked (use *viennent de débarquer*). 8. I fear that her French will hardly suffice when she finds herself in France (*en France*). 9. I don't want to buy anything in this store. 10. Have you found the menu? 11. I have everything I need (*tout ce qu'il me faut*) in my trunks. 12. This time (*cette fois*) I will take account of the limited space at my disposal. 13. The train will not wait; it is already a quarter of an hour late. 14. I know (*Je le sais bien*); as soon as the conductor calls, "All aboard!" the train will leave the station. 15. They will never dare to leave (use *partir*) without (*sans*) me. 16. What are you doing now (*maintenant*)? Are you dressing yourself or are you brushing your hair? (Use present tense of both verbs.) 17. To begin with, I am going to order a good dinner. 18. He will never pay such a price. 19. They would never take him for a Frenchman. 20. Perhaps I shall eat a better breakfast than you. 21. No, I don't want to go up immediately; I will wait for (*attendrai*) my friend. 22. The elevator hasn't stopped. At what (*à quel*) floor is your suite? 23. If everybody wants to make a pig of himself, it's all the same to me. 24. I prefer to taste my dinner in advance. 25. Perhaps she is ready (*prête*) to sit down at the table. 26. I welcome only my friends. 27. The people on foot arrived safe and sound, but the car overturned on the way.

28. In the lobby of the hotel, I met three friends whom (*que*) I had not seen since two weeks ago. 29. He plunged into the crowd and disappeared. 30. He followed me to my room. 31. Very well, sir, if (*si*) you wish a room exposed to the sun, it will be necessary to pay the price. 32. He will not dare to ask me five hundred francs a week. 33. This suite has no bath; show me another (*un autre*), please. 34. My things are half unpacked; I am not yet (*pas encore*) ready to go down; besides, I am not hungry. 35. Really (*Vraiment*)? For myself, I am dying of hunger. 36. There are even (*même*) white curtains (*des rideaux blancs*) in my friend's room. 37. Both rooms are large and spotless. 38. The waiter seized the tip and preceded us to Number 40 (*quarante*).

FOR FURTHER STUDY

Learn thoroughly the regular and irregular verbs given in the following Conjugation Lists, in all their forms. Compose one hundred sentences in French, employing these verbs in various tenses, together with the vocabulary you have learned in the past lessons. Drill yourself; review, and review again, since each review increases immeasurably the value of past study. Review is the best insurance against forgetfulness.

REGULAR AND IRREGULAR CONJUGATIONS

PARLER, *to speak* (1)

(First Conjugation—Regular Verb)

Present Tense

Fr: je parle, tu parles, il parle, elle parle.
Pron: zhuh parl, tu parl, eel parl, el parl.
Eng: I speak, thou speakest, he speaks, she speaks.

Fr: nous parlons, vous parlez, ils (elles) parlent.
Pron: noo par-lonh, voo par-lay, eel (el) parl.
Eng: we speak, you speak, they speak.

NOTE: The familiar form with *tu* (thou) is used only between intimate relatives and intimate friends, or in speaking to children and animals, or in addressing Deity.

Imperfect Tense

Fr: je parlais, tu parlais, il (elle) parlait.
Pron: zhuh par-leh, *tu* par-leh, eel (el) par-leh.
Eng: I was speaking, thou wast speaking, he (she) was speaking.
  I used to speak he (she) used to speak.

NOTE: *ais*, *ait*, and *aient* are all pronounced *eh*, like the *e* in *bet*.

Fr: nous parlions, vous parliez, ils (elles) parlaient.
Pron: noo par-lee-onh, voo par-lee-ay, eel (el) par-leh.
Eng: we were speaking, you were speaking, they were speaking.
  we used to speak, you used to speak, they used to speak.

Past Definite Tense (formal)

Fr: je parlai, tu parlas, il parla, elle parla.
Pron: zhuh par-lay, *tu* par-lah, eel par-la, el par-la.
Eng: I spoke, thou spokest, he spoke, she spoke.

Fr: nous parlâmes, vous parlâtes, ils (elles) parlèrent.
Pron: noo par-lahm, voo par-laht, eel (el) par-lair.
Eng: we spoke, you spoke, they spoke.

Future Tense

Fr: je parlerai, tu parleras, il parlera, elle parlera.
Pron: zhuh par-ler-ay, *tu* par-ler-ah, eel par-ler-ah, el par-ler-ah.
Eng: I shall speak, thou wilt speak, he will speak, she will speak.

Fr: nous parlerons, vous parlerez, ils (elles) parleront.
Pron: noo par-ler-onh, voo par-ler-ay, eel (el) par-ler-onh.
Eng: we shall speak, you will speak, they will speak.

Potential or Conditional Tense

Fr: je parlerais, tu parlerais, il (elle) parlerait.
Pron: zhuh par-ler-eh, *tu* par-ler-eh, eel (el) par-ler-eh.
Eng: I should speak, thou wouldst speak, he (she) would speak.

The plural forms of the Conditional are the same as the Future except that an *i* is inserted after the infinitive ending: *nous parleri*ons, *vous parleri*ez, but *ils parleraient*.

The endings of the Conditional are the same as those of the Imperfect Tense.

Present Subjunctive Tense

Fr: je   parle, tu   parles,   il (elle) parle.
Pron: zhuh parl, *tu* parl,   eel (el) parl.
Eng: I may speak, thou mayst speak, he (she) may speak.

Fr: nous parlions,   vous parliez,   ils (elles) parlent.
Pron: noo par-lee-onh, voo par-lee-ay, eel (el) parl.
Eng: we may speak, you may speak, they   may speak.

NOTE: The Imperfect Subjunctive is not given in this book, since it has purposely been omitted from the lesson text as being of little value in an elementary study of French.

Imperative Mood

Fr: parle,   qu'il parle,   parlons,
Pron: parl,   keel parl,   par-lonh,
Eng: speak thou, let him speak, let us speak.

Fr: parlez,   qu'ils parlent.
Pron: par-lay,   keel parl.
Eng: you speak,   let them speak.

The Present Participle	The Past Participle
Fr: parlant	parlé
Pron: par-lanh	par-lay
Eng: speaking	spoken

COMPOUND TENSES OF *Parler:*

Past Indefinite Tense (I have spoken, I did speak, or I spoke, etc.)— j'ai parlé, tu as parlé, il a parlé, elle a parlé; nous avons parlé, vous avez parlé, ils ont parlé, elles ont parlé.

Pluperfect Tense (I had spoken, etc.)—j'avais parlé, tu avais parlé, il avait parlé, elle avait parlé; nous avions parlé, vous aviez parlé, ils (elles) avaient parlé.

Past Anterior Tense (I had spoken, etc.)—j'eus parlé, tu eus parlé, il eut parlé, elle eut parlé; nous eûmes parlé, vous eûtes parlé, ils (elles) eurent parlé.

Future Anterior Tense (I shall have spoken, etc.)—j'aurai parlé, tu auras parlé, il aura parlé, elle aura parlé; nous aurons parlé, vous aurez parlé, ils (elles) auront parlé.

Conditional Anterior Tense (I should have spoken, etc.)—j'aurais parlé, tu aurais parlé, il aurait parlé, elle aurait parlé; nous aurions parlé, vous auriez parlé, ils (elles) auraient parlé.

Perfect Tense, Subjective Mood—compounded with the Present Subjunctive of *Avoir*—(I may have spoken, etc.)—j'aie parlé, tu aies parlé, il (elle) ait parlé; nous ayons parlé, vous ayez parlé, ils (elles) aient parlé.

The Perfect Infinitive (To have spoken)—avoir parlé.

The Perfect Participle (Having spoken)—ayant parlé.

POLIR, *to polish* (2)

(Second Conjugation—Regular Verb)

Present Tense

Fr: je polis, tu polis, il (elle) polit.
Pron: zhuh po-lee, tu po-lee, eel (el) po-lee.
Eng: I polish, thou dost polish, he (she) polishes.

Fr: nous polissons, vous polissez, ils (elles) polissent.
Pron: noo po-lees-sonh, voo po-lees-say, eel (el) po-leess.
Eng: we polish, you polish, they polish.

Imperfect Tense (I was polishing, I used to polish, etc.)—je polissais, tu polissais, il polissait, elle polissait; nous polissions, vous polissiez, ils (elles) polissaient.

Past Definite Tense (I polished, etc.)—je polis, tu polis, il polit, elle polit; nous polîmes, vous polîtes, ils (elles) polirent.

Future Tense (I shall polish, etc.)—je polirai, tu poliras, il polira, elle polira; nous polirons, vous polirez, ils (elles) poliront.

Conditional Tense (I should polish, etc.)—je polirais, tu polirais, il polirait, elle polirait; nous polirions, vous poliriez, ils (elles) poliraient.

Present Subjunctive Tense (I may polish, etc.)—je polisse, tu polisses, il polisse, elle polisse; nous polissions, vous polissiez, ils (elles) polissent.

Imperative Mood

Fr: polis, qu'il polisse, polissons, polissez.
Eng: polish thou, let him polish, let us polish, you polish.

Fr: qu'ils (qu'elles) polissent.
Eng: let them polish.

The Present Participle (Polishing)—polissant.
The Past Participle (Polished)—poli.

NOTE: The compound tenses are conjugated with *Avoir* and the Past Participle, as shown in the case of *Parler,* page 587.

VENDRE, *to sell* (3)

(Third Conjugation—Regular Verb)

Present Tense

Fr: je   vends, tu   vends, il (elle) vend.
Pron: zhuh vawnh, *tu*   vawnh, eel (el)   vawnh.
Eng: I   sell,   thou sell,   he (she) sells.

Fr: nous vendons,   vous vendez,   ils (elles) vendent.
Pron: noo vawnh-donh, voo vawnh-day, eel (el)   vawnh-d.
Eng: we   sell,   you sell,   they   sell.

Imperfect Tense (I was selling, used to sell, etc.)—je vendais, tu vendais, il vendait, elle vendait; nous vendions, vous vendiez, ils (elles) vendaient.

Past Definite Tense (I sold, etc.)—je vendis, tu vendis, il vendit, elle vendit; nous vendîmes, vous vendîtes, ils (elles) vendirent.

Future Tense (I shall sell, etc.)—je vendrai, tu vendras, il vendra, elle vendra; nous vendrons, vous vendrez, ils (elles) vendront.

Conditional Tense (I should sell, etc.)—je vendrais, tu vendrais, il vendrait, elle vendrait; nous vendrions, vous vendriez, ils (elles) vendraient.

Present Subjunctive Tense (I may sell, etc.)—je vende, tu vendes, il vende, elle vende; nous vendions, vous vendiez, ils (elles) vendent.

Imperative Mood

Fr: vends,   qu'il vende, vendons.
Eng: sell thou, let him sell, let us sell.

Fr: vendez,   qu'ils (qu'elles) vendent.
Eng: you sell, let them sell.

The Present Participle (Selling)—vendant.
The Past Participle (Sold)—vendu.

NOTE: The compound tenses are conjugated with *Avoir* and the Past Participle, as in the cases of *Parler* and *Polir,* on the previous pages.

Avoir, *to have* (4)

(Irregular Verb)

Present Tense

Fr: j'ai, tu as, il a, elle a.
Pron: zhay, tu ah, eel ah, el ah.
Eng: I have, thou hast, he has, she has.

Fr: nous avons, vous avez, ils (elles) ont.
Pron: nooz avons, vooz a-vay, eelz (elz) onh.
Eng: we have, you have, they have.

Imperfect Tense (I was having [I had, I used to have], etc.)— j'avais, tu avais, il avait, elle avait; nous avions, vous aviez, ils (elles) avaient.

Past Definite Tense (I had, etc.)—j'eus, tu eus, il eut, elle eut; nous eûmes, vous eûtes, ils (elles) eurent.

Future Tense (I shall have, etc.)—j'aurai, tu auras, il aura, elle aura; nous aurons, vous aurez, ils (elles) auront.

Conditional Tense (I should have, etc.)—j'aurais, tu aurais, il aurait, elle aurait; nous aurions, vous auriez, ils (elles) auraient.

Present Subjunctive Tense (I may have, etc.)—j'aie, tu aies, il ait, elle ait, nous ayons, vous ayez, ils (elles) aient.

Imperative Mood

Fr: aie, qu'il ait, ayons, ayez, qu'ils (elles) aient.
Eng: have thou, let him have, let us have, have, let them have.

The Present Participle (Having)—ayant.
The Past Participle (Had)—eu.

NOTE: The compound tenses are conjugated with appropriate forms of *Avoir* and the Past Participle (*eu*); thus, *ayant eu* (having had).

Être, *to be* (5)

(Irregular Verb)

Present Tense

Fr: je suis, tu es, il est, elle est.
Pron: zhuh swee, tu eh, eel eh, el eh.
Eng: I am, thou art, he is, she is.

Fr: nous sommes, vous êtes, ils   sont, elles sont.
Pron: noo sum,   vooz eht, eel sonh, el   sonh.
Eng: we are,   you are, they are,   they are.

Imperfect Tense (I was, I used to be, etc.)—j'étais, tu étais, il était, elle était; nous étions, vous étiez, ils (elles) étaient.

Past Definite Tense (I was, etc.)—je fus, tu fus, il fut, elle fut; nous fûmes, vous fûtes, ils (elles) furent.

Future Tense (I shall be, etc.)—je serai, tu seras, il sera, elle sera; nous serons, vous serez, ils (elles) seront.

Potential or Conditional Tense (I should be, etc.)—je serais, tu serais, il serait, elle serait; nous serions, vous seriez, ils (elles) seraient.

Present Subjunctive Tense (I may be, etc.)—je sois, tu sois, il soit, elle soit; nous soyons, vous soyez, ils (elles) soient.

Imperative Mood

Fr: sois,   qu'il soit,   soyons,   soyez,   qu'ils soient.
Eng: be thou, let him be, let us be, be you, let them be.

The Present Participle (Being)—étant.
The Past Participle (Been)—été.

NOTE: The compound tenses are conjugated with *Avoir* and the Past Participle (*été*). Certain verbs (e.g., Aller, Arriver, Partir, Sortir, and Venir) conjugate their compound tenses with forms of *Être* (instead of with *Avoir*). For example: *je serai arrivé* (I shall have arrived). All reflexive verbs conjugate their compound tenses with forms of *Être,* as follows:

ALLER, *to go* (6)

(Irregular Verb)

Present Tense

Fr: je vais, tu   vas,   il va,   elle va.
Pron: zhuh vay, t*u*   vah, eel vah, el   vah.
Eng: I   go, thou goest, he goes, she goes.

Fr: nous allons, vous allez, ils (elles) vont.
Pron: nooz al-lonh, vooz al-lay, eel (el)   vonh.
Eng: we   go,   you go,   they   go.

Imperfect: j'allais, tu allais, il allait, nous allions, vous alliez, ils allaient. *Past Definite:* j'allai, tu allas, il alla, nous allâmes, vous allâtes, ils allèrent. *Future:* j'irai, tu iras, il ira, nous irons, vous irez, ils iront. *Conditional:* j'irais, tu irais, il irait, nous irions, vous iriez, ils iraient. *Present Subjunctive:* j'aille, tu ailles, il aille, nous allions, vous alliez, ils aillent. *Imperative Mood:* va, qu'il aille, allons, allez, qu'ils aillent. *Present Participle:* allant. *Past Participle:* allé (conjugated with *être*).

ACCUEILLIR, *to welcome* (7)

(Irregular Verb)

Present Tense

Fr: j'accueille, tu accueilles, il (elle) accueille.
Pron: zhak-*keu*-ee, tu ak-*keu*-ee, eel (el) ak-*keu*-ee.
Eng: I welcome, thou welcomest, he (she) welcomes.

Fr: nous accueillons, vous accueillez, ils (elles) accueillent.
Pron: nooz ak-*keu*-ee-onh, vooz ak-*keu*-ee-ay, eelz (elz) ak-*keu*-ee.
Eng: we welcome, you welcome, they welcome.

Imperfect: j'accueillais, tu accueillais, il accueillait, nous accueillions, vous accueilliez, ils accueillaient. *Past Definite:* j'accueillis, tu accueillis, il accueillit, nous accueillîmes, vous accueillîtes, ils accueillirent. *Future:* j'accueillerai, tu accueilleras, il accueillera, nous accueillerons, vous accueillerez, ils accueilleront. *Conditional:* j'accueillerais, tu accueillerais, il accueillerait, nous accueillerions, vous accueilleriez, ils accueilleraient. *Present Subjunctive:* j'accueille, tu accueilles, il accueille, nous accueillions, vous accueilliez, ils accueillent. *Imperative Mood:* accueille, qu'il accueille, accueillons, accueillez, qu'ils accueillent. *Present Participle:* accueillant. *Past Participle:* accueilli.

DÉCOUVRIR, *to discover* (8)

(Irregular Verb)

Present Tense

Fr: je découvre, tu découvres, il (elle) découvre.
Pron: zhuh day-coov-r, tu day-coov-r, eel (el) day-coov-r.
Eng: I discover, thou discoverest, he (she) discovers.

Fr: nous découvrons, vous découvrez, ils (elles) découvrent.
Pron: noo day-coov-ronh, voo day-couv-ray, eel (el) day-coov-r.
Eng: we discover, you discover, they discover.

Imperfect: je découvrais, tu découvrais, il découvrait, nous découvrions, vous découvriez, ils découvraient. *Past Definite:* je découvris, tu découvris, il découvrit, nous découvrîmes, vous découvrîtes, ils découvrirent. *Future:* je découvrirai, tu découvriras, il découvrira, nous découvrirons, vous découvrirez, ils découvriront. *Conditional:* je découvrirais, tu découvrirais, il découvrirait, nous découvririons, vous découvririez, ils découvriraient. *Present Subjunctive:* je découvre, tu découvres, il découvre, nous découvrions, vous découvriez, ils découvrent. *Imperative Mood:* découvre, qu'il découvre, découvrons, découvrez, qu'ils découvrent. *Present Participle:* découvrant. *Past Participle:* découvert.

MOURIR, *to die* (9)

(Irregular Verb)

Present Tense

Fr: je meurs, tu meurs, il (elle) meurt.
Pron: zhuh meur, tu meur, eel (el) meur.
Eng: I am dying, thou art dying, he (she) is dying.

Fr: nous mourons, vous mourez, ils (elles) meurent.
Pron: noo moo-ronh, voo moo-ray, eel (el) meur.
Eng: we are dying, you are dying, they are dying.

Imperfect: je mourais, tu mourais, il mourait, nous mourions, vous mouriez, ils mouraient. *Past Definite:* je mourus, tu mourus, il mourut, nous mourûmes, vous mourûtes, ils moururent. *Future:* je mourrai, tu mourras, il mourra, nous mourrons, vous mourrez, ils mourront. *Conditional:* je mourrais, tu mourrais, il mourrait, nous mourrions, vous mourriez, ils mourraient. *Present Subjunctive:* je meure, tu meures, il meure, nous mourions, vous mouriez, ils meurent. *Imperative Mood:* meurs, qu'il meure, mourons, mourez, qu'ils meurent. *Present Participle:* mourant. *Past Participle:* mort (conjugated with *être*).

TENIR, *to hold* (10)

(Irregular Verb)

Present Tense

Fr: je   tiens,   tu   tiens,   il (elle) tient.
Pron: zhuh tee-ănh, *tu*   tee-ănh, eel (el) tee-ănh.
Eng: I   hold,   thou holdest, he (she) holds.

Fr: nous tenons,   vous tenez,   ils (elles) tiennent.
Pron: noo tuh-nonh, voo tuh-nay, eel (el)   tee-en.
Eng: we hold,   you hold,   they   hold.

Imperfect: je tenais, tu tenais, il tenait, nous tenions, vous teniez, ils tenaient. *Past Definite:* je tins, tu tins, il tint, nous tînmes, vous tîntes, ils tinrent. *Future:* je tiendrai, tu tiendras, il tiendra, nous tiendrons, vous tiendrez, ils tiendront. *Conditional:* je tiendrais, tu tiendrais, il tiendrait, nous tiendrions, vous tiendriez, ils tiendraient. *Present Subjunctive:* je tienne, tu tiennes, il tienne, nous tenions, vous teniez, ils tiennent. *Imperative Mood:* tiens, qu'il tienne, tenons, tenez, qu'ils tiennent. *Present Participle:* tenant. *Past Participle:* tenu.

S'ASSEOIR, *to sit down* (11)

Present: je m'assieds, tu t'assieds, il s'assied, nous nous asseyons, vous vous asseyez, ils s'asseyent. *Imperfect:* je m'asseyais, tu t'asseyais, il s'asseyait, nous nous asseyions, vous vous asseyiez, il s'asseyaient. *Past Definite:* je m'assis, tu t'assis, il s'assit, nous nous assîmes, vous vous assîtes, ils s'assirent. *Future:* je m'asseoirai, tu t'asseoiras, il s'asseoira, nous nous asseoirons, vous vous asseoirez, ils s'asseoiront. *Conditional:* je m'asseoirais, tu t'asseoirais, il s'asseoirait, nous nous asseoirions, vous vous asseoiriez, ils s'asseoiraient. *Present Subjunctive:* je m'asseye, tu t'asseyes, il s'asseye, nous nous asseyions, vous vous asseyiez, ils s'asseyent. *Imperative Mood:* asseye-toi, qu'il s'asseye, asseyons-nous, asseyez-vous, qu'ils s'asseyent. *Present Participle:* s'asseyant. *Past Participle:* assis.

DEVOIR, *to owe* (12)

Present: je dois, tu dois, il doit, elle doit, nous devons, vous devez, ils (elles) doivent. *Imperfect:* je devais, tu devais, il devait, nous devions, vous deviez, ils devaient. *Past Definite:* je dus, tu dus, il dut, nous dûmes, vous dûtes, ils durent. *Future:* je devrai, tu devras, il devra, nous devrons, vous devrez, ils devront. *Conditional:* je devrais, tu devrais, il devrait, nous devrions, vous devriez, ils devraient. *Present Subjunctive:* je doive, tu doives, il doive, nous devions, vous deviez, ils doivent. *Imperative Mood:* dois, qu'il doive, devons, devez, qu'ils doivent. *Present Participle:* devant. *Past Participle:* dû.

FALLOIR, *to be necessary* (13)

NOTE: *Falloir* is a defective verb; that is, it is used only in a certain few of the usual verb forms—in this case, only in the third person singular.

Present: il faut, it is necessary. *Imperfect:* il fallait, it was necessary. *Past Definite:* il fallut, it was necessary. *Future:* il faudra, it will be necessary. *Conditional:* il faudrait, it would be necessary. *Present Subjunctive:* il faille. *Past Indefinite:* il a fallu. *Past Participle:* fallu.

POUVOIR, *to be able* (14)

Present: je puis (peux), tu peux, il peut, elle peut, nous pouvons, vous pouvez, ils (elles) peuvent. *Imperfect:* je pouvais, tu pouvais, il pouvait, nous pouvions, vous pouviez, ils pouvaient. *Past Definite:* je pus, tu pus, il put, nous pûmes, vous pûtes, ils purent. *Future:* je pourrai, tu pourras, il pourra, nous pourrons, vous pourrez, ils pourront. *Conditional:* je pourrais, tu pourrais, il pourrait, nous pourrions, vous pourriez, ils pourraient. *Present Subjunctive:* je puisse, tu puisses, il puisse, nous puissions, vous puissiez, ils puissent. *Present Participle:* pouvant. *Past Participle:* pu.

RECEVOIR, *to receive* (15)

Present: je reçois, tu reçois, il reçoit, elle reçoit, nous recevons, vous recevez, ils (elles) reçoivent. *Imperfect:* je recevais, tu recevais, il recevait, nous recevions, vous receviez, ils recevaient. *Past Definite:* je reçus, tu reçus, il reçut, nous reçûmes, vous reçûtes, ils reçurent. *Future:* je recevrai, tu recevras, il recevra, nous recevrons, vous recevrez, ils recevront. *Conditional:* je recevrais, tu recevrais, il recevrait, nous recevrions, vous recevriez, ils recevraient. *Present Subjunctive:* je reçoive, tu reçoives, il reçoive, nous recevions, vous receviez, ils reçoivent. *Imperative Mood:* reçois, qu'il reçoive, recevons, recevez, qu'ils reçoivent. *Present Participle:* recevant. *Past Participle:* reçu.

SAVOIR, *to know* (16)

Present: je sais, tu sais, il sait, elle sait, nous savons, vous savez, ils (elles) savent. *Imperfect:* je savais, tu savais, il savait, nous savions, vous saviez, ils savaient. *Past Definite:* je sus, tu sus, il sut, nous sûmes, vous sûtes, ils surent. *Future:* je saurai, tu sauras, il saura, nous saurons, vous saurez, ils sauront. *Conditional:* je saurais, tu saurais, il saurait, nous saurions, vous sauriez, ils sauraient. *Present Subjunctive:* je sache, tu saches, il sache, nous sachons, vous sachez, ils sachent. *Imperative Mood:* sache, qu'il sache, sachons, sachez, qu'ils sachent. *Present Participle:* sachant. *Past Participle:* su.

VALOIR, *to be worth* (17)

Present: je vaux, tu vaux, il vaut, elle vaut, nous valons, vous valez, ils (elles) valent. *Imperfect:* je valais, tu valais, il valait, nous valions, vous valiez, ils valaient. *Past Definite:* je valus, tu valus, il valut, nous valûmes, vous valûtes, ils valurent. *Future:* je vaudrai, tu vaudras, il vaudra, nous vaudrons, vous vaudrez, ils vaudront. *Conditional:* je vaudrais, tu vaudrais, il vaudrait, nous vaudrions, vous vaudriez, ils vaudraient. *Present Subjunctive:* je vaille, tu vailles, il vaille, nous valions, vous valiez, ils vaillent. *Imperative Mood:* vaux, qu'il vaille, valons, valez, qu'ils vaillent. *Present Participle*: valant. *Past Participle:* valu.

VOIR, *to see* (18)

Present: je vois, tu vois, il voit, elle voit, nous voyons, vous voyez, ils (elles) voient. *Imperfect:* je voyais, tu voyais, il voyait, nous voyions, vous voyiez, ils voyaient. *Past Definite:* je vis, tu vis, il vit, nous vîmes, vous vîtes, ils virent. *Future:* je verrai, tu verras, il verra, nous verrons, vous verrez, ils verront. *Conditional:* je verrais, tu verrais, il verrait, nous verrions, vous verriez, ils verraient. *Present Subjunctive:* je voie, tu voies, il voie, nous voyions, vous voyiez, ils voient. *Imperative Mood:* vois, qu'il voie, voyons, voyez, qu'ils voient. *Present Participle:* voyant. *Past Participle:* vu.

VOULOIR, *to want* (19)

Present: je veux, tu veux, il veut, elle veut, nous voulons, vous voulez, ils (elles) veulent. *Imperfect:* je voulais, tu voulais, il voulait, nous voulions, vous vouliez, ils voulaient. *Past Definite:* je voulus, tu voulus, il voulut, nous voulûmes, vous voulûtes, ils voulurent. *Future:* je voudrai, tu voudras, il voudra, nous voudrons, vous voudrez, ils voudront. *Conditional:* je voudrais, tu voudrais, il voudrait, nous voudrions, vous voudriez, ils voudraient. *Present Subjunctive:* je veuille, tu veuilles, il veuille, nous voulions, vous vouliez, ils veuillent. *Imperative Mood:* veuillez (please). *Present Participle:* voulant. *Past Participle:* voulu.

BOIRE, *to drink* (20)

Present: je bois, tu bois, il boit, elle boit, nous buvons, vous buvez, ils (elles) boivent. *Imperfect:* je buvais, tu buvais, il buvait, nous buvions, vous buviez, ils buvaient. *Past Definite:* je bus, tu bus, il but, nous bûmes, vous bûtes, ils burent. *Future:* je boirai, tu boiras, il boira, nous boirons, vous boirez, ils boiront. *Conditional:* je boirais, tu boirais, il boirait, nous boirions, vous boiriez, ils boiraient. *Present Subjunctive:* je boive, tu boives, il boive, nous buvions, vous buviez, ils boivent. *Imperative Mood:* bois, qu'il boive, buvons, buvez, qu'ils boivent. *Present Participle:* buvant. *Past Participle:* bu.

CONNAÎTRE, *to be acquainted with* (21)

Present: je connais, tu connais, il connaît, elle connaît, nous connaissons, vous connaissez, ils (elles) connaissent. *Imperfect:* je connaissais, tu connaissais, il connaissait, nous connaissions, vous connaissiez, ils connaissaient. *Past Definite:* je connus, tu connus, il connut, nous connûmes, vous connûtes, ils connurent. *Future:* je connaîtrai, tu connaîtras, il connaîtra, nous connaîtrons, vous connaîtrez, ils connaîtront. *Conditional:* je connaîtrais, tu connaîtrais, il connaîtrait, nous connaîtrions, vous connaîtriez, ils connaîtraient. *Present Subjunctive:* je connaisse, tu connaisses, il connaisse, nous connaissions, vous connaissiez, ils connaissent. *Imperative Mood:* connais, qu'il connaisse, connaissons, connaissez, qu'ils connaissent. *Present Participle:* connaissant. *Past Participle:* connu.

CRAINDRE, *to fear* (22)

Present: je crains, tu crains, il craint, elle craint, nous craignons, vous craignez, ils (elles) craignent. *Imperfect:* je craignais, tu craignais, il craignait, nous craignions, vous craigniez, ils craignaient. *Past Definite:* je craignis, tu craignis, il craignit, nous craignîmes, vous craignîtes, ils craignirent. *Future:* je craindrai, tu craindras, il craindra, nous craindrons, vous craindrez, ils craindront. *Conditional:* je craindrais, tu craindrais, il craindrait, nous craindrions, vous craindriez, ils craindraient. *Present Subjunctive:* je craigne, tu craignes, il craigne, nous craignions, vous craigniez, ils craignent. *Imperative Mood:* crains, qu'il craigne, craignons, craignez, qu'ils craignent. *Present Participle:* craignant. *Past Participle:* craint.

DIRE, *to say, tell* (23)

Present: je dis, tu dis, il dit, elle dit, nous disons, vous dites, ils (elles) disent. *Imperfect:* je disais, tu disais, il disait, nous disions, vous disiez, ils disaient. *Past Definite:* je dis, tu dis, il dit, nous dîmes, vous dîtes, ils dirent. *Future:* je dirai, tu diras, il dira, nous dirons, vous direz, ils diront. *Conditional:* je dirais, tu dirais, il dirait, nous dirions, vous diriez, ils diraient. *Present Subjunctive:* je dise, tu dises, il dise, nous disions, vous disiez, ils disent. *Imperative Mood:* dis, qu'il dise, disons, dites, qu'ils disent. *Present Participle:* disant. *Past Participle:* dit.

RIRE, *to laugh* (24)

Present: je ris, tu ris, il rit, elle rit, nous rions, vous riez, ils (elles) rient. *Imperfect:* je riais, tu riais, il riait, nous riions, vous riiez, ils riaient. *Past Definite:* je ris, tu ris, il rit, nous rîmes, vous rîtes, ils rirent. *Future:* je rirai, tu riras, il rira, nous rirons, vous rirez, ils riront. *Conditional:* je rirais, tu rirais, il rirait, nous ririons, vous ririez, ils riraient. *Present Subjunctive:* je rie, tu ries, il rie, nous riions, vous riiez, ils rient. *Imperative Mood:* ris, qu'il rie, rions, riez, qu'ils rient. *Present Participle:* riant. *Past Participle:* ri.

ECRIRE, *to write* (25)

Present: j'écris, tu écris, il écrit, elle écrit, nous écrivons, vous écrivez, ils (elles) écrivent. *Imperfect:* j'écrivais, tu écrivais, il écrivait, nous écrivions, vous écriviez, ils écrivaient. *Past Definite:* j'écrivis, tu écrivis, il écrivit, nous écrivîmes, vous écrivîtes, ils écrivirent. *Future:* j'écrirai, tu écriras, il écrira, nous écrirons, vous écrirez, ils écriront. *Conditional:* j'écrirais, tu écrirais, il écrirait, nous écririons, vous écririez, ils écriraient. *Present Subjunctive:* j'écrive, tu écrives, il écrive, nous écrivions, vous écriviez, ils écrivent. *Imperative Mood:* écris, qu'il écrive, écrivons, écrivez, qu'ils écrivent. *Present Participle:* écrivant. *Past Participle:* écrit.

FAIRE, *to make, do* (26)

Present: je fais, tu fais, il fait, elle fait, nous faisons, vous faites, ils (elles) font. *Imperfect:* je faisais, tu faisais, il faisait, nous faisions, vous faisiez, ils faisaient. *Past Definite:* je fis, tu fis, il fit, nous fîmes, vous fîtes, ils firent. *Future:* je ferai, tu feras, il fera, nous ferons, vous ferez, ils feront. *Conditional:* je ferais, tu ferais, il ferait, nous ferions, vous feriez, ils feraient. *Present Subjunctive:* je fasse, tu fasses, il fasse, nous fassions, vous fassiez, ils fassent. *Imperative Mood:* fais, qu'il fasse, faisons, faites, qu'ils fassent. *Present Participle:* faisant. *Past Participle:* fait.

SUIVRE, *to follow* (27)

Present: je suis, tu suis, il suit, elle suit, nous suivons, vous suivez, ils (elles) suivent. *Past Participle:* suivi. [All other tenses of *suivre* are like *vendre* (3).]

SORTIR, *to go out* (28)

Present: je sors, tu sors, il sort, elle sort, nous sortons, vous sortez, ils (elles) sortent. *Imperfect:* je sortais, tu sortais, il sortait, nous sortions, vous sortiez, ils sortaient. *Past Definite:* je sortis, tu sortis, il sortit, nous sortîmes, vous sortîtes, ils sortirent. *Future:* je sortirai, tu sortiras, il sortira, nous sortirons, vous sortirez, ils sortiront. *Conditional:* je sortirais, tu sortirais, il sortirait, nous sortirions, vous sortiriez, ils sortiraient. *Present Subjunctive:* je sorte, tu sortes, il sorte, nous sortions, vous sortiez, ils sortent. *Imperative Mood:* sors, qu'il sorte, sortons, sortez, qu'ils sortent. *Present Participle:* sortant. *Past Participle:* sorti (conjugated with *être*).

Partir, to go away, is conjugated like *sortir* (28).

METTRE, *to put* (29)

Present: je mets, tu mets, il met, elle met, nous mettons, vous mettez, ils (elles) mettent. *Past Definite:* je mis, tu mis, il mit, nous mîmes, vous mîtes, ils mirent. *Present Participle:* mettant. *Past Participle:* mis. [All other forms of *mettre* are like *vendre* (3).]

Prendre, *to take* (30)

Present: je prends, tu prends, il prend, elle prend, nous prenons, vous prenez, ils (elles) prennent. *Imperfect:* je prenais, tu prenais, il prenait, nous prenions, vous preniez, ils prenaient. *Past Definite:* je pris, tu pris, il prit, nous prîmes, vous prîtes, ils prirent. *Future:* je prendrai, tu prendras, il prendra, nous prendrons, vous prendrez, ils prendront. *Conditional:* je prendrais, tu prendrais, il prendrait, nous prendrions, vous prendriez, ils prendraient. *Present Subjunctive:* je prenne, tu prennes, il prenne, nous prenions, vous preniez, ils prennent. *Imperative Mood:* prends, qu'il prenne, prenons, prenez, qu'ils prennent. *Present Participle:* prenant. *Past Participle:* pris.

Courir, *to run* (31)

Present: je cours, tu cours, il court, elle court, nous courons, vous courez, ils (elles) courent. *Imperfect:* je courais, tu courais, il courait, nous courions, vous couriez, ils couraient. *Past Definite:* je courus, tu courus, il courut, nous courûmes, vous courûtes, ils coururent. *Future:* je courrai, tu courras, il courra, nous courrons, vous courrez, ils courront. *Conditional:* je courrais, tu courrais, il courrait, nous courrions, vous courriez, ils courraient. *Present Subjunctive:* je coure, tu coures, il coure, nous courions, vous couriez, ils courent. *Imperative Mood:* cours, qu'il coure, courons, courez, qu'ils courent. *Present Participle:* courant. *Past Participle:* couru.

CARDINAL NUMERALS

0	zéro (zay-roh)	14	quatorze (kat-orz)
1	un, une (unh, *u*n)	15	quinze (kănh-z)
2	deux (d*eu*)	16	seize (sez)
3	trois (trwah)	17	dix-sept (dee-set)
4	quatre (kat-r)	18	dix-huit (deez-*u*-eet)
5	cinq (sank)	19	dix-neuf (dee-n*euf*)
6	six (seess)	20	vingt (vănh)
7	sept (set)	21	vingt et un (vănh teh unh)
8	huit (*u*-eet)	22	vingt-deux (vănht-d*eu*)
9	neuf (n*euf*)	30	trente (trawnh-t)
10	dix (deess)	31	trente et un (trawnh-teh-unh)
11	onze (onh-z)	32	trente-deux (trawnh-t-d*eu*)
12	douze (dooz)	40	quarante (ka-ranh-t)
13	treize (trez)	50	cinquante (sanh-kant)

60	soixante (swa-sanh-t)	92	quatre-vingt-douze
70	soixante-dix (swa-sanh-t-	93	quatre-vingt-treize, etc.
	deess)	100	cent (sawnh)
71	soixante-onze	101	cent un (sawnh unh)
72	soixante-douze	102	cent deux (sawnh d*eu*)
73	soixante-treize, etc.	200	deux cents
80	quatre-vingts (kat-r-vanh)	220	deux cent vingt
90	quatre-vingt-dix (kat-r-vanh-	1000	mille (meel)
	deess)	8000	huit mille
91	quatre-vingt-onze (kat-r-	1,000,000	un million (unh meel-
	vanh-tonh-z)		yonh)

ORDINAL NUMERALS

1st	premier (pruh-mee-ay)	10th	dixième (deez-ee-em)
	(masculine form)	11th	onzième (onh-zee-em)
	première (pruh-mee-air)	12th	douzième (dooz-ee-em)
	(feminine form)	13th	treizième (trez-ee-em)
2nd	deuxième (d*euz*-ee-em)	14th	quatorzième (ka-torz-ee-em)
3rd	troisième (trwaz-ee-em)	15th	quinzième (kǎnh-zee-em)
4th	quatrième (kat-ree-em)	16th	seizième (sez-ee-em)
5th	cinquième (sank-ee-em)	17th	dix-septième (dee-set-ee-em)
6th	sixième (see-zee-em)		etc., *-ième* being added to
7th	septième (set-ee-em)		the end of the Cardinal Nu-
8th	huitième (*u*-eet-ee-em)		merals to form the Ordinals.
9th	neuvième (n*euv*-ee-em)		

TRANSLATIONS OF EXERCISES

Lesson II: English into French

1. Il est dans la cour. 2. Elle est à la porte. 3. Ils sont à la maison. 4. Nous sommes dans la rue. 5. La chaise est dans le vestibule. 6. J'ai un lit et un sofa. 7. Vous n'avez pas peur. 8. Ma chambre est au rez-de-chaussée. 9. Ils ont une fenêtre entre la salle à manger et la cuisine. 10. Il a une chambre au-delà du salon. 11. Nos chaises sont au premier étage. 12. Ses bibliothèques sont sous l'escalier. 13. Votre tapis est sur son plancher. 14. La souris est au-dessous de mon fauteuil. 15. Leur table est près de son lit. 16. J'ai une chaise pour mon bureau. 17. Il est au-dessus de la cheminée. 18. Je suis content qu'ils ne soient pas dans la rue. 19. Elle a sommeil, mais elle n'est pas malade. 20. Qu'a-t-il? Il n'est pas sur la chaise.

Lesson III: English into French

1. Qui est dans le salon? Monsieur Lenoir. 2. Monsieur Leblanc a-t-il une belle maison? 3. Non, mais c'est un très bel homme. 4. Ce sont vos amis qui sont à la porte. 5. N'avez-vous pas quelque chose à dire? 6. Oui, j'ai quelque chose à vous dire, mais vous n'avez rien à me dire. 7. Elle n'a pas de mère; elle n'a qu'une amie. 8. Votre père est-il un ami de mon professeur? 9. J'ai des pêches et de la crème à manger aujourd'hui. 10. Mademoiselle Lebon est avec sa mère dans la cuisine. 11. J'ai envie de dire quelque chose à votre professeur. 12. Le sucre n'est pas dans la salle à manger. 13. Je ne suis pas votre père, mais je suis votre ami. 14. N'est-il pas son père? 15. L'amie de ma mère est très malade. 16. Des souris sont sous l'escalier, et une pêche est sur le plancher. 17. Je n'ai pas d'argent, mais j'ai tant d'enfants que je suis très heureuse. 18. Les mères sont toutes belles. 19. Elle a un beau tapis au mur, du plafond jusqu'au plancher. 20. J'ai tant de pêches que je n'ai pas envie de manger.

Lesson V: French into English

1. I have eaten (ate) some meat. 2. My mother roasted the chicken. 3. He has sold the cow. 4. The cow which he has sold (sold) used to eat (was eating, ate) the cabbages. 5. Before eating a chicken, one roasts it. 6. We do not sell our children. 7. The cook (feminine) will roast the meat before we eat (shall eat) the dinner. 8. If I had not sold the cow, we should have nothing to eat today. 9. While I was roasting the meat, my friends were eating bonbons (candies). 10. They will not sell the chickens before roasting them.

Lesson VI: French into English

—We left the house in the little village where we were living, a week ago. Now the ship is approaching the coast of France. Tomorrow morning we shall disembark in Havre.

—Do you remember the hours of preparation for this voyage?—the confusion of the last moments when we wished to throw into the trunks all our possessions, without taking account of (realizing) the limited space at our disposal—the tremendous hurry of the departure in the taxi, which, after having arrived half an hour late, nearly overturned five times on the way to the station—the fear of having missed the train?

—Yes, but at last we found ourselves in the railway coach. We had just got our baggage checks and we were climbing into the coach at the moment when the conductor called, "All aboard!"

—Yes, I remember. And on board the ship when we were leaving the harbor of New York I couldn't find my passport!

—Horrible! And that very evening you found it in your valise, in which you had put it.

—But look! the ship is stopping. We are going to drop anchor. Soon the port officials will come aboard, and tomorrow we shall find ourselves in the city of Havre. We have arrived.

Lesson VII: French into English

After leaving the ship we got into a taxi which was found near the wharf. We gave the chauffeur the name of a good hotel, and after ten minutes of zigzagging through the crowd of bicyclists, automobiles, and people on foot, we arrived safe and sound.

We were getting out of the taxi when a boy seized our bags and disappeared into the lobby of the hotel. We followed him to the desk, where another employee welcomed us.

—What do you desire, gentlemen?

—Two rooms with bath.

—Very well, gentlemen, we have a fine suite exposed to the sun, both rooms large and excellently furnished. Do you wish to see them at once?

—How much is it (necessary to pay) per week?

—Three hundred francs a week, gentlemen, or fifty francs a day. And I assure you that the suite is well worth the price. The bellboy will show it to you. Do you wish to go up immediately?

The boy precedes us to the elevator. It is evident that everybody takes us for Americans, otherwise they would never dare to ask us such a price for two rooms. The elevator stops at the fourth floor and the boy leads us to Number Thirty-seven. The rooms are truly fine, with large windows which let the sun in through white-and-rose curtains. From the rug on the floor to the coverlet, everything is spotless and charming after the fatigue of the journey. There is even a telephone on a little table in a corner. In spite of the three hundred francs a week, we are well pleased with our rooms.

As soon as the boy goes away with a magnificent tip, we begin to lay out our things; but when they are half unpacked, the desire to plunge into cold water seizes us, and we repair to the bathroom to efface the dust of travel.

—When you have finished washing, shaving, cleaning your teeth, and dressing—in short, when you have brushed your hair, polished your fingernails, and smoothed (curled) your eyebrows, perhaps you will think (imagine) that you are ready to go downstairs. As for me, I'm dying of hunger.

Lesson VIII: French into English

—Well, here we are sitting down for a quarter of an hour, and I don't see the waiter.

—Calm yourself, old boy! We just sat down, two minutes ago at the most. As for the waiter, here he is coming now. Are you going to have everything brought that is (written) on the menu?

—No, of course not! I find on it so many dishes that I never encountered in my textbooks that I don't know what to do or what to choose.

—All right. Choose at your convenience. For myself, I don't wish to wait any longer.—Waiter! The consommé to begin with; then some roast beef, juicy, with fried potatoes and string beans.

—Very good! And you, sir? You wish—?

—Oh, I too—I cannot resist either the roast beef with fried potatoes or the string beans. My friend is saving me the trouble of choosing, and I am glad of it.

—Good, gentlemen, I'll be back in an instant.

—You did well, my friend. Veal sweetbreads, soufflés, and an infinity of rare and delicate dishes are waiting for us in all the restaurants of France; but at present a simple and well-prepared dinner suits us better. To continue the same idea, you will find that of all the things that will strike your eyes in the French stores, the most useful are the cheapest, and the strange and startling ones are expensive, without satisfying any real need. However, I fear that all the French clerks, on seeing Americans approach, will raise the prices of all their merchandise. We'll have to be on our guard, even in buying a pin!

—But here's the waiter bringing the consommé. For dessert—

—Good heavens! Already you are beginning to talk about the dessert, and we haven't ordered the wine yet.

—(To the waiter) Some white wine, please. I don't like the red wine—the common wine which many French people drink instead of water.

—As I was saying, my friend, you may spend the time poring over the menu while I eat dinner. I have already chosen my dessert. I shall have strawberries with cream, little cakes, and naturally some black coffee with a small glass of brandy. What do you think of that?

—Keep right on, chatterbox! You don't allow yourself the pleasure of thinking about the delicacies. I prefer to taste them in advance. Besides,

I must choose a dessert which fits in with this white wine which I drink to your health!

—To your health! It is useless to wish you a good appetite.

Lesson IX: English into French

1. Nous demeurions dans un petit village près du Havre. 2. Vous rappelez-vous où vous avez mis mon passeport? 3. Je crains que vos amis soient dans le taxi qui a versé en route au village. 4. J'ai jeté ma valise dans le taxi et j'ai crié le nom de mon hôtel. 5. Enfin j'ai trouvé la station et je suis monté dans le wagon au moment que le train s'arrêtait. 6. Il ne veut pas attendre à bord du vaisseau. 7. Ils viennent de débarquer. 8. Je crains que son français ne suffise guère quand elle se trouvera en France. 9. Je ne veux rien acheter dans ce magasin. 10. Avez-vous découvert le menu? 11. J'ai tout ce qu'il me faut dans mes malles. 12. Cette fois je me rendrai compte du peu d'espace dont je dispose. 13. Le train n'attendra pas; il est déjà un quart d'heure en retard. 14. Je le sais bien; aussitôt que le chef de train criera: "En voiture!" le train quittera la station. 15. Ils n'oseront jamais partir sans moi. 16. Que faites-vous maintenant? Vous vêtez-vous (vous habillez-vous) ou vous brossez-vous les cheveux? 17. Pour commencer, je vais commander un bon dîner. 18. Il ne payera jamais un tel prix. 19. On (*one* or *they; ils* would refer to certain definite persons as *they*) ne le prendrait (*prendraient* if *ils* is used) jamais pour un Français. 20. Peut-être je ferai un meilleur déjeuner que vous. 21. Non, je ne veux pas monter tout de suite; j'attendrai mon ami. 22. L'ascenseur ne s'est pas arrêté. A quel étage est votre appartement? 23. Si tout le monde veut se faire gourmand, ça m'est égal. 24. Je préfère goûter mon dîner d'avance. 25. Peut-être elle est prête à s'asseoir à la table. 26. Je n'accueille que mes amis. 27. Les gens à pied sont arrivés sain et sauf, mais l'automobile a versé en route. 28. Dans le foyer de l'hôtel j'ai rencontré trois amis que je ne vois pas depuis deux semaines (or *quinze jours*). 29. Il s'est plongé (or *s'est jeté*) dans la foule, et a disparu. 30. Il m'a suivi à ma chambre. 31. C'est bien (or *très bien*), monsieur, si vous voulez une chambre exposée au soleil, il faudra payer le prix. 32. Il n'osera pas me demander cinq cents francs par semaine. 33. Cet appartement n'a pas de bain; montrez-moi un autre, s'il vous plaît. 34. Mes biens (or *affaires*) sont à demi déballés; je ne suis pas encore prêt à descendre; de plus, je n'ai pas faim. 35. Vraiment? Moi, je meurs de faim. 36. Il y a même des rideaux blancs dans la chambre de mon ami. 37. Les deux chambres sont larges et sans tache. 38. Le garçon a saisi le pourboire et nous a précédés au numéro quarante.

VOCABULARY

A

à, at, to, on, in, by
accueillir, to welcome
acheter, to buy
ailleurs(d'-), furthermore
aimer, to like, to love
aller, to go
amener, to lead
ami(e), m. or f. friend
ancre, m. anchor
anglais(e), English
appétit, m. appetite
apporter, to bring
approcher(s'—de), to approach
après, after
argent, m. money, silver
arrêter, to stop
arriver, to arrive, to reach
ascenseur, m. elevator, lift
asseoir(s'-), to seat
assez, enough
attendre, to wait for, await
au, to the (masculine singular form)
aucun(e), no, not one
au-dessous, beneath
au-dessus, above
aujourd'hui, today
au jus, juicy
aussi, also
aussitôt (que), as soon as
autour, around
autre, other
autrement, otherwise
avance(d'-), in advance
avant, before
avec, with

B

bain, m. bath, bathroom
balancer, to swing

bavard(e), chatterbox
beau (belle), fine, beautiful
beaucoup, many
belle, f. of *beau*
besoin, m. need
bête, f. beast, adj. dumb
bibliothèque, f. bookcase, library
bien, well; *(-que),* although
biens, goods, things, property
bientôt, soon
billet, m. ticket, note
bizarre, strange
blanc (blanche), white
bois, m. wood
bon (bonne), good
bonbon, m. bonbon, candy
bord(à-), on board
braver, to dare, to brave
briser, to break
brosser, to brush
bruit, m. noise
bureau, m. desk, office

C

cadrer, to fit with
café, m. coffee
calmer, to calm
cas, m. case
ce (cette), this, that
cent, hundred
cependant, however
chaise, f. chair
chambre, f. room, bedroom
charmant(e), charming
château, m. castle
chaud(e), hot, warm
chef, m. chief, cook
chemin, m. road; *(-de fer),* railroad
cheminée, f. fireplace

cher (*chère*), dear, costly
chercher, to seek, look for
cheveux, m. pl. hair
chez, at the place (home) of
choisir, to choose
chose, f. thing
chou, m. cabbage
cinq, five
cinquante, fifty
cœur, m. heart
coin, corner
combien, how many, how much
commander, to order
commis, m. clerk (in a store)
comme, like, as
compte, m. account, bill
connaître, to be acquainted with
consommé, m. clear broth, soup
content(*e*), glad, content
continuer, to continue
contre, against
convenance, f. convenience
côte, f. coast
coup(*tout d'un-*), all at once
courir, to run
coûter, to cost
couvre-lit, m. coverlet
couvrir, to cover
craindre, to fear
crème, f. cream
crier, to cry out, call out
cuisine, f. kitchen
cuisinière, f. cook (female)

delà(*au-*), beyond
délicat(*e*), delicate
délicieux (*délicieuse*), tasty
demain, tomorrow
demander, to ask
demeurer, to reside, live
demi(*e*), half
dent, f. tooth
départ, m. departure
déposer, to lay down
depuis, since
dernier (*dernière*), last
derrière, behind
des, of the (m. plural) *de + les*
descendre, to go down, get down
désirer, to desire, to wish
dessert, m. dessert
deux, two
deuxième, second
devant, before
devoir, to owe, ought
Dieu, m. God
dîner, m. dinner
dire, to say
disparaître, to disappear
dix, ten
donc, then, now
dont, of which, of whom, whose
donner, to give
doute, m. doubt
droit(*e*), right, straight
du, of the (m. singular form)
  de + le

D

dans, in, into
déballer, to unpack
débarquer, to disembark
découvrir, to discover, uncover
dedans, within
déjà, already
déjeuner, m. lunch, breakfast

E

eau, f. water
éclatant(*e*), startling
écrire, to write
effacer, to wipe out, efface
effet, m. effect
en, in; of it, of them
encore, again, still, yet

enfant, m. child
enfin, finally, at last
entendre, to hear, understand
entre, between, among
entrer, to enter
envie, f. desire
épargner, to spare
épingle, f. pin
escalier, m. stairs, stairway
espace, f. space
et, and
étage, m. floor, landing
été, m. summer
eux, pron. m. them
exposer, to expose

F

faim, f. hunger
faire, to make, to do
falloir, to be necessary
fatigue, f. weariness
faux (fausse), false
fenêtre, f. window
fer, m. iron
finir, to finish
fois, f. time
foule, f. crowd
foyer, m. lobby, hearth
frais (fraîche), fresh
fraise, f. strawberry
franc, m. franc
frapper, to strike, knock
frère, m. brother
frire, to fry
frit(e), fried
froid(e), cold

G

garçon, m. boy, waiter
gâteau, m. cake
gens, m. pl. people
glacer, to freeze

gourmand(e), m. or f. glutton
goûter, to taste
grand(e), big, large, tall

H

habiller(s'-), to get dressed
halter, to stop, halt
haricot, m. string bean
hâte, f. haste
hausser, to raise
heure, f. hour
heureux (heureuse), happy
hiver, m. winter

I

idée, f. idea
imaginer, to imagine
indiquer, to indicate
infinité, f. infinity
inutile, useless

J

jamais, never, ever
jaune, yellow
je, I
jeter, to throw
jour, m. day
jus, m. juice
jusqu'à, until, up to

L

laisser, to leave, to let
laver, to wash
le (la), the
lequel (laquelle), which
leur, their, theirs, to them
lieu, m. place
lit, m. bed
livre, m. book
lorsque, when
lourd(e), heavy
lumière, f. light

M

magasin, m. store
magnifique, magnificent
maintenant, now
mais, but
maison, f. house
maître, m. master
mal, badly
malade, ill, sick
malgré, in spite of
malle, f. trunk
manger, to eat
manquer, to lack, to miss
marchandise, f. merchandise
marché, n. market; (*bon-*), cheap
matin, m. morning
mauvais(e), bad
méditer, to meditate, ponder, pore
meilleur(e), better
même, even; self
mer, f. sea
mère, f. mother
messieurs, m. gentlemen
mets, m. dish (of food)
mettre, to put
meuble, m. piece of furniture
meubler, to furnish
mieux, better
mis, put (past part. of *mettre*)
moi, me, I, myself
mon (*ma*), my
monde, m. world; (*tout le monde*),
  everybody
monsieur, m. sir, gentleman
monter, to climb, go up
montrer, to show
mouiller, to wet
mur, m. wall

N

naturellement, naturally
nettoyer, to clean

ni, neither, nor
noir(e), black
nom, m. name
non, no
notre, our
nuit, f. night

O

obéir, to obey
objet, m. object
œil, m. eye
oiseau, m. bird
on, one, they
ongles, m. fingernails
oreille, f. ear
oser, to dare
oui, yes
ouvrir, to open

P

par, through, by
parler, to speak
parvenir, to reach to
pas, m. step, pace
pas, not
passer, to pass
payer, to pay
pêche, f. peach
peine, f. pain, trouble
pendant, during, while
pendre, to hang
père, m. father
permettre, to allow
personne, f. person; nobody
petit(e), little, small
peur, f. fear
peut-être, perhaps
pièce, f. room, division
pied, m. foot
plaine, f. plain
plaire, to please
plaisir, m. pleasure

plancher, m. floor
plat, m. dish
plonger, to plunge
pluie, f. rain
plus, more
polir, to polish
pomme, f. apple
pomme de terre, f. potato
porte, f. door
porteur, m. carrier, porter
poser, to place
poulet, m. chicken
pour, for
pourboire, m. tip
pourquoi, why
pouvoir, to be able, can
précéder, to precede
préférer, to prefer
prendre, to take
près(-de), near
presque, almost, nearly
prêt(e), ready
prix, m. price, prize
puis, then

Q

quai, m. wharf
quand, when, whenever
quart, m. quarter
que, that, which, whom, than, if
quel(-le), which, what
quelque, some
qui, who, which
quitter, to leave, quit

R

rappeler, to recall
raser, to shave
recevoir, to receive
refuser, to refuse, to deny
rencontrer, to meet
rendre, to give back

retard(en-), late
revenir, to come or go back
rideau, m. curtain
rien, anything, nothing
rire, to laugh
ris(-de veau), sweetbread
rosbif, m. roast beef
rose, pink, rose color
rôtir, to roast
rouge, red
route, f. way
roux (rousse), reddish
rue, f. street

S

sain(e), sound, well
saisir, to seize
salle, f. room
salon, m. parlor
sans, without
santé, f. health
satisfaire, to satisfy
sauf (sauve), safe
savoir, to know
semaine, f. week
sentir, to know, to feel, to smell
sept, seven
si, if, so
simple, simple
sœur, f. sister
soif, f. thirst
soir, m. evening
soleil, m. sun, sunlight
sommeil, m. sleep
son (sa), his, her, its
sortir, to go out
soufflé, puffed, as in a kind of food
souhaiter, to wish
souillure, f. dirt
sourcil, m. eyebrow
sous, under
souvenir(se—de), remember

sucre, m. sugar
suffire, to be enough
suite, f. that which follows
suivre, to follow
sur, upon
sûr(e), sure

T

table, f. table
tache, f. spot
tâche, f. task
tant, so many, so much
tapis, m. rug
tel, telle, such, such a
temps, m. time, weather
tenir, to hold
tête, f. head
ton (ta), thy
toujours, always
tout(e), all
tracer, to trace
travers(à-, au-), across, through
trente, thirty
très, very
trois, three
troisième, third
trouver, to find

U

un (une), one, a
utile, useful

V

vache, f. cow
vaisseau, m. vessel, ship
veau, m. calf, veal
vendre, to sell
venir, to come
véritable, true, real
verre, m. glass, tumbler
vers, toward
verser, to upset, to overrun, to pour
vert(e), green
vêtir, to dress
viande, f. meat
vieux (vieille), old
ville, f. city
vin, m. wine
voici, here, here is, see here
voilà, there, there is, look
voiler, to veil
voir, to see
voiture(en-), all aboard (in carriage)
votre, your
vôtre, yours
vouloir, to wish
vraiment, truly, really

W

wagon, m. coach

Y

y, there, to it, on it
yeux, m. pl. eyes

TOPICAL VOCABULARY

QUESTION WORDS

où? where?
  ici, là, here, there
  sur, sous, on, under

devant, derrière, in front of, behind
loin de, près de, far from, near

dans, hors de, in, out

à, de, to, from

à gauche, à droite, to the left, to the right

partout, nulle part, everywhere, nowhere

voici, voilà, here is, there is

comment? how?

bien, mal, well, badly

vite, lentement, quickly, slowly

si, très, so, very

à voix basse, à haute voix, softly, aloud

quand? when?

toujours, jamais, always, never

souvent, rarement, often, rarely

après, avant, after, before

maintenant, plus tard, now, later

le matin, l'après-midi, le soir, in the morning, afternoon, evening

aujourd'hui, hier, demain, today, yesterday, tomorrow

combien? how much (how many)?

beaucoup, peu, many, few

plus, moins, more, less

tant, assez, so much, enough

trop, trop peu, too much, too little

tout, rien, all, nothing

n'est-ce pas? isn't it so?

oui, non, yes, no

et, aussi, ou, and, also, or

mais, si, peut-être, but, if, maybe

certainement, pas du tout, certainly, not at all

pourquoi? why?

parce que, because

pour, in order to

je ne sais pas, I don't know

qu'est-ce qui? what?

ceci, cela, this, that

qu'est-ce qui est arrivé? what happened?

que veut dire cela? what does that mean?

qui? who, whom?

moi, toi, lui, elle, I or me, you, he or him, she or her

nous, vous, eux, elles, we, you, they or them (masculine), they or them (feminine)

tout le monde, personne, everybody, nobody

DESCRIPTIVE WORDS
(words in parentheses are feminine forms)

bon, mauvais, good, bad (*bonne, mauvaise*)

petit, grand, small, big (*petite, grande*)

pauvre, riche, poor, rich

triste, heureux, sad, happy (*triste, heureuse*)

beau, laid, handsome, ugly (*belle, laide*)

vrai, faux, true, false (*vraie, fausse*)

même, autre, same, other

blanc, noir, white, black (*blanche, noire*)

bleu, jaune, blue, yellow (*bleue, jaune*)

vert, rouge, green, red (*verte, rouge*)

gris, brun, gray, brown (*grise, brune*)

jeune, vieux, young, old (*jeune, vieille*)

fort, faible, strong, weak (*forte, faible*)

court, long, short, long (*courte, longue*)

premier, dernier, first, last (*première, dernière*)

doux, dur, sweet, harsh; soft, hard (*douce, dure*)

plein, vide, full, empty (*pleine, vide*)

sec, mouillé, dry, wet (*sèche, mouillée*)

habile, bête, clever, stupid

calme, inquiet, calm, worried (*calme, inquiète*)

meilleur, pire, better, worse

THE HOME

la famille, the family

le père, la mère, the father, the mother

l'homme, la femme, the man, the woman

le garçon, la jeune fille, the boy, the girl

le fils, la fille, the son, the daughter

le grand-père, la grand'mère, the grandfather, the grandmother

le neveu, la nièce, the nephew, the niece

le frère, la sœur, the brother, the sister

l'oncle, la tante, the uncle, the aunt

un ami, une amie, a (boy) friend, a (girl) friend

les parents, les enfants, the parents, the children

la maison, la rue, the house, the street

la cuisine, la salle à manger, the kitchen, the dining room

le salon, la chambre, the drawing room, the bedroom

la pièce, la salle de bain, the room, the bathroom

le plafond, le plancher, le mur, the ceiling, the floor, the wall

les meubles, the furniture

la table, la chaise, the table, the chair

la lampe, le lit, the lamp, the bed

le piano, la radio, the piano, the radio

le canapé, la fauteuil, the sofa, the armchair

l'image, le tapis, the picture, the rug

THE PERSON

le corps, the body

la tête, the head

les cheveux, the hair

le visage, the face

une oreille, an ear

le nez, the nose

la bouche, the mouth

les yeux, the eyes

la langue, the tongue

la dent, the tooth

le menton, the chin

le cou, the neck

une épaule, a shoulder
le bras, the arm
la main, the hand
le doigt, the finger
le pied, the foot

la santé, health
comment allez-vous? how are you?
je vais bien, I feel all right
j'ai mal à . . . , I have a pain in . . .
le médecin, le malade, the doctor, the patient
avoir de la fièvre, rester au lit, to have fever, to remain in bed
se reposer, to rest

les vêtements, clothing
le chapeau, the hat
le complet, the suit
la robe de soie, the silk dress
le soulier, the shoe
le bas de laine, the woolen stocking
la chaussette, the sock
la cravate, the tie
la chemise, the shirt
le manteau, lady's coat

le pardessus, man's overcoat
le mouchoir, the handkerchief
la paire de gants, the pair of gloves
porter, to wear
ça me va, that suits me

pleurer, rire, to cry, to laugh
aimer, haïr, to love, to hate
s'amuser, s'ennuyer, to have a good time, to be bored
se fâcher, to become angry
oublier, se souvenir de, to forget, to remember
oser, avoir peur de, to dare, to be afraid to
se lever, se coucher, to get up, to go to bed
s'endormir, se réveiller, to fall asleep, to awaken
s'habiller, se déshabiller, to get dressed, to undress
sortir, rentrer, to go out, to come back
marcher, courir, to walk, to run
se mettre en route, être de retour, to start out, to be back
naître, mourir, to be born, to die

MEALS

j'ai faim, I'm hungry
j'ai soif, I'm thirsty
manger, boire, eat, drink
le repas, the meal
le petit déjeuner, breakfast
le déjeuner, lunch
le dîner, dinner
goûter, to taste
fumer, to smoke
le pain, bread
le petit pain, roll
du beurre, butter

du fromage, cheese
de la viande, meat
des légumes, vegetables
un œuf, an egg
le potage, soup
le dessert, dessert
les fruits, fruit
le gâteau, cake
le lait, milk
le café, coffee
le thé, tea
l'eau, water

le vin, wine
le verre, glass
la tasse, cup
la bouteille, bottle
la serviette, napkin
la cuillère, spoon

le couteau, knife
la fourchette, fork
le restaurant, restaurant
le garçon, waiter
l'addition, bill
le pourboire, tip

SHOPPING

la boutique, shop
le magasin, store
acheter, vendre, to buy, sell
payer, devoir, to pay, owe
l'argent, money
le tailleur, tailor
la couturière, dressmaker
le boucher, la boucherie, butcher, butcher shop
le boulanger, la boulangerie, baker, bakery

l'épicier, l'épicerie, grocer, grocery
le magasin de nouveautés, gents' furnishing shop
la blanchisserie, laundry
la confiserie, candy shop
combien? how much?
bon marché, cheap
trop cher, too expensive
coûter, to cost

TRAVEL

le voyage, the trip
voyager en chemin de fer, to travel by rail
voyager en auto, en avion, to travel by auto, by plane
le billet, the ticket
l'horaire, timetable
la mille, mile
la gare, station
voler, to fly
l'aërodrome, airdrome
le terrain d'atterrissage, the landing field

se mettre en route, arriver, to start out, to arrive
aller à toute vitesse, to go full speed
s'arrêter, to stop
traverser, to cross
le train, the train
l'avion, the plane
le bateau, the boat
regarder par la fenêtre, to look out of the window
le paysage, the countryside
le pont, the bridge

THE COUNTRY

le monde, the world
le ciel, the sky
une étoile, a star
le nuage, the cloud

le vent, the wind
la terre, the land, earth
la montagne, the mountain
la vallée, the valley

le fleuve, the river
le lac, the lake
la mer, the sea
au bord de la mer, at the seashore
l'océan, the ocean
la plage, the beach
le pays, the country
la campagne, the countryside
le champ, the field
le bois, the wood

un arbre, a tree
la feuille, the leaf
le jardin, the garden
la ferme, the farm
pêcher à la ligne, to fish
nager, to swim
se baigner, to go bathing
faire une promenade, to take a
 walk
faire le canotage, to go boating

THE YEAR

les jours de la semaine, the days of
 the week
lundi, Monday
mardi, Tuesday
mercredi, Wednesday
jeudi, Thursday
vendredi, Friday
samedi, Saturday
dimanche, Sunday

les mois de l'année, the months of
 the year
janvier, January
février, February
mars, March
avril, April
mai, May
juin, June
juillet, July
août, August
septembre, September
octobre, October
novembre, November
décembre, December

la fête, the holiday
l'anniversaire de naissance, birthday
Pâques, Easter

Noël, Christmas
le Jour de l'An, New Year's Day
les grandes vacances, summer vacation

le temps, les saisons, the weather,
 the seasons
en été, en hiver, in summer, in
 winter
en automne, au printemps, in fall,
 in spring
il fait beau, mauvais, the weather
 is good, bad
il fait froid, chaud, the weather is
 cold, warm
il fait du vent, du soleil, it's windy,
 sunny
il neige, il pleut, it is snowing, raining
quel temps fait-il? what kind of
 weather is it?
j'ai froid, chaud, I'm cold, warm

quelle heure est-il? what time is it?
il est une heure, it is one o'clock
il est deux heures et demie, it is
 half-past two
il est trois heures quart, it is a quarter after three

il est quatre heures vingt, it is twenty after four

il est cinq heures moins un quart, it is a quarter to five

il est six heures moins dix, it is ten minutes to six

midi, minuit, noon, midnight

la montre, the watch

je suis en retard, en avance, I am late, ahead of time

je suis à l'heure, I am on time

POLITE TALK

bonjour, good day

Monsieur, Madame, Mademoiselle, Sir, Ma'am, Miss

permettez-moi de vous présenter, allow me to introduce to you

enchanté, delighted

pas de quoi, don't mention it, you're welcome

au revoir, so long

s'il vous plaît, please

merci, thank you

EXAMINATION QUESTIONS

Translate the following into French:

1. In the yard at the house.
2. On the wall of my bedroom on the third floor beyond the window.
3. Above the bookcase near his bed.
4. I am distressed that you are afraid.
5. He has a bedroom beyond the parlor.
6. That gentleman is my professor and my father's friend.
7. I have so much money; I am very happy.
8. I have eaten some meat.
9. Before eating a chicken one roasts it.
10. Do you recall the small amount of space we had at our disposal?
11. Soon the port officials will come aboard, and tomorrow we shall find ourselves in the city of Havre.
12. We left the house in the little village where we were living, a week ago.
13. It was evident that everybody took us for Americans; otherwise they would never have dared to ask such a price for two rooms.
14. There was even a telephone on a little table in a corner.
15. After leaving the ship, we got into a taxi which was found near the wharf.
16. What do you desire, gentlemen?
17. How much is it necessary to pay per week?
18. In spite of the three hundred francs a week, we are well pleased with our rooms.
19. We've just sat down, two minutes ago at the most.
20. We must be on our guard; they are expensive.

21. My friend is saving me the trouble of choosing, and I am glad of it.
22. Veal sweetbreads, soufflés, and an infinity of rare and delicate dishes are waiting for us in all the restaurants of France; but at present a simple and well-prepared dinner suits us better.
23. It is useless to wish you a good appetite.
24. I will have strawberries with cream, little cakes, and naturally black coffee with a little glass of cognac.
25. To your health! I prefer to taste them in advance.

Translate the following into English:

26. Nous sommes contents; ils ont faim.
27. Je suis content qu'ils ne soient pas dans la rue.
28. Ma chambre est au rez-de-chaussée.
29. J'ai quelque chose à vous dire, Monsieur Lebon.
30. Mes amies sont toutes belles et leurs enfants sont tous beaux.
31. Vous avez du sucre et de la crème.
32. J'ai tant de pêches que je n'ai pas envie de manger.

33. Votre père, est-il un ami de mon professeur?
34. Les mères sont toutes belles.
35. Je ne suis pas votre père, mais je suis votre ami.
36. Elle a un beau tapis au mur, du plafond jusqu'au plancher.
37. J'ai des pêches et de la crème à manger aujourd'hui.
38. Le soir même, nous nous sommes trouvés en retard.
39. C'en est assez! Moi, je meurs de faim.
40. En effet, vous faites un meilleur dîner que moi.
41. Nous voici, mon vieux, et j'en suis bien content.
42. Ils nous attendent, et moi, je ne sais que faire.
43. C'est un dessert qui cadre avec ce vin blanc.
44. De plus, ils coûtent cher.
45. Enfin, j'ai trouvé la station et je suis monté dans le wagon au moment que le train s'arrêtait.
46. Il ne veut pas attendre à bord du vaisseau.
47. Non, je ne veux pas monter.
48. Peut-être elle est prête à s'asseoir à la table.
49. Il m'a suivi à ma chambre.
50. Le garçon a saisi le pourboire et nous a précédés au numéro quarante.

FOR FURTHER STUDY

Concise French Grammar, by A. B. Swanson. (Henry Holt & Co., New York.)

French à la Mode, by Edith Pattou. (Houghton Mifflin, Boston.)

Conversational French, by Albert Mann. (The Macmillan Co., New York.)

Joie de Lire, by Ruben Pfeiffer. (Henry Holt & Co., New York.)

XIII

Spanish Self Taught

HOW TO STUDY SPANISH

WITHOUT grammar, a language could not exist any more than a building could stand without a framework. Yet our first acquaintance with a house or with a language tells us little about its supporting structure—that is, if we learn about it in the usual way. The grammar or skeleton is best understood *after* we have used the language and formed an idea of what it is all about. For this reason the following lessons endeavor to teach the beginner how to use Spanish in expressing simple ideas, and then how to build original conversation from the raw materials of grammar.

The speaking and the understanding of a language should be learned at the same time, word for word, sentence for sentence, since making the sounds always deepens the impression received by the ear. One cannot form a complete picture of any word without speaking it oneself. Therefore our study of Spanish is preceded by instruction in pronouncing Spanish words whose sound combinations are typical of the language.

Most important of all is the matter of faithful study. Each lesson must be learned and rehearsed until it is completely mastered; otherwise the mind cannot retain it. Between lessons the student should repeat to himself Spanish words, idioms, and sentences until he has trained himself to *think* in the language. He should choose objects and ideas of daily experience, thus forming chains of mental association which will make forgetting impossible. The observance of these few rules will help to make the learning of Spanish simple and thorough.

PRONUNCIATION

ALPHABET SOUNDS

The following letters are pronounced in Spanish in practically the same way as they are in English: *f, l, m, n, p,* and sometimes *s* and *x*

a has the value of *a* halfway between the *a* in *fat* and the *a* in *father*

e has usually the value of *a* in *gate,* sometimes that of *e* in *get*

i has the value of *ee* in *see*

o has the value of *o* in *both*

u, when pronounced, is like *oo* in *pool;* it is silent after *q,* and likewise between *g* and *e* or between *g* and *i* unless it is marked with a dieresis (*ü*). This *u* with dieresis (*ü*) is pronounced like *w*

b and *v* in Spanish have practically the same sound—that of a soft *b*. Spaniards are apt to consider the English *b* and *v* sounds too loud and explosive

c coming before *a, o,* or *u* has the value of *k;* before *e* or *i* it is given as *th* in *thought* (Castilian), and in some Spanish-speaking countries as *s*

d at the beginning of a word has the value of the English *d,* but between two vowels or at the end of a word it is given as *th* in *then,* very softly

g coming before *e* or *i* has the value of a rough *h* (the sound you make when clearing your throat); everywhere else it is given as in the English word *got*

j always is given as a rough *h*

q is always followed by a silent *u* and has the sound of *k*

r is slightly trilled, except when it ends a word

s is soft as in *sell;* it is never like the English *z* when it is followed by *n* or *m*

t is given more lightly and delicately in Spanish than in English

x in certain old spellings like *Mexico* and *Quixote* is given like a rough *h* (Mexico—Máy-hee-ko; Quixote—Kee-hó-teh); otherwise it has the value of the English *x*

z has the value of *th* in *thought,* and in some Spanish-speaking countries as *s*

y used as a vowel has the value of *ee* in *see;* when used as a consonant it is pronounced as in *young*

ch, ll, ñ, and *rr* are considered not as combinations but as separate symbols of the Spanish alphabet. Thus *ch* has the same value in Spanish as in the English word *child;* *ll* serves for the English *ly,* as in *milla* (pronounced *meel-ya*); *ñ* serves for the English *ny,* as in *leña* (pronounced *lane-ya*); and *rr* is clearly trilled on the tip of the tongue (*r-r-r-r*).

The letter *h,* while common enough in written Spanish, has no sound whatever in the spoken language.

Only approximate sounds can be indicated by the rough-and-ready phonetic spelling used in this book. But in the absence of a Spanish-speaking instructor the student will be enabled to learn to pronounce Spanish words intelligibly, if not with absolute accuracy. The way to put the finishing touches to your Spanish is to converse with people who speak Spanish.

The rules of Spanish accent are quite simple: the emphasis or accent is given to the last syllable only when that syllable ends in a consonant (except *n* or *s*) or when the last syllable bears an accent mark (´); emphasis is given to the next-to-the-last syllable when the word ends in a true diphthong (*ia, io, ua, ie, uo, ue, iu, ui*), a vowel (*a, e, i, o, u*), or *n* or *s,* unless some other syllable bears a written accent (´); when the stress falls on a syllable that contains a diphthong it is the strong vowel (*a, o, u*) which receives the emphasis; when the stress falls on a syllable containing the diphthongs *ui* or *iu,* it is the second of these vowels that receives the stress.

LESSON I

Spanish: El hombre habla, come, anda, y trabaja.
Pronounced: El óm-breh áhb-la, kó-meh, áhn-da, ee tra-bá-ha.
English: The man speaks, eats, walks, and works.

Span: El perro come y corre, pero no habla.
Pron: El páir-r-ro kó-meh ee cór-r-reh, páir-o no áhb-la.
Eng: The dog eats and runs, but not speaks.
  (does not speak.)

Span: La mujer habla español. Yo hablo inglés.
Pron: La mooháir áhb-la es-pan-yól. Yo áhb-lo een-gléhs.
Eng: The woman speaks Spanish. I speak English.

Span: El niño habla francés; usted lo escribe.
Pron: El néen-yo áhb-la fran-théhs; oos-tédth lo es-crée-beh.
Eng: The child speaks French; you it write.
  (write it.)

Span: Nosotros hablamos con ustedes ahora.
Pron: nos-ó-tros ahb-lá-mos con oos-tédth-es a-ór-a.
Eng: We speak with you (plural) now (at pres.)

Span: El escribe su lección; ella no hace nada.
Pron: El es-crée-beh soo lek-thee-ón; él-ya no á-theh ná-da.
Eng: He writes his lesson; she not does nothing.
                                                  (is doing nothing.)

Read again the suggestions for study and apply them carefully to this lesson. Review the Alphabet Sounds, so that your first pronunciation of the above words may be as accurate as possible. Remember that the above phonetic spelling is only suggestive of the true pronunciation. Memorize every Spanish word.

LESSON II

The student has already noticed that the words *habla* (speaks) and *come* (eats) end differently, the first in *a* and the second in *e*. Farther along in Lesson I occurs the word *escribe* (write, writes), which ends in *e*. These words belong to three different conjugations of verbs, *habla* to the first, *come* to the second, and *escribe* to the third. The three regular Spanish conjugations are given on pages 639–643. Before going further the student should study the three regular conjugations and those of the irregular verbs *ser* (to be), *estar* (to be), and *haber* (to have), on pages 644–647. Only the present indicative of these verbs should be studied at first.

After studying the verb forms mentioned, write in Spanish:

1. We speak, eat, walk, and work. 2. They eat and run, but (they) do not speak. 3. You (sing.) write and speak Spanish. 4. You (plural) walk with us. 5. I possess nothing (I not possess nothing).

Notice that *usted* (you, singular) calls for the same verb ending as do *él* (he) and *ella* (she), and *ustedes* (you, plural) calls for the same verb ending as do *ellos* (they, masculine) and *ellas* (they, feminine). In Spanish we say: *usted habla* (you speak) and *él habla* (he speaks); or *ustedes hablan* (you speak) and *ellos hablan* (they speak). The reason for this is that *usted* and *ustedes,* though meaning *you,* are considered in Spanish as third-person pronouns. *Vd.*, sometimes written *Ud*, is a contracted form of *Usted* (you) and therefore takes a verb in the third person. The second person (represented in English by *thou, thee, thy, thine, ye,* etc.) is used in Spanish only in addressing close friends or relatives, and the Deity.

Notice also that the masculine word *hombre* (man) requires a masculine article *el* (the); and the feminine word *mujer* (woman) requires a feminine article *la* (the). Every Spanish noun, except a very few abstract expressions, is either masculine or feminine.

LESSON III

Span: Yo tengo   hambre.   Usted   tiene   pan.
Pron: Yo táin-go   áhm-breh.   Oos-tédth tee-én-eh pahn.
Eng: I   have   hunger.   You   have   bread.
(I am hungry.)

Span: Nosotros tenemos   sed.   Ustedes   tienen   agua.
Pron: Nos-ó-tros ten-áim-os sedth. Oos-tédth-es tee-én-en áhg-wa.
Eng: We   have   thirst. You   have   water.
(We are thirsty.)

Span: El tiene   miedo.   Ella tiene   un perro.
Pron: El tee-én-eh mee-áidth-o. Él-ya tee-én-eh oon páir-ro.
Eng: He has   fear.   She has   a   dog.
(He is afraid.)

Span: Tenemos   sueño.   La madre   tiene   vergüenza.
Pron: Ten-áim-os swáin-yo. La máhd-reh tee-én-eh bear-gwén-tha.
Eng: We have   sleep.   The mother has   shame.
(We are sleepy.)   (Mother is ashamed.)

Span: Tengo   frío,   pues calor;   tengo un   resfriado.
Pron: Táing-go frée-o, pwes cah-lór; táing-go oon res-free-áh-tho.
Eng: I have   cold,   then heat;   I have a   cold.
(I am cold, then hot;)

Span: Un resfriado   es terrible.   Estoy enfermo.
Pron: Oon res-free-áh-tho es ter-rée-bleh. Es-tóy en-fáir-mo.
Eng: A   cold   is terrible.   I am ill.

Span: Tienen   ganas   de dormir.   Tienen   razón.
Pron: Tee-én-en gáh-nas day dor-méer. Tee-én-en ra-thóne.
Eng: They have desires of to sleep. They have reason.
(They want to sleep.)   (They are right.)

LESSON IV

Several uses of the verb *tener* (to have) were illustrated in Lesson III; some of these resemble the English uses of the verb *to possess*. Those which do not resemble English are idiomatic forms in Spanish. For instance, the only correct way to say, "I am sleepy," in Spanish is (*Yo*) *tengo sueño* (I have sleep). The student should note further that the personal pronouns *I, you, he, she, we,* and *they* can just as well be omitted in Spanish, provided the verb form itself indicates clearly which person is meant. The personal pronouns are used whenever particular emphasis or clearness of meaning is desired. For instance, one says in Spanish: *Usted escribe; ella no hace nada* (You are writing; she is doing nothing); but *Juan no escribe; no hace nada* (John is not writing; [he] is doing nothing). No confusion of meaning can result in the second example from omitting the pronoun *él* (he) because we are dealing with only one person; but if *ella* (she) had been omitted in the first example, *usted* would be taken as the subject of both *escribe* and *hace,* making nonsense. Two different verbs (Lesson III) both mean *to be* (*ser* and *estar*). The sentences read: *Un resfriado es terrible. Estoy enfermo.* Here *es* means *is* and *estoy* (from *estar*) means *am.* But where *es* (a form of *ser*) is used a perpetual fact is stated; and where *estoy* is used a changeable condition is described. The verb *estar* is also used in describing place or position even though such location may be permanent, thus: *San Juan es una ciudad; ESTÁ lejos de aquí* (San Juan is a city; it lies [it is] far from here). Other distinctions are made between the uses of *ser* and *estar;* and these must be learned through experience with the language rather than by reference to rules.

NOTE: *Estoy enfermo* (I am sick—a temporary condition). *Soy enfermo* (I am sickly—a permanent condition).

Write in Spanish: 1. I have water; I am not thirsty. 2. She has bread, but she is hungry. 3. *She* has a dog; *he* is not afraid. 4. You are hot; you have not a cold. 5. We work (are working); we are not cold. 6. We are sleepy; we want to (go to) sleep. 7. A man is (see *ser*) not a child. 8. He is (see *estar*) ill; he is (see *estar*) here with us. 9. Juan (pronounced *Hwan*) is ashamed. 10. Mother is right.

In the lessons that follow, pronunciation and English meaning will seldom be indicated on the lesson page; instead, reference must be made to the previous rules for pronunciation and to the vocabulary and conjugation lists at the end of this section. Most Spanish verbs follow the three regular conjugations in all their forms; but many other Spanish verbs are irregular in certain of their forms. Some, like *ser* and *haber,* are extremely irregular; while others, like *escribir,* have only one irregular form (*escrito,* instead of *escribido,* in the past participle). So it is seen that even the irregularities of Spanish verbs fall into definite groups. An irregular verb typical of each of these groups is conjugated on pages

647–656. Only the irregular forms are given for most of the verbs listed, it being understood that the forms not given are regular for all verbs in that same group. Each example verb is numbered, and every verb in the lesson text which bears the same number is conjugated like the example.

LESSON V

Memorize the following expressions:

Vámonos: *Let us go.*

Tengo que: *I have to; I must.*

Hay: *There is; there are.*

Por supuesto: *Of course.*

Se hallan: *(There) are found.*

Se venden: *(There) are sold.*

Hasta la vista: *Until I see you.*

Por contra: *On the other hand.*

Por aquí: *This way.*

Cerca de: *Near to.*

Henos aquí: *Here we are.*

Si no me equivoco: *If I am not mistaken.*

No me gustan: *They don't please me; I don't like, etc.*

¡Buenos días! *Good day!*

Translate into English:

—Vámonos (Let's go) a la bodega. Yo tengo que comprar (1) muchas cosas para la cocina.

—¿Hay (5) una bodega aquí cerca? Yo también necesito (1) algo.

—Sí. ¡por supuesto! Hay varias tiendas en la calle de los Moros. Se hallan (1) allí bodegas, carnicerías, lavanderías y almacenes donde se venden (2) muchos artículos de utilidad. En la callejuela a la derecha hay una farmacía, una ferretería y una mercería; por aquí a la izquierda, se hallan un sastre y un zapatero. Cerca de la plaza están una buena fonda y dos o tres pequeños restaurantes.

—Henos aquí en la bodega. ¡Buenos días, señor! Necesitamos naranjas y limones y, si no están caras a presente, unas bananas. ¿Cuanto valen (are worth) estas naranjas?

—Cuarenta centavos la docena, señoritos; están muy baratas. Por contra, las manzanas están fuera de sazón y valen veinticinco centavos la libra.

—Está bien. No me gustan (1) las manzanas; yo tomaré; (2) una docena de naranjas y media docena de limones. Necesito también doce huevos, una libra de café, cinco libras de azúcar y dos panes. Y usted, Pedro, si no me equivoco (1) usted quiere algo.

—Sí amigo mío, me gustarían (1) unas bananas.— ¡No muchas, señor! Las tres bastan. ¡Gracias!

—¡Les doy (15) muchas gracias a ustedes, señoritos! ¡Hasta la vista!

NOTE: Every article, every pronoun, and every adjective must agree in gender and number with the noun it modifies or stands for.

Those adjectives whose masculine form ends in *o* simply change that to *a* in order to form the feminine: e.g., *barato, barata.* Masculine adjectives ending in *an* or *on* are usually changed to feminine adjectives by adding an *a;* masculine adjectives of nationality (*francés, español*) which end in a consonant form their feminine the same way; that is, by adding *a.* The same is true of masculine adjectives ending in *or,* with the exception of the words *mayor* and *menor, mejor* and *peor, superior* and *inferior, exterior* and *interior, anterior* and *posterior.*

Adjectives which end in any other way are the same in both masculine and feminine genders. But for the sake of easy pronunciation certain adjectives like *bueno, malo, alguno, santo, ninguno, grande, uno, primero, tercero,* and *ciento* become: *buen, mal, algún, san, gran, primer,* etc. (that is, they drop the last syllable) before a singular masculine noun; e.g., *el buen café; San Antonio. Cien* and *gran* are used before masculine or feminine singular nouns.

Translate into Spanish: 1. I have to go to the butcher shop. 2. Is there a hardware store near by? 3. Yes, of course! There are many stores in this street, if I am not mistaken. 4. Let us go, then. You want something? 5. Yes, if they are sold in these stores and if they are not expensive. 6. I like cheap things, too, if they are good. This way! 7. Here we are! The stores are found in this little street.

LESSON VI

Memorize the following expressions:

Tendría Vd. la bondad de—: *Will you have the goodness to—.* ¿Mande Vd.? *What did you say?* Yo quisiera: *I should like.* Es decir: *That is to say.* Tenga la bondad de: *Have the kindness to.* Se come muy bien: *One eats well; they serve good meals.* Tengo mucho gusto en conocerle: *I have great pleasure in knowing you.* A la disposición de Vd.: *At your service.* O: *Or.* ¡Que duerma Vd. bien! *May you sleep well!* La noche: *Tonight; the night.* ¡Igualmente! *The same to you!* ¡Hasta luego! *Until then; until later!* Le agradezco: *I thank you (or him, or her).*

Translate into English:

—Tenga Vd. (usted) la bondad de decirme (to tell me) dónde está una buena fonda.
—¿Mande Vd., señor?

—¿Vd. no ha (4) entendido (8)? Digo (I say) ¿dónde está una buena fonda o posada, es decir, un hotel? Yo soy viajero, y estoy muy cansado; yo quiero (want) acostarme (1).

—¡Yo entiendo perfectamente, señor! Tenga la bondad de acompañarme (1) dos manzanas hasta la calle Gómez donde está la posada San Pedro. Allí se come muy bien y los aposentos le gustarán.

—¡Muchas gracias, señor! Permítame (10) presentarme a Vd., Rafaél Casablanca, su servidor.

—Tengo mucho gusto en conocerle (9), señor. Me ofrezco (9), Miguel Alvarez, a la disposición de Vd.

—Le agradezco (9) infinamente sus informes; y, si no me equivoco, hemos (4) llegado (1) a la posada. ¡Hasta la vista, señor!

—¡Hasta luego! ¡Que duerma Vd. (May you sleep) bien la noche!

—¡Igualmente!

NOTE: *Me, te, se, nos,* and *vos* are employed as objects of verbs used reflexively: *me ofrezco* (I offer myself). They are also used passively where no agent is expressed: *se venden* (are sold); and as datives of interest: *permítame* (imperative, meaning: Permit me). Occasionally the use is reciprocal, as in *Se dan la mano* (They give the hand to each other; i.e., shake hands). This lesson illustrates also the simple indirect object, as in *decirme* (to tell me).

A personal pronoun, object of an infinitive, an imperative, or a gerund is attached to the verb like a suffix: *decirme, permítame, permitiéndome* (to tell me, permit me, permitting me).

Notice that *le* (you, him, her, it) is used as the indirect object of a verb, as in *Le agradezco* (I thank you).

Begin the study of all forms of all the example verbs given in the conjugation lists, covering as much ground as possible with each succeeding lesson. Compose sentences illustrating the use of all these verbs, accustoming yourself to use them without hesitation.

LESSON VII

Memorize the following expressions:

Una casa de huéspedes: *A boarding house.* A las siete: *At seven o'clock.* Por lo resto: *For the rest.* Antes de acostarse: *Before going to bed.* A la una: *At one o'clock.* Favor de decirme: *Please do me the favor of telling me.* Va a pasearse por el parque: *He goes for a walk through the park.* Después de bañarse: *After bathing.* ¿Quién sabe? *Who knows?* Algunas veces: *Sometimes.* Hace frío: *It is cold (weather).* Se pasan de moda: *They go out of style.* Conmigo: *With me.* Yo no me atrevo a:

I don't dare to. Tal vez: *Perhaps.* El café negro sigue (from *seguir*): *The black coffee follows.* Pasados por agua: *Soft boiled.* Hay que: *It is necessary to.*

Translate into English:

LA COCINA

—Muy importante en una casa de huéspedes es la cocina. A las siete de la mañana se sirve (14) el desayuno.—
—¿Qué es el desayuno?
—Es la primera comida del día. Consiste (10) generalmente en tostadas, huevos pasados por agua, frutas (naranjas o toronjas), café con leche, y, tal vez, un cereal. Al almuerzo se come una sopa, fideos o arroz con tomate y carne, ensalada y frutas. El almuerzo se sirve a la una de la tarde. A los ocho se sirve la comida principal que consiste en un plato de carne o de pescado con legumbres y después una ensalada. Luego se sirven unos postres—fruta, pasteles con queso, o tortas y dulces. El café negro sigue (14) naturalmente. Antes de acostarse (1) se come la cena, de chocolate o leche con galletas.

LA ROPA

—Favor de decirme, amigo, ¿cómo se viste (14) el hombre cuando va (he is going) a pasearse (1) por el parque?
—Primero, después de bañarse, se pone (he puts on) la ropa interior, la camisa con cuello y corbata, los calcetines, el pantalón, los zapatos, el chaleco y el saco, y antes de salir (going out) en la calle se pone el sombrero y el sobretodo. Algunas veces lleva (1) un par de guantes y un bastón. Cuando hay una lluvia fuerte y se moja (1) el traje, hay que mudar (1) de ropa. La ropa de hombre se hace (is made) de varios materiales:—la tela de lana, de algodón, de lino, de fieltro, y de seda. Los zapatos se hacen de cuero, y los sombreros que se llevan en el verano se hacen de paja o de jipijapa.
—¿Y que lleva la mujer cuando sale (she goes out) de la casa?
—Los trajes de señora se pasan de moda con tanta frecuencia que yo no me atrevo (2) a describirlos. Yo sé (know) que llevan medias y faldas y blusas y camisas, y naturalmente zapatos. Cuando hace frío llevan sombreros y abrigos. Por lo resto, ¿quién sabe? (who knows?)

Translate into Spanish: 1. Please (do me the favor to) tell me what a man wears when he goes out on the street. 2. Of what materials are the clothes of women (ladies' clothes) made? 3. We do not wear overcoats in the summer. 4. What does a man (do) when his clothing gets wet? 5. I do not like a man who carries gloves and a cane. 6. I need socks and underwear; are they sold at the store (*almacén*)? 7. After bathing (*bañarme*) I found that I had (*tenía*) one sock. 8. When it is cold I wear a felt hat; in the summer I wear a panama hat (*a hat of etc.*). 9. I don't dare to go for a walk (*pasearme*) through the park.

LESSON VIII

Memorize the following expressions. Compose original Spanish sentences in which these may be used. Practice using them again and again until they seem as natural to you as English.

Por lo común; de ordinario: *Commonly; ordinarily.* Piso bajo: *First (ground) floor.* Piso principal: *Second (main) floor.* Primer piso: *Second (sometimes third) floor.* Verdad; es verdad: *True; that's true.* ¿No es verdad? *Isn't that true?* ¡Ya lo creo! *I should say so!* Dejándonos de bromas: *Seriously; all joking aside.* Fíjese Vd. en este niño: *Notice particularly this child.* En cuanto a: *As for.* ¡Qué cosa más bonita! *What a beautiful thing!* ¡Cuidado! *Look out! Take care!* Conque: *So; so then; so that.* ¡Salud! *Hello!* ¡Buenos noches! *Good night!* ¡Buenas tardes! *Good afternoon!* Hace calor: *It is warm (weather).*

Hace ocho días: *A week ago.* Hace poco rato: *A short while ago.* Lo mismo da: *That's all the same; that makes no difference.* ¡De ningún modo! *Not at all!* ¡Ya voy! *I'm coming!* De veras: *Really.* Vd. es muy amable: *You are very kind.* A mi parecer: *As it seems to me.* ¡Buen provecho! *Enjoy your dinner! Hearty appetite!* Nada de eso: *Nothing like that.* De intento: *Intentionally.* ¿Cuánto se paga? *What is the charge?* Al fin: *At last.* No obstante: *Nevertheless.* De vez en cuando: *From time to time.* Está la comida; la comida está en la mesa: *Dinner is served.* No hay de que: *Don't mention it (after being thanked).* ¿Qué hay? ¿Qué es eso? *What is it? What's the matter?* ¿Qué tiene Vd.? *What have you? What's the matter with you?* ¡De buen grado! *Gladly! With pleasure!* ¿Cómo está Vd.? *How are you feeling?* A ver: *Let's see.* Todo va bien: *All goes well.* Muy bien: *Very good.*

LESSON IX

Study as in the eighth lesson:

De mi gusto: *To my liking.* Dar una propina: *To give a tip.* Pierda Vd. cuidado: *Don't be afraid; don't worry.* ¡Y tanto! *And how!* Bien puede: *Go ahead and do it (say it, etc.)*. A veces: *At times*. Respecto a: *In respect to; regarding*. No me extraña: *It doesn't surprise me*. Se me figura que: *It strikes me that; I have an idea that*. Muy señor mío: *Dear sir (beginning a letter)*. Atto. S. S. (Atento y seguro servidor): *Very truly yours*. Mi querido amigo: *My dear friend*. S.S.S.q.b.s.m. (Su seguro servidor que besa su mano): *Your devoted servant who kisses your hand; very sincerely yours*.

Tener prisa: *To be in a hurry*. Tener presente: *To recall; to remember*. ¿Cómo se llama su hermano? *What is your brother's name?* ¿Qué se hace? *What's up? What's being done?* Me alegro: *I am glad*. Si lo decía yo: *I told you so*. ¡Salud! ¿Cómo está Vd.? *How are you?* Sin novedad: *The same as ever; as usual*. De nuevo: *Again; once more*. ¿Qué hay de nuevo? *What's new?* Guardar cama: *To stay in bed*. Pronto: *At once; quickly; soon*. En la actualidad: *At the present time*. ¡Dios mío! *Heavens!* ¡Dispénseme Vd.! *Pardon me!* Lo siento mucho: *I am sorry about it*. No hay molestia alguna: *No harm's done*. ¡Válgame Dios! *Good Lord!* No vale la pena: *It is not worth while*. ¿Por qué? *Why?* No deje de hacerlo: *Don't fail to do it*. Porque: *Because*.

LESSON X

Study the following types of business correspondence, with the accompanying special vocabulary. Spanish business letters follow very strict form, quite different from the free-and-easy American style. The two letters which follow include a number of the commonest formal expressions. Especial attention is called to the heading, the opening, and the closing of the sample correspondence given below.

VOCABULARY

Sres.: abbreviation of *Señores:* Siguientes: *Following*. Sírvanse (reflexive; third person plural subjunctive): *Please*. Tan pronto como le sea posible: *As soon as it may be possible (for you)*. Muebles de oficina: *Pieces of office furniture*. Madera de caoba: *(wood of) mahogany*. Sillones giratorios: *Swivel chairs*. Que señala su catálogo: *Which your catalog lists*. Mesita para máquina de escribir: *Small table for typewriter*. Mesa larga: *Long table*. Modelo número: *Model number*. Desearía [from *desear* (1)] me remitan (1): *I should like you to send me*. A la mayor brevedad: *With the greatest promptness*. Con factura: *With invoice*. Mi dirección: *My address*. Haciéndome el descuento: *Making me the discount*. De Vds. atto. s.s.q.e.s.m.: *Very truly yours* (literally: *Your attentive and faithful servant who grasps your hand*).

Muy señor nuestro: *Our very dear sir; Dear sir.* Hemos recibido: *We have received.* Del cte.: *Of the current month.* La suya: *Your (letter).* De enviarle: *To send you.* En la que: *In which (letter).* Escritorio: *Office.* Hace Vd. pedido: *You (make) order.* Citadas: *Quoted.* Su carta: *Your letter.* No podemos remitarle: *We cannot send you.* Por no tener en existencia: *Because of not having it in stock.* Adjunta encontrará (13): *Attached you will find.* A su cuenta: *Charged to you.* Que se sirvió pedirnos: *Which you kindly ordered of us.* Esperando estará conforme: *Hoping it will be satisfactory.* Contestación: *Reply.*

CARTA

Maracaibo 16 de junio de 1958.

Sres. Rodriguez Hermanos
Caracas.

Muy señores míos:

Sírvanse enviarme, tan pronto como les sea posible, los siguientes muebles de oficina, en madera de caoba, que señala su catálogo:

Dos sillones giratorios, número 3 del catálogo.

Tres mesitas para máquina de escribir, número 8.

Una mesa larga, modelo número 5½.

Dos mesas, número 4.

Desearía me remitan estos muebles a la mayor brevedad, con factura, haciéndome el descuento usual.

De Vds. atto. s.s.q.e.s.m.

Manuel González.

Mi dirección: Libertad, 17.

CONTESTACIÓN

Caracas 20 de junio de 1958.
D. Manuel González
Libertad, 17
Maracaibo.

Muy señor nuestro:

Hemos recibido la suya del 16 del cte., en la que hace Vd. pedido de muebles de escritorio. Tenemos el gusto de enviarle todos los artículos correspondientes a los números citados en su carta, excepto la mesa, modelo número 5½, que no podemos remitirle, por no tener en existencia a presente.

Adjunta encontrará factura a su cuenta por los muebles que se sirvió pedirnos, con esa excepción.

Esperando estará conforme, y agradeciéndole su pedido, somos de Vd. attos. s.s.q.e.s.m.

Rodríguez Hermanos.

In the answering letter (*Contestación*), notice that the sender's address and the date are immediately above the name of the addressee. This is equally correct with the form shown in the first letter. D. Manuel González: *D.* is the abbreviation of *Don,* a courteous form of address. The feminine of Don (D.) is Doña (Da.).

WRITTEN EXERCISES

Compose two letters and two replies in Spanish, using as many of the terms given in the Sample Letters as you can from memory; but vary the arrangement and contents of your letters so as not to copy the Sample Letters entirely. Write a short letter to a friend, leaving out all the formal heading except the sender's address and the date. Begin with: "Mi querido Jaime," or "Amigo mío." Close with: "S.S.S. y amigo," or "Su amigo que mucho le estima (Your friend who is very fond of you)." Gather material for the letters from the foregoing lessons, using your letters as a general review of past study.

LESSON XI

IN A RESTAURANT

Llame Vd. al mozo: *Call the waiter.* Escoger (2) un plato: *To choose a dish.* ¿Qué desean los señores? *What do the gentlemen wish?* ¿Qué hay en la lista? *What's on the menu?* Carne asada: *Roast meat.* Bien asada: *Well roasted.* Poco asada: *Rare (roasted).* Sírvase (14) pasarme: *Please pass me.* Pagar la cuenta: *To pay the bill.* ¿Se le ofrece (9) algo? *Is there anything you would like?* El cuchillo: *Knife.* Tráigame (33) la ensalada: *Bring me the salad.* La cucharita: *Teaspoon.* Sentarse (1) a la mesa: *To sit down at the table.* La cuchara: *Soup spoon.* Saludar a un amigo: *To greet a friend.* Dejar caer (26) el tenedor: *To drop the fork.* Derramar la crema: *To pour (or spill) the cream.*

INTRODUCTIONS

—Señor C——, permítame presentarle a Vd. un amigo mío.
—¡Ricardo Moreno, servidor de Vd., señor!

—Mucho gusto en conocerle, señor Moreno.

—El gusto es mío. Espero (*I hope*) que Vd. sea indulgente conmigo. Me (*to me*) es difícil expresarme en español.

—Me parece (*It seems to me*) que Vd. lo habla muy bien, señor.

—Vd. es muy amable.

ON A JOURNEY

En la estación: *In the (railway) station.* Un itinerario: *A timetable.* Buscar (1) mi baúl: *To hunt (look) for my trunk.* El viaje: *The trip; the voyage.* Llevar mi maleta: *To carry my suitcase.* Al andén: *On the platform.* La próxima salida: *The next (train) departure; sailing (of a ship).* El despacho de billetes: *The ticket office.* ¡Al tren! *All aboard (train)!* Tomar un billete: *To get a ticket.* Billete sencillo: *One-way ticket.* La sala de equipajes: *The baggage room.* Facturar mi baúl: *To check my trunk.* Abordo del vapor: *On board the ship.* ¡Feliz viaje! *Have a good trip!* Reservar un camarote: *To reserve a stateroom.* El talón: *The check stub.* Conseguir (*or* sacar) un pasaporte: *To secure a passport.* Esperar a un amigo: *To wait for a friend.* ¡Adios! *Good-bye!* Un billete de ida y vuelta: *A round-trip ticket.*

LESSON XII

REVIEW

Write from memory the Spanish translations of the following expressions:

I am very pleased to know you (take great pleasure in knowing you). The same to you! Until later! Good-bye! Good day! At your service! They serve good meals. Hello! Good afternoon! Many thanks! That is to say. I should like. At seven o'clock. It is cold (weather). Sometimes. After bathing. Please. Perhaps. I don't dare to. Soft boiled. I should say so! It is necessary to—. What a lovely (beautiful) thing! Look out! Ordinarily. Isn't that true? Second floor. So that; so then. A week ago. Gladly! Intentionally. You are very kind. Not at all! What's the matter? What's the charge? As it seems to me. From time to time. How are you (feeling)? Very good. Dear Sir. To my liking. I have an idea that—. Regarding. Very truly yours. At times. To give a tip. It doesn't surprise me. Don't worry. At once; quickly. What's your sister's name? Why? To stay in bed. How are you? The same as ever. I'm glad. Because. What's up? To be in a hurry. Good lord! Pardon me! Again. I'm very sorry (about it). It's not worth while. No harm's done. At the present time. Roast meat. Bring me the salad. To pay the bill. To greet a friend.

Please pass me—. To spill the cream. To choose a dish. To drop the knife. To call the waiter. To sit down at the table. All aboard! To check the trunk. To reserve a stateroom. A timetable. To wait for a friend. The next sailing. A round-trip ticket.

SPECIAL VOCABULARY TO BE MEMORIZED

Café caliente: *Hot coffee.* Tortillas: *Omelettes.* Café frío: *Cold coffee.* La mantequilla: *Butter.* Café con leche caliente: *Coffee with hot milk.* El biftec: *Beefsteak.* Pan francés: *French loaf.* El tocino: *Bacon.* El chorizo: *Sausage.* Pan blanco: *White bread.* La chuleta: *Chop.* Huevos crudos: *Raw eggs.* Pescado asado: *Baked fish.* Huevos bien cocidos: *Medium-boiled eggs.* Pescado cocido: *Boiled fish.* Huevos duros: *Hard-boiled eggs.* Pescado frito: *Fried fish.* Huevos fritos: *Fried eggs.* Las ostras: *Oysters.* El pollo frito: *Fried chicken.* El rosbif: *Roast beef.* Jugoso: *Juicy; medium.* Carne de ternera: *Veal.* Carne de carnero: *Lamb,* or *mutton.* Tierno -a: *Tender.* Duro -a: *Tough.* La papa *or* patata: *Potato.* El tomate: *Tomato.* La col: *Cabbage.* La cebolla: *Onion.* Carne de puerco: *Pork.* Frijoles: *Beans.* La batata: *Yam.* El guisante: *Pea.* El apio: *Celery.* El nabo: *Turnip.* La remolacha: *Beet.* El pepino: *Cucumber.* La zanahoria: *Carrot.* La pera: *Pear.* El higo: *Fig.* La ciruela: *Cherry.* La fresa: *Strawberry.* El durazno: *Peach.* La frambuesa: *Raspberry.* La zarzamora: *Blackberry.* La aceituna: *Olive.* El melón: *Melon.* La uva: *Grape.* La piña: *Pineapple.* La sandía: *Watermelon.* La calabaza: *Squash.* La coliflor: *Cauliflower.*

For further study, use the English-Spanish Vocabulary at the end of this section, together with the foregoing lessons, in constructing original sentences in Spanish. Daily incidents and common objects are excellent for such compositions. The following lists of articles, adjectives, pronouns, and numbers will be found of great help in this work. The Spanish-English Vocabulary should be reviewed frequently, each important word being used as the nucleus of an original phrase or sentence. Finally, very special attention should be given to memorizing the foregoing lists of idiomatic expressions, not only because they illustrate the common way of speaking, but also because the Spanish of daily conversation could not be spoken or understood without knowing them.

DEFINITE ARTICLES

	Masculine	Feminine	Neuter
Sing.	el	la	lo
Plur.	los	las	

DEMONSTRATIVE ADJECTIVES

SINGULAR

Masculine	Feminine
este: *this*	esta: *this*
ese: *that*	esa: *that*
aquel: *that*	aquella: *that*

PLURAL

Masculine	Feminine
estos: *these*	estas: *these*
esos: *those*	esas: *those*
aquellos: *those*	aquellas: *those*

Ese, esa, esos, esas point out a thing (or things) near the person whom you are addressing. *Aquel, aquella, aquellos, aquellas* point out a thing (or things) away from both the speaker and the person addressed.

PRONOMINAL ADJECTIVES

SINGULAR

Masculine	Feminine
mi: *my*	mi: *my*
nuestro: *our*	nuestra: *our*
tu: *thy*	tu: *thy*
vuestro: *your*	vuestra: *your*
su: *your, his, her*	su: *your, his, her*
su: *your, their*	su: *your, their*

PLURAL

Masculine	Feminine
mis: *my*	mis: *my*
nuestros: *our*	nuestras: *our*
tus: *thy*	tus: *thy*
vuestros: *your*	vuestras: *your*
sus: *your, his, her*	sus: *your, his, her*
sus: *your, their*	sus: *your, their*

POSSESSIVE PRONOUNS

SINGULAR

Masculine	Feminine
mío: *mine*	mía: *mine*
nuestro: *ours*	nuestra: *ours*
tuyo: *thine*	tuya: *thine*
vuestro: *yours*	vuestra: *yours*
suyo: *your, his, hers*	suya: *your, his, hers*
suyo: *yours, theirs*	suya: *yours, theirs*

PLURAL

Masculine	Feminine
míos: *mine*	mías: *mine*
nuestros: *ours*	nuestras: *ours*
tuyos: *thine*	tuyas: *thine*
vuestros: *yours*	vuestras: *yours*
suyos: *yours, his, hers*	suyas: *yours, his, hers*
suyos: *yours, theirs*	suyas: *yours, theirs*

Note that *tu, tuyo,* etc. and *vuestro, vuestra,* etc. are familiar forms, used in addressing relatives, close friends, and the Deity.

Note also that before possessive pronouns the definite article is used in most instances; e.g., to the question, *¿De quién es el libro? ¿Es el suyo?* (Whose is the book? Is it yours?) the answer would be, *Sí, es el mío. Las plumas son las mías también* (Yes, it is mine. The pens are mine, too).

DEMONSTRATIVE PRONOUNS

SINGULAR

Masculine	Feminine	Neuter
éste: *this, the latter*	ésta: *this, the latter*	eso: *that*
ése: *that*	ésa: *that*	aquello: *that*
aquél: *that, the former*	aquélla: *that, the former*	esto: *this*

PLURAL

Masculine	Feminine
éstos: *these, the latter*	éstas: *these, the latter*
ésos: *those*	ésas: *those*
aquéllos: *those, the former*	aquéllas: *those, the former*

CARDINAL NUMBERS

0 cero		29 veintinueve	
1 uno -a		30 treinta	
2 dos		31 treinta y uno	
3 tres		32 treinta y dos, etc.	
4 cuatro		40 cuarenta	
5 cinco		41 cuarenta y uno, etc.	
6 seis		50 cincuenta	
7 siete		51 cincuenta y uno, etc.	
8 ocho		60 sesenta	
9 nueve		61 sesenta y uno, etc.	
10 diez		70 setenta	
11 once		71 setenta y uno, etc.	
12 doce		80 ochenta	
13 trece		81 ochenta y uno, etc.	
14 catorce		90 noventa	
15 quince		91 noventa y uno, etc.	
16 dieciséis		100 ciento	
17 diecisiete		101 ciento y uno, etc.	
18 dieciocho		200 doscientos -as	
19 diecinueve		300 trescientos -as	
20 veinte		400 cuatrocientos -as	
21 veintiuno		500 quinientos -as	
22 veintidós		600 seiscientos -as	
23 veintitrés		700 setecientos -as	
24 veinticuatro		800 ochocientos -as	
25 veinticinco		900 novecientos -as	
26 veintiséis		1000 mil	
27 veintisiete		2000 dos mil, etc.	
28 veintiocho			

ORDINAL NUMBERS

1st	primero -a	17th	décimoséptimo -a
2nd	segundo -a	18th	décimoctavo -a
3rd	tercero -a	19th	décimonoveno -a
	tercio -a	20th	vigésimo -a
4th	cuarto -a	21st	vigésimo -a primero -a
5th	quinto -a	22nd	vigésimo -a segundo -a
6th	sexto -a	30th	trigésimo -a
7th	séptimo -a	40th	cuadragésimo -a
8th	octavo -a	50th	quincuagésimo -a
9th	nono -a	60th	sexagésimo -a
10th	décimo -a	70th	septuagésimo -a
11th	undécimo -a	80th	octogésimo -a
12th	duodécimo -a	90th	nonagésimo -a
13th	décimotercio -a	100th	centésimo -a
14th	décimocuarto -a	1000th	milésimo -a
15th	décimoquinto -a	1,000,000th	millonésimo -a
16th	décimosexto -a		

Ordinals are rarely used above 20th. Cardinal numbers are used after that.

EXAMPLE VERBS CONJUGATED

NOTE: First Conjugation verbs always end the infinitive with -*ar* (illustrated by *Dejar*); Second Conjugation verbs always end the infinitive with -*er* (illustrated by *Comer*); Third Conjugation verbs always end the infinitive with -*ir* (illustrated by *Añadir*). The regular forms of any Spanish verbs belong to one of these three conjugations; and one may recognize the particular conjugation by noting whether the infinitive ends in -*ar,* -*er,* or -*ir.*

Study every form given in the following Conjugation Lists, noting whether it is regular or irregular, *and in what the irregularities consist.* Otherwise in Spanish conversation and writing you will be constantly making grammatical mistakes.

DEJAR, *to leave* (1)
(Regular, First Conjugation)

Present Tense

yo dejo: *I leave*
tú dejas: *thou leavest*
usted (él, ella) deja: *you (he, she) leave(s)*

nosotros dejamos: *we leave*
vosotros dejáis: *ye leave*
ustedes (ellos, ellas) dejan: *you (they) leave*

Imperfect Tense

yo dejaba: *I was leaving*

tú dejabas: *thou wast leaving*
Vd. (él, ella) dejaba: *you (he, she) were (was) leaving*

nosotros dejábamos: *we were leaving*
vosotros dejabais: *ye were leaving*
Vds. (ellos, ellas) dejaban: *you (they) were leaving*

Note: In the following conjugations the pronouns yo, tú, él, Vd. etc. will be omitted in order to avoid needless repetition.

Preterite Tense

dejé: *I left*
dejaste: *thou didst leave*
dejó: *you (he, she) left*

dejamos: *we left*
dejasteis: *ye did leave*
dejaron: *you (they) left*

Future Tense

dejaré: *I shall leave*
dejarás: *thou wilt leave*
dejará: *you (he, she) will leave*

dejaremos: *we shall leave*
dejaréis: *ye will leave*
dejarán: *you (they) will leave*

Potential or Conditional Tense

dejaría: *I should leave*
dejarías: *thou wouldst leave*
dejaría: *you (he, she) would leave*

dejaríamos: *we should leave*
dejaríais: *ye would leave*
dejarían: *you (they) would leave*

Present Subjunctive Tense

deje: *I may leave*

dejes: *thou mayst leave*

deje: *you (he, she) may leave*

dejemos: *we may leave*

dejéis: *ye may leave*

dejen: *you (they) may leave*

Imperative Mood

deja: *leave (thou)*

deje: *(you) leave, let him (her) leave*

dejemos: *let us leave*

dejad: *leave (ye)*

dejen: *(you) leave, let them leave*

The Gerund

dejando: *leaving*

The Past Participle

dejado: *left*

NOTE: Following are tenses of *Dejar* compounded with the verb *Haber*. As in English, practically any verb may be compounded with *Haber* (to have), and in all such cases *Haber* is conjugated as in the following examples, the past participle of the particular verb being used throughout.

Perfect Tense

he dejado: *I have left*

has dejado: *thou hast left*

ha dejado: *you have (he, she has) left*

hemos dejado: *we have left*

habéis dejado: *ye have left*

han dejado: *you (they) have left*

Pluperfect Tense

había dejado: *I had left*

habías dejado: *thou hadst left*

había dejado: *you (he, she) had left*

habíamos dejado: *we have left*

habíais dejado: *ye have left*

habían dejado: *you (they) have left*

Future Perfect Tense

habré dejado: *I shall have left*

habrás dejado: *thou wilt have left*

habrá dejado: *you (he, she) will have left*

habremos dejado: *we shall have left*

habréis dejado: *ye will have left*

habrán dejado: *you (they) will have left*

Conditional Past Tense

habría dejado: *I should have left*

habrías dejado: *thou wouldst have left*

habría dejado: *you (he, she) would have left*

habríamos dejado: *we should have left*

habríais dejado: *ye would have left*

habrían dejado: *you (they) would have left*

Perfect Subjunctive

haya dejado: *I may have left*
hayas dejado: *thou mayst have left*
haya dejado: *you (he, she) may have left*

hayamos dejado: *we may have left*
hayáis dejado: *ye may have left*
hayan dejado: *you (they) may have left*

Perfect Infinitive

haber dejado: *to have left*

Perfect Gerund

habiendo dejado: *having left*

NOTE: The imperfect and future subjunctives are not used in this book.

COMER, *to eat* (2)
(Regular, Second Conjugation)

Present Tense

como: *I eat*
comes: *thou eatest*
come: *you (he, she) eat(s)*

comemos: *we eat*
coméis: *ye eat*
comen: *you (they) eat*

Imperfect Tense

comía: *I was eating*
comías: *thou wast eating*
comía: *you were (he, she was) eating*

comíamos: *we were eating*
comíais: *ye were eating*
comían: *you (they) were eating*

Preterite Tense

comí: *I ate*

comiste: *thou didst eat*

comió: *you (he, she) ate*

comimos: *we ate*

comisteis: *ye did eat*

comieron: *you (they) ate*

Future Tense

comeré: *I shall eat*

comerás: *thou wilt eat*

comerá: *you (he, she) will eat*

comeremos: *we shall eat*

comeréis: *ye will eat*

comerán: *you (they) will eat*

Potential or Conditional Tense

comería: *I should eat*

comerías: *thou wouldst eat*

comería: *you (he, she) would eat*

comeríamos: *we should eat*

comeríais: *you (they) would eat*

comerían: *you (they) would eat*

Present Subjunctive Tense

coma: *I may eat*

comas: *thou mayst eat*

coma: *you (he, she) may eat*

comamos: *we may eat*

comáis: *ye may eat*

coman: *you (they) may eat*

Imperative Mood

come: *eat (thou)*

coma: *(you) eat, let him (her) eat*

comamos: *let us eat*

comed: *eat (ye)*

coman: *(you) eat, let them eat*

The Gerund

comiendo: *eating*

The Past Participle

comido: *eaten*

AÑADIR, *to add* (3)
(Regular, Third Conjugation)

Present Tense

añado: *I add*

añades: *thou addest*

añade: *you (he, she) add(s)*

añadimos: *we add*

añadís: *ye add*

añaden: *you (they) add*

Imperfect Tense

añadía: *I was adding*
añadías: *thou wast adding*
añadía: *you were (he, she was) adding*

añadíamos: *we were adding*
añadíais: *ye were adding*
añadían: *you (they) were adding*

Preterite Tense

añadí: *I added*
añadiste: *thou didst add*
añadió: *you (he, she) added*

añadimos: *we added*
añadisteis: *ye added*
añadieron: *you (they) added*

Future Tense

añadiré: *I shall add*
añadirás: *thou wilt add*
añadirá: *you (he, she) will add*

añadiremos: *we shall add*
añadiréis: *ye will add*
añadirán: *you (they) will add*

Potential or Conditional Tense

añadiría: *I should add*
añadirías: *thou wouldst add*
añadiría: *you (he, she) would add*

añadiríamos: *we should add*
añadiríais: *ye would add*
añadirían: *you (they) would add*

Present Subjunctive Tense

añada: *I may add*
añadas: *thou mayst add*
añada: *you (he, she) may add*

añadamos: *we may add*
añadáis: *ye may add*
añadan: *you (they) may add*

Imperative Mood

añade: *add (thou)*
añada: *(you) add, let him add, let her add*

añadamos: *let us add*
añadid: *add (ye)*
añadan: *(you) add, let them add*

The Gerund

añadiendo: *adding*

The Past Participle

añadido: *added*

HABER, *to have* (4)
(Auxiliary Verb)

Present Tense

he: *I have*   hemos: *we have*
has: *thou hast*   habéis: *ye have*
ha: *you have, he, she has*   han: *you (they) have*

Imperfect Tense

había: *I was having*   habíamos: *we were having*
habías: *thou wast having*   habíais: *ye were having*
había: *you were (he, she was)* · habían: *you (they) were having*
     having

Preterite Tense

hube: *I had*   hubimos: *we had*
hubiste: *thou hadst*   hubisteis: *ye had*
hubo: *you (he, she) had*   hubieron: *you (they) had*

Future Tense

habré: *I shall have*   habremos: *we shall have*
habrás: *thou wilt have*   habréis: *ye will have*
habrá: *you (he, she) will have*   habrán: *you (they) will have*

Potential or Conditional Tense

habría: *I should have*   habríamos: *we should have*
habrías: *thou wouldst have*   habríais: *ye would have*
habría: *you (he, she) would have*   habrían: *you (they) would have*

Present Subjunctive Tense

haya: *I may have*   hayamos: *we may have*
hayas: *thou mayst have*   hayáis: *ye may have*
haya: *you (he, she) may have*   hayan: *you (they) may have*

Haber (5)
(Impersonal)

Present Tense: hay: *there is, there are.*
Imperfect Tense: había: *there was, there were.*
Preterite Tense: hubo: *there was, there were.*
Future Tense: habrá: *there will be.*
Potential or Conditional Tense: habría: *there would be.*
Present Subjunctive Tense: haya: *there may be.*
The Gerund: habiendo: *having.*
The Past Participle: habido: *had.*

Ser, *to be* (6)

Present Tense

soy: *I am*
eres: *thou art*
es: *you are, he, she is*

somos: *we are*
sois: *ye are*
son: *you (they) are*

Imperfect Tense

era: *I was*
eras: *thou wast*
era: *you were, he, she was*

éramos: *we were*
erais: *ye were*
eran: *you (they) were*

Preterite Tense

fuí: *I was*
fuiste: *thou wast*
fué: *you were, he, she was*

fuimos: *we were*
fuisteis: *ye were*
fueron: *you (they) were*

Future Tense

seré: *I shall be*
serás: *thou wilt be*
será: *you (he, she) will be*

seremos: *we shall be*
seréis: *ye will be*
serán: *you (they) will be*

Potential or Conditional Tense

sería: *I should be*
serías: *thou wouldst be*
sería: *you (he, she) would be*

seríamos: *we should be*
seríais: *ye would be*
serían: *you (they) would be*

Present Subjunctive Tense

sea: *I may be*   seamos: *we may be*
seas: *thou mayst be*   seáis: *ye may be*
sea: *you (he, she) may be*   sean: *you (they) may be*

Imperative Mood

                                   seamos: *let us be*
sé: *be (thou)*   sed: *be (ye)*
sea: *be (you), let him be, let her* sean: *(you) be, let them be*
  be

The Gerund   ### The Past Participle

siendo: *being*   sido: *been*

ESTAR, *to be* (7)

Present Tense

estoy: *I am*   estamos: *we are*
estás: *thou art*   estáis: *ye are*
está: *you are, he, she is*   están: *you (they) are*

Imperfect Tense

estaba: *I was*   estábamos: *we were*
estabas: *thou wast*   estabais: *ye were*
estaba: *you were, he, she was*   estaban: *you (they) were*

Preterite Tense

estuve: *I was*   estuvimos: *we were*
estuviste: *thou wast*   estuvisteis: *ye were*
estuvo: *you were, he, she was*   estuvieron: *you (they) were*

Future Tense

estaré: *I shall be*   estaremos: *we shall be*
estarás: *thou wilt be*   estaréis: *ye will be*
estará: *you (he, she) would be*   estarán: *you (they) will be*

Potential or Conditional Tense

estaría: *I should be*

estarías: *thou wouldst be*

estaría: *you (he, she) would be*

estaríamos: *we should be*

estaríais: *ye would be*

estarían: *you (they) would be*

Present Subjunctive Tense

esté: *I may be*

estés: *thou mayst be*

esté: *you (he, she) may be*

estemos: *we may be*

estéis: *ye may be*

estén: *you (they) may be*

Imperative Mood

está: *be thou*

esté: *be (you), let him be, let her be*

estemos: *let us be*

estad: *be (ye)*

estén: *be (you), let them be*

The Gerund

estando: *being*

The Past Participle

estado: *been*

ENCENDER, *to kindle* (8)
(*e* changes to *ie* when the stress falls upon it.)

Present Tense

enciendo: *I kindle*

enciendes: *thou dost kindle*

enciende: *you kindle, he, she kindles*

encendemos: *we kindle*

encendéis: *ye kindle*

encienden: *you (they) kindle*

Present Subjunctive Tense

encienda: *I may kindle*

enciendas: *thou mayst kindle*

encienda: *you (he) may kindle*

encendamos: *we may kindle*

encendáis: *ye may kindle*

enciendan: *you (they) may kindle*

Imperative Mood

enciende: *kindle (thou)*

encienda: *(you) kindle, let him, her kindle*

encendamos: *let us kindle*

encended: *kindle (ye)*

enciendan: *(you) kindle, let them kindle*

AGRADECER, *to thank* (9)

(*c* changes to *zc* in the first singular of the present tense and in all of the present subjunctive.)

Present Tense

agradezco: *I thank*

agradeces: *thou dost thank*

agradece: *you thank, he, she thanks*

agradecemos: *we thank*

agradecéis: *ye thank*

agradecen: *you (they) thank*

Present Subjunctive Tense

agradezca: *I may thank*

agradezcas: *thou mayst thank*

agradezca: *you (he, she) may thank*

agradezcamos: *we may thank*

agradezcáis: *ye may thank*

agradezcan: *you (they) may thank*

Imperative Mood

agradece: *thank (thou)*

agradezca: *(you) thank, let him, her thank*

agradezcamos: *let us thank*

agradeced: *thank (ye)*

agradezcan: *(you) thank, let them thank*

REDUCIR, *to reduce* (10)

(*c* changes to *zc* in the first singular of the present tense and in all of the present subjunctive.)

Present Tense

reduzco: *I reduce*

reducimos: *we reduce*

reduces: *thou dost reduce*   reducís: *ye reduce*
reduce: *you reduce, he, she reduces*   reducen: *you (they) reduce*

Preterite Tense
(*c* changes to *j; i* drops out of 3rd plural.)

reduje: *I reduced*   redujimos: *we reduced*
redujiste, *thou didst reduce*   redujisteis: *ye reduced*
redujo: *you (he, she) reduced*   redujeron: *you (they) reduced*

Present Subjunctive Tense

reduzca: *I may reduce*   reduzcamos: *we may reduce*
reduzcas: *thou mayst reduce*   reduzcáis: *ye may reduce*
reduzca: *you (he, she) may reduce*   reduzcan: *you (they) may reduce*

Imperative Mood

reduzcamos: *let us reduce*
reduce: *reduce (thou)*   reducid: *reduce (ye)*
reduzca: *(you) reduce, let him, her*   reduzcan: *(you) reduce, let them*
reduce   reduce

JUGAR, *to play* (11)
(*u* changes to *ue* when stress falls upon it.)

Present Tense

juego: *I play*   jugamos: *we play*
juegas: *thou playest*   jugáis: *ye play*
juega: *you play, he, she plays*   juegan: *you (they) play*

Present Subjunctive Tense
(*g* changes to *gu* when followed by an *e*.)

juegue: *I may play*   juguemos: *we may play*
juegues: *thou mayst play*   juguéis: *ye may play*
juegue: *you (he, she) may play*   jueguen: *you (they) may play*

650

SPANISH SELF TAUGHT

Imperative Mood

juega: *play (thou)*

juegue: *(you) play, let him, her play*

juguemos: *let us play*

jugad: *play (ye)*

jueguen: *(you) play, let them play*

MOVER, *to move* (12)
(*o* changes to *ue* when stress falls upon it.)

Present Tense

muevo: *I move*

mueves: *thou dost move*

mueve: *you move, he, she moves*

movemos: *we move*

movéis: *ye move*

mueven: *you (they) move*

Present Subjunctive Tense

mueva: *I may move*

muevas: *thou mayst move*

mueva: *you (he, she) may move*

movamos: *we may move*

mováis: *ye may move*

muevan: *you (they) may move*

Imperative Mood

mueve: *move (thou)*

mueva: *(you) move, let him, her move*

movamos: *let us move*

moved: *move (ye)*

muevan: *(you) move, let them move*

CONTAR, *to count* (13)
(*o* changes to *ue* when stress falls upon it.)

Present Tense

cuento: *I count*

cuentas: *thou countest*

cuenta: *you count, he, she counts*

contamos: *we count*

contáis: *ye count*

cuentan: *you (they) count*

Present Subjunctive Tense

cuente: *I may count*

contemos: *we may count*

cuentes: *thou mayst count* contéis: *ye may count*
cuente: *you (he, she) may count* cuenten: *you (they) may count*

Imperative Mood

contemos: *let us count*
cuenta: *count (thou)* contad: *count (ye)*
cuente: *(you) count, let him, her* cuenten: *(you) count, let them*
count count

SERVIR, *to serve* (14)
(*e* changes to *i* when stress falls upon it.)

Present Tense

sirvo: *I serve* servimos: *we serve*
sirves: *thou servest* servís: *ye serve*
sirve: *you serve, he, she serves* sirven: *you (they) serve*

Preterite Tense

serví: *I served* servimos: *we served*
serviste: *thou didst serve* servisteis: *ye served*
sirvió: *you (he, she) served* sirvieron: *you (they) served*

Present Subjunctive Tense

sirva: *I may serve* sirvamos: *we may serve*
sirvas: *thou mayst serve* sirváis: *ye may serve*
sirva: *you (he, she) may serve* sirvan: *you (they) may serve*

Imperative Mood

sirvamos: *let us serve*
sirve: *serve (thou)* servid: *serve (ye)*
sirva: *(you) serve, let him, her* sirvan: *(you) serve, let them serve*
serve

The Gerund ### The Past Participle

sirviendo: *serving* servido: *served*

DAR, *to give* (15)

Present Tense

doy: *I give*   damos: *we give*
das: *thou givest*   dais: *ye give*
da: *you give, he, she gives*   dan: *you (they) give*

Preterite Tense

dí: *I gave*   dimos: *we gave*
diste: *thou gavest*   disteis: *ye gave*
dió: *you (he, she) gave*   dieron: *you (they) gave*

DORMIR, *to sleep* (16)

(*o* changes to *ue* when stress falls upon it; *o* changes to *u* in the gerund, third person singular and plural of the preterite, and first and second persons plural of the present subjunctive.)

Present: duermo, duermes, duerme, dormimos, dormís, duermen.
Preterite: dormí, dormiste, durmió, dormimos, dormisteis, durmieron.
Pres. Subj.: duerma, duermas, duerma, durmamos, durmáis, duerman.
Imperative: duerme, *sleep (thou);* duerma, *sleep (you), let him, her sleep;* durmamos, *let us sleep;* dormid, *sleep (ye);* duerman, *sleep (you), let them sleep.*
Gerund: durmiendo.
Past Participle: dormido.

DECIR, *to say, tell* (17)
(here *e* changes to *i,* except in a few forms.)

Present: digo, dices, dice, decimos, decís, dicen.
Preterite: dije, dijiste, dijo, dijimos, dijisteis, dijeron.
Future: diré, dirás, dirá, diremos, diréis, dirán.
Conditional: diría, dirías, diría, diríamos, diríais, dirían.
Pres. Subj.: diga, digas, diga, digamos, digáis, digan.
Imperative: di, *say (thou);* diga, *say (you), let him, her say;* digamos, *let's say;* decid, *say (ye);* digan, *say (you), let them say.*
Gerund: diciendo.
Past Participle: dicho.

Sentir, *to feel sorry* (18)
(*e* changes to *ie; e* changes to *i.*)
NOTE: Italics are used here and below to call attention to
unusual forms in a tense.

Present: siento, sientes, siente, sentimos, sentís, *sienten.*
Preterite: sentí, sentiste, *sintió,* sentimos, sentisteis, *sintieron.*
Pres. Subj.: sienta, sientas, sienta, *sintamos, sintáis,* sientan.
Imperative: siente, *feel (thou);* sienta, *(you) feel, let him feel; sintamos,
let us feel;* sentid, *feel (ye);* sientan, *(you) feel, let them
feel.*
Gerund: sintiendo.
Past Participle: sentido.

Salir, *to go out* (19)

Present: salgo, sales, sale, salimos, salís, salen.
Future: saldré, saldrás, saldrá, saldremos, saldréis, saldrán.
Conditional: saldría, saldrías, saldría, saldríamos, saldríais, saldrían.
Pres. Subj.: salga, salgas, salga, salgamos, salgáis, salgan.
Imperative: sal, *go (thou) out; salga, you (let him) go out; salgamos,
let us go out;* salid, *go (ye) out; salgan, (you) (let them)
go out.*

Oler, *to smell* (20)
(*o* changes to *hue.*)

Present: huelo, hueles, huele, olemos, oléis, *huelen.*
Pres. Subj.: huela, huelas, huela, olamos, oláis, *huelan.*
*Imperative: huele, smell (thou); huela, (you) smell, let him smell;
olamos, let us smell;* oled, *smell (ye); huelan, (you) (let
them) smell.*

Oír, *to hear* (21)
(*i* changes to *y.*)

Present: oigo, *oyes, oye,* oímos, oís, *oyen.*
Pres. Subj.: oiga, oigas, oiga, oigamos, oigáis, oigan.
Imperative: oye, hear (thou); oiga (you) hear; oigamos, let us hear;
oíd, *hear (ye); oigan, (you) (let them) hear.*

CABER, *to fit, contain* (22)

Present: quepo, cabes, cabe, cabemos, cabéis, caben.
Preterite: cupe, cupiste, cupo, cupimos, cupisteis, cupieron.
Future: cabré, cabrás, cabrá, cabremos, cabréis, cabrán.
Conditional: cabría, cabrías, cabría, cabríamos, cabríais, cabrían.
Pres. Subj.: quepa, quepas, quepa, quepamos, quepáis, quepan.
Imperative: cabe, *contain (thou); quepa, (you) (let him) contain; que-*
        pamos, let us contain; cabed, *contain (ye); quepan, (you)*
        (let them) contain.

IR, *to go* (23)

Present: voy, vas, va, vamos, vais, van.
Imperfect: iba, ibas, iba, íbamos, ibais, iban.
Preterite: fuí, fuiste, fué, fuimos, fuisteis, fueron.
Pres. Subj.: vaya, vayas, vaya, vayamos, vayáis, vayan.
Imperative: ve, *go (thou); vaya, (you) (let him) go (Go!); vayamos,*
        let us go; id, *go (ye); vayan, (you) (let them) go.*
Gerund: yendo.
Past Participle: ido.

CAER, *to fall* (24)

Present: caigo, caes, cae, caemos, caéis, caen.
Preterite: caí, caíste, *cayó,* caímos, caísteis, *cayeron.*
Pres. Subj.: caiga, caigas, caiga, caigamos, caigáis, caigan.
Imperative: cae, *caiga, caigamos,* caed, *caigan.*
Gerund: cayendo.
Past Participle: caído.

PODER, *to be able to* (25)
(*o* changes to *ue; o* changes to *u.*)

Present: puedo, puedes, puede, podemos, podéis, *pueden.*
Preterite: pude, pudiste, pudo, pudimos, pudisteis, pudieron.
Future: podré, podrás, podrá, podremos, podréis, podrán.
Conditional: podría, podrías, podría, podríamos, podríais, podrían.
Pres. Subj.: pueda, puedas, pueda, podamos, podáis, *puedan.*
Imperative: puede, pueda, pudamos, poded, *puedan.*
Gerund: pudiendo.
Past Participle: podido.

HACER, *to make, do* (26)

Present: hago, haces, hace, hacemos, hacéis, hacen.
Preterite: hice, hiciste, *hizo,* hicimos, hicisteis, hicieron.
Future: haré, harás, hará, haremos, haréis, harán.
Conditional: haría, harías, haría, haríamos, haríais, harían.
Pres. Subj.: haga, hagas, haga, hagamos, hagáis, hagan.
Imperative: haz, haga, hagamos, haced, *hagan.*
Gerund: haciendo.
Past Participle: hecho.

VENIR, *to come* (27)

Present: vengo, vienes, viene, venimos, venís, *vienen.*
Preterite: vine, viniste, vino, vinimos, vinisteis, vinieron.
Future: vendré, vendrás, vendrá, vendremos, vendréis, vendrán.
Conditional: vendría, vendrías, vendría, vendríamos, vendríais, vendrían.
Pres. Subj.: venga, vengas, venga, vengamos, vengáis, vengan.
Imperative: ven, *venga, vengamos,* venid, *vengan.*
Gerund: viniendo.
Past Participle: venido.

PONER, *to put, place* (28)

Present: pongo, pones, pone, ponemos, ponéis, ponen.
Preterite: puse, pusiste, puso, pusimos, pusisteis, pusieron.
Future: pondré, pondrás, pondrá, pondremos, pondréis, pondrán.
Conditional: pondría, pondrías, pondría, pondríamos, pondríais, pondrían.
Pres. Subj.: ponga, pongas, ponga, pongamos, pongáis, pongan.
Imperative: pon, *ponga, pongamos,* poned, *pongan.*
Gerund: poniendo.
Past Participle: puesto.

TENER, *to have* (29)

Present: tengo, tienes, tiene, tenemos, tenéis, *tienen.*
Preterite: tuve, tuviste, tuvo, tuvimos, tuvisteis, tuvieron.
Future: tendré, tendrás, tendrá, tendremos, tendréis, tendrán.
Conditional: tendría, tendrías, tendría, tendríamos, tendríais, tendrían.
Pres. Subj.: tenga, tengas, tenga, tengamos, tengáis, tengan.
Imperative: ten, *tenga, tengamos,* tened, *tengan.*

QUERER, *to like* (30)

Present: quiero, quieres, quiere, queremos, queréis, *quieren.*
Preterite: quise, quisiste, quiso, quisimos, quisisteis, quisieron.
Future: querré, querrás, querrá, querremos, querréis, querrán.
Conditional: querría, querrías, querría, querríamos, querríais, querrían.
Pres. Subj.: quiera, quieras, quiera, queramos, queráis, *quieran.*
Imperative: quiere, quiera, queramos, quered, *quieran.*

TRAER, *to carry* (31)

Present: traigo, traes, trae, traemos, traéis, traen.
Preterite: traje, trajiste, trajo, trajimos, trajisteis, trajeron.
Present Subj.: traiga, traigas, traiga, traigamos, traigáis, traigan.
Imperative: trae, *traiga, traigamos,* traed, *traigan.*
Gerund: trayendo.
Past Participle: traído.

SABER, *to know* (32)

Present: sé, sabes, sabe, sabemos, sabéis, saben.
Preterite: supe, supiste, supo, supimos, supisteis, supieron.
Future: sabré, sabrás, sabrá, sabremos, sabréis, sabrán.
Conditional: sabría, sabrías, sabría, sabríamos, sabríais, sabrían.
Pres. Subj.: sepa, sepas, sepa, sepamos, sepáis, sepan.
Imperative: sabe, *sepa, sepamos,* sabed, *sepan.*

VER, *to see* (33)

Present: veo, ves, ve, vemos, veis, ven.
Imperfect: veía, veías, veía, veíamos, veíais, veían.
Pres. Subj.: vea, veas, vea, veamos, veáis, vean.
Imperative: ve, vea, veamos, ved, vean.
Gerund: viendo.
Past Participle: visto.

ESCRIBER, *to write* (34)

Regular except for the Past Participle: escrito.

EXERCISES TRANSLATED

LESSON IV

English to Spanish

1. Yo tengo agua; no tengo sed. 2. Ella tiene pan, pero tiene hambre. 3. Ella tiene un perro: él no tiene miedo. 4. Vd. tiene calor; Vd. no tiene un resfriado. 5. Nosotros trabajamos; no tenemos frío. 6. Tenemos sueño; tenemos ganas de dormir. 7. Un hombre no es un niño. 8. Está enfermo; está aquí con nosotros. 9. Juan tiene vergüenza. 10. La madre tiene razón.

LESSON V

Spanish to English

—Let's go to the grocery store. I have to buy many things for the kitchen.

—Is there a grocery near here? I also need something.

—Yes, of course! There are several shops in Moros Street (literally: *the street of the Moors*). There are found these groceries, butcher shops, laundries, and stores where many articles of utility are sold. In the alley (little street) to the right there are a pharmacy, a hardware store and a haberdashery; over here, to the left, are (found) a tailor and a shoe-maker. Near the square are a good hotel and two or three little restaurants.

—Here we are at the grocery. Good day, sir! We need oranges and lemons and, if they are not expensive (dear) at present, some bananas. How much are these oranges worth?

—Forty cents a (the) dozen, young gentlemen; they are very cheap. On the other hand, the apples are out of season and are worth twenty-five cents a pound.

—All right. I don't like apples; I'll take a dozen oranges and half a dozen lemons. I need also twelve eggs, a pound of coffee, five pounds of sugar and two (loaves of) bread. And you, Peter, if I am not mistaken you want something.

—Yes (my friend), I should like some bananas.—Not many, mister! The three are enough. Thanks!

—I thank you very much (give you many thanks), young gentlemen! Until I see you again (literally: *until* [I have the pleasure of] *the sight* [of you]).

Lesson VI

English to Spanish

1. Yo tengo que ir a la bodega. 2. ¿Hay una ferretería aquí cerca? 3. ¡Sí, por supuesto! Hay muchos almacenes en esta calle, si no me equivoco. 4. Vámonos, pues. ¿Vd. quiere algo? 5. Sí, si se venden en estos almacenes, y si no están caros. 6. Me gustan las cosas baratas también, si son buenas. ¡Por aquí! 7. ¡Aquí hemos (llegado)! Los almacenes se hallan en esta callejuela.

Lesson VI

Spanish to English

—(Will) you have the goodness to tell me where is a good hotel?
—Beg pardon, sir?
—You didn't understand? I say, where is a good inn, (that) is to say, a hotel? I am a traveler, and I am very tired; I want to go to bed.
—Now I understand perfectly, sir! Have the kindness to accompany me two blocks, as far as Gómez Street where (there) is the Hotel San Pedro. There one eats very well (the food is very good) and the rooms will please you.
—Many thanks, sir! Allow me to present myself to you, Rafaél Casablanca, at your service.
—I am very pleased to know you, sir (literally: *I have much pleasure in knowing you*). I place myself at your service, Miguel Alvarez (literally: *I offer myself, M. A., at your disposition*).
—I thank you ever so much for your information; and if I am not mistaken we have arrived at the hotel. Until I see you again, sir!
—Until then! May you sleep well tonight!
—The same to you!

Lesson VII

Spanish to English

THE KITCHEN (COOKING, CUISINE, MEALS)

—In a lodging house the cuisine is very important. At seven in the morning breakfast is served.—

—What is the *desayuno*?

—It is the first meal of the day. It consists generally of (pieces of) toast, soft-boiled eggs, fruit (orange or grapefruit), coffee with milk, and, perhaps, a cereal. At lunch one eats soup, spaghetti or rice with tomato and meat, salad and fruit. Lunch is served at one in the afternoon. At eight is served the principal meal which consists of a dish of meat or of fish with vegetables, and afterward a salad. Then some desserts are served—fruit, pies with cheese, or cakes and candies. Black coffee follows, naturally. Before going to bed one eats a supper of chocolate or milk with crackers.

THE CLOTHING

—(Do me the) favor of telling me, (my) friend, how a man dresses when he is going to take a walk through the park.

—First, after bathing, he puts on underwear, shirt with collar and tie, socks, trousers, shoes, vest and sack coat, and before going out in the street he puts on hat and overcoat. Sometimes he carries a pair of gloves and a cane. When there is a heavy rain and the clothing gets wet, it is necessary to change the clothes. Men's clothing is made of several materials: woolen cloth, cotton, linen, felt, and silk. Shoes are made of leather, and hats which are worn in summer are made of straw or of panama fiber.

—And what does a woman wear when she goes out of the house?

—Ladies' clothes go out of style so frequently that I don't dare to describe them. I know that they wear stockings and skirts and blouses and shirtwaists, and naturally shoes. When the weather is cold they wear hats and overcoats. For the rest, who knows?

LESSON VII

English to Spanish

1. Hágame el favor de decirme qué lleva un hombre cuando sale en la calle. 2. ¿De qué tela se hacen los trajes de señora? 3. No llevamos abrigos en el verano. 4. ¿Qué hace un hombre cuando se moja su traje (ropa)? 5. No me gusta un hombre que lleve guantes y un bastón. 6. Necesito calcetines y ropa interior; ¿Se venden al almacén? 7. Después de bañarme, hallé que tenía un calcetín. 8. Cuando hace frío yo llevo un sombrero de fieltro; en el verano llevo un sombrero de jipijapa. 9. No me atrevo a pasearme por el parque.

LESSON X

Spanish to English

LETTER

Maracaibo, June 16th, 1958.

Rodriguez Brothers,
Caracas.

Gentlemen (Dear sirs):

Please send me, as promptly as possible, the following pieces of office furniture in mahogany, as listed in your catalogue (which your catalogue lists):

Two swivel chairs, catalogue number 3.

Three small typewriter tables, number 8.

One long table, model number 5½.

Two tables, number 4.

I should like you to send me these pieces at the earliest possible date (with the greatest promptness), with invoice, giving me the usual discount.

Very truly yours,

Manuel González.

Address: 17 Liberty Street.

REPLY

Caracas, June 20th, 1958.
Mr. Manuel González,
17 Liberty Street,
Maracaibo.

Dear sir:

We are in receipt of (have received) your (communication) of the 16th instant, in which you place an order for office furniture. We are pleased to send you all the articles corresponding to the numbers quoted in your letter, except the table, model number 5½, which we cannot ship to you because it is out of stock at present. Attached you will find invoice made out to you for the pieces which you were pleased to order of us, with this exception.

Hoping that it will be satisfactory, and thanking you for your order, we are,

Very truly yours,
Rodríguez Brothers.

SPANISH–ENGLISH VOCABULARY

A

a, to, in, at, on
abrigo, m., overcoat
acompañar, to accompany
acostarse, to retire, go to bed
agradecer, to thank
agua, f., water
alegrarse, to be glad
algo, m., something
alguno-a, some, any
almacén, m., store
almuerzo, m., lunch
allí, there
amigo, m., friend
antes, before
aquí, here
artículo, m., article
arroz, m., rice
atento-a, solicitous
atreverse, to dare
azúcar, m., sugar

B

bajo-a, low, lower
bañarse, to bathe
barato-a, cheap
bastar, to be enough
bastón, m., cane
besar, to kiss
bien, well
blusa, f., blouse
bodega, f., grocery
bondad, f., goodness, kindness
broma, f., joke
bueno-a, good

C

café, m., coffee
calcetín, m., sock
calle, f., street
callejuela, f., alley
cama, f., bed
camisa, f., shirt
cansado-a, tired, weary
cansar, to weary
carne, f., meat
carnicería, f., butcher shop
caro-a, dear, expensive
casa, f., house
cena, f., supper
cerca, near
cereal, m., cereal
ciento-a, hundred
cinco-a, five
cocina, f., kitchen, cooking
comida, f., meal, dinner
común-a, common
como, how, why, as
comprar, to buy
con, with
conocer, to know
consistir, to consist
contar, to count
contra, against
corbata, f., necktie
cosa, f., thing
creer, to believe
cuando, when
cuanto, how many
cuarenta, forty
cuello, m., collar

cuero, m., leather
cuidado, m., care

CH

chaleco, m., vest

D

dar, to give
de, of, from
decir, to say
dejar, to leave, to stop
derecho-a, right
desayuno, m., breakfast
describir, to describe
después, then, afterwards
día, m., day
Dios, m., God
dispensar, to forgive
doce, twelve
docena, f., dozen
donde, where
dos, two
dulce, sweet; m., candy

E

en, in
encender, to set fire to
ensalada, f., salad
entender, to understand
equivocarse, to be mistaken
ese-a, that; *ése-a,* pron., that
este-a, this; *éste-a,* pron., this
esto, this

F

falda, f., skirt
farmacia, f., pharmacy
ferretería, f., hardware store
fideos, m. plural, spaghetti,
    vermicelli
figurarse, to imagine
fijarse, to notice

fin, m., end
fonda, f., hotel
frecuencia, f., frequency
frío-a, cold
fruta, f., fruit
fuera, out, outside
fuerte, strong, heavy, loud, etc.

G

galleta, f., cracker
generalmente, generally
gracias, f. plural, thanks
grado, m., degree
grande, large, great
guante, m., glove
guardar, to keep
gustar, to please
gusto, m., taste, pleasure

H

hacer, to make, to do
hallar, to find
hasta, until, as far as
hermana, f., sister
hermano, m., brother
hombre, m., man
huéspedes, m. plural, guests
huevo, m., egg

I

infinamente, infinitely
informes, m. plural, information
izquierdo-a, left-hand

J

jipijapa, f., panama straw
jugar, to play

L

lavandería, f., laundry
leche, f., milk
legumbre, f., vegetable

libra, f., pound
limón, m., lemon
lo, the; it
luego, then, later

LL

llamar, to call
llegar, to arrive
llevar, to carry, to wear
lluvia, f., rain

M

malo-a, bad, sick
mandar, to command
mano, f., hand
manzana, f., apple, city block
mañana, f., tomorrow
más, more
mayor, larger
media, f., stocking
medio-a, half
mejor, better
menor, less
mercería, f., haberdashery
mi, my
mío-a, my, mine
mover, to move
mismo-a, same
moda, f., style
modo, m., way, means
mojarse, to get wet
molestia, f., trouble, harm
mucho-a, many, much
muy, very

N

nada, f., nothing
naranja, f., orange
necesitar, to need
negro-a, black
ninguno-a, none

noche, f., night
novedad, f., newness, news
nuevo-a, new

O

obstante, withstanding
ocho, eight
ofrecer, to offer

P

pagar, to pay
paja, f., straw
pan, m., bread, loaf
pantalón, m., trousers
par, m., a pair
para, for
parecer, to appear
parecer, m., opinion
parque, m., park
pasar, to pass
pasearse, to take a walk
pastel, m., pie
pena, f., bother
peor, worse
pequeño-a, small, little
perder, to lose
permitir, to permit, allow
pescado, m., fish (prepared)
pez, f., fish (in the sea)
piso, m., floor
plato, m., dish (of food), plate
plaza, f., square, plaza, market
poder, to be able
poner, to put on, to lay
por, through, by
posada, f., hotel
postre, m., dessert
presentar, to present
primero-a, first
primero, first, firstly
prisa, f., haste, hurry

Q

que, that, what, which
querer, to like, want, love
querido-a, dear, loved
queso, m., cheese
quien, who, whom

R

reducir, to reduce
resto, m., rest, remainder
ropa, f., clothing

S

saber, to know, know how
saco, m., sack coat
salir, to go out
santo-a, sacred, holy, St.
sastre, m., tailor
sazón, f., season
se, self, one
seguir, to follow
seguro-a, faithful
señor, m., gentleman, sir
señora, f., lady, madam
señorita, f., young lady
señorito, m., young gentleman
sentir, to feel (sorry)
servidor, servant
servir, to serve
si, if
sí, yes
siete, seven
sin, without
sobretodo, m., overcoat
sombrero, m., hat
sopa, f., soup
su, his, her, its, your
suyo-a, his, her, yours

T

tal, such

también, also
tan, so, so much
tanto-a, so much, so
tarde, late
tarde, f., afternoon
tercero-a, third
tienda, f., store
todo, all
tomate, m., tomato
tomar, to take
toronja, f., grapefruit, quince
torta, f., cake
tostada, f., toast
traje, m., dress, clothes
tres, three

U

uno-a, one; a, an
utilidad, utility, usefulness

V

valer, to be worth
varios-as, several, various
veinticinco, twenty-five
vender, to sell
ver, to see
verano, m., summer
veras, f. plural, truth
verdad, f., truth
vestirse, to dress
vez, f., time
viajero, m., traveler
vista, f., sight

Y

y, and
ya, already

Z

zapato, m., shoe
zapatero, m., shoemaker

ENGLISH–SPANISH VOCABULARY

A

a, *un, uno, una*
accompany, *acompañar*
afternoon, *tarde,* f.
against, *contra*
all, *todo-a*
alley, *callejuela,* f.
allow, *permitir*
already, *ya*
and, *y*
any, *alguno-a*
appear, *parecer*
apple, *manzana,* f.
arrive, *llegar*
article, *artículo,* m.
as, *tan, como*
at, *a*

B

bad, *malo-a*
bathe, *bañarse*
bed, *cama,* f.
before, *antes*
believe, *creer*
better, *mejor*
black, *negro-a*
block (city), *manzana,* f.
blouse, *blusa,* f.
bother, *molestia,* f.
bread, *pan,* m.
breakfast, *desayuno,* m.
brother, *hermano,* m.
butcher shop, *carnicería,* f.
buy, *comprar*

C

cake, *torta,* f.
call, *llamar*
candy, *dulce,* m.
cane, *bastón,* m.

care, *cuidado,* m.
carry, *llevar*
cereal, *cereal,* m.
cheap, *barato-a*
cheese, *queso,* m.
clothing, *traje,* m.; *ropa,* f.
coffee, *café,* m.
cold, *frío-a; resfriado,* m.
collar, *cuello,* m.
command, *mandar*
common, *común*
consist, *consistir*
cooking, *cocina,* f.
count, *contar*
cracker, *galleta,* f.

D

dare, *atreverse*
day, *día,* m.
dear, *caro-a, querido-a*
describe, *describir*
dessert, *postre,* m.
dinner, *comida,* f.
do, *hacer*
dozen, *docena,* f.
dress, *traje,* m.

E

egg, *huevo,* m.
eight, *ocho*
end, *fin,* m.
enough (to be), *bastar*

F

faithful, *seguro-a*
feel (sorry), *sentir*
find, *hallar, encontrar*
first, *primero-a*
fish (prepared), *pescado,* m.
five, *cinco*

floor, *piso, suelo,* m.
follow, *seguir*
for, *para*
forgive, *dispensar*
forty, *cuarenta*
frequency, *frecuencia,* f.
friend, *amigo,* m.
from, *de*
fruit, *fruta,* f.

G

generally, *generalmente*
gentleman, *señor,* m.
give, *dar*
glad (to be), *alegrarse*
good, *bueno-a*
goodness, *bondad,* f.
grapefruit, *toronja,* f.
great, *grande*
glove, *guante,* m.
go, *ir*
go out, *salir*
grocery, *bodega,* f.
guest, *huésped,* m. or f.

H

haberdashery, *mercería,* f.
half, *medio-a*
hand, *mano,* f.
hardware store, *ferretería,* f.
harm, *molestia,* f.; *daño,* m.
haste, *prisa,* f.
heavy, *pesante, fuerte*
her, *la;* poss., *su*
here, *aquí*
hers, *suyo-a*
him, *le*
his, *su, suyo-a*
hotel, *posada, fonda,* f.
house, *casa,* f.
how, *cómo*

how many, *cuanto-a*
hundred, *ciento-a*
hurry, *prisa,* f.

I

if, *si*
imagine, *figurarse*
in, *en*
infinitely, *infinamente*
information, *informes,* m. pl.
it, *le, la, lo*
its, *su*

J

joke, *broma,* f.

K

keep, *guardar*
kindness, *bondad,* f.
kiss, *besar*
kitchen, *cocina,* f.
know, *saber*

L

lady, *señora,* f.
large, *grande*
larger, *mayor*
later, *luego*
laundry, *lavandería,* f.
lay, *poner*
leather, *cuero,* m.
leave, *dejar*
left, *izquierdo-a*
lemon, *limón,* m.
little, *pequeño-a*
loaf, *pan,* m.
lose, *perder*
loud, *fuerte*
love, *querer*
low, *bajo-a*
lower, *inferior*

M

madam, *señora,* f.
make, *hacer*
man, *hombre,* m.
many, *mucho-a*
meal, *comida,* f.
means, *modo,* m.
meat, *carne,* f.
milk, *leche,* f.
mine, *mío-a*
more, *más*
move, *mover*
much, *mucho-a*
my, *mi, mío-a*

N

near, *cerca de*
necktie, *corbata,* f.
new, *nuevo-a*
newness, *novedad,* f.
night, *noche,* f.
none, *ninguno-a*
not, *no*
nothing, *nada,* f.
notice, *fijarse*

O

offer, *ofrecer*
on, *sobre, a*
one, *un, uno, una*
opinion, *parecer,* m.; *opinión,* f.
orange, *naranja,* f.
out, *fuera*
outside, *afuera*
over, *sobre*
overcoat, *sobretodo, abrigo,* m.

P

pair, *par,* m.
panama straw, *jipijapa,* f.
park, *parque,* m.
pass, *pasar*
pay, *pagar*

permit, *permitir*
pharmacy, *farmacia,* f.
pie, *pastel,* m.
play, *jugar*
pound, *libra,* f.
present, *presentar*
put, *poner*

R

rain, *lluvia,* f.
reason, *razón,* f.
rest, *resto,* m.
retire, *acostarse*
rice, *arroz,* m.
right, *derecho-a*

S

sack coat, *saco,* m.
sacred, *santo-a*
salad, *ensalada,* f.
same, *mismo-a*
say, *decir*
season, *sazón,* f.; *estación,* f.
see, *ver*
self, *se*
sell, *vender*
servant, *servidor,* m.
serve, *servir*
seven, *siete*
several, *varios-as*
shirt, *camisa,* f.
shoe, *zapato,* m.
shoemaker, *zapatero,* m.
sick, *enfermo-a*
sight, *vista,* f.
sir, *señor,* m.
sister, *hermana,* f.
skirt, *falda,* f.
small, *pequeño-a*
smell, *oler*
so, *tan*
sock, *calcetín,* m.

solicitous, *atento-a*
some, *alguno-a*
something, *algo*, m.
sorry (to feel), *sentir*
soup, *sopa*, f.
spaghetti, *fideos*, m. pl.
square, *plaza*, f.
stocking, *media*, f.
stop, *dejar*
store, *almacén*, m.; *tienda*, f.
straw, *paja*, f.
street, *calle*, f.
strong, *fuerte*
style, *moda*, f.
sugar, *azúcar*, m.
summer, *verano*, m.
supper, *cena*, f.
sweet, *dulce*, m.

T

take, *tomar*
take a walk, *pasearse*
tailor, *sastre*, m.
taste, *gusto*, m.
thank, *agradecer*
thanks, *gracias*, f. pl.
that, rel. *que;* adj. *ese-a*
then, *pues, luego*
there, *allí*
their, *su*
theirs, *suyo-a*
thing, *cosa*, f.
third, *tercero-a*
this, *este-a*
through, *por*
tie, *corbata*, f.
time, *vez*, f.
tired, *cansado*
to, *a*
toast, *tostada*, f.
tomato, *tomate*, m.
tomorrow, *mañana*, f.

traveler, *viajero*, m.
trouble, *molestia*, f.
trousers, *pantalón*, m.
truth, *veras*, f. pl.; *verdad*, f.
twelve, *doce*

U

under, *bajo de*
understand, *entender*
until, *hasta*
utility, *utilidad*, f.

V

vermicelli, *fideos*, m. pl.
very, *muy*
vest, *chaleco*, m.

W

walk, *andar*
water, *agua*, f.
way, *modo*, m.
wear, *llevar*
weary, *cansado*
well, *bien*
wet, *mojado-a*
wet (to get), *mojarse*
what, *qué*
when, *cuando*
where, *donde*
which, *cual, que*
who, *quien, que*
whom, *que*
why, *por qué*
with, *con*
without, *sin*
withstanding, *obstante*
worse, *peor*
worth (to be), *valer*

Y

yet, *todavía*

young gentleman, *señorito,* m.
young lady, *señorita,* f.

your, *su*
yours, *suyo-a*

TOPICAL VOCABULARY

QUESTION WORDS

dónde, where
adónde, to where
  aquí, allí, here, there
  sobre, debajo de, on, under
  delante de, detrás de, in front of, behind
  lejos de, cerca de, far from, near
  dentro de, fuera de, inside, outside
  en, a, de, in, to, from
  a la izquierda, a la derecha, to the left, right
  en todas partes, en ninguna parte, everywhere, nowhere
cómo, how
  bien, mal, well, badly
  rápidamente, lentamente, fast, slowly
  tan, muy, so, very
  en voz baja, alta, softly, aloud
cuándo, when
  siempre, jamás, always, never
  a menudo, raramente, often, rarely
  después, antes, after, before
  ahora, más tarde, now, later
  por la mañana, tarde, noche, in the morning, afternoon, evening
  hoy, ayer, mañana, today, yesterday, tomorrow

cuánto-a, cuántos-as, how much, how many
  mucho, poco, a lot, a little
  más, menos, more, less
  tanto, bastante, demasiado, so much, enough, too much
  todo, nada, everything, nothing
no es verdad, isn't it true (so)
  sí, no, yes, no
  y, también, and, also
  pero, si, quizá, but, if, maybe
  seguramente, de ningún modo, certainly, not at all
por qué, para qué, why
  porque, because
  para, in order to
  no sé, I don't know
qué, what
  esto, eso, this, that
qué sucedió, what happened
qué significa eso, what does that mean
quién, quiénes, who
a quién, a quiénes, (to) whom
  yo, tú, él, ella, Vd., I, thou, he, she, you
  nosotros, vosotros, ellos, ellas, Vds., we, you, they, you
  todo el mundo, nadie, everybody, nobody

DESCRIPTIVE WORDS

bueno-a, malo-a, good, bad
pequeño, grande, small, big

pobre, rico, poor, rich
triste, alegre, sad, happy

hermoso, feo, handsome, ugly
verdad, mentira, true, false
mismo, otro, same, other
blanco, negro, white, black
azul, amarillo, blue, yellow
verde, rojo, green, red
gris, pardo, gray, brown
joven, viejo, young, old
fuerte, débil, strong, weak

corto, largo, short, long
primero, último, first, last
dulce, duro, sweet, harsh
lleno, vacío, full, empty
seco, mojado, dry, wet
hábil, tonto, clever, stupid
tranquilo, inquieto, calm, worried
mejor, peor, better, worse

THE HOME

la familia, the family
el padre, la madre, the father, the mother
el hombre, la mujer, the man, the woman
el muchacho, la muchacha, the boy, the girl
hijo, hija, son, daughter
abuelo, abuela, grandfather, grandmother
sobrino, sobrina, nephew, niece
hermano, hermana, brother, sister
tío, tía, uncle, aunt
amigo, amiga, boy friend, girl friend
los padres, los hijos, parents, children

la casa, la calle, the house, the street
cocina, comedor, kitchen, dining room
el salón, dormitorio, drawing room, bedroom
cuarto, cuarto de baño, room, bathroom
suelo, techo, floor, ceiling
la pared, the wall
los muebles, the furniture
la mesa, la silla, table, chair
lámpara, cama, lamp, bed
piano, radio, piano, radio
sofá, butaca, sofa, armchair
el cuadro, alfrombrilla, picture, rug

THE PERSON

el cuerpo, the body
la cabeza, the head
el pelo, hair
cara, face
oreja, ear
la nariz, the nose
boca, mouth
ojo, eye
lengua, tongue
el diente, tooth

barba, chin
cuello, neck
hombro, shoulder
brazo, arm
la mano, hand
dedo, finger
el pie, foot

la salud, the health
cómo está Vd., how are you

estoy bien, I feel all right
tengo dolor de, I have a pain in
médico, enfermo, doctor, patient
la fiebre, fever
guardar cama, to stay in bed

ropa, clothing
sombrero, hat
vestido, suit
falda de seda, silk dress
zapato, shoe
media de lana, woolen stocking
el calcetín, sock
corbata, tie
camisa, shirt
sobretodo, overcoat
pañuelo, handkerchief
los guantes, gloves
llevar, to wear
eso me cae bien, that fits me
llorar, reír, to weep, laugh

amar, odiar, to love, hate
divertirse, aburrirse, to have a good time, to be bored
enfadarse, to become angry
olvidarse, acordarse, to forget, to remember
atreverse, tener miedo, to dare, to be afraid
levantarse, acostarse, to get up, to go to bed
ponerse la ropa, quitar la ropa, to get dressed, undressed
despertarse, dormir, to wake up, fall asleep
salir de, entrar en, to go out of, to go into
andar, correr, to walk, run
ponerse en camino, estar de vuelto, to start out, be back
nacer, morir, to be born, to die

MEALS

tengo hambre, I'm hungry
tengo sed, I'm thirsty
comer, beber, to eat, drink
comida, meal
desayuno, comida, breakfast, dinner
cena, supper
saber, to taste
fumar, to smoke
el pan, bread
panecillo, roll
mantequilla, butter
queso, cheese
la carne, meat
la legumbre, vegetable
huevo, egg
sopa, soup
el postre, dessert

fruta, fruit
el pastel, cake
la leche, milk
el café, coffee
el té, tea
el agua, water
vino, wine
vaso, glass
taza, cup
botella, bottle
servilleta, napkin
cuchara, spoon
cuchillo, knife
tenedor, fork
el restaurante, restaurant
mozo, waiter
cuenta, check
propina, tip

Shopping

tienda, shop
comprar, vender, buy, sell
pagar, deber, pay, owe
dinero, money
el sastre, tailor
costurera, seamstress
carnicero, carnicería, butcher, butcher shop
abacero, abacería, grocer, grocery

lavandera, lavandería, laundress, laundry
confitero, confitería, confectioner, candy shop
cuánto, how much
barato, caro, cheap, dear
costar, to cost
panadero, panadería, baker, bakery shop

Travel

el viaje, trip
viajar por ferrocarril, to travel by rail
viajar en automóvil, por avión, by auto, by plane
el billete, ticket
horario, timetable
milla, mile
la estación, station
volar, to fly
aeródromo, aerodrome
terreno de aterrizaja, landing field

ponerse en camino, llegar, to start out, arrive
ir a gran velocidad, to go full speed
pararse, to stop
atravesar, to cross
el tren, train
el avión, airplane
el buque, boat
mirar por la ventanilla, to look out of the window
el paisaje, the landscape
el puente, bridge

The Country

mundo, world
cielo, sky
estrella, star
la nube, cloud
viento, wind
tierra, land
montaña, mountain
el valle, valley
río, river
lago, lake
el mar, sea
la orilla del mar, seashore
océano, ocean

playa, beach
el país, country
el campo, countryside, field
el bosque, woods
el árbol, tree
hoja, leaf
el jardín, garden
hacienda, farm
pescar, to fish
nadar, to swim
bañarse, to bathe
dar un paseo, to take a walk
un paseo en bote, boat ride

The Year

los días de la semana, the days of the week
lunes, Monday
martes, Tuesday
miércoles, Wednesday
jueves, Thursday
viernes, Friday
sábado, Saturday
domingo, Sunday

los meses del año, the months of the year
enero, January
febrero, February
marzo, March
abril, April
mayo, May
junio, June
julio, July
agosto, August
septiembre, September
octubre, October
noviembre, November
diciembre, December

fiesta, holiday
el cumpleaños, birthday
Pascuas, Christmas
Pascuas Floridas, Easter
el día del año, New Year's Day

las vacaciones, vacation

el tiempo y las estaciones, weather and seasons
en el verano, in the summer
invierno, winter
otoño, autumn
primavera, spring
hace buen tiempo, mal tiempo, the weather is good, bad
hace calor, frío, it's warm, cold
sopla el viento, hay sol, it's windy, sunny
nieva, llueve, it's snowing, raining
qué tiempo hace, what kind of weather is it
tengo frío, calor, I'm cold, warm

qué hora es, what time is it
es la una, son las dos, it's one, two
y media, half past
y cuarto, menos cuarto, quarter after, quarter to
y cinco, menos cinco, five after, five to
el reloj, watch
mediodía, medianoche, midday, midnight
temprano, tarde, early, late
ser puntual, to be punctual

Polite Talk

buenos días, good day
Señor, Señora, Señorita, Mr., Mrs., Miss
permítame presentarle a Vd., allow me to introduce to you

encantado, delighted
gracias, thanks
no hay de que, don't mention it
hasta la vista, so long

EXAMINATION QUESTIONS

Translate the following into Spanish:

1. The woman speaks Spanish; you write it.
2. He writes his lesson; you are doing nothing.
3. We are hot; she is thirsty; Mother has a cold.
4. Mother is right; the dog wants to (go to) sleep.
5. San Francisco is a city far from here.
6. On the other hand, we are working.
7. If I am not mistaken, he is ill.
8. I have to buy many things for the kitchen.
9. Near the square are a good hotel and two or three little restaurants.
10. How much are these oranges worth?
11. All right, I don't like apples; I'll take a dozen of oranges and half a dozen of lemons.
12. I need also twelve eggs, a pound of coffee, five pounds of sugar, and two loaves of bread.
13. I am very pleased to know you, sir.
14. May you sleep well tonight!
15. At lunch one eats soup, spaghetti or rice with tomato and meat, the salad and fruits.
16. Lunch is served at one in the afternoon.
17. And what does a woman wear when she goes out of the house?
18. When there is a heavy rain and the clothing gets wet, it is necessary to change the clothes.
19. Sometimes he carries a pair of gloves and a cane.
20. Ladies' clothes go out of style so frequently that I don't dare to describe them.
21. Ordinarily it is warm.
22. My dear friend, how are you?
23. I should like a small typewriter table, model number 8.
24. We have the pleasure of sending you all the articles mentioned in your letter.
25. Call the waiter. I should like to pay the bill.

Translate the following into English:

26. El perro come, pero no trabaja.
27. (Él) no escribe nada ahora.
28. Ustedes tienen sueño, pero yo tengo vergüenza.
29. Juan está enfermo; tiene un resfriado terrible.
30. Por contra, está aquí con nosotros.
31. La madre tiene razón.
32. Yo tengo agua; no tengo sed.
33. Ella tiene un perro; él no tiene miedo.
34. Vd. tiene calor; Vd. no tiene un resfriado.
35. Juan tiene vergüenza.
36. Sí, si ve venden en estos almacenes, y no están caros.
37. Tenga la bondad de decir: ¡Le agradezco!
38. Antes de acostarse, va a pasearse por el parque.
39. No llevamos abrigos en el verano.
40. No me gusta un hombre que lleve guantes y un bastón.
41. Después de bañarme, hallé que tenía un calcetín.
42. Cuando hace frío, yo llevo un sombrero de fieltro; en el verano llevo un sombrero de jipijapa.

43. No me atrevo a pasearme por el parque.
44. La comida está en la mesa ¿no es verdad?
45. No vale la pena de guardar cama.
46. Hemos recibido la suya del cte.

47. ¿Se le ofrece algo? Sí. Tráigame la ensalada.
48. ¡Cuidado! ¿Qué hay? ¿Qué tiene usted?
49. ¡Dispénseme usted! ¡Lo siento mucho!
50. ¿Dar una propina? ¡Ya lo creo!

FOR FURTHER STUDY

BRIEF SPANISH GRAMMAR FOR BE-GINNERS, by Lawrence Wilkins. (Henry Holt & Co.)

CUENTOS CONTADOS, by J. Pittaro. (D. C. Heath & Co., Boston.)

INVITATION TO SPANISH, by Madrigal and Madrigal. (Simon & Schuster, New York.)

PRIMER CURSO DE ESPAÑOL, by Pittaro and Green. (D. C. Heath & Co., Boston.)

SPANISH AMERICAN LIFE, by John Crow. (Henry Holt & Co., New York.)

XIV

An Introduction to Latin

THE VALUE OF LATIN

LATIN is a "dead" language, and yet, if that oft-repeated statement is true, it is one of the liveliest ghosts imaginable. Of course nowhere in the world today do people speak to one another about groceries and health, or even art and philosophy, in Latin. But there is not one Western nation whose language does not contain words which are the direct descendants of the Latin tongue. Some words are still the same both in form and meaning, such as *labor* and *animal,* while others are changed because of their many sound intermarriages with other languages, such as the Greek.

Naturally, not all the words in use today are derived from Latin, but a great number owe their existence to the power of the Roman Empire whose boundaries stretched so far, and whose influence was so important, that wherever a Roman soldier marched he left a trace of his language behind him. The modern tongues of Italy, France, Spain, and Portugal are most closely allied to the original Latin, while more than two-thirds of our English words come from the same source. Latin words themselves are still used in many of the professions: science, law, and medicine. The Church, by adopting Latin as its official language, did much to familiarize unschooled people with the forms of Latin. All of us have heard sung, or have sung ourselves, that beautiful old Christmas hymn, "Adeste, Fideles."

In Latin, all letters are pronounced. Consonants are pronounced as they are in English. Vowels are pronounced approximately as in Spanish. The diphthong *ae,* which is frequent in Latin, is pronounced as the *i* in the word "mine."

The value of knowing Latin words in their various constructions rests on the light they throw on words which we use today. "Aqueduct," for instance, is a combination of the Latin word *aqua,* meaning water, and a past form of the verb *ducere,* meaning to lead. "That which leads water" is certainly a practical explanation of an aqueduct. When we are able to recognize the skeletons of words and see how they have changed through the ages, when we are able to perceive that they have a history like that of painting or music, words then take on a subtle magic, our vocabulary increases in richness and variety, and our use of words is bound to become more exact. The man who has read the Latin classics in their original tongue has acquired a background of culture which will do much toward broadening his interests in the modern world. A knowledge of Latin is a great aid to expression, and it is through the clear expression of our thoughts and ideals that we are understood and appreciated by the age in which we live.

LESSON I

English grammar is closely allied to the Latin, but there is one noticeable difference. Most Latin words change their endings according to their use in a sentence. In English, because we are so anxious to do everything rapidly, these endings have disappeared, and in the sentences, "The farmer kicked the horse," and "The horse kicked the farmer," the forms of "horse" and "farmer" do not vary, although in the first sentence the farmer was the subject, being the author of the action, and the horse was the object, being the recipient of the blow, while in the second example the horse was the subject and the farmer the object. This difference in syntax cannot be discovered by examining the words in English: it is the sense and their relative positions in the sentence which tell us who did the kicking. In Latin there could be no mistake. When the farmer, *agricola,* does the kicking, he is in the nominative or subjective case, and the horse which is the object has a case ending which we immediately perceive to be objective, or accusative, as it is called in Latin grammar. On the other hand, when the horse kicks the farmer, *agricola* changes to *agricolam,* and the ending (-*m*) tells the Latin student that the farmer was not the subject of the verb but the object of it. We can therefore see how important it is to be able to recognize the various case endings of nouns before we can attempt to translate sentences.

CASES OF NOUNS

Latin nouns have six cases to distinguish their meanings in sentences: nominative, genitive, dative, accusative, ablative, and vocative. The nominative is used for the subject of a sentence; the genitive to denote possession, such as "mother's" hat; the dative for the indirect object, like the English objective with "to" and "for"; the accusative for the direct object; and the ablative for adverbial phrases, which in English are usually denoted by the noun and a preposition, as "from," "in," "on," "with," etc. The vocative is used only when a person is addressed, as for instance: "O mother, here is your book." "Mother" would be placed in the vocative case for this use of the word.

See if you can tell what Latin cases would be used in translating the nouns (italicized) in the following sentences:

1. The *men* make *wine* in the *vats.*
2. *Helen's sister* gave *Mark* the *letter.*
3. *Venus,* you are the *queen* of *goddesses.*
4. *Cicero* was a great *orator* in the *senate.*

Now see whether your list tallies with this: *men,* nominative; *wine,* accusative; *vats,* ablative; *Helen's,* genitive; *sister,* nominative; *Mark,* dative ("to" is understood); *letter,* accusative; *Venus,* vocative; *queen,* nominative; *goddesses,* genitive; *Cicero,* nominative; *orator,* nominative; *senate,* ablative.

In English, as we have mentioned before, the form of a noun changes only in the plural and possessive (genitive), and other relations are indicated by prepositions. There are prepositions in Latin, too, but often they are omitted and their presence indicated only by a case ending. Every Latin noun has a stem, or base, as it is sometimes called, and an ending which, as we have seen, is subject to change according to the use of the word in the sentence. To *decline* a noun is to give all its possible forms in a regular order, both in the singular and the plural. These forms, when grouped together, are called *declensions.*

Nouns of the First Declension end in *a* in the nominative case and *ae* in the genitive, and they are all feminine except a few which are obviously masculine in meaning, such as *agricola,* the word for "farmer." This means that whenever you see a word ending in *a* in a vocabulary list, you know that it shares the same endings as all other nouns of the First Declension. The regular declension for these nouns ending in *a* is as follows:

First Declension

PUELLA, AE,—fem., a girl.

Cases	Singular		Endings	Plural		Endings
Nom.	*puella*	a girl	*-a*	*puellae*	girls	*-ae*

Cases	Singular		Endings	Plural		Endings
Gen.	*puellae*	of a girl	-ae	*puellarum*	of girls	-arum
Dat.	*puellae*	to a girl	-ae	*puellis*	to girls	-is
Acc.	*puellam*	a girl	-am	*puellas*	girls	-as
Abl.	*puella*	by or with a girl	-a	*puellis*	by or with girls	-is

The stem is found by dropping the *ae* of the genitive case. *Puell-* is therefore the stem of *puella*. When words are listed in the vocabularies, the genitive is always given to indicate the stem, since it is to the stem that the special case endings are attached. Some of the more familiar words belonging to the First or *A* Declension are: *agricola,* farmer; *aqua,* water; *Gallia,* Gaul; *terra,* land, earth; *tuba,* trumpet; *provincia,* province; *littera,* letter (of alphabet); *litterae* (plural form of *littera*), epistle; *fuga,* flight; *luna,* moon; and *nauta,* sailor.

Now the relationship between English and Latin words can readily be seen. What Latin words do the following suggest: aquatic, territory, provincial, literal, fugitive, agriculture, lunar, and nautical? You can see how our familiarity with these English words will help us to recognize their Latin cousins at sight, perhaps without ever having seen them before. For instance, if we see the word *copia* in a Latin sentence and have never met with it before, its meaning can be discovered with a little mental agility. What English word does *copia* suggest? "Copious," of course. Another word for "copious" in English is "plentiful," and so we are not surprised to learn that the noun *copia* actually means abundance or plenty.

By taking the stems of these new words and adding the endings of the First Declension to which they all belong, it is possible to decline them in their different forms, bearing in mind their various meanings. See if you are able to translate these nouns: *nautarum, Gallia, luna, fugae* (in three ways), *tubis* (in two ways), *provinciam, agricolas*. Remember there are no Latin words for "a," "an," or "the." They are "understood," meaning that although they are not expressed in Latin, they are translated in English. *Luna* is "a" moon or "the" moon, according to the context. Try now to translate the following English forms into their proper Latin equivalents: with the sailors, of Gaul, in the letters, flight (accusative), the provinces (accusative), of a moon, for the farmer, with a trumpet, to the earth. In order to find out whether your translations are correct, merely consult the case endings and meanings as they are listed in the table of the First Declension above.

VERB FORMS

Before we can attempt to translate even one whole simple sentence, we must investigate Latin verb forms. In English, we precede our verb forms with personal pronouns: *I, thou* or *you, he, she, we, you* (plural), and *they*. In Latin these pronoun subjects are not expressed, but are indicated by the endings as follows:

	Singular	*English*	*Plural*	*English*
1st Person	*-o* or *-m*	I	*-mus*	we
2nd Person	*-s*	you or thou	*-tis*	you (plural)
3rd Person	*-t*	he, she, or it	*-nt*	they

Note: Nouns are usually in the 3rd person.

FIRST CONJUGATION

All verbs whose infinitives end in *-are* belong to the First Conjugation, and their present active tenses are as follows:

AMARE, to love. Stem: AM-; Conjugation vowel, A.

Present Indicative Active

amo	I love	*amamus*	we love
amas	you love	*amatis*	you love
amat	he, she, or it loves	*amant*	they love

Amo also means, "I am loving" and "I do love." By this time you must have recognized the relationship between the Latin word meaning "to love" and the English "amatory," meaning "loving."

In order to read Latin easily, it is important to have a wide vocabulary. Only a few words can be included in this Latin section, but if you learn them, you will have a good framework on which to build a more complete vocabulary. Verbs of the First Conjugation which are often met with include: *laudare,* to praise; *narrare,* to relate or tell; *portare,* to carry; *pugnare,* to fight; *parare,* to prepare; *appellare,* to name; *sonare,* to sound; *liberare,* to set free; *aedificare,* to build; *laborare,* to work; and *monstrare,* to show. Knowing these, you can easily perceive the origin of the following English words: sonorous, laudatory, narrate, portable, pugnacious, demonstrate, edifice, and labor. If some of these

English words have not been a part of your vocabulary up to date, this is an excellent time to start using them in conversation, which will help fasten their Latin prototypes in your memory.

Now that you are acquainted with one declension and one tense of a conjugation, a few short sentences may be attempted. Remember that the subject of a verb is in the nominative case, and that its object is in the accusative. Also be sure that the verb agrees with its subject in number. If only one farmer loves, the verb ending will be *-t,* but if more than one farmer loves, the ending of the verb will be *-nt.* It is a Latin convention that the verb is generally placed at the very end of the sentence irrespective of where it occurs in its English equivalent. Translate the following into English: Puella nautam amat; Tubae sonant; Fabulam narro; Patriam amamus; Nautae aquam portant; Agricola puellam laudat. If you have noticed carefully, you will see that in the third sentence there is a word whose meaning you have not been told. Ignoring the ending, which we have learned is subject to change, we have *fabul-.* In spite of the difference in spelling, we recognize a relative of the English "fable." To see whether our deduction is correct, we have only to check up its sense with the main verb. "I am relating a story." That is certainly good English. There is another word which is even more closely connected with the Latin form: "fabulous." When we speak of a fabulous tale, we mean one that has been made up—one that is difficult to believe; in other words, one that is more imaginative than historical.

In order to ask a question in Latin, it is customary to add the letters *ne* to the emphatic word, which usually is placed first. Unfortunately there are no short words which correspond to our "yes" and "no." In replying, it is necessary to repeat the whole sentence in the affirmative, or, if the negative is desired, the whole sentence is repeated with *non,* not, placed directly before the verb. *Amasne patriam?* obviously means, "Do you love your fatherland?" *Amo patriam* would be the affirmative answer to this query, and *Non amo patriam* or *Patriam non amo* would be the negative reply. When the *non* is placed first, it indicates a decided negation, like our slang expression, "I should say I don't love my fatherland." For practice answer the following questions: *Laborasne? Puellae lunam monstrasne? Tubam sonasne? Portasne agricolae aquam?* If you have translated these correctly, you have recognized the dative case in *puellae* and *agricolae.* The second sentence reads, "Are you pointing out the moon to the girl?" and the third reads, "Are you carrying water to the farmer?" Notice that indirect objects in the dative case are always placed before the direct object, contrary to our English custom.

LESSON II

SECOND DECLENSION

We have learned that the First Declension can be distinguished by the genitive case-ending *-ae*. The genitive singular is always the key to the five declensions of nouns. The Second Declension has nouns ending in *-i* in this case. In the nominative singular, they end either in *-us, -er, -ir,* or *-um*. They are all masculine except the ones ending in *-um,* which are neuter. Learn the following declensions carefully ("m." indicates the masculine gender; "n.," the neuter.)

NUNTIUS, m., messenger.   PUER, m., boy.   AGER, m., field.

Singular

Nom.	nuntius	puer	ager
Gen.	nunti	pueri	agri
Dat.	nuntio	puero	agro
Acc.	nuntium	puerum	agrum
Abl.	nuntio	puero	agro

Plural

Nom.	nuntii	pueri	agri
Gen.	nuntiorum	puerorum	agrorum
Dat.	nuntiis	pueris	agris
Acc.	nuntios	pueros	agros
Abl.	nuntiis	pueris	agris

VIR, m., man.   BELLUM, n., war.

Singular

Nom.	vir	bellum
Gen.	viri	belli
Dat.	viro	bello
Acc.	virum	bellum
Abl.	viro	bello

Plural

Nom.	viri	bella
Gen.	virorum	bellorum
Dat.	viris	bellis

| Acc. | *viros* | *bella* |
| Abl. | *viris* | *bellis* |

By separating the endings from the stems, we find *-us* (*-er, -ir*), *-i, -o,* *-um, -o* in the singular, and *-i, -orum, -is, -os, -is* in the plural of the masculine nouns of the Second Declension. The neuter endings differ only in the nominative singular where *-um* replaces *-us,* and in the nominative and accusative plural, which both end in *-a.* So you can see that neuter nouns, whether in the nominative or accusative, have the same endings in the singular. Note carefully, however, that in the plural they all end in *-a* in the nominative and accusative, regardless of declension, as you will see when you study the third and fourth declensions. This naturally causes some confusion in translation, which, however, is readily straightened out by trying the neuter noun first as the subject and then as the object of the verb, selecting as your final choice the case which makes sense. For instance, *Nautae bellum amant* obviously means: "Sailors love war," and *bellum* is recognized as an accusative. Any doubts as to whether it should be classed as a nominative are removed when we attempt to translate the sentence: "War loves sailors." Do you see that, besides not making sense, this translation would be erroneous because "sailors" is evidently not in the accusative case and could therefore not be the object of the verb? Observing the *-nt* ending of the verb, we see that its subject must be plural, which is one way of immediately eliminating *bellum,* whose plural would have to be *bella.* In addition to these many case signs, accurate translation, particularly of simple sentences, is partially assured by the word order. A subject usually comes before its object. Notice that nouns of the second declension ending in *-ius* and *-ium* form their genitive singular in *-i* instead of *-ii,* which would be difficult to indicate by pronunciation.

The following nouns (each followed by the genitive singular) belong to the Second Declension, which you will meet with frequently in your reading; *amicus, -i,* friend; *equus, equi,* horse; *murus, -i,* wall; *annus, -i,* year; *legatus, -i,* ambassador or lieutenant; *liber, libri,* book; *oppidum, -i,* town; *frumentum, -i,* grain; *periculum, -i,* danger; and *telum, -i,* weapon. Which of these Latin words are the ancestors of the following: legation, mural, library, virile, equine, amicable, annual, and bellicose?

You have been shown that the First Conjugation verbs can be distinguished by the *-are* of their infinitive ending, and you are to learn a little later that there are other regular conjugations which can be recognized by their infinitives. However, some verbs are called "irregular." This means that we are not able to learn a set list of endings for all their cases, because they are strictly individual and must be learned by themselves. Usually irregular verbs are those which are used most often in speech, such as "to be," "to go," and "to be able." For the time being it will serve our purpose to learn only the Present Indicative of the verb "to be," whose infinitive form is *esse,* as follows:

Singular		*Plural*	
sum	I am	*sumus*	we are
es	thou art (you are)	*estis*	you are
est	he, she, it is	*sunt*	they are

Apparently the forms which we have been rehearsing have little practical value and seem disconnected, and yet, if you try, you will find that you are already able to translate fairly complicated Latin sentences into English. *Amicus nautae agricola est* becomes "The sailor's friend is a farmer" just as quickly as our eyes are able to read the Latin. Read the following sentences, referring to declensions and conjugations only when you are unable to get the meaning after a few minutes of intelligent observation: *Puella memoriam pueri laudat; Patria viri Gallia est; Nuntii legatis litteras portant; Sumus amici agricolae.* Even though you had never seen the noun *memoriam* before, its close relation to the English must have hinted that its meaning is "memory," and the sentence reads: "The girl praises the boy's memory." The second is simply, "The man's fatherland is Gaul." In the third we again come upon the dative, or perhaps it might be the ablative, in *legatis.* The translation might read: "The messengers are carrying letters *with* the ambassadors," or *"to* the ambassadors." Since our common sense tells us that if the ambassadors were along they would not need messengers also, we decide in favor of the "to the ambassadors" with little hesitation. "We are friends of the farmer" is the simple statement made in the fourth sentence.

Ask the following questions of yourself and answer them in good Latin, remembering that the whole question must be repeated to say, "Yes," and that to say "No" the whole question must be reiterated with *non* placed directly before the verb: *Sonantne tubas legati? Amici sumusne? Esne amicus puellae? Aedificantne legati oppidum?*

ADJECTIVES

Latin adjectives—those descriptive words without which any language would be drab indeed—are declined like nouns, and, in order to agree with the nouns which they modify in gender, they have a masculine, feminine, and neuter form. Adjectives of the First and Second Declensions have feminine forms like nouns of the First Declension, and masculine and neuter forms like masculine and neuter nouns of the Second Declension, as follows:

BONUS, -A, -UM, good or kind. Stem: BON-

Singular

Masculine	Feminine	Neuter
Nom. *bonus*	*bona*	*bonum*
Gen. *boni*	*bonae*	*boni*
Dat. *bono*	*bonae*	*bono*
Acc. *bonum*	*bonam*	*bonum*
Abl. *bono*	*bona*	*bono*

Plural

Masculine	Feminine	Neuter
Nom. *boni*	*bonae*	*bona*
Gen. *bonorum*	*bonarum*	*bonorum*
Dat. *bonis*	*bonis*	*bonis*
Acc. *bonos*	*bonas*	*bona*
Abl. *bonis*	*bonis*	*bonis*

An adjective agrees with its noun in gender, number, and case whether it is directly attached to the noun or appears in the predicate describing a noun that is the subject of the verb "to be." *Puella parva est,* "The girl is small," illustrates the agreement of the adjective "small." If we were to translate "small" from English into Latin in this sentence, we would first ask ourselves these questions about the noun which it modifies: Is it singular? Yes. Is it masculine, feminine, or neuter? It is a noun of the First Declension ending in -*a*, which is not obviously masculine, so it must be feminine. What is the case of *puella*? It is in the nominative case because it is the subject of the sentence. Having found out the gender, number, and case of *puella,* we have only to consider the adjective *parvus, -a, -um.* The endings of the noun and the adjective are here identical, but this need not always be true. We have already learned that, although *agricola* belongs to the First Declension, it is nevertheless masculine because of its meaning; therefore, in translating "The farmers are good," we write *Agricolae boni sunt,* using the masculine plural nominative form instead of the feminine plural nominative form, which would be *bonae* to correspond to *agricolae.*

Commit to memory some of the following common adjectives: *magnus, -a, -um,* great, large; *parvus, -a, -um,* small, little; *multus, -a, -um,* much (plural, many); *longus, -a, -um,* long, tall; *altus, -a, -um,* high, deep, tall; *malus, -a, -um,* bad; *carus, -a, -um,* dear; *latus, -a, -um,* broad, wide; and *novus, -a, -um,* new.

With the aid of these new words, you should now be able to understand the following: *Puella longas litteras pueri parvi laudat; Multi viri oppidum magnum aedificant; Tuba magna nautae alti nova est.* The phrase *nautae alti* illustrates how the masculine gender of *nauta* must be determined from its descriptive adjective. Many English words must have suggested themselves to you in reading this new vocabulary, such as magnate, altitude, latitude, novel, malignant, and innovate.

LESSON III

IMPERFECT INDICATIVE TENSE

We have already seen how verbs of the First Conjugation ending in *-are* are conjugated in the Present Tense. Now observe how the Imperfect Indicative, expressing continuous action in the past, is formed by adding to the present stem the tense sign *-ba-* plus the personal endings, as follows:

Imperfect Indicative

amabam	I was loving	*amabamus*	we were loving
amabas	you were loving	*amabatis*	you were loving
amabat	he was loving	*amabant*	they were loving

The Future Indicative is formed from the Present stem plus the tense sign *-bi-* plus the personal endings. The *i* is dropped before the *-o* of the first person singular, and before the *-nt* of the third person plural it becomes *u,* as follows:

Future Indicative

amabo	I shall love	*amabimus*	we shall love
amabis	you will love	*amabitis*	you will love
amabit	he will love	*amabunt*	they will love

In vocabulary lists verb forms, or "principal parts," are given. If the verb is regular, you will be able to construct all the tenses from the four principal parts, which are the first person singular of the present indicative; the present infinitive; the perfect indicative; and the perfect participle. For instance, the principal parts of the verb "to love" are *amo, amare, amavi, amatus.* Regular verbs of the First Conjugation form their principal parts all in the same way, as *celo, celare, celavi, celatus,* to conceal; *servo, servare, servavi, servatus,* to save; *convoco, convocare, convocavi, convocatus,* to call together; *supero, superare, superavi, superatus,* to defeat or to surpass; *vulnero, vulnerare, vulneravi, vulneratus,* to wound. From three of these come the English words: convocation, superior, vulnerable.

In order to learn the use of the Present, Imperfect, and the Future Indicative tenses, translate the following: *vocatis, amat, vulnerabamus, servabat, narrabam, pugnant, convocabunt, superabatis, laudamus, sumus.* Let us try *vulnerabamus.* First we must find the stem, which we do by omitting the ending *-are* from the Present Infinitive, leaving *vulner-.* The tense sign is *-abamus;* by checking with our conjugation of the Imperfect we find it to be the First Person Plural of the Imperfect Indicative.

Translate these sentences: *Portabam picturas; Amabat puellam; Viri magni pugnabunt.* You will have translated the first sentence, "I was carrying the pictures." To express "for whom" or "to whom" in Latin we use the *Dative* case. If the sentence reads, "I was carrying the pictures to the farmer," the Latin is *Picturas agricolae portabam. Legatus nuntio signum dat* is translated, "The lieutenant gives a signal to the messenger." Translate: *Diligentia pueri est magna; Boni servi sumus; Puer puellae pulchram picturam dabat.*

Further forms of *esse,* to be, are as follows:

Imperfect Indicative

Singular		Plural	
eram	I was	*eramus*	we were
eras	you were	*eratis*	you were
erat	he, she, it was	*erant*	they were

Future Indicative

Singular		Plural	
ero	I shall be	*erimus*	we shall be
eris	you will be	*eritis*	you will be
erit	he will be	*erunt*	they will be

Do you understand the following sentences easily? If so, you have mastered quite a bit of Latin already. If not, you should review the preceding pages.

AN INTRODUCTION TO LATIN

688 AN INTRODUCTION TO LATIN

Malus dominus eris. Equus niger viri in silva est. Libri magistri erant pulchri. Servi miseri dominos malos non amant. Servae fidae dominam caram amabant.

The Ablative (or the 5th Case) is used to express the means or the instrument without a preposition. *Pilis pugnant.* (They fight with javelins.) *Servus gladio dominum vulnerat.* (The servant wounds the master with a sword.) Add the following words to your vocabulary: *castra, -orum;* neuter plural, camp; *niger,* black; *pilum,* javelin; *malus,* bad; *hiemo, hiemare, hiemavi, hiematus,* to pass the winter; *filia,* daughter; *pulcher, pulchra, pulchrum,* beautiful.

When the word *nonne* or *num* precedes a question, an affirmative answer is expected. In speeches, several such questions are sometimes asked one after another, for the rhetorical effect on the hearers. The great orator Cicero often made use of these "rhetorical questions." *Num in casa nostra viri liberi sumus?* (Are we not free men [even] in our own house?) *Nonne servi fidi sunt?* (Are the slaves not faithful?)

The Latin Perfect tense describes action as completed at the present time. It also describes the action of the English Simple Past. To find the stem, drop the *-i* from the Perfect Indicative Active, *amavi;* stem *amav-*. The singular endings are *-i, -isti, -it;* and the plural, *-imus, -istis, -erunt*.

The Pluperfect or Past Perfect represents an action as having been completed before some past action. Find the stem, add the sign of the Pluperfect tense, *-era,* and then add the regular personal endings.

The Future Perfect tense represents an action as taking place before some definite time in the future. To the stem, add the tense sign *-eri* plus the regular personal endings.

AMARE, *to love*

Perfect Indicative Active		*Pluperfect Indicative Active*	
amavi	I have loved or I loved	amaveram	I had loved
amavis	you have loved	amaveras	you had loved
amavit	he has loved	amaverat	he had loved
amavimus	we have loved	amaveramus	we had loved
amavistis	you have loved	amaveratis	you had loved
amaverunt	they have loved	amaverant	they had loved

Future Perfect Indicative Active

amavero	I shall have loved
amaveris	you will have loved
amaverit	he will have loved

amaverimus	we shall have loved
amaveritis	you will have loved
amaverint	they will have loved

ESSE, *to be*

Perfect		Pluperfect	
fui	I was, I have been	*fueram*	I had been
fuisti	you have been	*fueras*	you had been
fuit	he has been	*fuerat*	he had been
fuimus	we have been	*fueramus*	we had been
fuistis	you have been	*fueratis*	you had been
fuerunt	they have been	*fuerant*	they had been

Future Perfect

fuero	I shall have been
fueris	you will have been
fuerit	he will have been
fuerimus	we shall have been
fueristis	you will have been
fuerint	they will have been

Analyze the following verb forms: *occupavi; paraverint; pugnavisti; fuerat; amaverunt; eritis; fueristis; vocabo; laudamus; dant.*

To express place, we generally use the following prepositions:

> *in,* with the ablative, for the place "in" or "on" which
> *a* or *ab,* with the ablative, for the place "from" which
> *e* or *ex,* with the ablative, for the place "out of" which
> *in,* with the accusative, for the place "into" which
> *ad,* with the accusative, for the place "to" which

Note that the ablative denotes a permanent condition, or rest, while the accusative denotes a transient condition, or change. This makes it simple to understand *ad murum,* to the wall; *in agris,* on the fields; *ex provincia,* from the province; *ad astras,* to the stars; *ad silvas,* to the woods. Translate into Latin: into the ditch, on the land, in the water, from the house.

You should be able to read quite a little Latin now. *Translate:* Dominus servos e provinciis convocaverit. In castris puellam pulchram servaveras. Vir filiis filiabusque copiam librorum dedit (-*que means "and"; it is affixed where there is an enumeration*). Filia agricolae ad magistrum libros multos et magnos portavit. Servus domino caro numerum magnum pilorum et gladiorum dederat.

REVIEW

Repeat the First Declension. Do you remember what gender First Declension nouns usually are?

What is an *Ablative?* A *Dative?* An *Accusative?*

Where in the sentence do we place the Latin verb? Build up a simple Latin sentence.

Conjugate the Present Indicative Active of *amo;* of *esse.*

Words belonging to the Second Declension generally are masculine or neuter. Decline a noun of each gender.

Sentences are not answered in Latin with either "yes" or "no," but by repeating the whole sentence. Use *ne, num,* and *nonne* correctly in asking questions.

An adjective agrees with its noun in gender, number, and case. Use the word *parvus,* small, with a masculine, a feminine, and a neuter noun, both in the singular and plural. Make *parvus* modify each of the following words: *agricola, filius, femina, bellum, tuba, hortus, pilum.*

Write all the English words you can think of which are derived from these Latin words: *fidus, magnus, magister, porto, longus, signum, numerus, terra, multus.*

Decline, conjugate, and translate: provincia, -ae; luna, -ae; nauta, -ae; tuba, -ae; laudo, -are; paro, -are; monstro, -are; annus, -i; liber, libri; frumentum, -i; magnus, -a, -um; carus, -a, -um; altus, -a, -um; celo, -are; supero, -are; niger, nigra, nigrum; hiemo, -are; copia, -ae; convoco, -are.

Give the Latin Nominative and the Genitive singular and the gender of these words: book, daughter, trumpet, messenger, signal, war, story, horse, native land.

Repeat the tenses of *amo* and *esse* through the Perfect Indicative Active forms.

Translate these sentences at sight: *Puellae donum dabis. Equus albus est in agro agricolae. Erimus boni amici magistri. Legati a muro copias vocaverunt.*

Try to translate the following little story, referring to the English rendering below only when you are unable to proceed:

CAROLUS ET POMA

Carolus agricolae filius erat et bonus puer sed malos amicos habebat. Agricola filio calathum pomorum plenum dedit. In calatho erant multa et bona poma sed pauca vitiata.

Puer calathum celavit sed vitiata poma maculaverunt bona, et mox nulla bona erant. Tum agricola filium monuit: "Pauca vitiata poma maculant multa bona. Sic mali amici bonos pueros vitiabunt."

CHARLES AND THE APPLES

Charles was the son of a farmer and a good boy, but he had bad friends. The farmer gave his son a basket filled with apples. In the basket were many good apples, but a few bad ones.

The lad concealed the basket, but the spoiled apples tainted the good ones, and soon none were good. Then the farmer admonished his son: "A few tainted apples spoil many good ones. In the same manner bad friends will bring good boys to ruin."

LESSON IV

It will probably interest the student to learn what many of our everyday abbreviations stand for, and we here list a few of the more common ones:

A.D.	—*Anno Domini*—	In the year of Our Lord
Aet.	—*Aetatis*—	The age of
A.M.	—*Ante Meridiem*—	Before noon
	Artium Magister—	Master of Arts
etc.	—*et cetera*—	and so on
i.e.	—*id est*—	that is
I.H.S.	—*In hoc signo*—	In this sign
I.N.R.I.	—*Iesus Nazarenus Rex*	
	Iudaeorum—	Jesus Nazarene, King of the Jews
P.M.	—*Post Meridiem*—	After noon
	—*Post Mortem*—	After death
P.S.	—*Post Scriptum*—	After writing
S.P.Q.R.	—*Senatus Populusque*	The senate and the people of Rome
	Romanus—	

Here follow a few everyday quotations. If you learn these by heart and, whenever a suitable occasion presents itself, are able to use one or two, you can give the impression a great deal more readily of having enjoyed the advantages of a classical education.

> *Carpe diem.*—Seize the opportunity. HORACE.
> *Literally,* Pluck the day.
> *Alea iacta est.*—The die is cast. CAESAR.
> *Docendo discitur.*—We learn by teaching. SENECA.

Festina lente.—Make haste slowly. AUGUSTUS.
Rara avis.—A rare bird. HORACE.
Omnia mutantur.—All things change. OVID.
Semper idem.—Always the same. CICERO.
O tempora, O mores.—Oh, the times, oh, the customs.
CICERO.

THIRD DECLENSION

We are now proceeding with our regular work, and shall begin by examining the large group of words belonging to the Third Declension. Unlike the First and Second Declensions, the words belonging to the Third may be either masculine, feminine, or neuter. All words whose Genitive singular ends in *-is* belong to the Third Declension.

Very frequently the Nominative and the stem of the noun are the same in Third Declension words. The terminations vary slightly from the First and Second Declensions and should be committed to heart. Nominative has various endings—*s, l, n;* genitive—*is;* dative—*i;* accusative—*em;* ablative—*e.* The plural runs as follows: nominative—*es;* genitive—*um;* dative—*ibus;* accusative—*es;* ablative—*ibus.* There is no difference between the declension of masculine and feminine words. Here follow two examples:

VICTOR, *victor*	SOROR, *sister*
Stem: VICTOR	Stem: SOROR

Singular		*Singular*	
Nom.	*victor*	Nom.	*soror*
Gen.	*victoris*	Gen.	*sororis*
Dat.	*victori*	Dat.	*sorori*
Acc.	*victorem*	Acc.	*sororem*
Abl.	*victore*	Abl.	*sorore*

Plural		*Plural*	
Nom.	*victores*	Nom.	*sorores*
Gen.	*victorum*	Gen.	*sororum*
Dat.	*victoribus*	Dat.	*sororibus*
Acc.	*victores*	Acc.	*sorores*
Abl.	*victoribus*	Abl.	*sororibus*

The following words are much used, and you must decline them carefully, so that the case endings will become just as familiar as the First and Second Declensions. Also study their meanings; you will find that a great many resemble English words closely.

arbor, -oris, tree	*aedifico, -are, -avi, -atus,* to build
explorator, -oris, explorer	*vastro, -are, -avi, -atus,* to lay waste
imperator, -oris, general	*monstro, -are, -avi, -atus,* to show
mercator, -oris, merchant	*latus, -a, -um,* broad, wide
quis, who	*ubi,* where, when

What Latin words do the following English words suggest?—"sorority," "edifice," "feminine," "arbor."

"To parse" a noun means listing, first, its declension; second, its nominative and genitive singular; third, its gender; fourth, its number; fifth, its case; sixth, the rule, why it is in that particular case. In the sentence: *Victores murum altum aedificabunt,* if we parse *murum,* we find:

Murum, second declension, *murus, muri;* masculine gender, singular number, accusative case (it is being erected), direct object of the verb *aedificabunt.*

Translate these sentences, and parse the nouns: *Amici mercatorum agros multos et latos vastabant. Magister sorori parvae pulchrum librum monstravit. In silva multae et magnae arbores fuerunt. Dominus ad feminam bonam dona pulchra portaverit.*

The reason for exercising your mind on these declensions and parsing is really the same as physical exercising. By doing it over and over, we become subconsciously acquainted with the various forms the words change to, and then when we read, our mind unconsciously places them in their right relation. The more you do it, the easier it becomes.

INTERROGATIVE PRONOUNS

When we have a question which cannot readily be answered by yes or no, we use an "interrogative" pronoun. An "interrogative" pronoun asks a question, "who," "which," "what." We also use an "adverb." An "adverb" of interrogation asks a question with reference to *time, place, manner,* or *reason.* "When" shall we go? "Where" do we go? "How" shall we go? "Why" shall we go?

You have just learned the adverb of place *ubi,* "where," and the interrogative pronoun *quis,* "who." In those questions we do not use the little word *ne.* A few sentences will illustrate this: *Quis es?* Who are you? *Ubi soror pueri erat?* Where was the sister of the boy?

In many nouns of the Third Declension the nominative differs very little from the stem. Remember we find the stem by using the Genitive less *is*. Usually these differences are for reasons of "phonetics," or what one might call "good sound." Latin is a "euphonious," or clear and melodious, language, and that is why consonants change so often. We do it in English and are hardly aware of it; of course the Romans were not aware of it in their everyday life either. We say, "an apple," simply because "a apple" does not sound well. A great deal of slang is an attempt at modeling the language into "rounded" sounds, and where such slang becomes universal, it finally is adopted as part of the language. "Can not" has become "can't"; "is not," "isn't," in everyday speech.

MILES, m. *soldier*	DUX, m. *leader*	FRATER, m. *brother*
Stem: MILIT-	Stem: DUC-	Stem: FRATR-

Singular

Nom.	*miles*	*dux*	*frater*
Gen.	*militis*	*ducis*	*fratris*
Dat.	*militi*	*duci*	*fratri*
Acc.	*militem*	*ducem*	*fratrem*
Abl.	*milite*	*duce*	*fratre*

Plural

Nom.	*milites*	*duces*	*fratres*
Gen.	*militum*	*ducum*	*fratrum*
Dat.	*militibus*	*ducibus*	*fratribus*
Acc.	*milites*	*duces*	*fratres*
Abl.	*militibus*	*ducibus*	*fratribus*

Several words which are frequently met with follow. You will know their meaning from English words in many cases.

iudex, -icis, judge

lapis, -idis, stone

liberi, -orum, m. children

pater, -tris, m. father

telum, -i, weapon

caput, -itis, n. head

comes, -itis, m. companion

rex, regis, m. king

pes, pedis, m. foot

quid? (inter. pron.), what?

clamor, -oris, shout, noise

oppugno, -are, -avi, -atus, to attack

decimus, -a, -um, tenth

circum, preposition with accusative, around

cum, preposition with ablative, with

Don't get mixed up in these words; they resemble each other very much, and are very simple:

libero, -are, -avi, -atus—to set free (verb)
liber, -era, -erum—free (adjective)
liberi, -orum—free-born children (noun). This noun is called
   plurale tantum, because several are used as one.
liber, libri—book

The English words "liberate," "liberty," "library," "librarian," recall these Latin words.

What Latin words do these English words suggest?—"judicial," "fraternity," "decimal," "paternal."

To express "accompaniment," in company with, or in conflict with, we use *cum* and the Ablative case.

Puer cum patre est.	The boy is with his father.
Caesar cum Gallis pugnavit.	Caesar fought with the Gauls.

Translate these English sentences into Latin: The general and his children are good friends. The girl was with her brother in the native land of the Gauls. Caesar gives a signal to his faithful soldiers. The judge's mother and sister were unhappy.

Analyze and parse each English word first, recite your declensions, and then write them. You will have very little difficulty if you have memorized the various lessons well.

The translation follows here. Do not make use of it until you are through with your own. *Dux cum liberis boni sunt amici. Puella cum fratre in patria Gallorum erat. Caesar signum fidis militibus dat. Iudicis mater et soror miserae erant.*

After this the translation of the following Latin sentences will cause no trouble:

Malus vir lapide militem vulneravit. Caesar tuba decimae legioni victoriam nuntiavit. Liberi iudicis patri tela monstrabunt. Duces cum multis militibus oppida magna oppugnaverant. Dux cum fratre erat.

The declension of neuters belonging to the Third Declension varies from masculine and feminine words, in that the Nominatives and Accusatives Singular and Plural respectively agree. This follows the same rule with other words as it did in the Second Declension.

We shall give you a typical example:

CAPUT, n. *head*	FLUMEN, n. *river*	CORPUS, n. *body*
Stem: CAPIT-	Stem: FLUMIN-	Stem: CORPOR-

Singular

Nom. *caput*	*flumen*	*corpus*
Gen. *capitis*	*fluminis*	*corporis*

Dat.	*capiti*	*flumini*	*corpori*
Acc.	*caput*	*flumen*	*corpus*
Abl.	*capite*	*flumine*	*corpore*

Plural

Nom.	*capita*	*flumina*	*corpora*
Gen.	*capitum*	*fluminum*	*corporum*
Dat.	*capitibus*	*fluminibus*	*corporibus*
Acc.	*capita*	*flumina*	*corpora*
Abl.	*capitibus*	*fluminibus*	*corporibus*

With these new declensions you can understand the saying: *Mens sana in corpore sano.* "A sound mind in a sound body."

Also, the English expressions "capital punishment," "corporate action," take on new meaning.

LESSON V

We have become well acquainted with the three declensions now, and shall continue to analyze verbs. They are divided into four classes, called conjugations, which really follow the declensions of nouns rather closely as to their stem. An example of each follows:

	Present Indicative	Present Infinitive	Perfect Indicative	Perfect Participle	Stem Vowel
1st	*amo*	*amare*	*amavi*	*amatus*	*a*
2nd	*deleo*	*delere*	*delevi*	*deletus*	*e*
3rd	*duco*	*ducere*	*duxi*	*ductus*	*e*
4th	*audio*	*audire*	*audivi*	*auditus*	*i*

The same rules as to stem, tense sign, and personal endings are followed when forming the various Indicative tenses in the second conjugation as in the first. That is why it is important to know the first one thoroughly; the latter ones follow very easily. Here follows the typical conjugation of a verb of the Second Conjugation:

DELEO, *I ruin, break off*
Stem: DELE

Indicative Active

| *Present* | *Perfect* |
| I ruin | I have ruined |

deleo	*delemus*	*delevi*	*delevimus*
deles	*deletis*	*delevisti*	*delevistis*
delet	*delent*	*delevit*	*deleverunt*

	Imperfect I was ruining		**Pluperfect** I had ruined
delebam	*delebamus*	*deleveram*	*deleveramus*
delebas	*delebatis*	*deleveras*	*deleveratis*
delebat	*delebant*	*deleverat*	*deleverant*

	Future I shall ruin		**Future Perfect** I shall have ruined
delebo	*delebimus*	*delevero*	*deleverimus*
delebis	*delebitis*	*deleveris*	*deleveritis*
delebit	*delebunt*	*deleverit*	*deleverint*

A number of verbs which are conjugated in the same manner follow:

habeo, -ere, -ui, -itus—to have, to hold
moneo, -ere, -ui, -itus—to warn, to advise
moveo, -ere, -i, -tus—to move
teneo, -ere, -ui, . . . —to hold
timeo, -ere, -ui, . . . —to fear
video, -ere, vidi, visus, . . . —to see

You can easily pick the Latin words out of English ones such as "tenacious," "homicide," "timid," and "admonish."

Test your knowledge of the verb forms on the following: *habuit, deleverunt, videmus, portavit, vastas, tenuisti, timebo, deleveratis, videt, vidit.*

Here are a few English sentences; translate them into Latin. It is a good idea to make up some more sentences yourself; this section is too limited to permit us to give you many. "We have feared the enemy." "He has loved the girl." "He saw the river." "He feared the noise of the companion."

When we desire to express the manner in which a certain task was performed, or the quality of a certain person, place, or object, we mostly use the ablative with *cum*, letting the adjective describe the object. An example will serve: "With many tears he advised me to be careful." *Multis cum lacrimis me monuit timere.* "Julius was a boy with a slow mind." *Julius erat puer cum animo tardo.* "He writes with great care." *Magna cum diligentia scribit.*

Translate the following sentences from English into Latin: The good teacher will advise the brother and sister. The judge and the king have been in the small town. The children feared the man's companion. We fought with bad men, but were not the victors.

Here follows an exercise which you should conduct very carefully yourself, and pronounce the words aloud. We take this occasion to advise you to do a great deal of your studying aloud. You will find that you can remember your conjugations much more easily; the sound of your own voice carries you through. Also the fact that you pronounce the words in full makes them remain in your consciousness.

Here are a few Latin questions; read them and answer them in Latin: Quid vidisti? Suntne magni lapides in flumine? Timesne clamorem hominum? Num duces castra moverunt? Quis habet magnum caput?

To conclude this lesson, here are a few Latin sentences; read them several times and then try to translate them at sight:

Rex magnum flumen in silva vidit. Niger equus corpus magnum sed caput parvum habet. Milites maxima cum diligentia oppidum servaverunt. Filius regis bonos comites habebit. Homines castra moverint.

Do your best to translate this without help of the translation below, and if you do get caught, be certain that you carefully analyze the reasons why. Study the tense and the case of each verb and noun; we are certain that you should be able to do this without help. This is the English: The king saw a large river in the forest. The black horse has a large body but a small head. The soldiers saved the city with the greatest effort. The son of the king will have good companions. The men will have moved the camp.

LESSON VI

We noticed that in the First Declension *a* seemed the predominant vowel; in the Second Declension it was *o*. Therefore the First Declension often is spoken of as the *a* declension, the Second Declension as the *o* declension. Similarly we speak of the Third Declension as the *i* or Consonant Declension, because the "stem" ends either in a consonant or in *i*. We are now going to study those words whose stem is formed by adding *i* to the base. These are: 1st. The masculine and feminine nouns ending in *es* and *is* whose genitive has the same number of syllables as the nominative; in other words, those distinguished from words like *soror, sororis,* where a full syllable is added.

   2nd. Nouns ending in *-ns, -rs.*
   3rd. Nouns ending in *-s* or *-z* following a consonant.
   4th. Neuter nouns ending in *-e, -al,* or *-ar.*

Here follows the complete declension of such nouns, which will render the rules easier to understand:

| IGNIS, m. *fire* | HOSTIS, m. *enemy* | MARE, n. *sea* |
| Stem: IGNI- | Stem: HOSTI- | Stem: MARI- |

Singular

Nom.	*ignis*	*hostis*	*mare*
Gen.	*ignis*	*hostis*	*maris*
Dat.	*igni*	*hosti*	*mari*
Acc.	*ignem*	*hostem*	*mare*
Abl.	*igne* or *-i*	*hoste*	*mari*

Plural

Nom.	*ignes*	*hostes*	*maria*
Gen.	*ignium*	*hostium*	*marium*
Dat.	*ignibus*	*hostibus*	*maribus*
Acc.	*ignes* or *-is*	*hostes* or *-is*	*maria*
Abl.	*ignibus*	*hostibus*	*maribus*

We are adding a list of words; many will once more be familiar to you.

animal, -alis, -ium, n. animal
caedes, -is, -ium, f. slaughter
mons, montis, -ium, m. mountain
nox, noctis, -ium, f. night

pars, partis, -ium, f. part
porta, -ae, f. gate
ripa, -ae, f. embankment
urbs, urbis, -ium, f. city

You have heard about "riparian rights," "ignition sparks," "urban conditions," the "portal of the cathedral," "marine laws," "nocturnal prowlings." All these words will now have a great deal more meaning for you, and we hope that the study of Latin, as this little work presents it, will encourage you to make use of these frequently.

A. Can you translate the following sentences?

Ripae fluminis altae erant. Caput pars corporis est. Caesar cum hostibus saepe pugnavit. Agros ab urbe ad montem vastavit. Milites a portis urbis tela portabunt. Multa animalia fuerunt in mari.

B. And can you render these easily in Latin?—"The brother and sister of the general see the large rivers." "There have been many fires on the mountain." "The enemy will pass the winter in the city." "The soldiers announced their victory to Caesar with great shouts." "The little children had feared the large animals."

Here are the correct forms of these sentences:

A. The embankments of the river were high. The head is part of the body. Caesar often fought with the enemies. He has laid waste the fields from the city unto the mountain. The soldiers will bear the arms from the gates of the city. There were many animals in the sea.

B. Frater et soror ducis magna flumina vident. Multi ignes in monte fuerant. Hostis in urbe hiemabit. Milites magna cum clamore Caesari victoriam nuntiaverunt. Parvi liberi magna animalia timuerant.

We have now studied the nouns of the Third Declension, and shall review our work. If you find that you can do the review work without difficulty, you will know that you are progressing satisfactorily.

Write all the English words you know derived from *arbor, hostis, ignis, caput, frater, femina, homo, corpus, miles, urbs.*

Give the nominative, the genitive, and the gender in Latin of the following words: "gate," "light," "king," "mother," "tree," "soldier," "sea."

Give the Latin verbs in their four major tenses for the following English ones: "to move," "to give," "to announce," "to storm," "to seize," "to lay waste," "to warn."

Write a short Latin sentence containing an ablative of manner, of accompaniment, of means.

Decline the following nouns: *dux, lumen, mare, mater.*

Read the following sentences at sight: Puella feminae librum dat. Viri malum consulem non amaverant. Viri mali consulem non amaverant. Multi mercatores montes et mare videbunt. Serva a domina ad matrem dona pulchra portabat.

We will close our review with a short story; study this well before you look at the translation. If you are unable to bring the construction of either a noun or a verb to mind, then compare the forms with those listed and repeat the tables entirely.

EQUUS MARCI

Marcus puer sororem Iuliam habebat. Pater liberorum multos equos in agro habebat. Liberi equum nigrum amabant quem pater Marco dederat. Equus dominum parvum circum agrum et in silvam saepe portabat. Soror Marci magnos equos timebat sed Marcus ad equum frumentum portavit et ei aquam dedit. Mali pueri lapidibus animal pulchrum vulneraverant et mater liberorum magna cum diligentia equum celabat.

THE HORSE OF MARCUS

The boy Marcus had a sister Julia. The father of the children had many horses in his field. The children loved a black horse, which the father had given Marcus. Often the horse carried his small master around the field and into the forest. The sister of Marcus was afraid of the large horses, but Marcus carried grain to the horse and gave him water. Bad boys had wounded the beautiful animal with stones, and the mother of the children concealed the horse with great care.

LESSON VII

Everybody knows and has seen Roman numerals on churches, hospitals, state capitols, etc., stating the year in which the buildings were erected. This is still an almost universal practice.

	Cardinals			*Ordinals*
1	unus, -a, -um	I	1st	primus, -a, -um
2	duo, -ae, duo	II	2nd	secundus
3	tres, tria	III	3rd	tertius
4	quattuor	IV	4th	quartus
5	quinque	V	5th	quintus
6	sex	VI	6th	sextus
7	septem	VII	7th	septimus
8	octo	VIII		octavus
9	novem	IX		nonus
10	decem	X		decimus
11	undecim	XI		undecimus
12	duodecim	XII		duodecimus
13	tredecim	XIII		tertius decimus
14	quattuordecim	XIV		quartus decimus
15	quindecim	XV		quintus decimus
16	sedecim	XVI		sextus decimus
17	septendecim	XVII		septimus decimus
18	duodeviginti	XVIII		duodevicesimus
19	undeviginti	XIX		undevicesimus
20	viginti	XX		vicesimus
21	viginti unus	XXI		vicesimus primus
29	undetriginta	XXIX		undetricesimus
30	triginta	XXX		tricesimus
40	quadraginta	XL		quadragesimus
50	quinquaginta	L		quinquagesimus
60	sexaginta	LX		sexagesimus

Cardinals			Ordinals
70	septuaginta	LXX	septuagesimus
80	octoginta	LXXX	octogesimus
90	nonaginta	XC	nonagesimus
100	centum	C	centesimus
200	ducenti, -ae, -a	CC	ducentesimus
300	trecenti	CCC	trecentesimus
400	quadringenti	CD	quadringentesimus
500	quingenti	D	quingentesimus
600	sescenti	DC	sescentesimus
700	septingenti	DCC	septingentesimus
800	octingenti	DCCC	octigentesimus
900	nongenti	DCCCC	nongentesimus
1000	mille	M	millesimus
2000	duo milia	MM	duomillesimus

Latin numerals are not difficult to learn. Familiar English words frequently are based on a Latin numeral.

Compare such everyday words, as: "to sing a duet," "to play in a quartet," "the band is composed of a sextet." On the piano we span an "octave." We speak of a "septuagenarian," an "octogenarian," a "non-agenarian," and a "centenarian." A "simplex," "duplex," or "triplex" apartment denotes an apartment with one, two, or three stories respectively.

The Latin adjectives *singuli, bini, terni,* meaning "single," "double," "triple," give us such words as "single," "binary," and "ternary."

THE CALENDAR

There is another large group of words derived from Latin which we constantly use; in fact, we cannot properly picture our lives without it. This is the "calendar" division of time going back directly to the Romans. The Latin names for the months follow:

Ianuarius	*Maius*	*September*
Februarius	*Iunius*	*October*
Martius	*Iulius*	*November*
Aprilis	*Augustus*	*December*

Some of these names go back to the time that Rome was governed by "consuls"; some to emperors, for instance *Iulius* and *Augustus;* and obviously the last four months of the year are nothing but numerals. The Roman year began with March; this accounts for September being the 7th month.

The 1st, 5th, and 13th of the month were holidays and were named *Kalendae, Nonae,* and *Idus.* Shakespeare has familiarized us in his *Julius Caesar* with the "Ides of March"; where March was the first month of the year, the first "Ides" was an important holiday. There were also certain days on which all slaves were free and could do as they pleased without having to work. Their masters frequently provided an unlimited quantity of food and drink, so that such days ended in "Bacchanalia," which means there was too much pledging to the god Bacchus, the god of drink. Several days of festivity occurred in January; these days were devoted to Saturnus, and the orgies which accompanied them have led to the expression "Saturnalia." The extraordinary development of races, games, and gladiatorial fights in the large circuses, seating as many people as ours do today, and provided for the common people, led to the expression "panem et circenses." In other words, the slaves and lower classes were usually kept quiet and pleased if only on their holidays those in power provided plenty of "bread and entertainment." That entertainment was also afforded by watching lions devouring helpless Christians shows that as a race we have traveled far since the days of the haughty Roman emperors.

Adjectives of the Third Declension almost always follow the declension of nouns ending in *i.* Those which end in *er,* like *acer,* have a feminine ending: *acris,* and a neuter: *acre.* They are declined without any exception to the general rules. Those which end in *is* are the same throughout the masculine and feminine; the neuter ends in *e.* In other words, their genitive plural ends in *ium,* and their ablative in *i.*

When we wish to express the "time within which" something occurred, or the time "when" something occurred, we use the ablative without a preposition. For instance: "They were fighting in the tenth hour." *Decima hora pugnabant.* "Many towns were stormed in one year." *Multa oppida uno anno oppugnata sunt.*

Several new words follow. Learn these painstakingly; you will frequently need them.

aestas, -atis, f. summer	*celeritas, -atis,* f. swiftness
hora, -ae, f. hour	*mensa, -ae,* f. table
navis, -is, f. ship	*periculum, -i,* n. danger
vigilia, -ae, f. watch	*gravis, -e,* heavy
levis, -e, light (in weight)	*omnis, -e,* all, every
propero, -are, -avi, -atus, to hurry	*libenter,* gladly

What Latin words do you discern in "nautical," "civil," "accelerate," "temporary," "levity," "peril," and "fortitude"?

Translate the following sentences:

Virtus civium magna erat. Tertia hora nautae frumentum ex navibus in oppidum portaverunt. Libri in mensa magna sunt. Brevi tempore servi regis liberabuntur. Centurio levi gladio pugnaverit. Viri in agris libenter laboraverant. Decima legio a Gallis non saepe superata erat.

The virtue of the citizens was great. In the third hour, the sailors carried the grain out of the ships into the town. The books are on the large table. In a short time the slaves of the king will be freed. The captain (*centurio* literally means "soldier in charge of one hundred") will have fought with a light sword. The men gladly labored in the fields. Not frequently had the tenth legion been vanquished by the Gauls.

Adjectives of the Third Declension not ending in *-er* or *-is,* and not of the Comparative degree, have one ending. *Potens* (powerful) is a typical example. We will decline it in full:

SINGULAR

Masculine and Feminine	Neuter
Nom. *potens*	*potens*
Gen. *potentis*	*potentis*
Dat. *potenti*	*potenti*
Acc. *potentem*	*potens*
Abl. *potenti*	*potenti*

PLURAL

Nom. *potentes*	*potentia*
Gen. *potentium*	*potentium*
Dat. *potentibus*	*potentibus*
Acc. *potentes*	*potentia*
Abl. *potentibus*	*potentibus*

LESSON VIII

The verbs we have studied so far have all been in the *Active Voice.* That is to say, in our examples so far the subject of the sentence was also the performer of the action. "The boy loved the horse." "The soldiers fought for Caesar." A verb, however, may also be in the *Passive Voice.* In that case the subject of the sentence undergoes an action. "The horse was beloved by the boy." "The boys were punished."

When a verb is used only in the *active voice,* we call it an "Intransitive Verb." Such are: "to walk," "to run."

Some verbs are "Impersonal"; for instance, "it rains."

In Latin the passive voice is expressed through endings peculiar to each conjugation. For the First Conjugation they are *-r, -ris, -tur, -mur, -mini, -ntur*. The Second Conjugation does not vary from the first in the formation of the Passive endings.

Passive Voice

AMARE	DELERE
Present Indicative	*Present Indicative*
I am beloved	I am destroyed
amor	deleor
amaris	deleris
amatur	deletur
amamur	delemur
amamini	delemini
amantur	delentur
Imperfect Indicative	*Imperfect Indicative*
I was beloved	I was destroyed
amabar	delebar
amabaris	delebaris
amabatur	delebatur
amabamur	delebamur
amabamini	delebamini
amabantur	delebantur
Future Indicative	*Future Indicative*
I shall be beloved	I shall be destroyed
amabor	delebor
amaberis	deleberis
amabitur	delebitur
amabimur	delebimur
amabimini	delebimini
amabuntur	delebuntur

We do not use the Perfect stem in the Passive voice. The Perfect, Pluperfect, and Future Perfect tenses in the Passive voice are made by joining the participial stem with the endings as of adjectives. They have to agree with their subject as to gender, number, and case. Use *sum* for the perfect, *eram* for the pluperfect, and *ero* for the future perfect.

Passive Voice

AMARE	DELERE
Perfect Indicative	*Perfect Indicative*
I have been beloved	I have been destroyed
amatus sum	*deletus sum*
etc.	etc.
Pluperfect Indicative	*Pluperfect Indicative*
I had been beloved	I had been destroyed
amatus eram	*deletus eram*
etc.	etc.
Future Perfect	*Future Perfect*
I shall have been beloved	I shall have been destroyed
amatus ero	*deletus ero*
etc.	etc.
Present Infinitive	*Present Infinitive*
to be beloved	to be destroyed
amari	*deleri*
Perfect Infinitive	*Perfect Infinitive*
to have been beloved	to have been destroyed
amatus esse	*deletus esse*

We also present a list of words:

proelium, -i, n. battle	*promoveo, -ere,* to move forward
stella, -ae, f. star	*retineo, -ere,* to retain, to detain
vicus, -i, m. village	*semper,* always
defessus, -a, -um, tired	*saepe,* often
navigo, -are, to sail	*culpo, -are,* to blame

What Latin words can you trace in "navigate," "constellation," "culpable," "promote," "potential"?

We use the ablative with *a* or *ab* when we wish to denote the "personal agent" with a passive verb. For instance: "The small girl is praised by her mother." *Parva puella a matre laudatur.* "The sword was carried by the sailor." *Gladius a nauta portabatur.*

Read the following:

Puer bonus a matre non saepe culpabitur. Agri a militibus vastabuntur. Corpus equi multis lapidibus vulnerabatur. Dominus in mari navigavit. Liberi a Iulia amantur. Frumentumne in oppidum portatum est? Defessae legiones in castris retinebantur. Signa brevi tempore promota erunt. Urbs magna a duce forti deleta est. Decima hora ab exploratore celeri moneberis. Ubi castra Caesaris erant?

Which English words are derived from *annus, brevis, fortis, velox?*

The following is a short story which will explain to you why our George Washington is often called "The Cincinnatus of America." The city Cincinnati was thus named to honor the Father of our Country.

CINCINNATUS

Cincinnatus agricola Romanus erat et in agro laborabat. Miles non erat, sed patriam amabat. Roma in magno periculo erat et nuntii ad Cincinnatum mittebantur. Nuntii bonum virum in agro arantem videbant. Cincinnato periculum patriae narraverunt et eum ad bellum vocaverunt. Tum Cincinnatus erat dictator. Potens imperator erat et brevi tempore hostes superavit et victor ad agros properavit. Agricola fortis ab omnibus amatus et laudatus est.

CINCINNATUS

Cincinnatus was a Roman farmer and had always worked in the field. He was not a soldier, but he loved his country. Rome was in great peril and messengers were sent to Cincinnatus. The messengers saw the good man plowing in the field. They told Cincinnatus the danger to the country and summoned him to the war. Then Cincinnatus was dictator. He was a mighty general and vanquished the enemies in a short while, and hastened as victor to the country. The brave farmer was beloved and praised by all.

The verb *possum* means "I am able," and is conjugated like the verb *sum, esse.* Wherever the sound is harsh the two *ss* change to *t.* One must think of it as being *pot sum.* Its principal parts are *possum, posse, potui.* The Indicative Present reads:

possum	*possumus*
potes	*potestis*
potest	*possunt*

Imperfect: *poteram;* Future: *potero;* Perfect: *potui;* Pluperfect: *potueram;* Future Perfect: *potuero;* Perfect Infinitive: *potuisse;* Present Participle: *potens,* powerful.

Study these words:

cotidianus, -a, -um, daily	*cresco, -ere,* to grow
palus, -udis, f. swamp	*compleo, -ere,* to fill
debeo, -ere, -ui, -itus, owe, ought, must	*fere,* almost

Of course the bookkeeping term *"debit* side" means the side that must be paid. In a few lessons you will learn the verb *credo,* which means to believe, to trust, so that is the *credit* side of our ledger. Can you sift the Latin words out of these English ones?—"complementary," "population," "possible."

LESSON IX

Verbs of the Third Conjugation end in *-ere* in their Present Infinitive. The Third Person Plural ends in *-unt* in the Present Indicative. Most of those verbs are irregular in their Perfect Indicative and Past Participle. Much reading, however, familiarizes us with the various forms, and dictionaries and vocabularies give the various tenses. Otherwise they are conjugated with all the regular endings as you know them.

duco, ducere, duxi, ductus, to lead	*amitto, -ere, -isi, -issus,* to lose
educo, -ere, eduxi, eductus, to lead out	*pono, -ere, posui, positus,* to place
	curro, -ere, cucurri, cursus, to run
mitto, -ere, misi, missus, to send	*relinquo, -ere, reliqui, relictus,* to leave
trans, across	*lux, lucis,* f. light
iter, itineris, n. journey	

The following is the conjugation of *duco* in the Indicative of the Active Voice. Note that the endings of the Future differ from those of the First and Second Conjugations.

Present	Imperfect	Future
I lead	I led (was leading)	I shall lead
duco	*ducebam*	*ducam*
ducis	*ducebas*	*duces*
ducit	*ducebat*	*ducet*
ducimus	*ducebamus*	*ducemus*

| ducitis | ducebatis | ducetis |
| ducunt | ducebant | ducent |

Perfect	Pluperfect	Future Perfect
I have led (I led)	I had led	I shall have led
duxi	duxeram	duxero
duxisti	duxeras	duxeris
duxit	duxerat	duxerit
duximus	duxeramus	duxerimus
duxistis	duxeratis	duxeritis
duxerunt	duxerant	duxerint

The Passive is formed according to the rules previously given for the first two conjugations.

We often express the "cause" of a certain action by using an ablative, and usually without a preposition. "The man ran from fear." *Vir timore cucurrit.* "The mothers will praise their children for their diligence." *Matres liberos diligentia laudabunt.*

Translate these sentences: *Caesar auxilia trans flumen duxerit. Rex multas et longas litteras ad centurionem scripsit. Prima luce princeps in castris auxilia reliquit.*

Translate the following into Latin: In time of war, the men leave the women and children in the town. The horse ran with great swiftness. The soldiers ran because of their great fear. At daybreak we had led the soldiers out of the camp. I shall write long letters and send them to my friends. The end of the journey will be in a swamp.

So many similar constructions and examples have been discussed above that we do not give you the translation. Should anything be very difficult, then apply yourself to that special question once more with great zeal and you will readily understand it.

civitas, -tatis, f. state
cohors, -hortis, f. cohort
eques, -itis, m. horseman
nomen, -inis, n. name
obses, -idis, m. and f. hostage

oratio, -onis, f. speech
pedes, -itis, m. foot soldier
vulnus, -eris, n. wound
par, paris, adj. equal
vox, vocis, f. voice

When in English we use a verb, noun, or adjective describing a noun, verb, or adjective, specifying its peculiar qualities, so that we get an answer to the question: "In what respect?" then in Latin we use an Ablative.

He was King in name, not fact. *Rex nomine non facto erat.*
The boy was small in body. *Puer corpore parvus erat.*

He was not surpassed in courage. *Virtute non superabatur.*
The horses of the general are equal in speed. *Equi ducis
    celeritate pares sunt.*

Adjectives expressing quality are compared in Latin, as follows:

longus, longior, longissimus,	long, longer, longest
brevis, brevior, brevissimus,	short, shorter, shortest
velox, velocior, velocissimus,	swift, swifter, swiftest
miser, miserior, miserrimus,	unhappy, more unhappy, most unhappy

The following adjectives are irregular and should be memorized:

bonus, melior, optimus,	good, better, best
malus, peior, pessimus,	bad, worse, worst
magnus, maior, maximus,	great, greater, greatest
parvus, minor, minimus,	small, smaller, smallest
multus, plurimus,	much, most
multi, plures, plurimi,	many, more, most
senex, senior, maximus natu,	old, older, oldest
iuvenis, iunior, minimus natu,	young, younger, youngest
exterus, exterior, extremus,	outward, outer, outermost, last
inferus, inferior, infimus,	low, lower, lowest
posterus, posterior, postre-mus, postumus,	following, later, last, next
superus, superior, supremus, summus,	above, higher, highest, last

Frequently the comparative and superlative are formed by using *magis,*
more, and *maxime,* most.

A few adjectives have no positive, but are formed from prepositions:

citerior, citimus,	hither, hithermost
interior, intimus,	inner, innermost
prior, primus,	former, first
propior, proximus,	nearer, nearest, next
ulterior, ultimus,	farther, last

Of course a great many everyday English words have been suggested
by this list. Write them all down and read them over carefully; it will
render the study of the Latin words a great deal easier. Think also of
words like "juvenile," "priority," "facility," etc.

mos, -ris, m. custom, habit   *collis, -is,* m. hill

nihil, n. nothing
gero, -ere, gessi, gestus, to carry on
quam, than, as possible
quomodo, how

acriter, sharply
celeriter, quickly
atque, and also, and
fortiter, bravely

An adverb describes a verb, an adjective, or another adverb. For instance: "He sings *well.*" "He is *nearly* through." "He sings *unusually* well." An adverb may express time, manner, place, degree, affirmation, negation, or, as an interrogative adverb, it may ask a question. Examples: *lately; poorly; there; very; yes; no; not; when? where? how? why?*

We form an adverb in Latin by changing the ending of adjectives belonging to the *a* or *o* declension. We add *e* to the base. *Latus,* adjective; *late,* adverb. Third declension adjectives are formed by adding *-ter* or *-iter.* The comparison is the same as that of adjectives, except that the comparative ends in *-ius* and the superlative in *-e.*

late, latius, latissime   widely, more widely, most widely
acriter, acrius, acerrime   sharply, more sharply, most sharply

When we wish to express a degree of difference, we use the ablative without a preposition. "The wall is four feet higher." *Murus quattuor pedibus altior est.* "The boy is a year older than his sister." *Puer anno senior est quam soror.*

Translate these sentences: Diu atque acriter pugnaverunt. Bella in extremis finibus Galliae gesta sunt. Milites fortes magna oppida hostium facillime delere possunt. Mons plurimis pedibus altior colle erat. Femina minus facile atque minus celeriter cucurrit quam filia. Milites Germani brevissimo itinere et magna cum celeritate ad urbem properaverant et muros deleverant.

A few expressions often met with include: *minus facile,* less easily; *diu atque acriter,* long and bitterly; *quam fortissime,* as bravely as possible; *prima luce,* at daybreak; *prima aetate,* when still very young.

We shall now read a short story about Cornelia, a famous Roman lady.

ORNAMENTA CORNELIAE

Cornelia femina Romana erat et optima mater. Filios habebat Tiberium et Gaium Gracchum. Mater et filii Romam, maximam urbem incolebant. Diligentia Corneliae matris Gracchi Graecas litteras atque bonos mores docebantur. Companiae femina Corneliae sua ornamenta, quae pulcherrima erant, monstrabat, et laudabat. Corneliae dixit, "Habesne nulla ornamenta?" Cornelia respondit, "Mei pueri ornamenta sunt mea."

The Jewels of Cornelia

Cornelia was a Roman lady and a very good mother. She had as sons Tiberius and Gaius Gracchus. Mother and sons lived at Rome, the largest city. The Gracchi were taught Greek literature and good morals through the devoted care of their mother Cornelia. A woman from the Campagna showed her jewels, which were very beautiful, to Cornelia, and praised them. She said to Cornelia, "Don't you have any ornaments?" Cornelia answered, "My boys are my jewels."

Translate the following English words and write their comparative, superlative, and adverbial forms: sharp, quick, swift, small, faithful.

Translate these sentences into Latin: Peace is better than war. The ships were very small. The river is rather long and very deep. Many bridges have been built across wide rivers.

The Fourth Declension consists of nouns whose genitive singular ends in *-us.* Those ending in *-us* in the nominative are masculine; those ending in *-u* are neuter.

Singular	*Plural*

FRUCTUS, *fruit.* Stem: FRUCT-

Singular	*Plural*
Nom. *fructus*	Nom. *fructus*
Gen. *fructus*	Gen. *fructuum*
Dat. *fructui*	Dat. *fructibus*
Acc. *fructum*	Acc. *fructus*
Abl. *fructu*	Abl. *fructibus*

CORNU, *horn.* Stem: CORN-

Nom. *cornu*	Nom. *cornua*
Gen. *cornus*	Gen. *cornuum*
Dat. *cornui*	Dat. *cornibus*
Acc. *cornu*	Acc. *cornua*
Abl. *cornu*	Abl. *cornibus*

The nouns *artus* and *tribus* have their Dative and Ablative plural *artubus* and *tribubus.* The word *domus,* house, is irregular; it also is feminine. *Manus,* hand; *porticus,* portal; *acus,* needle; *idus,* used in the Plural only, 13th of the month; *tribus,* district, are also feminine. They are declined regularly. Learn the declension by heart: *domus, domus, domui, domum, domo,* in the singular; and in the plural: *domus, domorum, domibus, domos, domibus.*

> *domi,* at home; *domum,* to the home; *domo,* from the house
> *impetus, -us,* m. attack   *dexter, -tra, -trum,* right (hand)
> *occasus, -us,* m. setting   *sinister, -tra, -trum,* left (hand)
> *sol, solis,* m. sun   *sustineo, -ere, -ui, -tentus,* withstand

What Latin words do "manual," "domestic," "solar," "sinister," suggest?

When speaking of "part of a whole" we use the Genitive in Latin. With numbers sometimes the Ablative with *de* or *ex* is used.

> Part of the soldiers.   *Pars militum.*
> The bravest of the men.   *Fortissimi virorum.*
> One of the boys.   *Unus ex pueris.*

Some expressions are typical and found in many authors: *solis occasu,* at sunset; *a dextro cornu,* on the right wing; *a sinistro cornu,* on the left wing; *ab summo colle,* on the top of the hill; *ab superior parte,* on the highest part.

The Fifth and last Declension offers very little difficulty. Nouns belonging to the Fifth Declension are mostly feminine; their Genitive singular ends in *-ei.*

	Singular	Plural		Singular	Plural
	DIES, m. *day*			RES, f. *thing*	
Nom.	*dies*	*dies*	Nom.	*res*	*res*
Gen.	*diei*	*dierum*	Gen.	*rei*	*rerum*
Dat.	*diei*	*diebus*	Dat.	*rei*	*rebus*
Acc.	*diem*	*dies*	Acc.	*rem*	*res*
Abl.	*die*	*diebus*	Abl.	*re*	*rebus*

More words belonging to the Fifth Declension are:

> *acies, -ei,* f. line of battle   *ius, -ris,* n. right, law (3rd declension)
> *spes, -ei,* f. hope   *pauci, -ae, -a,* few (adjective of 1st and 2nd)
> *locus, -i,* m. place (2nd declension)   *amicus, -i,* m. friend (2nd declension)

Adjectives meaning dear, faithful, friendly, suitable, useful, and their opposites, as unfaithful, etc., take the Dative.

The place is suitable for a camp. *Locus castris idoneus est.*

The slaves are faithful to their masters. *Servi dominis fidi sunt.*

Translate: Part of the army was unfriendly to the general. A faithful son can be useful to his old father. The house had been on the right bank of the river. The attack at sunset was useless. The day was a few hours longer than the night. At the lower part of the river there had been a bridge.

Translate these back into English: Aestate dies noctibus longiores sunt. Locus castris idoneus fuit, sed aciei inutilis. Boni cives rei publicae fidi semper fuerunt. Pauci amicorum militum ad collem missi erunt. Tela militibus sunt utilissima. Romani locum idoneum castris viderunt.

There is a large group of words whose declensions are defective. That is, through the centuries parts have become obsolete and are no longer in use. A few should be studied, as they are frequently met with in reading, and some are also used by us as expressions in their own right. Among the following not all are defective:

indoles, natural aptitude

scientia, science

specimen, specimena, proof, specimen

vestis, -is, f. clothing, vestment

posteri, posterity

nuptiae, wedding feast

poema, poem

insidiae, ambush (hence insidious)

arma, -orum, n. weapons, arms

deliciae, darling

reliquae, remnants

gratias, thanks (accusative plural)

opera, work, plural of *opus, operis,* n.

vesper, -eris, m. evening

rus, ruris, n. the country, land

With names of cities and towns, when expressing the place, in Latin, one does not use a preposition. One uses the ablative when the condition is permanent, and the accusative when it is an action or in a state of transition. "He goes out of Rome." *Exit Roma.* "He goes to Rome." *Romam it.*

Answer the following questions to yourself in Latin: Amatne mater filium filiamque? Ubi sunt femina ducum et liberi? Quid est in superiore parte muri?

LESSON X

We are now through with the nouns and adjectives and have only the Fourth Conjugation to study, after which most Latin, as the layman meets with it, should come to you easily. Verbs of the Fourth Conjugation end in *-ire* in the Present Infinitive; the Perfect stem mostly ends in *-iv*, and the participial stem with a *-t*. The Passive follows the normal rules, and if you have studied the other verbs well, you will master the Fourth Conjugation with very little trouble.

We present a skeleton outline:

INDICATIVE
ACTIVE

Present	*Imperfect*	*Future*
I hear	I heard	I shall hear
audio	audiebam	audiam
audis	audiebas	audies
audit	audiebat	audiet
audimus	audiebamus	audiemus
auditis	audiebatis	audietis
audiunt	audiebant	audient

Perfect	*Pluperfect*	*Future Perfect*
I have heard	I had heard	I shall have heard
audivi	audiveram	audivero
audivisti	audiveras	audiveris
audivit	audiverat	audiverit
audivimus	audiveramus	audiverimus
audivistis	audiveratis	audiveritis
audiverunt	audiverant	audiverint

Verbs that follow the same conjugation, for instance, are: *munio*, to fortify; *servio*, to serve.

The Passive Tenses of *audio* are listed below:

INDICATIVE
PASSIVE

Present	*Imperfect*	*Future*
I am heard	I was heard	I shall be heard

audior	*audiebar*	*audiar*
audiris	*audiebaris*	*audieris*
auditur	*audiebatur*	*audietur*
audimur	*audiebamur*	*audiemur*
audimini	*audiebamini*	*audiemini*
audiuntur	*audiebantur*	*audientur*

Perfect	*Pluperfect*	*Future Perfect*
I have been heard	I had been heard	I shall have been heard
auditus sum	*auditus eram*	*auditus ero*
etc.	etc.	etc.

Pres. Inf. Pas.	*Perf. Inf. Pas.*
audiri	*auditus esse*

When we wish to express duration of time or space, we use the Accusative.

They came six miles. *Milia passuum sex venerunt.*
They fought five hours. *Quinque horas pugnaverunt.*

Word study:

latitudo, -inis, f. width	*captivus, -i,* m. captive
longitudo, -inis, f. length	*deus,* m. god
maneo, -ere, mansi (mansus) to remain	*dea,* f. goddess
pateo, -ere, -ui, to extend	*ordo, -inis,* m. rank, order
longe, far	*quot?* how many?
quam longe? how far?	*alter,* the other
quam diu? how long?	*alius,* other

A few adjectives, viz., *alius,* other; *alter,* the other; *ullus,* any; *nullus,* none; *uter,* which; *neuter,* neither; *solus,* alone; *totus,* whole; and *unus,* one, though regular in their plural declensions, have in the Genitive the ending *-ius,* and in the Dative *-i,* in all genders.

What Latin words come to your mind when meeting with these English ones?—"latitude," "remain," "neutral," "invincible," "alternate," and "deity."

Answer these questions in Latin: Quot horas homines laborabunt? Quam longe venisti? Quam diu vixit? Laborasne totum diem? Utra puella melior est?

Write all the English words suggested to you by these Latin ones. *utilis, ordo, vita, captivus, bene, impetus.*

Translate the following phrases into Latin: How long? As bravely as possible. At sunset. On the left wing. On the top of the hill. Late in the day.

Read the following sentences at sight: Equi milia passuum quinque cucurrerunt. Iter ad flumen facillimum est. Nullius orationes quam Ciceronis meliores sunt. Octo horas quam fortissime pugnaverant. Solis occasu nuntius audiebatur. Alia oppida munientur, alia delebuntur.

FORUM ROMANUM

Forum Romanum erat inter Capitolium et Palatium. Primo parvae tebernae utrimque erant. Post multos annos consules et imperatores templa in Foro aedificaverunt. In templo Concordiae senatores convenie-bant. In rostris Cicero et alii oratores ad populum orationes habebant. Undique altae columnae atque simulacra deorum et statuae virorum erant. Togati Romani in Foro saepe conveniebant. Hinc Via Sacra legiones Romanae ad bellum educebantur. Via Sacra legiones victores magnis cum clamoribus in Forum veniebant. Nunc in Foro ruinae un-dique videntur. Nihil manet nisi pauca vestigia antiquae gloriae Roma-norum.

THE FORUM AT ROME

The Roman forum was between the Capitol hill and the Palatine hill. At first there were a few small shops on both sides. After many years the consuls and the emperors built temples in the Forum. In the temple of Concordia the senators held their meetings. In that speaker's chair Cicero and other orators made their speeches to the populace. On all sides were high columns and images of the gods and statues of heroes. In the Forum the aristocratic Roman citizens often met (*togati* literally means "men wearing the toga"; this was worn only by the aristocrats). From here along the Via Sacra the Roman legions were led out to war. And along the Via Sacra the victorious legions returned into the Forum with loud acclaim. At present one sees ruins on all sides of the Forum. Nothing remains but a few remnants of the ancient glory of the Romans.

Below is a list of Latin phrases the student will often find quoted.

Ad finem	to the finish	*Ad valorem*	at exact value
Ad infinitum	endlessly	*Alias*	other (name)
Ad nauseam	until one is dizzy	*Alibi*	other place

Alma Mater	Fostering Mother (one's college)
Alter ego	other self
Ante bellum	before the war
Aqua vitae	the water of life (alcohol)
Bona fide	in good trust
Cave canem	beware of the dog
Ceteris paribus	other things being equal
Corpus Christi	the body of Christ
De gustibus non disputandum	about taste there is no arguing
Deo volente	with God's will
Deus vobiscum	may God be with you
Dramatis personae	the people in the drama or the occurrence
Ecce homo	Behold the man
E pluribus unum	one out of many
Excelsior	higher, onward
Exit	this is the way out (from the verb *exire*)
Ex officio	on account of his official position
Facsimile	similar to the fact (replica)

Gloria in excelsis	glory in the highest
Habeas corpus	you (shall) have the body
In extremis	in the last moments
In pace	in peace
In situ	on the original spot
In statu quo	in the exact state of
Inter nos	between us
In toto	in the whole
Ipse dixit	he says it himself
Labor omnia vincit	work conquers everything
Lapsus linguae	a lapse of the tongue
Lares et Penates	the household gods one's own hearth
Mea culpa	my fault
Mens sana in corpore sano	a healthy mind in a sound body
Mirabile dictu	amazing to say
Modus operandi	the manner one must go to work
Moriturite salutamus	we who are about to die, greet thee
Multum in parvo	there is much in small things
Ne plus ultra	nothing better
Nolens volens	not wanting it
Nulli secundus	second to nothing

Omnia ad Dei Gloriam	everything for the glory of God
Pater Noster	our father
Pax vobiscum	may peace be with thee
Per annum	a year
Per capita	a head
Per diem	a day
Per se	in itself
Prima facie	on first evidence
Pro bono publico	for the public good
Pro et con	for and against
Pro rata	according to ration / according to number
Pro tempore	for the present time
Quid nunc	what now?
Requiescat in pace	may he rest in peace
Res republica	business pertaining to the Republic
Semper fidelis	always true
Sine dubio	without doubt
Summum bonum	the highest good

Sine qua non	without which nothing
Te Deum laudamus	you, God, we praise
Tempus fugit	time speeds on
Terra firma	real earth (solid ground)
Una voce	with one voice, without dissension
Ultimatum	the last thing
Vade mecum	come with me
Vade retro, Satane	go away, Satan
Veni, vidi, vici	I came, I saw, I conquered
Versus	against
Via	by way of
Vice versa	this way and that way (the terms being exchanged)
Vivat rex	may the king live
Viva voce	with loud voice

A few of the mottoes of our states may interest you:

Ad astra per aspera	To the stars through hardships	Kansas
Labor omnia vincit	Work conquers everything	Oklahoma
Aliis volat propriis	She flies with her own wings	Oregon
Esse quam videri	To be, rather than to seem to be	North Carolina

Latin	Translation	State
Montani semper liberi	Mountaineers are always free	West Virginia
Justitia omnibus	Justice for all	District of Columbia
Salus populi suprema est lex	The good of the people is the supreme law	Missouri
Cedant arma togae	Peace has her victories as well as war (Let arms yield to the toga.)	Wyoming
Nil sine numine	Nothing without divinity.	Colorado
Animis opibusque parati, dum spiro spero	We are prepared with our souls and our labor, and as long as we breathe we will hope	South Carolina
Qui transtulit sustinet	He who brought us across the sea will safeguard us	Connecticut
Sic semper tyrannis	Thus always to tyrants	Virginia
Crescit eundo	It grows as it goes	New Mexico
Ense petit placidam sub libertate quietem	With the sword she seeks calm repose in freedom	Massachusetts
Dirigo	I shall sail my own boat	Maine
Regnant populi	May the people rule themselves	Arkansas

Read the following short story at sight:

TARPEIA

Sabini cum Romanis bellum gerebant et agros Romanorum vastabant. Romanum exercitum ducebant et urbem intraverunt sed Capitolium capere non poterant. Ubi ab Capitolio non longe aberant, puellam Tarpeiam, filiam ducis Romani, portantem aquam extra moenia viderunt. Dux Sabinorum putavit puellam in Capitolium exercitum ducere posse, et dixit se Tarpeiae praemium daturum esse. Puella dixit se habituram esse res quas in sinistris manibus gererent. Sabini aureos anulos e armillas in sinistris manibus gerebant. Brevi tempore Sabini in Capitolio stant et Tarpeiae praemium dare parant. In puellam scuta iaciunt; nam scuta Sabinorum erant in sinistris manibus. Tarpeia interficitur; Sabini Capitolium occupant.

(*puto, -are, -avi, -atus,* to think; *armilla, -ae,* f. bracelet; *interficio, -ere, -feci, -fectus,* to kill.)

TARPEIA

The Sabines were at war with the Romans and had ravaged the Roman fields. They were driving the Roman army ahead and had entered the city but could not capture the Capitol. When they were not far away from the Capitol hill they saw Tarpeia, the daughter of the Roman general, carrying water outside the walls. The general of the Sabines thought that the girl could lead the army into the Capitol, and he said that she, Tarpeia, would be given a gift. The girl said that she would want to receive those things which they were carrying in their left hands. The Sabines were wearing golden rings and bracelets on their left hands. In a short time the Sabines were standing on the Capitol and were preparing to give Tarpeia her present. They threw their shields on the girl, because the shields were in the left hands of the Sabines. Tarpeia was killed, and the Sabines occupied the Capitol.

LESSON XI

The only group of words still requiring our careful scrutiny are the "pronouns." A *pro-noun* is a word used in the place of a noun. We use them for brevity and for better sound. "'I saw Jane as she walked down the street" sounds better than "I saw Jane as Jane walked down the street." If you study that sentence, you will notice that in the first one Jane is the "direct object" and would in Latin be in the accusative case. In the second part of the sentence Jane is the subject. In other words, pronouns agree with the nouns to which they belong, so far as gender and number are concerned, but not in "case." There are many kinds of pronouns; we shall study them one by one.

First the "relative pronouns," "who," "which," and "that," in Latin *qui.* "I saw the man who came." *Virum qui venit vidi.* "The city which you see is Rome." *Urbs quam vides Roma est.*

Qui is masculine; *quae,* feminine; *quod,* neuter. The declension follows:

	SINGULAR			PLURAL		
	Mas.	*Fem.*	*Neut.*	*Mas.*	*Fem.*	*Neut.*
Nom.	*qui*	*quae*	*quod*	*qui*	*quae*	*quae*

Gen.	*cuius*	*cuius*	*cuius*	*quorum*	*quarum*	*quorum*
Dat.	*cui*	*cui*	*cui*	*quibus*	*quibus*	*quibus*
Acc.	*quem*	*quam*	*quod*	*quos*	*quas*	*quae*
Abl.	*quo*	*qua*	*quo*	*quibus*	*quibus*	*quibus*

Translate the following sentences:

Viderunt custodem cuius amicus ex urbe missus erat. Milites missi sunt qui fines Gallorum popularentur. Loca ad quae properavimus tuta erant. Caesar per nuntios certior factus est tres partes copiarum trans flumen fuisse, quartam partem in castris relictam esse. Vidistine impedimenta quibus imperator potitus est?

mitto, -ere, -ssi, -ssus, to send

qui, sometimes means *ut,* so that

relinquo, -ere, reliqui, relictus, to leave

locus, -i, m. (pl., *loca, -orum,* n.) place

propero, -are, -avi, -atus, to hurry

potior, -iri, -itus sum, get possession of

The "interrogative pronouns" ask a question. "Who are you?" The interrogative pronouns are: "who," "which," "what." In Latin they are: *quis,* who, and the adjective *qui,* what.

The declension of *quis* runs as follows:

| | SINGULAR | | PLURAL | | |
	M. and *F.*	*Neut.*	*Mas.*	*Fem.*	*Neut.*
Nom.	*quis*	*quid*	*qui*	*quae*	*quae*
Gen.	*cuius*	*cuius*	*quorum*	*quarum*	*quorum*
Dat.	*cui*	*cui*	*quibus*	*quibus*	*quibus*
Acc.	*quem*	*quid*	*quos*	*quas*	*quae*
Abl.	*quo*	*quo*	*quibus*	*quibus*	*quibus*

There is no difference in the declension of the "relative pronoun" *qui* and the "interrogative pronoun" *qui.* Often the little word *num* is used, like the English word "whether."

Answer these Latin questions in Latin, after first translating them:

Quibus telis milites utentur? Quem Romae vidisti? Quis puer a patre laudatur?

A "personal pronoun" shows by its form whether it refers to the speaker (first person, I), the one spoken to (second person, you), or the one spoken of (third person, he). The personal pronouns are *ego* for the first person and *tu* for the second. The third person is the same as the demonstrative *is.*

We only use the personal pronouns in Latin to give greater emphasis to a statement which is very positive in fact already. "I, Cicero, warn you." *Ego, Cicero, vos moneo.*

The declension of the personal pronouns follows the usual manner:

| | FIRST PERSON | | SECOND PERSON | |
	Singular	Plural	Singular	Plural
Nom.	ego	nos	tu	vos
Gen.	mei	nostrum, nostri	tui	vestri, vestrum
Dat.	mihi	nobis	tibi	vobis
Acc.	me	nos	te	vos
Abl.	me	nobis	te	vobis

A "reflexive pronoun" refers back to the subject. They are declined like the personal pronouns of the same persons, except that they have no nominative: "of myself," *mei;* "of yourself," *tui;* and so on. The reflexive of the third person serves for all genders and for both numbers. *Sui* may mean of himself, of herself, of itself, of themselves. The sense of the sentence must make that clear.

The declension of the third person reflexive pronoun is thus:

	Singular	Plural
Gen.	sui	sui
Dat.	sibi	sibi
Acc.	se, sometimes sese	se or sese
Abl.	se, sometimes sese	se or sese

Study these words: *deditio, -ionis,* f., surrender; *neque,* neither; *dedo, -ere, dedidi, deditus,* to give up; *quaero, -ere, quaesivi, quaesitus,* to ask; *respondeo, -ere, -di, responsus,* to answer.

What Latin words do "egotism," "me," "response," and "vision" suggest?

Translate the following: Tu me vides. Nos vos laudamus. Ego me video.

Also translate: You praised us. We came with you. We saw you.

Answer these: Cur tu melior me es? Tune te saepe laudas? Quis vobis dona dedit?

The "possessive pronouns" denote the possessor of the noun to which they belong. "This book is mine." The Latin possessive pronouns are the adjective forms of the personal and reflexive pronouns. They are used exactly as adjectives, and so they agree with their nouns in gender, number, and case. The possessive pronouns are:

meus, -a, -um, mine
noster, -tra, -trum, ours
tuus, -a, -um, your, yours (singular, when belonging to one)
vester, -tra, -trum, your, yours (plural, when belonging to more than one)
suus, -a, -um, his, her(s), their(s)

The gender of a possessive pronoun does not agree with the gender of the person to whom it refers, but with the gender of the noun possessed.

Marcus loves his mother.	*Marcus matrem suam amat.*
Julia loves her mother.	*Iulia matrem suam amat.*
Julia loves her father.	*Iulia patrem suum amat.*

Many verbs compounded with the prepositions *ad, ante, con, in, inter, ob, post, prae, pro, sub, super* use the dative. Remember this when reading, as it often clarifies a whole sentence.

praesum, -esse, -fui, to have command of
supersum, -esse, -fui, to survive, to be left over
praesto, -are, -iti, -itus, to excel, surpass

Brutus was in command of the ships. *Brutus navibus praeerat.*
He placed Brutus in command of the ships. *Brutum navibus praeposuit.*
Translate: Caesar exercitui praefuit. Romani omnibus virtute praestiterunt. Laudabimini, pueri, et a matre vestra et a magistro vestro. Dei semper comites nostri sunt, et rebus hominum praesunt.
Fero, "I carry," is one of the most irregular verbs, and its compounds are also irregular. The four tenses are: *fero, ferre, tuli, latus.* Some frequently met with composite verbs are:

confero, conferre, contuli, collatus, to bring together
differo, differre, distuli, dilatus, to scatter, to differ
effero, efferre, extuli, elatus, to bring out, to carry away
infero, inferre, intuli, illatus, to bring in, upon, against
bellum inferre, to make war on
signa inferre, lit., to bear the standards on, to advance
expugno, -are, -avi, -atus, to take by storm

What Latin words do the following suggest?—"conference," "transfer," "to infer," "to differ."

Translate: Scimus Caesarem Germanis bellum intulisse. Decima legio signa infert et urbem expugnat. Inter se lingua legibusque differunt.
"Demonstrative pronouns" point out an object; they are used either substantively or adjectively. They are:

hic, this (near the speaker)	*is,* that
iste, that (near you)	*idem,* the same
ille, that (remote from both speaker and the person addressed)	

The declension of HIC is typical:

	SINGULAR			PLURAL		
	Mas.	*Fem.*	*Neut.*	*Mas.*	*Fem.*	*Neut.*
Nom.	*hic*	*haec*	*hoc*	*hi*	*hae*	*haec*
Gen.	*huius*	*huius*	*huius*	*horum*	*harum*	*horum*
Dat.	*huic*	*huic*	*huic*	*his*	*his*	*his*
Acc.	*hunc*	*hanc*	*hoc*	*hos*	*has*	*haec*
Abl.	*hoc*	*hac*	*hoc*	*his*	*his*	*his*

ILLE is declined as follows:

	SINGULAR			PLURAL		
	Mas.	*Fem.*	*Neut.*	*Mas.*	*Fem.*	*Neut.*
Nom.	*ille*	*illa*	*illud*	*illi*	*illae*	*illa*
Gen.	*illius*	*illius*	*illius*	*illorum*	*illarum*	*illorum*
Dat.	*illi*	*illi*	*illi*	*illis*	*illis*	*illis*
Acc.	*illum*	*illam*	*illud*	*illos*	*illas*	*illa*
Abl.	*illo*	*illa*	*illo*	*illis*	*illis*	*illis*

ISTE is declined like *ille* (the genitive is *istius*) and *ipse*, gen. *ipsius*. You will have no trouble with those declensions, we think.

Is is more irregular; here is the declension:

	SINGULAR			PLURAL		
	Mas.	*Fem.*	*Neut.*	*Mas.*	*Fem.*	*Neut.*
Nom.	*is*	*ea*	*id*	*ii* or *ei*	*eae*	*ea*
Gen.	*eius*	*eius*	*eius*	*eorum*	*earum*	*eorum*
Dat.	*ei*	*ei*	*ei*	*iis*	*iis*	*iis*
Acc.	*eum*	*eam*	*id*	*eos*	*eas*	*ea*
Abl.	*eo*	*ea*	*eo*	*iis*	*iis*	*iis*

IDEM is declined like *is;* the singular genitive runs: *eiusdem, eiusdem, eiusdem,* and the genitive plural: *eorundem, earundem, eorundem.*

Can you trace the Latin words in "action," "identify," and "national"?

The "intensive pronoun" is *ipse,* which is used with the personal or demonstrative pronouns to give greater emphasis to a statement. "He himself said it." *Ille ipse dixit.* The genitive is *ipsius* in all genders, and in the plural it is: *ipsorum, ipsarum, ipsorum.*

Translate: Iste tuus amicus est, sed eorum inimicus. Ille dixit se habere litteras a Lentulo. Eodem tempore Caesar suas legiones laudari iussit. Scies eum amicum quem ad te missi. Caesar suum amicum vocavit et eius virtutem laudavit.

We translate: He is your friend, but their enemy. He said that he had letters from Lentulus. At the same time Caesar ordered that his legions be praised. You will know that friend whom I have sent to you. Caesar has called his friend and has praised his courage.

Pronouns which do not refer to definite persons or things are called "indefinite pronouns." The most common ones are:

> *aliquis,* masc. and fem.; neut., *aliquid;* someone, something
> *quisque,* masc. and fem.; neut., *quidque;* each one, everyone, everything
> *quidam, quaedam, quiddam,* a certain one

The adjective forms are:

> *aliqui, aliqua, aliquod,* any
> *quisque, quaeque, quodque,* each
> *quidam, quaedam, quoddam,* a certain
> *quantus, -a, -um,* how great, how much
> *post,* after, behind
> *initium, -ti,* neut., beginning
> *reverto, -ere, -ti, -sus,* to return
> *revertor, -i, reversus sum,* to turn back
> *interea,* in the meantime
> *propterea quod,* because, on account of

What words do these English words suggest?—"initial," "initiation," "revert."

We will close this brief Latin course with a few *fabulae faciles:*

MURI SPARTAE

Quidam ex Spartano quaesivit: "Cur muros non habet Sparta?" Spartanus respondit: "Nostra urbs muros optimos habet, incolarum fortium virtutem."

THE WALLS OF SPARTA

Somebody asked a Spartan: "Why does Sparta not have walls?" The Spartan answered: "Our city has the very best walls, the courage of the brave inhabitants."

VIRTUS SPARTANA

Rex Spartanus dixit: "Mei cives numquam quaesiverunt, 'Quot sunt hostes?' sed 'Ubi sunt?' "

THE VALOR OF SPARTA

A Spartan king said: "Never have my citizens asked: 'How many enemies are there?' but: 'Where are they?' "

IOCUS CICERONIS

Femina quaedam, iuniorem se esse simulans quam erat, dixit se triginta tantum annos habere; cui Cicero dixit: "Verum est, nam hoc viginti annos audio."

THE JOKE OF CICERO

A certain woman, pretending to be younger than she was, said that she was thirty years old; Cicero said to her: "That is true, for I heard that twenty years ago."

EXAMINATION QUESTIONS

Translate the following into Latin:

1. Farmers love the land.
2. Do the messengers carry letters from Gaul?
3. We are ambassadors of the city.
4. They are not friends of the girl.
5. The men were building high walls.
6. The farmers will hide much grain in the town.
7. The sailor's danger will be great.
8. Many men have fought with javelins.
9. There are many provinces in Gaul.
10. Caesar called together the senate in the name of the Roman people.
11. Who is the leader of the Roman soldiers?
12. The king moved his soldiers around the enemy.
13. The black horse fears the soldiers' weapons.
14. Gaul is now part of Rome.
15. Julia has a beautiful little horse.
16. In the second hour, the soldiers gladly carried the weapons from the ships into the city.
17. The beautiful little animal was wounded by bad boys with stones.
18. New villages have been built by the tired soldiers after the battle.
19. Will you always be able to grow in mind?
20. At dawn, the general led the foot soldiers out of the city and across the bridge.
21. The king was in fact a hostage of the cohorts.

22. Charles is more unhappy than Julia.
23. The Roman horsemen fought bravely but were not able to overcome the Helvetians.
24. When still very young, Caesar wished to lay waste the lands of the Germans.
25. Rome is often called the Eternal City.

Translate the following into English:

26. Puella tubam sonat.
27. Agricolae fabulam puellarum narrasne?
28. Agricolae fabulam puellarum non narro.
29. Vir pueris agros agricolae monstrat.
30. Muros novos oppidi parvi aedificabamus.
31. Equus frumentum agricolae portabit.
32. Legati in patria cara hiemabuntne?
33. Periculum belli in Gallia magnum erat.
34. Nuntius ad astras puellas pulchras laudavit.
35. Agricola filio caro Carolo calathum pomorum bonorum malorumque plenum dedit.
36. Ubi nuntii in Roma tela imperatoris celaverunt?

37. Quis gladio lato mercatorem vulneravit?
38. Milites Romani pilis gladiisque populum Galliae oppugnaverunt.
39. Rex militesque in ripa fluminis circum portam magnam partem urbis vastaverunt.
40. Nocte imperator Romanus in montibus altis castra hostis videt et igne delere viros monet.
41. Parvi liberi magna cum clamore patri equum parvum pulchrumque monstraverunt.
42. Ubi urbs populi Romani est?
43. In Italia in ripis fluminis est.
44. Cincinnatus ab agris ad Romam nuntiis vocabatur.
45. Tempore periculi vir magnus patriam servare potest.
46. Iter trans montes altos et per paludes magnas duxit.
47. Latinum scribere posse bonum est.
48. Prima luce Caesar ab castris legiones educet.
49. Post mortem Caesaris Marcus Antonius ad populem Romanum in nomine civitatis orationem magnam fecit.
50. Post Iulium Caesarem imperatores Romani in sua honore nominem Caesaris semper ferebant.

FOR FURTHER STUDY

First Year Latin, by Smith and Thompson. (Allyn & Bacon, Boston.)

Latin First Year, by Berry and Lee. (Silver Burdett Co., New York.)

Latin First Year, by K. P. Harrington. (Ginn & Co., Boston.)

New Latin Grammar, by Charles E. Bennett. (Allyn & Bacon, Boston.)

XV

Mathematics Made Easy

READING AND WRITING NUMBERS

ARABIC SYSTEM

OUR NUMBER SYSTEM was invented by the Arabs. The value of each numeral depends upon its *place* in relation to other numbers. For example:

4 is read as four
40 is read as forty
400 is read as four hundred.

In the first position the numeral 4 represents four units. In the second position, 4 represents 4 × 10 units. In the third position, 4 represents 4 × 100 units. In order to facilitate the reading of large numbers, we group them in units of three and usually separate the groups by commas:

60,458,907,657

In each group the first numeral on the right is units; the second, tens; the third, hundreds. The above number is read as "sixty billion, four hundred fifty-eight million, nine hundred seven thousand, six hundred fifty-seven." In reading integers (whole numbers) aloud you need not use "and." Numbers may be read the shortest way possible. 1,406 may be read "fourteen hundred six," instead of "one thousand four hundred six."

Exercise 1

Read the following figures:

(a) 55,646,808	(d) 10,000,458,975	(g) 465,672,408
(b) 4,900,009	(e) 808,009,606	(h) 80,763,029
(c) 106,456,837	(f) 77,050,731,310	(i) 5,679,005,050

Exercise 2

Write the following figures:

(a) Eighty million, seven hundred sixty-three thousand, twenty-nine.
(b) Ten billion, four hundred fifty-eight thousand, nine hundred seventy-five.
(c) Four million, nine hundred thousand, nine.
(d) Fifty-five million, six hundred forty-six thousand, eight hundred eight.

DECIMALS

In the Arabic system, the value of the numeral is multiplied by ten as we move from right to left. To express values less than 1, we use the decimal point. The value of the numeral is divided by 10 as we move from the decimal point to the right:

.4444

The above decimal is read as "Four thousand four hundred forty-four ten thousandths."

Read the following figures as stated here:

.4—four tenths
.04—four hundredths
.004—four thousandths
.0004—four ten thousandths

Relation between the decimals and numerals:

.4 is 1/10 of 4
.04 is 1/100 of 4
.004 is 1/1000 of 4
.0004 is 1/10,000 of 4

When reading an integer and decimal, insert "and" when you get to the decimal point, thus:

1,808.08 is read "eighteen hundred eight *and* eight hundredths."
500.05 is read "five hundred and five hundredths."

Exercise 3

Read the following figures:

| (a) | 55,055.5 | (c) | 100,006.676 | (e) | 703,703.703 |
| (b) | 6,967.67 | (d) | 14,580.8856 | (f) | 1,505.069 |

(g)	2,960.0008	(j)	5,000.005	(m)	729.0086
(h)	22,022.0022	(k)	9,009.009	(n)	7,007.7007
(i)	4,678.009	(l)	40,004.0004	(o)	3,033.033

Exercise 4

Write the following as decimals:

(a) Six hundred and six hundredths.
(b) Twelve hundred twelve and twelve thousandths.
(c) Fifty thousand and fifty thousandths.
(d) One million, six hundred thousand, fifty-four and fifty-four thousandths.
(e) Fourteen hundred four and fourteen hundred four ten thousandths.

FUNDAMENTAL OPERATIONS, PROOFS, AND SHORT CUTS

ADDITION

To develop accuracy and speed in addition, we suggest the following practices:

1. When adding a column of figures, name or think of results only. For example, in adding 3, 7, 8, 4, we say "10, 18, 22." This is shorter than "three and seven are ten; ten and eight are eighteen"; etc.

2. Whenever possible, group the numbers; that is, combine two or more numbers at sight into a single number, just as you group the letters s-p-e-e-d in reading the word. Practice alone can develop this skill. Notice the grouping indicated in the following column of figures:

$$
\left.\begin{matrix} 3 \\ 4 \\ 2 \end{matrix}\right\} \quad 9 \qquad \text{The first group is read as 9}
$$

$$
\left.\begin{matrix} 6 \\ 2 \\ 2 \end{matrix}\right\} \quad 19 \qquad \text{The second group is read as 10}
$$

$$
\left.\begin{matrix} 4 \\ 2 \end{matrix}\right\} \quad 25 \qquad \text{The third group is read as 6}
$$

$$
\left.\begin{matrix} 9 \\ 3 \end{matrix}\right\} \quad 37 \qquad \text{The fourth group is read as 12}
$$

——————— The results in succession are 9, 19, 25, 37.

The long way would give eight subtotals and the final answer. The timesaving feature is obvious.

3. It is advisable to memorize those combinations which occur frequently so that the response becomes mechanical. Practice saying $7+8=15$, $7+5=12$, $8+5=13$, etc.

4. Develop the habit of proving the answer. Good business practice demands that all computations should be checked for accuracy.

PROOFS FOR ADDITION

(a) Add the columns the opposite way. If you started at the top and added down, reverse the process to prove the result.

(b) Cashier's Method: Add each column of figures separately, but do not carry from one column to the next. Arrange the totals as follows:

6,408	(From right to left)	
3,394	The first column totals	25
6,786	The second column totals	29
735	The third column totals	21
8,092	The fourth column totals	23
25,415		25,415

Exercise 5 (Oral)

The purpose of this drill is to develop speed. Read at sight the sum of each combination. Continue until you can complete the exercise in twenty seconds:

7	5	4	9	4	4	6	3	8	6	8	3	9	1	8	5
2	3	6	1	5	2	6	9	2	3	8	2	2	7	3	2

3	1	4	2	4	1	6	1	2	6	3	5	8	5	7	9
7	1	3	1	4	8	2	4	2	1	3	5	4	9	6	6

5	7	3	9	6	8	7	8	6	9	8	7	4
1	5	1	9	8	7	4	9	5	7	5	7	9

Exercise 6 (Oral)

Drill in grouping. Make groups of two figures each, as you add. Name the results only. Thus in problem "a," starting at the top, by adding in groups of two numbers the results are: 13, 23, 31, 41, 52, 63.

	(a)	(b)	(c)	(d)	(e)	(f)	(g)	(h)	(i)	(j)
	4	5	8	7	8	6	4	7	9	9
	9	7	5	7	4	6	7	8	8	3
	3	4	7	4	6	4	5	6	5	7
	7	6	2	8	3	4	1	2	6	8
	6	2	4	5	3	2	2	6	3	6
	2	7	6	7	4	8	7	4	3	9
	8	6	9	6	2	5	4	7	6	5
	2	1	1	1	9	6	5	4	2	5
	5	4	2	3	4	2	3	5	3	4
	6	4	7	4	5	4	7	3	7	5
	4	5	4	5	2	4	4	1	2	6
	7	5	3	6	8	3	2	5	9	2
Totals ..	..	..	..	..	..	..	..	..	..	..

Exercise 7

Find the annual total sales for each department and the monthly total for all departments:

a.   REPORT ON SALES

Month	Millinery	Clothing	Shoes	Handbags	Totals
January	2,945.67	9,805.37	1,468.35	943.70	....
February	2,060.50	7,468.90	948.30	784.36	....
March	4,673.00	12,229.40	2,960.25	1,549.39	....
April	4,039.20	13,770.35	2,472.78	2,046.37	....
May	1,846.39	9,456.40	2,006.37	1,273.44	....
June	2,635.30	8,895.70	3,785.79	946.30	....
July	1,846.35	6,907.00	1,862.57	683.47	....
August	1,536.70	7,780.50	1,740.63	749.37	....
September	5,638.42	11,436.70	3,246.73	1,936.22	....
October	3,075.09	13,738.25	2,872.94	1,039.79	....
November	2,482.25	11,640.40	3,050.70	946.37	....
December	2,009.45	9,720.65	1,986.37	1,830.95	....
Totals	....	....	....	....	....

Prove by checking the final totals of the vertical columns against the final totals of the horizontal columns.

Compute the annual payroll for each department and the monthly total for all departments.

b.

PAYROLL

Month	Millinery	Clothing	Shoes	Handbags	Totals
January	736.20	1,150.00	450.00	205.00	. . . .
February	694.35	1,379.85	435.75	205.00	. . . .
March	927.80	1,839.25	565.45	240.75	. . . .
April	875.45	1,010.90	490.90	298.35	. . . .
May	706.30	1,025.45	412.60	205.50	. . . .
June	789.75	1,655.30	401.30	201.25	. . . .
July	637.45	940.15	257.00	149.00	. . . .
August	705.25	1,015.00	298.50	205.90	. . . .
September	1,023.60	2,095.75	570.35	220.70	. . . .
October	750.65	2,140.50	485.70	215.30	. . . .
November	700.10	1,730.90	448.40	290.25	. . . .
December	530.00	1,809.35	420.15	340.00	. . . .
Totals	. . . .	. . . .	. . . . . .	. . . . . .	. . . .

Prove your answers by the method used in (a).

Compute the annual expenses for each department and the monthly expenses for all departments.

c.

EXPENSES

Month	Millinery	Clothing	Shoes	Handbags	Totals
January	217.23	976.63	249.74	107.30	. . . .
February	231.34	1,086.47	220.37	85.46	. . . .
March	341.15	1,146.28	346.86	97.74	. . . .
April	316.17	1,230.81	292.41	148.50	. . . .
May	240.56	944.35	263.60	125.83	. . . .
June	231.67	939.75	313.79	132.27	. . . .
July	195.78	849.62	236.95	96.39	. . . .
August	210.90	1,230.79	247.57	103.70	. . . .
September	375.23	1,197.43	324.93	170.46	. . . .
October	285.44	1,039.36	267.66	125.75	. . . .
November	294.50	1,246.20	319.32	139.80	. . . .
December	278.71	947.00	230.27	167.29	. . . .
Totals	. . . .	. . . .	. . . . . .	. . . . . .	. . . .

Prove your answers.

d. Add and prove the results.

46.05	563.07	4,680.55
268.178	649.607	549.8609
49.602	70.5401	72.004
94.7305	68.0099	3,663.32
636.093	42.3	987.6984

e. Add horizontally and prove the results.

1) $7.21+8.3+9.04+6.21+4.05+7.5+6.6+19=$
2) $.46+5.7+37+7.56+.26+4.8+15+.32=$
3) $.9+3.05+.8+.304+7.46+.29+.076+20=$
4) $8.5+2.73+.26+.09+3.805+.37+12+.35=$
5) $22+9.009+.73+9.01+.906+.84+.009+24=$

SUBTRACTION

The usual method of "making change" is to add from the amount of the sale to the next higher money unit. If the amount of the sale is 47¢ and the clerk is giving change of $1.00, he gives the customer 3¢ and says 50¢, then he gives 50¢ and counts $1.00. He subtracts by adding to 47¢ an amount that brings it up to $1.00. We apply this method to subtraction.

(a) Deduct 21.24 from 96.24

96.79	$4+5=9$ The difference is 5
21.24	$2+5=7$ The difference is 5
75.55	$1+5=6$ The difference is 5
	$2+7=9$ The difference is 7

(b) Deduct 94.17 from 635.25

635.25   We cannot deduct 7 from 5.
94.17   We therefore borrow one from the next higher
541.08   unit, the ten column, and raise 5 to 15.

$$7+8=15$$

We used one of the "ten" units leaving 1 as a remainder.

$$1+0=1$$
$$4+1=5$$
$$9+4=13$$

Since we borrowed one unit from the hundreds column, we reduced the 6 to 5.

The *minuend* is the number which is to be reduced. The *subtrahend* is the number which is deducted from the minuend.

$$639 \text{ minuend}$$
$$\underline{-47} \text{ subtrahend}$$
$$592 \text{ remainder}$$

Exercise 8 (Subtraction)

a.	9	8	6	7	8	9	8	7	9
	3	2	2	4	3	5	1	2	4

b.	15	14	18	17	18	16	17	13	16
	9	7	5	9	4	7	4	5	3

c.	24	27	22	21	26	28	23	20	25
	17	16	13	15	19	14	12	11	18

d.	32	38	34	37	30	35	31	36	33
	27	29	22	21	26	23	28	24	25

e.	46	53	67	80	44	92	39	71	63
	38	45	59	72	36	88	24	64	59

f.	59	48	73	62	36	76	28	32	54
	30	39	67	54	28	62	15	27	47

You should repeat this exercise until you can complete it in 60 seconds.

Exercise 9

	Old Balance	Deposit	Checks	New Balance
a.	654.39	145.70	269.35	?
b.	329.36	285.63	347.60	?
c.	840.09	248.27	193.38	?
d.	1269.75	132.24	478.26	?
e.	746.32	398.47	348.12	?
f.	1927.36	408.35	976.33	?

	Old Balance	Deposit	Checks	New Balance
g.	468.70	571.28	630.74	?
h.	1055.48	94.62	587.37	?
i.	361.05	281.35	118.32	?
j.	941.83	483.79	589.73	?
k.	736.27	632.28	730.56	?

To prove your results, add the old balance and deposit; then add the checks and new balance. The totals should agree.

Exercise 10

Find the net amount for each invoice. Then total all columns and prove your results.

	Invoice Amount	Discount	Net Amount
a.	236.47	4.73	. . . .
b.	93.32	.93	. . . .
c.	781.28	23.44	. . . .
d.	967.90	19.36	. . . .
e.	343.83	10.31	. . . .
f.	563.76	5.64	. . . .
g.	834.45	16.64	. . . .
h.	175.53	5.26	. . . .
i.	62.27	1.24	. . . .
j.	129.00	2.58	. . . .
Totals			

MULTIPLICATION

In order that you may understand the subject matter presented in this section, it will be necessary to know the terms used.

Multiplicand is the unit or number which is to be multiplied.

Multiplier is the multiplying number.

Product is the result of multiplication.

The multiplicand and multiplier are called *factors:*

$$2 \times 3 = 6$$
$$15 \text{ yards} \times 4 = 60 \text{ yds.}$$

2 is the multiplicand; 3 is the multiplier; 6 is the product; 2 and 3 are factors.

When you speak of 15 yards of cloth, 20 machines, $500, 8 bushels, you are using *concrete* numbers, but when you say 15, 20, 5, 8 you are using *abstract* numbers. The multiplier is always an abstract number. If the multiplicand is a concrete number, the product is expressed in terms of the same unit. In the example given above, the answer is 60 *yards*.

Exercise 11 (Oral)

Multiply at sight, using as multipliers 2, 3, 4, 5, 6, 7, 8, 9. Repeat this drill until you can do these problems at the rate of 120 a minute. 4, 7, 6, 9, 11, 3, 8, 2, 5, 12, 13.

PROVING MULTIPLICATION

1. Interchange the multiplier and multiplicand

```
Illustration  4695         Proof  347
              347                 4695
             -----               -----
            32865                1735
            18780                3123
            14085                2082
          -------                1388
          1629165               -----
                               1629165
```

2. Divide the product by either factor

```
              4,695
        347)1,629,165
            1388
            ----
            2411
            2082
            ----
             3296
             3123
             ----
             1735
             1735
             ----
```

Exercise 12

a. Make the extensions for each of the following:

79 Doz. shirts	@	$22.50	$......
24 Doz. collars	@	3.75	......
37 Doz. pajamas	@	16.50	......
19 Doz. ties	@	8.75	......
13 Doz. ties	@	6.60	......
18 Doz. hats	@	27.50	......
11 Doz. hats	@	42.00	......
18 Doz. prs. socks	@	3.85	......
22 Doz. gloves	@	16.75	......
9 Doz. hdkfs.	@	2.90	......
15 Doz. underwear	@	6.75	......
		Total	$......

b. Find the total value:

61 yd.	@	$.75	$......
78 yd.	@	.49	......
35 yd.	@	1.05	......
136 yd.	@	.64	......
78 yd.	@	.78	......
226 yd.	@	.99	......
		Total	$......

c. Find the total payroll:

Employee	Hours	Rate	Wages
A	37	$.80	$......
B	44	.67	......
C	39	.44	......
D	42	.72	......
E	48	.42	......
F	36	.85	......
G	29	.65	......
H	44	.75	......
I	40	.59	......
J	35	1.30	......
K	38	.87	......
		Total Payroll	$......

SHORT CUTS

There are ways of shortening our calculations, thereby saving time and labor. We present a few practical short cuts. Use them wherever possible to get results quickly and possibly avoid making mistakes.

1. To multiply an integer by 10, 100, 1000, etc.
   Add as many zeros to the multiplicand as there are zeros in the multiplier.

$$765 \times 10 = 7{,}650$$
$$765 \times 100 = 76{,}500$$
$$765 \times 1000 = 765{,}000$$

If the multiplicand has a decimal, move the point to the right as many places as there are zeros in the multiplier.

$$14.05 \times 10 = 140.5$$
$$14.05 \times 100 = 1{,}405$$
$$14.05 \times 1000 = 14{,}050$$

2. To multiply a number by 11, 101, 1001, etc.
   First step: Multiply by 10, 100, 1000, etc.
   Second step: Add the multiplicand to the product.

$76 \times 10 = 760$	$76 \times 100 = 7{,}600$	$76 \times 1000 = 76{,}000$
$76 \times 1 \quad 76$	$76 \times 1 \quad 76$	$76 \times 1 \quad 76$
$76 \times 11 \quad 836$	$76 \times 101 \quad 7{,}676$	$76 \times 1001 \quad 76{,}076$

3. To multiply a number by 9, 99, 999, etc., multiply by 10, 100, 1000, etc.; then deduct the multiplicand.

$176 \times 10 = 1{,}760$	$176 \times 100 = 17{,}600$	$176 \times 1000 = 176{,}000$
$176 \times 1 \quad 176$	$176 \times 1 \quad 176$	$176 \times 1 \quad 176$
$176 \times 9 \quad 1{,}584$	$176 \times 99 \quad 17{,}424$	$176 \times 999 \quad 175{,}824$

4. To multiply a number by a fractional part of a hundred the fractional parts of a hundred are called *aliquot parts*. The ones frequently used are listed below. You should memorize them in order to use them effectively.

Halves	*Quarters*	*Eighths*
50 = ½ of 100	25 = ¼ of 100	12½ = ⅛ of 100
	75 = ¾ of 100	37½ = ⅜ of 100
		62½ = ⅝ of 100
		87½ = ⅞ of 100

Sixteenths	Thirds	Sixths
6 1/4 = 1/16 of 100	33 1/3 = 1/3 of 100	16 2/3 = 1/6 of 100
	66 2/3 = 2/3 of 100	83 1/3 = 5/6 of 100

To multiply a number by a fractional part of a hundred, first multiply by 100 and then multiply by the fractional part of a hundred.

Illustration: $762 \times 33\ 1/3$
First step: $762 \times 100 = 76,200$
Second step: $76,200 \times 1/3 = 25,400$

5. To multiply a number by aliquot parts of 1, 100, or 1000, study the following table. The fraction in the first column indicates the aliquot part of 1, 10, 100, 1000.

	1.	10.	100.	1000.
⅛	.12½	1¼	12½	125
¼	.25	2½	25	250
½	.5	5	50	500
⅝	.62½	6¼	62½	625
¾	.75	7½	75	750
⅞	.87½	8¾	87½	875

Principle: When the multiplier is an aliquot part of a number, use the latter as a multiplier and then multiply the answer by the fractional part of the number.

Illustrations: $24 \times 8¾$ $8¾ = ⅞$ of 10
Short cut: $24 \times 10 = 240$ $240 \times ⅞ = 210$
                   720×625 $625 = ⅝$ of 1,000
                   $720 \times 1000 = 720,000$ $720,000 \times ⅝ = 450,000$

Skill in using aliquot parts reduces the mechanics of computations to a minimum.

Exercise 13

Make the following extensions mentally:

a) 60 hammers @ .33⅓ ......   h) 48 trowels @ .25 ......
b) 56 saws   @ .87½ ......   i) 66 screens @ .66⅔ ......
c) 88 locks   @ .62½ ......   j) 74 knives   @ .99 ......
d) 32 bolts   @ .06¼ ......   k) 96 batteries @ .06¼ ......
e) 42 brushes @ .83⅓ ......   l) 101 hammers @ .49 ......
f) 72 pliers   @ .37½ ......   m) 99 saws   @ .65 ......
g) 36 planes   @ .50 ......   n) 101 bulbs   @ .13 ......

o) 76 bolts   @ .09 . . . .   s) 99 knives   @ .27   . . . .
p) 99 brushes @ .84 . . . .   t) 64 funnels   @ .12½ . . . .
q) 78 pliers   @ .99 . . . .   u) 25 strainers @ .16   . . . .
r) 24 planes   @ .75 . . . .   v) 24 sockets   @ .06¼ . . . .

Exercise 14

Find the invoice amount:

46 ft. of 2-in. galvanized pipe	@	.40 . . . .
32 ½-in. valves	@	.87½ . . . .
6 wash basins	@	19.40 . . . .
280 ft. 1-in. galvanized pipe	@	.11 . . . .
6 bathtubs	@	85.00 . . . .
6 escutcheons	@	.65 . . . .
5 2-in. gate valves	@	4.25 . . . .

Exercise 15

a) 62½ is what part of 100?. . .   j)   1¼ is what part of   10?. . .
b)   2½ is what part of   10?. . .   k) 66⅔ is what part of 100?. . .
c) .12½ is what part of   1?. . .   l)   6⅔ is what part of   10?. . .
d) .75 is what part of   1?. . .   m) 875 is what part of 1000?. . .
e) .33⅓ is what part of   1?. . .   n) .16⅔ is what part of   1?. . .
f) 625 is what part of 1000?. . .   o) 16⅔ is what part of 100?. . .
g) 250 is what part of 1000?. . .   p) .83⅓ is what part of   1?. . .
h)   7½ is what part of   10?. . .   q) 37½ is what part of 100?. . .
i) .66⅔ is what part of   1?. . .   r)   6¼ is what part of   10?. . .

DIVISION

The following terms are used in division:

Dividend is the quantity or number which is to be divided into parts.
Divisor is the number by which the dividend is to be divided.
Quotient is the result of division.

As we pointed out under multiplication, much of the mechanics can be reduced by using short cuts wherever possible. Some of these devices are presented below.

1. To divide by 10, 100, 1000, etc., point off as many decimal places to the left as there are zeros in the divisor.

$$678.5 \div 10 = 67.85$$
$$678.5 \div 100 = 6.785$$
$$678.5 \div 1000 = .6785$$

2. To divide by an aliquot part of a number, divide by the number and multiply the result by the inverted fraction.

Example 1—   480 ÷ 2½   2½ = ¼ of 10
             480 × 4/10 = 192

In other words, multiply by 4, and divide by 10.

Example 2—   480 ÷ 25   25 = ¼ of 100
             480 × 4/100 = 19.2

Example 3—   480 ÷ 250   250 = ¼ of 1000
             480 × 4/1000 = 1.92

PROVING DIVISION

To prove the result, multiply the divisor by the quotient and add the remainder, if any.

To prove the last example:

$$250 \times 1.92 = 480$$

Exercise 16

Divide at sight:

a. 120 by 2½
b. 90 by 7½
c. 600 by 25
d. 900 by 75
e. 444 by .25
f. 90 by 33⅓
g. 490 by .87½
h. 48 by .5
i. 500 by 16⅔
j. 480 by .16⅔
k. 60 by .83⅓
l. 35 by 833⅓
m. 24 by .25

n. 320 by 6¼
o. 3000 by 375
p. 1200 by 16⅔
q. 5000 by 625
r. 14000 by 875
s. 150 by .33⅓
t. 3500 by 500
u. 450 by 50
v. 400 by 125
w. 1800 by 750
x. 900 by .37½
y. 500 by 12½
z. 900 by 33⅓

Exercise 17

a. 968.75 ÷ 6.25
b. 43335 ÷ 963
c. 1809 ÷ 27
d. 44160 ÷ 128
e. 19683 ÷ 729

f. 1342.70 ÷ 2.90
g. 8464 ÷ 18
h. 59832 ÷ 72
i. 1175 ÷ 35
j. 2809 ÷ 53

FRACTIONS

An integer is a whole number, like 5. A fraction is a part of a unit, like ½ gallon, ½ pound, ¾ yard, and so forth. A fraction indicates division; therefore, ¾ means that the unit is divided into four equal parts, each of which is called a fourth (and in this fraction we are representing three fourths).

The number above the line is the *numerator,* and the number below the line, the *denominator.* The denominator expresses the names of the parts, like halves, fourths, sixths, and so forth. The numerator shows the number of parts. In the fraction ¾, the unit is divided into four equal parts and the fraction is three parts of the unit.

Which is larger, ⅛ or ¼ of the same unit?

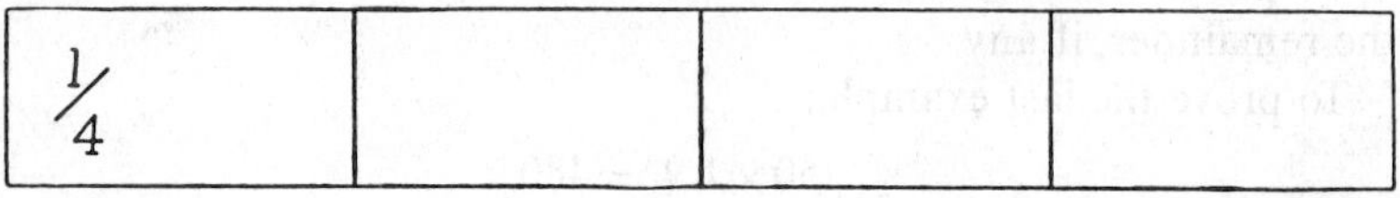

FIGURE 1

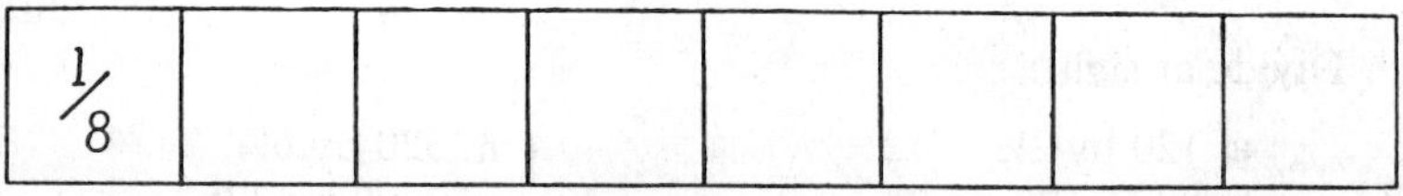

FIGURE 2

In Figure 1, the unit was divided into fourths, and in Figure 2, into eighths. When the denominator is increased and the numerator remains the same, the value of the fraction decreases. When the numerator is increased and the denominator remains the same, the value of the fraction increases.

WRITING FRACTIONS

Fractions may be expressed in two ways:

a. As a common fraction, with the numerator and denominator separated by the division sign, written either: $\frac{1}{2}$ *or* ½.
   Example: ⅔, ⅘, ¾, etc.

b. As a decimal fraction:
   .66⅔, .8, or .75.

In decimal fractions, the denominator is always 10, 100, 1000, o⁻ any power of 10. The denominator is not written, but is indicated b⁻ the position to the right of the decimal point.

INTERCHANGE OF FRACTIONAL FORMS

The arithmetical calculations may be shortened sometimes by using the common fraction form and at other times by using a decimal fraction form. To compute the cost of 68½ yards at 14¼¢ the multiplication is done more easily if we change the fractions ½ and ¼ to decimal fractions:

$$
\begin{array}{r}
.1425 \\
68.5 \\
\hline
7125 \\
11400 \\
8550 \\
\hline
\$9.76125 \quad \text{Answer } \$9.76
\end{array}
$$

To compute the cost of 60 pounds at .12½¢ the work is shortened by changing .12½ to ⅛ of $1.00.

$$60 \times \$⅛ = \$7.50$$

USE OF DECIMAL POINTS

1. *Multiplication*—The number of decimal places in the product is equal to the decimal places in the factors. Example:

$$16.4 \times .32 = 5.248$$

   There is one decimal place in the multiplicand and there are two places in the multiplier. Therefore, there should be three decimal places in the product.

2. *Division*—When the divisor has a decimal fraction we move the decimal point as many places as it is necessary to change the fraction to an integer (whole number). Carry the decimal point in the dividend the *same number of places* to the right and if necessary add zeros. Example: $641 \div .72$

$$
\begin{array}{r}
890.27 \\
72. \overline{)64100.00} \\
576 \\
\hline
650 \\
648 \\
\hline
200 \\
144 \\
\hline
560 \\
504 \\
\hline
56
\end{array}
$$

We move the decimal point two places in the divisor and dividend and add two zeros after the decimal point in the dividend in order to continue the division to two decimal places.

3. *Addition* and *Subtraction*—Write the numbers so that the decimals line up properly and the figures are placed in the proper column one under the other. Example:

Subtract

658.5
  92.007
———
566.493

Exercise 18 (Oral)

Change the following to decimal fractions:

5/10   6/100   5/1000   1/4   1/8   7/8
3/8   1/16   5/8   3/4   1/2   1/3   2/3

Change the following to common fractions:

a. .5
b. .05
c. .125
d. .75
e. .1666⅔
f. .6666⅔
g. .3333⅓
h. .875
i. .0125
j. .4

k. .015
l. .025
m. .25
n. .8333⅓
o. .005
p. .8
q. .08
r. .008
s. .0625
t. .375

Exercise 19

Perform the operations indicated:

a. 8.005×68
b. 94.2×1.45
c. 75.06×405
d. .0916×2.2
e. 64.36×.134
f. .8503×.18
g. 7.09×.53

h. 675÷1.5
i. 675÷.15
j. 675÷.015
k. .675÷.015
l. 6.75÷.15
m. 86.4÷.024
n. 5.4÷.036

SELLING BY THE HUNDRED

What is the value of 413 lbs. @ 60¢ cwt. (cwt. means 100 pounds)?
The quantity and the unit price are not alike. Therefore we change
413 lbs. to cwt.

$$413 \div 100 = 4.13 \text{ cwt.}$$
$$4.13 \times .60 = 2.4780 \text{ or } \$2.48.$$

Principle: The multiplier must be expressed in terms of the price
unit.

SELLING BY THE THOUSAND

What is the value of 24000 shingles @ 6.40 per M (thousand)?
The unit price is M. Therefore we change 24000 to the same unit.

$$24000 \div 1000 = 24 \text{ units}$$
$$\$6.40 \times 24 = \$153.60$$

Exercise 20

(a) At sight, change the following quantities to units of 100: 300;
6,037; 175; 75; 8,637; 2,637; 4,235; 80,680; 467.5; 83.27.
(b) At sight, change the following quantities to units of 1000: 5000;
65000; 8649; 400; 50; 8496.5; 2840; 93785; 150608; 724.
(c) Find the cost. (Use short cuts wherever possible.)

800 @ .12½ per c	2,000 @ 4.50 per M
1800 @ .20 per c	10,000 @ 1.55 per M
450 @ 1.33⅓ per c	500 @ 8.00 per M
240 @ .87½ per c	800 @ 5.00 per M
50 @ .80 per c	625 @ 8.00 per M

Exercise 21

Find the total cost.

a.   9980 lbs. of beef   @ 12.50 per cwt.
b.   4672 ft. of lumber   @ 37.00 per M
c. 18400 shingles   @ 4.25 per M
d.   720 lbs. of bran   @ 1.05 per cwt.
e. 1250 fence posts   @ 9.00 per C
f. 14500 tiles   @ 12.25 per M
g. 2500 envelopes   @ 4.10 per M
h. 10250 sheets   @ 3.15 per M
i. 2200 lbs. oats   @   .85 per cwt.
j.   475 lbs. nails   @ 6.00 per cwt.

COMMON FRACTIONS

A *common fraction* is one whose numerator is less than the denominator.

An *improper fraction* is a fraction whose numerator is larger than the denominator, such as 7/5, 4/3, etc.

A *mixed number* includes an integer and a fraction, such as 46⅓, 21⅝, etc.

CHANGING FRACTIONS TO HIGHER TERMS

A unit may be divided into halves, quarters, eighths, etc.: 1=2/2 or 4/4 or 8/8, etc.

Since all these fractions equal 1 they are equal to each other: 2/2=4/4=8/8.

To change halves to quarters, we multiply the numerator and denominator by 2.

$$2/2 \times 2/2 = 4/4$$

In other words we do not change the *value* of a fraction when we multiply the numerator and denominator by the same number.

1/4=?/12;   3/4=?/12;   1/5=?/20   4/5=?/20

Rule: To change a fraction to higher terms, divide the higher denominator by the lower denominator; then, using the quotient as a multiplier, multiply the numerator and denominator.

CHANGING FRACTIONS TO LOWER TERMS

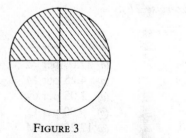

FIGURE 3

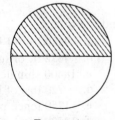

FIGURE 4

In Figure 3 the unit is divided into fourths; in Figure 4 the unit is divided into halves. The shaded part in Figure 3 covers 2/4 of the unit and in Figure 4, 1/2 of the unit. It is obvious from the illustration tha

2/4 = 1/2. To change from fourths to halves we divide the numerator and denominator by 2.

$$2/4 \div 2/2 = 1/2$$

$$\frac{2 \div 2}{4 \div 2} = \frac{1}{2}$$

$$4/8 = ?/2 \qquad 4/6 = ?/3 \qquad 6/15 = ?/5$$

Rule: To change a fraction to lower terms, divide the higher denominator by the lower denominator; then, using the quotient as a divisor, divide the numerator and denominator.

Exercise 22

a. At sight reduce to higher terms:

1/2 to eighths	2/3 to sixths
1/4 to twentieths	4/5 to thirtieths
1/6 to twelfths	3/8 to twenty-fourths
1/3 to twelfths	3/4 to twelfths
1/5 to fifteenths	5/6 to twelfths
1/8 to sixteenths	3/5 to tenths

b. At sight reduce to lower terms:

4/8 to fourths	14/20 to tenths
4/6 to thirds	15/27 to ninths
5/15 to thirds	12/16 to eighths
2/16 to eighths	4/20 to fifths
4/12 to thirds	6/24 to fourths
14/16 to eighths	4/32 to eighths

c. Reduce to eighths: 1/4, 1/2, 3/4
   Reduce to sixteenths: 1/8, 3/8, 5/8, 1/2, 3/4
   Reduce to twentieths: 1/2, 1/4, 2/5, 3/10, 3/4, 4/5
   Reduce to hundredths: 1/5, 1/4, 1/10, 3/4, 4/5, 10/25, 3/50

LEAST COMMON DENOMINATOR

How many feet in 3 yds. and 2 feet? We cannot add yards and feet because the units are different. However, we can change 3 yards to 9 feet and then add 2 feet, making a total of 11 feet.

Add 3/4 and 1/8. We cannot add fourths and eighths. Therefore we change 3/4 to 6/8 and, adding 6/8 and 1/8, we get 7/8.

Add 1/3, 1/2, and 1/4. We must reduce all fractions to a common denominator. 12 is exactly divisible by each denominator, 3, 2, and 4. Therefore we reduce the fractions to twelfths 1/3=4/12, 1/2=6/12, 1/4=3/12, 4/12+6/12+3/12=13/12 or 1 1/12.

The lowest number which is exactly divisible by all the given denominators is called the *least common denominator.*

Exercise 23

Find the least common denominator:

a. 1/5, 1/6
b. 1/3, 1/6, 1/4
c. 1/2, 1/4, 1/6
d. 1/4, 1/8, 1/2
e. 1/2, 1/5
f. 1/2, 1/5, 1/10
g. 1/6, 1/3, 1/9

h. 1/5, 1/10, 1/20
i. 1/3, 1/6, 1/2, 1/8
j. 1/2, 1/4, 1/8, 1/6
k. 1/4, 1/8, 1/2, 1/12
l. 1/5, 1/10, 1/4, 1/2
m. 1/20, 1/5, 1/10, 1/25, 1/4
n. 1/6, 1/4, 1/12, 1/8

ADDITION OF FRACTIONS

Add: 1/8, 3/8, 5/8. Answer: 9/8 or 1 1/8. Since all the denominators are alike, we add the numerators, 1, 3, and 5. We added eighths; therefore the result is 9 eighths (9/8).

If the denominators are not alike, we reduce the fractions to equivalent fractions with a *least common denominator* and add numerators.

Add: 3/16, 1/4, 5/8, 1/2. The least common denominator is *16.*

$$\begin{array}{rl} & \textit{sixteenths} \\ 3/16 = & 3/16 \\ 1/4 = & 4/16 \\ 5/8 = & 10/16 \\ 1/2 = & \underline{8/16} \\ & 25/16 = 1\ 9/16 \end{array}$$

Exercise.24

Add the following mentally:

a. 1/2, 1/3, 1/6
b. 1/4, 1/3, 1/12
c. 1/3, 1/4, 1/6
d. 1/2, 1/10, 1/5

e. 1/3, 1/4, 1/6
f. 1/2, 3/4, 5/8
g. 1/4, 2/3, 5/6
h. 1/8, 3/4, 1/16

SUBTRACTION OF FRACTIONS

Find the difference between 1/2 and 3/8. The denominators are not alike. The first step is to change the fractions to equivalent fractions having the least common denominator, which is 8. $4/8 - 3/8 = 1/8$.

Problem: From 89¼ take 83⅝.

$$
\begin{array}{r}
& 8 \\
& \overline{} \\
89¼ & 2 \\
83⅝ & 5 \\
\hline
\text{Answer:} \quad 5 & ⅝
\end{array}
$$

Explanation: The least common denominator is 8.

We cannot deduct 5/8 from 2/8. Therefore we take one unit from the integer, and change it to 8/8. $8/8 + 2/8 = 10/8$. Subtracting 5/8 from 10/8 we get 5/8. $88 - 83 = 5$.

Exercise 25

Find the difference mentally:

a. $1/5 - 1/10$ f. $3/4 - 2/3$
b. $2/3 - 5/12$ g. $4/5 - 1/3$
c. $5/6 - 2/9$ h. $1/3 - 1/7$
d. $3/4 - 1/5$ i. $3/8 - 1/3$
e. $3/4 - 2/5$ j. $1/2 - 2/15$

MULTIPLICATION OF FRACTIONS

To multiply an integer by a fraction:

10×15 feet equals how many feet? $8 \times 2/3$ equals how many thirds? 16/3. Since the numerator is larger than the denominator, it is an improper fraction. To change to a mixed number divide the numerator by the denominator. $16/3 = 5\ 1/3$.

The process of multiplying an integer by a fraction involves two steps:

1. Multiply the integer by the numerator.
2. Divide the product by the denominator.

a. *To multiply a fraction by another fraction:*

$$4/7 \times 3/5 = 12/35$$

Multiply the numerators to find the new numerator; then multiply the denominators to find the new denominator.

b. *To multiply a mixed number by a mixed number:*

$$6\tfrac{1}{4} \times 12\tfrac{1}{3}$$

First Solution:

$$6\tfrac{1}{4} = 25/4 \qquad\qquad 12\tfrac{1}{3} = 37/3$$
$$25/4 \times 37/3 = 925/12 = 77\ 1/12$$

Solution: Change the mixed numbers to improper fractions; multiply the numerators and denominators; then change the improper fraction to a mixed number.

Second Solution:

6¼	Multiply $6 \times 1/3 = 2$
12⅓	" $12 \times 1/4 = 3$
———	" $1/4 \times 1/3 = \quad 1/12$
2	" $12 \times 6 = 72$
3 1/12	———
72	77 1/12
———	
77 1/12	

Third Solution:

6¼ = 6.25   Change the fractions to equiva-
12⅓ = 12.33⅓   lent decimals and multiply.

6.25
12.33⅓ $625 \times \tfrac{1}{3} = 208\tfrac{1}{3}$ etc.
———
208⅓
1875   There are four decimal places in
1875   the multiplier and multiplicand;
1250   therefore we point off four deci-
625   mal places in the product.
—————
77.0833⅓ = 77 1/12

Exercise 26

I. Find the product mentally and reduce to lowest terms:

a. $1/2 \times 1/3$	f. $2/3 \times 1/2 \times 3/5$
b. $3/7 \times 4/5$	g. $4/7 \times 2/3 \times 1/2$
c. $3/4 \times 2/3$	h. $4/9 \times 2/5 \times 3/10$
d. $1/3 \times 5/6$	i. $3/5 \times 4/5 \times 2/3$
e. $3/12 \times 2/5$	j. $1/3 \times 9/10 \times 6/7$

II. Find the product:

a. $24 \times 5/8$
b. $72 \times 5/6$
c. $783 \times 4/9$
d. $320 \times 11/16$
e. $2436 \times 7/12$
f. $63 \times 15\ 1/3$
g. $846 \times 20\ 1/6$
h. $42 \times 8\ 1/4$
i. $375 \times 22\ 2/5$

j. $180\ 1/3 \times 24\ 1/4$
k. $172\ 1/6 \times 54\ 2/3$
l. $84\ 1/2 \times 7\ 1/4$
m. $906\ 2/5 \times 83\ 1/2$
n. $235\ 1/4 \times 32\ 7/10$
o. $36\ 5/8 \times 12\ 1/2$
p. $195\ 2/3 \times 17\ 1/4$
q. $3186\ 3/5 \times 10\ 1/10$
r. $866\ 1/2 \times 42\ 3/8$

ESTIMATING RESULTS

Short cuts may be used to estimate results when we deal with large numbers which cannot be solved mentally. In this way, we avoid absurd answers.

Example 1. 77 yds. @ 48¢. Which is the correct amount? $3.70? $.37? $369.60? $36.96?

We can estimate the result by using 75 in place of 77: $75 = \frac{3}{4}$ of 100, $\frac{3}{4} \times 100 \times .48 = \$36.00$. The correct answer is slightly higher, because the quantity is slightly more than 75 yds. Therefore the correct answer is $36.96.

Example 2. Find the cost of 65 dozen @ 35¢. Which is the correct answer? $2.28? $22.75? $227.50?

If we use 37½¢ in place of 35¢, and 64 in place of 65, we can solve the problem mentally, thus: $64 \times \$\frac{3}{8} = \$24.00$.

The nearest answer given is $22.75, which is correct. In estimating the result we use 64 because it is divisible by the denominator 8. We substitute 37½¢ instead of 35¢ because the former is an aliquot part of a dollar.

Exercise 27

By the estimating process, select the approximate answer which is nearest the exact answer.

a. $49 \times 32 = 160?\ 1600?\ 16,000?$
b. $19 \times 45 = 90?\ 9000?\ 900?$
c. $32 \times 126 = 4000?\ 400?\ 40,000?$
d. $97 \times 456 = 456,000?\ 45,600?$
   $4560?$
e. $48 \times 36.50 = 18,000?\ 1800?\ 180?$
f. $900 \div 35 = 2700?\ 270?\ 27?$
g. $40,000 \div 23 = 16,000?\ 1600?\ 160?$
h. $3965 \div 127 = 320?\ 32?\ 3.2?$
i. $796 \div 37 = 200?\ 2000?\ 20?$

j. 7972 ÷ 250 = 32? .32? 320? 3200?   m. 51 × 19 = 100? 1,000? 10,000?
k. 6397 ÷ 71 = 90? 9000? 900?   n. 480 ÷ 22 = 2500? 250? 25?
l. 8010 × 63 = 50,000? 5000?   o. 360 × .65 = 24? 240? 2400?
   500,000?

PROBLEMS

Thus far the fundamental operations, which include addition, subtraction, multiplication, and division, have been reviewed, and practical short cuts explained. These are the arithmetical tools with which you have to work. Complete mastery of these fundamentals is necessary in order to solve the problems which will be given in this section. To solve a problem you must know three things:

a. What facts are given?
b. What fact or facts must we find?
c. What are the calculations (addition, subtraction, multiplication, division), which numbers are to be grouped, and in what order are the calculations to be performed to solve the problem?

The first two steps, *a* and *b*, are matters of interpretation. If you read the problem *carefully*, you should have no difficulty. The third step requires a knowledge of the fundamental principles of arithmetic. Many problems are patterned after one or more of the following types:

Type 1. What is ⅔ of $24.00?
Type 2. ⅔ of what number is $16.00?
Type 3. What part of $24.00 is $16.00?

Solution Type 1:
Facts given: The whole number and a fraction.
Find: The product.
Method: Multiply the multiplicand ($24.00) by the fraction (⅔).
$$⅔ × \$24.00 = \$16.00$$

Solution Type 2:
Facts given: A factor (⅔) and a product ($16.00).
Find: The other factor. (*Of what number* indicates that we must find a missing factor.)
Method: Divide the product by the fraction. (In the section on multiplication we proved the result by dividing the product by either factor.) The product is $16.00 and the given factor is ⅔.
$$\$16.00 ÷ ⅔ = \$24.00$$

(To divide a number by a fraction, we use the *numerator* as a divisor and the *denominator* as a multiplier; in other words, we *invert* the fraction.)

Solution Type 3:

   Facts given: A product, $16.00, and one factor, $24.00.

   Find: The other factor.

   Method: $16.00 ÷ $24.00 = 16/24 or ⅔.

This type has one thing in common with Type 2, namely, we must find the missing factor. In Type 2 the multiplicand was missing, in Type 3 the multiplier is missing. Therefore the operation is the same— division.

In Type 3, you must be careful in selecting the numbers as the product and factor respectively. The product is divided by the factor to find the missing factor. The given factor can be easily identified, because it always follows the expression "what part of ...." This is the divisor or denominator of the fraction 16/24.

PROBLEMS

In the following problems, identify the pattern or type as 1, 2, or 3. List the facts given—what you are required to find—and solve. Always *recheck* the calculations.

1. A retailer's gross profit is ⅓ of the selling price. What is his gross profit on a sale of $1.50?

2. The operating expenses are 1/6 of the sales. If the sales are $24,030.00, what are the operating expenses?

3. The cost of goods is $75.00 and the selling price is $100.00. What part of the selling price is the cost?

4. An employee worked 30 hours and received $15.00. If he had worked 40 hours, what amount would he receive?

5. A secretary typed 16 pages of a report, which is ⅘ of the total number. How many pages in the entire report?

6. At the end of a year a clerk's salary was increased 20%. If the new salary rate is $18.00 per week, what was the old salary?

7. A dealer bought 100 radios @ $65.00 net. He sold ½ of this number at a mark-up of ½ of cost; ⅔ of the remainder at a mark-up of ¼ of cost; the remainder at a loss of 1/10 of cost. What was the gross profit or loss on sales?

8. A jobber buys shirts @ $15.00 a dozen and sells them @ $22.50 a dozen. What part of the selling price is the profit? What part of the cost is the profit?

9. A man spends $450 for rent, which is ⅖ of his annual income. What is his income per month?

10. A lake has a total frontage of 3 miles, 160 feet. A owns 2 miles; B owns 1440 feet; C owns the remainder. What part of the lake frontage does C own? (5280 feet in a mile.)

PERCENTAGE

What part of 28 is 7?

What part of 60 is 45?

The answers may be expressed as *fractions:*

$$7/28 = ¼ \qquad\qquad 45/60 = ¾$$

or as *hundredths:*

$$¼ = 25/100 \qquad\qquad ¾ = 75/100$$

or as *decimals:* .25; .75

or as *per cents:* 25%; 75%

It simplifies the comparison of two numbers or quantities if we use *hundredths* as a measure of comparison. Every fraction can be reduced to hundredths by dividing the numerator by the denominator and continuing the division to as many decimal places as the problem requires.

Example: Change 24/25 to a decimal.   *Answer:* .96

$$\begin{array}{r} .96 \\ 25\overline{)24.00} \\ 22\ 5 \\ \hline 150 \\ 150 \\ \hline \end{array}$$

Per cent means *by the hundred.* It is usually expressed by this sign "%." Five per cent may be written

$$5/100 \quad \text{or} \quad .05 \quad \text{or} \quad 5\%$$

Do you see any difference between *a.* .1, *b.* 10%, and *c.* .1%? *a* and *b* have the same value, namely 10/100. *c* is 1/10 of 1% or 1/10 of 1/100 = 1/1000. Whenever the decimal and % are used, it denotes a fractional part of one per cent.

In percentage problems, the basis of comparison is 100/100 or 100%. The method of solving the problems is the same as the problems in fractions solved in the preceding chapter.

READING PERCENTAGES

Since per cent means hundredths, we use two decimal places, thus .29 is read "twenty-nine per cent." To convert a decimal to per cent form, move the decimal point two places to the right and place % after the number. Conversely, to convert a per cent form to a decimal, point off two places to the left, drop the per cent symbol, and read as a decimal.

.055 is read "five and five-tenths per cent."
.1525 is read "fifteen and twenty-five hundredths per cent."

Read the following expressions as per cent:

1. 17/100
2. .95
3. .9
4. .0775
5. ¾

6. .5%
7. 5/1000
8. ⅓
9. .16⅔
10. ⅞

Exercise 28

Change to per cent form (use % after the expression):

1. .06
2. .72
3. .725
4. .005

5. .96¼
6. .87½
7. .0012½
8. .0175

9. .0005
10. .005/100
11. .001/10
12. 1.25

Change to decimal form:

13. 70%
14. 5%
15. 12½%
16. 33⅓%

17. ½%
18. .75%
19. 1/10%
20. .05%

21. 1¼%
22. ⅝%
23. ⅔%
24. 1½%

Change to decimal and per cent forms:

25. ¼
26. ⅛
27. 1/6
28. ⅞

29. ⅔
30. 45/80
31. 16/80
32. 35/90

33. 17/85
34. 5/11
35. 30/80
36. 16/25

TERMS IN PERCENTAGE

Learn the following terms:
Base is the number or quantity which represents 100/100 or the multiplicand.
Rate is the number of hundredths or the multiplier.
Percentage is the product of the base and rate.

Amount is the sum of the base and the percentage.
Difference is the base less the percentage.

Type 1. *The base and rate are given to find the percentage.*

(a) What is 15% of $880?

Change the rate to a decimal and multiply.

Solution:

$$
\begin{array}{r}
\$880 \\
.15 \\
\hline
4400 \\
880 \\
\hline
\$132.00
\end{array}
$$

(b) What is 66⅔% of $1500?

$$66\tfrac{2}{3}\% = \tfrac{2}{3} \qquad \$1500 \times \tfrac{2}{3} = \$1000$$

Fractions, decimals, and per cents may be reduced from one form to another. Whenever we can convert a per cent to an aliquot part, as in the above example, we simplify the calculation by using the equivalent aliquot part.

COMMUTATIVE LAW IN MULTIPLICATION

We may interchange multiplier and multiplicand without changing the result. Thus the problem, 28% of $125, may be converted to 125% of $28.

We converted the multiplicand $125 into the multiplier 125%, and the multiplier 28% was changed to the multiplicand $28. The results of either multiplication is the same:

$$28\% \text{ of } \$125 = \$35.00$$
$$125\% \text{ of } \$28 = 35.00$$

Rule for Type 1: Base × Rate = Percentage.

Exercise 29

Find the percentage at sight:

1. 80% of $45
2. 75% of $240
3. 16⅔% of $1800
4. 62½% of $8000
5. 87½% of $560

6. 125% of $400
7. 112½% of $1600
8. .5% of $660
9. 12½% of $4000
10. 83⅓% of $2400

11.	27% of $3333.33	16.	32% of $250
12.	45% of $2000	17.	36% of $2500
13.	16% of $1250	18.	18% of $666.66
14.	66% of $1666.66	19.	40% of $750
15.	56% of $125	20.	35% of $6000

Type 2. *The base and percentage are given to find the rate.*

> $40. is what part of $120?
> $40. is what per cent of $120? or what per cent of $120. is $40.?
> $120. × ?% = $40.
> The base is $120. The percentage is $40. Rate?
> *Solution:* $40. ÷ $120. = Rate.
> 40/120 = ⅓ = 33⅓%   Proof: $120. × ⅓ = $40.

Rule for Type 2: To find the rate, divide the percentage by the base.
Note: The number after "per cent of ......" is the base.

Exercise 30

What per cent of:

1.	$45 is $18?	5.	$2.00 is $.75?	9.	$410.00 is $287.00?
2.	$96 is $16?	6.	$1.50 is $.30?	10.	$31.00 is $15.50?
3.	$960 is $120?	7.	$40.80 is $8.16?		
4.	$.50 is $.20?	8.	$335.00 is $97.50?		

Type 3. *The rate and percentage are given to find the base.*

> 84 is ⅓ of what number?
> 84 is 33⅓% of what number? or, ? × 33⅓% = 84.

We are given the rate 33⅓% and the percentage 84. The missing number is the *base.*
This is similar to Type 2 of problems in fractions.

> *Solution:* 84 ÷ ⅓ = 252. (In division by fractions, the denominator is the multiplier.) Proof: ⅓ of 252 = 84.

Rule for Type 3: Percentage divided by the rate equals the base.

Exercise 31

Find the number of dollars of which

1.	$ 90.00 is 15%	4.	$735.00 is 87½%
2.	696.00 is 30%	5.	32.00 is 12½%
3.	480.00 is 66⅔%	6.	96.00 is 6¼%

7. $ 30.00 is 75%
8. 720.00 is 40%
9. 60.00 is 125%
10. 20.00 is 133 1/3%
11. 45.00 is .5%
12. 90.00 is 3/4%
13. 777.00 is .87 1/2%

14. $ 20.00 is 1/6%
15. 6.90 is 23%
16. 7.20 is 18%
17. 168.00 is 42%
18. 10.80 is 12%
19. 16.50 is 33%
20. 11.20 is 6 1/4%

Type 4. *Per cent of Increase.*

Problem: A number increased by 25% equals 150. What is the number?

Solution: The missing number is the base or 100%. When we increase it by 25%, we get 125% of the number. Therefore the rate is 125%.

$$? \times 125\% = 150$$
$$150 \div 5/4 = 120$$

Proof: $120 \times 5/4 = 150$.

Rule for Type 4: When the problem indicates an increase, be sure to add the increase to 100%.

Type 5. *Per cent of Decrease.*

Problem: A number decreased by 10% equals 810. What is the number?

Solution: The missing number is the base or 100%. Deducting 10% from the base, we get 90%.

$$? \times 90\% = 810$$
$$810 \div 9/10 = 900$$

Proof: $900 \times 90\% = 810$.

Rule for Type 5: When the problem indicates a decrease, deduct the per cent of decrease from 100% and proceed in accordance with the solution for Type 2 problems.

Exercise 32

What number increased by

1. 25% of itself is 300?
2. 10% of itself is 242?
3. 33⅓% of itself is 98?
4. 40% of itself is 9800?
5. 100% of itself is 36?

6. 62½% of itself is 65?
7. 87½% of itself is 900?
8. 5% of itself is 1050?
9. 30% of itself is 910?
10. 250% of itself is 1050?

Exercise 33

What number decreased by

1. 25% of itself is 9?
2. 10% of itself is 90?
3. 33⅓% of itself is 120?
4. 40% of itself is 120?
5. 50% of itself is 45?

6. 62½% of itself is 300?
7. 87½% of itself is 14?
8. 15% of itself is 1700?
9. 30% of itself is 560?
10. 12½% of itself is 56?

How to Solve Problems in Percentage

Five types of problems in percentage have been presented. To solve the problems that follow, it is necessary to recognize the type in order to get the correct result. You will find it helpful to arrange your solution in this form:

a. Facts given:
b. Find:
c. Solution:

Each type of problem is illustrated below.

Type 1 Problem: An investor realized a profit of 8% in his investment of $4850.00. What was his profit?

Facts given: Base, $4850.00. Rate, 8%.
Find: Profit (percentage).
Solution: Base × Rate = Percentage.
$4850 × .08 = $388.

Type 2 Problem: January sales were $10,500. February sales were $787.50 less than January. What was the per cent of decrease?

Facts given: Base (January sales).
Percentage (February *decrease of sales*).
Find: The rate (per cent of decrease).
Solution: Percentage ÷ Base = Rate.
$787.50 ÷ $10,500 = .075 or 7½%.
Proof: $10,500. × .075 = $787.50

Type 3 Problem: The operating expenses of a retail store for one year were $10,547. This is 26½% of the net sales. What were the sales?

Facts given: Percentage (operating expenses).
Rate (per cent of net sales).
Find: The base (net sales).

Solution: Percentage ÷ Rate = Base.

1% of sales is $10,547 ÷ .265 = $398.

100% of sales is $398 × 100 = $39,800.

Proof: $39,800 × .265 = $10,547.

Type 4 Problem: A salesman's salary was increased from $60 to $70 per week. What was the rate of increase?

Facts given: Base (old salary).

Amount (new salary).

Find: The per cent of increase.

Solution: Increase ÷ Base = Rate.

The increase = $70 − $60 = $10.

The rate = $10 ÷ $60 = 1/6 or 16 2/3%.

Type 5 Problem: A suit marked $35 was reduced to $29.75. What was the mark-down per cent?

Facts given: Base (original sales price).

Difference (marked-down price).

Find: The per cent of decrease.

Solution: Decrease ÷ Base = Rate.

The decrease is $35 − $29.75 = $5.25.

$5.25 ÷ $35 = 15%.

PROBLEMS IN PERCENTAGE

1. A wholesaler sold radios at $45, which was 40% less than the list price. What was the list price?

2. The 1940 census of a city was 165,430. The 1950 census was 173,715. What was the rate of increase?

3. A retailer buys shirts @ $15.00 a dozen. He makes 40% gross profit on cost. What is the sales price per shirt?

4. In 1946 a building and lot were assessed at $18,700, which represented an increase of 10% of the 1945 valuation. What was the assessed value in 1945?

5. After deducting a cash discount of 3%, a customer paid $353.08. What was the invoice amount?

6. An employer cut all salaries 15%. One employee received $9.00 less because of this reduction. What was his salary before the reduction?

7. A lawyer's income in 1946 was 18% more than in 1945. If his income in 1946 was $7,457.60, how much did he earn in 1945?

8. During March the operating expenses of a department store were 19% of the sales. If the expenses were $5440.84, what were the sales?

9. The sales were $4352 and the cost of sales, $2720. What was the per cent of gross profit on sales?

10. In problem 9 what was the per cent of gross profit on cost?

11. A commission merchant made sales as follows:

> 1015 bunches of bananas @ $2.10
> 970 " " " @ $1.80
> 1425 " " " @ $1.50

His commission is 7½% of sales. What were his commissions?

12. A salesman who works on a straight commission basis earned $3600. If his rate is 7½% on sales, what were his sales for the period?

13. Mr. Frohm sold a building for $126,500. The original cost to Mr. Frohm was $95,000. He spent $32,500 on permanent improvements and had a net income of $4,850 during the period of ownership. What was the per cent of profit or loss on this transaction?

14. A and B are in the retail grocery business. A's average mark-up is 33⅓% on cost, while B's average mark-up is 30% on sales. Assuming that each has net sales of $3,000 for January, which one has a greater gross profit, and what is the difference?

15. Mr. Franklin purchased 100 motors @ $10.00 less 5%. He sold 50% of them at a mark-up of 50% on cost; 30% of the remainder at a mark-up of 25% on cost, and the rest of the lot at a loss of 15% on cost. What was his gross profit or loss on the entire lot?

TRADE DISCOUNTS

In some industries it is customary to issue catalogues with list prices subject to *trade discounts*. When the market prices fluctuate upward or downward, the discounts are changed. This arrangement makes it possible to continue using the same catalogue indefinitely. *Trade discounts* are deductions from the list price.

Problem 1

An article is listed at $20 and the trade discount is 40%. What is the net selling price?

The list price is the base or 100%.

> 40% of $20.00 = $8.00 Trade Discount
> $20.00 − $8.00 = $12.00 Selling Price.

Problem 2

The list price is $75.00 less 20%, 10%, and 10%. Find the net selling price.

When there are two or more trade discounts, it makes no difference in what order the discounts are taken. To illustrate this point, we offer two solutions, one deducting the discounts in the order given, 20%, 10%, 10%, the other following the reverse order of discounts, 10%, 10%, and 20%.

Solution 1		*Solution 2*
20% of $75.00 = $15.00	*The first discount*	10% of $75.00 = $7.50
$75. − $15. = $60.	The price after the *first discount*	$75.00 − $7.50 = $67.50
10% of $60.00 = $6.00	*The second discount*	10% of $67.50 = $6.75
$60. − $6. = $54.00	The price after the *second discount*	$67.50 − $6.75 = $60.75
10% of $54.00 = $5.40	*The third discount*	20% of $60.75 = $12.15
$54.00 − $5.40 = $48.60	*Net Selling Price*	$60.75 − $12.15 = $48.60

Note that after the first discount is deducted, the following discounts are computed on the last remainder or the price after the previous discount is deducted. In other words, each discount is based on a different amount.

Exercise 34

Find the net selling price.

	List Price	Trade Discounts		List Price	Trade Discounts
a.	$8.00	25%, 10%	f.	$4.40	25%, 12½%, 5%
b.	$45.00	33⅓%, 10%, 5%	g.	$30.00	50%, 10%, 3%
c.	$16.00	40% and 12½%	h.	$40.00	15%, 10%, 5%
d.	$2.40	20%, 16⅔%	i.	$6.00	12½%, 5%, 5%
e.	$15.00	30%, 10%, 10%	j.	$18.00	33⅓%, 16⅔%, 10%

To find a single rate of discount equal to a discount series.

To shorten the calculation, we find a single rate of discount which is equivalent to a series of discounts.

Example: What single discount is equal to 15%, 10%, and 10%?

Let $1.00   = the list price
        .15   = the first discount
       ———
        .85   = the remainder after deducting the first discount
        .085   = the second discount (10% of .85)
       ———
        .765   = the remainder after deducting the second discount
        .0765 = the third discount (10% of .765)
       ———
        .6885 = the net selling price

    1.00 − .6885 = .3115 or 31.15%

Exercise 35

Find the single rate of discount equivalent to:

a. 25% and 10%
b. 33⅓%, 10%, and 5%
c. 40% and 12½%
d. 20% and 16⅔%
e. 30%, 10%, and 10%

f. 25%, 12½%, and 5%
g. 50%, 10%, and 3%
h. 15%, 10%, and 5%
i. 12½%, 5%, and 5%
j. 33⅓%, 16⅔%, and 10%

Discounts are also offered for payment of a bill within the discount period, which is indicated in the terms of the invoice. They are called *time discounts*. The retail merchants occasionally try to stimulate sales by offering goods at marked-down prices. These reductions in price are known as discounts or "Mark-down." The computation for finding the net selling price is based on Type 1 of percentage.

$$\text{Base} \times \text{Rate} = \text{Percentage}$$
$$\text{Base} - \text{Percentage} = \text{Net Selling Price}$$

Problems

1. A watch is listed at $45.00 less 40% and 5%. The cash discount is 2%. What is the net cost to the retailer?

2. Refrigerators are invoiced at $225.00 less 30%, 10%, and 5%. What is the net invoice cost?

3. Typewriters are listed at $85.00 less 20%, 10%, and 10%, with 2% for cash. Find the net cost if the dealer pays cash.

4. The net cost of a bathtub to a plumber is $48.00. If the trade discount is 40%, what is the list price?

5. A desk cost the retailer $60 less 33⅓% and 5%. What should the marked price be to yield a gross profit of 33⅓% on cost?

6. A merchant buys desk lamps at $45.00 per dozen less 20%. What should be the marked price per lamp to yield a gross profit of 50% on cost?

7. Find the list price of a washing machine of which the net invoice cost is $57.75 and the trade discount 45%.

8. A bicycle listed at $40 less 15%, 10%, and 10% was changed to $40 less 33⅓%. Was the net invoice amount increased or decreased and how much?

9. The marked-down price of stockings was 76¢. If the discount was 20%, what was the original selling price?

10. A valise is to be sold for $16.20 net. If the manufacturer is to offer a trade discount of 40% and 10%, at what price should it be listed?

PROFIT AND LOSS

Cost is the net price to the seller.

Selling Price is the amount the buyer pays for the goods.

Gross Profit is the difference between the selling price and the cost.

Overhead or *Operating Expenses* include the expenses incurred in the management of a business, such as rent, salaries, electric and telephone service, supplies, depreciation charges, etc.

Net Profit or *Loss* is the difference between gross profit and operating expenses.

If a camera costing $30 retails for $50, what is the gross profit per cent?

This is similar to Type 2—percentage.

The gross profit is $20.

To find per cent of gross profit, divide the percentage $20 by the base. The problem does not indicate whether per cent of gross profit is based on cost or selling price. In accordance with sound business practice, per cent of profit is usually computed on selling price. Sales are the basis. Gross profit is generally compared with sales, not with cost.

$20/$50 = 40% *gross profit on selling price.*

Profit and Loss problems are similar to the types in percentage and are solved in the same manner.

The base is usually the selling price.

The per cent of profit on sales is the rate.

The profit or loss is the percentage.

Exercise 36

Fill in the gross profit and per cent of gross profit on sales.

	Selling Price	Cost	Gross Profit	% Gross Profit on Sales
1.	2.40	1.20	....	....
2.	20.00	15.00	....	....
3.	5.40	3.60	....	....
4.	10.00	7.50	....	....
5.	1.75	1.26	....	....
6.	.75	.45	....	....
7.	1.25	.75	....	....
8.	5.50	3.50	....	....
9.	8.75	6.25	....	....

To Find the Selling Price, when the Cost and the Per Cent of Gross Profit on Sales are Given

A retailer buys hats at $24.00 a dozen. If his mark-up rate is 33⅓% on sales, what is the resale price per hat?

Facts Given: Cost per dozen and the mark-up rate on sales.

Find: Selling price per hat.

Solution:

Sales   = 1.00
Mark-up = .33⅓
Cost   = .66⅔

$\frac{33⅓}{66⅔}$ = ½ or 50% on Cost

$24.00 ÷ 12 = $2.00 Cost of 1 hat
$2.00 × 50% = $1.00 Profit
$2.00 + $1.00 = $3.00 Selling Price
Proof: $1.00 ÷ $3.00 = 33⅓%

Explanation:

Sales is the base, 100%. Cost is 66⅔% of Sales. We do not know the sales. However, we can convert the per cent rate on sales to an equivalent per cent rate based on cost by dividing the mark-up by the cost.

33⅓% on Sales = 50% on Cost

Base × Rate of Profit = Profit

Summary: To find the selling price when the cost and per cent of gross profit on sales are given:

1. Find the complement of the mark-up rate on sales (the difference between $1.00 and the mark-up rate).

2. Form a fraction with the given mark-up rate as the numerator and its complement as a denominator.

3. Multiply the cost by the result of Step 2.

Exercise 37

The complement of a % is the difference obtained by subtracting the given % from 100%. The complement of 25% is, therefore, 75%.

What is the complement of the following per cents?

1.	20%	6.	50%	11.	37½%
2.	40%	7.	30%	12.	14 2/7%
3.	12½%	8.	10%	13.	28 4/7%
4.	33⅓%	9.	16⅔%	14.	62½%
5.	35%	10.	45%	15.	66 2/3%

The per cents shown above represent per cent gross profit on Sales. Find the equivalent rates based on Cost.

Illustration: Per cent of gross profit on sales is 25%.

The complement is 75%. 25/75 = ⅓ = 33⅓%.

The equivalent per cent of gross profit on cost is 33⅓%.

Exercise 38

Using the equivalent rates computed in Exercise 36, find the gross profit and selling price. Prove all results.

	Cost	Mark-up Rate based on S.P.	Equivalent Rate based on Cost	Profit	Selling Price
1.	4.00	20%	....	....	....
2.	.75	40%	....	....	....
3.	2.10	12½%	....	....	....
4.	5.00	33⅓%	....	....	....
5.	.65	37½%	....	....	....
6.	.85	50%	....	....	....
7.	7.00	30%	....	....	....
8.	1.08	10%	....	....	....
9.	1.50	16⅔%	....	....	....
10.	.66	45%	....	....	....
11.	.45	37½%	....	....	....
12.	1.74	14 2/7%	....	....	....
13.	3.00	28 4/7%	....	....	....

Given cost, per cent of operating expenses, and per cent of net profit. Find the selling price. (Note per cents are based on selling price.)

Problem: A retailer buys tooth brushes @ $1.80 per dozen. His operating expenses are 30% of sales. If he desires to make a net profit of 10% on sales, at what price each must he sell the tooth brushes?

Given: Cost per dozen, per cent of operating expenses and per cent of desired profit on sales.

Find: Selling price per tooth brush.

Solution:

Selling Price = 100%
$1.80 + 30% + 10% = Selling Price
100% − 30% − 10% = 60%
$1.80 = 60% of Selling Price
$1.80 ÷ .6 = $3.00 Selling Price per doz.
$3.00 ÷ 12 = $.25 S. P. per brush

Proof: 30% of 3.00 = .90
10% of 3.00 = .30

Explanation:

All per cents are based on selling price.

Deduct the rate of expenses and rate of profit from selling price to find the per cent of cost. Apply the formula:

Percentage ÷ Rate = Base
$1.80 + .90 + .30 = $3.00

Exercise 39

Find the selling price.

	Cost	Operating Expenses	Desired Net Profit	Selling Price
1.	$ 18.00	25%	15%	....
2.	1.50	37½%	12½%	....
3.	1.05	20%	10%	....
4.	.95	33⅓%	16⅔%	....
5.	1.60	12%	8%	....
6.	8.50	10%	5%	....
7.	156.00		15%	....
8.	2430.00	13%	6%	....
9.	28.70	25%	5%	....
10.	125.00	12½%	10%	....

FINDING THE LIST PRICE

Problem: A manufacturer produces lawn mowers at a cost of $12.00. He desires to make a gross profit of $6.00 after allowing a trade discount of 40% on the list price. Find the list price.

Given: Cost, gross profit, and trade discount.

Find: List price.

Solution:

1. $12 + $6 = $18 Selling Price.

2. List Price = 100%.
   100% − 40% = Selling Price.

3. 60% of List Price = Selling Price.
   60% of the List Price = $18.

4. $18 ÷ .6 = $30 List Price.

Explanation:

1. Cost + Gross Profit = Selling Price.

2. List Price − Trade Discount = Selling Price.
   Since the trade discount is computed on list price, the latter equals 100% of the amount which we are required to find.

3. In line 1 we determined the selling price to be $18, which is 60% of the list price.

4. P ÷ R = B (Percentage divided by the rate equals the base).

Proof: 40% of $30 = $12 Trade Discount.
$30.00 − $12.00 = $18.00 Selling Price.

Exercise 40

Find the List Price.

	Cost	Gross Profit	Selling Price	Trade Disc.	List Price
1.	$ 1.50	.50	......	33⅓%	......
2.	4.50	2.25	......	10%	......
3.	15.00	6.00	......	25%	......
4.	3.00	1.20	......	30%	......
5.	20.00	10.00	......	40%	......
6.	33.00	12.50	......	35%	......
7.	12.00	16.80	......	20%	......
8.	2.60	1.30	......	37½%	......
9.	1.50	.90	......	60%	......
10.	3.50	1.50	......	16⅔%	......

Problems

1. An electric heating pad cost the retailer $1.65. At what price should he sell it to make a gross profit of 40% on selling price?

2. A haberdasher sells ties at $2.25 which cost $1.50. What is his mark-up rate? (Based on selling price.)

3. A manufacturer earns a gross profit of 33⅓% on cost. What is the per cent gross profit on sales?

4. A retailer buys saws @ $1.75 less 20%. His operating expenses are 20%. At what price must he sell to make a net profit of 10%?

5. A furniture dealer desires to make a net profit of 12½%. His operating expenses are 32½%. What should be the resale price of a dining-room suite which is listed at $600 less 30% and 10%?

6. An electric iron is listed at $4.50 less 40%. A retails it at 50% gross profit on cost; B retails it at 40% gross profit on selling price. Which one sells the iron cheaper? How much?

7. A shoe store sells shoes for $6.50 and makes a gross profit of 35% on sales. What is the cost?

8. A department store buyer is planning a 33⅓% reduction sale. He wishes to buy lamps to sell at $3 less 33⅓%. What price should he pay for the lamps in order to make a gross profit of 50% on cost?

COMMISSION AND BROKERAGE

When a farmer brings his fruit or vegetables to the market place and disposes of his products, he sells directly to the customer. Because of listance from markets or other inconveniences, the grower frequently ells through an agent called a commission merchant. The goods are hipped to the commission merchant, but the title or ownership remains with the shipper until the merchandise is sold. A few of the erms used in this type of business are briefly explained:

A *consignor* or *shipper* is the principal who ships the goods.

A *consignee* is the agent to whom the goods are forwarded.

A *consignment* or *shipment* refers to the goods to be sold by the commission merchant for the shipper.

A *broker* is an agent who buys or sells for the principal without handling the goods.

Commission or *brokerage* is the agent's compensation for his services.

Net proceeds is the difference between the sales and charges.

An *account sale* is an itemized statement of sales and charges which the commission merchant sends to his principal.

FINDING THE NET PROCEEDS

Problem: The Liberty Fruit Distributors received 800 bags of coconuts from The Mayaguez Trading Company to be sold on their account. The consignee sold 400 bags @ $4.10; 300 @ $3.75; and 100 @ $3.25. Freight and insurance was $.50 a bag, trucking $.25 a bag, and storage charges $40.00. Advertising costs were $15.00; commission 5%. What are the net proceeds?

Given: Consignment; sales; charges; rate of commission.

Find: Net proceeds.

Solution:

Sales:		
	400 bags @ $4.10 =	$1640.00
	300 bags @ 3.75 =	1125.00
	100 bags @ 3.25 =	325.00
Total:	800	$3090.00

Charges:		
Freight	.50 × 800 =	$400.00
Trucking	.25 × 800 =	200.00
Storage		40.00
Advertising		15.00
Commission	$3090 × .05 =	154.50
Total charges		809.50
Net proceeds		$2280.50

Exercise 41

	Selling Price	Rate Comm.	Expenses	Net Proceeds
1.	1360.50	5%	148.25	....
2.	3471.00	2%	420.75	....
3.	546.40	7½%	49.10	....
4.	2684.70	2½%	328.50	....
5.	1965.15	3%	248.95	....
6.	4175.00	2%	816.30	....
7.	627.60	8%	59.10	....
8.	1382.40	5%	322.80	....
9.	916.25	7½%	88.00	....
10.	1844.65	2%	428.35	....

Problems

1. The Liberty Fruit Company received a consignment of 3500 bunches of bananas from Jean Battista, Aguadilla, P. R. The consignee paid the following charges: freight, $1070.80; dock labor, $135.00; advertising, $10.00. They sold 800 bunches @ $2.10; 1200 bunches @ $1.85; 500 bunches @ $1.90; 600 bunches @ $1.50; 400 bunches @ $1.25. The commission rate is 7½%. Find the net proceeds.

2. N. Nagleberg & Co. received a consignment of 2500 boxes of oranges from Henry Baccardi. He sold 925 boxes @ $3.75; 650 boxes @ $3.50; 700 boxes @ $3.60; 225 boxes @ $3.40. The consignee advanced the following expenses: freight 70¢ a box, insurance $12.50; dock labor, $35.00; cartage 15¢ a box. The commission is 5%. Find the net proceeds.

3. In Problem 1, what was the percentage of expenses (include commission) on sales? (Continue to two decimal places.)

4. A commission merchant whose rate is 5% received $45.00 commission. What were the sales?

5. In Problem 1, the shipper's cost averaged 70¢ a bunch. What was his profit or loss?

6. John Langford shipped 1960 boxes of grapefruit to the Washington Fruit and Produce Co. to be sold on his account. The commission merchant advanced $1000 to the shipper, paid for freight 90¢ a box, insurance $14.75, cartage 10¢ a box, advertising $7.50, repacking $35.00, storage charges $39.20. 14 boxes were lost in repacking. The commission rate is 5%. The fruit was sold @ $3.75 per box. Find the net proceeds.

7. Frank Richardson sold through a commission merchant 3500 bushels of wheat @ 95¢ a bushel. The commission rate was 2½% and

the freight was 20¢ per hundred pounds. What were the net proceeds? (A bushel of wheat weighs 60 lbs.)

8. A lawyer was given for collection a claim of $160.00. He collected 75% of the claim and charged his client 15% for his services. How much should the lawyer pay his client?

INTEREST

In profit and loss, marking goods, commission and brokerage problems the rules of percentage were applied. In the solution of the problems we used one of the rules of percentage.

$$\text{Base} \times \text{Rate} = \text{Percentage}$$
$$\text{Percentage} \div \text{Base} = \text{Rate}$$
$$\text{Percentage} \div \text{Rate} = \text{Base}$$

Interest problems belong to this group. However, there is a new factor in computing interest, namely the interest period.

Thomas Brown borrowed $1000 from the bank for 60 days at 6%. Alfred Coyne borrowed $2000 for 30 days @ 6%. Michael Dunn borrowed $2000 for 60 days @ 3%. How much interest does Brown pay? Coyne? Dunn?

The factors to be considered in each problem are (a) the sum of money (b) the time (c) the interest rate. The money borrowed is called the *principal*. The unit of time is a year. Interest rate is expressed as a *per cent* for a year. The interest rates in the preceding problem are 6% and 3% for one year. The rule for computing interest is:

$$P \times R \times T = I$$
P—Principal; R—Rate; T—Time; I—Interest.

Bankers and businessmen compute interest on the basis of 360 days to the year, because of convenience. For example, 90 days, 60 days, 30 days, may be readily changed to simple fractions of a year, thus:

$$90/360 = 1/4 \text{ of a year}$$
$$60/360 = 1/6 \text{ of a year}$$
$$30/360 = 1/12 \text{ of a year}$$

For the same reason businessmen also use 30 days to the month instead of the exact number of days. Banks, however, use the exact number of days in the calendar month.

To Find the Interest

The solutions for the above problems are shown below:

Given: Principal, time, and rate

Find: Interest

THOMAS BROWN

Solution: $\$1000 \times 6/100 \times 60/360 = \$10.00$

ALFRED COYNE

Solution: $\$2000 \times 6/100 \times 30/360 = \$10.00$

MICHAEL DUNN

Solution: $\$2000 \times 3/100 \times 60/360 = \$10.00$

Why is the result the same in each case?

When the time is one year, the formula uses 1 (360/360) as the time factor. The interest for $250 @ 2% for 1 year is $\$250 \times 2/100 \times 1 = \$5.00$.

To shorten the calculations, use simple fractions of a year.

Days	Year
30	1/12
45	1/8
60	1/6
90	1/4
120	1/3
No. of days to the year	= 360

Exercise 42

Find the interest:

	Principal	Time		2%	3%	4%	6%
1.	$500.00	1	year	......	......	......	......
2.	$800.00	90	days	......	......	......	......
3.	$600.00	60	"	......	......	......	......
4.	$2400.00	30	"	......	......	......	......
5.	$240.00	75	"	......	......	......	......
6.	$1000.00	2½	years	......	......	......	......
7.	$400.00	180	days	......	......	......	......
8.	$4800.00	15	"	......	......	......	......
9.	$720.00	10	"	......	......	......	......
10.	$160.00	45	"	......	......	......	......

The *amount* is the principal plus the interest. Find the amounts in the preceding exercise.

The 60-Day Method

Businessmen usually borrow money from banks for 30-, 60-, or 90-day periods. The 60-day method is a short cut for computing interest for periods less than a year. The basis of this method is: 60 days = 1/6 of a year. When the interest is 6% for one year, we multiply 6/100 by 1/6 to find the equivalent rate for 60 days.

$$6/100 \times 1/6 = 1\%.$$

Rule: To find the interest on any sum of money for 60 days at 6% take 1% of the principal.
Example: What is the interest on $1328.25 for 60 days at 6%?
Answer: $13.28 (1% of $1328.25).
Proof: $1328.25 \times 6/100 \times 60/360 = $13.28.

If the period of time is a multiple of 60 days, find the interest for 60 days and multiply result by the multiple of 60 days. For example:

$$120 \text{ days} = 60 \times 2$$
$$180 \text{ days} = 60 \times 3$$
$$240 \text{ days} = 60 \times 4$$

For periods less than 60 days, we use an aliquot part of 60, thus:

$$6 \text{ days} = 1/10 \text{ of } 60$$
$$15 \text{ " } = \frac{1}{4} \text{ of } 60$$
$$20 \text{ " } = \frac{1}{3} \text{ of } 60$$
$$30 \text{ " } = \frac{1}{2} \text{ of } 60$$

Illustrations:

a. What is the interest on $400.00 for 240 days at 6%?

        Interest for   60 days = $4.00
            "   " 240 days = $4.00 × 4 = $16.00

b. What is the interest on $400.00 for 15 days at 6%?

        Interest for 60 days = $4.00
            "   " 15 days = $4.00 × ¼ = $1.00

c. What is the interest on $400.00 for 90 days at 6%?

        Interest for 60 days = $4.00
            "   " 30 days = $2.00
            "   " 90 days = $6.00

d. What is the interest on $400.00 for 18 days at 6%?

$$
\begin{array}{rl}
\text{Interest for } \underline{60 \text{ days}} = & \underline{\$4.00} \\
\text{``} \quad \text{``} \quad 6 \text{ days} = & .40 \\
\text{``} \quad \text{``} \quad \underline{12 \text{ days}} = & \underline{.80} \\
\text{``} \quad \text{``} \quad 18 \text{ days} = & \$1.20
\end{array}
$$

To facilitate the calculation, break up the time into periods which are aliquot parts of 60, thus:

$$
\begin{aligned}
72 &= 60 + 12 \\
54 &= 60 - 6 \\
24 &= 30 - 6 \\
36 &= 30 + 6 \\
80 &= 60 + 20 \text{ etc.}
\end{aligned}
$$

Exercise 43

Find the interest at 6% on $1500.00 for

1. 66 days	5. 90 days	9. 70 days	13. 39 days
2. 120 "	6. 6 "	10. 45 "	14. 72 "
3. 180 "	7. 36 "	11. 20 "	15. 90 "
4. 240 "	8. 10 "	12. 50 "	16. 18 "

Break up the following into periods which are multiples or aliquot parts of 60.

17. 66 days	21. 90 days	25. 70 days	29. 39 days
18. 40 "	22. 3 "	26. 76 "	30. 150 "
19. 36 "	23. 10 "	27. 57 "	31. 186 "
20. 75 "	24. 96 "	28. 21 "	32. 42 "

THE 60-DAY METHOD AT OTHER RATES

When the interest rate is more or less than 6%, the interest can be computed in the following manner:

First compute interest at 6%. Divide the interest at 6% by 6 and multiply by the required rate.

Example: Find the interest on $1800.00 for 30 days at 4%.

$$
\begin{array}{rl}
\text{Interest for } 60 \text{ days at } 6\% = & \underline{\$18.00} \\
\text{``} \quad \text{``} \quad 30 \text{ days at } 6\% = & 9.00 \\
\text{``} \quad \text{``} \quad 30 \text{ days at } 1\% = & \$9.00 \div 6 = \$1.50 \\
\text{``} \quad \text{``} \quad 30 \text{ days at } 4\% = & \$1.50 \times 4 = \$6.00
\end{array}
$$

Exercise 44

Find the interest by using the 60-day method:

Principal	Time	6%	5%	7%	4%	2%
1. $ 900.00	60 days	......	......	......	......	......
2. $1500.00	72 "	......	......	......	......	......
3. $2400.00	120 "	......	......	......	......	......
4. $ 300.00	36 "	......	......	......	......	......
5. $ 800.00	66 "	......	......	......	......	......
6. $ 600.00	90 "	......	......	......	......	......
7. $1600.00	45 "	......	......	......	......	......
8. $1000.00	180 "	......	......	......	......	......
9. $2000.00	180 "	......	......	......	......	......
10. $9000.00	80 "	......	......	......	......	......

COMPOUND INTEREST

If you place a sum of money in a savings bank, it draws a certain amount of interest at the end of the first interest date. This interest is now added on to the original amount, and the interest at the end of the next interest date is computed on this larger amount. You are now receiving interest on the interest. This is known as *compound interest*. If the interest is added once a year, it is compounded annually. If it is added twice a year, it is compounded semi-annually; if it is added 4 times a year, it is compounded quarterly. Compound interest may be computed as illustrated below. However, most banks use tables for this purpose.

Illustration:

Find the amount of $600.00 for 3 years at 6% compounded annually.

Principal at beginning	$600.00
Interest first year	36.00
Amount at end of first year	$636.00
Interest second year	38.16
Amount at end of second year	$674.16
Interest third year	40.4496
Amount at end of third year	$714.6096
Answer to the nearest cent	$714.61

$714.61 − $600.00 = $114.61, compound interest

BANK DISCOUNT

John Doe needs to pay for his purchases. He applies at his bank for a loan of $1500 for three months. The bank, having agreed to make the loan, asks John Doe to fill in a promissory note. John Doe fills in the note as follows:

No. 52   New York, March 15, 19—

    Three months after date I promise
To pay to the order of....MYSELF....$1500
Fifteen hundred........................dollars

                        JOHN DOE (signed)

John Doe endorses the note and gives it to the bank.

Banks usually deduct from the face value of the note the charge for their services. In this case, the bank will charge John Doe interest on $1500 for the period of the loan. This charge is called Bank Discount. It is customary for banks to figure the exact number of days from the date of discount to the maturity date of the note. This interval is called the Term of Discount.

HOW TO COMPUTE THE TERM OF DISCOUNT

Suppose the discount date in the above transaction is March 15, 1946. The note becomes due three months after March 15, or June 15. The exact number of days from March 15 to June 15 is arrived at in the following manner:

Term of Discount		*Bank Discount*	
March 15–31	16 days	Int. for 60 days........$15.00
April has	30 "	" " 30 " 7.50
May has	31 "	" " 2 " .... .50
June 1–15	15 "	" " 92 " $23.00

(Total term
  of discount)   92 days

The bank discount on $1500 for the 92 days at 6% is $23.00. After deducting the bank discount from the face value of the note, you get the net amount which will be credited to John Doe's account.

$1500 − $23.00 = $1477. This is called the net proceeds.

Exercise 45

Compute the term of discount:

	Date of Discount	Maturity Date	Term of Discount
1.	Jan. 5	March 5	. . . .
2.	Feb. 10	May 10	. . . .
3.	March 20	Apr. 19	. . . .
4.	Apr. 2	June 1	. . . .
5.	May 25	July 10	. . . .
6.	June 9	Sept. 9	. . . .
7.	July 17	Aug. 16	. . . .
8.	Aug. 5	Nov. 3	. . . .
9.	Sept. 30	Dec. 5	. . . .
10.	Oct. 1	Nov. 30	. . . .

How to Compute the Date of Maturity

a. *When time is expressed in months:*

A note dated April 10 becomes due three months after date. What is the date of maturity?

April 10 plus three months equals July 10. The number of months is added to the date of the note. The due date falls on the corresponding date of the note. If the maturity date falls on Saturday, Sunday, or a legal holiday, the maturity date is on the following business day.

b. *When the time is expressed in days:*

A note dated April 15 will be due 90 days after date. What is the date of maturity?

Number of days left in April (Apr. 30 − 15)	15 days
May	31 "
June	30 "
	76 days
July	14 "
Total number of days from April 15 to July 14	90 days

Note that we took a total after June 30 because we approached the required number of days. Fourteen additional days are required in July to bring the total up to 90.

Exercise 46

Find the maturity date:

	Date of Note	Time	Maturity Date
1.	Jan. 5	60 days	. . . .
2.	Feb. 10	90 "	. . . .
3.	March 20	20 "	. . . .
4.	Apr. 2	60 "	. . . .
5.	May 25	90 "	. . . .
6.	June 9	90 "	. . . .
7.	July 17	40 "	. . . .
8.	Aug. 5	50 "	. . . .
9.	Sept. 30	90 "	. . . .
10.	Oct. 1	80 "	. . . .

INTEREST-BEARING NOTES

No. 10   New York, N. Y., May 20, 19—

Ninety days. . . . . .after date I promise to pay to
the order of . . . . .WILLIAM STRAUSS. $1000.00
One Thousand 00/100. . . . . .Dollars
Value received with interest at 6%

JOHN HENDERSON (signed)

Payable at Commercial Bank and Trust Co.
150 Broadway, New York.

John Henderson is called the *maker* or drawer, and William Strauss the *payee*.

How much should the payee of the above note collect from John Henderson on the date of maturity? Since the note bears interest at 6%, the maker must pay in addition to the face value the interest on $1000.00 for ninety days. The amount is computed thus:

Face Value	$1000.00
Interest (on $1000 for 90 days)	15.00
Maturity Value	$1015.00

If this were a non-interest-bearing note, the maker would pay $1000.00.

To Find the Present Value of a Note

Let us assume that on June 19 the payee, William Strauss, is in need of funds. If his credit standing is satisfactory, he can discount the note at his bank. To transfer the note to the bank, William Strauss endorses his name. The endorsement guarantees to the bank that the signature of the maker is bona fide, and that the note will be paid by the endorser if the maker fails to pay. What are the net proceeds if the bank charges at the rate of 6%?

Given: The face value, time of note, date of discount, interest rate, discount rate.

Find: Discount, and Net Proceeds.

Solution:

$$P \times T \times R = \text{Interest}$$
$$P + I = \text{Maturity Value}$$
$$\text{M.V.} \times \text{Term of Discount} \times R = \text{Discount}$$
$$\text{M.V.} - D = \text{Net Proceeds (Present Value)}$$

Banks compute the discount on the maturity value of the note. They figure the exact number of days from the date of discount to the maturity date. The routine for computing the net proceeds follows.

1. *Find the Date of Maturity.*

    May 20 + 90 days..............................August 18

May (31 − 20)	.........11 days	(If August 18 falls on
June	...............30 "	Saturday or Sunday,
July	.................31 "	the note matures on
August	..............18 "	the following business
Total	...............90 "	day.)

2. *Compute the Maturity Value.*

    Interest for 90 days at 6% on $1000 is $15.00.
    Principal, $1000 + Interest, $15.00 = $1015.
    (The interest is computed for the time of the note at the specified rate of interest.)

3. *Find the Term of Discount.*

    From the date of discount, June 19, to the maturity date, August 18, there are 60 days.

    June (30 − 19) 11 + July 31 + August 18 = 60 days

4. *Compute the Discount* (on the maturity value).

    Interest on $1015.00 for 60 days at 6%............$10.15

5. *Compute the Discount.*

Maturity Value	$1015.00
Discount	10.15
Net Proceeds	$1004.85

When the time of the note is expressed in months, the date of maturity is computed by adding the number of months to the date of the note.

Exercise 47

Find the maturity value of the following notes bearing interest at 6%.

	Face of Note	Time		Face of Note	Time
1.	$1500.00	90 days	6.	$4400.00	30 days
2.	4500.00	3 mos.	7.	280.00	60 days
3.	500.00	60 days	8.	441.00	90 days
4.	5000.00	2 mos.	9.	720.00	6 mos.
5.	3600.00	1 mo.	10.	800.00	4 mos.

Exercise 48

Find the term of discount.

	Date of Note	Time	Date of Discount		Date of Note	Time	Date of Discount
1.	Jan. 15	60 days	Jan. 25	6.	June 8	2 mos.	June 20
2.	Feb. 1	90 "	Mar. 15	7.	July 3	3 "	Aug. 31
3.	Mar. 30	30 "	Apr. 9	8.	Aug. 25	4 "	Aug. 31
4.	Apr. 10	60 "	May 15	9.	Sept. 20	2 "	Oct. 10
5.	May 5	90 "	May 15	10.	Oct. 3	3 "	Oct. 10

Exercise 49

Find the discount and net proceeds. The interest rate and discount rate are 6%.

	Date of Note	Face Value	Time of Note	Date of Discount	Discount	Net Proceeds
1.	April 3	$1000.00	60 days	Apr. 3	....	....
2.	May 10	600.00	3 mos.	June 10	....	....
3.	June 20	1230.00	90 days	July 8	....	....
4.	July 25	900.00	2 mos.	Aug. 10	....	....
5.	Aug. 5	450.00	60 days	Aug. 10	....	....
6.	Sept. 10	1470.00	90 days	Nov. 5	....	....
7.	Oct. 20	762.00	30 days	Oct. 20	....	....
8.	Dec. 5	2000.00	3 mos.	Jan. 4	....	....

TAXES

Who pays the salaries of public school teachers, policemen, firemen, judges of municipal and county courts? Who pays for the construction of public buildings, the maintenance of health service, parks and recreation centers, and highway department? What are the sources of income for the town or city in which you reside?

Every resident is subject to one form of tax or another. A direct tax is a sum of money levied against an individual, his property, or his business for the support of the government. Examples of direct taxes are taxes on real estate, personal property, and income. Indirect taxes are taxes levied on tobacco, liquor, gasoline, imported goods, etc. What taxes do you pay directly or indirectly?

In this section we shall concern ourselves with one type of tax— real-estate taxes. Most of the money needed to run the state, county, and city government is collected from this source. First, the various units of government determine the sum of money which will be needed for the following year for government expenses and construction of buildings. This estimate of expenses is called a budget. A discussion of the legal procedure involved is beyond the scope of arithmetic.

Let us assume that Rosedale Manor has adopted a budget of $50,000 for next year. How much should be levied against each property owner? In order to distribute the tax on an equitable basis, each lot and building is valued for tax purposes. This value is known as an *assessed valuation,* and is usually less than the resale value of the property. Let us further assume that the total valuation of all real estate in Rosedale Manor is $2,000,000. The tax rate is computed by dividing the budget total by the total assessed valuation.

$$\$50,000 \div \$2,000,000 = .025$$

This rate may be expressed as

25 mills per dollar, or
$2.50   "   hundred dollars, or
$25.00   "   thousand dollars.

To change the tax rate from a dollar basis to a hundred-dollar basis, move the decimal point in the tax rate two places to the right. Why?

To change the tax rate from a dollar basis to a thousand-dollar basis, move the decimal three places to the right. Why?

A's property (which is situated in Rosedale Manor) is assessed at $15,000. What is the amount of tax levied against him?

Given: Assessed valuation and the tax rate.
Find: The tax.

Solution: Base×Rate=Tax
            $15,000×.025=$375.00
Proof: $375.÷$15,000.=.025

Care must be exercised to point off the correct number of decimal places in the answer. In this problem there are three decimal places in the rate; therefore we point off three decimal places to the left in the result. When the rate is per hundred dollars, divide the assessed valuation by 100 and proceed as above. When the rate is per thousand dollars, divide the assessed valuation by 1000 and proceed in the same manner.

Exercise 50

Find the tax rate:

	Assessed valuation	Amount of tax	Rate per dollar	Rate per $100	Rate per $1000
1.	$ 8,000,000	$ 120,000	....	....	....
2.	70,000,000	350,000	....	....	....
3.	40,000,000	700,000	....	....	....
4.	200,000,000	2,500,000	....	....	....
5.	100,000,000	3,000,000	....	....	....

Exercise 51

Change the tax rates per dollar to equivalent tax rates per hundred and per thousand dollars.

	Rate per dollar	Rate per $100	Rate per $1000
1.	.03½	....	....
2.	35 mills	....	....
3.	20 mills	....	....
4.	2¾ cents	....	....
5.	27.5 mills	....	....
6.	18.64 mills	....	....
7.	82.25 mills	....	....
8.	75 mills	....	....
9.	.075	....	....
10.	.01864	....	....

Note 1 mill is 1/10 of a cent and may be decimally expressed as $.001 or .1¢.

Exercise 52

Compute the tax.

	Assessed valuation	Tax rate	Tax
1.	$ 6,500	27.5 mills	. . . .
2.	12,000	$1.758 per $100	. . . .
3.	25,000	$8.254 per $1000	. . . .
4.	14,600	25 mills	. . . .
5.	10,500	$1.952 per $100	. . . .
6.	30,000	$12.581 per $1000	. . . .
7.	5,000	$1.5724 per $100	. . . .
8.	7,500	$14.079 per $1000	. . . .
9.	8,000	26.9 mills	. . . .
10.	6,000	$1.426 per $100	. . . .

The formulas explained in the chapter on Percentage may be applied to tax problems if you substitute the terms used in property taxes for the terms used in percentage.

Percentage	Taxes
Base	Assessed Valuation
Rate	Tax Rate
Percentage	Tax

The type problems illustrated below indicate how the percentage formulas are applied:

Type 1. Assessed Valuation $\times$ Tax Rate = Tax. This type has already been illustrated.

Type 2. Tax $\div$ Assessed Valuation = Tax Rate.
Problem. The tax levied on a building assessed at $6500 was $178.75. What was the tax rate?
Solution: $178.75 $\div$ $6500 = .0275 or 2¾%
Proof: $6500 $\times$ .0275 = $178.75

Type 3. Tax $\div$ Tax Rate = Assessed Valuation.
Problem. At 1.426 per hundred dollars the tax amounts to $85.56. What is the assessed valuation?

Solution: $85.56 $\div$ $\dfrac{1.426}{100}$ = $6000

Proof: $\dfrac{\$6000}{100} \times 1.426 = \$85.56$

Exercise 53

Fill in the missing number in the following problems:

	Assessed valuation	Tax rate	Tax levy
1.	$14,500	. . . .	$253.75
2.	. . . .	17.5 mills	$560.00
3.	$125,500	1.875 per 100	. . . .
4.	$1,500,000	. . . .	$1,875.00
5.	. . . .	12.582 per 1000	$10,694.70

DENOMINATE NUMBERS

Quantities are measured by standard units of measure established by law or custom, like a pound, a yard, a gallon, a bushel. A number used apart from a unit is abstract, such as 3. A number of articles, such as 3 desks, 3 typewriters, is concrete. A number of units, such as 3 yards, 3 pounds, 3 dollars, is a denominate number. When the numerical expression denotes one kind of unit, it is a simple number, such as 5 gallons. When the expression denotes two or more units, such as 5 gallons, 3 quarts, 1 pint, it is a compound number.

In the following list, state whether the numbers are abstract or concrete:

a. 15	e. 5 tons	i. 25
b. 8 hours	f. 25 houses	j. 1 year 4 months
c. 10 chairs	g. 40 quarts	k. 3 yds. 2 ft. 5 in.
d. 9 pounds	h. $100	l. 1000 sq. miles

This division presents problems in denominate numbers. A knowledge of tables of weights and measures is essential to solve these problems.

LINEAR MEASURE

Linear measure is used for measuring distances.

```
    12 inches (in.)=1 foot (ft.)
     3 feet        =1 yard (yd.)
     5½ yards      =1 rod (rd.)
   320 rods    ⎫
  1760 yards   ⎬ =1 mile (mi.)
  5280 feet    ⎭
```

OTHER LINEAR MEASURES

1 fathom = 6 feet (used in measuring depths at sea)
1 knot   = 1.15266 miles or 6080.27 ft. (used in measuring distances at sea)
3 miles   = 1 league

SQUARE MEASURE

Square measure is used for measuring areas of surfaces.

144 square inches (sq. in.)	= 1 square foot (sq. ft.)
9 square feet	= 1 square yard (sq. yd.)
30¼ square yards	= 1 square rod (sq. rd.)
160 sq. rd.	= 1 acre (A)
640 acres	= 1 square mile (sq. mi.)
1 square	= 100 sq. ft.

The *square* is the unit used for measuring roofing material.
The *acre* is the unit used for measuring land outside of cities.

CUBIC MEASURE

Cubic measure is used to measure volume of solids.

1728 cubic inches	= 1 cubic foot (cu. ft.)
27 cubic feet	= 1 cubic yard (cu. yd.)
128 cubic feet	= 1 cord (cd.)
1 cubic yard (of earth)	= 1 load

1 perch of stone is 1 rod long, 1½ ft. wide, 1 ft. high.
1 cord of wood is a pile 8 ft. long, 4 ft. wide, 4 ft. high.
1 cubic foot of water weighs 62½ lb. (avoirdupois).

LIQUID MEASURE

Liquid measure is used to measure liquids and capacities of tanks, reservoirs, etc.

4 gills	= 1 pint (pt.)
2 pints	= 1 quart (qt.)
4 quarts	= 1 gallon (gal.)
1 wine gallon	= 231 cubic inches

1 gallon of water weighs approximately 8⅓ lb. (avoirdupois)
1 cu. ft. of water weighs 62½ lb.

APOTHECARIES' FLUID MEASURE

Apothecaries' fluid measure is used by druggists.

60 minims (m.)	= 1 fluid drachm
8 fluid drachms	= 1 fluid ounce
16 fluid ounces	= 1 pint
8 pints	= 1 gallon

1 gallon of the apothecaries' measure is the same as 1 wine gallon.

DRY MEASURE

Dry measure is used for measuring grain, fruit, and produce.

2 pints (pt.)	= 1 quart (qt.)
8 quarts (qt.)	= 1 peck (pk.)
4 pecks (pk.)	= 1 bushel (bu.)

The unit of dry measure is the bushel, which contains 2150.42 cubic inches, or a cylinder 18½ inches in diameter and 8 inches deep.

MEASURES OF WEIGHT

Jewelers use troy weight, the druggist uses apothecary weight, and others use avoirdupois weight.

TROY WEIGHT

24 grains (gr.)	= 1 pennyweight (pwt.)
20 pennyweights	= 1 ounce (oz.)
12 ounces	= 1 pound (lb.)
1 carat	= 3.168 grains

The carat is used to measure diamonds. When used in connection with gold, it denotes fineness and means 1/24 part. Gold marked 14K (14 carat) means 14/24 of the weight is pure gold and 10/24 alloy.

APOTHECARIES' WEIGHT

20 grains	= 1 scruple (sc.)
3 scruples	= 1 dram (dr.)
8 drams	= 1 ounce (oz.)
12 ounces	= 1 pound (lb.)

AVOIRDUPOIS WEIGHT

16 ounces = 1 pound (lb.)
100 pounds = 1 hundredweight (cwt.)
2000 pounds = 1 ton (T.)
2240 pounds = 1 ton (long)

Coal is sold at the mines by the long ton. The government uses the long ton to compute the duty on goods taxed by the ton.

Other common measures:

A bushel (bu.) of wheat, potatoes, or peas weighs	60 pounds
A barrel (bbl.) of beef or pork weighs	200 pounds
A firkin of butter weighs	56 pounds
A barrel (bbl.) of flour weighs	196 pounds
A keg of nails weighs	100 pounds

REDUCTION OF DENOMINATE NUMBERS

Add 5 gallons and 10 gallons. Answer: 15 gallons.

Add 5 yards and 10 feet. We cannot add these quantities because the units are not alike. However, we can change 5 yards to 15 feet (without changing the value) and then add 10 feet, which gives a total of 25 feet.

Reduction of denominate numbers means changing the unit or denomination without changing the value, as in the above example.

Principle: Denominations that are unlike cannot be added.

Descending Reduction means changing from a higher to a lower unit, as from yards to feet, from pounds to ounces, etc.

Ascending Reduction means changing from a lower to a higher unit, as from quarts to gallons.

REDUCTION DESCENDING

Example: Reduce 8 gallons, 3 quarts, 1 pint to pints.

8 gallons = 32 quarts   (4 quarts = 1 gallon)
Add   3 quarts
       35 quarts

35 quarts = 70 pints   (2 pints = 1 quart)
Add   1 pint
Answer   71 pints

Exercise 54

Reduce:

1. 150 rods to yards.
2. 15 square miles to acres.
3. 20 gallons to pints.
4. 30 ounces to drachms.
5. 10 ounces to pennyweight.
6. 12 bushels to quarts.
7. 20 ounces to drams (apothecaries' weight).
8. 15 bushels potatoes to pounds.
9. 5 bbl. flour to pounds.
10. 3 carats to grains.
11. 5 bu., 2 pks., 6 qts. to pints.
12. 4 oz., 15 pwt., 19 grains to grains.
13. 2 pts., 12 oz., 7 drams to drams.
14. 1 gal., 2 qts., 1 pt. to pints.
15. 4 cu. yds., 20 cu. ft. to cubic inches.
16. 15 sq. yds., 6 sq. ft., 130 sq. in. to square inches.
17. 6 miles, 800 yds., 50 ft. to feet.
18. 1 yr., 3 wks., 5 days to days.

REDUCTION ASCENDING

Example: Change 57 pints to higher denominations. The denominations in ascending order are pints, quarts, gallons.

$$\begin{array}{r} 2\overline{)57} \\ 4\overline{)28 \text{ qts. 1 pt.}} \\ 7 \text{ gal.} \end{array}$$

Answer: 7 gal. 1 pt.

Exercise 55

Change to higher denominations:

1. 5000 in.
2. 400 sq. ft.
3. 3600 sq. rods.
4. 465 pts. (liquid measure).
5. 320 qts. (dry measure).
6. 560 grains (troy weight).

7. 3400 drachms (apothecaries' fluid measure).
8. 300 cu. ft.
9. 775 rods.
10. 250,000 ounces (avoirdupois).

ADDITION OF DENOMINATE NUMBERS

Add: 2 bu. 3 pks. 5 qts. 1 pt.; 2 pks. 7 qts.; 10 bu. 1 pk. 1 qt. 1 pt.;
6 bu. 2 pks.; 1 qt. 1 pt.

Bu.	Pk.	Qt.	Pt.
2	3	5	1
	2	7	
10	1	1	1
6	2	1	1
18	8	14	3
2	1	1	1
20	9	15	
	1	7	

20 bu.   1 pk.   7 qt.   1 pt.

Solution:
a. Arrange the units, writing the highest unit at the left end.
b. List the numbers in the columns under the units.
c. Total all columns.
d. Reduce to higher denominations.
e. 3 pts. = 1 qt., 1 pt.
   Add 1 qt. and 14 qts.
   15 qts. = 1 pk., 7 qts.
   Add 1 pk. and 8 pks.
   9 pks. = 2 bu. and 1 pk.

SUBTRACTION OF DENOMINATE NUMBERS

	150 A.	100 sq. rd.	15 sq. yd.	sq. ft.	sq. in.
From					
deduct	40	60	45		
	110	39	¼	= 2¼	
			—		36
				2	
	110 A.	39 sq. rd.	0	2 sq. ft.	36 sq. in.

Solution: First arrange the units in series, commencing with the highest unit at the left end. Write the numbers under the denominations. Start subtracting at the right end (smallest unit). We cannot deduct 45 sq. yds. from 15 sq. yds. Therefore we take one unit of the next higher order (sq. rds.) 1 sq. rd. = 30¼ sq. yds.

Adding 30¼ and 15 we get 45¼ sq. yds. 45¼ sq. yds. − 45 sq. yds. = ¼ sq. yd. Fractional parts of a denomination are reduced to lower denominations. ¼ sq. yd. is therefore changed to 2¼ sq. ft. Reducing ¼ sq. ft., we get 36 sq. in. One sq. rd. was changed to sq. yds. Therefore we deduct 60 from 99 and get 39 sq. rds. 150 A. less 40 A. = 110 A.

Exercise 56

Add:

1. 30 yds. 2 ft. 10 in.; 41 yds. 1 ft. 9 in.; 27 yds. 2 ft. 7 in.
2. 5 cwt. 72 lbs. 15 oz.; 18 cwt. 59 lbs. 12 oz.; 14 cwt. 91 lbs. 5 oz.
3. 39 gals. 2 qts. 1 pt.; 45 gals. 3 qts. 1 pt.
4. 40 A. 130 sq. rds.; 35 A. 110 sq. rds.; 75 A. 55 sq. rds.
5. 70 bu. 2 pk. 6 qts. 1 pt.; 45 bu. 3 pk. 7 qts.
6. 3 T. 6 cwt. 70 lbs.; 15 T. 18 cwt. 85 lbs.; 14 cwt. 65 lbs.
7. 9 cu. yds. 20 cu. ft.; 6 cu. yds. 22 cu. ft.; 15 cu. yds. 15 cu. ft.
8. 5 oz. 15 pwt. 23 gr.; 10 oz. 12 pwt. 15 gr.; 8 oz. 18 pwt. 8 gr.
9. 6 oz. 5 dr.; 8 oz. 7 dr.; 4 oz. 3 dr.; 11 oz. 5 dr.
10. 10 hrs. 15 min.; 8 hrs. 50 min.; 7 hrs. 30 min.; 8 hrs. 45 min.; 9 hrs. 15 min.

Subtract:

11. 41 yds. 1 ft. 10 in. − 30 yds. 2 ft. 9 in.
12. 18 cwt. 59 lbs. 12 oz. − 14 cwt. 91 lbs. 15 oz.
13. 45 gals. 1 qt. 1 pt. − 32 gals. 3 qts.
14. 40 A. 100 sq. rds. − 35 A. 130 sq. rds.
15. 70 bu. 2 pks. 6 qts. − 45 bu. 1 pk. 5 qts. 1 pt.
16. 15 T. 6 cwt. 70 lbs. − 3 T. 18 cwt. 85 lbs.
17. 9 cu. yds. 20 cu. ft. − 6 cu. yds. 22 cu. ft.
18. 10 oz. 12 pwt. 15 gr. − 5 oz. 15 pwt. 23 gr.
19. 6 oz. 5 dr. − 2 oz. 7 dr.
20. 10 hrs. 15 min. 10 sec. − 5 hrs. 30 min. 50 sec.

MEASURING DISTANCES, AREAS, AND VOLUMES

In the preceding section the units of measurements were listed in connection with denominate numbers. Problems relating to measurement of distances, areas, and volumes will now be discussed.

MEASURING DISTANCES

The distance from one point to another is measured by units listed in linear measure. The tailor uses a tape measure, which indicates inches and subdivisions of inches; the retailer uses a yardstick, the builder a steel tape (which is usually made in 5 ft., 6 ft., 50 ft., and 100 ft. lengths), and the surveyor measures by rods and chains. Custom and practice in each industry determine the basic unit of measurement. The symbol used to denote feet is ' to the right of the number; thus, 5' means five feet. The symbol for inches is ". 10" means ten inches. 5'10" is read "five feet ten inches."

Problem 1: Frank Falk wants to put a fence on the limits of his property, which borders on the public highway. The distance measures 500 feet. Find the cost, if the price is $7.95 a hundred lineal feet. Find the cost of posts at $.55 if the posts are 20 feet apart. Find the total cost of materials.

Given: The measurement of the fence, cost per hundred feet, spacing of posts, and cost per post.

Find: The cost of wire, of posts, and total cost of materials.

Solution:

1. $\frac{500}{100} \times \$7.95 = \$39.75$ cost of fence
2. $500 \div 20 = 25$
   $$\frac{1}{26 \text{ Posts required}}$$
3. $26 \times 55¢ = \$14.30$ Cost of posts
4. $\$39.75 + 14.30 = \$54.05$ Total cost

Explanation:

The price is quoted per hundred feet; therefore the length is divided by 100.

Posts are placed 20 ft. apart. An extra post is needed at the end.

Add cost of fence and posts.

PERIMETERS

The *perimeter* is the distance around an area. The perimeter of a plot of ground is the total of the measurements of all sides. If the area is a square, the perimeter is the total of the four sides. If the area is a circle, the perimeter is the circumference.

The measurement of circumference is based on the formula D×
3.1416=C or 2R×3.1416.

D is the diameter of the circle.

C is the circumference.

R is the radius.

3.1416 is approximately 3⅐. When exact measurements are not required, the work may be shortened by using 3⅐ in place of 3.1416.

The symbol π (read "pie") is frequently used in place of the factor
3.1416 in expressing formulas for circular measurements.

Problem 2: What is the distance around a circular reservoir, if the
radius is 750 feet?

Given: Radius of reservoir.

Find: The circumference.

Solution:	*Explanation:*
1. 2×750×3.1416=4712.4 feet	Apply the formula 2R×3.1416.

Problem 3: What is the radius of a circle whose circumference is
2827.44 feet?

Given: Circumference of circle.

Find: The radius.

Solution:	*Explanation:*
2827.44 divided by (2×3.1416) =450′	If the radius were one foot, the circumference would be 2×3.1416,
Proof: 2×450′×3.1416=2827.44	which equals 6.2832 (according to the formula given above).
	Since the circumference is 2827.44, the length of the radius is determined by dividing by the circumference of a circle whose radius is one foot.

In measurement problems the geometric figures commonly used
include the following:

A *rectangle* is a figure bounded by four straight lines and having four
right angles.

A *square* is a rectangle whose sides are all equal.

A *triangle* is a figure having three sides.

A *circle* is a figure bounded by a curved line every point of which is
equally distant from the center.

A *radius* is the distance from the center to the circumference.

Diameter is any line that passes through the center and whose terminals are in the circumference of a circle.

Altitude refers to the height of a figure.

PROBLEMS

1. At 5¢ a foot, what will it cost to paint a rail which encloses a rectangular field 450′ long and 210′ wide?

2. How many rolls of chicken wire are required to enclose a rectangular yard 165 feet long, 210 feet wide? There are 100 feet to a roll and the dealer does not sell less than a roll.

3. What is the distance around a race track if the diameter is 843 feet?

4. How many feet of molding will be required for four rectangular rooms whose measurements are 13′ 6″ × 11′ 4″; 18′ 2″ × 14′ 6″; 14′ 4″ × 15′ 6″, and 12′ 6″ × 16′.

5. The rear wheels of a wagon are 3′ in diameter. If they make 1000 revolutions, how far has the wagon traveled?

MEASURING AREAS

RECTANGLES

Study the terms:

The *base* is the horizontal line at the bottom of a figure.

The *altitude* is the vertical line or the height of the figure.

The area is the surface of a figure. Lateral surfaces are the areas of the sides of a figure like the walls of a building. The area of Figure 5 is 15 sq. ft. Square units are used to measure areas. The tables should be reviewed. (See page 787.)

FIGURE 5

The area of a rectangle is found by multiplying base × altitude. The formula is b × a = area. In Figure 5 the base and altitude are 5 and 3 units each; therefore the area = 3 × 5 or 15 sq. ft.

Problem 4: Find the cost to carpet a room which is 14′ wide and 18′ long. The carpet is 36″ wide and is laid lengthwise.

Given: Length and width of room.

Width of carpet and cost per yard.

Find: Cost to carpet the room.

Solution: 1. $14' \div 3' = 4\frac{2}{3}$ or 5 strips.

2. $5 \times \frac{18}{3} = 30$ yds.

3. $\$3.75 \times 30 = \$112.50$ Cost.

Explanation: 1. Since the carpet is laid lengthwise, we divide the width of the room by the width of the carpet to find the number of strips. (Dealers do not sell fractions of a width, therefore the nearest number is 5 strips.)

2. Each strip is 18′ long. Divide by 3 to change to yards.

3. Multiply the yardage by the unit price to find cost.

TRIANGLES

The area of the rectangle ABCD = 4″ × 2″ or 8 sq. in. By drawing a

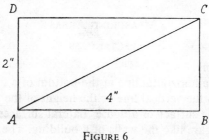

FIGURE 6

diagonal AC, we divide the area in half; therefore the triangle ABC or ADC = ½ of the area of the rectangle.

The formula for computing areas of triangles therefore is

$$\frac{b \times a}{2} = A$$

b—base
a—altitude
A—area

Problem 5: The gable end of a house (shaped like an inverted V) has a base of 20′ 3″ and a height of 2 yds. What is the area?

Given: Base and altitude.

Find: Area of triangle.

Solution:

   1. 20′ 3″ = 20¼′

     2 yds. = 6′

   2. $\dfrac{20¼' \times 6'}{2} = 60¾$ sq. ft.

Explanation: 1. Reduce all measurements to a common unit. In this case our unit is feet. Change 3″ to a ¼′ and 2 yds. to 6′.

   2. Apply the formula to find the area of triangles. ½b × a.

Circular Measurements

CIRCLES

The formula to find the area of a circle is 3.1416 × square of the radius. The square of a number is found by multiplying the number by itself. The square of 4 is 4×4 or 16. The square of 10 is 100, etc.

Problem 6: A tank has a diameter of 30″. What is the area of the cover?

Given: Diameter of tank.

Find: Area of cover.

Solution: 1. ½ of 30″ = 15″ Radius

   2. 3.1416 × 15″ × 15″ = 706.86 sq.″

Explanation: 1. To find the radius we take ½ of the diameter.

   2. Apply the formula for finding the area of a circle. The radius is repeated as a factor to square it.

CYLINDERS

Figure 7 is a cylinder with a diameter of 1″ and an altitude of 1½″. The lateral surface is a rectangle. This is obvious when we cut the cylinder vertically and unroll it as in Figure 8. The diameter is 1″; therefore the circumference of the cylinder is 1 × 3.1416. What is the base of the rectangle? The formula for the area of a rectangle is b × a. The formula

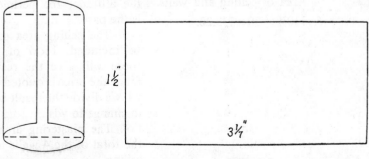

FIGURE 7   FIGURE 8

for the lateral area of a cylinder is c×a. To find the base of a cylinder use the formula of a circle. 2R×3.1416 or D×3.1416=C.

Problem 7: Find the cost of painting the sides of a water tank measuring 6' in diameter and 12' in height at 40¢ a sq. yd.
Given: Diameter, altitude, price per sq. yd.
Find: Area in sq. yds. and cost of painting.

Solution: 1. 6'=2 yds.
          12'=4 yds.
      2. 2×3.1416=6.2832 yds.
          Base
      3. 4×6.2832=25.1328
          sq. yds. Area
      4. 40¢×25.1328=$10.05.
          Cost

Explanation: 1. Change feet to yds. because the price is given in yds.
2. The formula to find the circumference is D×3.1416.
3. Find the area of the lateral surface by formula b×a=A.
4. The area and price have the same unit, viz., sq. yds.; therefore multiply the area by the unit price to find the cost.

Problem 8: Find the cost of plastering the walls and ceiling of a room 18' x 15' and 11' high @ 30¢ sq. yd. (no allowance for openings).
Given: Length, width, height, and cost per sq. yd.
Find: Areas of walls and ceiling and cost of plastering.

Solution: 1. 2(18'+15')=66'=22 yds.

      2. $22 \times \frac{11}{3} = 80\frac{2}{3}$ sq. yds. Area
            of four walls.

      3. $\frac{18 \times 15}{9} = 30$ sq. yds. Area
            of ceiling.

      4. $80\frac{2}{3} + 30 = 110\frac{2}{3}$ sq. yds.
          Area of ceiling and walls.

      5. $110\frac{2}{3} \times .30 = \$33.20$.

Explanation: 1. To find the perimeter, we add the length and width and multiply by 2. The four walls measure 66' or 22 yds.
2. The formula to find the area of a rectangle is b×a. The height of the room is the altitude; the perimeter is the base.
3. The ceiling area must be included. l×w of the room will give the result. Since the price is quoted per yd. we divide the result by 9 to change to yds.
4. The plastering area is the total of the 4 walls and ceiling.

         5. Multiply the total area by the unit price to find total cost of plastering.

PROBLEMS

1. How many yards in the 4 walls and ceiling of a room 17′×14′ ×9′?

2. The ridge of a gabled roof is 64′ and the rafters are 29′ 8″. How many bundles of shingles are required to cover the roof if each bundle covers 100 sq. ft.? (Dealers do not sell a fraction of a bundle.)

3. Find the cost of painting the sides of a water tank if the diameter is 10′ and the height is 15′, and the cost 30¢ sq. yd.

4. Find the cost of carpeting the room mentioned in problem 1, allowing for a border of 1′ on each side. The carpet is laid lengthwise, is 1 yd. wide, and costs $3.50 yd.

5. Find the cost of covering with tile a circular area with a diameter of 12′ @ $1.25 a sq. yd.

6. Find the cost of painting the walls and ceilings of the following rooms and corridors @ 25¢ a sq. yd., no allowance being made for windows and doors: 20′×15′; 12′ 6″×15′; 12′ 6″×9′; 30′×6′. The height of all the rooms is 9′.

7. Find the cost of carpeting rooms in problem 6 if the carpet is 1 yd. wide, is laid lengthwise, and costs $3.85 a yd.

SQUARE ROOT

What is a square? How many square feet in a square with sides 5 feet long? What is the length of a square with an area of 25 square feet?

When a number contains 2 equal factors it is a perfect square. 25 is a perfect square because the two factors are 5 and 5. The process of breaking down a number into equal factors is called "extracting the square root." The square root of 100 is 10. Proof: $10 \times 10 =$ the number.

How to Compute Square Root

Problem 1: Find the square root of 729.

    Solution:

```
        2  7
    2) 7,29
       4
   47) 3,29
       3,29
```

Proof: $27 \times 27 = 729$

Explanation:

1. Beginning at the right end of the number, group the digits b
pairs. The quotient will have one digit for each group in the dividend
There are two groups: the quotient will have two digits.

2. The largest perfect square contained in seven is four. The squar
root of 4 is 2. Write 2 in the quotient. Subtract the square of 2, whic
is 4, from the partial dividend, 7: the remainder is 3.

3. Bring down the next pair to get the next partial dividend: resul
329. The trial divisor is found by doubling the partial quotient 2
answer 4. This means that the trial divisor will be forty something be
cause the partial quotient is in the 10 column. The divisor will b
somewhere between 40 and 49. Forty something goes into 329 approx
imately 7 times. Write 7 in the quotient and trial divisor.

4. Multiply the last digit in the quotient, 7, by the trial divisor, 47
and deduct the result from the last remainder. The square root of 72ᵋ
is 27.

TO FIND THE SQUARE ROOT OF A NUMBER
WHICH IS NOT A PERFECT SQUARE

Problem 2: Find the square root of 800 and carry it out to 2 deci
mal places.

Solution:

```
        2 8. 2 8
    2) 8,00.00,00
       4
   48) 4,00
       3,84
  562)  16,00
       11,24
 5648)   4,76,00
         4,51,84
           24,16
```

Explanation:

1. Beginning at the decimal point an
moving to the right and left of the decima
point, group the digits by pairs as in th
preceding example. Note that two pairs c
zeros were added after the decimal poin
because we are required to carry out th
answer to two decimal places.

2. Proceed as in the first illustration. Re
member to double the partial quotient eacl
time to find the trial divisor. Thus the firs
partial quotient is 2. Therefore the follow
ing trial divisor is 4. The second partia
quotient is 28; therefore the trial divisor i
56. The third partial quotient is 28.2; there
fore the partial divisor is 564.

APPLICATION OF SQUARE ROOT TO TRIANGLES

Square root is used in connection with problems based on triangles
A right triangle is one which has one right angle. Figure 9 illustrate:
a right-angle triangle. The base is 4 inches, the altitude 3 inches. The

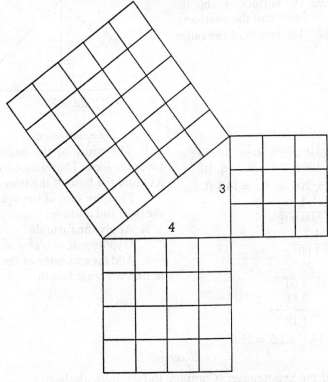

FIGURE 9

side opposite the right angle is called a *hypotenuse.* In Figure 9 the
length of the hypotenuse can be determined by the following method:

1. Square the base: $4 \times 4 = 16$.
2. Square the altitude: $3 \times 3 = 9$.
3. The square of the hypotenuse is equal to the sum of the squares
of the base and altitude. The relationship among base, altitude, and
hypotenuse is expressed briefly thus: $A^2 + B^2 = H^2$ or $\sqrt{A^2 + B^2} = H$. In
this formula A means altitude, B means base, H means hypotenuse.
The sign $\sqrt{}$ means square root.
4. Applying the formula, we get the following result: $16 + 9 = 25$
square inches. To find the length of the hypotenuse we take the square
root of 25, which is 5. For checking use the square root table on
page 964.

Problem 3: The distance from the ridge to the base of the gable is
10′, and the building is 20′ wide. The rafters extend 1.5′. What is the
length of the rafters?

Given: The altitude, double the
       base, and the overhang.

Find: The length of the rafter.

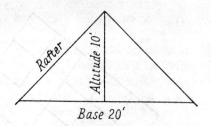

Rafter   *Altitude 10'*

Base 20'

<table>
<tr><td colspan="2">

Solution:
1.   The base is $20' \div 2 = 10'$
2. $10^2 + 10^2 = 200$ sq. ft.
3. $\sqrt{200}$ sq. ft. $= 14.1$ ft.

```
        1  4.1
      )2,00.00
       1
  24) 1 00
      96
 281)  4 00
      2 81
      ─────
      1 19
```

4. $14.1' + 1.5' = 15.6'$

</td><td>

Explanation:

1. The width of the building is twice the base. Therefore divide by 2 to find the base of the triangle.

2. Find the sum of the square of the base and altitude.

3. Apply the formula
    Hypotenuse $= \sqrt{a^2 + b^2}$

4. Add the extension of the rafter to find the total length.

</td></tr>
</table>

Exercise 57

Find the hypotenuse: (Continue to two decimal places.)

	Base	Altitude		Base	Altitude
1.	14″	7″	3.	12′	6′
2.	20′	25′	4.	12′	8′

Find the squares: Find the square root:

5.	42	7.	75	9.	6.869	11.	42.25
6.	105	8.	125	10.	375.769	12.	10.3684

Note: A table of squares and square roots may be found at the end of the section on Geometry.

MEASURING VOLUME

What is the difference between a square and a cube? How many dimensions does the square have? the cube?

To measure volumes or solids we must know length, width, and breadth or thickness. The method of measuring rectangular solids, cylinders, and cones will be explained in this section. Study the following terms:

MATHEMATICS MADE EASY

803

A rectangular solid is a solid that has six rectangular surfaces, like a brick.

A cylinder is a solid that is bounded by two circles parallel to each other and a uniformly curved surface, like a circular smokestack.

A cone is a solid that is bounded by one circle and a lateral surface which tapers uniformly to a point, like the top of a witch's hat.

Use the following formulas to find volume or capacity:

Solid	Formula
Rectangular solids	Length × width × thickness
Cylinder	Area of circle × height
Cone	⅓ of area of circle × height

Units commonly used in business are listed below:

A *cord* of wood is a pile 8′ long, 4′ wide, and 4′ high. This equals 128 cubic feet.

A *foot* of lumber, or board foot, is a board 1′ long, 12″ wide, and 1″ thick. Boards less than 1″ in thickness are measured as boards 1″ in thickness.

A *perch* of stone is a mass 16½′ long, 1½′ wide, and 1′ high. This equals 24¾ cubic ft. (In some areas the perch contains 16½ cu. ft.)

In measuring stonework, such as walls of buildings, the outside of the wall is measured for length. This is called the *girth.*

To compute *capacity of tanks,* we use the volume of 1 gallon, which equals 231 cu. in. One cubic foot contains approximately 7.48 gal.

Problem 1: How many gallons does a rectangular vat contain which measures 6′ × 4′ 2″ × 10′?
Given: Measurements of a rectangular vat.
Find: Capacity in gallons.

Solution:	*Explanation:*
1. $6' \times \frac{25'}{6} \times 10' = 250$ cu. ft.	1. Formula to find volume is l × w × t.
2. $250' \times 1728 = 432{,}000$ cu. in.	2. Change cu. ft. to cu. in.
3. $432{,}000 \div 231 = 1870$ gallons.	3. A gallon equals 231 cu. in. Divide volume by 231 to find number of gallons.

Problem 2: How many gallons does a cylindrical tank contain which measures 10′ in diameter and 6′ in height?

Solution:	*Explanation:*
1. $\frac{10'}{2} = 5'$	1. To find the radius, take ½ of the diameter.
2. $3.1416 \times 25 \times 6 = 471.24$ cu ft.	2. The area of the circle is 3.1416

3. $471.24 \times 1728 = 814{,}302.72$ cu. in.
4. $814{,}302.72 \div 231 = 3525.12$ gal.
5. $.12 \times 4 = .48$ qts.

Ans. 3526 gals.   .48 qts.

$\times 25$. The formula to find the volume of a cylinder is area of circle $\times$ height.

3. To change cu. ft. to cu. in. multiply volume by 1728.

4. 1 gal. 231 cu. in. To find the number of gallons in the cylinder divide its volume in cu. in. by 231.

5. Reduce gallons to qts.

Problem 3: How many cu. ft. are there in a cone whose diameter is 8′ and whose altitude is 15″?
Given: Measurements of the diameter and base of a cone.
Find: Volume in cu. ft.

Solution:

1. $8' \div 2 = 4'$

2. $\dfrac{3.1416 \times 16' \times 15}{3} = 251.328$ cu. ft.

Explanation:

1. To find the radius divide the diameter by 2.

2. The radius squared is 16. The formula to find the volume of a cone is ⅓ of area of circle × height. The area of the circle is 3.1416×4^2 or $3.1416 \times 16 \div 3$.

Problem 4: A pile of wood contains 12 cords. If it is 4′ wide and 8′ high, how long is it?
Given: Width, height, and volume.
Find: Length.

Solution:

1. $12 \times 128 = 1{,}536$ cu. ft. vol.

2. $4' \times 8' = 32$ sq. ft.

3. $1536 \div 32 = 48'$ long.

Proof: $4' \times 8' \times 32' = 1536$ cu. ft.

Explanation:

1. One cord equals 128 cu. ft. To find the volume of the pile multiply 5 cords by 128.

2. To find the area of a rectangle, use the formula base × altitude.

3. If the length were 1′ the pile would contain 32 cu. ft. Since the pile contains 1536 cu. ft. the length is equal to the quotient of $1536 \div 32$. $1536 \div 128$ cu. ft. $= 12$ cords.

Problem 5: Find the cost of 36 planks, $3'' \times 10'' \times 16'$ @ $36 per M (thousand feet). (3 in. in thickness, 10 in. in width, 16 ft. in length.)

Given: The number and measurements of planks and the cost per thousand feet.

Find: The cost.

Solution:

1. $\dfrac{36 \times 3 \times 10 \times 16}{12} = 1440$ board ft.

2. $1440 \div 1000 \times 36 = 51.84$.

Explanation:

1. There are 36 pieces. One board ft. is a board 1 ft. wide, 1 ft. long, 1 in. thick. We multiply the number of pieces by the thickness, width, and length of each piece. Since the width is expressed in inches, we divide by 12 to change it to feet.

2. Since the price is quoted at $36 per M, we divide 1440 by 1000 to find how many thousands we have. Then we multiply by the price.

NOTE: When the thickness is not mentioned, we assume it is 1″ or less and omit it in the calculation.

The width of lumber is always expressed in inches; therefore we always divide it by 12 to change to feet.

Exercise 58

Find the approximate number of gallons in the following vats:

1.	$8' \times 8' \times 4'$	3.	$4' \times 6' \times 8'$	5.	$2'4'' \times 2'4'' \times 6'$
2.	$10' \times 5' \times 6'$	4.	$5'3'' \times 4'8'' \times 9'$	6.	$10' \times 8' \times 5'$

Find the approximate number of gallons in the following cylindrical tanks:

	Diameter	Height			Diameter	Height
7.	8′	8′		10.	2′	8′
8.	10′	8′		11.	6′	12′
9.	4′	6′		12.	1′6″	6′

Find the volume of the following cones:

	Diameter	Altitude			Diameter	Altitude
13.	4″	9″		16.	4′	3 yds.
14.	4′	10′		17.	3′	8′
15.	6′	14′		18.	14′	12′

Find the number of cords in the following piles of wood:

19.	$20' \times 4' \times 4'$	21.	$32' \times 4' \times 6'$	23.	$12' \times 4' \times 6'$
20.	$12' \times 8' \times 4'$	22.	$16' \times 6' \times 8'$	24.	$18' \times 6' \times 10'$

Find the number of board feet:

25.	10 pcs. $2'' \times 4'' \times 12'$	28.	16 pcs. $4'' \times 4'' \times 18'$
26.	26 pcs. $1' \times 8'' \times 16'$	29.	4 pcs. $2'' \times 6'' \times 12'$
27.	30 pcs. $3'' \times 10'' \times 10'$	30.	50 pcs. $1'' \times 8'' \times 12'$

Find the cost in problems 25 to 30 if lumber costs $38 per M.

PROBLEMS

1. A ladder placed 6' away from a wall at the bottom touched a wall 8' from the ground. How long is the ladder? (Draw a diagram.)

2. What will it cost to paint the sides and bottom of a tank whose diameter is 8' and whose height is 9', @ 20¢ a sq. yd.?

3. A house has a gabled roof (shaped like an inverted V). Each side of the roof measures $18' \times 36'$. Find the cost of materials if shingles cost $6.50 a bundle. (The dealer does not sell a fraction of a bundle.)

4. A builder wants to place in the basement a storage tank that will hold 600 gallons of water (approximately). The available floor space is $6' \times 4'$. What is the minimum height of the tank?

5. A pile of timber $4' \times 6' \times 32'$ was cut from 6 acres of woodland. What was the average number of cords per acre?

6. Find the cost of excavating a cellar $21' \times 30' \times 8'$ @ $1.38 a cu. yd.

7. How many tons of anthracite coal can be stored in a bin $12' \times 8' \times 6'$. (One ton of anthracite coal equals approximately 36 cu. ft.)

8. The rates for excavating are $1.20 per cu. yd. of earth and $3.75 of rock. What is the cost of excavating a cellar $42' \times 60' \times 10'$ if $\frac{2}{3}$ of it is earth and $\frac{1}{3}$ rock?

9. A carton measures $16'' \times 14'' \times 12''$. How many cubic feet of space is required to store 90 cartons?

10. What does it cost to fill a tank with gasoline if the diameter is 36'' and the height 48'', at 14¢ a gallon? (Approximate the number of gallons.)

FOR FURTHER STUDY

GENERAL MATHEMATICS, by H. Crandall and F. E. Seymour. (D. C. Heath & Co., Boston.)

MATHEMATICS AT WORK, by G. H. Van Tuyl. (American Book Co., New York.)

MATHEMATICS FOR EVERYDAY USE, by William L. Schaaf. (Barnes & Noble, New York.)

PRACTICAL MATHEMATICS, by N. J. Lennes. (The Macmillan Co., New York.)

XVI

Elementary Algebra

THE USEFULNESS OF ALGEBRA

ALGEBRA is an extension of arithmetic. Because of the notation used, which is really a kind of shorthand, the average person who has never had the opportunity to study algebra is apt to have the impression that it is very difficult. We hope to convince you in this section that it is really simple and clear. To anyone who is interested in the marvelous things that science has produced, a knowledge of algebra is essential. Science, one of the most facinating branches of knowledge, is written in the language of mathematics—and algebra is the foundation of all mathematics.

Civil engineering, electrical engineering, mechanical engineering all depend on algebra. Skyscrapers and steam engines are constructed entirely according to algebraic formulæ. The telephone, the radio, the automobile, the airplane, the moving picture—in fact, every modern invention—would be impossible without algebra.

THE BASIS OF ALGEBRA

In arithmetic we learned to add, subtract, multiply, and divide *numbers.*

In algebra we learn to apply all these operations (and two new ones) to *letters* as well as numbers. We shall learn to add, subtract, multiply, and divide with these letters and numbers just as we did in arithmetic.

In algebra, instead of saying that we walked 5 miles or spent 10 dollars, we are more likely to say that we walked *a* miles or spent *b* dollars. The letters *a* and *b* are used to represent numbers. (In this case *a* stands for 5 and *b* stands for 10.)

It is easily seen that if someone else walked 20 miles and spent 35 dollars, we could also say that he walked *a* miles and spent *b* dollars, only in this case *a* stands for 20 and *b* stands for 35.

Again, let us suppose that we want to say in the language of algebra that a certain thing, a, is twice as much as another thing, b. We simply write

$$a = 2 \times b$$

Now, no matter what number we assign to b, a will always be twice as great. If $b = 2$, $a = 2 \times b = 2 \times 2 = 4$; if $b = 16$, $a = 2 \times 16 = 32$; and so on.

We see then that letters used in algebra *always represent numbers.* The first letters of the alphabet (a, b, c, d, etc.) are used to represent known numbers or numbers to which we can give any value we choose. The last letters of the alphabet (x, y, and z) are used to represent unknown numbers. Whenever we have no idea of the value of a certain number, we say "let x equal the value of that number," and work the problem to find the value of x. We shall learn how to do this.

Let us pause for a moment and see what the advantage is of using letters instead of numbers. Let us look at this simple principle: We know that the distance an express train travels equals the speed of the train times the length of time it travels. If it travels at the rate of 60 miles per hour for 2 hours, the distance it travels is 2×60 miles $= 120$ miles. In other words,

$$\text{distance} = \text{speed} \times \text{time of traveling}$$

If we abbreviate this we can say,

$$d = s \times t$$

If the speed is 45 miles per hour and the time it travels is 3 hours, then $s = 45$ and $t = 3$ and

$$d = 45 \times 3 = 135 \text{ miles}$$

We can name any speed we choose (letting s equal the number of miles per hour) and any length of time we choose (letting t equal that many hours), and we can always get the distance (d) by multiplying s by t.

The use of numbers gives only *one* solution to a given condition, while the use of letters gives as many solutions as we wish, because the letters can represent any numbers we choose to let them represent.

NEGATIVE NUMBERS

There is another difference between algebra and arithmetic. In arithmetic we work with numbers which were always greater than zero. In algebra we work with numbers which are less than zero as well as those which are greater than zero.

Any number that is less than zero is a *negative number,* and is always a minus quantity.

At first the notion of anything less than zero seems foolish. How can anything be less than nothing? Suppose you have absolutely no money. You are in a bad fix, to be sure, for your wealth is at zero; you have nothing. But cheer up! You are much better off than if you had borrowed $100 and spent it, for then you would owe $100 or, in the language of algebra, you would have *minus* $100. Your wealth would then be $100 less than zero, and only by earning $100 and paying your debt could you bring yourself back to zero.

Negative numbers always mean that something is lacking. They imply that something must be supplied to bring conditions back to normal. In a square hole 10 feet deep and 10 feet square, there are *minus* 1,000 cubic feet of dirt. This is like saying that 1,000 cubic feet of dirt are necessary to bring that hole back (fill it in) to its original state.

Negative numbers are always written with a minus sign (−) in front of them, thus:

$$-4, \ -6, \ -10, \ -a, \ -d, \ -x, \ -14a$$

Later on we shall learn how to add, subtract, multiply, and divide with these negative numbers.

POWERS AND ROOTS

There are only four processes in arithmetic: addition, subtraction, multiplication, and division. When we first studied arithmetic, we learned these four fundamental processes and used them only with *whole* numbers. Later on, when we were more advanced, we learned how to apply these four processes to fractions.

Now, in algebra, we learn to use the same four processes with letters as well as numbers, and find that in doing this we are obliged to use two new processes, called "raising to powers" and "extracting roots." The method of computing square root was introduced toward the end of our section on arithmetic, "Mathematics Made Easy." But in algebra we have more occasion to use roots.

Whenever a number is multiplied by itself one or more times, it is raised to a power. If it is multiplied by itself once, it is "squared." If it is multiplied by itself twice, it is "cubed." If it is multiplied by itself three times, it is "raised to the 4th power," and so on. The power to which a number is raised is written smaller to the upper right of the number, thus:

$$3 \times 3 = 3 \text{ squared or } 3^2 = 9$$
$$5 \times 5 \times 5 = 5 \text{ cubed or } 5^3 = 125$$
$$a \times a \times a \times a = a \text{ to the 4th power or } a^4$$

We are somewhat familiar with squares and cubes from arithmetic. We may recall some of those problems which called for the area of a square whose side was 5 inches, or the number of cubic inches in a cube whose side was 10 inches. These were very simple problems in arithmetic, and they are just as simple in algebra, except that in algebra we go much farther with this operation.

The extraction of roots is just the opposite of raising to powers. To find the square root of 81, for example, we must find some number which, when multiplied by itself once, will give us 81. Since 9×9 or $9^2 = 81$, we say that the square root of 81 is 9. For the same reason, since $5 \times 5 \times 5$ or $5^3 = 125$, we say that the cube root of 125 is 5. On page 964 of this book you will find a table of roots which you can use to solve some of the exercises which will be given later on.

SIGNS USED IN ALGEBRA

There are a number of signs and symbols used in algebra which we should memorize at once. These are the following:

$+$ (plus): the same as in arithmetic; $a+b$.

$-$ (minus): the same as in arithmetic; $a-b$.

$\times$ (multiplied by): actually the multiplication sign ($\times$) is seldom used in algebra. Either a dot is used or nothing at all. Thus

$$a \times b \text{ is written } ab \text{ or } a \cdot b$$
$$4 \times a \times c \text{ is written } 4ac \text{ or } 4 \cdot a \cdot c$$

The old familiar sign of division ($\div$) is seldom used in algebra. Instead of $17 \div 3$ we write $\dfrac{17}{3}$ Instead of $a \div b$ we write $\dfrac{a}{b}$.

We have seen that numbers raised to powers have the power written smaller to the upper right of the number. Thus, a^2 is read "a squared"; b^{12} is read "b to the 12th power."

The sign $\sqrt{}$ means square root. If there is a small number in front of it, it means the root indicated by that number; thus, $\sqrt[3]{}$ means cube root; $\sqrt[4]{}$ means 4th root; etc.

How to Express Yourself in Algebraic Signs

As a matter of practice it might be well to "translate" some ordinary terms into algebraic signs.

For example:

a times b times c times d minus a plus c, would be

$$abcd - a + c$$

The 5th root of 7 divided by a times the cube of b would be written

$$\frac{\sqrt[5]{7}}{ab^3}$$

a minus b plus the square root of 12 divided by 2 would be written

$$\frac{a-b+\sqrt{12}}{2}$$

EXERCISE I

Now see whether you can write the signs for the following:

1. b times c divided by a.
2. d times e plus the cube root of a.
3. 4 times b times c divided by b squared.
4. a plus 3 times b minus b cubed divided by 10.
5. minus b plus the square root of b squared divided by 2 times a.
6. the cube root of a times b times c.

See whether you can find the numerical value of each of the following:

7. 6^2+8^2
8. $3^2\times2^3$
9. $\sqrt{256}$
10. $8^2-\sqrt{36}$
11. $\sqrt{72}+3^4-\sqrt[3]{27}$
12. $\sqrt{3^2+4^2}$

FINDING VALUES BY SUBSTITUTION

Now let us go a step farther by substituting numbers for letters and finding the value of various expressions.

Let $a=2$ and $b=3$ and $c=4$ and $d=5$ in the following problems:

Find the value of $abcd$.

Substituting the values: $2\times3\times4\times5=120$.

Find the value of $\dfrac{cb}{a} - \sqrt[3]{c.}$

Substituting the values:

$$\frac{4\times3}{2} - \sqrt[3]{4} = \frac{12}{2} - 2 = 6 - 2 = 4.$$

Find the value of cd^2-a+b^2.

Substituting the values: $4\times5^2-2+3^2$

$$4\times25-2+9$$
$$100-2+9=107$$

EXERCISE II

Now see whether you can find the values of the following (remember that $a=2$, $b=3$, $c=4$, and $d=5$):

1. $\dfrac{cd}{a}$ 3. $\sqrt{b^2+c^2}$ 5. $\sqrt{10ad}$ 7. $\sqrt{4abc+4}$

2. b^2+c^2 4. $a+b-c+\dfrac{da}{2}$ 6. $\dfrac{c^2+4ac}{2a}$ 8. $\dfrac{cd-a}{b^2}$

POSITIVE AND NEGATIVE NUMBERS

Negative numbers are always less than zero and are always written with a minus sign in front of them. We must now learn how to add, subtract, multiply, and divide negative numbers.

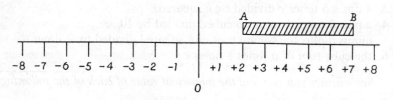

The diagram above is a straight line marked off with numbers. You will notice that zero is in the center and all the numbers to the *right* of zero are + (positive) while all the numbers to the *left* of zero are − (negative). Suppose we place a ruler (AB) 5 units long on the line so that A (the left end of the ruler) is over +2; then the other end, B, will be right over +7, or 2+5 (length of the ruler) = +7. As long as we read from A to B, we *add* 5 to whatever number the A end of the ruler is placed over. If A were moved up to 4, B would be over 9 (4+5=9). If we read from B to A, we *subtract* 5 from the number B is over. In the diagram, B is over 7 and A is over 2, or 7−5=2. If B were moved to the left so that it came over 5, then A would be right over 0, or 5−5=0.

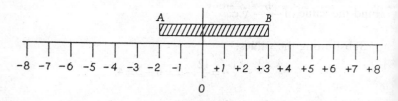

Now let us move the ruler still farther to the left so that B comes ove 3. Where is A now? We see that A is over −2. Then 3−5=−2. Suppos B were moved over zero, then A would be over −5, or 0−5=−5.

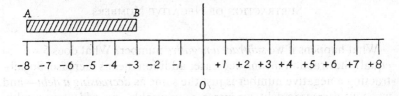

Now suppose B were moved over −3; then A would come over −8. or −3−5 = −8. Note the following examples:

$$4-6=-2 \qquad -5-3=-8$$
$$17-21=-4 \qquad 7+3-16=-6$$
$$-4+8=+4 \qquad -2+6-8-2=-6$$

EXERCISE III

See whether you can do the following:

1. $5-8=?$
2. $3-17=?$
3. $-7+12=?$

4. $-3+8=?$
5. $-5-2-2+10=?$
6. $-6+18-21-14=?$

It is extremely important to note right here that there are two ways of writing a positive number. We may write it either with or without the (+) sign in front of it. +8 is just the same as 8. 8 means +8.

Now let us look at one of the previous examples:

$$4-6=-2$$

This really means that

$$+4-(+6)=-2$$

In other words, we have *subtracted* +6 from +4. We could just as well *add* −6 to +4 and get the same result.

So *subtracting* +6 from +4 is just the same as *adding* −6 to +4:

$$4-(+6)=-2$$
$$4+(-6)=-2$$

There is no difference between *subtracting* a positive number and *adding* the same negative number. For instance:

$$5-(+6) \text{ is the same as } 5-6$$
$$5+(-6) \text{ is the same as } 5-6$$
$$10-(+4) \text{ is the same as } 10-4$$
$$10+(-4) \text{ is the same as } 10-4$$

SUBTRACTION OF NEGATIVE NUMBERS

What happens if we *subtract a negative* number? What does $5 - (-5)$ equal? Subtraction means decrease; addition means increase. So subtracting a negative number is just the same as *decreasing a debt*—and when we *decrease* a debt, we *increase* our wealth—we *add* to our wealth. If I owe you \$5, I have $-\$5$ in my pocket. $-\$5$ is the debt. To subtract from that $-\$5$ is to decrease that debt. If I decrease the debt by \$5, I wipe out the debt and become even. To wipe out the \$5 debt is to be \$5 richer than you were before, or you have added \$5 to your wealth.

This can be shown even more clearly when we think of an uneducated person using the double negative. We may overhear someone say, "I haven't nothing." This statement really means he has *something*, because if he had *not nothing* he must have *something*.

We see, then, that in subtracting a minus we always get a positive. We see also that subtracting a negative (minus) is the same as adding the same positive number. For example:

Take $\quad -6$ from $\quad +4$. Answer: $+10$
Take -10 from -10. Answer: 0
Take -14 from $\quad +3$. Answer: $+17$

It follows, then, that whenever we subtract a negative number we change the $-$ to $+$ and add.

MULTIPLICATION OF POSITIVE AND NEGATIVE NUMBERS

Let a friend represent a positive number, and let an enemy represent a negative number. We know that:

The friend of the friend is a friend.
a plus times a plus = a plus.

The friend of the enemy is an enemy.
a plus times a minus = a minus.

The enemy of the friend is an enemy.
a minus times a plus = a minus.

The enemy of the enemy is a friend.
a minus times a minus = a plus.

It would be well to memorize the following:

$$+ \times + = +$$
$$+ \times - = -$$
$$- \times + = -$$
$$- \times - = +$$

For example:

$$+3 \times +6 = +18 \quad (+ \times + = +)$$
$$+3 \times -6 = -18 \quad (+ \times - = -)$$
$$-3 \times +6 = -18 \quad (- \times + = -)$$
$$-3 \times -6 = +18 \quad (- \times - = +)$$

When the signs are the same, the answer is $+$; when the signs are different, the answer is $-$; like signs $+$, unlike $-$.

EXERCISE IV

See whether you can do the following:

1. $-3 \times -4 = ?$
2. $+5 \times -3 = ?$
3. $+7 \times -2 = ?$
4. $-5 \times +5 = ?$
5. $-2 \times -2 = ?$
6. $-3 \times -3 = ?$
7. $+4 \times -2 = ?$
8. $-6 \times +1 = ?$
9. $-11 \times -11 = ?$
10. $-6 \times 1 = ?$
11. $(-62) \times (-1) = ?$
12. $(3)(-4)(-3) = ?$
13. $(9)(-2)(1) = ?$
14. $(-1)(-1)(1) = ?$
15. $(10)(-1)(-1) = ?$
16. $(-8)(+8) = ?$
17. $(-2)(1)(-2) = ?$
18. $(1)(2)(3) = ?$
19. $(4)(-3)(2) = ?$
20. $(-9)(-8)(-1) = ?$
21. $(-3)(3)(-3) = ?$
22. $(2)(-2)(2) = ?$
23. $(1)(1)(-1) = ?$
24. $(2)(-4)(6) = ?$
25. $(-1)(-3)(-5) = ?$
26. $(1)(6)(-9) = ?$
27. $(-4)(-5)(-6) = ?$
28. $(5)(-10)(15) = ?$
29. $(-2)(-3)(-1) = ?$
30. $(2)(-3)(-1) = ?$

If you were asked what the square root of 9 is, you would say 3 and let it go at that. This is true, but it is only partly true. -3 is also a square root of 9 because -3×-3 also equals $9 (- \times - = +)$. Other negative numbers multiplied by themselves give positive numbers. In other words, the square root of any positive number is a positive and also the negative of the same number. For example, the square root of 4 is both $+2$ and -2; the square root of 25 is both $+5$ and -5; and so on.

But if you should ask what is the square root of -9, the answer would involve an entirely different system of numbers, known as imaginary numbers. These are vitally important in higher mathematics and engineering, and require much more advanced knowledge than we can present here.

DIVISION OF POSITIVE AND NEGATIVE NUMBERS

The same laws hold true for the division of negative and positive numbers as for multiplication, thus:

$$\frac{+4}{+2} = +2 \qquad\qquad \frac{+6}{-2} = -3$$

$$\frac{-8}{+2} = -4 \qquad\qquad \frac{-6}{-3} = +2$$

ADDITION AND SUBTRACTION IN ALGEBRA

ADDITION

Suppose I had 10 apples, and you gave me 5 apples and your brother gave me 7 apples. I would have a total of 22 apples.

Now suppose I had 10 apples and you gave me 5 bananas and your brother gave me 7 apples. I would have 17 apples and 5 bananas. Let us abbreviate this, letting a stand for apples and b for bananas. Then, in the first instance,

$$10a + 5a + 7a = 22a$$

and in the second instance,

$$10a + 5b + 7a = 17a + 5b$$

Suppose now that you had 3 apples, 2 bananas, and 14 cherries, and that I gave you 5 bananas, 6 cherries, and 3 dates. You would then have 3 apples, 7 bananas, 20 cherries, and 3 dates, or

$$\begin{aligned} 3a + 2b + 14c \\ \underline{+5b + 6c + 3d} \\ 3a + 7b + 20c + 3d \end{aligned}$$

It is clear, then, that in adding algebraic numbers we must separate them into similar terms and add up all those terms separately.

It is just like taking inventory in a store. You add up in separate columns the number of pounds of the various items, like tea, sugar, coffee etc., and the total will consist of your entire stock. Instead of saying that you have so many pounds all together of tea, coffee, sugar, etc., you say that you have so many pounds of tea *and* so many pounds of coffee *and* so many pounds of sugar, etc.

Of course this all applies to positive numbers. It also applies to negative numbers; and from what we have learned about negative numbers we should have no trouble in adding them. For example, to add:

$$6a - 2b + 3c \text{ and } 4a + 3b - 4c$$

we write the following:

$$\begin{array}{r} 6a - 2b + 3c \\ 4a + 3b - 4c \\ \hline 10a + b - c \end{array}$$

Note these examples:

$$-12a + 6a = -6a$$
$$5r - 8r = -3r$$
$$ax + 2ax - ax + 4ax = 6ax$$

EXERCISE V

See whether you can add:

1. $-11a + 9a - 12a - 2a + 31a = ?$
2. $16b - 3b + 7b - 15b = ?$
3. $10bc - 6bc + 12bc - 8bc = ?$
4. $2a - 5b + 3a + 2b = ?$
5. $-4c + 6b + 5c - 3b + 2c - b = ?$
6. $4a - 2b + c + 5b - 3a - 2c = ?$

DEFINITIONS

In algebra a single term not added to or subtracted from any other term is called a *monomial*. For example: 6, b, a^2, 12a, 2ax, 8bc, etc.

If two terms are indicated to be added or subtracted, the resulting expression is called a *binomial*. For example: $a + b$, $2x + 4y$, $a^2 - 2b$, etc.

A *trinomial* is an expression of three terms. For example: $a + b - c$, $x + y - z$, $a + 2b^2 - 5c$, etc.

Binomials and *trinomials* are also known as *polynomials*, a polynomial being an expression consisting of two or more terms. For example: $6a - 12b + 11c^2 - 4d + e$, $x - 2y + 3z - 4$, etc.

ADDITION OF POLYNOMIALS

To add the following polynomials:

$$3a - 2b + bc^2, \ 4b + 2bc^2, \ 3a + 7bc^2 + 11, \text{ and } 6b - 8$$

the problem should be arranged so that similar terms are in the same column; thus:

$$
\begin{array}{l}
3a - 2b + bc^2 \\
4b + 2bc^2 \\
3a + 7bc^2 + 11 \\
6b - 8 \\
\hline
6a + 8b + 10bc^2 + 3
\end{array}
$$

Add the following polynomials:

$a+k-x+5,\ 3a-2x+4,\ 7-3k+x,\ 6-3x-5a+k.$

$$
\begin{array}{l}
a + k - x + 5 \\
3a - 2x + 4 \\
-3k + x + 7 \\
-5a + k - 3x + 6 \\
\hline
- a - k - 5x + 22
\end{array}
$$

In the polynomial $2x^2 + 3x - 4$ you will see that the terms $2x^2$ and $3x$ appear. Just as square inches and inches are different things and cannot be added to each other, so x^2 and x are different and must be added separately. Therefore, if we add $2x^2 + 3x - 4$, $x^2 - 3x + 6$, $3x^2 - 2x - 2$, $2x^2 - x - 1$, we arrange as follows:

$$
\begin{array}{l}
2x^2 + 3x - 4 \\
x^2 - 3x + 6 \\
3x^2 - 2x - 2 \\
2x^2 - x - 1 \\
\end{array}
$$

and add thus:
$$8x^2 - 3x - 1$$

The answer cannot be made simpler by further addition.

EXERCISE VI

See whether you can add the following:

1. $8x + 7y - 4z$, $5x + 3z$, and $5x + 7y - 6z$.
2. $5d + 4d^2 + 6$, $d^2 + 2d - 1$, and $5d + 3d^2 - 8$.
3. $5x - 8y + 8z$, $12y - 12z + 2x$, and $10z - 5y$.
4. $2x - 10z$, $5x + 2y$, $3z - y$, and $3x - 4y + z$.

SUBTRACTION

Subtraction is extremely simple. You will remember that the subtraction of a positive number was the same as the addition of the same negative number. If you will memorize one simple rule, you will know how to subtract. The rule is as follows: In subtracting one algebraic expression from another, *change signs in the subtrahend and add.*

From $10a$ subtract $4a$.

$$\begin{array}{r} +10a \\ +\ 4a \text{ (subtrahend)} \\ \hline 6a \end{array}$$

We *changed the sign* of $4a$ to $-4a$ and *added* $10a$ and $-4a$, and obtained $6a$ as the result.

This process should be looked upon not as subtraction but as addition. *All subtraction must be looked upon as addition with the sign changed in the subtrahend.* This is necessary because there is no other way of subtracting negative numbers except by adding the same positive numbers. Inasmuch as algebraic expressions involve both negative and positive numbers and we cannot add some while subtracting others, there is this general rule for adding instead of subtracting in all cases.

1. From $10a$ subtract $-4a$.

$$\begin{array}{r} +10a \\ -\ 4a \text{ (subtrahend)} \\ \hline +14a \end{array}$$

We changed $-4a$ to $+4a$ and added $10a+4a=14a$.

2. Subtract $-3ax$ from $-7ax$.

$$\begin{array}{r} -7ax \\ -3ax \text{ (subtrahend)} \\ \hline -4ax \end{array}$$

We changed $-3ax$ to $+3ax$ and added it to $-7ax$.

3. Subtract $9ab^3$ from $-3ab^3$.

$$\begin{array}{r} -\ 3ab^3 \\ 9ab^3 \\ \hline -12ab^3 \end{array}$$

We changed $+9ab^3$ to $-9ab^3$ and added it to $-3ab^3$.

4. Subtract $3a-4b-5c+4$ from $a+7b-4c$.

$$\begin{array}{l} a+\ 7b-4c \\ 3a-\ 4b-5c+4 \\ \hline -2a+11b+\ c-4 \end{array}$$

We changed the signs in the subtrahend and added thus:

$$\begin{array}{l} a+\ 7b-4c \\ -3a+\ 4b+5c-4 \\ \hline -2a+11b+\ c-4 \end{array}$$

EXERCISE VII

1. Subtract $2x-3y+4$ from $3x+2y-8$.
2. Subtract $2x^2-4x+6$ from $3x^2+7x-3$.
3. Subtract $2a-2c-4$ from $a+3c+2$.
4. Subtract $3x-2y+z$ from $4x-3y+2z$.
5. Subtract $4x^2+7y^2-2z$ from $-6x^2-14y^2+3z$.

EQUATIONS

Whenever something equals something else, we have an *equation*. An equation is an equality. The following are three distinct equations:

$$6+4=10$$
$$3+7-2=4+4$$
$$11-2=20-2-9$$

Every equation has two parts: a left member or left side and a right member or right side. These two members or sides are separated by the *equals* sign $(=)$; thus:

$$\text{left member} = \text{right member}$$
$$18+2=20$$

The equals sign in any equation is like a fence. It is sometimes necessary to move terms from one side of the "fence" to the other side. Before a number can "jump over the fence" its sign must be changed. If it is plus it becomes minus, and if it is minus it becomes a plus:

$$18+2=20 \left\{ \begin{array}{l} +2=20-18 \\ 18\ =20-2 \end{array} \right.$$

Moving a term from one side of the "fence" to the other is called *transposing*. What we really do here is to add the same number to both sides of the equation. (This does not change the value of the equation.) In the preceding example we first added -18 to both sides and got $+2=20-18$; we then added -2 to both sides and got $18=20-2$. The -18 canceled the $+18$ in the first instance, leaving $+2$ on the left side. And the -2 canceled the $+2$, leaving 18 on the left side.

$$26+4=30$$

$$26 = 30 - 4$$

$$41-16=25$$

$$41 = 25+16$$

$$a+b=c$$

$$a = c-b$$

If $x-10=7$
    Then $x=7+10$ or $x=17$.

If $x+3=6$
    Then $x=6-3$ or $x=3$

If $x-2=0$
    Then $x=2$

EXERCISE VIII

See whether you can do the following (find the value of x or y):

1. $x-3=0$ 3. $x+17=42$ 5. $x-7=3$
2. $x+5-6=3$ 4. $y+21=37$ 6. $y+2=1$

If 4 oranges cost 20¢, 1 orange will cost 5¢. We found this by dividing 20 by 4.

Then if $4x=20$ (Divide both sides by 4.)
        $x=\ 5$
    If $6x=96$ (Divide both sides by 6.)
        $x=16$
    If $3x=12$ (Divide both sides by 3.)
        $x=\ 4$

EXERCISE IX

See whether you can do these (find the value of x):

1. $5x = 25$ 3. $7x = 63$ 5. $2x = 22$
2. $12x = 144$ 4. $9x = 81$ 6. $5x = 15$

Now let us go a step farther:

$$4x + 3 = 15 \quad \text{Find } x.$$
$$4x = 15 - 3$$
$$4x = 12$$
Ans. $\quad x = 3$

$$12x - 3x + 7 = 16 \quad \text{Find } x.$$
$$9x + 7 = 16$$
$$9x = 16 - 7$$
$$9x = 9$$
Ans. $\quad x = 1$

EXERCISE X

Find the value of x:

1. $x - 3 = 14$ 3. $4x = x + 2$ 5. $-6 - 5x = 19$
2. $2x = 5 - x$ 4. $3x + 4 = x - 6$ 6. $4x - 6 = 18$

If half a dozen eggs cost 30¢, 1 dozen cost 60¢. We found this by multiplying 30×2, or

$$\tfrac{1}{2} \text{ doz.} = 30$$
$$1 \text{ doz.} = 30 \times 2 \quad \text{(Multiply both sides by 2.)}$$
$$1 \text{ doz.} = 60$$

In other words:

$$\text{If } \tfrac{1}{2}d = 30$$
$$d = 30 \times 2$$
$$d = 60$$

$$\text{If } \tfrac{1}{3}x = 10 \quad \left(\tfrac{1}{3}x \text{ is written } \tfrac{x}{3} \right)$$
$$x = 10 \times 3 \quad \text{(Multiply both sides by 3.)}$$
$$x = 30$$

$$\text{If } \tfrac{x}{7} = 4$$
$$x = 4 \times 7 \quad \text{(Multiply both sides by 7.)}$$
$$x = 28$$

EXERCISE XI

Find the value of x:

1. $\dfrac{x}{3}=14$ 3. $\dfrac{x}{14}=17$ 5. $\dfrac{x}{10}=31$

2. $\dfrac{2x}{6}=20$ 4. $\dfrac{x}{3}=100$ 6. $\dfrac{x}{4}=9$

SOLVING EQUATIONS

By "solving an equation" is meant finding the value of x (or whatever other letter is taken to represent the unknown).

1. Solve $6x-7=3x+2$.

Collect the x's thus:

$$6x-3x-7= \quad +2$$

$$3x-7=+2$$

Transpose the -7 thus:

$$3x \quad =2+7$$

$$3x=9$$
$$x=3$$

Check by substituting 3 for x in the original problem, thus:

$$6x-7=3x+2$$
$$18-7=9+2$$
$$11=11$$

2. Solve $4t+3-t+5=t-10$.

Collect the t's thus:

$$4t+3-t+5-t= \quad -10$$

$$2t+8=-10$$

$$2t \quad =-10 \quad -8$$

$$2t=-18$$
$$t=-9$$

Check by substituting -9 for t in the original problem.

$$4t+3-t+5=t-10$$
$$-36+3+9+5=-9-10$$
$$-19=-19$$

3. Solve $x+2=\frac{x}{4}+8$.

First multiply both sides of the equation by 4 to change $\frac{x}{4}$ to x, thus:

$$4x+8=x+32$$

Next collect the $x's$ on the left side.

$$4x-x+8= \quad +32$$

$$3x+8=+32$$

$$3x \quad =32-8$$

$$3x=24$$
$$x=\ 8$$

Check by substituting 8 for x in the original problem.

$$x+2=\frac{x}{4}+8$$

$$8+2=\frac{8}{4}+8$$

$$8+2=2+8$$
$$10=10$$

4. Solve $-3+2x+2=\frac{2x}{4}-2x+6$.

First multiply both sides by 4 in order to change $\frac{2x}{4}$ to $2x$ (this is called clearing of fractions).

$$-12+8x+8=2x-8x+24$$

Next collect the x's on the left side, thus:

$$-12+8x+8-2x+8x=24$$
$$-12+14x+8=24$$
$$14x=28$$
$$x=2$$

Check by substituting 2 for x in the original problem.

$$-3+2x+2=\frac{2x}{4}-2x+6$$

$$-3+4+2=\frac{4}{4}-4+6$$

$$3=1-4+6$$

$$3=3$$

EXERCISE XII

Find the value of x:

1. $4x-2=3x+2$
2. $3x-20=8x+25$
3. $6x-3-3x=21$
4. $5x-7+2x=49$
5. $x+3-2x=2$
6. $2x+x-4=8$

APPLICATION OF EQUATIONS TO SIMPLE PROBLEMS

Before we apply these equations to problems, it is essential that we understand how to express ourselves algebraically.

For example, express the following algebraically: 3 times a certain number diminished by 5 equals the number increased by 7.

Let x be that certain number. Then 3 times that certain number is $3x$; and 3 times that certain number diminished by 5 is $3x-5$.

Now we are told that this equals the number increased by 7.

Hence $3x-5=x+7$.

EXERCISE XIII

See whether you can write the following algebraically and solve the equations:

1. Three times a certain number less 25 equals twice the number less 15. What is the number?
2. A certain number is doubled and the result increased by 10. The sum is 14. What is the number?
3. Twice a certain number added to 30 gives the same result as three times the number subtracted from 90. What is the number?

Now let us study a few problems and note carefully how we go about solving them.

PROBLEMS

The sum of three numbers is 22. The first number is 5 less than the second number, and the third number is 3 more than twice the second number. What are the numbers?

We note, first of all, that the sum of the three numbers is 22, but we do not know any of the numbers. We do know, however, that the first and third numbers both bear a definite relationship to the second number, as they are less and greater, respectively. Therefore, if we let x equal the second number, we can express the problem algebraically.

So we start by letting x = the second number.

Then the first number is 5 less than x, or $x-5$; and the third number is 3 more than twice x, or $2x+3$.

We know all these together = 22.

Therefore

$$
\underbrace{x-5}_{\text{1st no.}} \;+\; \underbrace{x}_{\text{2nd no.}} \;+\; \underbrace{2x+3}_{\text{3rd no.}} \;=\; \underset{\text{Total}}{22}
$$

$$x+x+2x = 22+5-3$$
$$4x = 24$$
$$x = 6 \quad \text{(second number)}$$
$$x-5 = 1 \quad \text{(first number)}$$
$$2x+3 = \underline{15} \quad \text{(third number)}$$
$$22 = \text{total}$$

A man can afford to spend $160 a week for part-time office help. If the part-time stenographer gets $20 a week and a bookkeeper gets ¾ as much as a salesman, how much does he pay each?

We note that there are three people to be paid. We are told that the stenographer gets $20 a week. Therefore it is only a question of finding how much the salesman and the bookkeeper get. Inasmuch as the bookkeeper gets ¾ as much as the salesman, it follows that x should be made to equal the salesman's salary, and $\dfrac{3}{4}x$ the bookkeeper's or $\dfrac{3x}{4}$.

Therefore:

$$
\underset{\text{salesman}}{x} \;+\; \underset{\text{bookkeeper}}{\dfrac{3x}{4}} \;+\; \underset{\text{stenographer}}{20} \;=\; \underset{\text{total}}{\$160}
$$

Multiplying by 4 to clear the fraction:

$$4x + 3x + 80 = 640$$
$$7x = 560$$
$$x = 80 \quad \text{(salesman's salary)}$$
$$\frac{3x}{4} = 60 \quad \text{(bookkeeper's salary)}$$

You can see at once that $80 + 60 + 20$ (the stenographer's salary) equals 160, or the total.

EXERCISE XIV

See whether you can do the following problems:

1. An uncle who is twice as old as his nephew is also twelve years older than his nephew. Find the age of each.
2. There are two numbers such that the larger is twice the smaller. If twelve is added to the larger, it will be six times as large as the smaller. Find the numbers.
3. A man is one year older than his wife; the age of their son is one third that of his mother. Their combined ages are 64 years. How old is each?

PARENTHESES

Suppose you order at a lunch counter a glass of milk and a piece of cake. You are served

milk + cake

If you know something about baking, you will realize that the cake is made up of flour and butter and sugar and eggs and milk. What you really eat is

milk + (flour + butter + sugar + eggs + milk)

All the ingredients in the parentheses, taken together, are called cake.

Numbers are like this cake; they can be separated into any number of ingredients. Thus: $4 = (5 - 1)$, $6 = (2 + 4)$, $18 = (12 + 6)$, etc. Of course these same numbers could be separated differently; for example, $18 = (9 + 9)$ or $(10 + 8)$, etc.

When we write $7 + 3$, we could just as well write it:

$7 + (4 - 1)$ or $7 + (2 + 1)$ or $7 + (6 - 3)$, etc.

All the numbers in parentheses are equal to 3. And if we remove the parentheses in each case, we shall always get the same result, namely, 10. Thus:

$$7+(4-1)=7+4-1=10$$
$$7+(2+1)=7+2+1=10$$
$$7+(6-3)=7+6-3=10$$

You will notice that in each case we *added* the two numbers in the parentheses to 7. You will remember that when we studied subtraction the rule was to change the sign and add. Now, if we *subtract* the numbers in the parentheses from 7 instead of adding them, it becomes necessary to change the signs of those numbers and add them. Thus:

$$7-(4-1)=7-4+1=4*$$
$$7-(2+1)=7-2-1=4$$
$$7-(6-3)=7-6+3=4$$

*Note that the $4-1$ becomes $-4+1$.

We removed the parenthesis, but this time we changed the sign of the numbers in the parenthesis, and so we have the RULE: *Whenever we remove a parenthesis with a minus sign in front of it, we change the signs of all the numbers or letters inside the parenthesis. Whenever we remove a parenthesis with a plus sign in front of it, we do not change the signs of the numbers or letters inside the parenthesis.*

Note the following examples:

$$6+(8-2+6)=6+8-2+6=18$$
$$6-(8-2+6)=6-8+2-6=-6$$
$$4-(-2-3+6)=4+2+3-6=3$$
$$a+(b-c+d)=a+b-c+d$$
$$x-(-y+z+2)=x+y-z-2$$

EXERCISE XV

See whether you can do the following:

1. $8+(3-1)=?$ 　　　 4. $x+(2x+3y-z)=?$
2. $9-(4+6-3)=?$ 　　 5. $x-(2a-b+3c-d)=?$
3. $17-(5-2+6)=?$ 　　 6. $x-(a+2x-3a+2)=?$

MULTIPLICATION IN ALGEBRA

We have seen that

$$a+a+a+a=4a$$

The number 4 is called the *coefficient* of *a,* and is written to the left of the letter. The coefficient before a letter tells us how many of that letter we have added together. Thus $7x$ is a short way of expressing the sum $x+x+x+x+x+x+x$.

We have also seen that

$$a \cdot a \cdot a \cdot a = a^4$$

The number 4 in this case is called the *exponent* of *a,* and is written to the right of and slightly above the letter, and is smaller than the usual number. Thus x^7 is a short way of expressing the product $x \cdot x \cdot x \cdot x \cdot x \cdot x \cdot x$. The coefficient and exponents are examples of what we meant by algebra shorthand mentioned at the beginning of this section. Note that in $3n^4$, 3 is the coefficient and 4 the exponent, while $3n^4$ itself is a shorthand notation for

$$n \cdot n \cdot n \cdot n + n \cdot n \cdot n \cdot n + n \cdot n \cdot n \cdot n$$

Note how the following may be simplified:

1. $a \cdot a \cdot a + a \cdot a \cdot a = a^3 + a^3 = 2a^3$
2. $x \cdot x \cdot x \cdot x \cdot x + x \cdot x \cdot x \cdot x \cdot x + x \cdot x \cdot x \cdot x \cdot x = x^5 + x^5 + x^5 = 3x^5$
3. $b \cdot b + b \cdot b + b \cdot b + b \cdot b + b \cdot b + b \cdot b + b \cdot b =$
$$b^2 + b^2 + b^2 + b^2 + b^2 + b^2 + b^2 = 7b^2$$

And the reverse:

4. $5x^3 = 5 \cdot x \cdot x \cdot x$
5. $3b^5 = 3 \cdot b \cdot b \cdot b \cdot b \cdot b$
6. $4n^2 = 4 \cdot n \cdot n$

Note these examples:

$5x^3$ 5 is the coefficient; 3 is the exponent.
$6a^2$ 6 is the coefficient; 2 is the exponent.
$8b^4$ 8 is the coefficient; 4 is the exponent.

Let us study this a little more closely. When just the letter appears without any exponent, like a, it really means a^1. For example, $a \times a$ is the same as $a^1 \times a^1$, which equals a^2, thus

$$a \times a = a^2$$
$$a \times a \times a = a^3$$
$$a \times a \times a \times a = a^4$$
$$a \times a \times a \times a \times a = a^5$$

Then $a^2 \times a^3 = (a \times a) \times (a \times a \times a) = a^5$.

Notice that we *add* the exponents of a^2 and a^3 instead of multiplying them.

$$a^2 \times a^3 = a^{2+3} = a^5$$

In the same way:

$$a^4 \times a^3 = a^{4+3} = a^7$$
$$x^2 \times x^4 = x^{2+4} = x^6$$
$$b^4 \times b^4 = b^{4+4} = b^8$$
$$a^{12} \times a^6 = a^{12+6} = a^{18}$$

This holds true for any number of letters. Thus:

$$a^4 b \times a^2 b^2 = a^6 b^3$$
$$a^5 b \times a^2 b^3 = a^7 b^4$$
$$a^2 \times a^3 b \times a^4 b = a^9 b^2$$

You will notice that we *added* all the exponents for each letter and wrote the sum in the answer.

EXERCISE XVI

See whether you can multiply these (remember to *add* the exponents):

1. $b^4 \times b^8 = ?$ 3. $x^4 \times x^2 = ?$ 5. $a^4 b^3 \times ab = ?$
2. $a^3 \times a^7 = ?$ 4. $a^3 b \times a^2 b^2 = ?$ 6. $bd^2 \times b^3 d^3 = ?$

If we have coefficients as well as exponents, we *multiply these coefficients* and *add the exponents*. Thus:

$$4a^2 \times 3a^4 = 12a^6$$

We multiplied the coefficients 4 and 3 and got 12. We added the exponents 2 and 4 and got 6.

$$5b^4 \times 3b^5 = 15b^9$$

We multiplied the coefficients 5 and 3 and got 15. We added the exponents 4 and 5 and got 9.

This holds true for any number of letters:

$$5ab \times 6a^2 = 30a^3b$$
$$6a^2b^2 \times 4a^3b^4 = 24a^5b^6$$
$$10a^3b^2c^4 \times 3a^4b^3c^2 = 30a^7b^5c^6$$
$$7x^4y^2z \times 4x^3y^3z^2 = 28x^7y^5z^3$$
$$4a^2b^3c^2 \times 8a^3c = 32a^5b^3c^3$$

EXERCISE XVII

See whether you can do these (remember to *multiply* the coefficients and *add* the exponents):

1. $3b^2 \times 4b^4 = ?$ 3. $7a^2 \times 4ab = ?$ 5. $6x^2y^2z^2 \times 4x^4y^3z^5 = ?$

2. $5a^2 \times 6a^4 = ?$ 4. $8bc^2 \times 3b^3c^4 = ?$ 6. $15\ a^3b^2c^4 \times 2bc = ?$

Remember our rule for multiplying unlike signs: like signs +, unlike signs −.

7. $8a^3b \times -3a^2b = ?$ 9. $5x^3y \times -10x^5y^2 = ?$

8. $-4ad \times -3a^2d^3 = ?$ 10. $x^2 \times x^3y \times x^4y^2 = ?$

So far we have learned to multiply single terms, or *monomials*. Now suppose we have to multiply polynomials. How do we go about it? You will remember that a polynomial was defined as an expression of two or more terms, like $2x+3y$, or $3a^2+4b^2$, or $6x^3+3y^3-2z^2$.

Let us see how we would multiply these:

Multiply $4x^2-3x+2$ by $5x$.

We arrange the problem as follows:

$$4x^2-3x+2$$
$$5x$$

and multiply each term of the trinomial by the monomial $5x$ as if there were three separate examples, thus:

$4x^2$	$-\ 3x$	$+\ 2$
$\times\ 5x$	$\times\ 5x$	$\times\ 5x$
$20x^3$	$-15x^2$	$+10x$

We write the complete example as follows:

$$4x^2-3x+2$$
$$5x$$
$$\overline{20x^3-15x^2+10x}$$

Note these examples:

$$6x^3-4x^2+3x$$
$$2x$$
$$\overline{12x^4-8x^3+6x^2} \quad \text{Ans.}$$

$$14a^2+2b^2-3ac$$
$$2c$$
$$\overline{28a^2c+4b^2c-6ac^2} \quad \text{Ans.}$$

$$3a^2b^3d+5a^3b^2d^2$$
$$4a^2bd$$
$$\overline{12a^4b^4d^2+20a^5b^3d^3} \quad \text{Ans.}$$

$$15a^3b^2c-3a^2b^3c+12ab^4c^2$$
$$-5a^2b^2c$$
$$\overline{-75a^5b^4c^2+15a^4b^5c^2-60a^3b^6c^3}$$

EXERCISE XVIII

Multiply:

1. $x+2b-cd$ by $2b$.
2. $x+3xy+2y$ by $2y$.
3. $4x^2-5x+2$ by x^2.
4. $10a+3b-4ac$ by $4a^2bc$.
5. $4a^2b-6bc+3c$ by $3ab$.
6. $2b^2+ab+a^3$ by $4ab^2$.

MULTIPLICATION OF POLYNOMIALS

We now know how to multiply a polynomial by a monomial. We shall next learn how to multiply one polynomial by another.

In arithmetic we say

$$5\times14=70$$

In algebra we do this another way and get the same result. Thus:

$$5\times14=5\times(10+4)=50+20=70$$

(We have multiplied the 10 by 5, then the 4 by 5, and added these results.)

For example:

$$6 \times 18 \text{ can be expressed: } 6(10+8) = 60+48 = 108$$
$$7 \times 10 \text{ can be expressed: } 7(8+2) = 56+14 = 70$$
$$8 \times 14 \text{ can be expressed: } 8(16-2) = 128-16 = 112$$
$$12 \times 6 \text{ can be expressed: } 12(10-4) = 120-48 = 72$$

EXERCISE XIX

See whether you can do these (remember to multiply both numbers in the parentheses separately by the number outside the parentheses and add the results):

1. $3(8+2)=?$
2. $7(14-3)=?$
3. $5(8-5)=?$

4. $4(10+2)=?$
5. $6(8-3)=?$
6. $4(10+3)=?$

7. $5(7+2)=?$
8. $2(9+4)=?$
9. $-1(6+7)=?$

The same rule is followed in multiplying letters. In multiplying an expression in parentheses by a letter, multiply each term in the parentheses separately by that letter and add the results:

$a(b+c)=ab+ac$ We multiplied b by a and c by a, and added.

$a(b-c)=ab-ac$ We multiplied b by a and c by a, and added.

$a(a+b)=a^2+ab$ We multiplied a by a and b by a, and added.

$a^2b(a^3+b^2)=a^5b+a^2b^3$ We multiplied a^3 by a^2b and b^2 by a^2b, and added.

$a^2bc^3(a^2+3b^3+c)=a^4bc^3+3a^2b^4c^3+a^2bc^4$ We multiplied each term in the parentheses by a^2bc^3, and added.

EXERCISE XX

See whether you can do these:

1. $x(x-y)=?$
2. $2x(x+3y)=?$
3. $3a^2(a+3b^2)=?$
4. $4a^3(a^2+3b+c)=?$

5. $ab(a^2+2ab)=?$
6. $2a^2(a^3+2a^4)=?$
7. $5ab^2(ab^2-3a^2b^3)=?$
8. $10a^3b^2(ab^3-4a^2b^2)=?$

Now let us multiply polynomials by one another. Let us apply the same simple principle to this, and we shall see that it is just as simple as ordinary multiplication.

$$(3x+2)(4x-7)=?$$

We write the example as shown below, thus:

$$3x+2$$
$$4x-7$$

and multiply just as if we had two separate examples, as follows:

$$3x+2 \qquad\qquad 3x+2$$
$$4x \qquad\qquad\qquad -7$$
$$\overline{12x^2+8x} \qquad\qquad \overline{-21x-14}$$

On adding the two results, we find

$$12x^2+\ 8x$$
$$\underline{-21x-14}$$
$$12x^2-13x-14$$

In practice, the complete example looks like this:

$$3x\ +\ 2$$
$$4x\ -\ 7$$
$$\overline{12x^2+\ 8x}$$
$$\underline{-21x-14}$$
$$12x^2-13x-14$$

You will see that we have multiplied each term in the upper line by each term in the lower line (first by $4x$ and then by -7), and then added the results.

This can be made clearer if we do it with actual numbers. If we wish to multiply 25 by 15, we can separate them as follows: $(20+5)(10+5)$. Now, multiplying these polynomials, we get:

$$20+\ \ 5$$
$$10+\ \ 5$$
$$\overline{200+\ 50}$$
$$\underline{\quad+100+25}$$
$$200+150+25=375$$

Examples:

1. $(5x^2+3x)$ $(2x^2+4x)$

$$5x^2 + 3x$$
$$2x^2 + 4x$$

$$10x^4 + 6x^3$$
$$+20x^3+12x^2$$

$$10x^4+26x^3+12x^2$$

2. $(3a+2b)$ $(4a-3b)$

$$3a + 2b$$
$$4a - 3b$$

$$12a^2+8ab$$
$$-9ab-6b^2$$

$$12a^2 - ab-6b^2$$

3. $(2x^2-3x+5)$ $(2x-1)$

$$2x^2-3x + 5$$
$$2x - 1$$

$$4x^3-6x^2+10x$$
$$-2x^2+ 3x-5$$

$$4x^3-8x^2+13x-5$$

EXERCISE XXI

See whether you can do these:

1. $(2x^2-8x)$ (x^2+2x) 4. $(3m^2-2m+7)$ $(2m^2-3m)$
2. (a^2+3ab) (a^3+2ab) 5. $(3x^2+5x-2)$ $(3x^2-2x)$
3. $(2x^2-3x-8)$ $(2x-4)$ 6. (x^3+2x^2+x) $(x-4)$

IMPORTANT SPECIAL PRODUCTS

There are three special kinds of products in algebra which are very important. These special products should be learned and memorized, as they will be extremely useful later on in our work. The first one is the square of a binomial.

I. $(a+b)^2=a^2+2ab+b^2$

This can be demonstrated in two ways. The first is ordinary multiplication:

$$
\begin{array}{r}
a + b \\
a + b \\
\hline
a^2 + ab \\
 + ab + b^2 \\
\hline
a^2 + 2ab + b^2
\end{array}
$$

The second is to take two units of length, a and b,

$$\underline{ a }$$

$$\underline{ b }$$

and lay them off on a straight line:

$$\underline{ a b }|$$

Then the length of this line is $a+b$. If we make a square of this (draw a square with each side equal to $a+b$), we can divide this square into 4

parts. The first part (I) is a square with a on each side, and its area is therefore a^2. The next part (II) has b for one side and a for the other therefore its area is ab. The third part (III) has a for one side and b for the other; therefore its area is also ab. The last part (IV) is a small square with b on each side, and therefore its area is b^2. We can easily see, then, that

$$(a+b)^2 = a^2 + 2ab + b^2$$

It is essential for you to memorize this rule: *The square of the sum of two terms is equal to the square of the first term, plus twice the product of the first term by the second term, plus the square of the second term.*

The second product is

II. $\qquad\qquad (a-b)^2 = a^2 + 2ab + b^2$

This can be seen from multiplication:

$$
\begin{array}{r}
a - b \\
a - b \\
\hline
a^2 - ab \\
- ab + b^2 \\
\hline
a^2 - 2ab + b^2
\end{array}
$$

It is essential for you to memorize this rule also: *The square of the difference of two terms is equal to the square of the first term, minus twice the product of the first term by the second term, plus the square of the second term.*

Now that we have learned these rules, let us apply them to a few examples:

$$(12)^2 = 144$$

Writing this as $(10+2)^2$, we get:

$$
\begin{aligned}
(10+2)^2 &= 10^2 + 2(10 \times 2) + 2^2 \\
&= 100 + 2(20) + 4 \\
&= 100 + 40 + 4 \\
&= 144
\end{aligned}
$$

Find the square of 24.

$$
\begin{aligned}
(24)^2 = (20+4)^2 &= 20^2 + 2(20 \times 4) + 4^2 \\
&= 400 + 2(80) + 16 \\
&= 400 + 160 + 16 \\
&= 576
\end{aligned}
$$

This result can also be obtained by means of the *second product* $(a-b)^2$ merely by letting $24=30-6$:

$$\begin{aligned}(24)^2=(36-6)^2&=30^2-2(30\times6)+6^2\\&=900-2(180)+36\\&=900-360+36\\&=576\end{aligned}$$

You will note that in the first example we let $24=20+4$ and applied the formula:

$$(a+b)^2=a^2+2ab+b^2$$

letting $a=20$ and $b=4$. In the second example we let $24=30-6$ and applied the formula:

$$(a-b)^2=a^2-2ab+b^2$$

letting $a=30$ and $b=6$. We always found $(24)^2=576$.

Of course we could let 24 equal the sum or difference of any two numbers we choose. For example:

$$\begin{aligned}(24)^2+(18+6)^2&=18^2+2(18\times6)+6^2\\&=324+2(108)+36\\&=324+216+36\\&=576\end{aligned}$$

No matter what two numbers make up 24, we can readily see that by applying the formula:

$$(a+b)^2=a^2+2ab+b^2$$
$$\text{or}$$
$$(a-b)^2=a^2-2ab+b^2$$

we *always* get the same result: 576

Let us study the following:

$$\begin{aligned}(x+1)^2&=x^2+2x+1\\(4+x)^2&=16+8x+x^2\\(x-2t)^2&=x^2-4tx+4t^2\\(7x-y)^2&=49x^2-14xy+y^2\\11^2=(8+3)^2&=64+48+9=121\\8^2=(7+1)^2&=49+14+1=64\\6^2=(10-4)^2&=100-80+16=36\end{aligned}$$

EXERCISE XXII

Now see whether you can do these:

1. $(14)^2 = (10+4)^2 = ?$ 4. $(x+y)^2 = ?$ 6. $(5-2y)^2 = ?$
2. $(22)^2 = (20+2)^2 = ?$ 5. $(2x-3y)^2 = ?$ 7. $(3a-y)^2 = ?$
3. $(48)^2 = (50-2)^2 = ?$

The third important product is called "the sum and difference of two terms" and is written:

III. $(a+b)\ (a-b) = a^2 - b^2$

This can be done by multiplication:

$$\begin{array}{r}
a - b \\
a + b \\
\hline
a^2 - ab \\
+ ab - b^2 \\
\hline
a^2 \qquad - b^2
\end{array}$$

(The $+ab$ and $-ab$ cancel each other.)

It is essential to memorize this rule: *The product of the sum and difference of two terms equals the difference of their squares.*

$$(x+y)\ (x-y) = x^2 - y^2$$
$$(c+d)\ (c-d) = c^2 - d^2$$

Let us apply this to a few examples:

1. $22 \times 18 = ?$
        Let $22 = 20 + 2$ (the same as $a+b$)
        Let $18 = 20 - 2$ (the same as $a-b$)
Then $22 \times 18 = (20+2)\ (20-2) = 20^2 - 2^2$
$$= 400 - 4$$
$$= 396$$

2. $31 \times 29 = ?$
        Let $31 = 30 + 1$
        Let $29 = 30 - 1$
Then $31 \times 29 = (30+1)\ (30-1) = 30^2 - 1^2$
$$= 900 - 1$$
$$= 899$$

3. $52 \times 40 = (46+6) \ (46-6) = 46^2 - 6^2$
$$= 2116 - 36$$
$$= 2080$$

4. $17 \times 7 = (12+5) \ (12-5) = 12^2 - 5^2$
$$= 144 - 25$$
$$= 119$$

5. $(x+2y) \ (x-2y) = x^2 - 4y^2$

6. $(3a+b) \ (3a-b) = 9a^2 - b^2$

EXERCISE XXIII

See whether you can do these:

1. $21 \times 15 = ?$ 3. $30 \times 20 = ?$ 5. $(3x+2y) \ (3x-2y) = ?$
2. $27 \times 17 = ?$ 4. $(a+2b) \ (a-2b) = ?$

DIVISION IN ALGEBRA

When we multiplied two letters with exponents and coefficients, we *added* the exponents of like letters and *multiplied* the coefficients. In division it is *exactly the reverse*. When we divide two letters with exponents and coefficients, we *subtract* the exponents of like letters and *divide* the coefficients. Thus

$$\frac{8c^3}{4c^3} = 2c^{3-2} = 2c$$

We divided the coefficient 8 by 4, and got 2.
We subtracted the exponent 2 from 3, and got 1.

$$\frac{16a^6}{4a^2} = 4a^{6-2} = 4a^4$$

We divided the coefficient 16 by 4, and got 4.
We subtracted the exponent 2 from 6, and got 4.

$$\frac{12x^{10}}{4x^2} = 3x^{10-2} = 3x^8$$

We divided the coefficient 12 by 4, and got 3.
We subtracted the exponent 2 from 10, and got 8.

$$\frac{15a^3b^6}{3ab} = 5a^{3-1}b^{6-1} = 5a^2b^5$$

We divided the coefficient 15 by 3, and got 5.

We subtracted the exponents 1 from 3, and 1 from 6, and got 2 and 5.

$$\frac{6c^2d^3}{3c^2d} = 2d^2$$

We divided the coefficient 6 by 3, and got 2.

We noted that we had c^2 divided by c^2, which is 1. We subtracted the exponent 1 from 3, and got 2.

Note that $\frac{c}{c} = 1$. Dividing a letter with an exponent by the same letter with the same exponent is always 1.

EXERCISE XXIV

See whether you can do these (remember to divide the coefficients and subtract exponents):

1. $\dfrac{6x^6}{3x^4} = ?$

2. $\dfrac{18a^3b^2}{6a^2b^2} = ?$

3. $\dfrac{10a^4b^2c^4}{5a^2bc^2} = ?$

4. $\dfrac{21a^7b^4}{7a^4b} = ?$

The rule of signs is the same in division as it is in multiplication, namely:

$$+ \text{ divided by } + = +$$
$$+ \text{ divided by } - = -$$
$$- \text{ divided by } + = -$$
$$- \text{ divided by } - = +$$

or, like signs $+$, unlike signs $-$. Thus:

$$\frac{+14a^3b^2}{-2ab} = -7a^2b$$

$$\frac{-6x^4y^3}{+3x^2y} = -2x^2y^2$$

$$\frac{-8x^3y^2}{-4xy} = 2x^2y$$

We saw in multiplication that when we multiplied a polynomial by a single term, we multiplied each term in the polynomial by that single term. In division we do the same thing, except that we divide each term. For example:

$$\frac{9x^4 - 12x^3 + 21x^2}{3x^2} = 3x^2 - 4x + 7$$

We divided the $9x^4$ first and got $\frac{9x^4}{3x^2} = 3x^2$.

Then we divided the $-12x^3$ and got $\frac{-12x^3}{3x^2} = -4x$.

And lastly we divided the $21x^2$ and got $\frac{21x^2}{3x^2} = +7$.

Examples:

$$\frac{25x^2y^2 + 30xy^4}{-5xy} = 5xy - 6y^3 \qquad \text{(Remember that } \frac{x}{x} = 1.\text{)}$$

$$\frac{ab + ad}{a} = b + d \qquad \text{(Remember that } \frac{a}{a} = 1.\text{)}$$

$$\frac{9x - 18x^3}{3x} = 3 - 6x^2$$

$$\frac{6a^2 + 8a - 12a^4}{2a} = 3a + 4 - 6a^3$$

EXERCISE XXV

See whether you can do these:

1. $\dfrac{14np^2 - 28n^2p^3}{7np} = ?$

2. $\dfrac{16a^4b^5 - 24a^5b^6 - 32a^6b^7}{8a^2b^3} = ?$

3. $\dfrac{49xy - 63x^2y^3 + 7xy^2}{7xy} = ?$

4. $\dfrac{18a^2x - 6a^3x^2 + 36a^4x^3}{6ax} = ?$

Dividing one polynomial by another polynomial is similar to long division in arithmetic. In arithmetic, long division is commonly arranged as follows:

```
                    2048    Quotient
Divisor    32 | 65536       Dividend
                64
               ───
                153
                128
               ───
                256
                256
               ───
```

The same arrangement is followed in algebra. Compare carefully each step in the following examples in algebra with the corresponding step of the example in arithmetic.

Example: Divide $2x^2 - 10x + 12$ by $x - 2$.
Solution:

$$
\begin{array}{r}
2x - 6 \qquad \text{Quotient} \\
\text{Divisor} \quad x - 2 \overline{\smash{\big)}\ 2x^2 - 10x + 12} \quad \text{Dividend} \\
2x^2 - 4x \\
\hline
- 6x + 12 \\
- 6x + 12 \\
\hline
\end{array}
$$

Example: Divide $n^2 + n - 6$ by $n - 2$.
Solution:

$$
\begin{array}{r}
n + 3 \qquad \text{Quotient} \\
\text{Divisor} \quad n - 2 \overline{\smash{\big)}\ n^2 + n - 6} \quad \text{Dividend} \\
n^2 - 2n \\
\hline
3n - 6 \\
3n - 6 \\
\hline
\end{array}
$$

Example: Divide $x^3 - 6x^2 + 11x - 6$ by $x - 3$.
Solution:

$$
\begin{array}{r}
x^2 - 3x + 2 \qquad \text{Quotient} \\
\text{Divisor} \quad x - 3 \overline{\smash{\big)}\ x^3 - 6x^2 + 11x - 6} \quad \text{Dividend} \\
x^3 - 3x^2 \\
\hline
- 3x^2 + 11x \\
- 3x^2 + 9x \\
\hline
+ 2x - 6 \\
+ 2x - 6 \\
\hline
\end{array}
$$

You will notice that in all these examples we started by dividing the first term of the divisor into the first term of the dividend, and placing the result above the line (getting the first term of the quotient). We multiplied the divisor by this result, and placed the answer under the corresponding term of the dividend. We then subtracted, and in the subtraction we were careful to change the signs and add. The new result we then treated like the original dividend. The operation is then repeated until the problem is completed, each new term of the quotient being placed next to the previous one.

See whether you can do these problems in division:

Divide:

1. $a^2 - 6a + 8$ by $a - 4$.   3. $n^3 - n^2 - 9n + 9$ by $n + 3$.
2. $4p^2 - 8np + 3n^2$ by $2p - 3n$.   4. $18a^2 + 45a^3 + 18a^4$ by $3a^2 + 6a$.

FACTORING

Factoring, like division, is the reverse of multiplication. In multiplication we multiplied two numbers together and obtained a product. In factoring we take that product and break it up into the two numbers.

In multiplication we say: $2 \times 5 = 10$.

In factoring we say: 10 can be "broken up" into two *factors:* 2 and 5.

Any numbers which, when multiplied together, will give a certain number are called *factors* of that certain number.

We learned that when we multiply a binomial by a single term we get

$$a(b + c - d) = ab + ac - ad$$

That is, we multiply each letter separately in the parentheses by the single letter outside the parentheses.

Now we can say that $ab + ac - ad$ can be broken up or factored into $a(b + c - d)$, because we knew that when we multiplied $a(b + c - d)$ we got $ab + ac - ad$. In other words, (a) is one factor and $(b + c - d)$ is another factor.

Now suppose we are given an expression with several terms and are asked to break it up or factor it. How do we go about it? For example, find the factors of $4a^2b^2 - 32ab$.

First we notice that ab is contained in both terms. We also notice that 4 will go into both terms evenly (it will go into the first term once and into the second term eight times). We therefore know that $4ab$ will go into both terms evenly. $4ab$, then, is one factor, and whatever remains by dividing $4ab$ into $4a^2b^2 - 32ab$ will be the other factor. Hence we divide:

$$\frac{4a^2b^2 - 32ab}{4ab} = ab - 8$$

The two factors are $4ab$ and $(ab - 8)$

or $4ab(ab - 8) = 4a^2b^2 - 32ab$

Whenever we factor a polynomial we always look to see whether there is a common term which is contained in all the terms of the polynomial. If there is one, we then divide the polynomial by this common term and put the result in a parenthesis.

This process of picking out the common term is extremely simple. We do it all the time whenever we talk. Instead of saying, for example, "Mr. Jones owns a boat and Mr. Jones owns a car and Mr. Jones owns a radio and Mr. Jones owns a house," we simply say that "Mr. Jones owns (a boat, and a car, and a radio, and a house)."

The factors of:

$$ax + ay + ab = a(x + y + b)$$
$$5ax + 10a^2x^2 + 30a^3x^2 = 5ax(1 + 2ax + 6a^2x)$$
$$6a^2 + 8a - 12a^4 = 2a(3a + 4 - 6a^3)$$

EXERCISE XXVII

See whether you can factor these:

1. $3ax - 15a^2x = ?$
2. $12b^3y + 8b^2y^2 - 4by = ?$
3. $ay - abc - aby = ?$
4. $3c^2 - 12c - 18c^4 = ?$
5. $5ad + 10a^2d^2 - 15a^3d = ?$

Now suppose you came across the following sentence. How would you make it simpler and shorter?

Mrs. a has a cat and Mrs. a has a dog and Mrs. b has a cat and Mrs. b has a dog.

Naturally you would write it first this way:

Mrs. a has (a cat and dog)
and Mrs. b has (a cat and dog).

Then you would write it

(Mrs. a and Mrs. b) have (a cat and dog).

If the cat and dog are abbreviated to c and d, we get:

$$ac + ad + bc + bd \quad \text{(1st sentence)}$$
$$a(c + d) + b(c + d) \quad \text{(2nd sentence)}$$
$$(a + b)(c + d) \quad \text{(last sentence)}$$

Note these examples:

$$3(a - b) + c(a - b) = (3 + c)(a - b)$$
$$x(a + b) + y(a - b) = (x + y)(a + b)$$

$$4a(2x-7)-3(2x-7)=(4a-3)(2x-7)$$
$$2m+bm+2z+bz=(2+b)m+(2+b)z=(2+b)(m+z)$$
$$3ax-6bx-ay+2by=3x(a-2b)-y(a-2b)=(3x-y)(a-2b)$$
$$ac-ax+bx-bc=a(c-x)-b(c-x)=(a-b)(c-x)$$

EXERCISE XXVIII

See whether you can do these:

1. $4(x+2y)+a(x+2y)=?$ 3. $ax+ay+bx+by=?$
2. $a(x^2+2)+b(x^2+2)=?$ 4. $4by+7by+8ax+3ax=?$

We have already seen that:

$$(a+b)^2=a^2+2ab+b^2$$
$$(a-b)^2=a^2-2ab+b^2$$
$$(a+b)(a-b)=a^2-b^2$$

We memorized these formulæ and understand them thoroughly. Now let us put them in the language of factoring and say

The factors of $a^2+2ab+b^2$ are $(a+b)(a+b)$
The factors of $a^2-2ab+b^2$ are $(a-b)(a-b)$
The factors of a^2-b^2 are $(a+b)(a-b)$

We will use these three typical formulæ a great deal in factoring. The first or second formula will apply to any expression that is the sum or the difference of two squares. All we need do in order to determine whether a given expression *is* the sum or difference of two squares is to take the square root of the first term, add to it or subtract it from the square root of the last term, and multiply this by itself (square it). If the result is the given expression, that expression is a perfect square. For example:

Is x^2+4x+4 a perfect square?
    The square root of x^2 is x.
    The square root of 4 is 2.

$$(x+2)^2=x^2+4x+4$$
$$\text{Ans.}\quad \textit{Yes.}$$

The factors are $(x+2)^2$.

Factor the following:

$$a^2+12a+36=(a+6)^2$$
$$(a+6)^2=a^2+12a+36$$

You will note that the middle term is always twice the product of the square root of the first and the square root of the second terms. If it is not twice this product, the expression is *not* a perfect square. Thus:

$$9c^2 + 12c + 4$$

The middle term is $12c$.
The square root of the first term is $3c$.
The square root of the last term is 2.

$$2 \times 3c = 6c, \text{ and } twice\ 6c \text{ is } 12c.$$

Therefore $9c^2 + 12c + 4$ is a perfect square with factors:

$$(3c + 2)(3c + 2)$$

If this expression were:

$$9c^2 + 8c + 4$$

the middle term, $8c$, would *not* be twice the first and last term; hence it would *not* be a perfect square.

Find what is necessary to make these expressions perfect squares:

$$a^2 + ? + b^2$$

The $\sqrt{a^2} = a$; the $\sqrt{b^2} = b$. Twice $ab = 2ab$.
Therefore $a^2 + 2ab + b^2$.

$$x^2 + ? + 25$$

$\sqrt{x^2} = x$; $\sqrt{25} = 5$. Twice $5x = 10x$.
Therefore $x^2 + 10x + 25$.

$$1 + ? + 16t^2$$

$\sqrt{1} = 1$; $\sqrt{16t^2} = 4t$. Twice $4t = 8t$.
Therefore $1 + 8t + 16t^2$.

The first thing to do, then, when factoring a trinomial (three-term expression), is to find out whether or not it is a perfect square. If it is, apply the formula:

$$a^2 + 2ab + b^2 = (a + b)^2$$

or if the middle term is preceded by a minus sign:

$$a^2 - 2ab + b^2 = (a - b)^2$$

Factor the following:

$$9x^2 + 6x + 1$$

The $\sqrt{9x^2} = 3x$; the $\sqrt{1} = 1$.

$9x^2 + 6x + 1$, being a perfect square, is of the form $a^2 + 2ab + b^2$, whose factors are $(a+b)^2$ or $(a+b)(a+b)$. Hence the factors of $9x^2 + 6x + 1$ are $(3x+1)^2$ or $(3x+1)(3x+1)$.

EXERCISE XXIX

See whether you can factor the following (remember $a^2 + 2ab + b^2 = (a+b)^2$; $a^2 - 2ab + b^2 = (a-b)^2$):

1. $x^2 + 4x + 4 = ?$
2. $a^2 + 6a + 9 = ?$
3. $y^2 - 10y + 25 = ?$
4. $b^2 - 14b + 49 = ?$

The third formula in the group which we learned is

$$a^2 - b^2 = (a+b)(a-b)$$

Let us apply this to factoring the difference of two squares. Thus:

$$a^2 - x^2 = (a+x)(a-x)$$
$$x^2 - 1 = (x+1)(x-1)$$
$$16 - t^2 = (4+t)(4-t)$$
$$4x^2 - 9 = (2x+3)(2x-3)$$

Whenever you see the difference of two squares, apply the formula:

$$a^2 - b^2 = (a+b)(a-b)$$

For example:

$$x^4 - 81 = (x^2+9)(x^2-9)$$

But $x^2 - 9$ is also the difference of two squares, or

$$x^2 - 9 = (x+3)(x-3)$$

Therefore $x^4 - 81 = (x^2+9)(x+3)(x-3)$.

FOR FURTHER STUDY

ALGEBRA: AN INTERESTING LANGUAGE, by E. R. Breslich. (Newsome & Co., New York.)

ALGEBRA FOR HOME STUDY, by William L. Schaaf. (New Home Library, Doubleday & Co., New York.)

ESSENTIALS OF ALGEBRA, by W. W. Hart. (D. C. Heath and Co., Boston.)

MATHEMATICS FOR THE MILLIONS, by Lancelot Hogben. (W. W. Norton Co., New York.)

PRACTICAL ALGEBRA, by C. B. Upton. (American Book Co., New York.)

XVII

Plane Geometry

WHAT PLANE GEOMETRY IS

WE ALL HAVE first-hand experience with the objects whose properties are studied in geometry. For instance, we know that a block of wood, a stone, and a chunk of coal are solid figures. *Solid* geometry is the study of the properties of solid figures.

The boundary of a solid figure is a *surface*. For example, the surface of a ball is what we call the outside of the ball. The surface of a cube consists of the six faces. The surface of a cylinder, such as a tin can, consists of the top, the bottom, and the rounded part joining them.

Not all surfaces are boundaries of solids. The flat surface called a *plane*, for example, is not the boundary, by itself, of any solid. The study of figures drawn on a plane is called *plane geometry,* and such figures are called *plane figures*. They are made up of points and lines. The figure made up of three points joined by three lines is called a *triangle.* The

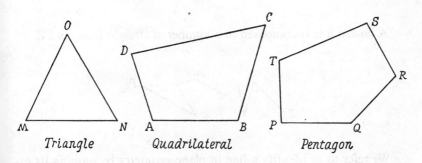

DIAGRAM 1. Types of plane figures.

figure made up of four points joined by four lines is called a *quadrilateral.* In the same way, five points joined by five lines form a *pentagon,* etc. All these figures have one general name—they are called *polygons*. The prefix "poly" means many; the suffix "gon" means side.

In speaking of plane figures, we usually label each point with a different letter of the alphabet, using capital letters, and read these letters in succession. For instance, the quadrilateral on the previous page is read as ABCD, the pentagon is PQRST, etc.

LINES AND ANGLES

LINES

A *line* is the path of a moving point. The simplest line is a straight line. The best example of a straight line is a string stretched taut between two points, like *AB*.

A ————————————————— *B*

There are several kinds of lines. A *curved* line is one of which no part is straight, as *CD*.

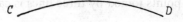

C ⌒ *D*

A *broken* line is composed of a number of straight lines, as *EF*.

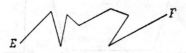

E ⋀⋁⋀⋁ *F*

We refer to or identify a line in plane geometry by naming its extremities (between which it runs), as *AB* in the first diagram, *CD* in the second diagram, and *EF* in the last diagram (above).

To "produce" a line means to prolong it. For instance, to produce the line *AB* means to prolong it through point *B*. To produce the line

BA means to prolong it through point *A*. The order in which the extremities of the line are named thus indicates the direction in which to prolong it.

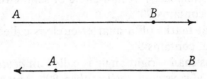

To bisect a line means to divide it into two equal parts, thus:

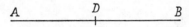

The point *D* bisects the line *AB*. It divides the line *AB* into two equal parts: *AD* and *DB*.

ANGLES

If a straight line, *OA*, rotates about one of its points, *O*, until it reaches any position, such as *OB*, the amount of this rotation is called an *angle*.

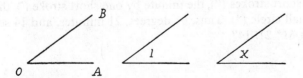

The angle in the figure shown above is designated by *AOB*.

The vertex letter (*O*) of an angle should always be read between the other letters. Frequently a number or letter is placed inside the angle, in which case it is read "angle 1" or "angle x," as in the figures above.

When the straight line *OA* rotates about *O,* the point *A* travels along a path called a circle. Every angle determines part of a circle, and its size is referred to in *degrees.* A complete rotation of line *OA* about *O* produces a complete circle. We say that the complete circle contains 360 degrees (written 360°). A half-circle or semi-circle contains 180°; a quarter-circle contains 90°.

The angle that marks off a quarter-circle is called a *right angle.* A right angle, then, contains 90°.

Any angle less than a right angle is called an *acute* angle. An acute angle, therefore, always contains less than 90°. Any angle greater than a right angle and less than a straight angle is called an *obtuse angle.* An obtuse angle, therefore, always contains more than 90° and less than 180°.

A *straight angle* is a straight line (180° or half a circle).

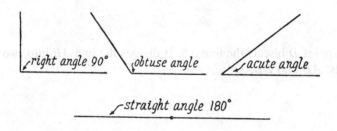

It is easily seen, then, that a circle contains two straight angles or four right angles.

Angles are measured in degrees, minutes, and seconds. (The size of an angle has nothing to do with the length of its sides.) There are 60 seconds in a minute, and 60 minutes in a degree. The second is indicated by two short strokes (″), the minute by one short stroke (′), the degree by a small circle (°). Thus, 61 degrees, 21 minutes, and 14 seconds is written: 61° 21′ 14″.

CONSTRUCTING WITH GEOMETRICAL TOOLS

The tools used in plane geometry are the straight-edge and the compasses. The *straight-edge* is merely an unmarked length made of wood, metal, or plastic material with which we can draw straight lines. A ruler is not a straight-edge, because it has markings on it, but we can use it as a straight-edge by disregarding the markings. The *compasses* are made by joining two bars at one end of each bar. The other end of one bar has a sharp point, while the other end of the other has a pencil point or pen-point attached. If the compasses are opened, and the sharp end stuck

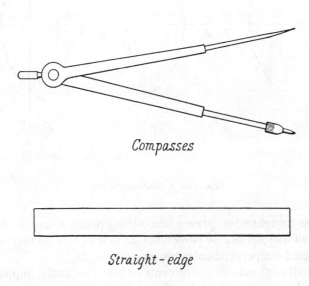

Compasses

Straight - edge

DIAGRAM 2. Geometrical tools.

into a plane surface like a sheet of paper, the pencil point can be made to draw a circle. In this section we shall learn how to use these two instruments to construct some simple geometrical figures.

We shall first use the straight-edge and compasses to bisect a line. Suppose that we have been given the line AB to bisect. We open the compasses so that the two points are at a distance greater than half the length of line AB. Placing the sharp point of the compasses on the end A of the line AB, we allow the writing point to travel, making an arc of about 120°. Without changing the angle between the legs of the compasses, place the sharp point on the end B of the line AB and draw a second arc cutting the first. If the directions are carefully followed, the two arcs drawn will cut each other at two points (labeled X and Y in the figure).

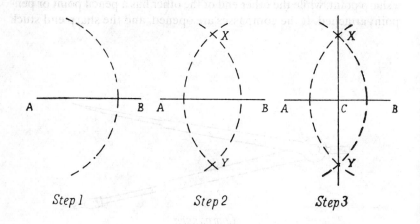

DIAGRAM 3. Bisecting a line.

With the straight-edge, draw a line joining points X and Y. This line will bisect line AB and be perpendicular to it as well. In fact, we have constructed the perpendicular bisector of line AB.

We shall next use our instruments to bisect an angle. Suppose that we have been given the angle AOB to bisect. We open the compasses to any convenient angle, and place the sharp point on the vertex O of the angle. We then allow the writing point to travel, making an arc long enough to cut both sides of the angle. Suppose side OA is cut at point X and side OB is cut at point Y. Without altering the angle between the legs of the compasses, we then place it with the sharp point at X and draw an arc lying inside the angle. Still keeping the legs of the compasses in the same position, place the sharp point at Y and draw a second arc cutting the first arc, say at point P. With the straight-edge, draw a line joining points O and P. The line OP will bisect the angle AOB.

Since the method given above for bisecting an angle can be used for angles of any size, it will work for the special case when the angle given is a straight angle. There is one slight change which must be made, however. Before drawing the arcs with centers at X and Y, we must open the legs of the compasses somewhat wider than when drawing the arc with center *O*. Let us go through with the complete construction in this case.

We start with the straight angle *AOB*. With the legs of the compasses opened to any angle, we draw the arc *XY* as before. Next we open the legs of the compasses more and then draw the arcs with centers *X* and *Y*, meeting at point *P*. Finally, we draw line *OP*.

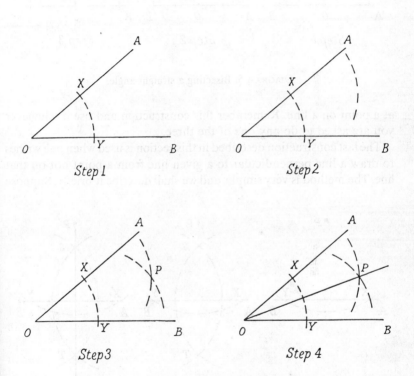

DIAGRAM 4. Bisecting an angle.

Since a straight angle has 180°, and since we have bisected angle *AOB*, it follows that angle *AOP* and angle *POB* are both equal to 90°. In other words, line *OP* is perpendicular to line *AB* at point *O*. In this construction, therefore, we do three things at once—we bisect a straight angle, we construct an angle of 90°, and we construct a perpendicular

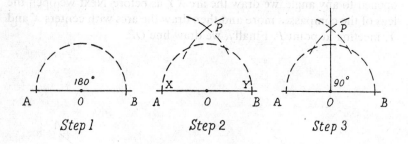

Step 1   Step 2   Step 3

DIAGRAM 5. Bisecting a straight angle.

at a point on a line. Remember this construction and use it whenever you are asked to do any one of the three.

The last construction described in this section is used when one wishes to draw a line perpendicular to a given line from a point not on that line. The method is very simple, and we shall describe it briefly. Suppose

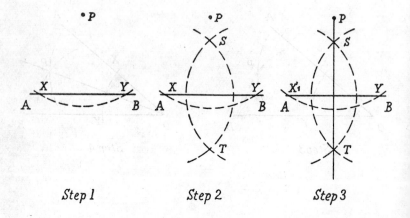

Step 1   Step 2   Step 3

DIAGRAM 6. Dropping a perpendicular.

we have been asked to construct a line from point *P* which shall be perpendicular to line *AB*. First, open the compasses so that the distance between the sharp point and the writing point is greater than the distance from point *P* to line *AB*. Place the sharp point on *P* and draw an arc *XY* cutting line *AB* at the two points *X* and *Y*. Finally, bisect line *XY* as described in the first construction. The perpendicular bisector you construct will pass through point *P* and will, consequently, be perpendicular to line *AB*.

Since the perpendicular will pass through the three points *P, S,* and *T,* and since all you need is two points to draw a line, you can simplify the construction by leaving out either all the arcs which lie above the line *AB* or all the arcs which lie below *AB*. Again, you may find it necessary to extend line *AB* either to the left or to the right in order to find the points *X* and *Y*. This can very easily be done and presents no great problem.

A line which starts from one vertex of a triangle and is perpendicular to the side opposite is called an *altitude*. The construction of an altitude is an example of construction of a perpendicular to a line from a point

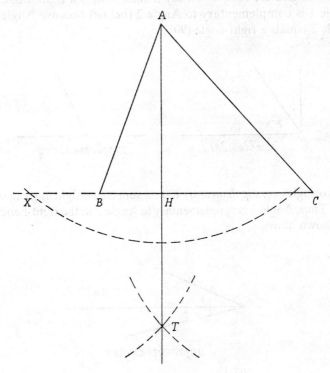

DIAGRAM 7. Constructing an altitude.

not on it. In the diagram you can trace the steps and see how the altitude can be constructed.

1. Construct an angle of 45°.
2. Draw a triangle and construct the three perpendicular bisectors of the sides.
3. Draw a triangle and construct the three angle bisectors.
4. Draw an angle and divide it into four equal parts.
5. Draw any line and divide it into four equal parts. Check by measuring each part.
6. Draw a triangle and construct the three altitudes.

GENERAL TERMS NEEDED

Two angles are *complementary* if their sum is a right angle. Thus, Angle 1 is complementary to Angle 2 (below) because Angle 1 plus Angle 2 equals a right angle (90°).

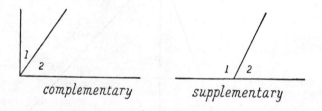

complementary   supplementary

Two angles are *supplementary* if their sum is a straight angle (a straight line). Thus, Angle 1 is supplementary to Angle 2 in the right-hand drawing shown above.

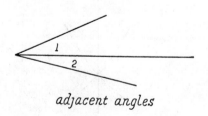

adjacent angles

Two angles that have a common side and a common vertex are called *adjacent* angles. Thus, Angle 1 is adjacent to Angle 2 because they both have a common vertex and a common side (the middle line).

Two angles are *vertical* if, when they are placed apex to apex, their sides are mutually continuous (see diagram below). Two intersecting straight lines always form four vertical angles. Thus, Angle 1 and Angle 2 are vertical angles; Angle 3 and Angle 4 are vertical angles (below).

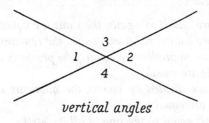

vertical angles

Two lines are *perpendicular* if they meet at right angles. "Perpendicular" always means "at right angles." A perpendicular angle measures 90°.

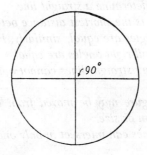

A *proposition* is a statement the truth of which is to be demonstrated or proved. Geometry consists of a number of propositions. Each proposition starts off with a hypothesis and a statement of what is to be proved. The hypothesis is really the conditional part of the proposition —it is what is given to you. The proof is a statement of what you are to prove.

A *theorem* is essentially the same as a proposition. A *corollary* is a theorem easily derived from another theorem. A *postulate* is a geometric axiom.

AXIOMS

An *axiom* is a self-evident fact. There is no necessity to prove an axiom. For instance, "We all must eat to live" is an axiom. There is no necessity to prove it; it just is a fact and is admitted by everybody.

Another axiom is: "No two bodies can occupy the same space at the same time." That is just common sense.

There are a few important axioms which we must learn and memorize. They are as follows:

1. *Things equal to the same thing, or to equal things, are equal to each other.*

2. *If equals are added to equals, the sums are equal.*

3. *If equals are subtracted from equals, the remainders are equal.*

4. *If equals are multiplied by equals, the products are equal. (Hence, doubles of equals are equal.)*

5. *If equals are divided by equals, the quotients are equal. (Hence, halves of equals are equal.)*

6. *The whole is equal to the sum of all its parts.*

7. *The whole is greater than any of its parts.*

8. *A quantity may be substituted for an equal one in an equation or in an inequality. (Called "substitution.")*

9. *One straight line, and only one, can be drawn through two points. Two points therefore determine a straight line.*

10. *A straight line is the shortest distance between two points.*

11. *All straight angles are equal; similarly, halves of straight angles are equal—therefore all right angles are equal.*

12. *Two intersecting straight lines cannot both be parallel to a third straight line.*

13. *A geometric figure may be moved from one position to another without change of form or size.*

14. *Two straight lines can intersect in only one point.*

SYMBOLS AND ABBREVIATIONS

For convenience in writing the precepts and propositions of geometry, a number of symbols and abbreviations are used. Instead of writing "triangle," "angle," etc., every time, we use the equivalent symbol given in the following table:

$+$ plus or added to.	$<$ is less than.
$-$ minus or diminished by.	$\therefore$ therefore, or hence.
$=$ equals, or is equivalent to.	$\perp$ perpendicular, or is perpendicular to.
$\cong$ congruent.	
$\neq$ is not equal to.	$\underline{\text{ls}}$ perpendiculars.
$>$ is greater than.	$\parallel$ parallel, or is parallel to.

∥s parallels.
∼ is similar to, or similar.
∠ angle.
⩟ angles.
△ triangle.
⩟ triangles.

▱ parallelogram.
⊡ parallelograms.
⊙ circle.
Ⓢ circles.
⌒ arc, as $\overset{\frown}{AB}$, meaning arc *AB*.

ax.	axiom.	iden.	identity.
circum.	circumference.	int.	interior.
comp.	complement.	isos.	isosceles.
cor.	corollary.	rt.	right.
corr.	corresponding.	st.	straight.
def.	definition.	sub.	substitution.
ext.	exterior.	sup.	supplementary,
hy.	hypotenuse.		or supplement.
hyp.	hypothesis.		

TRIANGLES

A triangle is a three-sided figure. We classify triangles according to sides or according to angles.

If we consider the sides of triangles, there are three kinds, namely, (1) the *scalene* triangle, which is a triangle whose three sides are all of different lengths; (2) the *isosceles* triangle, which has two equal sides; (3) the *equilateral* triangle, which has all three sides equal.

If we classify triangles with respect to angles, we have three kinds, namely, (1) an *obtuse* triangle, in which one angle is an obtuse angle (greater than 90°); (2) an *acute* triangle, in which all angles are acute (less than 90°); (3) a *right* triangle, of which one angle is a right angle.

The *base* of a triangle is the side on which the triangle appears to rest. The other sides are sometimes called arms or legs. The *vertex angle* of a triangle is the angle opposite the base. The side opposite the right angle in a right triangle is called the *hypotenuse*. The *altitude* of a triangle is the length of a line drawn from the vertex angle to the base and perpendicular to it. The sum of the angles of a triangle is always equal to 180°.

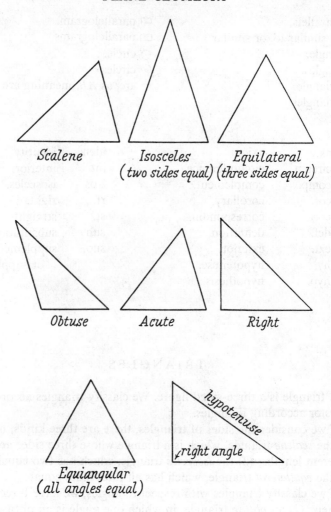

DIAGRAM 8. Kinds of triangles.

There are three classifications of triangles, namely, *congruent* triangles, *similar* triangles, and *equivalent* triangles.

When we say that two triangles are *congruent,* we mean that they will coincide exactly if one is superimposed on the other. In congruent triangles all sides and angles of one triangle equal all corresponding sides and angles of the other triangle. For example, triangles *ABC* and *A′B′C′* are congruent because the side *AB* of triangle *ABC* equals the side *A′B′*

of triangle $A'B'C'$, and the sides BC and AC of triangle ABC *equal the sides* $B'C'$ and $A'C'$ of triangle $A'B'C'$.

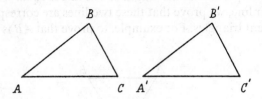

The angles A, B, and C of triangle ABC are equal, respectively, to the angles A', B', and C' of triangle $A'B'C'$.

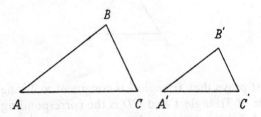

By two *similar* triangles we mean two triangles whose angles are equal and whose sides are proportional. Similar triangles are not necessarily congruent triangles. One triangle may be larger or smaller than the other, but the angles of one must be equal to the corresponding angles of the other. In the diagram, triangle ABC is similar to triangle $A'B'C'$ because angle A equals angle A', and angle B equals angle B', and angle C equals angle C'.

By *equivalent* triangles we mean triangles whose areas are equal. These triangles are not necessarily congruent or similar, but their areas

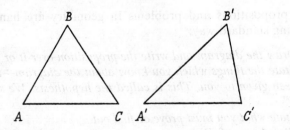

must be equal. The accompanying diagram shows two equivalent triangles. The area of triangle ABC equals the area of triangle $A'B'C'$.

Congruent Triangles

In order to prove that the length of one line is equal to the length of some other line, we prove that these two lines are corresponding sides of congruent triangles. For example, to prove that *AB* is equal to *CD,*

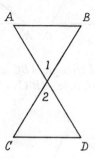

we must first prove that Triangle 1 is congruent to Triangle 2 because *AB* is a side of Triangle 1 and *CD* is the corresponding side of Triangle 2, and if these two triangles are congruent, the corresponding sides must be equal. To prove that one angle is equal (in degrees) to another angle, we must prove that they are both corresponding angles of congruent triangles. Thus, in the diagram above, if we want to prove angle *B* equal to angle *C*, we must prove Triangle 1 congruent to Triangle 2, for if these two triangles are congruent, the corresponding angles are equal.

THE METHOD OF GEOMETRY

All propositions and problems in geometry are handled in the following standard way:

1. *Draw the diagram and write the proposition over it or next to it.*
2. *State the things which you know about the diagram—things which have been given to you. This is called the hypothesis. We shall write it* "given."
3. *State what you must prove or find out.*
4. *Give the proof. Write your statements to the left and the reason for these statements to the right.*

Proposition I

Vertical angles are equal.

GIVEN *AB* and *CD* are straight lines which intersect to form angles
1 and 2.

TO PROVE $\angle 1 = \angle 2$.

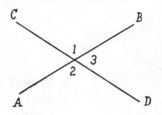

PROOF

STATEMENTS	REASONS
1. $\angle 1 + \angle 3 = 180°$	1. $\angle 1 + \angle 3$ forms a straight angle.
2. $\angle 2 + \angle 3 = 180°$	2. $\angle 2 + \angle 3$ forms a straight angle.
3. $\therefore \angle 1 = \angle 2.$	3. Axiom 1.

To our list of axioms and postulates, we now add two which are
extremely important:

15. *Two triangles are congruent if two angles and the included side of
one are equal to two angles and the included side of the other. (In
symbols, the △ are ≅ by a.s.a.)*

16. *Two triangles are congruent if two sides and the included angle of
one are equal to two sides and the included angle of the other. (In
symbols, the △ are ≅ by s.a.s.)*

With these postulates, we are now able to solve a great number of
problems. Where proof is not supplied, the problem should be worked
out by the reader. Let us first see some sample problems worked out
so that we can become accustomed to the method of proof.

PROBLEM 1

GIVEN *C* is the mid-point of line *BE* and ∠3 and ∠4 are right ∠s.
TO PROVE *AB* = *DE*, *AC* = *CD*.

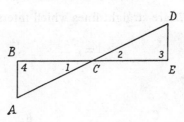

PROOF

STATEMENTS	REASONS
1. ∠1 = ∠2.	1. Vertical ∠s are equal (Proposition I).
2. *BC* = *CE*.	2. Given.
∠3 = ∠4.	
3. ∴ △*BAC* ≅ △*CDE*.	3. a.s.a.
4. ∴ *AB* = *DE*.	4. Corresponding parts of equal ∠s are =.
AC = *CD*.	

PROBLEM 2

GIVEN △*ABC* is isosceles, ∠1 = ∠2.
TO PROVE ∠3 = ∠4, *AD* = *DC*.

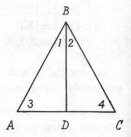

PROOF

STATEMENTS	REASONS
1. *AB* = *BC*.	1. Given. *ABC* is an isos. △.
2. ∠1 = ∠2.	2. Given.
3. *BD* = *BD*.	3. Identity.
4. ∴ △*ABD* ≅ △*CBD*.	4. s.a.s.
5. ∴ *AD* = *DC*.	5. Corresponding parts of ≅ ∠s are equal.
∠3 = ∠4.	

Problem 3

GIVEN $\angle 1 = \angle 2$, $AB = BC$.
TO PROVE $AD = DC$, $\angle 3 = \angle 4$.

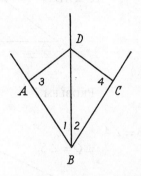

Problem 4

GIVEN $\angle 1 = \angle 2$, $\angle 3 = \angle 4$.
TO PROVE $AB = CD$, $AC = BD$.

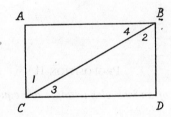

Problem 5

GIVEN $\angle B = \angle C$, $\angle 1 = \angle 2$.
TO PROVE $BE = DC$.

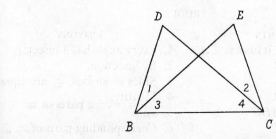

PROBLEM 6

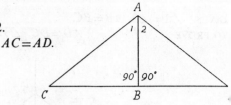

GIVEN $AB \perp CD$, $\angle 1 = \angle 2$.
TO PROVE $\qquad AC = AD$.

PROBLEM 7

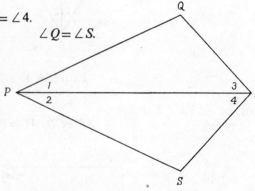

GIVEN $\angle 1 = \angle 2$, $\angle 3 = \angle 4$.
TO PROVE $\qquad \angle Q = \angle S$.

PROPOSITION II

The base angles of an isosceles triangle are equal.

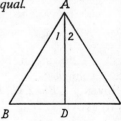

GIVEN ABC is an isosceles $\triangle$.
TO PROVE $\qquad \angle B = \angle C$.

PROOF

STATEMENTS	REASONS
1. Draw AD so that it bisects $\angle A$.	1. Every angle has a bisector.
2. Then $\angle 1 = \angle 2$.	2. By bisection.
3. $\qquad AB = AC$.	3. Sides of an isos. $\triangle$ are equa
4. $\qquad AD = AD$.	4. Identity.
5. $\therefore \triangle ABD \cong \triangle ADC$.	5. s.a.s.
6. $\therefore \angle B = \angle C$.	6. Corresponding parts of $\cong \triangle$

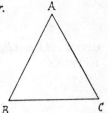

COROLLARY. *An equilateral triangle is equiangular.*

This is given as a corollary because it follows easily from the main theorem on isosceles triangles. The proof, in written form, is as follows:

GIVEN $\triangle ABC$, $AB=BC=CA$.

TO PROVE $A=\angle B=\angle C$.

PROOF

STATEMENTS	REASONS
1. $AB=BC$.	1. Given.
2. $BC=CA$.	2. Given.
3. $\angle B=\angle C$. $\angle C=\angle A$.	3. Base angles of an isosceles $\triangle$ are equal.
4. $\angle A=\angle B=\angle C$.	4. Axiom 1.

A theorem which is easily derived from another theorem is called a *corollary,* and stated without proof. Here are more corollaries of the theorem on isosceles triangles:

COROLLARY. *The bisector of the vertex angle of an isosceles triangle divides it into two congruent triangles.*

COROLLARY. *The bisector of the vertex angle of an isosceles triangle bisects the base.*

COROLLARY. *The bisector of the vertex angle of an isosceles triangle is perpendicular to the base.*

The following problems all are solved by using the theorem on isosceles triangles:

PROBLEM 8

GIVEN $OA=OD$, $AB=CD$.

TO PROVE $OB=OC$.

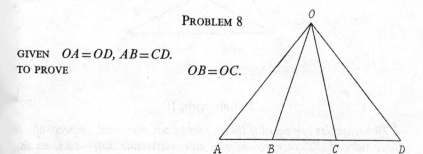

PROBLEM 9

GIVEN $AB = AD, BC = CD.$
TO PROVE $\angle ABC = \angle ADC.$

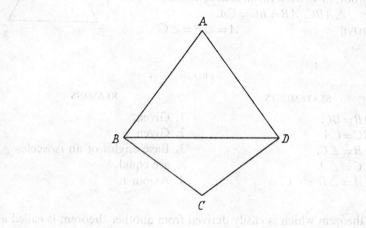

PROBLEM 10

GIVEN $AB = AC, BD = CE.$
TO PROVE $BE = CD.$

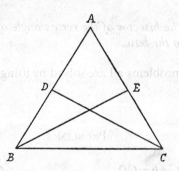

PROPOSITION III

Two triangles are equal if three sides of one are equal, respectively, t
three sides of the other. (Side, side, side = side, side, side—s.s.s. = s.s.s.

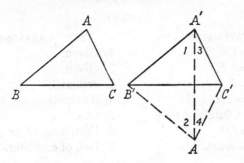

GIVEN $\triangle ABC$ and $A'B'C'$, with $AB=A'B'$, $BC=B'C'$, $AC=A'C'$.
TO PROVE $\triangle ABC \cong \triangle A'B'C'$.

PROOF

STATEMENTS	REASONS
1. Place $\triangle ABC$ so that BC shall coincide with $B'C'$ and A and A' lie on opposite sides of $B'C'$.	1. Axiom 13. $BC=B'C'$, given.
2. Draw AA'.	2. Axiom 9.
3. $\triangle AB'A'$ is isosceles. $\therefore \angle 1 = \angle 2.$	3. $AB=A'B'$, by hyp. Proposition II.
4. $\triangle AC'A'$ is isosceles.	4. $AC=A'C'$ by hyp.
5. $\therefore \angle 3 = \angle 4.$	5. Axiom 2.
6. $\therefore \angle 1 + \angle 3 = \angle 2 + \angle 4.$	6. Axiom 2.
7. Or $\angle A = \angle A'$.	7. Substitution.
8. $\therefore \triangle AB'C' \cong \triangle A'B'C'$. i.e. $\triangle ABC = A'B'C'$.	8. s.a.s.

We have now learned that the base angles of an isosceles triangle are equal and that when three sides of one triangle are respectively equal to three sides of another triangle, the two triangles are equal.

Let us now apply these new propositions to some problems:

PROBLEM 11

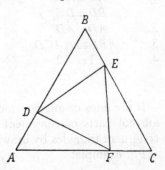

GIVEN $AB=BC=CA$.
$AD=BE=CF$.
TO PROVE $\triangle DEF$ is equilateral.

PROOF

STATEMENTS	REASONS
1. $AB = BC = CA$.	1. Given.
2. $AD = BE = CF$.	2. Given.
3. $BD = CE = FA$.	3. Axiom 3.
4. $\angle A = \angle B = \angle C$.	4. An equilateral $\triangle$ is equiangular.
5. $\triangle ADF \cong \triangle DBE \cong \triangle CFE$	5. s.a.s.
6. $DE = EF = FD$	6. Corr. sides of $\cong$ $\triangle$ are equal.
7. $\triangle DEF$ is equilateral.	7. Def. of equilateral $\triangle$.

PROBLEM 12

GIVEN ABC and BDC are two isosceles $\triangle$ on the same base BC.
TO PROVE $\angle 1 = \angle 2$.

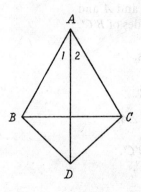

PROOF

STATEMENTS	REASONS
1. $AB = AC$. $BD = DC$.	1. Hyp.
2. $AD = AD$.	2. Identity.
3. $\therefore \triangle ABD \cong \triangle ACD$.	3. s.s.s.
4. $\therefore \angle 1 = \angle 2$.	4. Corresponding parts of $\cong$ $\triangle$ are equal.

If the lines or angles which we wish to prove equal to one another are not parts of congruent triangles, we try to make them parts of congruent triangles by drawing additional lines.

For example:

PROBLEM 13

GIVEN $AB=AC$, $BD=DC$.
TO PROVE $\angle B = \angle C$.

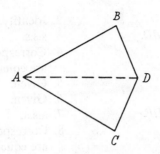

PROOF

STATEMENTS	REASONS
1. Draw line *AD*.	1. Axiom 9.
2. Then, in triangles *ABD* and *ACD*:	2. Given.
$\qquad AB=AC$.	
$\qquad BD=DC$.	
3. $\qquad AD=AD$.	3. Identity.
4. $\therefore \triangle ABD \cong \triangle ACD$.	4. s.s.s.
5. $\qquad \therefore \angle B = \angle C$.	5. Corresponding parts of $\cong$ ⧍ are equal.

If we cannot prove the required pair of triangles $\cong$, we prove the congruence of another pair of triangles whose corresponding parts will enable us to prove the equality of the required pair. In the following we do this very thing:

PROBLEM 14

GIVEN $AB=CD$, $AC=BD$, $\angle 1 = \angle 2$.
TO PROVE $CE=BF$.

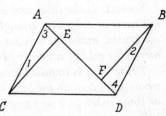

CE and *BF* are parts of triangles *AEC* and *BDF*. In order to prove these two triangles congruent, we must first prove that $\triangle ACD \cong \triangle ABD$, because we can then prove $\angle 3$ equal to $\angle 4$ and hence have two angles and a side of $\triangle AEC$ equal to two angles and a side of $\angle BFD$.

PROOF

STATEMENTS	REASONS
1. $AC=BD.$	1. Given.
$AB=CD.$	
2. $AD=AD.$	2. Identity.
3. $\therefore \triangle ACD \cong \triangle ABD.$	3. s.s.s.
4. Then $\angle 3 = \angle 4$	4. Corresponding parts of $\cong \triangle$ are equal.
5. $\angle 1 = \angle 2$	5. Given.
6. $AC=BD.$	6. Given.
7. $\therefore \triangle AEC \cong \triangle BDF.$	7. a.s.a.
8. $\therefore CE=BF.$	8. Corresponding parts of $\cong \triangle$ are equal.

Now let us review what we have learned, and see whether we can summarize it so as to know, once and for all, how to go about proving lines and angles equal to one another.

In order to prove lines and angles equal, we must

First: Pick out two triangles which contain these lines and angles, and prove these two triangles congruent by one of the three methods:

           1.   *a.s.a. = a.s.a.*
           2.   *s.a.s. = s.a.s.*
           3.   *s.s.s. = s.s.s.*

The method used will depend entirely on the hypothesis. If you are given two angles and can pick out a common side, use method 1; if you are given two sides and can find two corresponding angles equal, use method 2; if you are given two sides and can find a common side, use method 3.

Second: If the lines and angles whose equality we wish to prove are not parts of congruent triangles or parts of triangles which we can prove congruent, make them parts of triangles which we can prove congruent merely by adding a line or two.

Third: If it is impossible to prove the congruence of the two triangles whose sides contain the lines we wish to prove equal, prove the congruence of some other pair or pairs of triangles whose corresponding parts will help to prove the congruence of the first triangles.

Now see whether you can do these:

PROBLEM 15

GIVEN   *ABC* is an isosceles △, *BD=BE*.
TO PROVE   *FE=FD*.

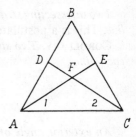

PROBLEM 16

GIVEN   *BC=AD*, ∠1=∠2.
TO PROVE   *BA=CD*.

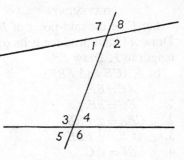

PARALLEL LINES

Parallel lines are lines which never meet, no matter how far they may be produced. The most familiar example of parallel lines is a car track.

When one line intersects two or more lines, it is called a transversal. The angles formed by these lines and the transversal are named as follows:

5, 6, 7, and 8 are *exterior* angles.
1, 2, 3, 4 are *interior* angles.
5 and 8 ⎫ are *alternate exterior*
6 and 7 ⎬   angles.
1 and 4 ⎫ are *alternate interior*
2 and 3 ⎬   angles.
3 and 7 ⎫
8 and 4 ⎪ are called *corresponding*
5 and 1 ⎬   angles.
6 and 2 ⎭

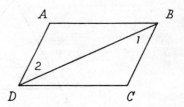

When two parallel lines are crossed by a transversal, we have eight angles formed, the names of which are the same as in the diagram given above.

Two intersecting straight lines cannot both be parallel to a third straight line. This is a postulate; we will refer to it hereafter as Axiom 17.

COROLLARY. *Two straight lines parallel to a third line are parallel to each other.*

PROPOSITION IV

An exterior angle of a triangle is greater than either remote interior angle.

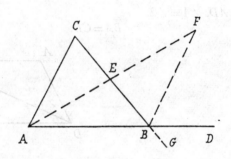

GIVEN   △*ABC* and the ext. ∠*CBD*.
TO PROVE   ∠*CBD* > ∠*C* or ∠*A*.

PROOF

STATEMENTS	REASONS
Let *E* be the mid-point of *BC*. Draw *AE* and produce it its own length to *F*. Draw *FB*.	
In △*ACE* and *FBE*,	
AE = *EF*.	
1. *EC* = *BE*.	1. Construction.
2. ∠*CEA* = ∠*FEB*.	2. Vertical ∠ are equal.
3. △*ACE* ≅ △*FBE*.	3. s.a.s.
4. ∠*EBF* = ∠*C*.	4. Corresponding parts of ≅ △ are equal.
5. ∠*CBD* > ∠*EBF*.	5. Axiom 7.
6. ∴ ∠*CBD* > ∠*C*.	6. Substitution.

NOTE: By joining the mid-point of *AB* to *C*, etc., it follows that
$\angle ABG > \angle A$, $\angle ABG = \angle CBD$.

$$\therefore \angle CBD > \angle A.$$

PROPOSITION V

*Two lines are parallel if a transversal to these lines makes a pair of
alternate interior angles equal.*

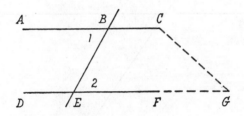

GIVEN   *AC* and *DF* are crossed by a transversal in *B* and *E* so that
$\angle 1 = \angle 2$.

TO PROVE $AC \| DF$.

PROOF

STATEMENTS	REASONS
AC and *DF* either meet or are parallel.	
1. Suppose they are not parallel and consequently they meet in some point *G* (on *DF* produced).	1. Two lines in a plane are | or intersect.
2. Then $\angle A'BE$ is the exterior angle of $\triangle BEG$.	2. Def. of exterior angle.
3. $\therefore \angle A'BE$, or $\angle 1$, is greater than $\angle 2$.	3. Proposition IV.
4. But $\angle 1 = \angle 2$.	4. Given.
5. $\therefore AC$ and *DF* cannot meet and are parallel.	5. If they meet, it contradicts the hypothesis that $\angle 1 = \angle 2$.

COROLLARY. *Two lines are parallel if a transversal to these lines makes a pair of corresponding angles equal.*

GIVEN   *AB* and *CD*, intersected by *EF* so that $\angle 1 = \angle 2$.
TO PROVE   *AB*‖*CD*.

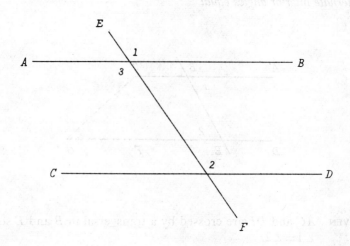

PROOF

STATEMENTS	REASONS
1. $\angle 1 = \angle 2$.	1. Given.
2. $\angle 1 = \angle 3$.	2. Proposition I.
3. $\angle 2 = \angle 3$.	3. Axiom 1.
4. $\therefore AB \| CD$.	4. Proposition V.

PROPOSITION VI

If two lines are parallel, a transversal to these lines makes a pair of alternate interior angles equal.

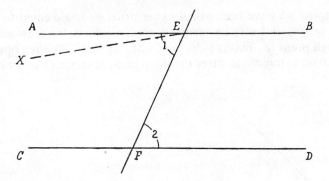

GIVEN $AB \| CD$ AB, CD cut by transversal in E and F.
TO PROVE $\angle 1 = \angle 2$.

PROOF

STATEMENTS	REASONS
1. Construct XE with $\angle XEF = \angle 2$. $XE \| CD$.	1. Two lines are $\|$ if a transversal makes a pair of alternate angles equal.
2. XE coincides with AB.	2. Axiom 17.
3. $\angle XEF = \angle AEF$ or $\angle 1$.	3. Two ∠ are equal if they can be made to coincide.
4. $\angle 1 = \angle 2$.	4. Substitution.

COROLLARY. *If two lines are parallel, a transversal to these lines makes a pair of corresponding angles equal.*

PARALLEL LINE CONSTRUCTIONS

The last two theorems give us a means of constructing parallel lines by using the straight-edge and compasses. There are at least two ways in which this can be done. We shall discuss both ways. First, however, let us try to construct an angle which will be equal to a given angle.

Suppose we have been asked to construct an angle equal to angle *AOB* below, and with its vertex at point *O'*. First, we draw any line through point *O'*. This is to be our "working line." We then open the compasses to any angle, place the sharp point at vertex *O*, and with the

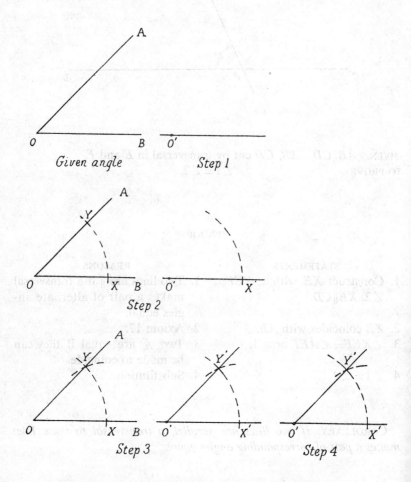

Diagram 9. Constructing an angle equal to a given angle.

writing point draw an arc cutting *OA* at *X* and *OB* at *Y*. Without changing the angle between the compasses' legs, we place the sharp point at *O'* and draw an arc cutting the working line at *X'*. Next, we set the compasses so that the sharp point is at *X* and the writing point is at *Y*. Without moving the legs of the compasses, we place the sharp point at *X'* and draw an arc cutting our first arc at Y'. Finally, we draw line $O'Y'$ with the straight-edge. Angle $Y'O'X'$ will equal angle YOX. You should be able to prove that this is so by proving $\triangle XOY = \triangle X'O'Y'$ (s.s.s.).

Now let us study how to construct parallel lines. Suppose that we have been given a line AB and a point P not on the line. We wish to construct a line which shall pass through point P and be parallel to line AB. Our

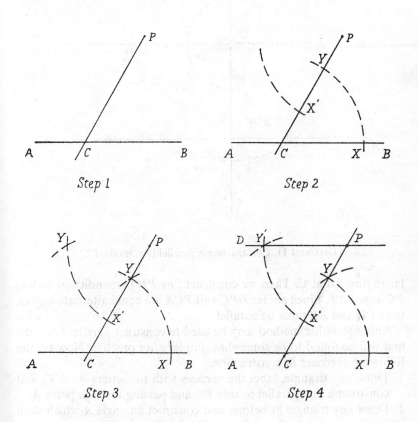

Step 1   Step 2

Step 3   Step 4

DIAGRAM 10. Constructing a parallel line, method 1.

procedure is as follows: First, we draw any line through point P cutting line AB, say at point C. Next, we construct an angle which is equal to angle PCB and also forms alternate interior angles with respect to it. Let this angle be angle DPC. Then DP will be parallel to line AB. The diagrams show the construction fully. Study them to understand the construction.

A second method for constructing a parallel is illustrated below. Again, suppose we have been asked to construct a line passing through point *P* and parallel to line *AB*. First, we construct line *PC* perpendicu-

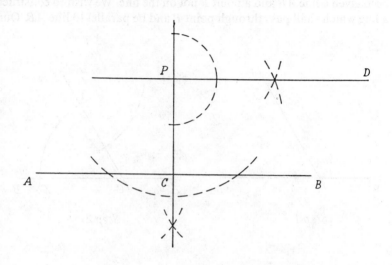

DIAGRAM 11. Constructing a parallel line, method 2.

lar to line *AB* at *C*. Then we construct line *PD* perpendicular to line *PC* at point *P*. Since angles *DPC* and *PCA* are equal alternate angles, lines *PD* and *AB* must be parallel.

Although either method may be used to construct parallel lines, the first will be found to be somewhat simpler after practice. Now try the following exercises in construction:

1. Draw any triangle, label the vertices with the letters *A, B, C*, and construct a line parallel to side *BC* and passing through point *A*.
2. Draw any triangle as before, and construct an angle *A* which shall be equal to angle *B* and lie outside the triangle. Do the same with angle *C*.
3. Construct a triangle whose angles are equal to those of any triangle *ABC* which you have drawn.
4. Construct any triangle. Then construct another triangle which is congruent to the first, and the sides of which are parallel to those of the first triangle.
5. Draw any six-sided figure. Then construct a five-sided figure, three sides of which shall be parallel to any three sides of the first figure.

PROPOSITION VII

The sum of the angles of a triangle is equal to a straight angle (180°).

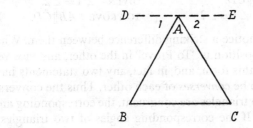

GIVEN △*ABC*.
TO PROVE ∠*A* + ∠*B* + ∠*C* = a st. ∠.

PROOF

STATEMENTS	REASONS
Through *A* draw *DE*‖*BC*.	
1. ∠1 = ∠*B*.	1. Prop. VI.
2. ∠2 = ∠*C*.	2. Prop. VI.
3. ∠*A* + ∠1 + ∠2 = a st. ∠.	3. Axiom 6.
4. ∴ ∠*A* + ∠*B* + ∠*C* = a st. ∠.	4. Substitution.

COROLLARY 1. *In a triangle there can be at most one obtuse angle or one right angle.*

COROLLARY 2. *The acute angles of a right triangle are complementary.*

COROLLARY 3. *If two triangles have two angles of the one equal respectively to two angles of the other, the third angles are equal.*

COROLLARY 4. *Two triangles are congruent if two angles and the side opposite one of them are equal respectively to two angles and the corresponding side of the other* (s.a.a. = s.a.a.).

COROLLARY 5. *Each angle of an equiangular triangle is 60°.*

COROLLARY 6. *Two right triangles are congruent if the hypotenuse and an acute angle of one triangle are equal to the hypotenuse and an acute angle of the other triangle.*

COROLLARY 7. *Two right triangles are congruent if an arm and an acute angle of one triangle are equal to an arm and the corresponding acute angle of the other triangle.*

PLANE GEOMETRY

CONVERSES

If we write two propositions on parallel lines next to each other like this:

GIVEN $AB\|CD$.   GIVEN $\angle 1 = \angle 2$.

TO PROVE $\angle 1 = \angle 2$ TO PROVE $AB\|CD$,

we cannot help but notice a striking difference between them. What is "Given" in one proposition is "To Prove" in the other, and vice versa. Propositions having this form, and, in fact, any two statements having this form, are said to be *converses* of each other. Thus the converse of the statement "If two triangles are congruent, the corresponding angles are equal" will be, "If the corresponding angles of two triangles are equal, the triangles will be congruent."

The important thing to notice about converse statements is that if one is true, the other need not be true. Thus the converse of our first theorem on parallel lines is true, but the converse of the statement about the angles of congruent triangles is not true. We cannot, therefore, assume the truth of the converse of a theorem from the truth of the theorem itself. A proof is required.

The converse of our theorem, "The base angles of an isosceles triangle are equal" is "If two angles of a triangle are equal, the triangle is isosceles." To prove this, we make use of the Corollary 4 of the previous theorem.

PROPOSITION VIII

If two angles of a triangle are equal, the triangle is isosceles.

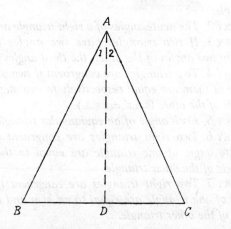

GIVEN $\triangle ABC$ with $\angle B = \angle C$
TO PROVE $AB = AC$

PROOF

STATEMENTS	REASONS
1. Construct line AD bisecting angle A.	1. Every angle has a bisector.
2. $\angle 1 = \angle 2$.	2. Bisection.
3. $\angle B = \angle C$.	3. Given.
4. $AD = AD$.	4. Identity.
5. $\triangle ABD = \triangle ACD$.	5. s.a.a. (Cor. 4, Prop. VII).
6. $AB = AC$.	6. Corr: sides of $= \triangle$ are equal.

COROLLARY. *An equiangular triangle is equilateral.*

VARIOUS KINDS OF TRIANGLES

THE EQUILATERAL TRIANGLE

Each angle in an equilateral triangle equals 60°.

An equilateral triangle can be divided into two congruent right triangles whose acute angles equal 30°.

Thus ABC is composed of rt. $\triangle\!\!\!\!\triangle$ ABD and BDC.

$\angle A = 60°$ and $\angle D = 90°$. Hence $\angle 1 = 30°$.

$\angle C = 60°$ and $\angle D = 90°$. Hence $\angle 2 = 30°$.

$AD = DC$ because they are corresponding parts of congruent triangles.

But $AD + DC = AC$ or AB or BC because $AC = AB = BC$, being sides of an equilateral $\triangle$.

$\therefore AB = AD + DC$.

But since $AD = DC$, $AB = 2AD$.

$\therefore AD = \frac{1}{2}AB$.

THE RIGHT TRIANGLE

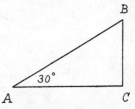

If $\angle A = 30°$, then $\angle B = 60°$ and $AB = 2BC$ or $BC = \frac{1}{2}AB$ (which was just demonstrated).

If $\angle A = 45°$, then $\angle B = 45°$ and $AC = BC$. (This is called an isosceles right triangle.)

Now let us apply what we have learned to some practical problems:

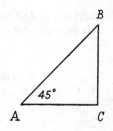

PROBLEM 17

Fifty feet behind a church, the steeple top makes an angle of 45° with the ground. How high is the steeple?

This is an isosceles right triangle one of whose sides is 50 feet. $BC = 50'$. Hence AB must be 50 feet.

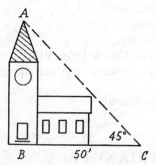

PROBLEM 18

The top of a hill is 500′ higher than the bottom, and the angle of inclination of the hill is 30°. How long will it take a car going 50 feet per second to climb the hill?

This is a right triangle, ABC, whose acute angle, A, is 30°. Hence $BC = \frac{1}{2}AB$ (see p. 885). This hill is consequently 1,000 feet long. At 50′ per second, the car will climb the hill in 20 seconds.

PROBLEM 19

The angle at which light strikes a mirror ($\angle 1$) equals the angle at

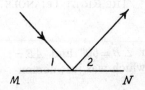

which it is reflected (∠2). Prove that a mirror is always exactly half-way between image and object.

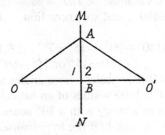

GIVEN MN is a mirror, O the object, and O' the image. OO' is a
straight line ⊥ MN.
TO PROVE   OB = BO'.

PROOF

STATEMENTS	REASONS
Draw any line, *OA*, from *O* to the mirror.	
Join *AO'*.	
1. Then ∠OAB = ∠BAO'.	1. Angle of incidence = angle of reflection.
2. *AB = AB*.	2. Identity.
3. ∠1 = ∠2.	3. All right ∠ are =.
4. ∴△OMB ≅ △BMO'.	4. a.s.a.
5. And *OB = BO'*.	5. Corresponding parts of ≅ △ are equal.

PROBLEM 20

A rock projects into a bay. A ship at *C* sights the top of the rock *A* and finds the angle *ACB* = 30°. It sails 1000 feet away and, sighting *A* again, finds the angle to be 15°. How high is the rock?

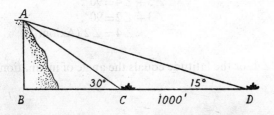

We know that $\angle CAB = 60°$ because $\triangle CAB$ is a rt. $\triangle$ one of whose acute $\angle$ is 30° (therefore the other acute $\angle$ must be 60°).

We know that $\angle BAD$ must be $180° - 90° - 15°$ because the sum of 3 $\angle$ of a triangle $= 180°$; and we know that $\angle ABD$ is a right $\angle$ and $\angle BDA$ is 15°.

Hence $\angle BAD = (180° - 90°) - 15° = 75°$, $\angle BAC = 60°$.

$$\therefore \angle CAD = 15° \text{ or } 75° - 60°$$

$\therefore \triangle CAD$ is isosceles — base angles are equal.

$\therefore AC = 1000'$ — sides of an isosceles $\triangle$.

$\therefore AB = 500'$ because in a rt. $\triangle$ with a 30° acute $\angle$, the side opposite this acute $\angle$ is equal to one-half the hypotenuse.

PROBLEM 21

The latitude of any point on the earth is found merely by sighting on the North Star (which is directly over the North Pole) and noting the angle between it and the horizon. Prove that this is so.

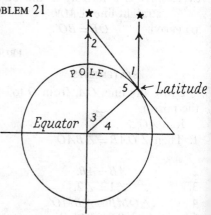

PROOF

In the diagram, the North Star is shown directly over the Pole. $\angle 4$ is the latitude of the observer. $\angle 5 = 90°$. $\angle 3 + \angle 4 = 90°$ because the Pole is 90° to the equator. The distance from the earth to the North Star is regarded as infinite; hence the line of sight is parallel to the pole line (or axis of the earth); hence $\angle 1 = \angle 2$ (Prop. VI). Then we have:

$$\angle 1 = \angle 2.$$
$$\angle 3 + \angle 4 = 90°.$$
$$\angle 3 + \angle 2 = 90°.$$
$$\therefore \angle 4 = \angle 2 \text{ (Axiom 1).}$$

$\therefore \angle 4 = \angle 1$, or the latitude equals the angle of inclination of the North Star.

SIMILAR TRIANGLES

We have learned how to prove triangles *congruent*, and have been able to apply this knowledge to proving lines and angles *equal*.

Now we shall learn how to prove triangles similar, and we shall see how useful these similar triangles are.

We define similar triangles as two triangles all of whose corresponding angles are equal. We say that if in $\triangle ABC$ and $\triangle A'B'C'$ $\angle A = \angle A'$, $\angle B = \angle B'$, $\angle C = \angle C'$ then $\triangle ABC \sim \triangle A'B'C'$.

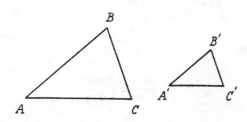

There is something more about triangles which we say is necessary if they are to be similar; that is, that their corresponding sides, instead of being equal (as in the case of congruent triangles), are in proportion. By this we mean that if $\triangle ABC \sim \triangle A'B'C'$, then

AB is to $A'B'$ as BC is to $B'C'$ as AC is to $A'C'$.

We remember from arithmetic that a proportion is a statement of equality of two ratios.

We say a is to b as c is to d is a proportion. This we write as follows:

$$a:b = c:d.$$

We might just as well write it:

$$\frac{a}{b} = \frac{c}{d}$$

for it means the same thing.

A few examples of numerical proportions would be:

$$3:6 = 4:8;$$
$$5:10 = 10:20;$$
a cent: a dime = a dime: a dollar.

These three proportions are to be read as follows:

3 is to 6 as 4 is to 8;
5 is to 10 as 10 is to 20;
a cent is to a dime as a dime is to a dollar.

The two dots (:) always mean "is to." The equal sign means "as." These all could be written as equal fractions; thus:

$$\frac{3}{6} = \frac{4}{8}$$

$$\frac{5}{10} = \frac{10}{20}$$

$$\frac{cent}{dime} = \frac{dime}{dollar}.$$

The first and fourth terms of a proportion are called the *extremes;* the second and third, the *means.*

When the means of a proportion are equal, *either* mean is said to be the *mean proportional* between the first and last terms. Thus, in the proportion, $a:b = b:c$, b is the mean proportional between a and c.

Proposition IX

In any proportion, the product of the means is equal to the product of the extremes.

GIVEN $a:b = c:d$.
TO PROVE $ad = bc$.

PROOF

$$\frac{a}{b} = \frac{c}{d} \qquad \text{(GIVEN)}$$

Clearing of fractions, *i.e.,* multiplying both members by bd,

$$ad = bc. \qquad \text{(Axiom 4.)}$$

This important proposition gives us the key to solving propositions. For example:

$$6:8 = 12:x—\text{Find } x.$$

We simply multiply the *extremes* together and the *means* together and divide one by the other:

$$6x = 96.$$
$$x = 16.$$
CHECK: $6:8 = 12:16.$

$$4:x = 16:8. \quad \text{Find } x.$$

$$16x = 32; x = 2.$$
CHECK: $4:2 = 16:8.$

$$x:10 = 3:5. \quad \text{Find } x.$$

$$5x = 30.$$
$$x = 6.$$
CHECK: $6:10 = 3:5.$

EXERCISE II

See whether you can do these:
Find x in each example:

1. $5:x = 3:6$
2. $2:7 = 6:x$
3. $12:3 = x:1$

4. $x:17 = 4:34$
5. $10:12 = 20:x$
6. $6:x = 8:16$

7. $x:9 = 12:36$
8. $\frac{1}{2}:x = 261:522$
9. $.3:x = 27:270$

PROPOSITION X

If three terms of one proportion are equal to the corresponding terms of a second proportion, then the fourth term of one is equal to the fourth term of the other.

GIVEN $a{:}b=c{:}x$ $a{:}b=c{:}y$
TO PROVE $x=y$

PROOF

STATEMENTS		REASONS
1. $a{:}b=c{:}x$	$a{:}b=c{:}y$	1. Given.
2. $ax=bc$	$ay=bc$	2. Prop. X.
3. $ax=ay$		3. Axiom 1.
4. $x=y$		4. Axiom 5.

The propositions on proportions look like and actually are algebraic rules. We connect them with geometry by the following postulate:

AXIOM 18. *A line parallel to one side of a triangle divides the other two sides into segments that are proportional.*

In symbols, if *DE* (in the drawing below) is drawn parallel to side

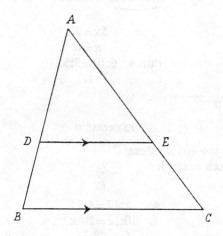

BC of $\triangle ABC$, then we can write these proportions by Axiom 18:

$$AD{:}DB=AE{:}EC \quad\quad AD{:}AB=AE{:}AC \quad\quad AB{:}DB=AC{:}EC$$

For example, suppose that $AD=12$, $DB=8$, $AE=15$. Then, using the first proportion above, we find

$$12{:}8=15{:}EC$$
$$12\times EC=120$$
$$EC=10$$

See whether you can do these (the letters refer to the drawing on preceding page):

1. $AD=10$ $AB=15$ $AE=12$ $AC=?$
2. $AB=20$ $DB=9$ $AC=24$ $CE=?$
3. $AD=8$ $DB=6$ $AC=18$ $AE=?$
4. $AD=16$ $CE=9$ $DB=AE$ $AE=?$
5. $AD=2(DB)$ $AC=30$ $AE=?$

PROVING TRIANGLES SIMILAR

We have already defined similar triangles as triangles whose corresponding angles are equal and whose corresponding sides are proportional. Now let us see how we can prove triangles similar and how we can make use of these similar triangles.

If two triangles are similar their corresponding sides are proportional. Suppose we have two triangles, ABC and $A'B'C'$.

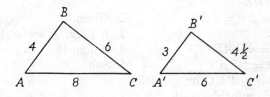

$AB=4$, $BC=6$, $AC=8$.
$A'B'=2$, $B'C'=3$, $A'C'=4$.

We say that

$AB{:}A'B'=4{:}2$.
$BC{:}B'C'=6{:}3$.

But $4{:}6=2{:}3$ is a perfect proportion, because $2\times6=4\times3$ (Prop. X). Hence $AB{:}BC=A'B'{:}B'C'$, and the sides of $\triangle ABC$ are proportional to the sides of $\triangle A'B'C'$.

PROPOSITION XI

Two triangles are similar if the three angles of one are equal respectively to the three angles of the other.

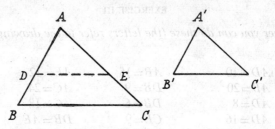

GIVEN in △ *ABC* and *A'B'C'*,

$\angle A = \angle A'$, $\angle B = \angle B'$, and $\angle C = \angle C'$.

TO PROVE $\triangle ABC \sim \triangle A'B'C'$.

PROOF

STATEMENTS	REASONS
1. Place $\triangle A'B'C'$ upon $\triangle ABC$, $\angle A'$ on $\angle A$, taking the position $\triangle ADE$.	1. Axiom 13.
2. $\angle ADE = \angle B' = \angle B$.	2. Given.
3. $DE \parallel BC$.	3. If 2 cor. ∠ are =, lines are ∥.
4. $AB:AD = AC:AE$.	4. Axiom 18.
5. $AB:A'B' = AC:A'C'$.	5. Sub.
By placing $\triangle A'B'C'$ on $\triangle ABC$ so that $\angle B'$ coincides with $\angle B$, we can show that $AB:A'B' = BC:B'C'$.	
6. $\therefore \dfrac{AB}{A'B'} = \dfrac{BC}{B'C'} = \dfrac{AC}{A'C'}$,	6. Steps similar to those preceding.
7. But $\angle A = \angle A'$, $\angle B = \angle B'$, $\angle C = \angle C'$.	7. Given.
8. $\therefore \triangle ABC \sim \triangle A'B'C'$.	8. Their corresponding ∠ are equal. Their corresponding sides are proportional.

COROLLARY 1. *Two triangles are similar if two angles of the one are equal respectively to two angles of the other.*

COROLLARY 2. *Two right triangles are similar if an acute angle of the one is equal to an acute angle of the other.*

COROLLARY 3. *A line parallel to one side of a triangle cuts off a triangle similar to the given triangle.*

COROLLARY 4. *If two triangles are similar to a third triangle, they are similar to each other.*

Two triangles are similar if an angle of the one is equal to an angle of the other, and the sides including these angles are proportional.

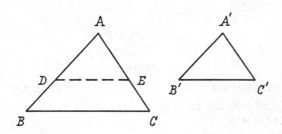

GIVEN   In $\triangle ABC$ and $A'B'C'$,
$\angle A = \angle A'$, and $AB:A'B' = AC:A'C'$.

TO PROVE $\triangle ABC \sim \triangle A'B'C'$

PROOF

STATEMENTS	REASONS
1. Place $\triangle A'B'C'$ upon $\triangle ABC$ so that $\angle A'$ coincides with $\angle A$ and $\triangle A'B'C'$ takes position $\triangle DAE$.	1. Axiom 13. Given. Sub.
2. $AB:A'B' = AC:A'C'$.	2. Converse of Axiom 18.
3. $AB:AD = AC:AE$ $DE \parallel BC$.	3. Cor. Prop. V.
4. $\angle B = \angle ADE$ and $\angle C = \angle DEA$. $\therefore \triangle ABC \sim \triangle ADE$ (or $\triangle A'B'C'$).	4. Prop. XI.

Two triangles are similar if their corresponding sides are proportional.

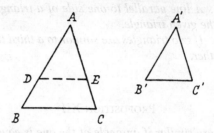

GIVEN   In △ ABC and $A'B'C'$,

$$\frac{AB}{A'B'}=\frac{BC}{B'C'}=\frac{AC}{A'C'}$$

TO PROVE   △$ABC \sim$ △$A'B'C'$.

PROOF

STATEMENTS	REASONS
On AC and AB, lay off $AD=$ $A'C'$ and $AE=A'B'$.	
Draw DE.	
1. $AB:A'B'=AC:A'C'$.	1. Given.
2. $AB:AE=AC:AD$.	2. Sub.
3. △$ADE \sim$ △ABC.	3. Prop. XII.
4. $AB:AE=BC:ED$.	4. Def. of similar △.
5. But $AB:A'B'=BC:B'C'$.	5. Given.
6. $ED=B'C'$.	6. Prop. X.
7. ∴△$A'B'C' \cong$ △ADE.	7. s.s.s.
8. ∴△$A'B'C' \sim$ △ABC.	8. Sub.

Now let us summarize what we have learned about similar triangles:

First: If three angles of one triangle equal three angles of another triangle, the two triangles are similar.

Second: If an angle of one triangle is equal to an angle of another triangle and the sides including the angles are in proportion, the two triangles are similar.

Third: If the corresponding sides of two triangles are in proportion to one another, the two triangles are similar.

Just as *congruent triangles* are used to prove lines *equal,* so *similar triangles* are used to prove lines *proportional.* By Proposition X, we know that if we have three quantities in a proportion given, we can always get the fourth or unknown quantity, because *the product of the means equals the product of the extremes.*

If, therefore, we know three sides of one triangle and only one side of a similar triangle, we can find the other sides of that similar triangle merely by solving the proportion.

Let us study a few examples to illustrate the use and practical application of similar triangles:

PROBLEM 22

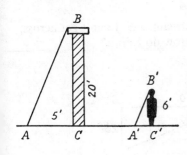

A wall 20 feet high throws a shadow 5 feet long. How long will *your* shadow be if you are 6 feet tall?

Since the sun is inclined at the same angle for both your shadow and the wall's shadow, it follows that the two triangles ABC (the wall and its shadow) and $A'B'C'$ (you and your shadow) are similar. ($\angle A = \angle A'$, $\angle B = \angle B'$ and $\angle C = \angle C'$.)

Hence:

$$5':20'=x':6'$$
$$\text{or } 20x=30 \text{ (Prop. X)},$$
$$x=1.5'.$$

Answer: 1½ feet.

PROBLEM 23

Mount Washington is 6000′ high. I hold a foot rule absolutely level and 1 foot away from my eye, and the mountain appears 3″ high. How far away am I from the mountain?

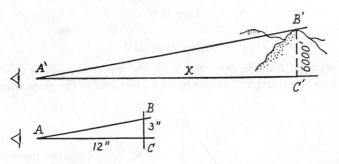

Here we have two similar triangles, ABC and $A'B'C'$. In the small triangle ABC the rule was held 1 foot away (AC) and the mountain measured 3″ (*BC*). In reality the mountain is "*x*" feet away (*A′C′*) and is 6000′ high (*B′C′*). Hence:

$$1':3''=x':6000'$$
$$\text{or } 1':\tfrac{1}{4}'=x':6000'-(3''=\tfrac{1}{4}').$$
$$\tfrac{1}{4}x=6000'.$$
$$x=24000'=4\tfrac{1}{2} \text{ miles.}$$

PROBLEM 24

I want to find the distance across a stream, *AB*. I can't get across, and I am on the same side as point *A*. How do I do it?

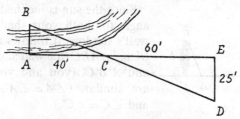

I measure off any distance, *AE*, at right angles to *AB*. This I do by putting a stake at *A* and a stake at *E* and connecting both stakes with a taut string. I measure this distance and find that it is 100 feet. At *E* I turn at right angles and go over to some point, *D*, say, 25 feet. I now line up *B* with *D* and move along this line until I reach the string. This point I call *C*. I now measure *AC* and find it to be 40 feet. Then: $\triangle ABC \sim \triangle CDE$ because $\angle 1 = \angle 2$ (vertical $\angle$) and $\angle A = \angle E$ (right angles).

Then
$$AC:CE=AB:DE$$
or $40:60=AB:25-AC=40', CE=100'-40'=60'$ and $DE=25'$.
$$\therefore 60AB=1000.$$
$$AB=16\tfrac{2}{3}'.$$

PROPOSITION XIV

In any right triangle, the altitude on the hypotenuse divides the tri-angle into two triangles, similar to each other and to the given triangle.

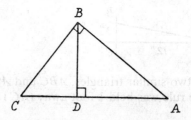

GIVEN in the rt. $\triangle ABC$, BD the $\perp$ to hypotenuse CA.

TO PROVE $\triangle BCD \sim \triangle ACB \sim \triangle BDA$.

PROOF

STATEMENTS	REASONS
Each $\triangle$ is a rt. $\triangle$.	
1. In $\triangle ACB$ and BCD, $\angle C = \angle C$.	1. Identity.
2. $\therefore \triangle BCD \sim \triangle ACB$.	2. Prop. XIII, cor. 2.
3. In $\triangle ACB$ and BDA, $\angle A = \angle A$.	3. Identity.
4. $\therefore \triangle ACB \sim \triangle BDA$.	4. Prop. XI, cor. 2.
5. $\therefore \triangle BCD \sim \triangle ACB$.	5. Prop. XI, cor. 4.

PROPOSITION XV

In a right triangle, the altitude upon the hypotenuse is the mean proportional between the segments of the hypotenuse, and either arm is the mean proportional between the hypotenuse and the segment adjacent to that arm.

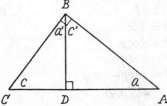

GIVEN in the rt. $\triangle ABC$, BD the altitude upon the hypotenuse AC.

TO PROVE   (1) $CD:DB = DB:DA$.
        (2) $CA:BA = BA:DA$.
        (3) $CA:CB = CB:CD$.

PROOF

STATEMENTS	REASONS
1. $\triangle ABC \sim \triangle BCD \sim \triangle BDA$.	1. Prop. XIV.
Since $\triangle BCD \sim \triangle BDA$,	
2. $\therefore CD:DB = DB:DA$.	2. Def. of similar triangles.
Since $\triangle ABC \sim \triangle BDA$,	
3. $\therefore CA:BA = BA:DA$.	3. Def. of similar triangles.
Since $\triangle ABC \sim \triangle BCD$,	
4. $\therefore CA:CB = CB:CD$.	4. Def. of similar triangles.

Note: $\angle a$ or $\angle A = \angle a'$ and $\angle c$ or $\angle C = \angle c'$.

900   *PLANE GEOMETRY*

PROPOSITION XVI

The sum of the squares of the arms of a right triangle is equal to the square of the hypotenuse.

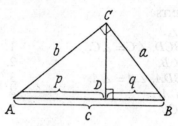

GIVEN ACB, a rt. $\triangle$, having its rt. $\angle$ at C.

TO PROVE $a^2+b^2=c^2$

PROOF

STATEMENTS	REASONS
1. Draw $CD \perp AB$,	1. Prop. XV.
$p:b=b:c.$	
$\therefore b^2=c\times p.$	
Similarly $a^2=c\times q.$	
$a^2+b^2=c\times p+c\times q.$	
$=c(p+q).$	
2. $a^2+b^2=c^2.$	2. Sub.

COROLLARY. *The square of either arm of a right triangle is equal to the square of the hypotenuse, diminished by the square of the other arm.*

This proposition is one of the most important in all mathematics. It is known as the *Pythagorean Theorem* because it was first demonstrated by Pythagoras about 500 B.C.

EXERCISE IV

Now see whether you can use the Pythagorean Theorem to solve these problems. Refer to the table of square roots on pages 964–966 when necessary.

1. The sides of a right triangle are 6″ and 8″. Find the hypotenuse.
2. A ladder 25 feet long leaning against a wall reaches 24 feet up the wall. How far from the foot of the wall is the foot of the ladder?
3. A gate four feet high and three feet wide has two braces reaching diagonally from corner to corner. How long is each brace?
4. A path runs diagonally across a lot 20 yd. wide and 21 yd. long. How long is the path?

5. What is the length of the longest line you can draw on a sheet of paper 6" long and 4" wide?
6. A gable in the form of an isosceles triangle has a width of 24 ft. and a height of 5 ft. How long must the rafters be?
7. The equal sides of an isosceles triangle are 12" long, and the base is 6" long. Find the length of the altitude to the base.
8. The sides of a square are 7" long. How long is the diagonal?

QUADRILATERALS

Any four-sided figure is called a *quadrilateral;* "lateral" means side, "quadri" means four.

There are six kinds of quadrilaterals: namely, parallelogram, trapezoid, rectangle, square, rhombus, and trapezium.

A *parallelogram* is a quadrilateral having both pairs of its opposite sides parallel.

A *trapezoid* is a quadrilateral having two, and only two, sides parallel.

A *rectangle* is a parallelogram whose angles are right angles.

A *square* is an equilateral rectangle.

A *rhombus* is an equilateral parallelogram.

A *trapezium* is a quadrilateral having no sides parallel.

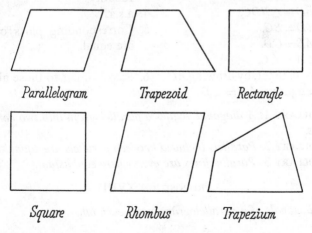

Parallelogram   Trapezoid   Rectangle

Square   Rhombus   Trapezium

An *isosceles trapezoid* is a trapezoid whose nonparallel sides are equal.

The parallel sides of a trapezoid are called its *bases,* and are distinguished as *upper* and *lower.*

The *altitude* of a trapezoid or a parallelogram is a perpendicular between the parallel sides.

The *diagonal* of a quadrilateral is a line which joins opposite vertices.

PROPOSITION XVII

The opposite sides and the opposite angles of a parallelogram are equal.

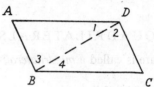

GIVEN ▱*ABCD*.

TO PROVE $AD = BC$, $AB = CD$, $\angle A = \angle C$, $\angle B = \angle D$.

PROOF

STATEMENTS	REASONS
1. Draw diagonal *BD*.	1. Two points determine a line. Axiom 9.
2. $AD \| BC$, $AB \| DC$.	2. The opp. sides of a ▱ are ‖ (Definition).
3. $\angle 1 = \angle 4$, $\angle 3 = \angle 2$. $BD = BD$.	3. Prop. VI. Identity.
4. $\triangle ABD \cong \triangle BDC$.	4. a.s.a.
5. $AD = BC$. $AB = CD$. $\angle A = \angle C$.	5. Corresponding parts of ≅ ▲ are equal.
6. In like manner, by drawing *AC*, we can prove $\angle B = \angle D$.	6. Steps similar to those above.

COROLLARY 1. *A diagonal divides a parallelogram into two congruent triangles.*

COROLLARY 2. *Parallels included between parallels are equal.*

COROLLARY 3. *Parallel lines are everywhere equidistant.*

PROPOSITION XVIII

The diagonals of a parallelogram bisect each other.

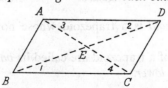

GIVEN ▱*ABCD*, diagonals *AC* and *BD* intersecting at *E*.
TO PROVE *AE=EC* and *BE=ED*.

PROOF

STATEMENTS	REASONS
1. In △ *AED* and *BEC*, *AD=BC*.	1. The opposite sides of a ▱ are equal. Prop. XVII.
2. *AD‖BC*.	2. Opposite sides of a ▱ are ‖ (Definition).
3. ∠1=∠2 and ∠3=∠4.	3. If two lines are ‖, a transversal makes a pair of alternate interior ∠ equal. Prop. VI.
4. △*AED*≅△*BEC*.	4. a.s.a.
5. ∴ *AE=EC* and *BE=ED*.	5. Corresponding parts of ≅ △ are equal.

PROPOSITION XIX

A quadrilateral is a parallelogram if the opposite sides are equal.

GIVEN   *AB=CD, AD=BC*.
TO PROVE *ABCD* is a ▱.

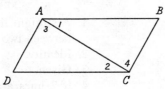

PROOF

STATEMENTS	REASONS
1. Draw *AC*.	1. A straight line can be drawn between two points.
2. *AC=AC*.	2. Identity.
3. *AB=CD* and *AD=BC*.	3. Given.
4. △*ABC*≅△*ACD*.	4. s.s.s.
5. ∠1=∠2 and ∠3=∠4.	5. Corresponding angles of ≅ △ are equal.
6. *AB‖CD* and *AD‖BC*.	6. If the alternate interior ∠ are equal, the two lines are ‖.
7. *ABCD* is a ▱.	7. A quadrilateral is a ▱ if the opposite sides are ‖.

Proposition XX

A quadrilateral is a parallelogram if the same two sides are both equal and parallel.

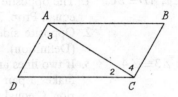

GIVEN $AB \parallel CD$, $AB = CD$.
TO PROVE $ABCD$ is a $\square$.

PROOF

STATEMENTS	REASONS
1. Draw AC.	1. A straight line can be drawn between two points.
2. $AC = AC$.	2. Identity.
3. $AB \parallel CD$.	3. Given.
4. $\angle 1 = \angle 2$.	4. If 2 lines are $\parallel$, the alternate interior angles are equal.
5. $AB = CD$.	5. Given.
6. $\triangle ABC \cong \triangle ACD$.	6. s.a.s.
7. $\angle 3 = \angle 4$.	7. Corresponding angles of $\cong$ ⚠ are equal.
8. $AD \parallel BC$.	8. If the alternate interior angles are equal, the lines are $\parallel$.
9. $ABCD$ is a $\square$.	9. A quadrilateral is a $\square$ if the opposite sides are $\parallel$.

Proposition XXI

A quadrilateral is a parallelogram if the diagonals bisect each other.

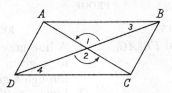

GIVEN $AE = EC$, $DE = EB$.
TO PROVE $ABCD$ is a $\square$.

PROOF

STATEMENTS	REASONS
1. $AE = EC$ and $ED = BE$.	1. Given.
2. $\angle 1 = \angle 2$.	2. Vertical angles are equal.
3. $\triangle ABE \cong \triangle DEC$.	3. s.a.s.
4. $\angle 3 = \angle 4$ and $AB = CD$.	4. Corresponding parts of $\cong$ $\triangle$ are equal.
5. $AB \parallel CD$.	5. If the alternate interior angles are equal, the lines are $\parallel$.
6. $ABCD$ is a $\square$.	6. A quadrilateral is a $\square$ if the same two sides are both equal and $\parallel$.

Proposition XXII

If three or more parallels intercept equal segments on one transversal, they intercept equal segments on every transversal.

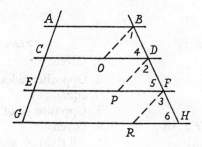

GIVEN $AB \parallel CD \parallel EF \parallel GH$, and $AC = CE = EG$.
TO PROVE $BD = DF = FH$.

PROOF

STATEMENTS	REASONS
1. Draw *BO, DP,* and *FR*∥*AG.*	1. A line may be constructed ∥ to a given line and passing through a given point.
2. *BO*∥*DP*∥*FR.*	2. Lines ∥ to the same line are ∥ to each other.
3. ∠1 = ∠2 = ∠3. ∠4 = ∠5 = ∠6.	3. Corresponding ∠ of ∥ lines are equal. (Cor. Prop. VI.)
4. *BO* = *AC, DP* = *CE, FR* = *EG.*	4. Proposition XVII, Corollary 2.
5. *AC* = *CE* = *EG.*	5. Given.
6. *BO* = *DP* = *FR.*	6. Axiom 1.
7. △*BOD* ≅ △*DPF* ≅ △*FRH.*	7. s.a.a.
8. ∴ *BD* = *DF* = *FH.*	8. Corresponding sides of ≅ ∆ are equal.

COROLLARY 1. *The line parallel to one side of a triangle, bisecting another side, bisects the third side.*

COROLLARY 2. *The line that bisects a nonparallel side of a trapezoid and is parallel to the bases bisects the other nonparallel side.*

PROBLEM 24

GIVEN □*ABCD, AE*⊥*DC, CF*⊥*AB.*
TO PROVE *AE* = *CF.*

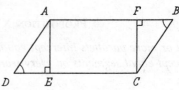

PROOF

STATEMENTS	REASONS
1. *ABCD* is a □.	1. Given.
2. *AD* = *BC.*	2. Opposite sides of a □ are equal.
3. ∠*D* = ∠*B.*	3. Opposite ∠ of a □ are equal.
4. *AE*⊥*CD* and *CF*⊥*AB.*	4. Given.
5. ∠*E* = ∠*F.*	5. All right ∠ are equal.
6. △*ADE* ≅ △*CFB.*	6. s.a.a.
7. *AE* = *CF.*	7. Corresponding sides of ≅ ∆ are equal.

PROBLEM 25

GIVEN ▱*ABCD*, *AE* = *CF*.
TO PROVE *AF* = *EC*.

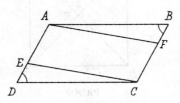

PROOF

STATEMENTS	REASONS
1. *ABCD* is a ▱.	1. Given.
2. *AB* = *CD* and *AD* = *BC*.	2. Opposite sides of a ▱ are equal.
3. *AE* = *CF*.	3. Given.
4. *DE* = *BF*.	4. If equals are subtracted from equals, the results are equal.
5. ∠*D* = ∠*B*.	5. Opposite ∠ of a ▱ are equal.
6. △*ABF* ≅ △*DEC*.	6. s.a.s.
7. *EC* = *AF*.	7. Corresponding sides of ≅ △ are equal.

PROBLEM 26

GIVEN Rectangle *ABCD*, diagonals *AC* and *BD*.
TO PROVE *AC* = *BD*. (The proof should be worked out by the student)

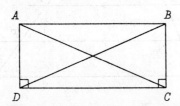

PROBLEM 27

GIVEN   Square *ABCD*, diagonals *AC* and *BD*.
TO PROVE $AC \perp BD$.

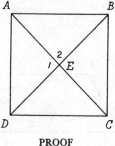

PROOF

STATEMENTS	REASONS
1. *ABCD* is a square.	1. Given.
2. *AD=AB*.	2. All sides of a square are equal.
3. *DE=EB*.	3. The diagonals of a ▱ bisect each other.
4. *AE=AE*.	4. Identity.
5. $\triangle ADE \cong \triangle AEB$.	5. s.s.s.
6. $\angle 1 = \angle 2$.	6. Corresponding ⚊ of ≅ ⚊ are equal.
7. $\angle 1$ is the supplement of $\angle 2$.	7. If two adjacent ⚊ have their exterior sides lying on a straight line, they are supplementary.
8. $\angle 1$ and $\angle 2$ are right ⚊.	8. Two ⚊ which are both equal and supplementary are right ⚊.
9. $AC \perp BD$.	9. Two lines are ⊥ to each other if they meet at right ⚊.

PROBLEM 28

If $AB \| CD \| EF \| GH$, $AC=CE=EG$, and $BD=3$, find *FH* and *DF*.

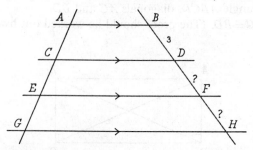

$FH = DF = 3$. If three or more parallel lines intercept equal segments on one transversal, they intercept equal segments on every transversal.

POLYGONS

We have learned that a plane figure of three or more points joined by lines is called a polygon. The more important polygons which we have already treated are the *triangle* (three sides) and the *quadrilateral* (four sides). Other polygons are the *pentagon* (five sides), the *hexagon* (six sides), the *heptagon* (seven sides), the *octagon* (eight sides), the *nonagon* (nine sides), the *decagon* (ten sides), and the *decodecagon* (twelve sides). A straight line, other than a side, joining any two vertices of a polygon is called a *diagonal*. Similar polygons are those whose corresponding angles are equal and whose corresponding sides are proportional.

A regular polygon is equiangular and equilateral. The radius of a circle inscribed in a regular polygon is called the *apothem* of the polygon. The apothem may also be defined as the perpendicular from the center of a regular polygon to any of its sides. The sum of the lines or sides of the polygon is its perimeter. The area of the polygon or any other plane figure is the surface included within its lines or sides.

PROPOSITION XXIII

The sum of the angles of a polygon of n sides is (n-2) straight angles.

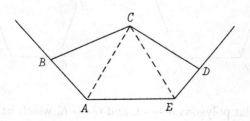

GIVEN   Polygon A - - - E having n sides.
TO PROVE   The sum of the angles of A - - - E is $(n-2)$ straight angles.

PROOF

STATEMENTS	REASONS
1. Draw diagonals *CA* and *CE*, making (*n*-2) △.	1. A straight line can be drawn through two points (Ax. 9).
2. The sum of the ∠ of a △ = one straight ∠.	2. Prop. VII.
3. The sum of the ∠ of (*n*-2) △ = (*n*-2) straight ∠.	3. If equals are added to equals, the sums are equal (Ax. 2).
4. The sum of the ∠ of (*n*-2) △ = the sum of the ∠ of polygon *A - - - E*.	4. The whole is equal to the sum of all its parts (Ax. 6).
5. ∴ The sum of the ∠ of polygon *A - - - E* equals (*n*-2) straight ∠.	5. Substitution. (Ax. 8).

COROLLARY 1. *The sum of the exterior angles of a polygon when each side is extended is two straight angles.*

COROLLARY 2. *Every angle of an equiangular polygon of n sides is equal to $\frac{n-2}{n}$ straight angles.*

PROPOSITION XXIV

Regular polygons which have the same number of sides are similar.

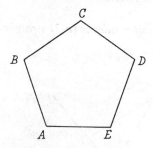 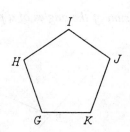

GIVEN   Regular polygons *A - - - E* and *G - - - K*, which have the same number of sides.

TO PROVE   Polygon *A - - - E* ∼ polygon *G - - - K*.

PROOF

STATEMENTS	REASONS
1. $\angle A = \angle B = \angle C = \angle D = \angle E$ $= \frac{n-2}{n}$ straight $\angle$.	1. An $\angle$ of an equiangular polygon equals $\frac{n-2}{n}$ straight $\angle$ (Prop. X, Cor. 2).
2. $\angle G = \angle H = \angle I = \angle J = \angle K$ $= \frac{n-2}{n}$ straight $\angle$.	2. As in Step 1.
3. $\angle A = \angle G$, $\angle B = \angle H$, etc.	3. Things equal to the same thing are equal each other (Ax. 1).
4. $AB = BC = CD = DE = EA$.	4. Definition of a regular polygon.
5. $GH = HI = IJ = JK = KG$.	5. As in Step 4.
6. $\frac{AB}{GH} = \frac{BC}{HI} = \frac{CD}{IJ} = \frac{DE}{JK} = \frac{EA}{KG}$.	6. If equals are divided by equals, the quotients are equal (Ax. 5).
7. $\therefore$ Polygon A - - - $E \sim$ polygon G - - - K.	7. Definition of similar polygons.

COROLLARY. *Any theorem true for a regular polygon is true for a circle. As the number of sides of a regular polygon increase, it finally becomes a circle, and its apothem becomes a radius.*

PROPOSITION XXV

The area of a regular polygon equals half the product of its perimeter and apothem.

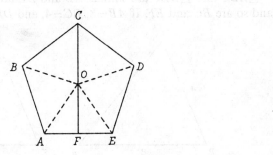

GIVEN Regular polygon A - - - E, perimeter P and apothem OF.
TO PROVE Area of polygon A - - - E equals $\frac{1}{2}(P \times OF)$.

PROOF

STATEMENTS	REASONS
1. Draw the radii *OA,* etc., from the center *O* to each vertex.	1. A straight line can be drawn through two points (Ax. 9).
2. All the △ have the same altitude.	2. In a ⊙ equal chords are equally distant from the center.
3. Area of $\triangle OAE = \frac{1}{2}(OF \times AE)$. The same is true of the other △.	3. Area of △ equals ½ base times altitude.
4. Area of △ $OAE + OAB + OBC + OCD$ and $ODE = \frac{1}{2}OF(AB + BC + CD + DE + EA)$.	4. If equals are added to equals, the sums are equal (Ax. 2).
5. ∴ Polygon $A \text{ - - - } E = \frac{1}{2}(P \times OF)$.	5. Substitution (Ax. 8).

COROLLARY 1. *The area of a circle equals one half the radius times the circumference.*

COROLLARY 2. *The area of a circle equals π times the square of the radius or πr². π is the ratio of the circumference to the radius of any circle, and is equal to 3⅐(3.1416).*

PROBLEM 29

Find the number of degrees in the sum of interior angles of a pentagon. The sum of the interior angles $= (n\text{-}2)$ st. △

$$= 5\text{-}2 \text{ st. } \angle$$
$$\text{or} \quad 3 \text{ st. } \angle$$
$$\text{or} \quad 3 \times 180°$$
$$= 540°.$$

PROBLEM 30

△ *ABC* and △ *DEF* are similar. *AB* and *DE* are corresponding sides and so are *BC* and *EF*. If *AB*=8, *BC*=4, and *DE*=6, find *EF*.

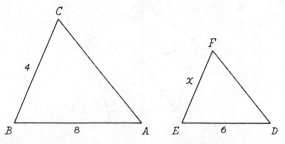

If two triangles are similar, the corresponding sides are proportional.

$$\frac{4}{x} = \frac{8}{6} \qquad 8x = 24$$
$$x = 3.$$

1. Find the number of degrees in each interior angle of an equiangular hexagon.
2. Find the number of degrees in the sum of the exterior angles of a decagon.
3. Find the number of degrees in each exterior angle of an equiangular polygon of 20 sides.
4. How many sides does an equiangular polygon have if each exterior angle contains 40°?
5. Find the area of a regular octagon whose side is 10 inches and whose apothem is 5 inches.
6. Find the area of a circle whose radius is 14 feet.

CIRCLES

A circle is a plane figure bounded by a single curved line called the circumference, every part of which is equally distant from a fixed point within called the center. A circle ($\odot$) may be designated by a capital letter near the center as $\odot A$ or by any three points on its circumference as $\odot BCD$. Any part of a circle is called an *arc* (as $\overgroup{BC}$). A *minor arc* is smaller than a semi-circle; a *major arc* is greater than a semi-circle. A radius is a line from the center to any point on the circumference, as *AD*.

A *chord* is a line joining two points on the circle, as *AB*. A *diameter* is a chord through the center, as *CD;* a diameter consists of two radii in a straight line bisecting the circle. A *secant* is a line cutting the circle at two points, as *EF*. A *tangent* is a line touching the circle at one point only (no matter how far extended), as *GH*, which touches the circle at *K* only.

A circle is circumscribed about a polygon if it passes through all the vertices of the polygon.

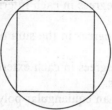

A circle is inscribed in a polygon if each side of the polygon is tangent to the circle.

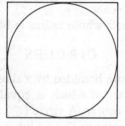

PROPOSITION XXVI

In a circle, equal chords cut off equal arcs.

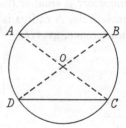

GIVEN Chord AB equals chord CD.

TO PROVE $\overgroup{AB} = \overgroup{CD}$.

PROOF

STATEMENTS	REASONS
1. Draw radii AO, OD, CO, OB.	1. A straight line can be drawn through two points (Ax. 9).
2. In $\triangle AOB$ and COD, chord $AB =$ chord CD.	2. Given.
3. $AO = OD$ and $CO = OB$.	3. Radii of a $\odot$.
4. $\triangle AOB$ and COD are $\cong$.	4. s.s.s.
5. $\angle AOB = \angle COD$.	5. Corresponding parts of $\cong$ $\triangle$ are equal.
6. $\therefore \overgroup{AB} = \overgroup{CD}$.	6. In the same circle, equal central $\angle$ have equal arcs.

CONVERSELY: *In a circle, equal arcs have equal chords.*

PROPOSITION XXVII

If a radius is perpendicular to a chord, it bisects the chord and its arc.

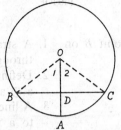

GIVEN $\odot$ O and radius $OA \perp$ to chord BC at D.

TO PROVE $BD = DC$ and $\overarc{BA} = \overarc{AC}$.

PROOF

STATEMENTS	REASONS
1. Draw radii OB and OC.	1. A straight line can be drawn through two points. (Ax. 9.)
2. In $\triangle$ BOD and DOC, $OB = OC$.	2. Radii of the same $\odot$ are equal.
3. $OD = OD$.	3. Identity.
4. $\angle ODB = \angle ODC$.	4. Both are right $\angle$ since $OD \perp BC$ at D.
5. $\triangle$ BOD and DOC are $\cong$.	5. If an arm and the hypotenuse of a right $\triangle$ equal the arm and hypotenuse of another, the two $\triangle$ are equal. (Prop. VII).
6. $\therefore BD = DC$ and $\angle 1 = \angle 2$.	6. Corresponding parts of $\cong$ $\triangle$ are equal.
7. $\therefore \overarc{BA} = \overarc{AC}$.	7. In the same circle, equal central $\angle$ have equal arcs.

PROPOSITION XXVIII

A radius is perpendicular to a tangent at the point of contact.

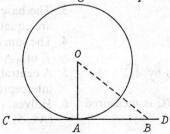

GIVEN ⊙ *O* and tangent *CD* tangent at *A* to radius *OA*.
TO PROVE   *OA* ⊥ to *CD*.

PROOF

STATEMENTS	REASONS
1. Draw *OB* to any point *B* on *CD* except *A*.	1. A straight line can be drawn through two points (Ax. 9).
2. *B* is outside of ⊙ *O*.	2. Definition. A tangent touches a ⊙ at one point only.
3. ∴*OA*<*OB*.	3. A line from the center of a ⊙ to a point outside the ⊙ is greater than the radius.
4. ∴*OA*⊥*CD*.	4. A ⊥ is the shortest line from a point to a line.

PROPOSITION XXIX

An angle inscribed in a circle is measured by one half of its intercepted arc.

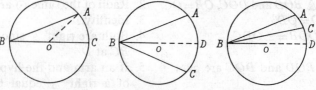

GIVEN   ⊙ *O* and inscribed ∠*ABC*.

TO PROVE   ∠*ABC* is measured by ½$\widehat{AC}$.
Case A. One side of the angle is a diameter.

PROOF

STATEMENTS	REASONS
1. Draw *OA*.	1. A straight line can be drawn through two points (Ax. 9).
2. *OA*=*OB*.	2. Radii of the same ⊙ are equal.
3. ∠*A*=∠*B*.	3. The base ∠s of an isosceles △ are equal.
4. ∠*A*+∠*B*=∠1.	4. The sum of the remote interior ∠s of a △ equals the exterior ∠.
5. ∠1 is measured by $\widehat{AC}$.	5. A central ∠ is measured by its intercepted arc.
6. ∴∠*B* or ∠*ABC* is measured by ½$\widehat{AC}$.	6. Halves of equals are equal (Ax. 5).

Case B. Neither side of the angle is a diameter.

1. Draw diameter *BD*.	1. A straight line can be drawn through two points (Ax. 9).
2. $\angle ABD$ is measured by $\frac{1}{2}\overarc{AD}$ and $\angle DBC$ is measured by $\frac{1}{2}\overarc{DC}$.	2. Case A (Above).
3. $\therefore \angle ABC$ is measured by $\frac{1}{2}\overarc{AC}$.	3. If equals are added to equals, the sums are equal (Ax. 2); and if equals are subtracted from equals, the remainders are equal (Ax. 3).

PROPOSITION XXX

A chord and a tangent make an angle measured by one half its intercepted arc.

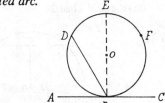 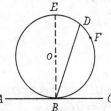

GIVEN ⊙ *O* with chord *DB* and with *AC* tangent to the circle at *B*.
TO PROVE $\angle DBC$ is measured by $\frac{1}{2}\overarc{DFB}$.

PROOF

STATEMENTS	REASONS
1. Draw diameter *EOB*.	1. A straight line can be drawn through two points (Ax. 9).
2. *EB* ⊥ to *AC*; $\angle EBC$ is a right $\angle$.	2. A radius is ⊥ to a tangent at point of contact (Prop. XXII).
3. $\overarc{EFB}$ is a semi-circle.	3. A diameter bisects a ⊙.
4. $\angle EBC$ is measured by $\frac{1}{2}\overarc{EFB}$.	4. A right $\angle$ is measured by $\frac{1}{2}$ a semi-circle as each contains 90°.
5. $\angle DBE$ is measured by $\frac{1}{2}\overarc{DE}$.	5. An $\angle$ inscribed in a ⊙ is measured by $\frac{1}{2}$ its intercepted arc (Prop. XXIII).
6. $\angle DBC$ is measured by $\frac{1}{2}\overarc{DFB}$.	6. If equals are added to equals, the sums are equal (Ax. 2), and if equals are subtracted from equals, the remainders are equal (Ax. 3).

PROBLEM 31

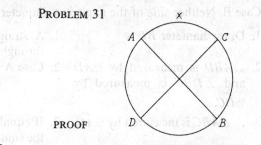

GIVEN $\overset{\frown}{AD}=\overset{\frown}{BC}$.
TO PROVE $AB=CD$.

PROOF

STATEMENTS	REASONS
1. $\overset{\frown}{AD}=\overset{\frown}{BC}$.	1. Given.
2. $\overset{\frown}{AC}=\overset{\frown}{AC}$.	2. Identity.
3. $\overset{\frown}{DC}=\overset{\frown}{AB}$.	3. If equals are added to equals, the results are equal.
4. $AB=DC$.	4. In the same circle, equal arcs have equal chords.

PROBLEM 32

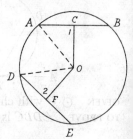

GIVEN   Circle O.
            $AB=DE$, $OC \perp AB$, $OF \perp DE$.
TO PROVE $OC=OF$.

PROOF

STATEMENTS	REASONS
1. Draw AO and OD.	1. A straight line can be drawn between two points.
2. $OA=OD$.	2. Radii of the same circle are equal.
3. $OC \perp AB$ and $OF \perp DE$.	3. Given.
4. $\angle 1$ and $\angle 2$ are rt. $\underline{\angle s}$.	4. Perpendiculars form right angles.
5. $AB=DE$.	5. Given.
6. $AC=CB$ and $DF=FE$.	6. A line from the center of a circle perpendicular to a chord bisects the chord.
7. $AC=DF$.	7. Halves of equals are equal.
8. $\triangle ACO \cong \triangle ODF$.	8. Hypotenuse leg = hypotenuse leg.
9. $OC=OF$.	9. Corresponding sides of $\cong$ $\underline{\angle s}$ are equal.

PROBLEM 33

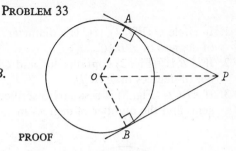

GIVEN Circle *O*
Tangents *PA* and *PB*.
TO PROVE *PA* = *PB*.

PROOF

STATEMENTS	REASONS
1. Draw *OA*, *OB*, and *OP*.	1. A straight line can be drawn between two points.
2. *PA* and *PB* tangent to circle *O*.	2. Given.
3. *PA* ⊥ *OA* and *PB* ⊥ *OB*.	3. A tangent is perpendicular to the radius at the point of contact.
4. ∠*A* and ∠*B* are rt. &.	4. Perpendiculars form right angles.
5. *OA* = *OB*.	5. Radii of the same circle are equal.
6. *OP* = *OP*.	6. Identity.
7. △*AOP* ≅ △*BOP*.	7. Hypotenuse leg = hypotenuse leg.
8. *PA* = *PB*.	8. Corresponding sides of ≅ & are equal.

PROBLEM 34

In circle *O*, ∠*A* contains 30°. Find the number of degrees in ∠*BOC*.

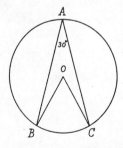

Angle *A* contains 30°. Since an inscribed angle is measured by half its intercepted arc, $\overset{\frown}{BC}$ contains 60°. Since a central angle is measured by its intercepted arc, ∠*BOC* contains 60°.

EXERCISE VI

1. In circle *O* (Fig. 1), *AC* is a diameter. If $\overarc{AB}=80°$, find the number of degrees in ∠*BAC*.
2. If ∠*BAC* (Fig. 2) contains 40° and *CD* is a tangent, find the number of degrees in ∠*BCD*.
3. If *ABCD* (Fig. 3) is a square inscribed in a circle and *AE* is a tangent, find the number of degrees in ∠*EAB*.

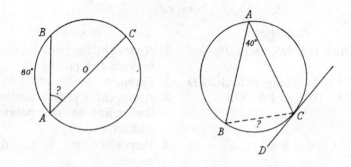

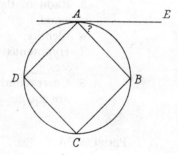

XVIII

Solid Geometry

WHAT SOLID GEOMETRY IS

In *plane* geometry we dealt with polygons and circles, which are the surfaces or planes of solid figures. In *solid* geometry we deal not only with plane figures but also with solid figures themselves, such as a block of wood, a ball, a mountain, and the like.

PLANES AND ANGLES

PLANES

A plane is the surface of any solid figure. A plane is determined by any three points which are not in a straight line. A plane has only two dimensions: length and width. A solid has three dimensions: length, width, and thickness.

A *locus* is the path of a point (a geometric figure) satisfying a given condition or given conditions. One *locus* or two or more *loci* determine a point or points. The intersection of two planes is the locus of all points in both planes.

SOLID ANGLES

A *dihedral* angle is formed by the intersection of two planes. A dihedral angle has two planes or surface sides. In the illustration, the planes intersect at *CB* and the intersection *CB* is the edge of the angle. A plane angle is the angle formed by the perpendiculars in the planes of the dihedral angle, perpendicular to the same point on the edge of the dihedral angle. The plane angles are all equal.

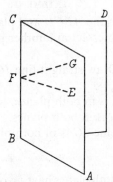

Angle *EFG* is the plane angle of the dihedral angle.

A *trihedral* angle is one that has three surfaces or plane sides.

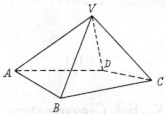

Thus, angle *V-ABC* is a trihedral angle. A *polyhedral* angle is any angle that has three or more surfaces or plane sides. The *vertex* is the point at which all the planes meet. An angle formed by two consecutive edges is called a face angle, as angle *AVB*.

PROPOSITION I

When two planes meet, their intersection is a straight line.

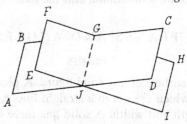

GIVEN   Plane *ABCD* intersecting plane *EFHI* at point *J*.
TO PROVE   *JG* is a straight line.

PROOF

STATEMENTS	REASONS
1. Plane *ABCD* and plane *EFHI* intersect at another point *G*.	1. If two planes intersect, they must have more than one point in common.
2. Draw straight line *JG*.	2. A straight line can be drawn through two points (Ax. 9).
3. *J* is in both planes.	3. Given.
4. *G* is in both planes.	4. See Step 1.
5. Line *JG* is in both planes.	5. A straight line joining any two points in a plane is in the plane.
6. Both planes have no other point in common or they would coincide.	6. A straight line and a point not on the line determine the plane.

7. The intersection of the two planes is in the straight line *JG*.

7. ∴The intersection of two planes is the place which contains the line common to both places.

Proposition II

If two parallel planes intersect a third plane, the intersections are parallel.

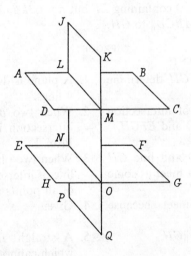

GIVEN   Plane *ABCD*‖ to plane *EFGH* and both intersected by plane *JKQP* at *LM* and *NO* respectively.

TO PROVE   *LM*‖ to *NO*.

PROOF

STATEMENTS	REASONS
1. *LM* and *NO* are in the same plane.	1. Given.
2. If *LM* and *NO* meet, then planes *ABCD* and *EFGH* must meet.	2. A straight line joining any two points in a plane is in that plane.
3. Planes *ABCD* and *EFGH* cannot meet.	3. ‖ planes cannot meet.
4. ∴*LM* is ‖ to *NO*.	4. Lines in the same plane that cannot meet are ‖.

PROPOSITION III

A plane which contains one of two parallel lines is parallel to the other line.

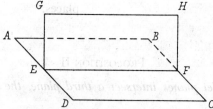

GIVEN   Plane *ABCD* containing *EF* but not *GH* and *GH*‖ to *EF*.
TO PROVE   Plane *ABCD*‖ to *GH*.

PROOF

STATEMENTS	REASONS
1. Lines *EF* and *GH* determine plane *EFGH*.	1. A plane is determined by two ‖ lines.
2. *EF* is the line of intersection of planes *ABCD* and *EFGH*.	2. When two planes meet, their intersection is a straight line. Prop. I.
3. If plane *ABCD* and line *GH* meet, they must meet at some point on *EF*.	3. When two planes intersect, the line of intersection is the locus of all points common to both.
4. They cannot meet because *EF*‖*GH*.	4. Given.
5. ∴ Plane *ABCD*‖*GH*.	5. A straight line and a plane which cannot meet are ‖.

PROPOSITION IV

Two planes are parallel if they are perpendicular to the same line.

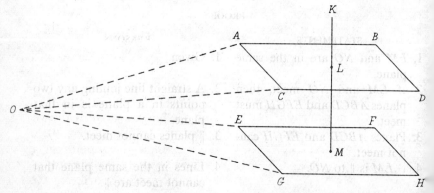

GIVEN $KM \perp$ to planes *ABCD* and *EFGH*.
TO PROVE   Plane *ABCD*‖ to plane *EFGH*.

PROOF

STATEMENTS	REASONS
1. If the two planes are not ‖, they meet at some point *O*.	1. Lines which are not ‖ meet.
2. If they meet at *O*, they cannot both be $\perp KM$.	2. Through a given point outside a given line, only one plane can be passed $\perp$ the given line.
3. But both planes $\perp KM$.	3. Given.
4. ∴ Plane *ABCD* and plane *EFGH* do not meet.	4. Steps 2 and 3.
5. Plane *ABCD* is ‖ plane *EFGH*.	5. Planes that do not meet are parallel.

PROPOSITION V

Only one perpendicular to a given plane can be drawn through a given point in that plane.

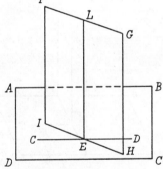

GIVEN   Plane *ABCD* and point *E* therein.
TO PROVE   Only one $\perp$ can be drawn to plane *ABCD* at *E* or *LE* $\perp$ to plane *ABCD*.

PROOF

STATEMENTS	REASONS
1. Draw *CD* in plane *ABCD*.	1. A straight line can be drawn between two points (Ax. 9).
2. Pass plane *FGHI* $\perp CD$ at *E*.	2. Through a given point in a given line only one plane $\perp$ to the line can be drawn.

3. Plane *FGHI* intersects plane *ABCD* at *HI*.

3. When two planes meet, their intersection is a straight line (Prop. I).

4. In plane *FGHI*, draw *LE* ⊥ *HI*; *LE* is the only line in plane *FGHI* that can be drawn ⊥ *HI* at *E*.

4. In one plane, one and only one ⊥ can be drawn to a straight line at a given point.

5. *CD* ⊥ *LE*.

5. If a line is ⊥ to a plane, it is ⊥ to every line passing through its foot, and Step 2.

6. *LE* ⊥ *HI*; *LE* ⊥ *CD*.

6. Steps 4–5.

7. ∴ *LE* ⊥ plane *ABCD*.

7. If a line is ⊥ to two intersecting lines at the point of intersection, it is ⊥ to the plane of the two lines.

PROPOSITION VI

If a line is perpendicular to a plane, every plane containing the given line is perpendicular to the given plane.

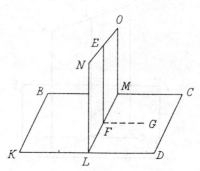

GIVEN　*EF* ⊥ to plane *ABCD* and plane *LMNO*, any plane containing *EF*.

TO PROVE　Plane *LMNO* ⊥ to plane *ABCD*.

PROOF

STATEMENTS	REASONS
1. Draw *FG* ⊥ to *LM* at *F*.	1. A ⊥ to a given line may be drawn at a given point.
2. *EF* ⊥ to *LF*.	2. If a line is ⊥ to a plane it is ⊥ to every line in the plane passing through its foot.

3. $\angle EFG$ is the plane $\angle$ of dihedral $\angle LEMG$.

   3. A plane $\angle$ of a dihedral $\angle$ is an $\angle$ formed by two straight lines, one in each plane of the dihedral $\angle$ and both $\perp$ to the edge at the same point.

4. $EF\perp$ to FG and $\angle EFG$ is a right $\angle$.

   4. See Reason 2.

5. Dihedral $\angle LEMG$ is a right $\angle$.

   5. If a plane $\angle$ is a right $\angle$, its dihedral $\angle$ is a right $\angle$.

6. $\therefore$ Plane $LMNO \perp$ to plane $ABCD$.

   6. Two planes are $\perp$ to each other if their dihedral $\angle$ are right $\angle$.

PROPOSITION VII

If two planes are perpendicular to each other, a line drawn in one plane perpendicular to their intersection is perpendicular to the other.

GIVEN   Plane $GHIJ \perp$ to plane $ABCD$ and $EF\perp$ to FH.
TO PROVE $EF\perp$ to plane $ABCD$.

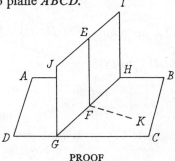

PROOF

STATEMENTS	REASONS
1. In plane $ABCD$ draw $FK\perp$ to FH.	1. A $\perp$ to a given line can be drawn through a given point.
2. $EF\perp FK$.	2. Given.
3. $\angle EFK$ is plane $\angle$ of dihedral $\angle IFHK$.	3. A plane $\angle$ of a dihedral $\angle$ is an $\angle$ formed by two straight lines, one in each plane of the dihedral $\angle$ and both $\perp$ to the edge at the same point.
4. Plane $GHIJ \perp$ plane $ABCD$.	4. Given.
5. $\angle EFK$ is a rt. $\angle$ or $EF\perp FK$.	5. If a dihedral $\angle$ is a rt. $\angle$, its plane $\angle$ is a rt. $\angle$.
6. $\therefore EF\perp ABCD$.	6. A $\perp$ to two intersecting lines at their point of intersection is $\perp$ to their plane.

COROLLARY. *If two planes are perpendicular to each other, a perpendicular to one plane at any point on their intersection is in the other plane.*

PROPOSITION VIII

If two intersecting planes are both perpendicular to a third plane, the third plane is perpendicular to their intersection.

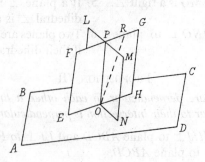

GIVEN Plane $ABCD \perp$ to planes $EFGH$ and LMN and PO their intersection.

TO PROVE Plane $ABCD \perp$ to PO.

PROOF

STATEMENTS	REASONS
1. Draw $RO \perp$ to plane $ABCD$.	1. A $\perp$ can be drawn to a plane through a given point in a given plane.
2. Plane $EFGH$ and plane $LMN \perp$ plane $ABCD$.	2. Given.
3. RO is in planes $EFGH$ and LMN.	3. If two planes are $\perp$ to each other, a $\perp$ to one at any point on their intersection is in the other plane (Prop. VII, Cor. 1).
4. RO coincides with PO.	4. When two planes meet, the line of intersection is the locus of all points common to both.
5. $\therefore$ Plane $ABCD \perp$ to PO.	5. Plane $ABCD$ is $\perp$ to RO, which coincides with PO; and Step 1.

COROLLARY. *If a line is not perpendicular to a plane, only one plane perpendicular to the given plane can be passed through that line.*

PROBLEM 1

GIVEN   Plane $m \parallel$ plane n.
$\quad\quad\quad AB \parallel CD$.
TO PROVE $AB = CD$.

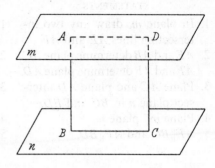

PROOF

STATEMENTS	REASONS
1. $AB \parallel CD$.	1. Given.
2. AB and CD determine plane AC.	2. Two parallel lines determine a plane.
3. Plane AC intersects planes m and n in AD and BC.	3. Two planes intersect in a straight line.
4. Plane $m \parallel$ plane n.	4. Given.
5. $AD \parallel BC$.	5. The intersections of two parallel planes with a third plane are parallel.
6. $ABDC$ is a $\square$.	6. A quadrilateral is a parallelogram if the opposite sides are parallel.
7. $AB = CD$.	7. Opposite sides of a parallelogram are equal.

PROBLEM 2

GIVEN   Plane $m \parallel$ plane n.
$\quad\quad\quad AB \perp$ plane m.
TO PROVE $AB \perp$ plane n.

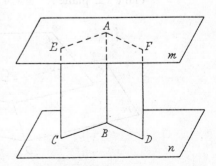

PROOF

STATEMENTS	REASONS
1. In plane *m,* draw any two intersecting lines *AE* and *AF.*	1. In a plane, any number of lines can be drawn through a point.
2. *AE* and *AB* determine plane *AC.* *AF* and *AB* determine plane *AD.*	2. Two intersecting lines determine a plane.
3. Plane *AC* and plane *AD* intersect plane *n* in *BC* and *BD.*	3. The intersection of two planes is a straight line.
4. Plane *m*‖ plane *n.*	4. Given.
5. *AE*‖*BC* and *AF*‖*BD.*	5. The intersections of two parallel planes with a third plane are parallel.
6. *AB* ⊥ plane *m.*	6. Given.
7. *AB* ⊥ *AE* and *AB* ⊥ *AF.*	7. If a line is perpendicular to a plane, it is perpendicular to every line in the plane passing through its foot.
8. *AB* ⊥ *BC* and *AB* ⊥ *BD.*	8. In a plane, a line perpendicular to one of two parallel lines is perpendicular to the other.
9. *AB* ⊥ plane *m.*	9. If a line is perpendicular to each of two intersecting lines at their point of intersection, it is perpendicular to their plane.

PROBLEM 3

GIVEN Plane *m* and plane *r* intersect in *CD.*
Plane *s* ⊥ *CD.*
TO PROVE Plane *s* ⊥ plane *m.*
Plane *s* ⊥ plane *r.*

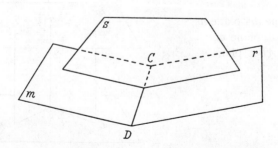

Problem 4

GIVEN   Plane $x \parallel$ line AB, plane $y \parallel$ line AB, plane z containing line AB intersects plane x and plane y on lines CD and EF.

TO PROVE $CD \parallel EF$.

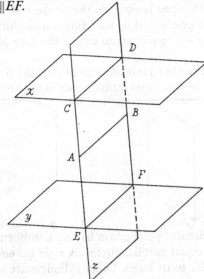

POLYHEDRONS

General Terms Needed

A solid has been defined as a figure which has length, width, and thickness, the boundaries of which are surfaces that may be plane or curved. A *polyhedron* is a solid bounded by parts of planes. The parts of the planes are the *faces,* the intersections are the *edges,* and the intersection of the edges are the *vertices.* The faces of a polyhedron are polygons. A straight line joining two vertices not in the same face is a diagonal. The faces of a *regular polyhedron* are all congruent regular polygons, and the polyhedral angles are congruent. The regular polyhedrons are *tetrahedron* (four faces), *hexahedron* (six faces), *octahedron* (eight faces), *dodecahedron* (twelve faces), and *icosahedron* (twenty faces).

Prisms and Cylinders

A *prism* is a polyhedron whose bases are congruent plane figures (such as triangles, squares, etc.) and whose sides are parallelograms.

The lateral edges of the prism are the intersections of the planes that comprise the lateral surfaces. A *right prism* is one whose bases are perpendicular to a lateral edge. A prism whose bases are parallelograms is called a *parallelepiped*. A *right parallelepiped* is one whose lateral edges are perpendicular to the bases. A *rectangular parallelepiped* is a right parallelepiped whose bases are rectangles. A rectangular parallelepiped whose faces are square is called a *cube*. The volume of a rectangular parallelepiped is equal to the product of its length, width, and altitude or the product of its base (area) and altitude.

The volume of a triangular prism equals the area of the base times the altitude.

The volume of a prism equals the area of the base times the altitude. Two prisms whose bases and altitudes are equal are equal.

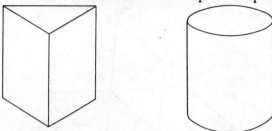

A *cylinder* is a circular polyhedron having a uniform diameter with bases which form equal parallel circles. A *right cylinder* is one whose axis is perpendicular to its bases. Other cylinders are *oblique*. A *circular cylinder* is one whose base is a circle. A *cylinder of revolution* is a right cylinder which is circular. It receives its name from the fact that it can be created by the revolution of a rectangle about one of its sides. The axis is the line about which it revolves. A right section of a cylinder or a prism is a section made by a plane perpendicular to a side.

PROPOSITION IX

The lateral area of a prism is equal to the product of a lateral edge and the perimeter of a right section.

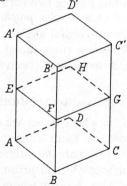

GIVEN Prism ABC, P the perimeter of right section $EFGH$, A the lateral area and E an edge.

TO PROVE $A = EP$.

PROOF

STATEMENTS	REASONS
1. AB', BC', etc., are ▱.	1. Definition.
2. $EF \perp$ to $B'B$, $FG \perp$ to $C'C$ etc.	2. A line $\perp$ to a plane is $\perp$ to every line passing through its foot.
3. $\square AB' = EF \times BB'$. $\square BC' = FG \times CC'$ etc.	3. Area of $\square$ = base $\times$ altitude.
4. ▱$AB' + BC' +$ etc. $= (EF + FG$ etc.$) \times E$.	4. If equals are added to equals the sums are equal (Ax. 2).
5. $\therefore A = EP$.	5. Substitution.

COROLLARY 1. *The lateral area of a right prism equals its altitude times the perimeter of its base.*

COROLLARY 2. *The lateral area of a circular cylinder equals a side times the perimeter of a right section.*

COROLLARY 3. *The lateral area of a right circular cylinder equals its altitude times the circumference of the base.*

PROBLEM 5

Find the lateral area of a right prism whose altitude is 10 and whose base is a right triangle and whose legs are 3 and 4.

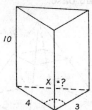

By the Pythagorean Theorem:
$$x^2 = 3^2 + 4^2$$
$$x^2 = 9 + 16$$
$$x^2 = 25$$
$$x = 5.$$

The perimeter of the base is $3 + 4 + 5 = 12$

$$\text{area} = \text{edge} \times \text{perimeter}$$
$$= (10)(12)$$
$$= 120.$$

1. Find the volume of a cube whose edge is 3 ft.
2. The dimensions of a rectangular parallelepiped are 2 yards, 4 yards, and 8 yards. Find the edge of a cube of the same volume.
3. Find the lateral area of a right prism whose altitude is 10 ft. and whose base is a square with a side of 4 ft.
4. The altitude of a right circular cylinder is 12 ft. and the radius of the base is 3 ft. Find the lateral area.

PYRAMIDS AND CONES

A pyramid is a polyhedron with a polygon as its base and the lateral planes or faces meeting at a point called the *vertex*. A *regular* pyramid is a pyramid whose base is a regular polygon and whose altitude is ⊥ to the base at its center. The lateral faces of a regular pyramid are congruent isosceles angles. The height of a regular pyramid is called its *altitude*. The slant height of a regular pyramid is the altitude of one of the lateral faces drawn from the vertex.

A *cone* is a polyhedron which has a circular base and sides ending in a vertex. The altitude of a cone is the perpendicular from the vertex to the base. The axis of the cone is a straight line from the vertex to the center of its base. A *right cone* is one whose axis is perpendicular to the base. A right circular cone is called a *cone of revolution* because it can be created by a right triangle turning about one of its legs as an axis. The slant height of a cone of revolution is the distance on the surface from the vertex to the base.

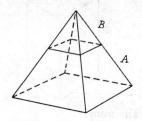

The *frustum* of a pyramid or cone is the part of the pyramid or cone next to the base left by cutting off the top portion by a plane parallel to the base. *A* is the frustum. The part of a pyramid or cone intersected by two planes, usually parallel, is also called a frustum. A pyramid or cone whose lateral planes or surfaces are cut off below the vertex by a plane (usually parallel to the base) is called a *truncated* pyramid or cone. The diagram on the next page shows a truncated cone.

Proposition X

The lateral area of a regular pyramid is equal to one half the slant height times the perimeter of the base.

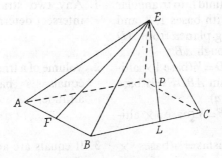

GIVEN   Regular pyramid *EABC*, slant heights *EF*, *EL*, etc., lateral area *m*, perimeter of base *ABCD*, *p*.

TO PROVE $m = \frac{1}{2}(EF \times p)$.

PROOF

STATEMENTS	REASONS
1. $\triangle EAB = \frac{1}{2}(EF \times AB)$ $\triangle EBC = \frac{1}{2}(EL \times BC)$, etc.	1. Area of a $\triangle$ equals ½ base times the altitude.
2. $\triangle EAB + EBC$, etc. $= \frac{1}{2}$ slant height $(AB + BC,$ etc.).	2. If equals are added to equals the sums are equal (Ax. 2).
3. $m = \frac{1}{2}(EF \times p)$.	3. Substitution.

COROLLARY 1. *The lateral area of a right circular cone is equal to the slant height times half the circumference of the base.*

Proposition XI

The volume of a pyramid is equal to one third the area of the base times the altitude.

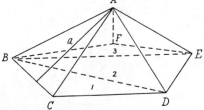

GIVEN   Pyramid *ABCDE*, volume *V*, Base *BCDE*, altitude *a*.

TO PROVE $V = \frac{1}{3}(\text{base } BCDE \times a)$.

PROOF

STATEMENTS	REASONS
1. Cut the pyramid into triangular pyramids with bases 1, 2, and 3 by passing planes from *AD* and *AE* through *AB*.	1. Any two straight lines that intersect determine a plane.
2. Prism *ABCD* = ⅓(base 1 × altitude *a*). Prism *ABDE* = ⅓(base 2 × altitude *a*). Prism *ABEF* = ⅓(base 3 × altitude *a*).	2. Volume of a triangular pyramid equals ⅓ base times the altitude.
3. Sum of prisms = ⅓(bases × altitude).	3. If equals are added to equals, the sums are equal (Ax. 2).
4. $V = \frac{1}{3}(\text{base} \times a)$.	4. Substitution.

COROLLARY. *The volume of a circular cone is equal to one third of the base times the altitude.*

EXERCISE II

1. Find the lateral area of a regular pyramid if the base is a square whose side is 6 ft. and whose slant height is 10 ft.
2. Find the lateral area of a right circular cone if the radius is 10 in. and the slant height is 4 in.
3. The altitude of a prism is 10 ft. and the base is a right triangle whose legs are 4 ft. and 6 ft. Find the volume of the prism.
4. Find the volume of a regular pyramid whose altitude is 15 yards and whose base is a square whose side is 5 yards.
5. The altitude of a right circular cone is 9 ft. and the radius of the base is 6 ft. Find the volume.

THE SPHERE

A *sphere* is a solid figure with a curved surface, every part of which is equally distant from a point within, called its *center*. A *radius* is a straight line from the center to the surface. A *diameter* is a line passing through the center from one point on the sphere to another point. A *great circle* of a sphere is a circle made by the intersection with the sphere of a plane passing through the center. Any other circle made by the intersection of a plane with the sphere is called a *small circle* of the sphere. One fourth of a great circle is called a *quadrant*. The axis of a circle of a sphere is the diameter which is perpendicular to the plane of the circle. Each end of the axis is called the *pole* of the circle.

A *spherical polygon* is a polygon on the surface a sphere made by three or more arcs of great circles. The arcs are the sides, and the points where the sides intersect are the vertices. A spherical angle is the angle formed by two intersecting great circles. A *spherical triangle* is a spherical polygon which has three sides. The *polar triangle* of a spherical triangle is another spherical triangle whose sides are the arcs of great circles which have the vertices of the given triangle as poles.

A *lune* is a part of a sphere whose boundaries are two semi-circles. The spherical angle made by the two arcs is called the *angle of the lune*.

PROPOSITION XII

A plane passing through a sphere cuts off a section that is a circle.

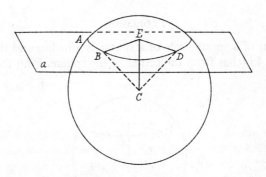

GIVEN   Sphere *C*, plane *a* cutting *C* in *ABD*.
TO PROVE   *ABD* is a circle.

PROOF

STATEMENTS	REASONS
1. Draw $CE \perp$ to plane a.	1. A line $\perp$ to a given plane can be drawn from a given point outside the given plane (Prop. VII, Cor.).
2. From B and D, any two points on the intersection draw BC, BE, ED and DC.	2. A straight line can be drawn through any two points (Ax. 9).
3. $CB = CD$.	3. Radii of a sphere are equal.
4. $BE = ED$.	4. If from a point outside a plane a $\perp$ and 2 equal oblique lines are drawn to a plane, the oblique lines meet the plane at equal distances from the foot of the $\perp$.
5. $\therefore ABD$ is a $\odot$.	5. Definition. A $\odot$ is a plane figure bounded by a single curved line, the circumference, every part of which is equally distant from the center.

COROLLARY 1. *When two spheres intersect, the intersection is a circle.*

COROLLARY 2. *A circle can be passed through any three points of a sphere.*

COROLLARY 3. *All great circles of a sphere intersect.*

PROBLEM 6

The radius of a small circle of a sphere is 3 inches and the plane of the circle is 4 inches from the center of the sphere. Find the radius of the sphere.

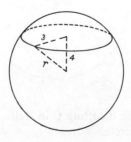

By the Pythagorean Theorem:

$$c^2 = a^2 + b^2$$
$$r^2 = 3^2 + 4^2$$
$$r^2 = 9 + 16$$
$$r^2 = 25$$
$$r = 5.$$

PROBLEM 7

1. The radius of a sphere is 13 inches. Find the area of a small circle whose plane is 5 inches from the center of the sphere.

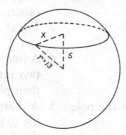

By the Pythagorean Theorem:

$$x^2 + 5^2 = 13^2 \qquad A = \pi r^2$$
$$x^2 + 25 = 169 \qquad A = \pi(12)^2$$
$$x^2 = 144 \qquad A = 144\pi \text{ sq. in.}$$
$$x = 12.$$

PROPOSITION XIII

On a sphere, a point which is a quadrant's distance from each of two other points, not the ends of a diameter, is the pole of the great circle through these points.

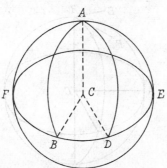

GIVEN   Sphere C, point A, quadrants AB and AD and $\odot FBDE$.
TO PROVE A is the pole of $\odot FBDE$.

PROOF

STATEMENTS	REASONS
1. Draw AC, BC, and CD.	1. A straight line can be drawn through any two points (Ax. 9).
2. $\widehat{AB}=90°$; $\widehat{AD}=90°$ $\widehat{AB}=\widehat{AD}$.	2. A quadrant = one quarter of a great circle or 90° (by definition) and things equal to the same things are equal to each other.
3. $\angle ACB = \angle ACD$.	3. Equal arcs have equal central $\angle$.
4. $AC \perp$ to plane BDE.	4. A line $\perp$ to the intersection of two intersecting lines is $\perp$ to their plane.
5. AC is the axis and A the pole of $\odot BDE$.	5. A diameter $\perp$ to the plane of the $\odot$ of a sphere is the axis of the $\odot$ and the end of the diameter is the pole of the $\odot$ (by definition).

CONVERSE. *The distance of all points on a great circle from a pole of the circle is a quadrant.*

COROLLARY. *All points on a great circle are a quadrant's distance from a pole of the circle.*

PROPOSITION XIV

A spherical angle is measured by the intercepted arc on the great circle of which the vertex is a pole.

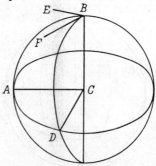

GIVEN   Sphere C, spherical angle ABD, B the pole of great circle of which $\overarc{AD}$ is an arc.

TO PROVE   Spherical $\angle ABD$ is measured by $\overarc{AD}$.

PROOF

STATEMENTS	REASONS
1. Draw EB and FB tangents to $\overarc{AB}$ and $\overarc{BD}$ respectively.	1. A tangent to a $\odot$ can be drawn at a point on the $\odot$.
2. Draw radii CB, CD, and CA.	2. A straight line can be drawn through two points (Ax. 9).
3. $CB \perp$ plane ACD.	3. A radius to the pole of a $\odot$ is $\perp$ to the plane of the $\odot$.
4. $CB \perp CD$.	4. If a line is $\perp$ to a plane, it is $\perp$ to every line in the plane passing through its foot.
5. $CB \perp BF$ and CD.	5. A tangent is $\perp$ to the radius of a $\odot$ at point of contact.
6. BF is in plane ACD.	6. Construction.
7. $CD \parallel BF$.	7. Lines $\perp$ to the same line are $\parallel$.
8. $CA \parallel BE$.	8. Steps 4–6.
9. $\angle EBF = \angle ACD$.	9. Two $\angle$s are equal if they are not in the same plane but have their sides respectively $\parallel$ and extending in the same direction.
10. $\therefore \angle ACD$ is measured by $\overarc{AD}$. $\therefore \angle EBF$ is measured by $\overarc{AD}$.	10. A central $\angle$ is measured by its intercepted arc and things equal to the same thing are equal to each other.
11. Spherical $\angle ABD$ is measured by $\angle EBF$.	11. A spherical angle is defined as the angle formed by the respective tangents drawn to the curves at their point of intersection.
12. $\angle ABD$ is measured by $\overarc{AD}$.	12. Things equal to the same thing are equal to each other. (Ax. 1).

XIX

Trigonometry

WHAT TRIGONOMETRY IS

In plane geometry we discussed planes and the figures drawn on these planes. In solid geometry we discussed solid figures. In trigonometry we shall discuss the measurement of magnitudes by studying the relationship of the sides and angles of triangles.

CONSTANTS, VARIABLES, AND FUNCTIONS

In trigonometry we begin with the right triangle and the measurement of its parts. In the diagram below, three similar right triangles have been drawn. They are similar because each has angles of 90°, 51°, and 39°.

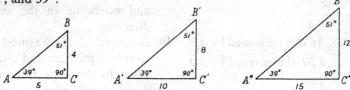

It follows that the corresponding sides are proportional. For instance:

$$\frac{BC}{AC}=\frac{B'C'}{A'C'}=\frac{B''C''}{A''C''}$$

Now suppose we are to change the size of angle A, leaving angle C equal to 90°. Then triangle ABC would no longer be similar to the other two triangles and we would then have: $\frac{BC}{AC}\neq\frac{B'C'}{A'C'}$ and $\frac{BC}{AC}\neq\frac{B''C''}{A''C''}$ In other words, the value of the ratio $\frac{BC}{AC}$ depends upon the value of the angle A.

In geometry we learned that the formula for the circumference of circle is $2\pi R$. The value of π is always 3.1416, and therefore π is calle a constant quantity. A *constant* quantity is one whose value in a formula never changes. The circumference and the radius are called *variable* quantities, depending, of course, on the size of the circle in question. Now if in any formula or equation the value of one variable quantity depends upon the value of another variable quantity, the first variable quantity is called a *function* of the second variable quantity. Thus, since the value of the ratio $\frac{BC}{AC}$ (first variable) depends upon the value of angle A (second variable), the ratio $\frac{BC}{AC}$ is called a function of angle A. In trigonometry this function is called the *tangent* of angle A and is written tan A; thus: $\tan A = \frac{BC}{AC}$. Similarly: tan B equals $\frac{AC}{BC}$.

To compute the value of tangent A, that is $\frac{BC}{AC}$, substitute the value of BC and AC as given in the illustration:

$\frac{BC}{AC} = \frac{4}{5} = .8000$ *or* tan $A = .8000$. Similarly, $\tan B = \frac{AC}{BC} = \frac{5}{4} = 1.25$.

THE TANGENT FUNCTION

In a right triangle we have for either of the acute angles a side *adjacent* or next to it, a side *opposite* it, and the *hypotenuse*. For any acute angle of a right triangle, the value of the tangent is equal to the ratio of the opposite side to the adjacent side, as shown in the illustration.

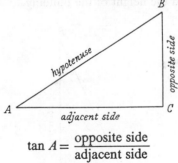

$$\tan A = \frac{\text{opposite side}}{\text{adjacent side}}$$

EXERCISE I

On page 952 there is a table of the natural trigonometric functions. Find the values of the following:

1. tan 45° =?
2. tan 30° =?
3. tan 27° =?
4. tan 72° =?

5. tan 36° =?
6. tan A = .3640 A =?
7. tan X = .7002 X =?
8. tan B = 1.3270 B =?

THE ANGLES OF ELEVATION AND DEPRESSION

In order to apply our new knowledge to the solution of problems, it is necessary that we know what is meant by the angle of elevation and the angle of depression. An *angle of elevation* is an angle measured upward from a horizontal line. Thus, in the illustration angle *A* (also called angle *BAC*) is the angle of elevation, because it is measured upward from *AC*.

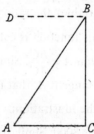

If *DB* is drawn parallel to *AC*, the angle *DBA* is measured downward from a horizontal line *DB*. Angle *DBA* is an *angle of depression*. Note that the angle of elevation equals the angle of depression because they are alternate interior angles of parallel lines.

Now let us apply this information to the solution of problems.

At a distance of 60 feet from the foot of a building, the angle of elevation is 58°. Find the height of the building.

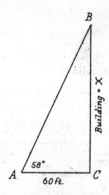

We draw a diagram in which *BC* represents the building whose height is the unknown *X*, and *AC* represents the distance of 60 feet.

$$\tan A = \frac{BC}{AC} = \frac{X}{60}$$

From the table of trigonometric functions we find tan 58° = 1.6003.

Therefore $1.6003 = \dfrac{X}{60}$

Clearing fractions $X = 60 \times 1.6003$ or 96.018 feet.

EXERCISE II

1. At a distance of 2000 feet from the base of a cliff, the angle of elevation to the top is 22°. Find the height of the cliff.
2. A lighthouse is 80 feet high. From the top of the lighthouse the angle of depression of a ship is 12°. How far is the ship from the lighthouse?
3. When the angle of elevation of the sun is 36°, how long a shadow will a flagpole 80 feet high cast?
4. Find to the nearest degree the angle of elevation of the sun when a stick 6 feet long casts a shadow whose length is 8 feet.

THE SIX TRIGONOMETRIC FUNCTIONS

Besides the tangent, there are other functions of either of the acute angles of the right triangles. In all, six different ratios of the sides can be obtained, thus giving either of the acute angles six functions. These six ratios constitute the six *functions,* which are as follows: *sine, cosine, tangent, cotangent, secant, cosecant.*

In the table below we give each of the functions with the ratio which corresponds to the function and the abbreviation which is used to represent the function:

NAME		RATIO	ABBREVIATION
1. sine	=	$\dfrac{\text{arm opposite the angle}}{\text{hypotenuse}}$	sin
2. cosine	=	$\dfrac{\text{arm adjacent to the angle}}{\text{hypotenuse}}$	cos
3. tangent	=	$\dfrac{\text{arm opposite the angle}}{\text{arm adjacent to the angle}}$	tan
4. cotangent	=	$\dfrac{\text{arm adjacent to the angle}}{\text{arm opposite the angle}}$	cot
5. secant	=	$\dfrac{\text{hypotenuse}}{\text{arm adjacent to the angle}}$	sec
6. cosecant	=	$\dfrac{\text{hypotenuse}}{\text{arm opposite to the angle}}$	csc

Use the capital letters to represent the angle of a right triangle and he corresponding small letters to represent the sides. As in the illustration, the functions of the two angles of a right triangle and the ratios which represent them are as follows:

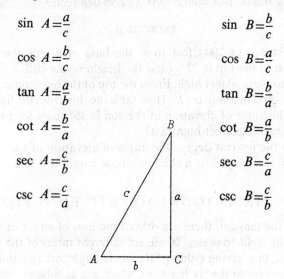

$$\sin A = \frac{a}{c} \qquad\qquad \sin B = \frac{b}{c}$$

$$\cos A = \frac{b}{c} \qquad\qquad \cos B = \frac{a}{c}$$

$$\tan A = \frac{a}{b} \qquad\qquad \tan B = \frac{b}{a}$$

$$\cot A = \frac{b}{a} \qquad\qquad \cot B = \frac{a}{b}$$

$$\sec A = \frac{c}{b} \qquad\qquad \sec B = \frac{c}{a}$$

$$\csc A = \frac{c}{a} \qquad\qquad \csc B = \frac{c}{b}$$

If in right triangle *ABC*, with angle *C* the right angle, $a=4$, $b=3$, and $c=5$, the value of the functions of angle *A* and angle *B* will be as follows:

$$\sin A = \frac{a}{c} = \frac{4}{5} \qquad\qquad \sin B = \frac{b}{c} = \frac{3}{5}$$

$$\cos A = \frac{b}{c} = \frac{3}{5} \qquad\qquad \cos B = \frac{a}{c} = \frac{4}{5}$$

$$\tan A = \frac{a}{b} = \frac{4}{3} \qquad\qquad \tan B = \frac{b}{a} = \frac{3}{4}$$

$$\cot A = \frac{b}{a} = \frac{3}{4} \qquad\qquad \cot B = \frac{a}{b} = \frac{4}{3}$$

$$\sec A = \frac{a}{b} = \frac{5}{3} \qquad\qquad \sec B = \frac{c}{a} = \frac{5}{4}$$

$$\csc A = \frac{c}{a} = \frac{5}{4} \qquad\qquad \csc B = \frac{c}{b} = \frac{5}{3}$$

PROBLEM 1

Find the value of the functions of angle *A* in the right triangle *ABC* with angle *C* the right angle if $a=4$ and $c=5$.

The value of b is not given. To find the unknown side b, we must use the Pythagorean Theorem; namely, the sum of the squares of the arms of a right triangle equals the square of the hypotenuse. Therefore:

$$a^2 + b^2 = c^2$$
$$4^2 + b^2 = 5^2$$
$$16 + b^2 = 25$$
$$b^2 = 25 - 16 \ or \ 9$$
$$\therefore b = 3.$$

Now that we know the value of the third side is 3, we proceed as before; that is,

$$\sin A = \frac{a}{c} = \frac{4}{5}$$

$$\cos A = \frac{b}{c} = \frac{3}{5} \text{ etc.}$$

PROBLEM 2

Find the value of the functions of angle A in triangle ABC if $\sin A = \frac{8}{15}$.

$$\sin A = \frac{a}{c} = \frac{8}{15} \therefore a = 8, \ c = 15$$

$$a^2 + b^2 = c^2 \text{ (Pythagorean Theorem)}$$
$$8^2 + b^2 = 15^2$$
$$64 + b^2 = 225$$
$$b^2 = 225 - 64 = 161$$
$$b = \sqrt{161}.$$

Proceed as before.

EXERCISE III

1. In the right triangle ABC with the right angle at C, $a = 5$, $b = 12$, and $c = 13$. Find the value of the functions of angle A and angle B.

2. In the right triangle ABC with the right angle at C, $a = 2$, $b = 5$, and $c = \sqrt{29}$. Find the values of the functions of angle A and angle B.

3. Find the value of the functions of angle A in right triangle ABC, with the right angle at C, if $a = 5$ and $c = 13$.

FUNCTIONS OF VARIOUS ANGLES

FUNCTIONS OF COMPLEMENTARY ANGLES

Complementary angles are those whose sum is a right angle. Therefore, in the right triangle ABC, angle A is the complementary

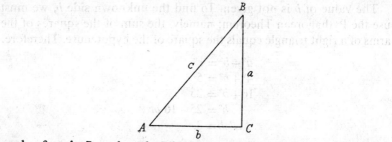

angle of angle B, and angle B is the complementary angle of angle A. Or, angle A equals 90° minus angle B, and angle B equals 90° minus angle A.

The functions of the complementary angles A and B are related, as you can see from the table:

$$\sin\ A = \frac{a}{c} \quad = \quad \cos\ B = \frac{a}{c}$$

$$\cos\ A = \frac{b}{c} \quad = \quad \sin\ B = \frac{b}{c}$$

$$\tan\ A = \frac{a}{b} \quad = \quad \cot\ B = \frac{a}{b}$$

$$\cot\ A = \frac{b}{a} \quad = \quad \tan\ B = \frac{b}{a}$$

$$\sec\ A = \frac{c}{b} \quad = \quad \csc\ B = \frac{c}{b}$$

$$\csc\ A = \frac{c}{a} \quad = \quad \sec\ B = \frac{c}{a}$$

Each function of an acute angle of a right triangle is equal to the cofunction of its complementary angle.

You may also observe from the table that each function has a reciprocal. For example, $\sin A = \frac{a}{c}$, but $\csc A = \frac{c}{a}$; $\cos A = \frac{b}{c}$, but $\sec A = \frac{c}{b}$; and $\tan A = \frac{a}{b}$, but $\cot A = \frac{b}{a}$. The same, of course, is true for angle B. Thus, if $\tan A = \frac{3}{4}$, $\cot A = \frac{4}{3}$, the reciprocal.

EXERCISE IV

1. In right triangle ABC, angle C is the right angle.

   a. If $\sin\ A = \frac{3}{7}$, find $\cos B$.

   b. If $\tan\ A = \frac{3}{11}$, find $\cot B$.

   c. If csc $A = \frac{8}{3}$, find sec B.

   d. If cos $A = \frac{2}{3}$, find sin B.

2. Find the missing function in each of the following:

   a. sin   60° =_____30°.   d. cos   2° =_____88°.

   b. tan 12° =_____78°.   e. cot 53° =_____37°.

   c. csc 40° =_____50°.   f. sec 19° =_____71°.

3. Express the following as a function of an angle less than 45°:

   a. sin 70°   b. tan 55°   c. sêc 72°

4. In right triangle ABC, angle C is the right angle.

   a. If sin $A = \frac{2}{3}$, find csc A.

   b. If tan $A = \frac{3}{4}$, find cot A.

   c. If cos $B = \frac{3}{8}$, find sec B.

THE FUNCTIONS OF THE ANGLE OF 45°

The functions of the angles of 45°, 30°, and 60° may be found very easily. First we will find the functions of the angle of 45°. In the isosceles right triangle ABC, $a = b$ and angle A equals angle B. Each angle equals 45°

If we give a the value of 1, then b has a value of 1, and since

$$a^2 + b^2 = c^2$$
$$1^2 + 1^2 = c^2$$
$$1 + 1 = c^2$$
$$2 = c^2$$
$$c = \sqrt{2}$$

Therefore:

$$\sin\ 45° = \frac{a}{c} = \frac{1}{\sqrt{2}}\ \text{or}\ \frac{1}{2}\sqrt{2} \qquad\qquad \csc\ 45° = \frac{c}{a} = \frac{\sqrt{2}}{1}\ \text{or}\ \sqrt{2}$$

$$\cos\ 45° = \frac{b}{c} = \frac{1}{\sqrt{2}}\ \text{or}\ \frac{1}{2}\sqrt{2} \qquad\qquad \sec\ 45° = \frac{c}{b} = \frac{\sqrt{2}}{1}\ \text{or}\ \sqrt{2}$$

$$\tan\ 45° = \frac{a}{b} = \frac{1}{1}\ \text{or}\ 1 \qquad\qquad \cot\ 45° = \frac{b}{a} = \frac{1}{1}\ \text{or}\ 1$$

THE FUNCTIONS OF THE ANGLES OF 30° AND 60°

We will now find the functions of the angles of 30° and 60°. In the equilateral triangle *ABD*, we draw the perpendicular bisector *BC*, dividing triangle *ABD* into two congruent right triangles.

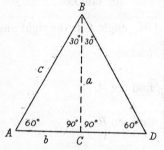

In triangle *ABC*, angle *A* equals 60°, angle *B* equals 30°, and angle *C* equals 90°. Since *b* equals ½*c* (equilateral triangle), *a* equals ½*c* $\sqrt{3}$. The value of *a* is derived from the equation

$$a^2 + b^2 = c^2$$
$$a^2 = c^2 - b^2$$
$$a = \sqrt{c^2 - b^2}$$
$$a = \sqrt{c^2 - \frac{1}{4}c^2}\ \left(b = \frac{1}{2}c;\ b^2 = \frac{1}{4}c^2\right)$$
$$a = \sqrt{\frac{3}{4}c^2}\ \text{or}\ 3\frac{c^2}{4}$$
$$a = \frac{1}{2}c\sqrt{3}$$

Therefore:

$$\sin\ \ 30° = \cos\ \ \ 60° = \frac{b}{c} = \frac{1}{2}$$

$$\cos\ \ 30° = \sin\ \ \ 60° = \frac{a}{c} = \frac{1}{2}\sqrt{3}$$

$$\tan\ \ 30° = \cot\ \ \ 60° = \frac{b}{a} = \frac{1}{3}\sqrt{3}$$

$$\cot 30° = \tan \quad 60° = \frac{a}{b} = \sqrt{3}$$

$$\sec 30° = \csc \quad 60° = \frac{c}{a} = \frac{2}{3}\sqrt{3}$$

$$\csc 30° = \sec \quad 60° = \frac{c}{b} = 2$$

Below is a summary of the values of the angles of 45°, 30°, and 60°.

Function	30°	45°	60°
sin	$\frac{1}{2}$	$\frac{1}{2}\sqrt{2}$	$\frac{1}{2}\sqrt{3}$
cos	$\frac{1}{2}\sqrt{3}$	$\frac{1}{2}\sqrt{2}$	$\frac{1}{2}$
tan	$\frac{1}{3}\sqrt{3}$	1	$\sqrt{3}$
cot	$\sqrt{3}$	1	$\frac{1}{3}\sqrt{3}$
sec	$\frac{2}{3}\sqrt{3}$	$\sqrt{2}$	2
csc	2	$\sqrt{2}$	$\frac{2}{3}\sqrt{3}$

EXERCISE V

Find the numerical value of each of the following:

1. sin 30° + cos 60°
2. tan 45° − cot 45°
3. cot 30° + 5 tan 60°
4. 2 sec 60° + 4 sin 30°
5. 8 (tan 60° + 5 cot 30°)
6. 8 tan 60° + 6 sin 30°
7. (4 csc 30° + 12 cos 60°) sin 30°
8. sin 60° + cos 45°
9. sin 30° tan 45° + sec 60° sec 30°
10. $\dfrac{\sin 30°}{\tan 45°}$

THE VALUES OF THE FUNCTIONS

We have shown you how to compute the values of the functions of angles 30°, 45°, and 60°. The functions of other acute angles can be computed, though not as easily. To save time, a table of the values of the functions of angles 0° to 90° is shown here. Since the function of each acute angle is equal to the cofunction of its complementary angle, only the values of the functions of angles 0° to 45° are needed. The values of the functions of angles 46° to 90° are equal to the cofunctions of angles 0° to 45°; that is, sin 40° equals cos 50° or sin 40° equals cos 50° equals .6428.

To use the table, therefore, *read down* for the values of the functions of angles 0° to 45°; *read up* for the values of the functions of angles 46° to 90°. Be sure to check the headings at the top and at the bottom of the table.

Note that the value of sines and cosines is never greater than 1; the value of tangents and cotangents ranges from 1 to infinity (∞); the value of secants and cosecants is never less than 1.

TABLE OF NATURAL TRIGONOMETRIC FUNCTIONS

Angle	Sine	Cosine	Tangent	Angle	Sine	Cosine	Tangent
1°	.0175	.9998	.0175	46°	.7193	.6947	1.0355
2°	.0349	.9994	.0349	47°	.7314	.6820	1.0724
3°	.0523	.9986	.0524	48°	.7431	.6691	1.1106
4°	.0698	.9976	.0699	49°	.7547	.6561	1.1504
5°	.0872	.9962	.0875	50°	.7660	.6428	1.1918
6°	.1045	.9945	.1051	51°	.7771	.6293	1.2349
7°	.1219	.9925	.1228	52°	.7880	.6157	1.2799
8°	.1392	.9903	.1405	53°	.7986	.6018	1.3270
9°	.1564	.9877	.1584	54°	.8090	.5878	1.3764
10°	.1736	.9848	.1763	55°	.8192	.5736	1.4281
11°	.1908	.9816	.1944	56°	.8290	.5592	1.4826
12°	.2079	.9781	.2126	57°	.8387	.5446	1.5399
13°	.2250	.9744	.2309	58°	.8480	.5299	1.6003
14°	.2419	.9703	.2493	59°	.8572	.5150	1.6643
15°	.2588	.9659	.2679	60°	.8660	.5000	1.7321
16°	.2756	.9613	.2867	61°	.8746	.4848	1.8040
17°	.2924	.9563	.3057	62°	.8829	.4695	1.8807
18°	.3090	.9511	.3249	63°	.8910	.4540	1.9626
19°	.3256	.9455	.3443	64°	.8988	.4384	2.0503
20°	.3420	.9397	.3640	65°	.9063	.4226	2.1445
21°	.3584	.9336	.3839	66°	.9135	.4067	2.2460
22°	.3746	.9272	.4040	67°	.9205	.3907	2.3559
23°	.3907	.9205	.4245	68°	.9272	.3746	2.4751
24°	.4067	.9135	.4452	69°	.9336	.3584	2.6051
25°	.4226	.9063	.4663	70°	.9397	.3420	2.7475
26°	.4384	.8988	.4877	71°	.9455	.3256	2.9042
27°	.4540	.8910	.5095	72°	.9511	.3090	3.0777
28°	.4695	.8829	.5317	73°	.9563	.2924	3.2709
29°	.4848	.8746	.5543	74°	.9613	.2756	3.4874
30°	.5000	.8660	.5774	75°	.9659	.2588	3.7321
31°	.5150	.8572	.6009	76°	.9703	.2419	4.0108
32°	.5299	.8480	.6249	77°	.9744	.2250	4.3315
33°	.5446	.8387	.6494	78°	.9781	.2079	4.7046
34°	.5592	.8290	.6745	79°	.9816	.1908	5.1446
35°	.5736	.8192	.7002	80°	.9848	.1736	5.6713
36°	.5878	.8090	.7265	81°	.9877	.1564	6.3138
37°	.6018	.7986	.7536	82°	.9903	.1392	7.1154
38°	.6157	.7880	.7813	83°	.9925	.1219	8.1443
39°	.6293	.7771	.8098	84°	.9945	.1045	9.5144
40°	.6428	.7660	.8391	85°	.9962	.0872	11.4301
41°	.6561	.7547	.8693	86°	.9976	.0698	14.3007
42°	.6691	.7431	.9004	87°	.9986	.0523	19.0811
43°	.6820	.7314	.9325	88°	.9994	.0349	28.6363
44°	.6947	.7193	.9657	89°	.9998	.0175	57.2900
45°	.7071	.7071	1.0000	90°	1.0000	.0000	

EXERCISE VI

1. Find the numerical value of each of the following:

   a. sin 70°
   b. tan 80°
   c. cos 69°

   d. sec 52°
   e. csc 48°
   f. cot 49°

2. In each of the following, find angle A:

   a. sin $A = .9063$
   b. tan $A = 5.6713$
   c. cos $A = .6157$

   d. sec $A = 4.1336$
   e. csc $A = 1.2868$
   f. cot $A = .2309$

OTHER RELATIONSHIPS AMONG THE FUNCTIONS

We have learned that the functions of an acute angle are equal in value to the cofunctions of its complementary angle; also that the sine and cosecant, cosine and secant and the tangent and cotangent of an acute angle are reciprocals. In addition, there are other relationships among the functions, a number of which will be shown here.

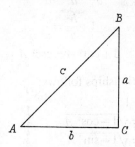

In the right triangle ABC,

$a^2 + b^2 = c^2$ (Pythagorean Theorem)

$\dfrac{a^2}{c^2} = \dfrac{b^2}{c^2} = 1$ (dividing by c^2)

$\sin^2 A + \cos^2 A = 1$ $\left(\sin A = \dfrac{a}{c}, \ \cos A = \dfrac{b}{c} \right)$

$\sin^2 A = 1 - \cos^2 A$ and $\cos^2 A = 1 - \sin^2 A$ (transposing)

$\sin A = \sqrt{1 - \cos^2 A}$ and $\cos A = \sqrt{1 - \sin^2 A}$ (taking the square root)

Also

$$\tan A = \frac{a}{b}, \text{ and } \sin A = \frac{a}{c} \text{ and } \cos A = \frac{b}{c}$$

$$\frac{a}{b} = \frac{\dfrac{a}{c}}{\dfrac{b}{c}}$$

$$\frac{a}{b} = \frac{a}{b}$$

$$\text{or } \tan A = \frac{\sin A}{\cos A}$$

Also

$$a^2 + b^2 = c^2$$

$$\frac{a^2}{b^2} + \frac{b^2}{b^2} = \frac{c^2}{b^2}$$

$$\frac{a^2}{b^2} + 1 = \frac{c^2}{b^2}$$

$$\tan^2 A + 1 = \sec^2 A$$

Also

$$a^2 + b^2 = c^2$$

$$\frac{a^2}{a^2} + \frac{b^2}{a^2} = \frac{c^2}{a^2}$$

$$1 + \frac{b^2}{a^2} = \frac{c^2}{a^2}$$

$$1 + \cot^2 A = \csc^2 A$$

A summary of the relationships follows:

1. $\sin^2 A + \cos^2 A = 1$
2. $\sin A = \sqrt{1 - \cos^2 A}$
3. $\cos A = \sqrt{1 - \sin^2 A}$
4. $\tan A = \dfrac{\sin A}{\cos A}$ and $\cot A = \dfrac{\cos A}{\sin A}$ (reciprocals)
5. $\tan^2 A + 1 = \sec^2 A$
6. $\cot^2 A + 1 = \csc^2 A$

Other relationships may be derived from the relationship $\tan A = \dfrac{\sin A}{\cos A}$.

1. $\sin A = \tan A \cos A \quad \left(\tan A \cos A = \dfrac{\sin A}{\cos A} \cos A \right)$

2. $\sin A = \dfrac{\cos A}{\cot A} \left(\tan A \; \cos A = \dfrac{\cos A}{\dfrac{1}{\tan A}} = \dfrac{\cos A}{\cot A} \; \text{[reciprocal of } \tan A] \right)$

3. $\sin A = \dfrac{\tan A}{\sec A} \left(\tan A \; \cos A = \dfrac{\tan A}{\dfrac{1}{\cos A}} = \dfrac{\tan A}{\sec A} \; \text{[reciprocal of } \cos A] \right)$

The relationships for the other functions are derived in like manner.

FINDING THE VALUES OF THE FUNCTION BY INTERPOLATION

Angles are measured not only in degrees but also in minutes and seconds. Thus, sixty seconds equal one minute and sixty minutes equal one degree. In ordinary problems, angles are measured in degrees and minutes, as 33°, 10′ or 33 degrees, 10 minutes.

The table of trigonometric functions which we have used gives the value of the functions of angles measured in degrees only. In more advanced treatises there are tables which give the measurement of angles in degrees, minutes, and seconds. Because our table measures angles in degrees only, we must use a process called *interpolation* when the angle is measured in degrees and minutes.

In using interpolation, we *add* the value of the minutes of the function to the value of the function if the function is a sine, cosine, or tangent; and we *subtract* the value of the minutes from the value of the function if the function is a cosine, cotangent, or cosecant (cofunction).

For example, let us find the value of sin 20°, 20′:

$$\left. \begin{array}{l} \sin 21° = .3584 \\ \sin 20° = .3420 \end{array} \right\} \text{table}$$
$$\text{difference} = .0164$$

$$20′ = \frac{20′}{60′} = \tfrac{1}{3}° \times .0164 = .0054\tfrac{2}{3} \text{ or } .0055$$

$$\left. \begin{array}{l} \sin 20° = .3420 \\ 20′ = .0055 \end{array} \right\} \text{add (function)}$$
$$\sin 20° \; 20′ = .3475$$

Let us find the value of cos 33°, 30′:

$$\left. \begin{array}{l} \cos 33° = .8387 \\ \cos 34° = .8290 \end{array} \right\} \text{table}$$
$$\text{difference} = .0097$$

$$\frac{30°}{60} = \frac{1}{2} \times .0097 = .0048\frac{1}{2} = .0049$$

$$\begin{aligned} \cos 33° &= .8387 \\ 30' &= .0049 \end{aligned} \quad \text{subtract (cofunction)}$$
$$\cos 33° \ 30' = .8338$$

We can also find the angle to the nearest minute if we are given the value of a function. For example, find the angle whose cosine is .8338. Solution:

$$\begin{aligned} \cos 33° &= .8387 \\ \cos 34° &= .8290 \\ \text{difference} &= .0097 \end{aligned}$$

$$\begin{aligned} \cos 33° &= .8387 \\ \cos \angle x &= .8338 \\ \text{difference} &= .0049 \end{aligned}$$

the ratio of the two differences $\dfrac{.0049}{.0097} = \dfrac{1}{2}\left(x60'\right) = 30'$

$$\angle x = 33° \ 30' \quad \textit{Ans.}$$

EXERCISE VII

1. Find the value of the following:
   a. sin 32° 10′
   b. tan 20° 40′
   c. cos 35° 20′
   d. cot 52° 30′

2. Find the angle whose
   a. sine is .4440
   b. tangent is .2700
   c. cosine is .7800
   d. cotangent is 2.8000

PROBLEM 3

Show that $\sin^2 A + \cos^2 A^2 = 1$ is true if angle A is 30°.

$$\sin^2 30° + \cos^2 30° = 1$$
$$\left(\frac{1}{2}\right)^2 + \left(\frac{\sqrt{3}}{2}\right)^2 = 1$$
$$\frac{1}{4} + \frac{3}{4} = 1$$

PROBLEM 4

Show that $\tan^2 A + 1 = \sec^2 A$ is true if angle A is $45°$.

$$\tan^2 45° + 1 = \sec^2 45°$$
$$(1)^2 + 1 = (\sqrt{2})^2$$
$$1 + 1 = 2$$
$$2 = 2$$

PROBLEM 5

Show that $\cot^2 A + 1 = \csc^2 A$ is true if angle A is $60°$.

$$\cot^2 60 + 1 = \csc^2 60°$$
$$\left(\frac{\sqrt{3}}{3}\right)^2 + 1 = \left(\frac{2\sqrt{3}}{3}\right)^2$$
$$\frac{3}{9} + 1 = \frac{(4)\,(3)}{9}$$
$$\frac{1}{3} + 1 = \frac{4}{3}$$
$$\frac{4}{3} = \frac{4}{3}$$

PROBLEM 6

Find the angle of elevation of the sun at the time when a pole 12 ft. high casts a shadow of 16 ft.

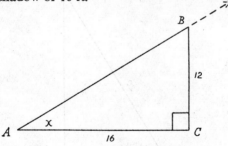

$\tan x = \dfrac{12}{16}$

$\tan x = \dfrac{3}{4}$

$\tan x = .75$

$\tan x = .7500$

$x = 37°$

Interpolating:

$\tan 37 = .7536$

$\tan 36 = .7265$

difference $.0271$

$\tan x = .7500$

$\tan 36 = .7265$

difference $.0235$

$\dfrac{.0235}{.0271}$ of $1° = 1°$

$36° + 1° = 37°$

PROBLEM 7

A boy flying a kite lets out 100 ft. of string. If the string makes an angle of 40° with the ground, find, correct to the nearest foot, the height of the kite above the ground.

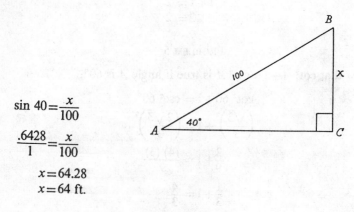

$$\sin 40 = \frac{x}{100}$$

$$\frac{.6428}{1} = \frac{x}{100}$$

$$x = 64.28$$
$$x = 64 \text{ ft.}$$

PROBLEM 8

A ladder 20 ft. long leans against a wall and makes an angle of 74° with the ground. How far, correct to the nearest foot, is the front of the ladder from the wall?

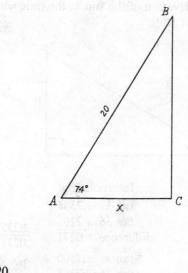

$$\cos 74 = \frac{x}{20}$$

$$\frac{.2756}{1} = \frac{x}{20}$$

$$x = 5.5120$$
$$x = 6 \text{ ft.}$$

PROBLEM 9

From the top of a lighthouse 300 ft. high, the angle of depression of a boat at sea is 22°. Find the distance, correct to the nearest foot, of the boat from the lighthouse.

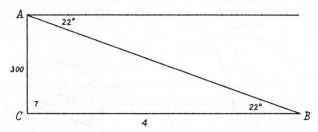

Since the angle of elevation is equal to the angle of depression, *B* is also 22°.

$$\cot 22 = \frac{x}{300}$$

$$\frac{2.4751}{1} = \frac{x}{300}$$

$$x = 742.5300$$
$$x = 743 \text{ ft.}$$

PROBLEM 10

The diagonal of a rectangle makes an angle of 57° with one side whose length is 14 ft. Find, correct to the nearest foot, the diagonal of the rectangle.

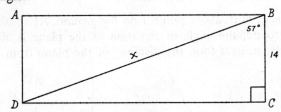

$$\sec 57° = \frac{x}{14}$$

$$\frac{1.8361}{1} = \frac{x}{14}$$

$$x = 25.7054$$
$$x = 26 \text{ ft.}$$

PROBLEM 11

Two tangents are drawn to a circle from an outside point. The tangents meet at an angle of 50° and the length of each tangent is 18 inches. Find, to the nearest inch, the distance from the center of the circle to the outside point.

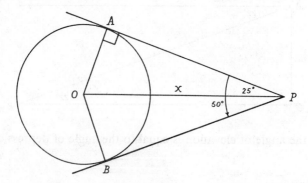

If $\angle APB = 50°$, then $\angle APO = 25°$. Draw radius AO at point of contact. The tangent is perpendicular to the radius at point of contact.

$$\sec 25° = \frac{x}{18}$$

$$\frac{1.1034}{1} = \frac{x}{18}$$

$$x = 19.8612$$
$$x = 20 \text{ inches}$$

PROBLEM 12

A plane is 1200 ft. above point A on the ground. At another point B on the ground, the angle of elevation of the plane is 50°. Find, correct to the nearest foot, the distance of the plane from point B.

$$\csc 50° = \frac{x}{1200}$$

$$\frac{1.3054}{1} = \frac{x}{1200}$$

$$x = 1566.4800$$
$$x = 1566 \text{ ft.}$$

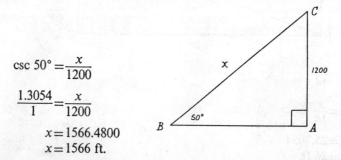

Exercise VIII

1. At a point 125 ft. from the base of a building, the angle of elevation of the top of the building is 65°. Find, correct to the nearest foot, the height of the building.

2. From the top of a building, the angle of depression of a car on the ground is 70°. If the car is 240 ft. from the foot of the building, find, correct to the nearest foot, the height of the building.

3. A ladder 15 ft. long rests against a building. If the foot of the ladder makes an angle of 62° with the ground, find, to the nearest foot, the height that the top of the ladder reaches on the wall.

4. A guy wire 122 ft. long runs from the top of a pole to the ground. If the wire makes an angle of 42° with the ground, find the height of the pole to the nearest foot.

5. The diagonal of a rectangle is 25 ft. and one side is 10 ft. Find to the nearest degree the angle opposite this side.

6. A boy flying a kite lets out 150 ft. of string. The string makes an angle of 24° with the ground. Another boy stands directly below the kite. Find to the nearest foot the distance between the two boys.

7. A plane rises at an angle of 10° with the ground. Find to the nearest foot the horizontal distance the plane travels after it has traveled the distance of 430 ft.

8. A ladder 30 ft. long leans against a building. If the foot of the ladder is 24 ft. from the building, find to the nearest degree the angle the ladder makes with the ground.

9. A guy wire is attached to the top of a pole which is 22 ft. high. If the wire is to make an angle of 19° with the ground, how far, correct to the nearest foot, must the wire be fastened from the foot of the pole?

10. A plank of wood leans against a building and makes an angle of 40° with the ground. If the foot of the plank is 10 ft. from the building, find, correct to the nearest foot, the length of the plank.

11. From a certain point A on the earth, the angle of elevation of the top of a building 300 ft. high is 29°. Find, correct to the nearest foot, the distance from point A to the top of the building.

THE OBLIQUE TRIANGLE AND ITS SOLUTION

So far we have concerned ourselves with the solution of the right triangle. But problems arise in which the right triangle cannot be used. We must have, therefore, formulas which will enable us to solve the *oblique* triangle, that is, the triangle which does not contain a right angle.

Before coming to these formulas, we must keep in mind that a tri-angle is determined by any three independent parts, one of which must be a side. These three parts are:

1. two sides and the included angle, or
2. two angles and the included side, or
3. two sides and the angle opposite one of them.

The formulas used in the solution of the oblique triangle are as follows:

1. The Law of Sines

The sides of a triangle are proportional to the sines of the opposite angles.

$$\frac{a}{\sin A} = \frac{b}{\sin B} = \frac{c}{\sin C}$$

or

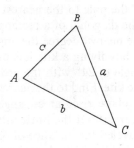

$$\frac{a}{b} = \frac{\sin A}{\sin B}$$

$$\frac{b}{c} = \frac{\sin B}{\sin C}$$

$$\frac{a}{c} = \frac{\sin A}{\sin C}$$

2. The Law of Cosines

The square of any side of a triangle is equal to the sum of the squares of the other two sides less twice the product of the two sides and the cosine of their included angle.

$$a^2 = b^2 + c^2 - 2bc \cos A \text{ or } a = \sqrt{b^2 + c^2 - 2bc \cos A}$$

$$b^2 = a^2 + c^2 - 2ac \cos B \text{ or } b = \sqrt{a^2 + c^2 - 2ac \cos B}$$

$$c^2 = a^2 + b^2 - 2ab \cos C \text{ or } c = \sqrt{a^2 + b^2 - 2ab \cos C}$$

3. The Law of Tangents

The difference between two sides of a triangle is to their sum as the tangent of one half the difference between the opposite angles is to the tangent of one half the sum of the opposite angles.

$$\frac{a-b}{a+b} = \frac{\tan \frac{1}{2}(A-B)}{\tan \frac{1}{2}(A+B)}$$

$$\frac{a-c}{a+c} = \frac{\tan \frac{1}{2}(A-C)}{\tan \frac{1}{2}(A+C)}$$

$$\frac{b-c}{b+c} = \frac{\tan \frac{1}{2}(B-C)}{\tan \frac{1}{2}(B+C)}$$

If b is greater than a, the $\angle B$ is greater than $\angle A$. To avoid negative quantities, the formula should be written

$$\frac{b-a}{b+a} = \frac{\tan \frac{1}{2}(B-A)}{\tan \frac{1}{2}(B+A)}$$

Application of the Law of Sines:

In triangle ABC, $\sin A = .3$, $\sin B = .5$, and $b = 20$. Find a and b.

$$\frac{a}{\sin A} = \frac{b}{\sin B}$$

$$\frac{a}{.3} = \frac{20}{.5}$$

$$.5a = 3.20$$
$$.5a = 6$$
$$5a = 60$$
$$a = 12 \; Ans.$$

Application of the Law of Cosines:

In triangle ABC, $a = 5$, $b = 9$, and $\cos C = \frac{7}{15}$. Find c.

$$c^2 = a^2 + b^2 - 2ab \cos C$$
$$c^2 = 5^2 + 9^2 - 2(5.9)\left(\frac{7}{15}\right)$$

$$c^2 = 25 + 81 - 42$$
$$c^2 = 64$$
$$c = 8 \; Ans.$$

Application of the Law of Tangents:

In triangle ABC, $a = 10$, $b = 6$, and $C = 100°$. Find to the nearest hundredth $\tan \frac{1}{2}(A - B)$

$$\frac{a-b}{a+b} = \frac{\tan \frac{1}{2}(A-B)}{\tan \frac{1}{2}(A+B)}$$

$$\frac{10-6}{10+6} = \frac{\tan \frac{1}{2}(A-B)}{\tan 40°} \quad (180° - C[100°] = A + B [80°] \; \frac{1}{2} \text{ of } 80° = 40°$$

$$\frac{4}{16} = \frac{\tan \frac{1}{2}(A-B)}{.8391}$$

$$\frac{1}{4} = \frac{\tan \frac{1}{2}(A-B)}{.8391}$$

$$4 \tan \frac{1}{2}(A-B) = .8391$$
$$\tan \frac{1}{2}(A-B) = .2097\frac{3}{4} = .21 \; Ans.$$

TABLE OF SQUARE ROOTS OF NUMBERS

N	0	1	2	3	4	5	6	7	8	9
1.0	1.000	1.005	1.010	1.015	1.020	1.025	1.030	1.034	1.039	1.044
1	1.049	1.054	1.058	1.063	1.068	1.072	1.077	1.082	1.086	1.091
2	1.095	1.100	1.105	1.109	1.114	1.118	1.122	1.127	1.131	1.136
3	1.140	1.145	1.149	1.153	1.158	1.162	1.166	1.170	1.175	1.179
4	1.183	1.187	1.192	1.196	1.200	1.204	1.208	1.212	1.217	1.221
1.5	1.225	1.229	1.233	1.237	1.241	1.245	1.249	1.253	1.257	1.261
6	1.265	1.269	1.273	1.277	1.281	1.285	1.288	1.292	1.296	1.300
7	1.304	1.308	1.311	1.315	1.319	1.323	1.327	1.330	1.334	1.338
8	1.342	1.343	1.349	1.353	1.356	1.360	1.364	1.367	1.371	1.375
9	1.378	1.382	1.386	1.389	1.393	1.396	1.400	1.404	1.407	1.411
2.0	1.414	1.418	1.421	1.425	1.428	1.432	1.435	1.439	1.442	1.446
1	1.449	1.453	1.456	1.459	1.463	1.466	1.470	1.473	1.476	1.480
2	1.483	1.487	1.490	1.493	1.497	1.500	1.503	1.507	1.510	1.513
3	1.517	1.520	1.523	1.526	1.530	1.533	1.536	1.539	1.543	1.546
4	1.549	1.552	1.556	1.559	1.562	1.565	1.568	1.572	1.575	1.578
2.5	1.581	1.584	1.587	1.591	1.594	1.597	1.600	1.603	1.606	1.609
6	1.612	1.616	1.619	1.622	1.625	1.628	1.631	1.634	1.637	1.640
7	1.643	1.646	1.649	1.652	1.655	1.658	1.661	1.664	1.667	1.670
8	1.673	1.676	1.679	1.682	1.685	1.688	1.691	1.694	1.697	1.700
9	1.703	1.706	1.709	1.712	1.715	1.718	1.720	1.723	1.726	1.729
3.0	1.732	1.735	1.738	1.741	1.744	1.746	1.749	1.752	1.755	1.758
1	1.761	1.764	1.766	1.769	1.772	1.775	1.778	1.780	1.783	1.786
2	1.789	1.792	1.794	1.797	1.800	1.803	1.806	1.808	1.811	1.814
3	1.817	1.819	1.822	1.825	1.828	1.830	1.833	1.836	1.838	1.841
4	1.844	1.847	1.849	1.852	1.855	1.857	1.860	1.863	1.865	1.868
3.5	1.871	1.873	1.876	1.879	1.881	1.884	1.887	1.889	1.892	1.895
6	1.897	1.900	1.903	1.905	1.908	1.910	1.913	1.916	1.918	1.921
7	1.924	1.926	1.929	1.931	1.934	1.936	1.939	1.942	1.944	1.947
8	1.949	1.952	1.954	1.957	1.960	1.962	1.965	1.967	1.970	1.972
9	1.975	1.977	1.980	1.982	1.985	1.987	1.990	1.992	1.995	1.997
4.0	2.000	2.002	2.005	2.007	2.010	2.012	2.015	2.017	2.020	2.022
1	2.025	2.027	2.030	2.032	2.035	2.037	2.040	2.042	2.045	2.047
2	2.049	2.052	2.054	2.057	2.059	2.062	2.064	2.066	2.069	2.071
3	2.074	2.076	2.078	2.081	2.083	2.086	2.088	2.090	2.093	2.095
4	2.098	2.100	2.102	2.105	2.107	2.110	2.112	2.114	2.117	2.119
4.5	2.121	2.124	2.126	2.128	2.131	2.133	2.135	2.138	2.140	2.142
6	2.145	2.147	2.149	2.152	2.154	2.156	2.159	2.161	2.163	2.166
7	2.168	2.170	2.173	2.175	2.177	2.179	2.182	2.184	2.186	2.189
8	2.191	2.193	2.195	2.198	2.200	2.202	2.205	2.207	2.209	2.211
9	2.214	2.216	2.218	2.220	2.223	2.225	2.227	2.229	2.232	2.234
5.0	2.236	2.238	2.241	2.243	2.245	2.247	2.249	2.252	2.254	2.256
1	2.258	2.261	2.263	2.265	2.267	2.269	2.272	2.274	2.276	2.278
2	2.280	2.283	2.285	2.287	2.289	2.291	2.293	2.296	2.298	2.300
3	2.302	2.304	2.307	2.309	2.311	2.313	2.315	2.317	2.319	2.322
4	2.324	2.326	2.328	2.330	2.332	2.335	2.337	2.339	2.341	2.343
5.5	2.345	2.347	2.349	2.352	2.354	2.356	2.358	2.360	2.362	2.364
6	2.366	2.369	2.371	2.373	2.375	2.377	2.379	2.381	2.383	2.385
7	2.387	2.390	2.392	2.394	2.396	2.398	2.400	2.402	2.404	2.406
8	2.408	2.410	2.412	2.415	2.417	2.419	2.421	2.423	2.425	2.427
9	2.429	2.431	2.433	2.435	2.437	2.439	2.441	2.443	2.445	2.447
6.0	2.449	2.452	2.454	2.456	2.458	2.460	2.462	2.464	2.466	2.468
1	2.470	2.472	2.474	2.476	2.478	2.480	2.482	2.484	2.486	2.488
2	2.490	2.492	2.494	2.496	2.498	2.500	2.502	2.504	2.506	2.508
3	2.510	2.512	2.514	2.516	2.518	2.520	2.522	2.524	2.526	2.528
4	2.530	2.532	2.534	2.536	2.538	2.540	2.542	2.544	2.546	2.548
6.5	2.550	2.551	2.553	2.555	2.557	2.559	2.561	2.563	2.565	2.567
6	2.569	2.571	2.573	2.575	2.577	2.579	2.581	2.583	2.585	2.587
7	2.588	2.590	2.592	2.594	2.596	2.598	2.600	2.602	2.604	2.606
8	2.608	2.610	2.612	2.613	2.615	2.617	2.619	2.621	2.623	2.625
9	2.627	2.629	2.631	2.632	2.634	2.636	2.638	2.640	2.642	2.644
7.0	2.646	2.648	2.650	2.651	2.653	2.655	2.657	2.659	2.661	2.663
1	2.665	2.666	2.668	2.670	2.672	2.674	2.676	2.678	2.680	2.681
2	2.683	2.685	2.687	2.689	2.691	2.693	2.694	2.696	2.698	2.700
3	2.702	2.704	2.706	2.707	2.709	2.711	2.713	2.715	2.717	2.718
4	2.720	2.722	2.724	2.726	2.728	2.729	2.731	2.733	2.735	2.737

N	0	1	2	3	4	5	6	7	8	9
7.5	2.739	2.740	2.742	2.744	2.746	2.748	2.750	2.751	2.753	2.755
6	2.757	2.759	2.760	2.762	2.764	2.766	2.768	2.769	2.771	2.773
7	2.775	2.777	2.778	2.780	2.782	2.784	2.786	2.787	2.789	2.791
8	2.793	2.795	2.796	2.798	2.800	2.802	2.804	2.805	2.807	2.809
9	2.811	2.812	2.814	2.816	2.818	2.820	2.821	2.823	2.825	2.827
8.0	2.828	2.830	2.832	2.834	2.835	2.837	2.839	2.841	2.843	2.844
1	2.846	2.848	2.850	2.851	2.853	2.855	2.857	2.858	2.860	2.862
2	2.864	2.865	2.867	2.869	2.871	2.872	2.874	2.876	2.877	2.879
3	2.881	2.883	2.884	2.886	2.888	2.890	2.891	2.893	2.895	2.897
4	2.898	2.900	2.902	2.903	2.905	2.907	2.909	2.910	2.912	2.914
8.5	2.915	2.917	2.919	2.921	2.922	2.924	2.926	2.927	2.929	2.931
6	2.933	2.934	2.936	2.938	2.939	2.941	2.942	2.944	2.946	2.948
7	2.950	2.951	2.953	2.955	2.956	2.958	2.960	2.961	2.963	2.965
8	2.966	2.968	2.970	2.972	2.973	2.975	2.977	2.978	2.980	2.982
9	2.983	2.985	2.987	2.988	2.990	2.992	2.993	2.995	2.997	2.998
9.0	3.000	3.002	3.003	3.005	3.007	3.008	3.010	3.012	3.013	3.015
1	3.017	3.018	3.020	3.022	3.023	3.025	3.027	3.028	3.030	3.032
2	3.033	3.035	3.036	3.038	3.040	3.041	3.043	3.045	3.046	3.048
3	3.050	3.051	3.053	3.055	3.056	3.058	3.059	3.061	3.063	3.064
4	3.066	3.068	3.069	3.071	3.072	3.074	3.076	3.077	3.079	3.081
9.5	3.082	3.084	3.085	3.087	3.089	3.090	3.092	3.094	3.095	3.097
6	3.098	3.100	3.102	3.103	3.105	3.106	3.108	3.110	3.111	3.113
7	3.114	3.116	3.118	3.119	3.121	3.122	3.124	3.126	3.127	3.129
8	3.130	3.132	3.134	3.135	3.137	3.138	3.140	3.142	3.143	3.145
9	3.146	3.148	3.150	3.151	3.153	3.154	3.156	3.158	3.159	3.161
10	3.162	3.178	3.194	3.209	3.225	3.240	3.256	3.271	3.286	3.302
1	3.317	3.332	3.347	3.362	3.376	3.391	3.406	3.421	3.435	3.450
2	3.464	3.479	3.493	3.507	3.521	3.536	3.550	3.564	3.578	3.592
3	3.606	3.619	3.633	3.647	3.661	3.674	3.688	3.701	3.715	3.728
4	3.742	3.755	3.768	3.782	3.795	3.808	3.821	3.834	3.847	3.860
15	3.873	3.886	3.899	3.912	3.924	3.937	3.950	3.962	3.975	3.987
6	4.000	4.012	4.025	4.037	4.050	4.062	4.074	4.087	4.099	4.111
7	4.123	4.135	4.147	4.159	4.171	4.183	4.195	4.207	4.219	4.231
8	4.243	4.254	4.266	4.278	4.290	4.301	4.313	4.324	4.336	4.347
9	4.359	4.370	4.382	4.393	4.405	4.416	4.427	4.438	4.450	4.461
20	4.472	4.483	4.494	4.506	4.517	4.528	4.539	4.550	4.561	4.572
1	4.583	4.593	4.604	4.615	4.626	4.637	4.648	4.658	4.669	4.680
2	4.690	4.701	4.712	4.722	4.733	4.743	4.754	4.764	4.775	4.785
3	4.796	4.806	4.817	4.827	4.837	4.848	4.858	4.868	4.879	4.889
4	4.899	4.909	4.919	4.930	4.940	4.950	4.960	4.970	4.980	4.990
25	5.000	5.010	5.020	5.030	5.040	5.050	5.060	5.070	5.079	5.089
6	5.099	5.109	5.119	5.128	5.138	5.148	5.158	5.167	5.177	5.187
7	5.196	5.206	5.215	5.225	5.235	5.244	5.254	5.263	5.273	5.282
8	5.292	5.301	5.310	5.320	5.329	5.339	5.348	5.357	5.367	5.376
9	5.385	5.394	5.404	5.413	5.422	5.431	5.441	5.450	5.459	5.468
30	5.477	5.486	5.495	5.505	5.514	5.523	5.532	5.541	5.550	5.559
1	5.568	5.577	5.586	5.595	5.604	5.612	5.621	5.630	5.639	5.648
2	5.657	5.666	5.675	5.683	5.692	5.701	5.710	5.718	5.727	5.736
3	5.745	5.753	5.762	5.771	5.779	5.788	5.797	5.805	5.814	5.822
4	5.831	5.840	5.848	5.857	5.865	5.874	5.882	5.891	5.899	5.908
35	5.916	5.925	5.933	5.941	5.950	5.958	5.967	5.975	5.983	5.992
6	6.000	6.008	6.017	6.025	6.033	6.042	6.050	6.058	6.066	6.075
7	6.083	6.091	6.099	6.107	6.116	6.124	6.132	6.140	6.148	6.156
8	6.164	6.173	6.181	6.189	6.197	6.205	6.213	6.221	6.229	6.237
9	6.245	6.253	6.261	6.269	6.277	6.285	6.293	6.301	6.309	6.317
40	6.325	6.332	6.340	6.348	6.356	6.364	6.372	6.380	6.387	6.395
1	6.403	6.411	6.419	6.427	6.434	6.442	6.450	6.458	6.465	6.473
2	6.481	6.488	6.496	6.504	6.512	6.519	6.527	6.535	6.542	6.550
3	6.557	6.565	6.573	6.580	6.588	6.595	6.603	6.611	6.618	6.626
4	6.633	6.641	6.648	6.656	6.663	6.671	6.678	6.686	6.693	6.701
45	6.708	6.716	6.723	6.731	6.738	6.745	6.753	6.760	6.768	6.775
6	6.782	6.790	6.797	6.804	6.812	6.819	6.826	6.834	6.841	6.848
7	6.856	6.863	6.870	6.877	6.885	6.892	6.899	6.907	6.914	6.921
8	6.928	6.935	6.943	6.950	6.957	6.964	6.971	6.979	6.986	6.993
9	7.000	7.007	7.014	7.021	7.029	7.036	7.043	7.050	7.057	7.064

N	0	1	2	3	4	5	6	7	8	9
50	7.071	7.078	7.085	7.092	7.099	7.106	7.113	7.120	7.127	7.134
1	7.141	7.148	7.155	7.162	7.169	7.176	7.183	7.190	7.197	7.204
2	7.211	7.218	7.225	7.232	7.239	7.246	7.253	7.259	7.266	7.273
3	7.280	7.287	7.294	7.301	7.308	7.314	7.321	7.328	7.335	7.342
4	7.348	7.355	7.362	7.369	7.376	7.382	7.389	7.396	7.403	7.409
55	7.416	7.423	7.430	7.436	7.443	7.450	7.457	7.463	7.470	7.477
6	7.483	7.490	7.497	7.503	7.510	7.517	7.523	7.530	7.537	7.543
7	7.550	7.556	7.563	7.570	7.576	7.583	7.589	7.596	7.603	7.609
8	7.616	7.622	7.629	7.635	7.642	7.649	7.655	7.662	7.668	7.675
9	7.681	7.688	7.694	7.701	7.707	7.714	7.720	7.727	7.733	7.740
60	7.746	7.752	7.759	7.765	7.772	7.778	7.785	7.791	7.797	7.804
1	7.810	7.817	7.823	7.829	7.836	7.842	7.849	7.855	7.861	7.868
2	7.874	7.880	7.887	7.893	7.899	7.906	7.912	7.918	7.925	7.931
3	7.937	7.944	7.950	7.956	7.962	7.969	7.975	7.981	7.987	7.994
4	8.000	8.006	8.012	8.019	8.025	8.031	8.037	8.044	8.050	8.056
65	8.062	8.068	8.075	8.081	8.087	8.093	8.099	8.106	8.112	8.118
6	8.124	8.130	8.136	8.142	8.149	8.155	8.161	8.167	8.173	8.179
7	8.185	8.191	8.198	8.204	8.210	8.216	8.222	8.228	8.234	8.240
8	8.246	8.252	8.258	8.264	8.270	8.276	8.283	8.289	8.295	8.301
9	8.307	8.313	8.319	8.325	8.331	8.337	8.343	8.349	8.355	8.361
70	8.367	8.373	8.379	8.385	8.390	8.396	8.402	8.408	8.414	8.420
1	8.426	8.432	8.438	8.444	8.450	8.456	8.462	8.468	8.473	8.479
2	8.485	8.491	8.497	8.503	8.509	8.515	8.521	8.526	8.532	8.538
3	8.544	8.550	8.556	8.562	8.567	8.573	8.579	8.585	8.591	8.597
4	8.602	8.608	8.614	8.620	8.626	8.631	8.637	8.643	8.649	8.654
75	8.660	8.666	8.672	8.678	8.683	8.689	8.695	8.701	8.706	8.712
6	8.718	8.724	8.729	8.735	8.741	8.746	8.752	8.758	8.764	8.769
7	8.775	8.781	8.786	8.792	8.798	8.808	8.809	8.815	8.820	8.826
8	8.832	8.837	8.843	8.849	8.854	8.860	8.866	8.871	8.877	8.883
9	8.888	8.894	8.899	8.905	8.911	8.916	8.922	8.927	8.933	8.939
80	8.944	8.950	8.955	8.961	8.967	8.972	8.978	8.983	8.989	8.994
1	9.000	9.006	9.011	9.017	9.022	9.028	9.033	9.039	9.044	9.050
2	9.055	9.061	9.066	9.072	9.077	9.083	9.088	9.094	9.099	9.105
3	9.110	9.116	9.121	9.127	9.132	9.138	9.143	9.149	9.154	9.160
4	9.165	9.171	9.176	9.182	9.187	9.192	9.189	9.203	9.209	9.214
85	9.220	9.225	9.230	9.236	9.241	9.247	9.252	9.257	9.263	9.268
6	9.274	9.279	9.284	9.290	9.295	9.301	9.306	9.311	9.317	9.322
7	9.327	9.333	9.338	9.343	9.349	9.354	9.359	9.365	9.370	9.375
8	9.381	9.386	9.391	9.397	9.402	9.407	9.413	9.418	9.423	9.429
9	9.434	9.439	9.445	9.450	9.455	9.460	9.466	9.471	9.476	9.482
90	9.487	9.492	9.497	9.503	9.508	9.513	9.518	9.524	9.529	9.534
1	9.539	9.545	9.550	9.555	9.560	9.566	9.571	9.576	9.581	9.586
2	9.592	9.597	9.602	9.607	9.612	9.618	9.623	9.628	9.633	9.638
3	9.644	9.649	9.654	9.659	9.664	9.670	9.675	9.680	9.685	9.690
4	9.695	9.701	9.706	9.711	9.716	9.721	9.726	9.731	9.737	9.742
95	9.747	9.752	9.757	9.762	9.767	9.772	9.778	9.783	9.788	9.793
6	9.798	9.803	9.808	9.813	9.818	9.823	9.829	9.834	9.839	9.844
7	9.849	9.854	9.859	9.864	9.869	9.874	9.879	9.884	9.889	9.894
8	9.899	9.905	9.910	9.915	9.920	9.925	9.930	9.935	9.940	9.945
9	9.950	9.955	9.960	9.965	9.970	9.975	9.980	9.985	9.990	9.995

FOR FURTHER STUDY

MODERN PLANE GEOMETRY, by J. R. Clark and A. S. Otis. (World Book Co., Yonkers, N. Y.)

A NEW GEOMETRY, by Herberg and Orleans. (D. C. Heath and Co., Boston.)

PLANE GEOMETRY, by A. Schultze, F. L. Sevenoak, and E. Schuyler. (The Macmillan Co., New York.)

PLANE GEOMETRY FOR HOME STUDY, by William L. Schaaf. (Doubleday and Co., New York.)

TRIGONOMETRY FOR HOME STUDY, by William L. Schaaf. (Doubleday and Co., New York.)

XX

Introduction to General Science

SCIENCE IN THE MODERN AGE

COMPARE YOUR LIFE today with that of your grandfather or great-grandfather. Travel was slow. There were no motorcars. Vehicles were mainly horse-drawn. Communication likewise was slow. Radio was not yet known; radio waves were first produced in 1887. No one then had even dreamed of television. The electric-light bulb and telephone had not yet been invented. People died by the thousands from epidemics and plagues whose causes had long been considered to be bad air, as in the case of malaria. Earlier, evil spirits had been blamed for cholera, bubonic plague, and smallpox.

During the latter part of the nineteenth century, Louis Pasteur in France and Robert Koch in Germany proved the causative factor of contagious disease to be microscopic bacteria. Once the germ theory of disease was established, rapid progress was made in the conquest of disease. The use of sterilized instruments practically eliminated the great risk of infection which had previously been present in surgery. More recently the discoveries of the wonder drugs, such as sulfa, the antibiotics, and isoniazid, have markedly reduced death rates from pneumonia, scarlet fever, typhoid, tuberculosis, and many other diseases.

The first successful flight of an airplane was accomplished in 1903 by the Wright brothers at Kitty Hawk, North Carolina. Since the Wright brothers' first flight, the speed of propeller-driven airplanes has risen from 31 miles an hour to over 600 miles an hour. The invention of the jet-propulsion engine has made it possible to increase the speed up to 760 miles an hour. In 1953, Major Charles Yeager flew an X-1A rocket plane at twice the speed of sound, or 1,650 miles an hour. It is now possible to circle the globe in little more than twenty-four hours.

Not long ago, talk of space travel and rockets to the moon was considered as sheer fantasy. Today these are rapidly coming into the realm of reality. Already, rocket-driven earth satellites outfitted with recording instruments have been launched from various places on the earth's surface. This rapid progress in part reflects the important program during 1957 and 1958 known as the International Geophysical Year, with thousands of participating scientists from fifty-five nations of the world cooperating to seek answers to questions such as these: Is the earth's climate changing? Are glaciers receding? Will melted ice sheets someday flood the coastal plains? What are cosmic rays and where do they come from? What causes the aurora borealis? What is the relationship between sunspots, solar flares, and long-range radio transmission? Can weather prediction on a long-range basis be improved? Can we build a space station for refueling of manned space flights to Mars or to the moon? What is the true shape of the earth?

The answers to these questions are important not only for our understanding of the universe but for practical applications to such problems as agriculture, air travel across the polar regions, radio and television communication, and navigation.

WHAT IS GENERAL SCIENCE?

General Science is a first view of many of the most interesting and important topics in the Physical Sciences and the Natural Sciences. It places much emphasis on the aspects of these topics which we meet with often in our daily life. Some idea of the range of General Science can be indicated by mentioning some of the subjects which we shall consider here: earth satellites and space travel; the functioning of rockets, jet propulsion, and the various means of transportation, including airplanes, automobiles, railroads, ships, and submarines; modern methods of communication, such as television and radio, as well as telephone and telegraph; the field of weather study, including weather prediction and weather measurements; food supply and health and hygiene; the releasing and use of atomic energy. In presenting such a wide variety of subject matter, we, of course, cannot attempt to give the thorough grounding which is to be found in the individual sciences of which General Science is a preview. The reader is therefore urged to follow his study of this General Science section by studying in turn the sections on Physics, Chemistry, Biology, Physiology, Astronomy, and Geology, in this book, where the fundamental principles of each science are clearly and carefully explained.

In the discussion which follows we include not only the specific topics which we have mentioned but also an introduction to *scientific method,* the procedure which all scientists follow in their research and in arriving at their conclusions. And since an understanding of scientific method is essential for the appreciation of all scientific discoveries and inventions, we turn to it now.

HOW SCIENTIFIC DISCOVERIES ARE MADE

We start our explanation of scientific method by giving two famous examples of the method at work.

THE DISCOVERY OF PENICILLIN

One day in September 1929, Dr. Alexander Fleming, returning to his hospital laboratory in London, stopped to examine the bacterial cultures which he had started a week before. He discarded a number of cultures which had been contaminated by other bacteria, and he was about to discard the rest when he noticed something unusual about one of them. This dish contained a patch of green mold surrounded by a clear area which separated it from a colony of staphylococcus. He immediately suspected that the mold contained a substance which possessed a powerful germ-killing effect. He consulted a mold expert, who described the specimen as a variety of penicillium, and the filtrate of the broth mold culture was therefore named *penicillin.* Though Fleming discovered the germicidal effect of the mold on this bacterial colony, he failed at first to realize that penicillin would kill germs within a living body. Fourteen years later, however, he obtained from Howard Florey, a pathologist at Oxford University, some yellow penicillin powder with which he was able to save the life of a friend who would otherwise have died of meningitis.

How are great scientific discoveries made? In the words of Pasteur, "There is no such thing as a scientific accident." What appears to be an accident is the impact of observed facts on a prepared mind. Perhaps others before Fleming had seen bacterial colonies and penicillium molds in a plate without realizing the significance of the clear area between them. Fleming was a laboratory research expert whose techniques and knowledge of germ culture and their interactions with living things was superb. Previously he had discovered lysozyme, a substance present in tears, which dissolves germs. It is also found in other body fluids such as sweat, saliva, mucus, and gastric juices. Fleming tentatively concluded that the clear area on his test plate was an example of "lysis." He tested his hypothesis by growing penicillium on agar and streaking six different kinds of germs across the dish: staphylococci; streptococci; bacilli of diphtheria, anthrax, and typhoid; and coli. The germs of the first four were destroyed, and the last two grew close up to the mold. This proved conclusively the presence of a powerful secretion from the mold, which was selective in nature and capable of killing germs.

ANTOINE LAVOISIER'S FAMOUS DISCOVERY

Two centuries ago it was commonly believed that objects lost weight when they burned. When a log of wood was burned, it appeared to lose most of its weight. This loss of weight was believed to be due to the escape of a fiery gas called phlogiston. Antoine Lavoisier, a French chemist, had a hunch that objects actually gained weight when they were burned. To test this hypothesis he burned sulfur, phosphorus, mercury, and tin in closed vessels. In each case he found that they combined with about one fifth of the air in the vessel. He also found by carefully weighing the substances before and after burning that these substances gained weight. He concluded that this increase in weight was a result of combination with a portion of the air called oxygen.

This discovery led to a realization that burning was in reality a speedy form of oxidation, the same process as occurs slowly when metal rusts.

WHAT WE MEAN BY SCIENTIFIC METHOD

There are certain methods of work followed by all scientists, including several steps. First, the scientist centers his attention upon a specific problem. In the case of Lavoisier this took the form of a question: Do substances gain or lose weight upon burning? Secondly, the scientist makes many careful observations and performs experiments. Here apparatus and techniques involving weight and measurements are required. Lavoisier burned many substances, all the while making careful measurements both before and after burning each substance—in an enclosed vessel so that nothing could be added or lost during the process. He also recorded his observations carefully in a notebook. Thirdly, the scientist draws a tentative conclusion or hypothesis. Lavoisier's hypothesis was that substances gain weight when burned. Fourthly, this hypothesis is subject to repeated verification. Lavoisier repeated his experiments many times and planned new ones. The true scientist is ready to discard his hypothesis if further experimental evidence proves him to be wrong. Fifthly, the hypothesis is now advanced to a higher stage called a theory—a large principle which helps explain an aspect of the working of the universe. A theory is also useful in predicting what will happen under a given set of environmental conditions, and it often has practical application. Thus it could be predicted that a substance such as iron or lead will increase in weight upon burning, and that is exactly what happens.

When the experimental method is used, comparison is made between one part, which is kept under natural conditions, and another part, which has been modified by one factor. Thus, to test the germicidal effect of penicillin, one dish, called the control, containing a certain bacterial colony, is compared with another dish containing the same kind of bacteria but to which some penicillin has been added. Since the dishes are kept under identical conditions, any change in the bacteria is attributed to the addition of the penicillin. The same principle of comparison is applied in all experiments.

Science, then, is both a body of organized knowledge and a method of work used to obtain evidence which leads toward certain conclusions. In many ways it is similar to the methods used by detectives in obtaining clues to solve crimes.

EXPLORING SPACE

In the film version of H. G. Wells's book, *The Shape of Things to Come,* a young couple are fired by a space gun to the moon while their fathers watch the ascent in the mirror of a giant telescope.

Man's unquenchable thirst for adventure impels him ever onward to uncover the mysteries of the unknown, even at the peril of his life.

The record height for a propeller-driven airplane was set in 1938 by the flight of an Italian Caproni 161 biplane to a height of 56,046 feet. The same year, two United States Air Force captains set a record when their balloon reached a height of 72,335 feet. In 1957 the Bell X-2, a jet plane, was piloted to an altitude of 126,000 feet, setting a new record.

A missile called the WAC Corporal B, launched from a V-2 rocket, has transmitted information to earth by radio at an altitude of 250 miles.

PENETRATING THE SOUND BARRIER

During the past 150 years man has devised ways of increasing speeds by developing more efficient engines—based in turn upon steam, internal combustion, jet and rocket propulsion. Not long ago scientists thought it would be impossible to travel faster than the speed of sound. At that speed (about 750 miles an hour), the air waves created by the plane's motion cannot get out of the way of the plane fast enough, and a turbulent confusion of air around the plane causes it to stumble and swirl out of the pilot's control. This is the *sound barrier* at which men and machines have been smashed to pieces. Once that barrier is penetrated through supersonic speed, the plane escapes its own air and sound waves and the flying becomes smooth.

Penetration of the sound barrier could take place only through radical change in plane design as well as increased engine power. Back-swept wings, turbo-jet and rocket engines have made this possible. There is another apparent limit to the speed of planes. Air friction would heat up the metal surface of a plane traveling at *2600 miles an hour* to a temperature of 900° F., destroying both plane and persons inside, even at an altitude of 40,000 feet where the atmospheric temperature is –65° F., that is 65° below zero. Perhaps, just as in the case of the sound barrier, the heat barrier may also be conquered.

SPACE TRAVEL

There are numerous obstacles to the conquest of space. The pull of earth's gravity must be overcome by any object attempting to get away from it. Weightlessness once the ship is out in space, a feeling akin to that of continuously falling, must be counteracted. The peril of being surrounded by an airless region creates such problems as the need for an adequate supply of oxygen, and artificial creation of atmospheric pressure around the body to keep it from exploding. These conditions can be met by using pressurized cabins and space suits and tanks of oxygen diluted with helium for breathing. Exposure to direct rays of the sun must also be controlled. Differences in temperatures from extreme heat on the side of the ship exposed to the sun and extreme cold on the other side would be insupportable. By painting checkerboard designs of black and white, it is hoped the contrast will be lessened.

Another important problem is the effect on the human body of sudden acceleration and deceleration of speed. During World War II, studies made of dive-bombing pilots revealed that they suffered brief periods of unconsciousness, or "blackout," when certain high rates of acceleration and deceleration were attained. During these blackout periods, lasting several seconds, the ship would be out of the pilot's control and in danger of accident. This problem exists likewise in space travel.

What are the limits of human endurance? Prospective pilots for the U.S. Navy and Air Force are put into huge whirling machines to test the effect of increased pressure produced by acceleration in various parts of the body. Acceleration is measured in terms of G's, one G being equivalent to the normal gravity, or 32 feet per second every second. Although some men can stand 10 to 17 G's against their chests and still think clearly, give and take orders, and manipulate controls, most men become unconscious even under 2½ to 5 G's.

Rocket Ships and Satellites

To get useful information about conditions in outer space, it is now possible to install man-made satellites in orbital motion around the earth. Such satellites are not powered; they maintain their altitude above the earth and continuous speed about it according to the same principles that govern planetary satellites in the solar system. The orbit of any satellite is determined and maintained by an exact balance of the downward force of gravity and the outward centrifugal force that is exerted on any body in rotation.

In recent years, men of all nations have contributed to development of rockets, high-speed computers, gyroscopic guidance systems, heat-resistant ceramics, and high-speed fuels. These now make space exploration feasible.

With the development of gigantic rockets capable of developing speeds of 18,000 miles an hour, satellites can be put into orbit, and the conquest of outer space has begun.

The principles of planetary motion were laid down over three hundred years ago by two famous physicists, Johannes Kepler and Isaac Newton. Gravity is the pull which keeps things on earth. Centrifugal force pulls away from the center. The small planes in an amusement park which are swinging on cables from a central pole rise off the ground because centrifugal force becomes greater than the force of gravity.

Applying these principles to satellite flight, it can be understood that when a rocket is shot into outer space at sufficient altitude and speed, the inward pull of gravity is balanced by an outward centrifugal force great enough to keep the satellite in orbit. Yet the centrifugal force must not be so great that the satellite will leave the earth's gravitational pull entirely. Once a satellite is in orbit it continues its motion according to Newton's principle of "inertia of motion," which states that *objects in motion tend to stay in motion in the same direction unless acted upon by outside force.* If you bat a baseball it keeps going in one direction for some distance, then curves toward the earth. The force applied to the ball initially was great enough to overcome gravity. Air resistance soon slows the ball and together with gravity overcomes the original centrifugal force. If air resistance could be overcome, the ball would continue traveling for a much longer period of time. This is what actually happens to satellites in outer space where gravitational pull is small and there is no air resistance. "Inertia of motion" enables satellites to continue in orbit without motors for long periods of time.

In order to reach the zone above earth where gravity and inertia of motion will keep the satellite in orbit, it is necessary to build a rocket which will travel through the atmosphere, then into outer space where no oxygen exists. Rocket fuels are required which need no air for burning. Rocket action is based on Newton's principle that *for every action there is an equal and opposite reaction.* Many illustrations of this principle may be obtained from daily living. Examples are the recoil of a gun after firing, and the flight of an air-filled balloon around the room in the opposite direction of the exhaust. Rockets which are used to carry satellites look like giant pencils. At present long-range rockets are made up in several stages. As the fuel is used up in one stage, the latter falls away and the motor of the next stage takes over. Each successive stage gets a running start from the speed attained by the preceding stage until the final speeds necessary to keep the satellite in orbit are attained.

The bottom rocket stage must be the strongest since it must overcome air resistance as well as gravitational pull against the weight of the whole rocket. The fuel of the first stage may be kerosene or alcohol. Tanks of liquid oxygen are needed to support combustion of the fuel. Blasts of hot expanding gases from the rear of the rocket produce an equal and opposite reaction, shooting the rocket out into space. The second stage supplies power and controls direction of the rocket. Fuels such as hydrazine combined with nitric acid are used at this stage. Directional control is achieved through gyroscopes and steering devices which automatically adjust direction of rear rocket nozzles to keep the rocket on its course. Mathematical computers with electronic "brains" control the position of the rocket motors. When correct height and path are reached, the second stage gives the third a spinning motion to keep it on the correct path. The last stage carries the satellite into orbit.

Instruments inside the satellites measure cosmic radiation, ultraviolet radiation produced by storms on the sun, temperature of the satellite (both inside and outside), and impact of micrometeorites. The latter are detected by tiny microphones and pressure gauges. Instruments are tightly packed like stacks of pancakes to save space and for protection. Tiny radios transmit information via short wave to earth. Protruding antennae help transmit radio signals.

The first man-made satellite was fired in 1957 by a carrier rocket to an altitude of approximately 600 miles, achieving a speed of approximately 18,000 miles per hour. At this height and speed, the unmanned satellite assumed an elliptical orbit around the earth, making one revolution every 96 minutes. The orbit of the satellite had a minimum altitude of about 143 miles and a maximum altitude of about 600 miles.

The satellite was spherical in shape, weighing about 184 pounds, with a diameter of 22 inches, and contained numerous instruments for recording space conditions.

Teams of scientists as well as amateurs throughout the world co-operate in tracking satellite movements with radio, radar, telescope, and camera. Information is fed into huge electronic "brains" which compute satellite tracks.

Before space travel can be feasible, a method must be developed for returning satellites and rocket ships safely to earth. At present satellites installed in orbits around the earth can maintain their speed and altitude only for a limited period of time. Friction caused by high speed through atmosphere will eventually burn up a satellite. Thus, at present, space travel would be a one-way stage. Scientists predict, however, that within only a few years this may no longer be the case. What was considered only a few decades ago subject for fictional fantasies is rapidly coming to be a reality.

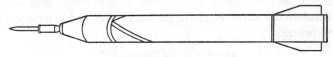

FIG. 1. Diagram of a Rocket.

It is hoped that eventually doughnut-shaped space stations will be established at an altitude of about 1,000 miles in space for the purpose of refueling space ships, and that space ships will be built to carry men and materials for space travel.

The cost of such a program is almost beyond imagination. Fuel, such as alcohol, hydrogen, and octane, costs about $5,000 a ton, and it will take 170 tons of fuel to lift every ton of weight to a space station. It is estimated that the cost of establishing a space station where men could live and work would be about four billion dollars.

WEATHER AND WEATHER MEASUREMENT

Weather refers to specific atmospheric conditions at a particular time and place. Climate refers to average weather conditions in a particular area over a period of months or years.

There have been many superstitious beliefs concerning weather. For example, if it rains on St. Swithin's Day, it is supposed to rain every day for forty days. If foot corns hurt, it's supposed to indicate bad weather ahead.

To have reasonable success in predicting weather conditions, it is necessary to understand the causes of weather changes. Reliable prediction is based on the science of meteorology and makes use of a number of instruments capable of measuring changes in atmospheric conditions.

A description of weather conditions includes temperature, moisture content of the air, air pressure, and direction of wind. Water vapor content, or humidity, together with temperature, determines cloud formation, amount of snow, rain, or even hail.

We know that in order to ventilate a room properly, windows must be opened from both top and bottom. This is because warm air in the room rises and escapes through the open window at the top. Cool air rushes in from outside through the open bottom window. Thus a continuous movement of air is maintained, with fresh air replacing the stale air. This same principle may be applied to the movement of large masses of air, which move due to changes of temperature. In the daytime the land absorbs the sun's heat more rapidly than does the ocean. Therefore warm air rises rapidly above the land to be replaced by a cool sea breeze. At night the sea is warmer, since water retains its heat longer than does the land. Therefore the warm air above the ocean rises and is replaced by a cool land breeze.

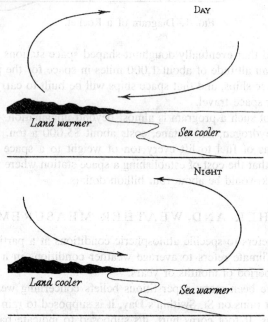

FIG. 2. Weather Fronts.

On a world scale, the air at the equator is much warmer than the air at the poles, due to the tilt of the earth's axis in relation to the sun. Warm air above the equator rises continuously, to be replaced by masses of cold air coming from both North and South poles. Rotation of the earth interrupts this movement somewhat.

When warm air rises it carries with it invisible water vapor from all bodies of water. Moisture may make up as much as 4 per cent of air by volume.

The troposphere is the lowest layer of the atmosphere. Most clouds form in it, and most storms take place in it. When conditions of temperature become unstable in this layer, changes of weather occur. Above the troposphere is the stratosphere, which is always cold. Above this is the ionosphere, where the atmosphere thins out almost to nothingness with increased altitude.

Actually, changes in temperature and movement of air masses are caused by the effect of the sun's rays heating up the earth, which in turn gives its heat back to the atmosphere, causing air masses to move as described previously. In daytime and in summer the earth receives and radiates back to the atmosphere more heat than it does at nighttime and during the winter. This explains daily and seasonal changes in weather.

FIG. 3. Direction of Prevailing Winds.

AIR PRESSURE

Air pressure is measured with an instrument known as the *barometer*. There are two principal types: mercury and aneroid. Changes in air pressure are due to two main factors. Cold air is heavier than warm air and causes the barometer to rise due to increased air pressure. Air containing a large amount of water vapor weighs less than a corresponding quantity of dry air and causes the barometer to fall.

PRINCIPLE OF THE MERCURY BAROMETER

Evangelista Toricelli, a pupil of Galileo, discovered that the pressure of air at sea level can hold up a column of mercury by pressure on the mercury in the dish. As the air pressure varies, the column of mercury rises or falls proportionally. A simple mercury barometer can be made with a glass tube about three feet long, sealed at one end and filled with mercury from a medicine dropper. Placed with the open end down in a beaker of mercury, the tube may be fixed to a ring stand and attached to a yardstick. The mercury will reach a level of about 30 inches, depending on altitude and weather conditions. Normal air pressure at sea level weighs 14.7 pounds per square inch and supports exactly 29.92 inches of mercury.

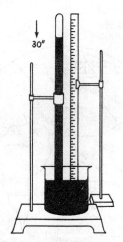

Fig. 4. Simple Mercury Barometer.

Since warm, moist air causes air pressure to be lowered, a falling barometer may mean rain or possibly a storm. A rising barometer is an indication of dry, cool, and fair weather.

Aneroid barometers register the air pressure acting directly on a metal box, which is pushed in or out and moves a needle when the pressure changes.

TEMPERATURE AND HUMIDITY

Mercury or red-colored alcohol thermometers are used to indicate temperature changes. Heat expands the liquid, forcing the level up; the liquid contracts and falls when it is cold. A special type of instrument known as the *maximum-minimum thermometer* is used to record the highest and lowest temperatures for the day.

The *rain gauge* is used to measure the amount of any precipitation or moisture which falls to the ground. Rain, snow, and hail are forms of precipitation. Rainfall and snowfall are measured in inches of water that collect in a cylinder.

Relative humidity is a measure of the amount of water vapor in the air compared to the amount of water vapor air can hold at that temperature. When the air holds all the moisture it possibly can at a particular temperature, its relative humidity is 100 per cent. A piece of filter paper soaked in cobalt chloride and allowed to dry may be used to determine air humidity. Dry air turns the paper blue; moisture turns it pink or red. An instrument known as a *sling psychrometer,* with wet- and dry-bulb thermometers, is used by the U.S. Weather Bureau to determine relative humidity. It is used by slinging it around to evaporate moisture on the wet bulb and comparing the reading with the dry bulb. Tables are consulted which give the relative humidity for known wet- and dry-bulb readings.

MEASUREMENT OF WINDS

Wind speed is measured by an instrument called the *anemometer,* which consists of four cups attached to metal bars and connected to a shaft. The speed at which the cups turn measures wind speed.

Wind direction is indicated by weather vanes marked N., E., S., W. The *radiosonde* is an instrument used to broadcast weather conditions from high altitudes.

WEATHER MAPS

Weather maps made up daily by the U.S. Weather Bureau are based on reports sent in by co-operative weather observers in many parts of the country. Wind direction is indicated by arrows; the speed is shown in miles per hour, with cold and warm fronts, amount and kind of clouds and precipitation. *Isobars* are solid curving lines that denote areas of equal barometric pressure. *Isotherms* are broken lines joining places of similar temperature.

When air masses of different kinds meet, a *front* is formed at the boundary line. Weather conditions depend upon the kinds of air masses and how they meet.

A *warm front* is produced when two air masses of different temperatures meet, the warm air mass advancing. Characteristic cloud formations are produced.

A *cyclone* is an area of low pressure marking the advance of a warm front. Winds blow in a large counterclockwise circle in the Northern Hemisphere. Winds blowing the opposite direction are anticyclones in areas of high pressure. *Tornadoes* are the most violent of all land storms,

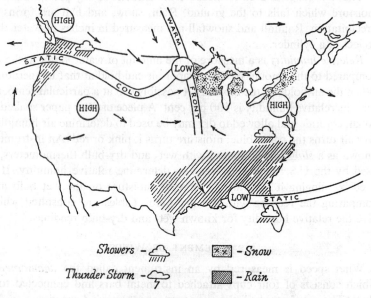

Showers –   ▨ – *Snow*
Thunder Storm –   ▨ – *Rain*

FIG. 5. Weather Map.

though they are only a few hundred feet in diameter. *Hurricanes* or *typhoons,* the most violent of all large storms, are formed at sea when air is pushed upward in a violent whirl. They extend from 100 to 600 miles in diameter over tropical oceans, and move into other regions. Tremendous damage has been done in recent years by hurricanes, especially along the Atlantic Coast.

THUNDERSTORMS AND LIGHTNING

When clouds are formed, some become charged with plus (+) electricity, others with minus (–) electricity. Since (+) and (–) charges attract one another, it is believed that the (–) charges leap over to a cloud having (+) charges. This discharge is said to be the cause of lightning. The rapid expansion and contraction of air as lightning passes through it is believed to cause thunder. Since trees are good conductors of electricity, it is dangerous to stand near them during a thunderstorm.

CLOUD FORMATION

Recognition of different types of cloud formation is essential to weather prediction and of interest to everyone. Size, shape, and altitude are essentials. The three main varieties of clouds are stratus, cumulus, and cirrus. *Stratus* clouds are flat and low, about 2,000 to 5,000 feet high, associated with rain and fog. A *cumulus* cloud is fluffy (like a ball of cotton), from 4,500 to about 10,000 feet high—often indicating thunderstorms ahead. *Cirrus* clouds (also known as mare's-tails) are always white, made of minute ice crystals, and extend from an altitude of 27,000 to 30,000 feet. Cloud formations are important to airplane pilots.

PRECIPITATION

When the air temperature drops, condensation of water vapor occurs, at first forming clouds, then *rain*.

Dew is formed after sundown by the condensation of moisture on cold objects near the earth such as plants.

Frost is formed instead of dew if the air temperature drops below 32° F. A *fog* is a cloud which hangs low over the earth.

Sleet and *hail* are formed when raindrops pass through air which is below freezing temperature.

Snow is formed in saturated air below freezing temperature. Water particles in the air form particles of ice which grow and form snow crystals.

MODERN TRANSPORTATION

THE STEAM ENGINE

About two thousand years ago, Hero, an Egyptian, devised the first machine which could operate without man or animal. The principle of Hero's machine may be illustrated as follows: A tin can with spouts punched at opposite sides at an angle and containing a small amount of water is heated until steam is produced. It will be discovered that the pressure produced by steam causes the can to spin.

In 1768, James Watt produced the first steam engine to be used in industry. At first the engine was used to raise coal from the bottom of mines. Later it was used to run textile machines and then locomotives. Heat energy is produced by burning coal or wood which turns water to steam. Movement of a slide valve from left to right permits the entry of steam first into one compartment, where it forces out a piston, which is attached to a crankshaft, which turns the flywheel. The valve slides back and steam enters through another opening, pushing the piston rod back into its original position.

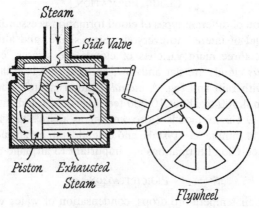

FIG. 6. Steam Engine.

Thus continuous motion of the flywheel is produced.

The first ship to use such an engine was Robert Fulton's steamship *Clermont* in its trip up the Hudson River in 1807. Today an improved engine known as the *steam turbine,* with blades carefully built to use steam energy more efficiently, has replaced the simple engine used by Fulton. Water turbines with huge blades are made to whirl by using the weight of water falling from dams to turn huge dynamos which produce much of our electricity. Steam turbines have been used to power large seagoing vessels, but they are being replaced by diesel engines, which give more power. Steam-driven engines are called *external-combustion engines* because they burn fuel for power outside the engine.

Liquid fuels, such as gasoline and oil, are the best fuels for use in engines because they vaporize easily and have a low *kindling temperature,* thus producing an explosion.

THE AUTOMOBILE ENGINE

The first gasoline-burning engine is credited to Nikolaus Otto, a German engineer, in 1886. This is now known as an *internal-combustion engine* because the fuel burns inside the engine to give it power. Utilizing this engine to provide power for a "horseless carriage," Henry Ford introduced methods of mass production and manufactured automobiles that were within the reach of the average man's pocketbook.

The internal-combustion engine is used widely in transportation today on land, sea, and in the air.

The *cycle of operation* consists of four strokes: the *intake stroke,* in which the intake valve opens as the piston moves down, allowing a mixture of gasoline vapor and air to enter the cylinder; the *compression stroke,* in which the intake and exhaust valves close, followed by the upward movement of the piston rod, causing a compression of the gases; the *ignition* or *power stroke,* in which the gases are ignited by the spark plug, causing an explosion that forces the piston down. This motion moves the crankshaft, which then causes the flywheel to turn. On the *exhaust stroke,* the exhaust valve opens as the piston moves up to force out the exhaust gases.

The cycle is repeated as the intake valve opens, permitting fresh gas vapor and air to enter the cylinder. Smooth operation depends upon the continued movement of the four strokes in proper sequence.

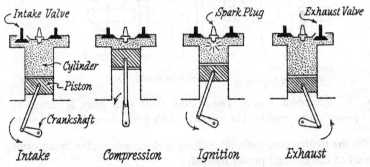

FIG. 7. Four Stage Operation in Gasoline Engine.

The *diesel engine* operates on the same principle as the four-stroke gasoline engine but with the following differences: On the *intake stroke,* only air enters through the intake valve. On the *compression stroke,* there is much greater compression of air than in the gas engine, producing intense heat. On the *fuel injection stroke,* a spray of oil is injected into the cylinder. Due to intense heat it vaporizes and burns immediately, producing an explosion which provides power to push the piston down with great force. On the *exhaust stroke,* the waste gases are expelled through the exhaust valve by the upward stroke of the piston.

Diesel engines are used widely in heavy transportation on land and sea because they use cheap fuel oil. They are heavier and stronger than the gasoline engines because of greater compression developed.

THE GEARSHIFT

Two sets of gears known as *transmission* and *differential* help turn the rear wheels of a car and move it either forward or backward. Large transmission gears, when linked with small differential gears attached to the rear wheels, can cause rapid movement of the latter. This is what happens when the car is in third gear or high speed. Shifting of gears enables gears of different sizes to mesh, thereby changing speeds of the rear wheels to first, second, or third speed. When the driver shifts into neutral, he puts his foot on the clutch, thus disengaging the two sets of gears and freeing the motion of the wheels altogether.

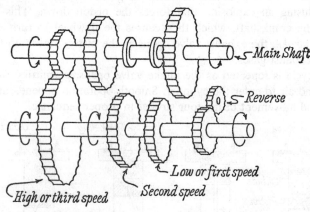

FIG. 8. Automobile Gears. The bottom shaft with gears is turned by the power of the engine. The top shaft with gears turns the rear wheels.

In the hydromatic shift, all shifting is done automatically according to speed of the car and power needed.

OCEAN TRAVEL

What makes a steel ship weighing thousands of tons float on water? That certain bodies float in water is explained by Archimedes' principle, which states that an object placed in a liquid is pushed up by a force equal to the weight of the liquid displaced by it. A bar of steel measuring 1 cubic foot in volume may weigh 400 pounds. It will sink in water because the latter weighs only 62.5 pounds per cubic foot. However, if the same weight of steel is hammered into thin sheets and shaped into a boat until the volume occupied by the same weight of steel is thereby increased 100 times, the steel will float because it is now being buoyed up by a much larger volume of water which has a buoyant force of 100 times 62.5 pounds, or 6,250 pounds.

Ships can carry heavy cargoes. Lines marked on the hulls indicate how far the hull of the ship may go down into the water and still be safely loaded. Ocean liners are powered either by high-speed steam turbines or diesel engines. In the largest ships, electric motors have tens of thousands of horsepower to drive the propellers.

SUBMARINES

Underwater craft have a set of valves capable of admitting sea water into special compartments, thereby allowing the ship to sink to any desired level. To cause the ship to rise to the surface, the water ballast can be driven out of the compartments by special electrically driven pumps.

Diesel engines are used to power submarines, and more recently atomic power is being used to enable submarines to remain under water for long periods of time.

THE AIRPLANE

The flight of an airplane depends upon the invisible ocean of air around us which exerts pressure equally in all directions. The use of airplanes has brought the peoples and places of the world much closer together than ever before.

The most important part of a plane is the wingspread. There must be greater air pressure below than above the wings; otherwise the plane will not rise. This is accomplished by shaping the wing in such a way that when the plane moves forward at a certain speed, a partial vacuum is created above the wing so that the air pressure below the wing produces a *lift*. The plane will continue to rise so long as the lift is greater than its own weight.

The principle of lift may be simply illustrated by holding a piece of paper in your hand and blowing across the top of it. The paper will rise because the speed of the air currents across the top of it results in a partial vacuum.

To produce lift, the airplane must be moved forward by its propellers at a certain speed. This is known as *thrust*. The counterforce of the air against the plane is known as *drag*. A plane's thrust must be greater than its drag in order for it to fly safely by producing enough lift. The nose of the plane is tilted upward to produce greater lift. Excessive tilting produces air turbulence, resulting in lowered lift.

The *ailerons* are the flaps on the rear edges of the wings. Raising or lowering them makes it possible for the pilot to bank or make sharp turns.

The *fuselage* is the body of the plane. In front are the seated pilot and his instruments.

Engines and *propellers* are mounted in the wings or in front of the fuselage in most planes.

Jet planes do not need propellers. Hot gases pushed out of the rear of a jet plane give the plane its energy for motion.

The *elevators* are used for climbing. The rudder is chiefly to keep the plane on a straight course when the air becomes rough.

Propeller-driven planes cannot be used to achieve supersonic speeds. They are being rapidly replaced by jet engines. Instead of using propellers, air is compressed and forced into a fuel chamber where fuel is injected and the mixture burned. The exhaust gases are forced out through the stovepipe at the rear at a speed of over 1,000 miles per hour. It is this action which produces the counteraction of forward thrust by the plane and continued compression of gases and air. Tremendous heat and the great noise produced are chief problems of jet aircraft. Much greater speed and altitude are chief potentialities of jet planes.

JET PROPULSION

Jet propulsion is based upon the principle of action and reaction discovered by Isaac Newton. It states that for every action there is an equal and opposite reaction. If you blow up a toy balloon and let it go, it will move rapidly away, rounded end first; the sound made by escaping air is due to the force of the air leaving the balloon. This is the action. The movement of the balloon in the opposite direction is the reaction. This is similar to the kick of a gun when it is fired or to the movement of a rocket as the hot blast of gases leaves its open end.

The principle of jet propulsion can be illustrated by attaching a small cylinder of compressed air or carbon-dioxide gas to the tail of a model jet plane. If you puncture the seal on the cylinder by shooting a needle into it from a special type of gun, the gas will escape and the plane will then shoot forth at a very rapid speed. The plane should be attached loosely to a guide wire to keep it from shooting out into space. At about ten feet from the starting point of the plane, a mass of soft putty or clay should be placed to catch the plane; and the experimenter must be careful to step quickly away from the rear end of the plane to avoid possible kickback from the escaping gas.

MODERN COMMUNICATION

Man's first attempt to communicate with his neighbors was probably by means of a shout. Then he may have realized that by cupping his hands alongside his mouth he could augment the sound of his voice and project it to a greater distance. Following this he found that he could make use of horns of animals, and he fashioned the first megaphones. These were followed by a variety of trumpets found useful in commanding masses of fighting men, who could be co-ordinated at a moment's notice to advance, retreat, or perform other actions. Among primitive peoples the tom-tom is one of the best-known means of communication. The cadence of the drums transmits messages to members of the tribe, summoning them whenever social, political, or religious gatherings require their presence. Another means of communication, used by the Indians and other primitive peoples, have been smoke signals.

Sounds of various kinds are used today as signals on oceangoing vessels, the number and length of blasts given indicating the intent of the vessel. Lightlists of each coast are on hand for purposes of identification of lighthouses, based upon duration of foghorn blasts and intervals between blasts. Flashes of light reflecting the sun's rays from mirrors are a simple but very effective method of communication.

TELEGRAPH AND TELEPHONE

Signal communication, whether through the use of sound or light, is an elementary form of telegraph. The telegraph is basically a circuit carrying an electric current, which the sender connects and breaks. The receiving set may record the electric signals in a variety of ways, the most usual being by sound signals. A basic type of telegraph receiver is an electromagnet which attracts a pliable strip of metal when the current is on and releases it when the current is broken. The "message" is heard in a series of long and short clicks. The Morse code—named for S. F. B. Morse, who in the middle of the nineteenth century designed the first efficient telegraph—is a simple, practical code of long and short signals for all the letters of the alphabet and the marks of punctuation. Modern telegraph systems have been designed which translate the signals into a design of holes punched on a tape. The tape is then passed into a special typing machine, and the original message is automatically decoded and typed out.

The invention of the telephone followed shortly after the telegraph. In the telephone, the vibrations of the human voice are transmitted electrically by the sending apparatus and translated back into intelligible sound vibrations at the receiver. The sender and receiver are basically identical: each consists of a sensitive diaphragm of soft iron which in vibrating affects a simple bar magnet, which in turn affects the electric current. The variations in strength of the current record the sound vibrations. At the receiver, these electrical impulses affect the magnet, which in turn makes the diaphragm vibrate exactly as the one which was being spoken into did. Voice is thus reproduced. It is interesting to note that in principle the microphone—so important in radio and television—is really nothing more than a highly developed telephone mouthpiece.

RADIO AND TELEVISION

Near the end of the last century wireless telegraphs and telephones were invented, leading to the development of radio as we know it today.

In radio transmission, sound waves are transformed into electrical impulses having the same form as sound waves. These impulses are then superimposed on an alternating electric current (called the carrier) in a separate circuit. This latter current is of extremely high frequency, and its exact frequency determines the wave length of the broadcast. The carrier current, which contains the sound impulses, is then amplified and radiated by the antenna of the broadcasting outfit. The receiving set, which has a tuning instrument to enable it to select only the desired wave length, separates the sound impulses from the carrier wave and amplifies them. Basically, then, the process is one of utilizing high-frequency radio waves to "carry" sound impulses—more or less as a wire carries them in the telephone.

The most recent development in communication is, of course, television. Television utilizes radio waves also. The impulses imposed on the radio circuits, however, are produced from light instead of sound. The variations of light and dark from each part of the object to be reproduced or the scene to be transmitted are transformed into electric impulses, amplified, and imposed on radio waves. The television receiver transfers light impulses back into an image which the viewer sees. Color television is based on the same principles, certain primary colors being picked up, transformed into electric impulses, transmitted, and recombined in the receiver in an image reproducing the original colors.

These modern forms of communication which we have discussed are taken up in greater detail in the chapter on Physics.

ATOMIC ENERGY

Today everyone is familiar with the sketch of the mushroom-shaped cloud and aware of the enormous amount of heat, light, and radioactivity caused by the explosion of an atomic bomb. Most people do not realize, however, that a normal amount of radioactive particles existed in all environments, even before the production of the atomic bomb. These other radioactive particles are *cosmic rays* emanating from outer space—probably from distant stars, whose disintegrating atoms release these powerful rays which ultimately reach us. The presence of these rays (and also those emanating from radium-tipped dials in watches) can easily be detected by the clicking sound of the instrument known as the *Geiger counter*.

Matter and energy appear to be different, though actually they are different forms of the same thing. Albert Einstein (1879–1955) showed the mathematical relationship between the two over forty years ago when he discovered the formula, $E = mc^2$ (Energy equals mass times the square of the speed of light). Henri Becquerel, in 1896, found strange invisible rays coming from uranium, which registered on photographic paper; he gave us the word radioactivity to describe this phenomenon. Frédéric Joliot-Curie, who in 1935 was the third member of the Curie family to win a Nobel prize in science, noticed that when alpha rays from the radioactive element polonium passed through beryllium they gave off other powerful rays which, when passed through paraffin, drove out the hydrogen nuclei (the center of the atom) with great force. These mysterious rays left no track in detecting devices and had no electric charge. They proved to be neutrons (part of the center of an atom), whose existence had been predicted by Rutherford ten years earlier.

Joliot-Curie exposed uranium, a naturally radioactive element, to a bombardment of neutrons, and discovered that two entirely different atoms were formed with much energy released. The total weight of the end-products was less than the combined weight of the uranium and the neutrons used to bombard it. This led to the conclusion that some matter was transformed into energy, sustaining Einstein's equation. This set the stage for production of the atom bomb.

Wherever uranium is found, it is present in two forms. One is U 238, which is heavier and makes up 99.3 per cent of the total. The lighter form is U 235, which makes up 0.7 per cent. Since U 235 is the more radioactive of the two, its value is greater. An instrument known as the *cyclotron* is used to study the properties of U 235. Atomic particles shoot into the center of this instrument and are enormously accelerated to a speed of over 100,000 miles per second. These atomic "bullets" may then be shot into the nucleus of U 235 atoms, thereby smashing them and producing many other elements, including radioactive phosphorus and iodine, plus a great amount of energy.

Dr. Lise Meitner and Dr. Frisch calculated that if all the atoms in a pound of U 235 were split, or underwent *fission*, as much energy as that produced by burning five million pounds of coal or exploding nine thousand tons of TNT would be given off.

A team of scientists of the Manhattan Project during World War II, including Enrico Fermi and Harold Urey, succeeded in slowing up the neutron bombardment, thus making possible a *chain reaction* of neutrons which would release more neutrons.

EFFECTS OF ATOMIC EXPLOSION

In addition to the intense heat of two million degrees produced by the explosion of the atom bomb, showers of neutrons and powerful gamma rays hit every object in their path with terrific impact. Destruction is enormous. In addition, the blast of air set in motion by the explosion destroys buildings two miles from the center. Radioactive dust or *fallout* is carried from the explosion for thousands of miles by winds and settles on plants, animals, and land.

The hydrogen bomb is even more powerful in its destructive capacity. Instead of fission of atoms, atomic *fusion* of hydrogen atoms occurs, resulting in the production of helium plus enormous amounts of energy. It is believed that the sun's heat and light come from the fusion of hydrogen atoms. The two million degrees heat of "fission" atomic energy is used to trigger off the "fusion" reaction.

INDUSTRIAL USES OF ATOMIC ENERGY

The fission or fusion of atoms need not be destructive. If controlled, we have here a great new source of energy which can be used for peaceful, constructive purposes.

By building atomic piles in machines called *nuclear reactors,* it is possible to control the energy released by smashed atoms. Heat given off by the atomic pile at Hanford, Washington, is so great that masses of cold water from the Columbia River are required to dissipate it. Someday this heat from atomic sources may be used to replace a good deal of the coal and oil used as fuel to run factory machines, to heat homes, and to provide energy to run trains and cars and planes.

The first atomic-powered submarines, the *Nautilus* and *Sea Wolf,* are already in use by the U.S. Navy. Oxygen is not required, thus enabling these submarines to remain submerged for long periods of time. Space taken up by oil may be used for storage of food and other essentials. Atom-powered engines for ships and aircraft are now feasible.

RADIOACTIVE ISOTOPES

In addition to using radioactive materials as a source of energy, there are many other applications of atomic energy. Radioactive phosphorus, for example, is used to trace processes occurring inside the bodies of plants and animals. This is done by "tagging" radioactive atoms to certain compounds, such as phosphorus, iodine, cobalt, iron, and carbon calcium, which are fed to animals and plants; Geiger counters are then used to detect the location of these compounds in the body.

Radioactive atoms may be used to locate tumors in the body, and radioactive iodine to check growth of tumors of the thyroid gland. Radioactive cobalt may be used instead of X rays for treatment of cancer. The speed of many life processes, such as circulation, manufacture of food by green plants, and digestion may be measured in the same way.

Radioactive materials save industry millions of dollars by finding flaws in metal castings, leaks in water pipes, impurities in steel, and tracing the flow of oil in pipes.

These are but a few examples of the peacetime uses of radioactive atoms. New uses are continually being discovered.

MAINTAINING OUR FOOD SUPPLY

Maintaining an adequate supply of food for the growing world population is one of the major problems in the world today. With our modern methods of communication and transportation, all people are neighbors. Yet many areas which are densely populated have food supply less than adequate to meet the needs of the population. For a number of years the United States and other countries and the United Nations agencies have been sending surplus food stores to various parts of the world. It is now realized that such measures can never be more than temporary stopgaps, and that it would be wiser for us to offer the aid of food technicians and scientists who would bring modern know-how to these areas, in order to assist the local population in developing their own resources into the needed food supply. Food scientists are continually experimenting with ways of improving and increasing our food supply.

THE IMPORTANCE OF PLANTS

According to the history of life as recorded in layers of rock, the first living organisms were plants. It has been known for a long time that the green leaves of plants are the food factories of the world. If green plants disappeared from the earth, our food supply would go with them. This is because green plants have the ability to make their own food from relatively simple chemicals, whereas animals depend upon plants for many essentials of nourishment.

To understand the unique ability of green plants to manufacture their own food, we need first of all to know that in the presence of sunlight, carbon-dioxide gas and water combine inside the leaf of a plant to produce sugar and oxygen gas, provided that the green matter *chlorophyl* is present. This process is known as *photosynthesis*.

The process of photosynthesis may be expressed in the following manner:

$$CO_2 \quad + \quad H_2O \quad \xrightarrow[\text{chlorophyl}]{\text{Sunlight}} \quad O_2 \quad + \quad C_6H_{12}O_6$$

| (carbon dioxide) | (water) | | (oxygen) | (sugar) |

Colorless plants—for example, mushrooms and molds—have no chlorophyl and are unable to make their own food.

Green plants not only make their food but in addition they release oxygen, which is so essential for all animal life and is basic in respiration.

The interdependence of green plant and animal life is demonstrated by the $CO_2 \rightarrow O_2$ cycle. The cycle may be illustrated by a sealed aquarium containing some green water plants and a goldfish. Why can such an aquarium be maintained indefinitely? If the aquarium receives sunlight, both fish and plants can live indefinitely, because the green plant takes in CO_2 and water, producing oxygen and food which are used up by the fish and reconverted to CO_2 and H_2O all over again. In other words, the wastes of the fish are utilized by the plant during the process of food-making. The plant also uses some of the O_2 and food which it manufactures for its own needs.

This same balance by exchange is also maintained between land animals and plants. Animals and men eat green plants and breathe out wastes which help plants to grow. Also, when the bodies of plants and animals decay, they add minerals to the soil.

THE ROLE OF BACTERIA

Bacteria play an important part in the balance of nature by causing decay. The first product of decay is ammonia. Other forms of bacteria

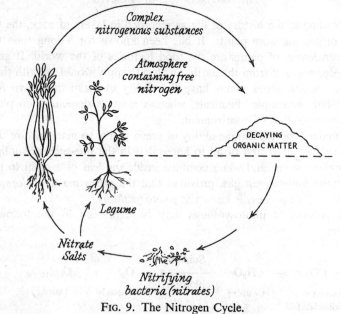

FIG. 9. The Nitrogen Cycle.

convert this ammonia into nitrites. Still others change nitrites into nitrates, which enter the soil and are absorbed by plant roots via soil water. Nitrates are essential to the building of protein substances in living protoplasm. This process, known as the nitrogen cycle, repeats itself over and over again.

Certain plants such as beans, clover, and alfalfa have nitrogen-fixing bacteria in their root nodules. These crops, which are particularly rich in proteins, are planted alternately by farmers to replenish the soil worn out by other crops. In addition, farmers add commercial fertilizers to the soil, often prepared from the bones of animals or fish and containing the minerals which plants remove from the soil.

Bacteria are used industrially for flavoring cheeses, souring milk, making sauerkraut, softening and flavoring meats, netting flax, curing tobacco, tanning leather.

Yeasts have an essential role in the fermentation of fruit to make alcoholic beverages, and in making bread and some kinds of cake.

Molds are valuable in flavoring certain cheeses, such as gorgonzola and blue cheese, and in the manufacture of antibiotics, such as penicillin, terramycin, and streptomycin.

CONSERVATION OF NATURAL RESOURCES

For a long time man has been destroying forests, partly for industrial purposes and partly accidentally by fire. As a result the bared land has suffered erosion, and millions of acres of topsoil have been blown away. Thus many areas have lost their fertility; unable to hold moisture, they will not grow any plants. Consequently, there has been a serious reduction in the quantity of food supply, both plant and animal, capable of sustaining human life. Many measures have been taken to conserve soil and water supply and to protect plant and animal life. These include: *reforestation* of depleted areas; *construction of dams* to provide reservoirs for irrigating desert lands; the use of *contour plowing* and *strip planting,* which prevents the run-off of rain water and soil in hilly areas; and the establishing of game laws in regions where wildlife may aid in maintaining the balance of life.

THE WAR BETWEEN INSECTS AND MAN

Insects are essential to man for cross-pollination of fruit-producing plants. Yet billions of dollars worth of crops are destroyed annually by insects of all types. In addition, many diseases such as malaria, sleeping sickness, and yellow fever are carried by insects. In many areas of the world, such as Africa and Asia, these diseases are still widely prevalent. Some scientists believe that should man become extinct his place would quickly be taken by the insect race, his chief competitor for food. If insects were permitted to grow unhindered, man's very existence would be threatened.

Some of the more harmful insects include the *codling moth,* whose larval stage lives in pears, plums, and apples; the *boll weevil,* which destroys a large part of our cotton crop; the *Japanese beetle,* which attacks vegetables and plant leaves; the *tent caterpillar,* so called because it builds tent-like webs between the branches of fruit trees and feeds on their leaves; and *termites,* which destroy timber.

Insects which carry disease germs include *flies* (typhoid), the *anopheles mosquito* (malaria), the *tsetse fly* (African sleeping sickness), and the *aëdes mosquito* (yellow fever).

The United States Department of Agriculture spends large sums of money on the study of insects, their habits, and their weaknesses—which makes it possible to open an attack upon them.

Insect poisons are of three types: stomach poisons, contact poisons, and fumigants. Insects which bite their food, such as beetles and grasshoppers, die when it has been sprayed with lead arsenate. Other insects, such as plant lice and scale insects, suck their food and must be suffocated by direct spraying with such preparations as lime, tobacco, sulphur, kerosene soap, and oil emulsions. DDT has been widely used as a contact poison against fleas, lice, and mosquitoes. It is found, however, that useful animals and birds are also poisoned by it. Also, many insects have built up a resistance to DDT. Poisonous sulphur dioxide and hydrocyanic acid gases kill certain insects by suffocation.

Mosquitoes, whose larval stages breathe through tubes extending above the surface of stagnant water, are suffocated by oil spread on the surface of the water, which clogs their breathing tubes. Oils in spray guns kill many insects which may be found in the home.

SCIENTIFIC BREEDING

In the early days of civilization, when man exchanged a nomadic existence for a more stable form of society, he found it necessary to domesticate animals and to sow fields to ensure a steady supply of food and clothing for his family. Thus wild forms of crops such as wheat, rye, and oats were gradually improved by selecting the largest and best plants and breeding them. The less desirable varieties were eliminated, and the best strains were maintained by inbreeding.

In the nineteenth century, Gregor Mendel (1822–1884) made a major contribution to the science of breeding by his discovery of certain basic laws of heredity. Countless developments have since been made in breeding. In America, Luther Burbank (1849–1926), known as the father of modern plant breeding, succeeded in developing and improving many varieties. Today we have giant forms of tobacco, larger tomatoes, much larger and tastier corn, and larger wheat plants capable of resisting diseases such as rust and wilt which formerly destroyed thousands of acres of wheat plants. Texas cattle now combine the good meat qualities of native animals with the heat- and disease-resistant qualities of Brahman cattle from India. These are but a few examples of improved varieties developed by the application of scientific principles.

COMMUNITY HEALTH PROBLEMS

A century ago, thousands upon thousands of people died of the ravages of smallpox, and many who survived were pockmarked for life. Epidemics of typhoid fever and bubonic plague were frequent and widespread. People died en masse of these and other diseases.

In Rome two thousand years ago the average age expectation was 22 years. Today it is 68 years in the United States. To what is this increase due?

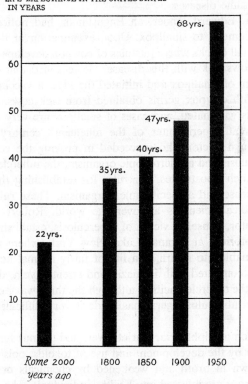

FIG. 10. Increase in Life Expectancy.

Doubtless one of the most important factors in prolonging the life span is the control of contagious disease. Epidemics and plagues which diminish whole populations have been brought under control and eliminated by a growth of scientific knowledge of causes and methods of transmission of these diseases.

Up to the time of Louis Pasteur, people commonly believed these diseases to be caused by demons inhabiting the bodies of unfortunate human beings. With the improvement of the microscope in the seventeenth and eighteenth centuries, the relationship between disease and bacteria became firmly established. In the nineteenth century Pasteur conducted numerous experiments to discover the specific causes of diseases. In 1868 he isolated the bacilli of two separate diseases that were attacking silkworms, and by developing a method for detecting the diseased silkworms and preventing the spread of contagion, he was able to save the silk industry of France and of other countries from destruction. He developed the system of protection against diseases such as anthrax in sheep and hydrophobia in man by vaccination of healthy individuals with weakened germs of the same diseases.

Earlier, Dr. Edward Jenner, an Englishman, had noticed that milkmaids were immune to smallpox. Upon examination of their hands he discovered small cracks where pustules of cowpox developed due to their handling of cows sick with this disease. He reasoned that cowpox must be a mild form of smallpox and initiated the idea of vaccinating healthy individuals with cowpox germs obtained from sick cows. Today every school child is vaccinated, and cases of smallpox are very rare.

Another great experimenter of the nineteenth century was Robert Koch, a German doctor who succeeded in proving the connection between tuberculosis and a microscopic organism, the tubercle bacillus. He developed "Koch's postulates," or rules for establishing the connection between a disease and a specific microorganism. These rules are in use today by medical scientists all over the world. Robert Trudeau, an American doctor, himself a victim of tuberculosis, established the famed Trudeau Sanatorium at Saranac Lake, New York, where patients were treated and enabled to return to a life of fairly normal activity. Today this disease is combated with isoniazid and streptomycin, drugs capable of destroying the tubercle bacillus, although the thick waxy coating which surrounds the tuberculosis germ has made it very difficult to penetrate with drugs.

Diseases such as diphtheria, scarlet fever, and tetanus have been conquered largely by the development and use of toxoids, poisons produced by germs grown in broth and weakened by chemicals or heat. These weakened poisons are injected into healthy individuals, who then develop active immunity against the diseases. Victims of a disease such as diphtheria may be given antitoxins developed in the blood sera of horses who have recovered from the disease. Poliomyelitis, commonly known as infantile paralysis, has been found to be caused by a virus. The Salk vaccine, consisting of dead polio germs, is used for the prevention of this disease.

Typhoid fever has been identified with a bacterium spread by polluted water as well as insect agents. The control of sewage disposal and of water supply is therefore of the utmost importance in maintaining community health. Methods of sanitation have been improved and methods of water purification developed so that possibility of transmission of water-borne germs has been eliminated in civilized countries throughout the world.

Malaria, yellow fever, and sleeping sickness have been brought under control in areas of the world where insect carriers of these diseases have been destroyed. In Africa and India and other countries where modern methods of control have not been fully established, these diseases still wreak havoc among the population.

Since diseases caused by germs are being successfully controlled through vaccination, "wonder drugs" such as sulfa drugs and antibiotics, improved sanitation and water supply and other public health measures, the chief public health problems are those diseases which are not caused by germs. Cancer and heart disease are among the chief killers of our population today.

SAFEGUARDING FOOD SUPPLY

To protect the public against the spread of disease via spoiled and adulterated foods, Pure Food and Drug Laws have been enacted by both state and federal governments. These laws require that certain standards of cleanliness be maintained in the handling, preparation, and canning of foods. Where adulterants are used, or any ingredients that might be harmful, these must be indicated on the labels.

Health department inspectors examine samples of milk and investigate those which show a high bacterial count. Inspection of dairies, cows, milking equipment, and pasteurization processes are made until the source of the high bacterial count is discovered. So long as the situation is not corrected the milk may not be sold.

Proper refrigeration is of the utmost importance in the storage of perishable foods, and food distributors are increasingly aware of the necessity for displaying produce and packaged goods under the temperature conditions which they require.

EXAMINATION QUESTIONS

1. Who first proved that bacteria cause contagious disease?
2. When, where, and by whom was the first successful flight of an airplane made?
3. What important discovery was made by Dr. Alexander Fleming?
4. What did Lavoisier discover about combustion?
5. What is a control in a scientific experiment?
6. What is the sound barrier?
7. What are the major difficulties in the way of space travel?
8. Why is rapid change in the rate of acceleration of a plane dangerous?
9. What does Newton's principle of "inertia of motion" state?
10. What conditions should be described in a weather report?
11. Why must windows be opened top and bottom for proper ventilation?
12. What causes movements of air masses?
13. What does a falling barometer indicate?
14. What is relative humidity?
15. What are hurricanes?
16. What causes lightning and thunder?
17. What was the name of the first steamship?
18. Why are liquid fuels such as gasoline and oil the best fuels for use in engines?
19. What are the four strokes of the gasoline engine?
20. Why are Diesel engines stronger than gasoline engines?
21. What is "drag" in airplane flight?
22. Describe a basic type of telegraph.
23. What instrument is really nothing more than a highly developed telephone mouthpiece?
24. What are cosmic rays?
25. What is the Geiger counter for?
26. Who first discovered radioactivity?
27. What instrument is used to smash atoms by bombardment?
28. How much energy can be produced from one pound of U 235?
29. How is the H bomb produced?
30. List some peacetime uses of atomic energy.
31. What are the primary "food factories" of the world?
32. Why are colorless plants like mushrooms and molds unable to make their own food?
33. What is the first product of decay?
34. What are some industrial uses of bacteria?
35. Who was Dr. Edward Jenner?

FOR FURTHER STUDY

EXPLAINING THE ATOM, by Selig Hecht. (Viking Press, New York.)

MICROBE HUNTERS, by Paul de Kruif. (Harcourt, Brace & Co., New York.)

NEW ADVANCES IN MEDICINE, by Morris Fishbein, M.D. (Doubleday & Co., New York.)

THE PHYSICAL NATURE OF FLIGHT, by Ray Holland, Jr. (W. W. Norton & Co., New York.)

ROCKETS, MISSILES AND SPACE TRAVEL, by Willy Ley. (Viking Press, New York.)

THE STORY OF SCIENCE, by David Dietz. (Dodd, Mead & Co., New York.)

XXI

Astronomy for Everybody

WHAT IS ASTRONOMY?

ASTRONOMY IS the science of the heavenly bodies—the sun, the planets, the moons, the comets, the meteors, the stars. Men have observed these bodies for centuries. In recent years, through wonderfully powerful telescopes, and with the aid of other valuable instruments, especially the spectroscope, astronomers have learned much about them. Aided by the exact science of mathematics and by the laws of physics, astronomers have measured the heavenly bodies—their size and mass, their relation to one another, their movement, their distance from the earth and from one another, their nature, and the like. Astronomy is of vital importance— it tells us particularly of our own earth, of the changes in its seasons, of the measurement of our time (by which our clocks are set), of the influence of the sun upon life, of the extent and nature of the great universe of which our solar system is but a tiny part.

Astronomy is one of the oldest sciences: even the ancients observed the starry heavens and made remarkably accurate observations. The ancients named the planets, which they could see with the naked eye, and called them *wanderers* (the word *planet* comes from a Greek word meaning *wanderer*) to distinguish them from the *fixed stars,* which appear not to move in their relative positions. *Astronomy* must not be confused with *astrology,* although the two terms were originally synonymous; astrology is today not a science, for it is concerned with fanciful interpretations of the assumed influence of heavenly bodies on human beings and earthly events.

The universe is a vast aggregate of stars, flaming variously, much like our sun in constitution, but most of those which are visible to us directly or through our telescopes are vastly larger than the sun. The nearest star to the sun is approximately 25,000,000,000,000 miles away, and any star is separated from the others that dot the heavens by similar and usually much greater distances.

Astronomers are just beginning to discern a pattern within our universe. They have discovered that the solar system—the sun and its planets and related smaller bodies—are part of a great grouping of about 40 billion stars called the *Galaxy*. Beyond our Galaxy we find independent aggregates of stars resembling our own Galaxy and floating in the vast oceans of space. These groupings are appropriately referred to as *island universes,* or more correctly as extra-galactic spiral nebulae. To date we have counted more than 250,000,000 of these island universes within the range of the 200-inch telescope at Mount Palomar. This telescope can see out to a distance so great that light (traveling at 186,000 miles a second) takes more than a billion years to reach us from the farthest stars recorded by the telescope. At this great distance we do not detect a thinning out of these nebulae, and it seems almost certain that our telescopes have not been able to reach any region of space which could be thought of as the limit of the universe. The distances which we have so far perceived are so great that astronomers measure them in "light-years," by which they mean the number of years that light from a given star takes to reach the earth (from which the distance can be calculated, since the speed of light is 186,000 miles per second). Some authorities on the extent and structure of the universe state that there is evidence to indicate that we must develop instruments capable of seeing out to *several more billion* light-years before we can discover the limits of the universe. Beyond and around the universe, perhaps, there is space without limit, extending to infinity. Difficult as it is for the imagination to conceive space without end, it is even more difficult to conceive an end to space—for what could be beyond that end?

The very magnitude of the universe and the evidence that it contains countless stars leads astronomers to the assumption that somewhere in the vast universe there must be other stars which have planets surrounding them just as our sun does. The very conditions which gave rise to life on earth may also prevail on such planets. The sheer weight of statistical probability prompts the conclusion that life may exist elsewhere in the universe. With some 250,000,000 island universes, each of which contains about 40,000,000,000 stars, whatever conditions gave rise to the planets and to life on earth must certainly have prevailed somewhere else in the universe, even though the probability be only one in a million. The probability is increased when we consider the fact that the planets with which we are familiar are made up of the same chemical elements that the spectroscope shows to be present in the distant stars. These elements are not distributed to each body, but astronomers have discovered no elements in the stars which do not exist on earth. Astronomers at the present time are fairly certain that a comparatively small star in our Galaxy, designated as Wolf 359, has a planetary system. But, despite the probabilities which we have mentioned, there is no direct evidence that life exists in that distant planetary system or anywhere else in the universe other than on earth.

THE SOLAR SYSTEM

We look at what we call the heavens from the surface of the earth, which is one of the planets revolving around the sun. The earth is our vantage point: from its surface, as from a plain bounded by the horizon, we gaze "up into the sky," observing the sun (and occasionally the moon and a star or two) by day, and the moon and "stars" (including the other planets which are visible to the naked eye) by night. Stars are, of course, present in the sky during the day, but they fade out of our sight, usually, in the brightness of the sun's light. If it were possible to render the earth transparent, or to remove it and the sun for a moment, so that you could be fixed in space where you are at this moment, you would see all around you, in every direction, what would appear to be the inside of a giant sphere, dotted with stars. That sphere is called the "celestial sphere," but, of course, it is imaginary only. No such sphere exists, for the stars are varying distances away.

The sun appears to rise each morning, to mount and cross the heavens, and to set each night at the opposite side of the horizon. Its light provides us with what we call our "day." Really, the earth rotates on its axis (a line drawn, as it were, through the earth between the North and South poles), making one rotation in every 24 hours. As a given point on the earth is rotated past the sun, so to speak, the sun appears to move past it, giving the illusion of the sun's motion. The earth is, at the same time, revolving around the sun, in a somewhat circular path with the sun as the center (actually, an ellipse, with the sun as one of the foci), which causes the sun to appear farther north or south in the sky at different seasons of the year. One revolution around the sun takes a year, or approximately 365¼ days (365 days on the calendar, the correction being made in leap years of 366 days every fourth year). The axis of the earth, as it revolves around the sun, is at an angle, and this angle changes relatively to the sun during the revolution, thus causing the sun's daily path across the sky to move north during the summer and south during the winter (as viewed from a place north of the equator).

Next to the sun, the moon is apparently the largest and brightest object in the sky. The moon is the earth's satellite; that is, it revolves around the earth, once in every 27¼ days. It also rotates on its axis, but the rate of its rotation is exactly equal to the rate of its revolution around the earth, so the moon always has the same "side" toward the earth. Really, the moon is a comparatively small celestial body, but it appears large to us because it is quite near. An orange at your elbow looks much larger than a man's head down the street, because the orange is nearer. The moon, indeed, is not a planet, for it does not revolve independently around the sun; but since it is "tied" to the earth, it is taken around the sun by the earth on its yearly journey.

The next brightest object in the heavens is a planet, the one called Venus, which can usually be seen in the west after sunset or in the east before sunrise. It may at first appear to be fixed, but repeated observation, night after night, will show that the visible planets move through the sky, passing by the constellations of fixed stars. For each planet, like the earth, revolves around the sun, in a greater or less elliptical *orbit* (the path the planet takes in its revolution). The planets (like the moon) shine by reflected sunlight; they have no source of light of their own, as does the sun. The stars are like our sun—they flame with their own light, and, owing to their great distance from the earth, they also appear to twinkle through the earth's atmosphere. The sun and its planets, which are "tied" to it by the force of gravitational attraction, together with some other minor bodies (including satellites of the planets), comprise our solar system.

The earth is about 93,000,000 miles from the sun (this distance varies somewhat at different times of the year, since the earth's orbit is not circular, but elliptical). Some idea of the mighty heat and light of the sun can be suggested when one thinks of how warm the sunshine feels on a bright summer day and remembers that it has come through an intervening space of some 93,000,000 miles! Light travels at the almost unimaginable speed of 186,000 miles per second; a beam of light, if it could be that much curved, would go round the earth several times in one second. Yet, at this speed, it takes light about eight minutes to travel from the sun to the earth. That is to say, the light that you are now reading by (if it is daylight) left the sun eight minutes ago. Radio or ether waves travel at the same speed, so that, although radio transmission is practically instantaneous in the small distances on the earth, a radio message from the earth to the sun would also take about eight minutes in transit.

Yet the distance of the earth from the sun is trifling compared with the greater distances of the outer planets. Neptune, for example, is 30 times as far from the sun as the earth—it takes the sun's light four hours to reach Neptune. So great is the distance of Neptune from the sun, indeed that it can receive only about 1/1000 as much light and heat as the earth receives.

Great as these distances seem, and huge though the solar system may appear to be if its outermost limit is something like 5,000,000,000 miles from the sun, something like 25,000,000,000,000 miles must be added to that to reach the nearest star. That is to say, in terms of time it takes light to travel, the earth is eight *light-minutes* from the sun, Neptune is four *light-hours* from the sun, and the nearest star, Proxima Centauri, is four *light-years* from the sun. Our solar system, therefore, is in no great danger of colliding with any star. The nearest star (which is in the constellation Centaurus) is visible to us by light which left that star four years ago. A light-year is a unit of distance equivalent to about 6,000,-000,000,000 miles.

Most stars, however, are not by any means so near as the one just mentioned. Some of the brightest stars are much farther away than that. The farthest source of light that can be seen with the naked eye is a faint splotch in the constellation Andromeda, which is so far away from the earth that its light, traveling 186,000 miles per second, takes a *million* years to traverse the intervening distance. It is beyond the power of the human imagination to realize what that means—the patch of light, which happens to be (as is revealed by the telescope) a spiral nebula, started the waves which today reach our eyes on their immense journey across space, before any creature very much like modern man ever appeared on the earth—in far past ages. There are points of light in the heavens even farther removed (visible through the telescope), but they are so far away that their distance cannot be determined with any accuracy.

When one thinks that recorded human history has taken not more than 7,000 years, and that even our sun, immense ball of fire though it is, is a pigmy beside most of the stars, the figures of astronomy dwarf the earth into comparative insignificance. The earth is of paramount importance to us, because we live on it.

THE PLANETS AS A GROUP

There are nine known planets which circle our sun in elliptical orbits. The five innermost planets (not counting the earth) can be seen with the naked eye; the more remote three can be seen only with a telescope. The period of revolution around the sun varies with each planet, the nearer planets having shorter periods. The planets also rotate on their axes, as does the earth. It is supposed that Mercury and Venus rotate in the same period as their revolutions, but this has not been definitely established.

The nine known planets are as follows:

NAME	AVERAGE DISTANCE FROM SUN
Mercury	36,000,000 miles
Venus	67,300,000 miles
Earth	92,900,000 miles
Mars	141,500,000 miles
Jupiter	483,000,000 miles
Saturn	886,000,000 miles
Uranus	1,782,000,000 miles
Neptune	2,793,000,000 miles
Pluto	3,670,000,000 miles

These planets all revolve around the sun, in elliptical orbits, in the same direction as the earth. The period of revolution around the sun varies, the nearer planets having shorter periods. Mercury, nearest the sun, completes its revolution or "year" in 88 days; Venus, in 225 days; Earth, in 365¼ days; Mars, in 687 days; Jupiter, in 11¾ years; Saturn, in 29½ years; Uranus, in 84 years; Neptune, in 164¾ years; Pluto in 249 years. So long does it take Neptune to make one complete revolution around the sun that, since it was discovered in 1846, it has not had time to make more than half its circuit.

The period of rotation of a planet is the length of that planet's year, just as the period of revolution is the length of its day. The period of rotation of Mercury is 88 days. The period of rotation of Venus is not exactly known because of the density of its atmosphere. The earth rotates in about 24 hours, and Mars in nearly the same time (longer by a half hour). Jupiter takes nearly 10 hours per rotation; Saturn, a few minutes more than that; Uranus, 10¾ hours; Neptune's period is 15¾ hours. The period of rotation for Pluto is 50 years; Pluto was considered to be a planet until observations of its relatively slow rate of rotation, together with its small size and high density, suggested that it is probably an escaped moon of Neptune.

The planets have different average diameters, as follows: Mercury, 3,100 miles; Venus, 7,700 miles; Earth, 7,913 miles (usually given in round numbers as 8,000 miles); Mars, 4,200 miles; Jupiter, 86,728 miles; Saturn, 71,520 miles; Uranus, 30,878 miles; Neptune, 31,000 miles; Pluto, about 4,000 miles. All are spherical, or nearly spherical, in shape like the earth, the sun, and the stars.

The maximum temperatures on the surface of the planets changes considerably. Maximum surface temperatures in degrees Fahrenheit is as follows for each of the planets: Mercury, 770°; Venus and Earth, 140°

Mars, 86°; Jupiter, –216°; Saturn, –243°; Uranus, –300°; Neptune, –330°; Pluto, –400°. (Note that the maximum temperatures decrease with increasing distances from the sun.)

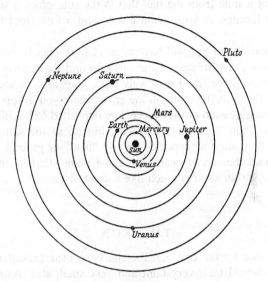

FIG. 1. The Solar System.

Mercury and Venus have no moons or satellites. The earth has one satellite, called the moon. Mars has two satellites, which revolve around it as the moon revolves around the earth. Jupiter has twelve satellites; Saturn, nine; Uranus, five; and Neptune, two. Pluto has no satellites.

Besides the nine planets and their satellites, the solar system also includes the so-called "minor planets," or asteroids (also called planetoids, meaning planet-like bodies). There are also the comets, meteors, and meteoric dust which travel within the limits of the solar system.

A good illustration of the size of the solar system, or rather of its planets in relation to one another, was given by the famous astronomer, Sir John Herschel. A modification of his representation follows:

Let a ball two feet in diameter represent the sun. Place this on a level field and walk 28 yards away from it. Drop at this point a tiny bead no bigger than the head of a pin—that represents Mercury. Walk 24 yards farther away, drop a small pea—that is Venus. Walk another 20 yards, drop another pea, and that is the earth. Still another 38 yards, or 110 yards from the "sun," drop a bead somewhat larger than that for Mercury—that is Mars. The minor planets or asteroids can be represented by tiny grains of sand and specks of dust at distances varying between 120 and 400 yards from the "sun" (the ball in the center of the field). Drop an orange of ordinary size about 400 yards from the sun—that is Jupiter. Place a slightly smaller orange 700 yards from the ball—that is Saturn. Four-fifths of a mile from the ball that is the sun, place a small plum— to represent Uranus. A large plum a mile and a fifth from the sun will be Neptune.

For the nearest star you will have to go 11,000 miles from your "sun," or farther than the other side of the earth, to find the relative position of that celestial neighbor! And now walk back your mile or so, and try to find the pea that was the earth, in the grass where you dropped it!

Finally, imagine each of the objects you deposited to be rolling around the ball (the "sun") at varying speeds, but all in the same direction. Except that they are not supported on any "field" or ground, the planets revolve around the sun in nearly the same plane—that is, they may be said to move within an area much like a great disk.

THE SUN

If it were not for the fact that the sun is so near (comparatively) to the earth, it would be a very faint and very small star. Astronomically defined, it is a dwarf star; and although it may be very much like other stars in constitution, it is in a stage of evolution that is perhaps almost peculiar to itself. It has been proved that it is a rotating, almost spherical body of flaming or incandescent gaseous matter, with a density about 1.4 times that of water, and containing some 70 of the elements (at least) which exist on the earth—though, of course, in an incandescent state.

The mean distance of the sun from the earth has been determined, with fair accuracy, as 92,900,000 miles. Since the earth's orbit is an ellipse, this distance varies, for the earth is sometimes nearer and sometimes farther away; but the variation, as compared with the total distance, is slight. The layman is likely to wonder how so great a distance can be accurately measured. More than one method is possible, and various observations have confirmed the figure given. The methods involve well-known principles of mathematics, especially of geometry and trigonometry, and are much like those used in surveying and other terrestrial computations.

By similar mathematical computations, the diameter of the sun is known to be about 864,000 miles. Its volume is something like 1,300,-000 times the volume of the earth, but its matter, being gaseous, is more tenuous (less solid). Its mass, or weight, is calculated as approximately

332,000 times the mass of the earth; if you care for figures, the sun weighs 2,000,000,000,000,000,000,000,000,000 tons! As compared with the earth, the gigantic size of the sun is really inconceivable. The sun has been radiating heat and light, a vast dissipation of energy, for millions upon millions of years, and will continue so to radiate for millions upon millions of years more. Of this vast amount of energy, the earth receives but a small part, for heat and light are being sent out into space in all directions from the sun, lighting all the planets and minor planets (whose own brightness is reflected sunlight). Sunlight is essential to life on the earth, and if the sun should explode (which is so unlikely as to be a negligible possibility) or be otherwise annihilated, life would soon cease, if indeed it were not wiped out by the tremendous chaos that would occur simultaneously with the sun's destruction.

By its gravitational attraction or pull, the sun keeps the various planets in their regular orbits and pulls them with it through space. For the sun, and the solar system with it, is known to be moving through space at the rate of about 12 miles per second. The sun itself is rotating on its axis, but since it is not rigid or solid, like the earth, the parts at the sun's equator rotate faster than those above and below the equator. The period of rotation is about 26 days, which means (since the sun is 864,000 miles in diameter) that the speed of a point on the equator can only be described as terrific.

Laymen have a fondness for hypothetical figures in astronomy. Let it be said, then, that the attraction of gravity on the sun is so great that if a man could stand there (he would, of course, be burned into incandescent gas particles long before he could get anywhere near the sun), he would weigh something like two tons, and would be crushed by his own weight.

The luminous surface of the sun, which appears to us as a disk, is called the photosphere. Above this there is a solar atmosphere of incandescent gas particles, called the chromosphere. Between the two there is still another layer, called the reversing layer. The sun exhibits various fascinating phenomena, including sunspots, faculae, and solar prominences. Solar storms in the sun's atmosphere are thousands of times more violent than the most terrific hurricane on the earth.

Sunspots are now known to occur in the photosphere at regularly recurring intervals of maximum number, about every 11⅓ years. A sunspot appears as a dark or black hole in the photosphere; really, the sunspot is very bright, but appears black by contrast with the comparatively greater brightness of the normal photosphere. The spot moves, carried along by the rotation of the sun. Some spots last a few days, others some months. They are of varying size. Occasionally they can be seen with the naked eye in a quick glance at the sun (the reader should be warned never to stare at the sun for even a few seconds, lest he severely injure his eyesight); usually, however, they can be observed only through powerful telescopes.

The exact significance of sunspots is not known, though there are several theories about them. A connection has been established between frequency of sunspots and magnetic storms on the earth, the latter coinciding with the prevalence of spots on the sun. The spots, if large (some of them extend 100,000 miles across), may slightly reduce the radiation of heat and light to the earth. The presence of sunspots may also affect radio transmission and reception on the earth.

The faculae are bright spots, brighter than the adjacent photosphere; they frequently occur near sunspots, or near the limb (edge) of the sun's disk. The spectroheliograph, an astronomical instrument, has established that sunspots and faculae are different manifestations of the same activity, for both show a large amount of calcium gas.

The solar prominences (seen best during total eclipse of the sun) are jets of flaming gas projected from the surface of the sun with great speed and to great heights. A prominence observed in the solar eclipse of May 29, 1919, rose from 130,000 miles to more than 500,000 miles above the sun's surface in less than seven hours. The earth would be like a tiny moth in a candle flame if caught in such a mass of fire.

In appearance, through the telescope, the sun's photosphere is mottled; it looks like a plate of rice soup. In reality, what appears to us as a surface is layer on layer of incandescent gases, chiefly hydrogen and helium in the higher parts. Helium was first discovered on the sun (by means of the spectroscope), and not until long afterward was it found on the earth. The surface temperature of the sun is computed to be 6,000 degrees Centigrade, which corresponds to about 11,000 degrees Fahrenheit (water boils on the earth at 212 degrees Fahrenheit). At the sun's center the temperature is terrific; one estimate places it at the probable figure of 18,000,000 degrees Centigrade.

Various physical and chemical forces are at work in and on the sun to produce its great radiation of light and heat. Light, in the great quantities produced by the sun, exerts a pressure. Of the energy radiated by the sun, the planets and their satellites receive only one part in 120,000,-000. The other parts are sent out into remote space—how far, or serving what purpose, or with what result, if any, is not known.

It used to be thought that the sun produced its energy by contracting. But even if the sun once filled the entire dimensions of the solar system its contraction to its present small size would not have kept up that stream of energy for more than a few million years.

It is now believed that the energy is due to a thermonuclear reaction in which hydrogen is fused to form helium through the intermediate action of carbon. In this process 564 million tons of hydrogen become 560 million tons of helium. Thus the sun loses mass at the rate of 4,000,000 tons a second. This mass is converted into energy in accordance with a prediction of Albert Einstein, who showed that if matter is annihilated, energy takes its place. There is no need, however, to be alarmed at this rapid loss in weight of the sun, for if the sun continues to lose 4 million tons of matter each second, it still has enough hydrogen to last many billions of years.

To reach the earth, the sun's rays must pass through our atmosphere, which diffuses the sunlight so as to cause the blue color of the sky, which we seem to see extending far up into space, but which is really our own atmosphere filled with diffused sunlight. On cloudy days, of course, the sun's rays are further obstructed, but never altogether, for even on the cloudiest days there is some light and heat from the powerful sun.

Perhaps the most awesome spectacle ever to be seen in the heavens is a total eclipse of the sun. So infrequent is this occurrence, and so scattered (or limited in width) is its area of totality—often taking place in regions of the earth that are inaccessible to most of us—that few people ever have the chance to view the phenomenon. An awesome spectacle to the casual observer, a total eclipse of the sun is a boon to astronomers, for only then can they observe the pearly white corona and make other investigations of the true nature of the sun and the sources of its energy. Eclipses blot out, for a few seconds or minutes, the bright photosphere, enabling astronomers to view the surrounding gases, the prominences, and the corona.

A solar eclipse is a beautiful sight indeed, especially because of the corona, which is a pearly white radiance forming a halo around the sun (which, hidden by the moon, appears to be a black disk). This corona extends out into space from the sun, in all directions, but in an irregular outline; the corona may be flung hundreds of thousands of miles from the surface of the sun, gradually diminishing in brightness. The light is about equal to that which is cast on the earth by a full moon: it is bright enough to permit good photographs of the landscape to be taken during a total eclipse of the sun.

The moon revolves around the earth once in about 28 days, while the earth revolves around the sun once in 365¼ days. The plane of the moon's orbit, however, is not the same path or level as the earth's orbital path around the sun, but is inclined at an angle of about 5° above and below. It can therefore be understood that occasionally, but not very often, the moon will pass between the sun and the earth, obscuring temporarily the stream of light from the sun and casting a shadow on the earth. If the sun is viewed from this shadow, it will seem to be partially obscured (a partial eclipse) or totally blotted out (a total eclipse).

Fortunately for astronomers, the moon's diameter and its distance from the earth are such that times occur when the moon, small though it is compared with the sun, can seem to slide over the sun's face and exactly cover it, casting a narrow pencil of shadow on the earth (seldom over 180 miles in width). Just before a total eclipse this shadow can some-

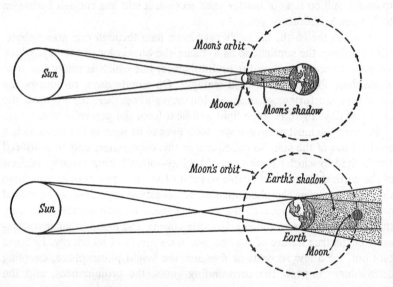

FIG. 2. The top drawing shows an eclipse of the sun. The moon is passing directly between the earth and the sun. The bottom drawing shows an eclipse of the moon, which takes place when the earth passes directly between the sun and the moon.

times be seen traveling along at the tremendous speed of 1,000 miles an hour—for the moon is revolving around the earth, the earth is revolving around the sun, and the earth is rotating on its axis, making the duration of total eclipse at any one point very short (the longest duration possible is a trifle less than eight minutes; the usual duration is two or three minutes).

Partial eclipses of the sun are rather frequently visible. Partial eclipses, however, are of very little value to astronomers. For their investigations they need the precious few moments of total eclipse.

At the instant of totality, the moon's racing shadow sweeps across the observer, putting him literally in the shade (the shadow of totality is called the umbra, and the adjacent shadow of partial eclipse, the penumbra). Just before totality, the observer can see "Baily's beads," tiny spots of light at the edge of the moon, caused by the last rays of the bright sun shining through the deep valleys between the mountains of the moon along that edge; and just before totality, when a small crescent of the sun is still visible, shadow bands, dancing vertically on the ground or buildings, can often be seen. Then, at the instant of totality, the stars pop out—they are invisible in the daytime because the sun's light is so diffused through the earth's atmosphere, except when it is blotted out by the moon during eclipse. The planets Mercury and Venus may gleam forth near the sun. The corona and perhaps a solar prominence or two are visible, surrounding the black disk that has supplanted the bright sun. A few rare moments of impressive spectacle, and the moon slips away, revealing first a thin crescent of the sun, which is so bright that it wipes out the stars and lights the earth, and the moon's shadow races into the distance, and, for most observers (who cannot chase eclipses over the earth), into eternity.

THE EARTH

Technically, the earth is a planet, an oblate spheroid in shape—that is, it is not perfectly spherical, being somewhat flattened at the poles and bulging somewhat at the equator. Ancient peoples believed the earth to be flat, like a dinner plate, floating on a sea of infinite extent. Many proofs exist of the spheroidal shape of the earth. Even the laymen can observe how a ship disappears over the horizon, masts last; or the fact that the stars are different when viewed from different points on the earth's surface (some, in the northern hemisphere, are never visible south of the equator, and vice versa); or that the earth casts a round shadow on the moon during a lunar eclipse. A general belief in the roundness of the earth is rather recent, but intelligent thinkers deduced its general shape even in ancient times.

The diameter of the earth is usually given in round numbers as 8,000 miles; actually, the diameter at the equator is slightly different from the diameter between the poles. The polar diameter is 7,899.6 miles; the equatorial diameter is 7,926.6 miles—a difference of 27 miles. The earth is fifth in size among the planets; it is the third in distance from the sun. The density of the earth is 5½ times that of water. It is a mass of solid matter (the liquid oceans at the surface are part of a very thin crust), more rigid than steel. Since the temperature is known to increase toward the earth's center, it was once believed that the center was a molten mass of metal. This view is no longer widely held; in fact, in the light of presen knowledge, it seems impossible. Though it is at a very high temperature, matter inside the earth is kept solid by the tremendous pressure exerted by the outer matter.

The earth revolves around the sun once in every 365¼ days, approximately. The path taken during this revolution is an ellipse, but it is nevertheless very nearly circular. The earth also rotates on its axis, which is a line drawn between the two poles, once in every sidereal day, which is exactly 23 hours, 56 minutes, and 4.095 seconds, but, for convenience, is taken to be 24 hours, a correction in calendars being made by the insertion of "leap years." Spinning thus through space, the axis of the earth does not remain in a constant position, but wobbles slightly (somewhat as a spinning top may be seen to wobble from the vertical), so that the North Pole changes its position slightly through the ages.

The North Star is so called because it would nearly coincide with the axis of the earth if that line were extended out into space from the North Pole. It is always visible in the northern hemisphere and is traditionally useful for mariners to steer by. But since the line of the earth's axis changes, the North Star is not always the same star. It has been so for some time, and will remain so for some time to come, but in 12,000 years, if anyone cares to know it, the North Star, instead of Polaris (as it is now), will be Vega.

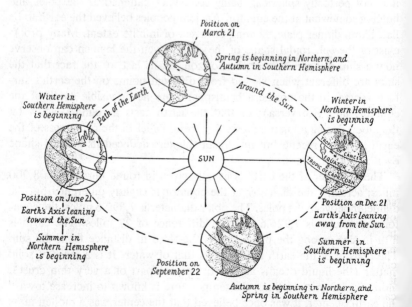

FIG. 3. Diagrammatic representation of the changing of the seasons.

The point at which the sun crosses the line of the earth's equator on the way north is called the vernal equinox (it occurs on March 21); the autumnal equinox is the point at which the sun crosses the equator on its way south (it occurs on September 22). These points (the equinoxes) coincide with points in the celestial sphere, which is to say, with certain stars or constellations, or almost so coincide. Owing to the wobbling of the earth's axis, this point in the heavens varies slightly from year to year. This change is called the precession of the equinoxes. In a period of 25,800 years the precession will rotate upon itself and the points will return to approximately the same corresponding points among the stars which they intersected at the beginning of that period.

The name of Sir Isaac Newton is associated with the law of gravitation, for he first stated that every particle of matter exerts a force of attraction for every other particle of matter, which varies inversely to the square of the distance between them, and also varies proportionately to their masses. Gravitation ties us to the earth, and makes us fall when we have no support beneath us. Gravitation also holds the earth together in its spheroidal shape, and keeps the moon revolving around the earth. By the force of gravity, too, the earth and the other planets are kept revolving around the sun, in orbits which vary somewhat, owing to the attraction of one planet for another, as well as of the sun for each planet. Careful observation and calculation of planetary perturbations enabled scientists to foretell the existence of the planet Neptune, and also of Pluto, discovered in 1930. Gravitation has been proved and measured experimentally in the laboratory, even for so small a body as a sphere of lead two feet in diameter.

The planets remain fixed in their orbits because of a balance between the force of gravity and what is called *centrifugal force*. This force is exerted from the center of an orbit outward on any object in rotation. Hence it is a force of exactly opposite direction to that of gravity, and the equilibrium between the two determines the position of a planet's orbit and also holds the planet constantly within its orbit.

Study of the earth's surface, which is a comparatively thin crust or shell, belongs to subjects other than astronomy, chiefly geography, geology, and meteorology. Immediately surrounding the earth is the atmosphere, consisting of air (principally nitrogen and oxygen, but containing many other gases in small quantities) and water vapor (concentrated in clouds, and falling as rain or snow). The atmosphere is necessary to life; it diffuses the sun's light and heat evenly over any particular region. Because of it we have the blue color of the daytime sky, and because of the refraction of the light waves as the sun sets, we get the beautiful and changing colors of the sunset. But this very same atmosphere is one of the astronomer's greatest difficulties, for he must allow for its refraction of the light from sun and moon and stars, and its impurities and the weather conditions taking place in it often interfere seriously with his observations. The atmosphere is held wrapped around the earth by the force of gravity.

How old is the earth? Not only astronomers, but physicists and geologists, have turned their attention to this question. Their various computations are based on the length of time it should take for certain changes to occur, which are known to have occurred. These changes are: the rate of decomposition of uranium, the rate of increase of the saltiness of the sea, and the rate of deposit of sediment. The age of the earth is now believed to be at least 3,000,000,000 or 4,000,000,000 years.

THE MOON

The moon is the earth's satellite: it revolves around the earth. This chief luminary of the night sky (when it is visible), in consequence of its nearness to the earth, has an important effect on the earth—namely, the tides.

FIG. 4. The mountains of the moon. The relative height of these mountains may be judged by comparing them with the building in the center, which represents the Empire State Building (1250 feet high). The mountains of the moon are higher than any on earth.

The moon shines by reflected sunlight. It is a spherical body, as can readily be ascertained by viewing it through a small telescope. The so-called "man in the moon," having the apparent configurations of a human face, is formed by the distribution of light and shadow caused by mountains and valleys and depressions on the moon's surface.

The moon's average distance from the earth (it varies slightly, since its orbit is a nearly circular ellipse) is 239,000 miles. Its diameter is 2,162 miles—about one fourth that of the earth. Its mass is about 1/80 that of the earth, and its volume about 1/49 that of the earth. With reference to the sun, the moon takes about 29½ days to revolve around the earth, thus nearly dividing the year into our twelve months, a lunar month being sometimes called a "moon." With reference to the stars, the period of revolution is about 27⅓ days. The difference is due to the different viewpoint of an observer on the earth, whose relative position is changed by the earth's revolution around the sun. The point of the moon's orbit nearest the earth is known as the *perigee;* the point farthest from the earth is the *apogee.*

The moon also rotates on its axis, with a period of rotation that exactly coincides with its period of revolution around the earth. The result is that the moon always keeps one face toward the earth and we are unable to see the back of the moon at any time. Actually we see a little more than half of the moon during the month of its revolution, because the moon "wobbles" a bit as it revolves around the earth. We have thus been able to map about 50 per cent of the moon's surface.

The illuminated portion that we see varies from completely dark (new moon), when the moon is between the sun and the earth, to completely bright (full moon), when the luminary is on the opposite side of the earth from the sun. These phases of the moon are familiar to everyone. From completely dark, the moon begins to go toward one side of the earth with respect to the sun (toward the east) and reveals a small crescent of the sun's reflected light (this crescent being usually called the new moon). Then appears the first quarter, or "half" moon, followed by the appearance called gibbous, and finally by the full moon, after which the phases occur in reverse order, through the last quarter and to the new moon again. Even when only a crescent of the sun's reflected light can be seen, the rest of the moon's disk is faintly visible. This is reflected earth-shine—sunlight reflected into space from the earth, caught by the moon, and reflected back to us again.

Though many fanciful romances have been written about "moon people," supposing that there is life on the moon, it is almost certain that the moon has little if any water, and no atmosphere, and without water and oxygen there can be no life on the moon. Without atmosphere there can be no weather and no sound—no howling winds, no freezing of water in crevices to split rocks, no wearing away of mountains by the action of wind and rain, no motion of even sand particles in storms. The surface of the moon, according to all indications, is a region heated to great temperatures (there being no diffusion through an atmosphere, as on the earth) in the sunlight, and extremely cold in the shade. The moon is a place where there is no life and where nothing ever happens; there is no volcanic activity—nothing; the moon is dead.

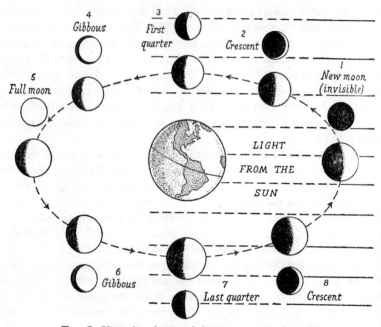

FIG. 5. How the phases of the moon are produced.

Through an ordinary glass the surface of the moon looks rather smooth, but through a more powerful telescope it is seen to be pitted with round, crater-like rings and depressions. These may be volcanic craters, similar to those on the earth, but on the moon they are no longer active. In height above the surrounding surface they rise to something like 20,000 feet. Dark and smooth-looking areas were first called seas or oceans, and they are still so called although it is now known that they are not oceans like those on the earth, for no such bodies of water exist on the moon. They may be areas of solidified lava emitted from now extinct volcanoes in the remote past. Anything much less than a mile in diameter cannot be clearly distinguished on the moon, so, of course, very small features of its surface are not observable. The total brightness of the moon

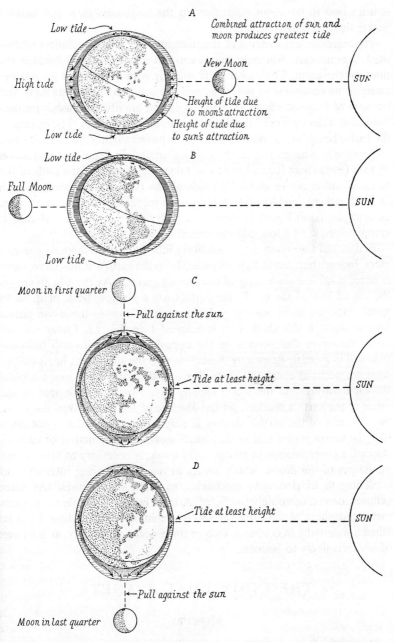

FIG. 6. How tides are produced through the pull of the sun and the moon.

is estimated to be about equivalent to the brightness of a 100 candle-power light 22 yards away.

The scientific explanation of the tides involves highly technical mathematical equations. Not only the moon, but also the sun, influences the tides on the earth. The moon pulls strongly with its force of gravity because of its comparative nearness, and the sun pulls rather strongly also because of its great size—although the pull of gravity diminishes proportionately to the square of the distance between two bodies. The oceans of the earth, being liquid and tenuous, can be pulled slightly out of their beds, so to speak. And as the earth revolves around the sun and rotates on its axis (even these forces have to be taken into account), the pulls of the sun and moon act to make high tide as the ocean waves seem to rush in (on beaches), and low tide as the waters recede once more. The ocean, as a whole, is no higher or deeper at high tide; the apparent change is compensated for by low tide elsewhere.

Eclipses of the moon are of relatively little interest to modern astronomers. Indeed, because of light refracted from the earth's atmosphere, there is never complete darkening of the moon's surface. As the sun shines on the round ball of the earth, the earth casts a shadow back of it, so to speak, tapering away into space like a cone. Whenever the moon passes into or through this shadow, it is eclipsed (see Fig. 2). Lunar eclipses occur whenever the moon is on the opposite side of the earth from the sun, and in a nearly or exactly direct line with the sun. But a lunar eclipse does not occur at every full moon, because the path of the moon around the earth varies, and the moon usually passes to either one side or the other of the earth's shadow. At the distance of the moon from the earth, the diameter of the earth's shadow is only 6,000 miles, so it is not often that the moon comes within that small space. A conjunction of circumstances, a co-ordination of forces, so to speak, is necessary to bring about an eclipse of the moon, which occurs at regular recurring intervals and according to fixed laws of mechanics, so that lunar eclipses, like solar eclipses, can be accurately predicted. A lunar eclipse is visible from whatever hemisphere of the earth the moon is shining on at the time (that is, when not actually in eclipse). Two or three occur every year, at least one of which is likely to be total.

THE INDIVIDUAL PLANETS

MERCURY

It is generally accepted that Mercury's period of rotation is equal to its period of revolution around the sun, or 88 days. Allowing for the sun's light "sliding over the edges," as Mercury's position changes due to a very eccentric orbit, something like 37 per cent of the planet's surface remains in eternal night, and the same proportion in eternal day, the other 26 per cent being alternately lighted up and plunged into darkness. Since Mercury is so close to the sun (36,000,000 miles), such day and night changes as may occur over about a quarter of its surface mean severe changes in temperature. There is little likelihood of life on Mercury.

Mercury appears to have little if any atmosphere. Its *albedo* (the proportion of sunlight it reflects) is so low (planets with atmospheres, like Venus, reflect much more sunlight than those lacking atmospheres) that it seems certain that there is little atmosphere of any kind on Mercury. Indeed, Mercury is quite faint in the sky, although it may be seen, a few days at a time, as a morning or evening star, just before sunrise or just after sunset.

No satellite revolves around Mercury. The mass of the planet is about 1/27 of that of the earth. Its diameter is about 3,100 miles. In general, it is very difficult to observe, even through telescopes, for it presents phases much like those of the moon as it revolves around the sun, revealing a varying amount of illuminated surface to the earth.

VENUS

Venus is very much like the earth in size and mass, and in having a dense atmosphere. If Venus rotates on its axis more rapidly than it revolves around the sun (the period of revolution being 225 days, as compared with the earth's 365¼ days), and if there is plenty of oxygen and water, there may be life on Venus, for the temperature is not more than 1½ times the earth's average, or somewhat like the earth's tropical regions, where life is very profuse. Unfortunately, little is known about Venus; shrouded in clouds, it is a planet of mystery. Pictures taken in infrared light (which penetrates haze) show clouds on Venus to be 35 to 80 miles thick as compared to those on earth, which are 2 to 7 miles deep.

Venus moves in an orbit between that of Mercury and the earth. It appears to us as by far the brightest object in the heavens besides the sun and moon—its light will even cast a shadow on the earth, when it is in its brightest phase. For Venus, like Mercury, displays phases much like those of the moon. Venus reflects actually 59 per cent of the sun's light, as compared with 44 per cent reflected by the earth, and only 7 per cent reflected by the moon. It is sometimes visible as an evening star, just after sunset, when the ancients called it Hesperus, and sometimes as a morning star, just before sunrise, when the ancients called it Phosphorus or Lucifer.

Indeed, in a favorable phase, Venus may be seen with the naked eye in daytime.

Venus is 67,300,000 miles from the sun. Its diameter is about 7,700 miles. Its mass is about 8/10 that of the earth. Venus has no satellite. According to present evidence, it seems probable that Venus may rotate on its axis rather rapidly; this, however, has not yet been proved. On account of the dense atmosphere, telescopic markings are rare or absent.

MARS

Mars captured the popular imagination during the later years of the nineteenth century as being quite possibly inhabited. Many romances have been written about imaginary life on Mars. The scientific belief now prevailing is that there is very little chance of life anything like ours on Mars.

Mars and all the other planets beyond it are called the superior planets, for the earth is between all of them and the sun. Mars is 141,500,000 miles from the sun. Its mean diameter is about 4,200 miles. Its mass is about 1/10 that of the earth. Solar light and heat cannot be more than half as intense on Mars as they are on the earth. Temperature measurements with sensitive thermocouples indicate that the temperature at the so-called polar cap in the Martian winter is 94° F. The equator measures 45° F. at noon and 9° F. at sunrise. There is probably little, if any, water or water vapor, and apparently little, if any, oxygen. The polar caps of "snow" which can be seen to melt with the seasons may be frozen carbonic-acid gas, for the temperature may be cold enough to freeze that gas or even liquefy air. Some recent evidence, however, indicates that it may be a very thin layer of ice. If there is life on Mars, it must be of a comparatively low order, corresponding to the lower forms of plant and animal life on the earth.

The great interest in Mars is partly due to the fact that it comes closer to the earth than any other major planet at a time favorable for observation—within some 35,000,000 miles, at its nearest point. Also, the period of rotation of Mars on its axis is very nearly the same as our day, or 24 hours and 37 minutes, while its period of revolution around the sun is nearly two of our years, or about 687 days. Owing to an inclination of the axis of Mars similar to that of the earth, the seasons on Mars also correspond somewhat to earthly seasons. Mars has two satellites or moons, named Phobos and Deimos, like the earth's moon, except much smaller (with diameters of not much more than 10 miles each) and much closer to the planet. Phobos revolves around Mars in 7½ hours, while Deimos takes 30¼ hours; since Phobos revolves three times as fast as the planet rotates, it would appear to a "Martian" to rise in the west and set in the east, while Deimos rises in the east and sets in the west.

To an earthly observer Mars appears as a fairly bright "star" of a reddish hue (Venus appears almost white). Many telescopic observations and photographs have been made, showing the famed "canals," or markings of the surface. It has been supposed that these so-called canals are works of engineering, devised by intelligent beings to conduct presumed water from the melting poles to the arid regions of the planet, to grow vegetation during suitable seasons. There is, of course, no astronomical evidence that such a hypothetical suggestion has any basis of truth. Astronomers have often violently disagreed on the probable nature of these markings. The more general opinion seems to be that they may be areas of vegetation, of a low order of plant life, which causes changes or "flowering" each "summer." All this, however, is merely speculation. The darker markings are permanent. It has even been suggested, not without reason, that the apparent configuration of the finer markings on Mars into canals is a subjective illusion—familiar in psychology as the tendency of the eye to make patterns out of irregular groupings of light and shade. Mars has a rare atmosphere—that much is agreed—and there are clouds, perhaps of two kinds, one of which may be made up of water vapor.

THE PLANETOIDS

As has already been said, a group of minor planets, also called asteroids or planetoids, more than 1,000 in number, are found for the most part between Mars and the next major planet, Jupiter. A few of the asteroids revolve in orbits that roam outside of the limits of the orbits of Mars and Jupiter. All these thousand or more asteroids revolve in variously eccentric orbits around the sun. The largest of them is Ceres, some 500 miles in diameter, discovered in 1801; some of those that have been observed are as small as ten miles or so in diameter. All are telescopic objects.

In 1852, 21 minor planets had been discovered and named. It began to appear that the large gap between Mars and Jupiter, in which astronomers thought another planet should be, was occupied by a host of small planets, all with very eccentric orbits, and sharp angles of inclination to the ecliptic. In those days, before photography came into use, hunting for such planetary objects was very laborious. Observers had to map sections of the sky and memorize the stars. Then, if a new planetoid swam into their ken (in Keats' immortal phrase), they could detect it. With the advent of photography, the search was made much easier, for a photographic plate exposed to a section of the heavens shows distant stars as points or disks of light, but a planet, moving rather rapidly with respect to the stars, photographs as a streak of light. So the search went on, until, by 1927, as many as 1,055 of these minor planets had been discovered, their orbits calculated, and themselves numbered and usually named. It is a task in itself for astronomical observatories to keep track of these small bodies, to watch them, and to see that they are not confused with one another.

More than 1,500 are known to exist, but the process of cataloguing the newer and smaller ones is slow and difficult. Some authorities hold that this host of minor planets represents a former single planet which at some time or other, in the remote past, exploded. Whether this is true or not, the minor planets are curiously interesting, and have often served a useful purpose in enabling astronomers to measure planetary distances.

Most of the planetoids revolve in a band lying between Mars and Jupiter. In 1898 the curious small planet Eros was discovered; the orbit of Eros is so eccentric that it comes within 14,000,000 miles of the earth—the nearest planetary body to the earth, except the moon. By means of Eros, new calculations of the sun's distance have been made, with great accuracy. Other minor planetoids include Pallas, 304 miles in diameter; Vesta, 243 miles; and Juno, 118 miles. Within the orbit of Venus are Apollo, Adonis, and Hermes, which were discovered in 1932, 1936, and 1937 respectively. Traveling out as far as the orbit of Saturn, the planetoid Hidalgo takes 13½ years to revolve completely around the sun, but most of the other asteroids take a shorter time.

JUPITER

Jupiter is the largest of the planets, and, next to Venus, the brightest in the sky. At a distance of 483,000,000 miles from the sun, it has a mean diameter of about 86,728 miles and revolves around that luminary in 11.86 years. Jupiter's day is about 10 hours; it rotates on its axis in that time. However, different latitudes exhibit slightly different times of rotation, indicating that Jupiter may be a gaseous body, at least on the surface. Certainly it is far less solid than the earth, for its density is 1.3 that of water, or very nearly the same as that of the sun (which is 1.4). Its mass is 320 times that of the earth, but less than 1/1000 that of the sun.

Many of the features of Jupiter can be observed through even a small telescope. It exhibits light and dark bands, and a peculiar and fairly permanent red spot, which has attracted the attention of observers since it was first discovered in 1878. No doubt many of these surface features are due to varying clouds, but the nature even of the conspicuous red spot is not yet known. Jupiter may radiate some heat, but it certainly radiates very little, if any, light of its own. Its light is due to reflected sunlight, of which it reflects 44 per cent of the comparatively small amount it receives at its great distance.

Jupiter has twelve satellites. The four outer ones revolve around the planet in a direction opposite to that of the eight inner moons, which suggests that they may have been acquired after the inner moons originated. The four brightest were discovered in 1610 by Galileo and are called the Galilean satellites, being named Io, Europa, Ganymede, and Callisto. The nearest satellite to Jupiter is 261,800 miles away, or farther than the moon is from the earth; the farthest is some 15,000,000 miles from the planet. Their diameters vary between less than 100 and more than 3,000 miles. The larger ones, the first four discovered, can readily be observed through a small telescope; they appear as black spots when passing in transit between the planet and the earth, and can be seen to cast circular shadows on the planet's surface.

If the shadow of one of Jupiter's moons can be observed on that planet, that moon is causing an eclipse of the sun on Jupiter, just as the earth's moon causes an eclipse of the sun on the earth. Jupiter's moons are also eclipsed on the far side of the planet from the sun, when they pass through the shadow cast by the planet into farther space. Such eclipses provide an interesting spectacle from the earth (through telescopes) and have been useful in computing more exactly the velocity of light.

SATURN

To earthly eyes looking through telescopes, Saturn is strangely beautiful. Within the "rings" of Saturn, the planet itself is poised like a bright silvery ball. At a distance of 886,000,000 miles from the sun, Saturn receives only 1/80 as much light and heat as the earth. Its time of revolution around the sun is almost 30 years; its period of rotation is a little more than 10 hours at its equator, and varies toward the poles, like that of Jupiter and the sun, showing that it is a fluid and probably a gaseous body. Its density, indeed, is only .7 that of water. It shows surface markings, chiefly spots, somewhat like those of Jupiter, though far less distinct, owing to the great distance from the earth. Saturn's mean diameter is 70,000 miles. Its mass is about 95 times that of the earth.

It is now known that Saturn has three rings, designated as A, B, and C. The outer diameter of A is 170,000 miles; of B, 145,000 miles; of C, 113,000 miles. A is 10,000 miles broad; B, 16,000 miles; C, 11,000 miles. The rings are between 20 and 40 miles thick; they appear very thin and film-like from the earth. They are somewhat transparent, Saturn being seen through them, and a star has been occasionally visible through them. The rings cast a shadow on the planet, however. They are believed to be made up of very fine particles—so fine that the rings appear to be continuous when viewed from the earth. The rings revolve around the planet; they shine by reflected sunlight. Possibly they were once a moon or moons that have disintegrated.

Saturn has at least nine satellites. The diameter of the largest is estimated at about 3,000 miles; the others are much smaller, one being only about 150 miles in diameter. Their distances from Saturn vary between 116,000 and 8,000,000 miles.

Knowledge of Saturn illustrates how difficult it often is to confirm telescopic discoveries of nonluminary bodies (that is, bodies which shine by reflected light) at such great distances. Even the number of Saturn's rings is sometimes disputed, other divisions being noted, or the division between B and C being denied (C is also called the "Crape Ring"). The rings of Saturn are sometimes presented edgewise to the earth, when they almost disappear from our view.

URANUS

Saturn was the outermost of the planets visible to and named by the ancients. Uranus, a telescopic planet, was discovered in 1781 by Sir William Herschel. Its distance from the sun is 1,782,000,000 miles; its diameter, 30,878 miles; its period of revolution, 84 years; its mass, almost 15 times that of the earth; its density, 1.36 that of water; its period of rotation, about 10¾ hours. The nature of Uranus appears to be about the same as that of Jupiter, Saturn, and Neptune. It reflects a good deal of the small amount of sunlight it receives, and can sometimes be seen with the naked eye; it appears slightly greenish in the telescope. Uranus has five satellites. Their distances from the planet vary between 119,000 and 364,000 miles.

NEPTUNE

The most interesting fact about Neptune is the manner of its discovery. In fact, Neptune is one of the triumphs of astronomical mathematics. Leverrier, a Frenchman, and also Adams, an Englishman, who worked independently, reached the conclusion that perturbations of the orbit of Uranus could be accounted for by a planet beyond Uranus, which would move in such and such an orbit and could be seen by looking in a certain part of the sky. Indeed, many facts about Neptune were predicted, and when the planet was discovered and the computations checked, the figures were found to be remarkably accurate.

Neptune is so far from the sun (2,793,000,000 miles), and of course so very far from the earth also, that few very definite facts and figures can be stated about it. It is known that it takes almost 165 years to revolve once around the sun; its diameter is 31,000 miles; it probably rotates in from 8 to 15 hours (uncertain); its mass is about 17 times that of the earth. Like the other large planets—Saturn, Jupiter, and Uranus—Neptune is shrouded in a thick atmosphere, probably heavy with clouds. In the sky, Neptune has the dimness of an eighth-magnitude star and cannot be seen with the naked eye. Neptune has two satellites.

PLUTO

Pluto was discovered in 1930 at the Lowell Observatory at Flagstaff, Arizona. This planet, if we may call it such, is small, possibly the size of Mercury or our own moon. Its orbit is very elliptical. The planet's period of revolution is about 250 years; its period of rotation is 50 years. Because of Pluto's small size and long rotational period, it has been suggested that Pluto is an escaped moon of Neptune. Its temperature must be so low that its atmosphere, if it has any, is liquefied or frozen. The density of Pluto is about 4 times that of water; Pluto's average distance from the sun is approximately 3,670,000,000 miles.

COMETS

Comets are fascinating, mischievous, not altogether dependable rascals, scampering through the solar system. Even though the reader may not have seen a comet himself, he knows that the more spectacular ones, at least, have what appears to be a glowing head with a long tail streaming out behind. Because of this tail, which looks like hair blown out by wind, comets received their name: the word comet comes from a Greek word which means "long-haired." Great comets, flaming through the sky, have often been viewed with dread, being regarded as dire omens. Even Shakespeare contributed to legend when he wrote the lines: "When beggars die, there are no comets seen; the heavens themselves blaze forth the death of princes."

So few comets are visible to the naked eye (and even then not all of them have tails) that people often think them rare. Many are known telescopically, however. The most famous great comet visible to the un-aided eye was Halley's comet, last seen in 1910. This comet will not be seen again until about 1985, for its period of revolution around the sun is about 75 years. And comets have enough light (largely reflected sun-light, apparently, though they may be partly self-luminous) to be visible only when they are near the sun. Halley's comet, after its appearance in 1910, swung out on its long journey through space at a terrific speed, passing somewhere between Saturn and Uranus in 1915, being somewhere beyond Neptune in 1930. It swung around and came back toward the sun in 1948, and started its long return trip. Not until about 1980, according to statistical indications, will it again be between Uranus and Saturn. Halley's comet, which moves in an orbit shaped like an elongated ellipse, was named after the astronomer who first calculated its period and identified it with a comet seen previously at intervals of about 75 years.

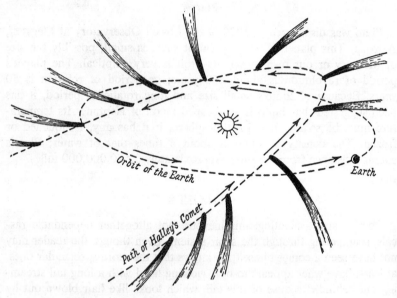

FIG. 7. The path of Halley's comet around the sun.

Many comets have such long periods that they do not return to the neighborhood of the sun within thousands, tens of thousands, or perhaps even hundreds of thousands of years. Many, therefore, have not yet been observed within the recorded history of man; at any time, indeed, a new comet may suddenly become visible as a flaming streak in the sky, though the likelihood is not great. Let it be said here, incidentally, that because of the known laws of celestial mechanics, no matter how near a comet may pass to the sun or to the earth, there is practically no chance that it will ever collide with any celestial body. Even should it do so, the mass of a comet is so small that it would probably have little or no effect. When Halley's comet passed between the earth and the sun in 1910, it could not be seen during the transit, proving that its mass, even at the head, was very small indeed. Of course the comet was readily visible every night—except during the short time just mentioned—until it left the sun's neighborhood for its long journey.

Comets come and go, and some have not been seen again. Some have been observed at regular periods of a few years, and then have disappeared; apparently they have disintegrated. The best description of the constitution of a comet is that it is a train of meteors—small pieces of matter streaming through space, somewhat more consolidated at and near the head or nucleus, and greatly attenuated in the tail, which may stretch into space for many millions of miles. Comets have been referred to as "the dirty icebergs of space." Indeed, the tails of comets which have long since left the neighborhood of the sun and have lost their visibility are still following behind, in the comets' orbits, and when these coincide with the orbit of the earth we see meteoric showers of "shooting stars," such as those that occur in August every year.

Although the orbits in which the planets move are elliptical, they are not so very far from being circular. Newton's law of gravitation showed that any celestial body revolving around another must follow a path that is a conic section—an ellipse, a parabola, or a hyperbola. The planets and some of the comets follow the path of an ellipse, one focus being the sun (an ellipse has two foci). Other comets follow the path of a parabola, and some seem to follow a hyperbolic path.

As compared with even the minor planets, the mass of a comet is very small. The round head, when there is little or no tail, is called the coma. If there is a tail, it is always directed away from the sun, no matter whether the comet is approaching or leaving the sun's neighborhood. The tail appears to be flung into space by some repulsive action of the sun—perhaps the force of the great radiation of light and heat from the sun. Yet this constant pushing away of matter from the comet's head appears not to reduce the comet so much as might be expected from its small mass. In the last analysis, so far as present knowledge goes, it can only be said that comets are still objects of considerable mystery to astronomers.

It is probable that all the comets belong within the limits of the solar system, though it has been argued that some may briefly enter the system from outer space. However, the limits of the solar system are circumscribed within a radius of something like 25,000,000,000,000 miles, which allows ample room for comets to complete their periodic journeys, even in many thousands of years, within that distance. It has been estimated that there may be as many as 120,000 comets in our solar system. The major planets, with their satellites, and all the minor planets, including the likelihood of many small ones not now known, cannot exceed 50,000 in number. Comets, incidentally, have been known for many centuries: records in Chinese annals are especially good, showing numerous appearances of Halley's comet during the past 2,000 years.

Although Halley called his comet the "Mercury among comets," believing it to have the shortest period of any, he was in error. Several comets have shorter periods than Halley's. The Mercury among the comets now known is Encke's comet, which is telescopic, and has a period of 3⅓ years. Some 60 comets are known with periods of less than 80 years.

Comets are divided into groups, each group associated with one of the major planets. Jupiter's family of comets numbers 50, with periods ranging between 3.3 and almost 9 years; Saturn's family consists of only four, with periods between 13 and 17.7 years; Uranus has only two, with a mean period of almost 37 years. There is some connection between each group or family and the planet from which it is named. Perhaps those more remote and giant planets are still in a state which enables them to cast off matter which takes the form of a comet and begins to revolve around the sun. Halley's comet belongs in Neptune's family, which numbers nine comets, with a mean period of about 71 years.

METEORS

Sometimes parts of comets' tails, but more often just isolated tiny bodies roaming through space, are many millions of meteors. They are not large enough ever to be visible by reflected sunlight. But when any of them hits the earth's atmosphere, its velocity—added to that of the earth if it meets the earth head on—as it passes through the air heats it to visible glowing, and it appears to earthly observers as a "shooting star." A meteor (properly only those seen as shooting stars are so called; the tiny bodies in outer space are more correctly called meteoroids) is, of course, not a star at all. Although it may seem very far away, it is not farther away than 100 miles, and is usually much nearer than that (even as near as 15 miles), for it must be within the earth's thin envelope of atmosphere.

The flash of a meteor is seldom longer than one second in duration. The body causing it is usually as small as or smaller than 2/10 of an inch in diameter, and weighs far less than an ounce, though some are considerably larger. Some 20,000,000 meteors with flashes bright enough to be visible to the unaided eye enter the earth's atmosphere, in different parts of the world, in one day. Though probably at least one survives the fiery ordeal to land on the earth every day, the chances of being struck by a meteor, or even of seeing one land, are extremely small. Besides those visible to the naked eye (on a clear, moonless night you should be able to see at least half a dozen in an hour, if you steadily watch the sky), many millions more are visible through telescopes. Most of these are burned up long before they reach the earth's surface.

After a meteor has landed on the earth, it is called a meteorite. A very few large ones, weighing some tons, are known, but they are rare. Small ones, of a few pounds, are not uncommon, and may be seen in almost any museum. They are usually metallic, containing chiefly iron and nickel, although some are more like common stones. One of the largest meteorites to strike the earth in recent times fell near Paragould, Arkansas, on February 17, 1930, breaking into many pieces—the heaviest of which weighed 820 pounds.

Comets appear to be composed of consolidated masses of meteoroids, more or less attracted by a common head or nucleus. The tails of comets, extending for many millions of miles, are composed of such bodies. When the earth passes through such tails, though the head of the comet may have passed by a great many years before, shooting stars are seen. Meteoric showers are usually associated with the orbit of some comet, especially the Leonid showers in October or November, which recur with especial brightness every 33 years. Such showers do not keep up indefinitely, for the masses of meteors become separated and dissipated as the years go by.

Many meteors are not associated with any comet, but seem to be roaming hit-or-miss through space. There are undoubtedly millions upon millions of such bits of cosmic matter which never come anywhere near the earth. The moon is bombarded by thousands of them all the time, but on that dead world they have no effect—since there is no air there, they do not even make a noise! Some meteors are believed to come from outer space, proving that all the starry universe is essentially of the same chemical composition.

THE STARS

We now leave our solar system and pass to the far more remote fixed stars—those bright points of light that dot the heavens nightly. The nearest star is something like 25,000,000,000,000 miles away from the sun, and is practically the same distance from the earth, the distance from the earth to the sun being so trifling in comparison. The light from that nearest star, traveling at the terrific speed of 186,000 miles per second, takes some four years to reach the earth. The distances of the stars are given in light-years; a light-year is the distance (about 6,000,000,000,000 miles) which light travels in one year, the farthest point of light that is visible with the unaided eye being in the neighborhood of 900,000 light-years away.

Anyone gazing up into a clear night sky notes two elementary facts: the stars vary in apparent brightness, and there is a kind of band of filmy light crossing the heavens which is known as the Milky Way, also called the Galaxy. At first glance the stars seem infinite in number, but those visible to the unaided eye can easily be counted. On a clear night only about 6,000 stars are visible to the naked eye. Of course with telescopes such as the 200-inch at Mount Palomar we can probably see about 1,000,000,000. Our Galaxy contains in the neighborhood of 40 billion stars. It is shaped very much like a watch and is approximately 8,000 light-years in its short diameter and 100,000 light-years across. By a differential star count in various directions, we can determine that the Galaxy is pinwheel-shaped, with two main arms. Our sun and its system of planets are 26,000 light-years from the center and on one of its arms. It is estimated that our Galaxy rotates once every 200,000,000 years.

Between stars in our Galaxy we sometimes find clouds of very tenuous matter. They are known largely because they obscure the light from the stars beyond, and therefore they look like dark patches in the sky. We call these clouds *dark nebulae*. If such a cloud is near a bright star, it glows, probably by fluorescence. We then call this fuzzy patch of light a *bright nebula*. We shall discuss nebulae further a little later.

The brightness of stars is classified numerically by magnitude: the higher the number, the fainter the star. Only 11 stars are of first magnitude, that is, of a brightness approaching that of Sirius (the Dog Star), which is the brightest fixed star in the heavens. Sirius, however, is brighter than the first magnitude, and is about 1,000 times as bright as the faintest stars visible to the naked eye, the faintest ones so visible being of the sixth magnitude. Of the fourth magnitude, there are 530 stars; of the fifth, 1,620 stars; of the sixth, 4,850 stars; and so on, the number steadily increasing with the faintness. Sirius, furthermore, is less than a billionth as bright as the sun, as seen from the earth, owing to the vast difference in distance.

Apparent motion of the stars is due to the combined effects of the earth's rotation on its axis and revolution around the sun.

The stars seem to be arranged in patterns or constellations. These were observed, and many of them named, by the ancients, who associated them with popular myths and legends. Appropriate pictures can be drawn to illustrate the major constellations by enclosing the proper stars in suitable outlines. The Big Dipper, for example, was called by the ancients Ursa Major, or the Great Bear. Other constellations in the north polar hemisphere of the heavens are Hercules, Boötes, Leo, Orion, Taurus, Perseus, Aries, Andromeda, Pegasus, etc. The brighter individual stars also have separate names, as Sirius, Betelgeuse, Polaris, Antares, Aldebaran, Arcturus, etc. Separate stars of the constellations are often distinguished by letters of the Greek alphabet, or by numbers.

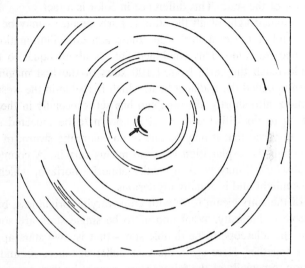

Fig. 8. The circular movement of stars in the heavens. The arrow points to the trail made by the North Star. This is so small that to the naked eye the North Star does not seem to move at all.

Unlike the planets, the stars shine by their own light, just as the sun does. Indeed, the sun is a dwarf star, but one of the more insignificant stars in the universe. Betelgeuse, for example, is so large that the earth could follow its customary orbit inside it! Yet Betelgeuse is very tenuous, being not more than 1/100 as dense as the earth's atmosphere. What is often called a vacuum in a physical laboratory is denser than such a star. Stars vary, not only in apparent brightness, but in size, temperature, and density. Some are very dense and not larger than some of the planets.

The Milky Way is revealed, through the telescope, as a dense mass of stars, seemingly concentrated around our solar system like a great wheel or spiral. The stars outside the Milky Way are thought to be merely outlying regions of this great Galaxy. Similar spirals can be observed as distant *nebulae,* which may be distant universes similar to ours. The nearest of these nebulae is almost a million light-years away.

While the planets appear to shine with a fairly steady light, the stars "twinkle" as we gaze at them. This twinkling is caused by refraction through the earth's atmosphere, which does not cause the planets to twinkle because they are of much greater apparent size. Even the brightest star is a mere point of light, while the disk of a planet can be readily discerned even through a small telescope. It may also be mentioned here that people with good color vision can distinguish apparent differences in the color of the stars. This difference in color is a fact.

The combined light of all the stars is fairly great, as may be seen on moonless and cloudless nights, when there is a faint illumination of the earth, called starshine. This combined light is about equal to the light that would reach the earth from 1,100 stars of the first magnitude. A phenomenon called the zodiacal light, which is visible in the west and up toward the zenith shortly after the sun has set, especially in the tropics, has nothing to do with the stars. It is known to be reflected sunlight, and it is supposed that it may be due to an encircling swarm of meteoroids, although the explanation is by no means certain. A counter-glow, or "Gegenschein," may be seen on the opposite horizon, which is also reflected sunlight and is equally mysterious.

Most of the stars gleam forth with an unvarying brightness, but many are variable in intensity. What appear to be single stars are sometimes shown by the telescope to be double stars—that is, two stars apparently very close together. Here again the vast stellar distances remind us that observation, especially of the fainter stars, cannot be very accurate, even with the most powerful telescopes. It is possible, too, that there are unknown obstructions to light, in the vast intervening spaces, which either lessen the starlight or perhaps blot out some stars altogether. There are also many cold bodies, comparatively speaking, which emit insufficient light to be visible through such great distances.

As compared with the brightness of our sun, Sirius would be 28 times as bright if we could be as near to it as we are to the sun. Under the same conditions, Canopus is probably 10,000 times as bright as the sun, while Arcturus is 100 times as bright. The difference in their apparent brightness, which is to say, in their magnitude, is of course due to their different distances from the earth. In general, however, stars as bright as 10,000 times our sun are rare; the number increases as they approach the sun in brightness, there being far more stars of brightness less than that of the sun than otherwise. The faintest known star is only 1/50,000 as bright as the sun.

Although the stars are described as "fixed," they only appear so, for all of them are moving, with speeds of from 10 to 100 miles per second, just as our sun and solar system are moving at the rate of 12 miles per second in the general direction of the constellation Hercules. Indeed, some stars revolve around others, forming double stars, which, however, appear single to the naked eye. If two stars very close together can be separated by the unaided eye, they are two separate stars, probably rather far apart; true double stars, one revolving around the other, cannot be distinguished with the naked eye.

The middle star in the tail of the Great Bear (Ursa Major) is a widely separated pair of stars that can be distinguished by good eyes. The two stars are not closer together than 11 times the distance of Neptune from the sun. More truly double stars are Sirius (in the constellation Canis Major) and Procyon (in Canis Minor), both "dog stars." Each has a companion star, of large mass, which can be telescopically discerned; the period of revolution for Sirius is 50 years, and for Procyon, 39 years. At least one half and perhaps three quarters of the stars in our Galaxy are double or multiple stars. The North Star, Polaris, is actually a system of three stars, and Castor is six.

Most of the stars vary between one third and three times the mass of our sun. A few, comparatively speaking, have very high masses, running up to 30, 50, and 70 or more times the mass of our sun. Betelgeuse, in Orion, has a mass nearly 100 times that of our sun. The stars of such large masses have a very low density and are very tenuous. In general, the brighter the star, the greater is its mass.

There are also many variable stars—that is, stars which do not emit the same amount of light steadily. Some of the variables are double stars in which the companion is often comparatively dark and may eclipse the brighter star as viewed from the earth. Algol is such an eclipsing variable. Other variables are pulsating; the difference in their light is due to the swelling and contracting of the stellar globe, inducing corresponding changes of temperature. The period of variation divides such stars into those varying in a few days and those varying through as many as 7,500 days.

Just as the spectroscope shows the chemical composition of the sun— the elements to be found there—the same instrument is of service in revealing the fact that the stars are of similar composition. It is also an aid in determining their surface temperatures. In general, it may be assumed that there are no elements in the stars which are unknown on earth, but the known elements—of which hydrogen, helium, calcium, and iron are particularly prominent—are in very different stages of ionization, owing to the great temperatures and pressures which exist in the stars. The whole subject is intimately bound up with the analysis of the atom, to which both astronomer and physicist turn their combined attention and knowledge.

THE EVOLUTION OF THE SOLAR SYSTEM

The apparent "order of the heavens" does not exclude change. In a million years, in thousands of millions of years, the stars exhibit—or would exhibit, if they could be observed that long—vast changes. A new star now and then appears to astronomers, called a "nova" (from the Latin word meaning "new"). It flares up brightly for a short time and then dies down. Various explanations are offered. It may be a collision or near-collision between two faint stars, but this is unlikely, for it is capable of demonstration that the laws of mechanics deny the likelihood of such collisions generally. Certainly it is a variable star, which for some reason has flared into unusual brightness.

Seven novae have been seen in the past hundred years. They are thought to represent explosions which eject large masses of gases. Sometimes the gas leaves from the entire surface of the star and then the star shrinks back. We then see a star surrounded by a shell of nebulosity which moves outward with great velocity. About once every six hundred years we see a supernova. These stars become so bright that they can be seen in the day sky. They may attain a brilliance equal to about 500,000,-000 suns. The Crab Nebula is thought to be the result of a supernova.

What may have happened to produce our solar system is a much more rare occurrence: the near-collision of one star (the sun) with some other star or sun. Just as the moon raises tides in the oceans of the earth (which, even considering the nearness of the moon, are very small in height as compared with the earth's diameter), if the sun did pass rather close (within a few million miles) to some other star, tides would have been raised to terrific heights on its surface. If the passing star came much closer still (within perhaps a million miles or so), such tides would be pulled out that they could not thereafter subside (as tides ordinarily do, like the tides on the earth), but, going out in two directions as great streamers, might revolve around the sun through space and become condensed into cooler bodies like the planets.

As each planet formed, taking the shape of a sphere (as a rotating body of gas is known to do), the sun would act on it much as the passing star acted on the sun, causing tides, and pulling out from the planet enough gaseous matter to form whatever satellites that planet may now possess. The formation of the satellites was therefore evidently the same as the formation of the planets, only on a much smaller scale.

Such a process of planet or satellite formation could not continue indefinitely, because of very definite and known laws of physics. The satellites, because of these laws, could not be made to give out matter to form moons around themselves. We know this did not happen.

Meanwhile, much of the ejected or pulled-out gaseous matter during the tidal eruption would remain uncondensed. The motions of the newly formed planets would be impeded, and as can be demonstrated by mathematics, they would take paths almost circular (actually elliptical) around the sun, which continues to attract them. After a time this intervening matter would be dissipated—drawn back to the sun or scattered into space.

Such a process of evolution for our solar system would have required a length of time approaching 7,000,000,000 years. The age of the earth, dating from its surface solidification only, is perhaps about 1,500,000,000 years.

The mass of the earth's moon being more nearly equal to that of the earth (about as 1 to 80) than the mass of any other satellite to its planet, a somewhat different explanation of the moon's origin is often suggested. It may be that the moon was torn from the earth when our world was in a much more liquid or condensed state than were the other planets when their satellites were born. However, it can just as well be assumed that the moon was born in the general cataclysm of the sun which brought forth the other planets and their attendant satellites.

THE UNIVERSE

Our Galaxy, then, contains stars (some of which may have planetary systems) and thin wisps of matter between stars which we call bright or dark nebulae. Before the advent of the more modern telescopes and refined methods of measuring distance, astronomers would occasionally see faint patches of light which looked very much like bright nebulae. In fact, they referred to them as nebulae. But when the distance to these objects was measured they were found to be well outside our Galaxy. When the more powerful telescopes were trained on them it was discovered that they were not composed of luminous gas, but rather of stars so close together, yet so distant from us, that they could scarcely be distinguished. The name nebula is still applied to these extra-galactic objects. In order to distinguish them from the bright nebulae in our own Galaxy we call them *spiral nebulae* because most of them exhibit a spiral shape.

Spiral nebulae are independent aggregates of stars. These "island universes" contain from 10,000,000,000 to 75,000,000,000 stars. The nearest extra-galactic nebula is the Great Nebula in Andromeda, which is about 1,000,000 light-years away. In both size and shape it is very similar to our Galaxy. Dr. Edwin Hubble, the world's greatest nebula authority, estimates that there are 250,000,000 of these star aggregates in the visible universe, and despite this multitude, the great universe of space is comparatively empty. He estimates that nebulae are spaced about 1,800,000 light-years apart, and if they were reduced to the size of marbles, their separation would be equal to 62,500 miles.

THE CONSTELLATIONS

We come back now to the night sky as it appears when we look up at it. The ancients noticed the stars and made patterns out of those which they could see from the early cradles of civilization around the ancient lands of the Mediterranean Sea. Greek, Roman, and Arabic names, in particular, have survived and are still used to designate many of the major constellations. Sometimes the star patterns were believed to indicate the forms of heroes, or animals, or objects, and sometimes maps are drawn to show such imagined shapes.

For convenience, stars are named and identified by referring them to the constellations of which they seem to form a part, ignoring the fact that they may be separated, in distance, by many millions of miles and by thousands of light-years. Even nebulae are identified in a similar way, as by mentioning "the nebula in Andromeda," for example. Stars are also identified and catalogued by right ascension and declination—a mathematical system used by astronomers.

As the earth revolves around the sun, that motion causes the sun apparently to cross the heavens each day, from sunrise to sunset, in a particular path. At night the sun is apparently crossing a similar path elsewhere in the world. The complete path so described (apparently) by the sun is called the ecliptic. The plane of the ecliptic shifts during the seasons, because of the shifting of the angle of the earth's axis as the earth revolves around the sun, causing the change in the seasons. But, no matter what the season, the ecliptic—the apparent path of the sun with respect to the stars—also marks out the path followed by the planets in their revolutions around the sun, for all the planets, including the earth, revolve nearly in the same plane. With respect to the stars this path appears rather wide, and it is called the zodiac.

The ecliptic, or path of the sun, is the middle line of the zodiac; the belt (which is entirely imaginary) extends about 8 degrees on each side of the ecliptic. The moon also appears to move in the zodiac. This path was divided by the ancients into twelve parts, or signs, called the signs of the zodiac. Each of these signs is identified with a constellation in that part of the sky. These twelve constellations are: Aries (the Ram), Taurus (the Bull), Gemini (the Twins), Cancer (the Crab), Leo (the Lion), Virgo (the Virgin), Libra (the Scales), Scorpio (the Scorpion)

Sagittarius (the Archer), Capricornus (the Goat), Aquarius (the Water-Carrier), and Pisces (the Fishes). Properly, the signs are divisions of the zodiac, each 30 degrees long, measuring from the vernal equinox, Aries being first. The precession of the equinoxes has shifted the apparent position of the constellations, so that the first "sign" is now occupied by Pisces.

To the north of the zodiac is the north polar hemisphere of the heavens, or of the celestial sphere. There are 27 northern constellations. To the south of the zodiac is the south polar hemisphere, with 48 constellations. The classically named constellations have legends associated with them which have come down to us with the lore of classical mythology.

The Big Dipper, in the northern hemisphere, is one of the easiest constellations to pick out. The two stars forming the points of the side farthest from the handle of the dipper are the "pointers," for a line drawn through them will point to Polaris, which is the North Star, almost coinciding with a line drawn through the North Pole of the earth.

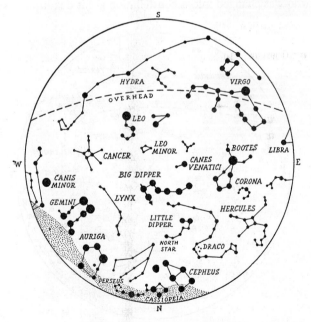

FIG. 9. The constellations as seen in the northern sky in the spring.

The so-called Big Dipper (which has also been called the Wagon, the Plow, and Charles' Wain or Cart) consists of only seven bright stars, a small portion of the constellation Ursa Major (Great Bear). The Hindus call them the seven Rishis. The brightest of the seven stars, designated by the Greek letter alpha, is one of the two pointers. The name "the Bear" is from the Greek legend of Callisto, who was transformed into that animal by Zeus, father of the gods, and translated to the heavens.

The Little Dipper, more exactly called Ursa Minor (Little Bear), is north of Ursa Major and almost at the pole. Indeed, the North Star, Polaris, is one of the stars in this constellation; the brightest in the group, it is of the second magnitude.

Famous Orion is conspicuously bright in the northern heavens. Betelgeuse, giant variable orb, is in this constellation; it is of a noticeable yellowish-red color; this star varies in brightness, being often brighter than the first magnitude and sometimes fainter. Rigel and Bellatrix, two other fairly bright stars, are in this group. There is a nebula in Orion which is visible to the naked eye—just below the "belt of Orion," which consists of three stars in a row. Orion, according to legend, was a mighty hunter who was changed into a constellation at his death.

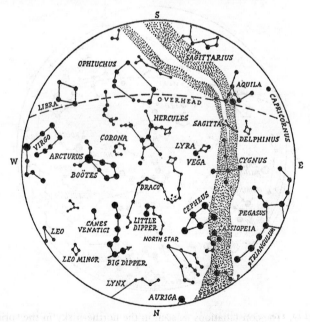

FIG. 10. The constellations as seen in the northern sky in the summer.

The Gemini, or the Twins, form the third sign of the zodiac. The two stars side by side are usually called Castor and Pollux. Castor is really a double star, as can be seen even through a small telescope, but Pollux appears to be the brighter. This constellation is, roughly, between Orion and Ursa Major.

Almost opposite Ursa Major, on the other side of the celestial pole, is Cassiopeia, in the shape of an uneven W. Below Cassiopeia is Andromeda. Situated in Andromeda is the great nebula, the brightest of such formations, some 900,000 light-years distant from the earth. It is visible with the naked eye. It is believed to be an "island universe," containing some millions of separate stars very much like those which make up our own system or universe. Some 86 novae or "new stars" have been seen to burst out in this nebula. Some of the November meteors each year are called Andromedids, after this constellation; these meteors are associated with Biela's comet, which seems to have disintegrated after its last appearance in 1852.

Adjacent to Andromeda, in the direction of Orion, is Perseus, her husband; in the constellation Perseus is the astronomically famous star Algol, which is an eclipsing variable.

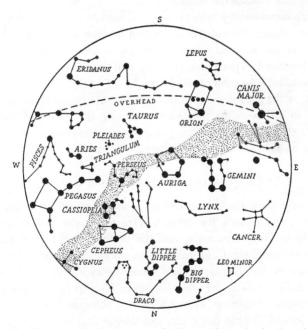

FIG. 11. The constellations as seen in the northern sky in the winter.

Between Perseus and Orion is Taurus, or the Bull, the second sign of the zodiac. Its brightest star is Aldebaran, which is mentioned by both

Hesiod and Homer. Taurus was the fabled bull which carried Europa across the seas to Crete. Taurus includes two famous star clusters, known as the Pleiades and the Hyades. Of the latter group, Aldebaran is the chief star; the seven Hyades are known by the mythological names of the seven daughters of Atlas and Aethra. The Hyades as a group were named in memory of their brother, Hyas, whom the sisters mourned.

The Pleiades are a very easily discerned tiny cluster of stars almost directly below Perseus. They represent the seven daughters of Atlas and Pleione—they are sisters of the Hyades. These stars are some 300 light-years distant from the earth.

Below Perseus and Andromeda, and midway between them, is Aries, or the Ram, the first sign of the zodiac. The so-called "first point of Aries," which, owing to the precession of the equinoxes, is now located in Pisces, is the zero point from which the right ascensions and longitudes of stars are measured, to locate them on the celestial sphere. The first point in Aries corresponds to the point where the equator of the celestial sphere crosses the ecliptic.

Swinging considerably around the pole, we come to Hercules, almost below Ursa Minor. Hercules is interesting because it is toward this constellation that our sun and planets are racing at the speed of 12 miles per second. Hercules is represented kneeling, and the constellation was therefore often called "the man on his knees."

Boötes, or the Plowman, is between and a little below Ursa Major and Hercules, in a descending line, Hercules being the lowest of the three. The bright star Arcturus is in this group. One of the other stars is double, consisting of a yellow and a blue star, one revolving around the other.

OBSERVATORIES AND PLANETARIUMS

The largest telescopes in the world for astronomical observations are in America, and include the 40-inch refractor at the Yerkes Observatory, Williams Bay, Wisconsin, and the 36-inch at the Lick Observatory, Mount Hamilton, California; while among the large reflectors are the 74-inch at the David Dunlop Observatory of the University of Toronto, the 69-inch at the Ohio Wesleyan University, and the 60-inch at the Carnegie Institution, Mount Wilson, California. The Hooker telescope on Mount Wilson has a concave mirror that is 100 inches in diameter. An 82-inch reflector, which was dedicated in 1939, is on Mount Locke near Fort Davis, Texas, and is operated jointly by the Universities of Texas and Chicago.

A 200-inch reflector, the largest in the world, is in the great observa tory on Mount Palomar, San Diego County, California, operated by the California Institute of Technology.

There are several "planetariums" in the United States, where in a circular building with a spherical dome a realistic reproduction of the heavens and the movement of the stars may be studied with some exactness. The two most important planetariums are in Chicago and New York.

Examination Questions

1. What is astronomy?
2. With what other science was astronomy originally synonymous?
3. What is the distance from the sun of the nearest star to the sun?
4. What is a light-year?
5. How many times does the earth rotate every twenty-four hours?
6. How long does one revolution of the earth around the sun take?
7. Where can the planet Venus usually be seen?
8. How far is the earth from the sun?
9. How long does it take light to travel from the sun to the earth?
10. If it were practicable, how long would it take a radio message to travel from the earth to the sun?
11. What are the nine known planets?
12. Which has the greater diameter, Earth or Saturn?
13. What is the form of the earth's orbit?
14. How many times as much as the earth does the sun weigh?
15. What is the computed Fahrenheit temperature of the surface of the sun?
16. What part of the energy radiated by the sun do the planets and their satellites receive?
17. How long does it take for the moon to revolve around the earth?
18. What is the shape of the earth?
19. Give the diameter of the earth in round numbers.
20. Give the exact length of a sidereal day.
21. What is the North Star now, and what will it be in 12,000 years?
22. What force holds the atmosphere wrapped around the earth?
23. Why is the same side of the moon always turned toward the earth?
24. What other body than the moon influences the tides on the earth?
25. What is the mass of Mercury compared with that of Earth?
26. What is the brightest object in the heavens besides the sun and moon?
27. What is the prevailing belief regarding life on Mars?
28. What is the difference in color between Mars and Venus?
29. What is the largest of the asteroids, and what is its diameter?
30. What is the nearest planetary body to the earth except the moon?
31. What are called the Galilean satellites?
32. What is the duration of Saturn's revolution around the sun?

33. Who discovered the planet Uranus?
34. How much larger than the earth is Neptune?
35. What is the period of revolution around the sun of Halley's comet?
36. How many comets are there estimated to be in our solar system?
37. What are meteors?
38. What are meteors commonly composed of?
39. What is the deduction from the belief that some meteors are believed to come from outer space?
40. How many stars are visible to the naked eye?
41. What is the distance of a light-year in miles?

42. What star is so large that the earth could follow its customary orbit inside it?
43. How does the size of Betelgeuse compare with that of our sun?
44. What are variable stars?
45. What instrument is used to show the chemical composition of the sun and the stars?
46. What is the estimated age of the earth dating from the surface solidification?
47. What relation in size does the moon bear to the earth?
48. What are spiral nebulae?
49. What is the path of the sun called?
50. How many bright stars are there in the Big Dipper?

FOR FURTHER STUDY

ASTRONOMY FROM A DIPPER, by Eliot C. Clarke. (Houghton Mifflin Co., Boston, Mass.)

ASTRONOMY FOR EVERYBODY, by Simon Newcomb. (New Home Library, Doubleday & Co., New York.)

BEGINNER'S GUIDE TO THE STARS, by Edgar G. Murphy. (G. P. Putnam's Sons, New York.)

FRIENDLY STARS, by Martha E. Martin. (Harper & Bros., New York.)

ROMANCE OF THE MOON, by Mary Proctor. (Harper & Bros., New York.)

ROMANCE OF THE SUN, by Mary Proctor. (Harper & Bros., New York.)

THROUGH SPACE AND TIME, by James Jeans. (The Macmillan Co., New York.)

XXII

Geology for Beginners

WHAT IS GEOLOGY?

GEOLOGY IS the study of the earth in all its aspects. The relation between earth and sky, between land and sea; the various land forms—mountains, hills, valleys, plains; the various bodies of water—oceans, lakes, rivers, streams; the natural resources near the surface of the earth—coal, oil, ores, minerals; the condition of the earth far below the surface, and the activity of subterranean forces such as volcanoes and geysers; the movements of the earth's crust, such as earthquakes; the action of glaciers and other large masses of ice upon the earth's surface; and the effect of the atmosphere upon the earth—all these phenomena are part of the subject matter of geology. And in addition to considering the forms and forces, the structures and processes of the earth, geology recounts the history of our planet from its origin to the present time. In the history of the earth, the history of man is in point of time only the last page; the history of the animals and plants that we know, only the last chapter; the history of life in any form, only a part of the story. The great, inanimate, impersonal earth has had a long, a strange, a fascinating history.

GENERAL INTEREST IN GEOLOGICAL PHENOMENA

Whenever we take a walk in the country we notice the principal features of the landscape—hills, valleys, streams, and rock formations. Now and again we wonder how these features came to be as they are, and often it is difficult to imagine a familiar landscape as having been very different in appearance at various times in the earth's history. In terms of a single human lifetime, the features of a familiar landscape are ancient and enduring; in terms of the earth's history, these same features are recent and temporary.

Certain landscape features and geologic phenomena are of such striking and spectacular interest that people travel great distances to see them, and it is a notable fact that exceptionally excellent examples of the results of great geological processes are presented to view in many parts of the United States, especially in the West. Several of our great national parks are areas of extraordinary geologic interest which are protected by law so that their great beauty and scientific importance will not in any way be impaired. Yellowstone, with its geysers; Yosemite, with its waterfalls; Mount Rainier and Glacier, with their glaciers; Grand Canyon, the greatest example in the world of stream erosion and rock stratification; Rocky Mountain, with its high peaks; Lassen Volcanic, with its recently active volcano; Carlsbad Caverns, with subterranean limestone formations; and in the East, an international park, famous Niagara Falls; and Acadia in Maine, with its rugged seacoast—these are only a few of the famous, mighty, natural exhibits.

LAND, SEA, AND AIR

The earth, as astronomy teaches us, receives most of its light and heat from the sun. Many of the phenomena which take place on the surface of the earth are influenced by the action of the sun; of all the heavenly bodies, the sun has at all times had the greatest effect upon the course of the earth's development. The moon, the earth's satellite, also is the cause of changes on the earth, particularly because of its important share in determining the tides of the ocean.

Apart from the influence of the sun and moon, and the very minor influence of other heavenly bodies, the changes which take place on the earth are due to causes which are to be found upon the earth itself.

In ancient times it was customary to speak of "the four elements"—fire, water, earth, and air. Although in a strictly scientific sense they are not elements, they correspond, in a very general yet exceedingly significant way, to the major divisions of the earth. For the surface of the earth is partly land (which is, even in our daily usage, "earth" in the narrow sense of the word) and partly water; and the whole earth is surrounded by air; and the interior of the earth, far below the surface, though not actually fire, is nevertheless exceedingly hot according to all indications. The solid portion of the earth's surface, the rocky portion, the truly earthy portion, is called the *lithosphere*. The portion of the surface which is water is called the *hydrosphere;* it includes the large bodies such as the oceans, and also the lakes, rivers, streams, and the water beneath the earth's surface. The air which envelops the earth is called the *atmosphere*. The earth's interior is known as the *centrosphere*.

The cooler outer portion of the lithosphere—to a depth of perhaps 30 or 40 miles—is spoken of as the earth's *crust*. Water covers almost three quarters of the earth's surface, all the continents together constituting only about one quarter. The extent of the earth's atmosphere is not known, but it is estimated to extend more than a hundred, perhaps a few hundred, miles from the earth's surface. However, the principal gaseous content of the atmosphere is relatively near the earth's surface.

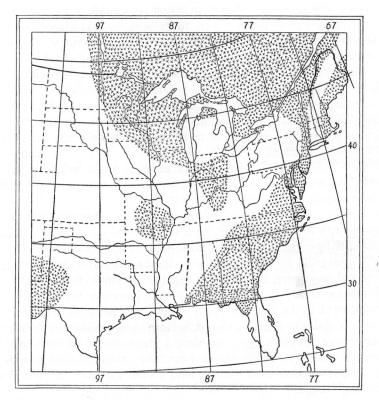

FIG. 1. Part of the United States during the Coal Period. The cross-hatched areas show the probable distribution of land, and the blank areas of water.

The portion of the atmosphere more than about six miles above the earth's surface is known as the *stratosphere;* it has been scientifically studied in balloon, airplane, and rocket flights, and found to be much more rarefied than the lower atmosphere, and to become increasingly so as it extends farther and farther from the earth.

The Rocky Surface of the Earth

If we stand and look out over a broad stretch of landscape, we are likely to be interested primarily in the larger features, the mountains and valleys, the hills and plains, the rivers and lakes. Yet, while we are observing the general form and contour, we begin to notice the extent to which the scene is one in which rocky masses or masses of vegetation predominate. If the valley at which we are looking is a fertile one largely covered with grass and other plant life, if the hillside is a dense forest, we do not give much thought to the rocky or earthy base which lies under these masses of vegetation. But if the scenery is rugged, with barren mountains and sandy plains, we can see the rocky material all about us.

Our interest in vegetation in a landscape is somewhat like our interest in houses visible in a wide expanse of land, or boats sighted at sea; it is essentially a personal interest, an interest in something over which we can have some control. For we can determine whether or not there shall be houses in a certain region, boats on a certain stretch of water, vegetation on a given stretch of land. We can build great cities where there were fields or forests before. But we cannot, except in minor ways, change the chief geologic features of the landscape, the mountains and valleys, the rivers and the sea.

In a city, with no natural landscape in sight, one hardly thinks of the rocky earth beneath; and even on a farm the daily concern is with the productivity of the soil, with the shallow, fertile layer of earth which rests on a great rocky foundation, and not with the rocky base itself. Architecture and agriculture, although so infinitely important to us, are incidental in relation to the unfolding of great geologic processes. For a description of the earth as the world in which we live, with countries, cities, rivers, and mountains individually named, we turn to geography. For an understanding of the earth as a great natural phenomenon, we must look to geology. Geology seeks to explain how these present conditions came to be, and to discover what changes have occurred through the ages since the earth began.

Types of Rocks

Geology deals with the earth's formations in their large aspects and also with the nature of the rocks of which these features are constituted. The rocks which form the earth's crust contain compounds of all the chemical elements, except a few gases (such as helium). Some of the elements are present in considerable quantities, others are quite scarce. Most of the elements have become oxidized through exposure to the air and are found in compounds containing oxygen. Of all the elements, oxygen is the most abundantly present in the earth's crust, constituting about 47 per cent of all rock material; next to oxygen is silicon, which constitutes 28 per cent; the principal metals, which rank next, constitute only about 2 per cent or 3 per cent each. It is silicon which is principally responsible for the fact that rocks have their familiar characteristics, though, of course, the other elements present affect the appearance of the rocks. Iron in a rock formation gives it a rusty color. So important is silicon in rock structure that it may be said to play a role in the mineral world comparable with that which is played by carbon in determining the character of all living matter (protoplasm).

It is customary to recognize three main classes of rock: *igneous, sedimentary,* and *metamorphic.*

IGNEOUS ROCKS

Igneous rocks (the word *igneous* is derived from the Latin word for "fire") are formed under the influence of heat below the surface of the earth, and are brought to the surface or very near the surface as a result of volcanic activity. Igneous rocks which have been brought to the surface and which are exposed while hardening are called *extrusive* rocks. Igneous rocks which do not quite reach the surface during volcanic activity but become solid somewhat below the surface are called *intrusive;* intrusive rocks in many instances later become exposed as a result of the wearing away of the surface rock.

In regard to texture, igneous rocks are classified principally as coarse-grained or fine-grained. The graining is determined by the rate at which the volcanic material cools. Extrusive rocks retain the fine grain of the molten mass. Intrusive rocks are formed more slowly, and during their solidification the minerals crystallize into larger grains.

Considering the characteristics of both texture and composition, intrusive igneous rocks are classified as follows:

Granite—coarse-grained, light color, high content of silica.
Diorite—coarse-grained, medium color, medium silica content.
Gabbro—coarse-grained, dark color, low content of silica, higher content of iron and magnesium oxides.

Extrusive igneous rocks are classified as follows:

Rhyolite—fine-grained, light color, high silica content.
Andesite—fine-grained, medium color, medium silica content.
Basalt—fine-grained, dark color, low content of silica.

SEDIMENTARY ROCKS

Sedimentary rocks are formed principally in shallow seas, by the piling up and hardening of the sediments carried down to the seas by streams, rivers, and other running water, or, in some instances, by wind. The particles which constitute the sediment may be coarse gravel, or grains of sand, or very fine dust, mud, or clay; the particles may have been broken off from igneous, metamorphic, or older sedimentary rock, but the new rocks which constitute the layers are quite different from the rocks from which the particles have come.

Sedimentary rocks are formed in layers, each layer being known as a *stratum* or bed. This stratification is caused by the fact that the water or other agent which transports the sediment varies in velocity, carrying only finer material when moving slowly, but bringing also coarser material when moving rapidly. Stratification also results from variations in the composition of the materials composing the sediment. Sedimentary deposits are changed into rocks as a result of great pressure, the filtering in of adhesive rock matter, and physical and chemical changes in the minerals.

Sedimentary rocks are classified according to the sediments from which they are formed, as follows:

> Conglomerate—formed from gravel and coarse fragments of stone.
> Sandstone—formed from sand.
> Shale—formed from clay or mud.
> Limestone—a special type of sandstone or shale composed almost entirely of the important chemical calcium carbonate.

Limestone is of special interest in that it is formed in large part from shells and other products associated with invertebrate animal life.

METAMORPHIC ROCKS

Metamorphic rocks are formed from igneous or sedimentary rocks as a result of powerful changes in temperature or pressure or other factors at work within the earth's crust. When a volcano is active in a given area, the molten mass, as we have already seen, forms igneous rocks on cooling. The presence of the volcano has a secondary effect in that the great heat acts upon the rocks already present in the region where the volcano is active. Although the heat does not cause these older rocks to become molten, it does bring about striking changes in the formation, degree of crystallization, and other characteristics. Similarly, earthquakes and other movements of the earth's crust, by the enormous power of the forces which stretch and strain and bend and tear the older rocks, cause profound changes in the character of the rocks. Metamorphic changes may also be brought about in rocks which have become buried under other tremendously heavy rock masses.

The more important metamorphic rocks are the following:

Gneiss—metamorphosed granite or coarse-grained sedimentary rocks.

Schist—metamorphosed shale which has become definitely crystalline in appearance. Mica schist is a familiar example.

Slate—metamorphosed shale which shows its clayey origin.

Quartzite—metamorphosed sandstone which has become crystalline.

Marble—metamorphosed limestone which has become crystalline.

ROCK WEATHERING

As we look out over a rocky landscape we see some large masses of solid rock which determine the basic structure of the region, and some loose mineral matter such as soil, clay, sand, gravel, or even larger loose rocks such as boulders. We know that beneath the loose material—called the *mantle*—if we dig deep enough we will strike solid rock. The solid rock, whether exposed to view or covered by mantle, is known as *bedrock*. The loose mantle consists principally of material which has been worn away from the bedrock by the action of the weather and other agencies. Any rock which is exposed to weathering by wind and rain will in time have its surface so worn that it will crumble into small particles which can readily be removed from the harder rock beneath. The weathering process is greatly aided by the fact that most rocks have cracks into which rain water can run, thus including the surfaces and base of the cracks in the area exposed to weathering. When water freezes in a crack, expansion may cause the crack to widen. The daily and seasonal variations in the heat from the sun also affect the course of weathering. When the action of the weather on rocks is purely mechanical, as that resulting from changes in temperature and pressure, the breaking down of the rock is known as *disintegration*. When the action involves changes in the minerals which constitute the rock, the process is looked upon as decay or *decomposition*.

Climate is a very important factor in determining the rate of weathering. In temperate climates, where there is considerable amount of rainfall, decomposition proceeds at a relatively rapid rate, and the mantle produced is rich in the chemical compounds which constitute fertile soil, capable of sustaining vegetation.

In arid regions, however, the mantle consists almost entirely of particles of the rock material which have been worn from the bedrock by physical disintegration, without any chemical change, and which do not make fertile soil.

Erosion

Weathering causes the surface of rocks and even the rocks themselves to break up and decay. *Erosion* is the term applied to any process which loosens and removes the rock material from one position to another. There are many important geologic agents which bring about erosion: streams and rivers, the waves of the oceans, glaciers, and wind, all transport rock material and bring about gradual but profound changes on the earth's surface.

The force of gravity is a very obvious but very important agent in erosion, for rock material which is loosened on cliffs and other high places drops or slides to the valley below; debris which accumulates at the base is known as *talus*. When the slope is gradual, the loose material as a rule moves downward slowly, but occasionally a very long, heavy rain may cause a sudden rapid movement, constituting a *landslide*.

Streams and Rivers

The power of streams to change the surface of the earth is perhaps the most amazing of all the forces of erosion.

Most streams have their sources in areas of frequent rainfall or of melting snow and ice. These areas are often high on the slopes of mountains or hills, and the water tends to run down the slopes even before definite streams are formed. Such water is called *runoff*. Water running down slopes is guided by the irregularities and depressions in the rock surface. In this way the course of the stream determines itself, flowing on and on, always seeking the nearest slope; and, being joined by other streams tending in the same direction, it continues as a wider stream; and then the enlarged stream repeats this process until it becomes a broad river flowing to the sea.

Streams do more than determine their course from source to mouth; for the most part they themselves construct the valleys in which they flow. Streams do not merely flow forward; they dig at the same time, and this digging is an astonishingly efficient process. In this way streams become powerful agents of erosion, for in flowing they wear away the surface over which they move, and carry the loosened rock material with them as sediment.

During its early stages, when it is moving most rapidly, a stream cuts down most actively into the surface over which it is flowing. Later it begins to dig at the sides of the valley which it has formed, and thus gradually widens the valley. The widening is accelerated by the fact that the stream tends to swing now to the right, now to the left, consequently bearing against first one side of its gully and then the other, making its course bend and wind. As it bends, the stream deposits some of its load, and the deposited sediment forms new land, a *floodplain,* along the side of the stream opposite the bend. As the stream winds its way the floodplain appears alternately on one side and then the other; and the valley, which is resulting from the erosive activity of the stream, is built on both sides.

Most streams as they proceed in their course are joined by lesser streams, *tributaries.* These tributaries flow into the larger streams because the larger streams, through their work of erosion, have made their valleys low points toward which near-by streams flowing down slopes necessarily make their way. It is an interesting fact that tributaries, although smaller than the main stream, ordinarily meet the main stream at its own level and do not have to drop over falls to reach the level of the main stream. This is because the very fact that the larger stream is a more powerful agent of erosion causes a comparatively steep slope for the final stage of the tributary, thus speeding up the erosive work of the tributary.

Although streams ordinarily flow in a bed which is comparatively gradual in its slope, even though the slope may change at various stages in the descent from the source to the mouth, occasionally there is a sudden vertical or almost vertical drop constituting *falls.* Falls may result from a variation in rock levels which existed before the stream made its way, or may be created by a stream in passing from more resistant to less resistant rock and wearing away the softer rock faster than the harder.

Niagara Falls illustrates the way in which falls can persist even when the work of erosion goes on actively. Originally, the falls of the Niagara River were nearer Lake Ontario than at present. As the river continued to pour over the shelf of hard rock to the base of soft rock, it wore away the soft rock, leaving an overhanging ledge of hard rock which in time dropped into the stream beneath from lack of support; then the falls dropped from the new edge of the hard rock a little further upstream, and again wore away the soft rock beneath until again the hard rock dropped from lack of support. This process has continued and still continues gradually but steadily.

When a stream flows into a lake it ordinarily deposits a large quantity of its sediment on the lake bottom; and likewise, when the stream, now widened into a river, finally reaches the sea, if the sea bottom descends very gradually from the coast line, the river deposits a large part of its sediment to form a great *delta.* Deltas often constitute extensive land areas. Among the most famous deltas are the Mississippi delta below New Orleans, the Nile delta which includes the city of Alexandria, and the delta formed by the Po, Adige, and neighboring rivers of Italy, somewhat south of Venice.

THE LANDSCAPE CYCLE

One of the most interesting applications of geology is the interpretation of scenery. The work of streams in changing the landscape follows a cycle which holds the utmost fascination for everyone who enjoys studying the surface of the earth.

The changes wrought by streams are far-reaching, yet the time required for appreciable change is such that one lifetime seldom witnesses changes that are readily recognizable. Nevertheless, in neighboring areas there are often contrasting landscapes brought to their present form by stream erosion and representing very different stages of the great cycle of stream development.

This cycle consists of a formative stage, a stage of youth, a stage of maturity, and a stage of old age.

The formative stage is the period when the runoff starts down the slopes. The narrow, rugged V-shaped valley of the rapidly moving stream is characteristic of the stage of youth. The valley with fully developed floodplains, constituting a relatively wide expanse, with hills rising at a distance from the river, is characteristic of the stage of maturity. By the time maturity is reached, all the river valleys of a given area have become connected in a system of streams and tributaries. As the cycle approaches old age, the rivers move more slowly and become wider, the valleys are broader, and the hills have been eroded down to form a gently rolling landscape. The level surface of late old age is known as a *peneplane;* the occasional hills, now no longer ranges, are called *monadnocks.*

Some idea of the rate at which this cycle advances is given in the estimate that it takes a stream about 7,000 years to lower the average landscape one foot. Yet in the tremendously long span of geologic time, landscapes may be leveled by stream erosion, and raised by forces active below the earth's surface and subjected again to the whole cycle of stream erosion, in some instances, once, in others, several times.

UNDERGROUND WATER

We can dig for a well almost anywhere and feel confident that sooner or later we will strike water. The water which we reach in this way is in the porous rocks below the earth's surface; much of it is rain water which has seeped through to this lower level instead of being carried away on the surface as runoff; some of it is water of volcanic origin; and some of it may have collected in the rock at the time that it was formed. At a certain depth (which varies according to the perviousness of the rock) below the surface, we reach a level beneath which for some distance the rocks are at all times saturated with water. This level is called the *water table*. The water below it is a continuous supply of ground water. Above the water table there is also water in the ground, but only in certain localities. Where the rock beneath the surface is porous and pervious, wells can readily be sunk to the water table. However, there is sometimes a bed of impervious rock between the surface and the water table. In such instances it is necessary to blast through the impervious rock to reach the level of ground water. Wells which have to be constructed through impervious rock are known as *artesian wells.*

If there is a fissure in the impervious rock, a *spring* will generally rise to the surface, if the level of the water table in that region is higher than that which the water near the fissure can reach because of the impervious rock above it. Water seeks its own level, and the water which flows up to form the spring is merely obeying this law. A spring has a steady current of water; water which merely flows out of the ground is known as *seepage.* Springs are also formed at points where the surface intersects the water table. When the water in a spring contains an unusually high content of mineral matter, we have mineral springs; those at Saratoga, Carlsbad, and Vichy, and many others are famous for their health-giving properties. Hot springs and geysers are due to phenomena associated with volcanoes and will be considered later.

Streams which flow over the surface of the earth usually have to dig their courses, as we have seen above. *Underground water* also tends to flow in a definite direction, but it makes its way more slowly than surface streams. It is easy to see, however, that this underground water is a very important factor in erosion, as it breaks down rock masses below the surface, and thus they are far more easily carried off when the surface erosion works its way down to a lower level and reaches the rocks which have disintegrated and decomposed through the activity of underground water. In some instances, particularly when the rock material is soluble, the work of the underground water is so effective that it excavates a hole, weakening the surface rock above so that it may in time collapse into the hole below.

Underground *caverns,* like famous Mammoth and Carlsbad Caverns, and those in the Shenandoah Valley of Virginia, are exceedingly interesting. These caverns are formed by the subsurface water which has brought the soluble matter in the rocks into solution; limestone and dolomite, because of their high degree of solubility, are the rocks in which caverns most readily form. When the caverns are below the water table they are, of course, filled with water, but when they are above the water table, the water drains off, leaving the large "chambers" and narrower "passages" connecting them, the whole network of a cavern often extending for many miles underground. In these caverns above the water table the small amounts of water in the ground above the caverns seep down to the cavern roof and act slowly upon the minerals there, causing a very gradual dripping of mineral material, forming large icicle-like masses known as *stalactites* which hang from the roof. As these stalactites form, the material which drips from them produces corresponding accumulations, *stalagmites,* rising from the floor of the cavern, which build up to meet the stalactites; and in meeting, they form columns. The minerals in the caves are quite varied, producing striking contrasts in the rocks, visible in many amazingly beautiful color effects.

LAKES

We have already seen that most of the water on the earth's surface tends to collect in streams and to make its way down slopes and through the weaker rocks until it reaches sea level and flows into the ocean. Some surface water collects in hollows, forming lakes. Some lakes have streams flowing into and out of them; others are fed only by springs and rainfall. Some lakes are formed in basins which have resulted from the action of subterranean forces on the earth's surface. Some lake basins in low-lying regions were orginally a part of the ocean, but have been completely surrounded by land through the building of sandbars. Many lakes are found in the mountains and are the result of the scraping of moving glaciers.

Lakes which have streams flowing in and out of them act as reservoirs for surplus stream water in periods of flood. At other times, however, a stream tends to drain a lake through which it flows, by depositing quite a bit of its load of sediment on reaching the lake, forming a delta at the lake shore, and gradually reducing the lake area until in time the lake disappears entirely, leaving only the stream which flows on its way.

Lakes which are fed only by springs and rainfall need an abundant supply of water to offset the evaporation which naturally takes place. In arid regions, shallow lakes may dry up almost entirely during dry seasons and be formed again when there is rainfall. Such lakes are often *salt lakes,* because the mineral matter brought into the lake by its springs is left on the lake bottom each time the water evaporates, thus steadily increasing the mineral content of the lake water; the Great Salt Lake in Utah is a famous example. Some salt-water lakes, on the other hand, may have been connected with the ocean at one time; this is probably true of the Caspian Sea.

Swamps are land areas that are saturated with water. Some swamps are poorly drained land areas which are not sufficiently depressed to constitute lakes; other swamps are former lakes which have become filled with vegetation. Swamps and the swampland occasionally found along the shore of lakes are of especial interest because the vegetation tends to decay in the water and form a mass of largely decomposed carbonaceous material known as *peat,* which is very valuable as fuel. Peat is the first stage in the process by which decaying vegetation is turned into coal.

GLACIERS

Among the great agents of erosion, glaciers are exceedingly important. Glaciers are moving masses of ice. They originate in great *snowfields* in areas which are cold enough to keep snow and ice from melting. In temperate climates the *snowline,* above which snow and ice do not melt, is high up in the mountains. In Arctic regions the snowline is at sea level. The temperature at different seasons causes fluctuations in the snowline in all regions. The well-known glaciers of the Alps and the Rocky Mountains flow away from snowfields situated quite high.

In the snowfields, snow gradually changes to ice. The pressure of new-fallen snow on the snow below, which has become compact from exposure and from such moisture as comes from the snow itself or from the water vapor in the air, causes a continual formation of glacial ice, the lower layers of which begin to move down the near-by slopes as soon as the amount of ice accumulated in the snowfield is more than the snowfield can retain. The glacier commences as an overflow of the basic ice, due to the accumulation of new ice and snow above, its direction determined by the direction of the existing slopes, its rate of movement by the steepness of the slopes. Glaciers move about a foot a day on an average. As long as new snow and ice accumulate in the snowfield, the glacier continues to move and it proceeds until it reaches the snowline, where the glacier necessarily commences to melt, giving rise to streams or lakes. Many famous rivers, among them the Rhine and the Rhone, originate as streams formed at the point where great glaciers reach the snowline and commence to melt. In Arctic regions, glaciers often reach the sea, and great chunks break off. These are the *icebergs* which drift out into open water and do not melt until they reach more temperate climes.

Ice sheets are the greatest glaciers, constituting huge ice blankets over large areas, including mountains, valleys, and plains. Now and again in earlier geologic times, ice sheets covered large parts of northern North America and northern Europe. Today most of Greenland is covered by an ice sheet, as is also the great continent of Antarctica.

We have already studied the process by which streams erode the areas through which they flow. Glaciers also are active agents of erosion, their work being known as glaciation. When a glacier commences to move into a valley it gathers up onto the base of its icy mass the fragments of rock lying loose in the valley. Consequently the underside and edges of the glacier are studded with rock fragments held tightly in the glacial mass. This rock matter acts as a cutting edge for the glacier as it moves, digging into the base and sides of the valley, cutting deeply and wearing away the rocky surfaces. At the same time these rocky fragments in the glacier are polished by their movement over the rocky surfaces and they become smoothly beveled.

The snowfields from which glaciers originate do an appreciable amount of eroding themselves, owing to occasional melting and changes in pressure. The snowfield is an irregular semicircular mass at the head of the glacier; as it wears away the rocks in the mountain area in which it is situated, it forms a semicircular valley head (a *cirque*) at the end of the valley occupied by the glacier. In regions from which glaciers and snowfields have disappeared, cirques are evidence of their previous presence. When several cirques, on adjacent sides of a mountain, break through the walls separating them, they leave a short peak or *horn* arising between them. The Matterhorn and Jungfrau are famous examples.

Although glaciers do not themselves excavate valleys, they greatly remodel the valleys through which they flow. Streams seek out the weaker rocks in determining their course; consequently young stream valleys show many sharp edges and sharp turns. Glaciers move more ponderously, wearing away anything which impedes their progress, and polishing the rocks over which they move. Consequently a glaciated valley is much more smoothly eroded than a stream valley; the base is broader, the sides less irregular; in place of the V-shaped valley of the young stream, we have the gently curved, U-shaped glacier valley.

An interesting effect of glaciation is the erosion of the base of the main valley to a lower level than the tributary valley which previously met the valley at grade. The tributary valleys end abruptly above the level of the main valley and their streams must drop into the valley below as falls. Good examples are found in the Yosemite Falls and the Bridal Veil Falls of the Yosemite Valley.

Great ice sheets are obviously far more powerful in their erosive activity than valley glaciers. Ice sheets not only move all loose mantle with them, but scoop basins in relatively soft rock. As the ice recedes, through melting and evaporation, lakes form in these basins. Lakes of glacial origin are particularly common in Canada, the New England States, and northern New York State. When a glacier recedes from an area, it leaves a trail of debris, composed of rock fragments carried in the glacier and materials from the base and sides of the valley loosened by the action of the glacier. Loose material of this sort is known as glacial *drift,* and, if smoothly polished, as *till.* If the debris consolidates and forms an appreciable mass it is known as a *moraine,* which in time may become covered with vegetation yet remain a very characteristic feature of an area once occupied by a glacier. Mounds of material accumulated beneath the glacier are called *ground moraines;* ridges of consolidated glacial drift or till formed at the end of the glacier and left exposed as the glacier receded are *terminal moraines.*

GLACIAL CLIMATES

When we speak of glacial periods we really mean periods during which large areas ordinarily free from glaciers were covered by them, particularly periods when a vast ice sheet was continuous over a tremendous area because the whole area was climatically suited to sustaining ice at the time. Among the various factors which undoubtedly combine to produce such a climate are the amount of energy received from the sun, the relation between land masses and sea masses, currents of the ocean, wind belts, and the proportion of the various constituents in the atmosphere. It has been estimated that if all the ice at present in the ice sheets of Greenland and Antarctica melted, the ocean levels would be raised 150 feet, thus submerging large areas now above sea level, including the great cities which are seaports. On the other hand, in an age of greater ice distribution, the level of the sea would be lower than at present, as the chief source of ice is atmospheric moisture deposited as snow, and the chief source of atmospheric moisture is the water vapor which has evaporated from the oceans.

EFFECTS OF THE ATMOSPHERE

One of the most striking indications that the atmosphere is an integral geologic part of the earth is found in the cycle of evaporation and condensation. Under the influence of the sun, water turns to vapor and evaporates from the surface of the oceans, lakes, and rivers, and becomes a part of the atmosphere. Then, with changes in temperature, in atmospheric pressure, and in wind currents, precipitation of the water vapor as rain or snow occurs, thus bringing the water back to the earth's surface; and whatever falls on land after a time makes its way back into bodies of water.

PHENOMENA OF THE ATMOSPHERE

Meteorology, the science of the atmosphere, describes and explains such important phenomena as changes in atmospheric temperature and pressure, humidity, winds, clouds, the various forms of condensation and precipitation of atmospheric water vapor, the electric phenomena of the atmosphere, and such more occasional atmospheric phenomena as thunderstorms, tornadoes, cyclones, hurricanes, and typhoons. Thus meteorology has as its subject matter what we commonly call the *weather*. All of these atmospheric phenomena, and the changes in weather and climate which they produce, are exceedingly important in geology because of their effects upon land and sea.

Atmospheric temperature is governed to a great extent by latitude and altitude. In the torrid zone, which is one of the five climate zones of the earth, the sun's rays are more direct than in the other four—the north and south frigid zones and the north and south temperate zones. The North Pole and South Pole receive the most oblique rays of the sun; in fact, at the poles the sun never rises higher than 23½ degrees from the horizon. Consequently the regions surrounding the poles are very cold because they receive much less heat than the torrid zone. Atmospheric temperature decreases one degree with each increase of about 300 feet in altitude above sea level, since the atmosphere is less dense at high altitudes and is therefore unable to retain the sun's heat in the way that the atmosphere at lower levels can.

Atmospheric pressure at sea level is usually 14.7 pounds per square inch, but grows less as the altitude increases. The atmospheric pressure as determined by the barometer drops one inch for every 900 feet of altitude for the first 10,000 feet. Whenever air currents rise, the atmospheric pressure is automatically lowered; the surrounding air then has a tendency to enter the low pressure region. Severe windstorms are created when this condition lasts for a certain number of days, and the centers of such regions move with great speed across land or sea.

Large storms, which may be over 2,000 miles in diameter, are known to meteorologists as *extra-tropical cyclones,* and are accompanied by rain as well as temperature changes. In the United States such cyclones generally move in an easterly direction. They are not as violent as the smaller, revolving storms called *tropical cyclones* or *hurricanes,* which do not usually exceed 600 miles in diameter. The central low pressure area of the tropical cyclone is known as the *eye;* this varies from 15 to 25 miles in diameter, and the winds surrounding it sometimes attain a velocity of 200 miles per hour. In the northern hemisphere these winds blow spirally, in a counterclockwise direction. Tropical cyclones are called *typhoons* in most of the Far East, and *baguios* in the Philippine Islands. Smaller in area than the cyclone, the *tornado* takes the form of a rapidly whirling, dark, funnel-shaped cloud; the eye or center is not more than about 200 feet in diameter, but the wind velocity may exceed 500 miles per hour.

Humidity is the condition of the atmosphere as regards the amount of moisture or water vapor which it contains. The atmosphere is said to be saturated when it contains all the water vapor it can hold; and the higher the temperature is, the more water vapor is needed to saturate the atmosphere. For example, the relative humidity is 50 when the atmosphere contains one half the quantity of moisture required to produce saturation. Precipitation (often rain or dew) results when the humidity is 100. The lowest relative humidity generally exists in warm areas that are located at a great distance from large bodies of water and are shielded by mountains from winds that bear moisture. Nevada, Arizona, New Mexico, and Utah have the lowest average relative humidity in the United States.

Clouds are composed of tiny drops of water or ice particles, and are generally formed by the condensation of vapor that occurs when a moist, warm air current rises and is cooled by the colder upper air. Rain is produced when such a current is cooled sufficiently to liberate a great deal of moisture. *Snow* is created when the cooling decreases the temperature to a point below 32° Fahrenheit, which is the temperature needed to freeze water. *Sleet* is rain that becomes frozen just before it reaches the earth. *Hailstones* are produced when drops of rain are carried upward and downward so that they are alternately covered with snow and more water.

A cloud that occurs at the earth's level is known as *fog,* made up of particles of water vapor which have been condensed by the mixing of layers of air having different temperatures. Fog is frequently seen in damp and low-lying sections, although it may be found also in many regions where the temperature varies to a great extent during the day or night. Thin fog is commonly known as *mist.* Near the coast of Newfoundland, fog is caused by the mixing of the cold air (from above the Labrador Current) with the warm air above the Gulf Stream. As a general rule, clouds are lower in moist or humid regions than in dry, arid areas, and higher in warm localities than in cold. Since the ground becomes cool at night before the atmosphere does, *dew* is often formed, resulting from the contact of the cold earth with the moisture in the warm air.

Another atmospheric phenomenon is *lightning*. This flashing illumination, which may appear in any of various forms such as forked and sheet lightning, is created by a discharge of electricity from a cloud. In order to produce lightning, the cloud must have become charged with a relatively greater potential (degree of electrification) than the land. When the electricity discharges, a lightning flash is produced. The sudden expansion of the air heated by the lightning flash causes a tremendous air wave which is heard as *thunder*. Summer lightning or heat lightning causes no thunder, being merely a reflection of an electrical discharge far beyond the horizon. Since lightning is seen instantaneously, while sound takes about five seconds to travel a mile, by estimating the time between the flash of lightning and the subsequent thunder, it is a simple matter to calculate one's distance from a thunderstorm.

Air currents produce *winds* in part because of the constant rotation of the earth. The torrid zone, which includes the equator, receives more heat from the sun than does any other part of the globe; and the air above the tropical regions is heated at the same time, and rises to high altitudes due to the pressure of the cooler air from both the north and the south. As the warm air cools and grows more dense, portions of it travel north or south, or descend once more to the earth, and the winds result from the currents thus formed. A basic wind system has been evolved whereby the earth is divided into nine sections, as follows: the *doldrums,* also called the low-pressure equatorial belt of calms, located in the torrid zone where the warmed air rises; the two *trade wind belts*—the northeast trade winds, north of the equator, blowing from the northeast, and the southeast trade winds, south of the equator, blowing from the southeast; the *horse latitudes,* located about the Tropic of Capricorn and the Tropic of Cancer, and consisting of two belts of calms between the prevailing westerly winds and the trade winds; the two prevailing *westerlies,* which blow toward the North Pole and the South Pole from the horse latitudes; and the *polar caps* at the poles. Such factors as ocean currents, variations in the rate of heating and cooling of land and sea, etc., affect or modify these major winds.

Weather at a given place on the earth is determined largely by the interaction of air masses of different temperatures and moisture content that pass over the locality. When air which has come down from the polar regions and has traveled over land areas passes over a city, that city will experience cool, dry weather. If, however, a mass of air coming from a tropical region and passing over water replaces the cooler air mass, the city will experience warm, humid weather. At the boundary between the two air masses, called the *front,* considerable air turbulence occurs; and as the warm air overrides the cold, or as the cold air digs in under and lifts the warm air, the warm, moist air becomes cooled, and rain results. When a front passes over a particular place, invariably a change in weather occurs. The passage of a front is almost always accompanied by precipitation and a change in wind direction.

EROSION BY WIND

The atmosphere acts upon the earth's surface not only through the rain and snow which it precipitates, but also by means of disturbances in it—the winds. The amount of dust and other fine particles of mantle carried by the wind is very considerable, and this is especially true in deserts and other arid regions where the surface level may be consider-

ably lowered as a result of continual removal of the loose material by
the wind. Sand and other sharp rock particles blown by the wind against
rocky surfaces aid in disintegrating the softer surface and in polishing
the harder stone.

Desert areas are regions of very scant rainfall. *Deserts* are found principally in a few latitudes, the desert areas in both the northern and southern hemispheres forming interrupted belts around the earth. The high
daytime temperatures and the strong contrasts in temperature between
day and night in the desert regions have a very definite effect in speeding
the rate of disintegration of rocks, thus making them very susceptible to
erosion by the wind.

Deposits made by the wind are principally of two kinds—dunes and
loess. In arid regions and along sandy seashores the sand is blown about
by the wind, and instead of settling again in an even layer, tends to
form *dunes* or mounds, the shape and size of which are dependent on the
usual direction of the wind and the effectiveness of some stone or bush
in acting as a windbreak.

Loess consists principally of the finely grained particles smaller than
sand, which are carried by the wind. It is characteristically a yellowish-
brown powdery substance which the wind deposits in compact masses.
Important areas of loess are found in the Mississippi Valley, in Central
Europe, and especially in northern China.

THE SEA

Sea areas constitute more than twice the land areas of the globe. The
deepest part of the sea is off the Philippine Islands, where the bottom
is over 6 miles below sea level. (The highest mountains rise 5½ miles
above sea level.)

The bottom of the ocean has not been very thoroughly charted, but
all soundings indicate that there is not the same amount of variation
within relatively small areas as on land. The large areas of great depths
are strikingly contrasted with comparatively shallow areas. The continents are surrounded by *continental shelves* covered with water seldom
deeper than 600 feet. The great depths average about 13,000 feet.

On all the coasts of the continents the shore is constantly being eroded
by the sea. When we think of the vast shore lines with the sea pounding
against great rocks or rolling to the edge of low-lying plains, we realize
what a tremendous agent of erosion the sea is.

Most of us have at one time or another observed the power of the
waves as they break against the shore. The waves and surface currents of
the sea result largely from the pressure and movement of winds. Wave

movement is complex, involving not only forward movement but also breaking, backwash, and undertow. The eroded material is separated by the waves into coarse and fine particles, certain wave currents being able to carry only the finer material.

A rugged coast, with rocks coming right to the shore, with bays here and there and islands which once were connected with the mainland—as for instance, the coast of Main—is known as a *shore line of submergence*. It has resulted from the submergence under water of the former more gradual approaches to the sea in this rugged area, due to a movement of the earth's crust, causing the land to settle to a lower level or raising the level of the sea. A *shore line of emergence* is low-lying, with sandy islands and sandbars, as, for example, the coast of Florida. Here the indication is that part of the earth's crust has risen, causing land formerly below the sea and part of the continental shelf to appear above the sea as the new coast line.

The cycle of erosion modifies both types of shore line. *Submerged shore lines* commence as rugged headlands, meeting the sea, with bays here and there. During the stage of youth the waves begin to erode the shore, forming cliffs and depositing part of the sediment to form beaches beneath the cliffs and in the bays. Later the bays become largely filled with beaches and gradually with vegetation, the headlands eroded so that the irregular shore has become fairly smooth, and when the coast line reaches maturity it is so simplified that it is entirely lacking in striking features.

Emerged shore lines commence their cycle as flat coastal plains. The water is shallow, and the waves, having no rocks to erode, expend their energy building up a sandbar at the point where they break, the bar being separated from the shore line by a lagoon. Sediment fills the lagoon and vegetation develops, gradually forming *tidal marshes*. In time, the waves wear away the sandbar and tidal marsh, and the resulting simplified shore line is similar to that of maturity in a shore line of submergence.

Some *islands* are formed through submergence of an irregular coast, high points becoming islands. Other islands, particularly those further at sea, are of volcanic origin, the lava having mounted from volcanoes beneath the sea to the surface, the islands being really the exposed tops of ranges of former volcanoes, as, for instance, the islands of Japan and Hawaii.

Tropical and subtropical islands present an interesting geologic feature in their *coral reefs,* which lie just at sea level and are exposed at low tide. If the reef surrounds the island, it is called a *fringing reef;* if the island has become partly submerged, there is a *lagoon* between the island and the *barrier reefs;* if the island has completely disappeared, the remaining circle of reef is called an *atoll;* the reefs and atolls of Bermuda and of the South Sea Isles are especially famous.

Ocean currents, such as the Gulf Stream and the Labrador Current, apparently result from the fact that in the tropics the sea is warmer than in the Arctic and Antarctic, and the currents flow from the warmer to the colder zones. These currents have a great effect on climate and consequently are indirectly important geologically.

Ocean tides are due to the gravitational pull on the earth by both sun and moon. The moon, being nearer, exerts the greater pull. This gravitational pull causes a bulge toward the moon on the side of the earth nearest the moon, and a bulge away from the moon on the side furthest from the moon. As the earth revolves around its axis every 24 hours, every point on its circumference is brought into line with the earth-moon axis twice a day, either toward the moon or away from it; and these are the high tides.

The effect of the moon's gravitational pull is most apparent on the ocean because this vast fluid body can respond so noticeably. Nevertheless, it is important to bear in mind that though it is less apparent, the particles of the lithosphere and atmosphere are also affected by this gravitational pull of the moon.

Sedimentation in ocean depths and shallow seas arises from the sediment which the sea derives from its own erosive activity and which is brought to it by streams, either as beaches at the shore, or in layers on the continental shelves, or as *oozes* on the deep-sea floor; the oozes are very fine clayey material sometimes containing large amounts of very primitive and simple forms of deep-sea plant and animal life.

In earlier geologic eras, large parts of the present continents were flooded by arms of the ocean, constituting shallow seas in which sedimentary rocks were formed. Most great sedimentary rock formations originated in this way, becoming exposed when the sea receded and dry land emerged once more.

MOVEMENTS IN THE ROCKS

Diastrophism is the general term applied to all movements of the earth's crust which cause changes of position in the earth's surface either by raising or lowering or tilting the level of a given area, or causing a horizontal movement sideways in one direction or another. Some of these movements take place gradually but steadily over a long period, others are more sudden, more violent. Earthquakes and volcanic eruptions are ordinarily of this latter sort; we shall consider them in detail after discussing the more general diastrophic movements.

When changes occur along the seacoast we have the phenomena of emergence or submergence, as we have already seen. Evidence of elevation of land from the sea is found in the presence of shells and fossils of sea organisms in land areas; and beach sand found inland also ordinarily indicates former submergence. The evidences of sinking of the land surface are found by taking soundings in the water offshore. Soundings show that the Hudson River Valley must have extended quite a distance beyond its present mouth at the end of Manhattan Island, as a true valley formation is found beneath the bay and outward along the continental shelf.

Horizontal change of position as a result of diastrophic activity is best demonstrated in areas where earthquakes have occurred. Often a road, railroad track, or fence is found to have been broken abruptly, and a whole section moved to right or left of its original position, as demonstrated by its lack of alignment with a section which has not been disturbed.

WARPS AND FOLDS

In a region where, due to diastrophic activity, there has been an upward or a downward movement, the earth's surface reveals a corresponding irregular uplift or depression which is particularly visible in exposed stratified rock. When strata, which were originally deposited horizontally, are seen to have been tilted, the general change of angle is known as a *warp*.

At various points in a landscape we may notice exposed strata which have been bent into rather regular curves, some quite strikingly arched, some more wave-like. Such curved formations are known as *folds*. Folds may either be curved upward or downward, and where they constitute a wave the two types are alternated. An upfold is called an *anticline;* a downfold is called a *syncline*.

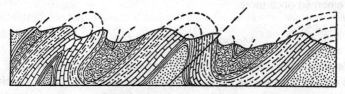

FIG. 2. Overthrown fold. The folded strata are so compressed that some folds are carried beyond the perpendicular and older strata appear above the younger. At left, a reversed or false dip is seen where the layers are overthrown. Near the middle, a fold has torn to a reversed fault.

FRACTURES, JOINTS, AND FAULTS

A *fracture* is a break in the earth's surface. If the walls of rock on either side of the fracture have not been displaced the fracture is called a *joint*. If the walls have been displaced so that parts which were continuous before the break took place are now out of alignment with one another, the fracture is called a *fault*. If the joint or fault shows a distinct separation between its two walls, it is called a *fissure*.

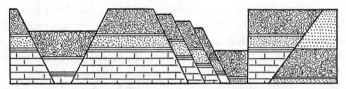

FIG. 3. Step and graben faults. Reading from left to right: graben, horst, three step-faults, vertical fault, reversed fault.

Jointing may occur during the final contractions in the cooling of a mass of molten rock material or as a result of diastrophic movements of the earth's crust. When jointing occurs during the cooling of a volcanic lava, it sometimes forms a series of closely spaced parallel fractures and one or more series of equally closely spaced fractures running either at right angles or obliquely in relation to the others. Such jointing breaks up the rocky mass into a great bed of columns, which become increasingly apparent as parts of the surface break away. One of the most famous examples of this columnar structure due to jointing is the Giant's Causeway in northern Ireland. Joints are of assistance to engineers in tunneling and mining. They are also convenient in quarrying unless they are so closely spaced as to make the quarried blocks smaller than desired.

The displacement of rock masses along the line of a fault may occur at the time of the fracture or take place later. The displacement is most apparent in sedimentary rocks, where a given stratum on one side of the fault and its original continuation on the other side are very clearly no longer directly opposite one another, but instead this stratum and the whole series of which it is part have moved either up or down in relation to the corresponding stratum on the opposite side. Faults are usually not quite vertical fractures; in fact, they are often fairly oblique.

Warping, folding, jointing, and faulting are all movements in the earth's crust which result from the forces of expansion, contraction, or twisting within the earth's interior. As yet we know so little about this deeper zone below the crust that we can only conjecture as to the forces at work there. However, we may find something of an analogy in an explosion within a house which, without destroying it, breaks the windows and cracks the plaster inside and the concrete walls outside.

UNCONFORMITY

When strata are parallel with one another and show a gradual change from one type to another, it is reasonable to assume that they were deposited successively under comparatively unchanged conditions. When there is a noticeable irregularity in the line in which two strata meet, or a decided difference in angle, as though the strata had been turned and then broken off, the point of transition is called an *unconformity*. When the lower strata are tilted as compared with the upper, an important movement must have taken place between the deposition of the two crust formations. When there is irregularity without change of angle, erosion must have occurred before the new rocks were laid down. Many instances reveal both crustal movements and erosion. Unconformities are readily recognized in rocks exposed to view as cross sections, and they immediately suggest something of the history of the region.

EARTHQUAKES

Earthquakes are shakings of the earth's crust due to disturbances within the earth's interior. The shaking may be gentle and perceptible only to delicate instruments, or it may be violent and cause great disasters. During one of the greatest earthquakes, which occurred in 1923 in Tokyo, Japan, 140,000 lives were lost and tremendous amounts of property destroyed. The great San Francisco earthquake of 1906, and the earthquake at Messina, in Sicily, in 1908 were also terrifying disasters.

The principal explanation of earthquakes lies in the yielding of the earth's crust to some strain from beneath, resulting in a displacement of the surface along an existing fault line, or the breaking of the crust, forming a new fracture. Many earthquakes occur along old fault lines, and the repetition in a given area undoubtedly corresponds to a definite weakness in the crust in that region.

Although earthquakes are ordinarily caused by profound movements below the earth's surface, studies along the San Andreas rift in California indicate that slow movements may cause strains along fault lines, bringing about minor surface movements, but accumulating the strain nevertheless until an active earthquake again relieves the strain.

It has been demonstrated, particularly through studies made during earthquake disturbances in southern California, that buildings with steel frames can withstand earthquake shocks relatively well, and frame houses are better than brick or stucco in this respect. The danger of damage is augmented when fires start as a result of broken electrical connections, because such fires cannot be efficiently fought when the water mains have been broken by the earthquake.

Earthquakes not infrequently occur below the sea, especially in the Pacific. They generate great waves, *tsunamis* (often incorrectly called "tidal waves"), as the principal evidence of their happening. Now that seismographs (instruments sensitive to and capable of recording both the direction and the distance as well as the intensity of the tremors) are located in all parts of the world, seismic (earthquake) activity is being studied constantly, and the indications are that minor disturbances of the crust are exceedingly frequent.

It is a significant fact that the areas most often the scenes of earthquakes are also the areas of volcanoes. In some instances earthquakes may be induced by volcanic activity, but for the most part the two phenomena occur independently. Nevertheless, it is not mere coincidence that they occur in the same areas; such regions are undoubtedly areas of relatively general unrest beneath the surface, and the two phenomena are manifestations of this unrest.

VOLCANOES

When a volcano erupts we have a dramatic indication of the nature of regions far below the earth's surface. Most volcanoes are of the familiar cone-shaped type, mountains with craters at the top. A vent in the earth's crust connects the crater with the earth's interior. Molten rock material from the earth's depths makes its way to the surface during the eruption of a volcano and pours out, often flowing for great distances. Mauna Loa in Hawaii has sent flows as far as 50 miles.

The molten material in a volcano is called *magma*. When an eruption takes place the magma expels volcanic gases and the molten mass which flows out, no longer containing the gases, is known as *lava*. The flowing lava is at white heat when eruption takes place, but it cools comparatively quickly when it is exposed to the air, and in cooling it solidifies, forming igneous rock.

Certain fragments of solid material broken from the solid surface of the volcano by the eruption are also ejected as *volcanic bombs* if they are large, as *volcanic cinders* if they are fine grains. These solid materials become cemented together as a result of the heat and pressure of the flowing lava, and form rocks along the sides of the volcano, the rocks composed of the larger fragments being known as *breccia;* those of the fine grains are known as *tuff.*

NOTABLE VOLCANIC ERUPTIONS

The outrush of volcanic gases from Mount Pelée in 1902 brought death and destruction to the island of Martinique in the Caribbean, the greatest volcanic disturbance in the vicinity of the United States in modern times. Molten lava from Vesuvius near Naples destroyed Pompeii and Herculaneum in 79 A.D. Vesuvius is quietly active at all times, and a powerful eruption took place in 1906. After being largely shattered by the eruption of 79 A.D., Vesuvius has rebuilt itself from its lava, breccia, and tuff to a height of 3,858 feet.

Two great explosive volcanoes in the neighborhood of Java in the East Indies, Tambora (which erupted in 1815) and Krakatoa (which erupted in 1883), are historically famous examples of eruptive activity. The noise of Krakatoa was heard in Australia, 1,750 miles away; a volcanic cloud arose 17 miles into the atmosphere, and the finest dust particles are known to have traveled all around the earth several times; waves as high as 100 feet were generated and swept over large parts of Java and Sumatra, destroying towns and taking 36,000 lives.

Lassen Peak in northern California became active in 1914, but ejected mostly gases and rock fragments. The absence of molten lava seems to indicate that it is becoming extinct.

The great volcanoes of Hawaii—Mauna Loa and Kilauea—are constantly active, discharging gas and lava in a quiet way without violent eruption.

VOLCANIC FLOWS THROUGH FISSURES

During violent eruptions the activity of the magma may cause fissures in the sides of the volcano, the magma pouring out through these fissures instead of rising and pouring over the top.

Eruptions do not only occur in volcanic cones. Fissures in the earth's surface may become outlets for volcanic activity; in such instances lava pours out in sheets, as in the lava fields of the Columbia River.

CAUSES OF VOLCANIC ACTIVITY

Volcanic activity is undoubtedly ultimately caused by changes in the earth's crust. In all probability, the magmatic material exists as a very hot, rigid mass in the depths of the crust or even below, in the earth's interior. The rigid mass beneath a given area tends to become liquid if the pressure upon it from the weight of the crust is lessened by movements of the crust which cause the rock masses to shift their position. Extensive erosion may also cause a great reduction of the weight of the crust. If a molten mass has formed as a result of a decrease in the pressure from above, and this mass is subject to pressure from the side as a result of increased pressure on the regions near it, the mass will tend to erupt upward through any convenient vent or opening in the crust. Inasmuch as lessened surface pressure in one area in many instances brings about increased surface pressure in a neighboring area, the two conditions necessary to imitate volcanic activity are likely to be present simultaneously. Once a volcano has become established in this way, it may persist for thousands of years, though erupting only occasionally.

VOLCANIC REGIONS

The earth's crust has belts of comparative weakness of structure where volcanic activity is likely to occur. There is such a belt around the Pacific Ocean, including the Andes in South America, the ranges of Central America and western Mexico, western United States and Canada, Alaska, the Aleutian Islands, and in Asia, Kamchatka, Japan, the Philippines, and the East Indies. There is another more broken chain across the Middle Atlantic, along the northern Mediterranean, and through Central Asia.

GEYSERS AND RELATED PHENOMENA

In some volcanic areas special phenomena associated with volcanoes but not involving volcanic eruption are found. *Fumaroles* are openings in rocks through which volcanic steam and other hot gases pour. *Hot springs* are currents of hot water which reach the surface in volcanic areas. Sometimes they actually boil; and under certain conditions they gush forth at intervals, erupting a column of hot water and steam. These columns, in some instances erupting as frequently as every hour, are known as *geysers,* of which there are world-famous examples in Yellowstone National Park.

The action of geysers results from the fact that the water at the base of the water column in a *geyser tube* often reaches the boiling point and turns to steam in the deeper earth interior because the heat at this depth is greater than above; the steam expands upward, forcing the water column to erupt at the surface. Geysers and related phenomena are the final state of volcanic activity when the magmas are cooling and consolidating.

MOUNTAINS

Some mountains are of volcanic origin, resulting from piling up of volcanic debris or from the pressure of intrusive magma which forces the upper crust into a dome-shaped mass without breaking through. Some are due to stream system erosion which may have started by the formation of various neighboring valleys in a plateau region, later breaking and dissecting the plateau to such an extent that the mountains remain. The

Grand Canyon of the Colorado, although deeply dissected by stream valleys, is still a plateau on top; but in time, as the valleys approach nearer and nearer to one another, it is probable that mountain forms will result.

Great mountain ranges and systems of ranges such as the Rocky Mountains and the Appalachians, the Andes, the Alps, and the Himalayas, are due, however, to more profound diastrophic activity, though modified by these other phenomena.

When faulting occurs, as we have already seen, two areas formerly in the same horizontal plane are forced out of alignment, one being raised, the other lowered. Where this occurs on a large scale and involves several nearly parallel fractures, mountains and valleys may be formed as blocks are raised and lowered.

Vast folding of the earth's crust brings about the most important of all mountain formations. We can recognize the folds particularly well where the mountain ranges are at least in part of sedimentary rock, and the bending in the strata indicates the extent to which up-folding or down-folding has taken place. Igneous and metamorphic rocks in relation to sedimentary rocks also are recognizably folded, and the presence of the igneous rocks is clear indication of some volcanic activity in the region. Nevertheless, sedimentary rocks are the principal rocks involved in building a fold mountain, indicating that the first stage prior to the uplift must have been a relative subsidence, followed by inundation by the sea, with sedimentary deposition in successive layers, perhaps interrupted by dry periods and again continued during further inundation; then a period in which the sedimentary rock consolidates; and finally, a great uplift of the strata, due to diastrophic movement of the crust, forms a new mountain range or system of ranges. These mountains are, of course, greatly modified in time by the forces of erosion.

An example of the relative shifting of exposed land areas is found in the Appalachian Mountains. The indications are that the area now occupied by the mountain system became, through subsidence at one time, a trough into which the sediment from the erosion of the land mass to the east deposited its sediment in strata and in great quantities. Such a trough is called a *geosyncline;* every indication shows it as a relatively weak portion of the crust. The folds, from their appearance, very clearly resulted from lateral and horizontal pressure. Ordinarily, folding on as large a scale as this commences mildly even during the original sedimentation as shown by the strata; the greatest diastrophism takes place after the emergence of the area, and results in a series of parallel ranges.

The part of the interior in closest contact with the cool crust is undoubtedly cooling or at least contracting, and it is felt that this process in the interior is largely responsible for the diastrophic movements above.

Movements of the interior are almost constantly occurring, as is indicated by seismograph records. Vast diastrophic surface upheavals are rare, however, occurring only periodically in the earth's history.

ISOSTASY

A general geologic theory which indicates in a simple way the relation between the more important diastrophic phenomena is known as *isostasy,* a conception of equilibrium in the earth's crust. It holds that the crust adjusts itself to changes in the surface, and that in the process of adjustment it causes other changes in the surface. Thus, in an area consisting of a mountain range which is in the process of being eroded and with the sediment carried by streams and deposited in a depressed area covered by shallow seas, the accumulating sediments, after long periods, weigh down on the crust below to such an extent that pressure is transmitted through the crust to the molten or plastic interior; then the whole mass below the sediments sinks, causing horizontal movement in one or another direction in the plastic mass below. This horizontal pressure causes a neighboring mass to press upward against the crust, and the upward pressure is met by strong resistance from the crust except at the important point where erosion has taken place, thus leaving less than the usual weight on the crust at that point. The pressure then causes an upward movement at this point, bringing about a new uplift.

THE EARTH'S INTERIOR

The lithosphere or outer shell of the earth, which we have called the crust, is in all probability 30 or 40 miles thick. The diameter of the earth is approximately 8,000 miles, consequently the earth's crust is at best only a very narrow zone as compared with the great depth of the earth's interior. The deepest mines are hardly more than a few thousand feet deep, so there is, of course, no direct evidence as to the nature of the interior. Volcanoes which bring up their magma from far below the surface prove that at least some depths are exceedingly hot, but these may be local conditions in the areas beneath the volcanoes or volcanic belts, and the magma may originate in an intermediate zone below the crust, which is hotter than the great interior. It is probable, however, that the interior is also hot, but not necessarily hot enough to cause the material of the interior to become or remain liquid. The interior is under such tremendous pressure from the crust that far greater heat would be needed to melt common minerals in the interior than is required on the surface of the earth where the pressure upon them is so very much less.

Seismographs, which measure earthquake shocks, are among our few

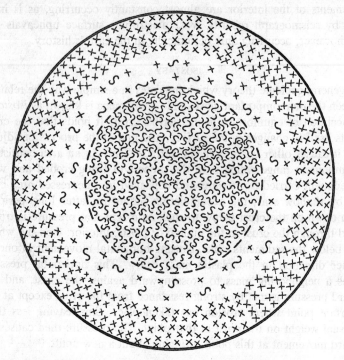

FIG. 4. The earth's interior. The center is believed composed mostly of iron, while the outer shell is probably of compounds of silicon. In the transition zone between the two, one element gradually replaces another.

indicators of conditions in the earth's interior. The study of the wave vibrations caused by earthquakes which are recorded on these instruments has revealed that the first waves set up by the disturbance pass *through* the interior of the earth, whereas the principal waves from the earthquake travel *around* the earth in the crust and parallel to the surface. Some indication of the solidity and fluidity of various zones may be gained from the variations in these waves.

Meteors, most of which consist primarily of iron and nickel, are supposed to be fragments of relatively simple bodies in the solar system, and it has been suggested that the earth's interior may resemble them in constitution.

MINERAL RESOURCES IN THE EARTH'S CRUST

Among the most important mineral resources in the earth are coal, oil (petroleum), iron, and other metallic ores.

Coal is a compact mass of plant debris which has lain submerged for so many geologic ages that it has become largely a mineral-like form of carbon, though containing appreciable quantities of other materials. The vegetation from which the coal was formed must have existed in great fresh-water swamps, the transformation to coal consisting in the decay of the vegetation and the consolidation of the decayed matter by pressure from sedimentation above or during diastrophic activities such as folding.

Because *oil* (*petroleum*) is a liquid, and "natural gas" is a vapor, they cannot constitute strata as coal does, but they must be formed within sufficiently porous rock to constitute a reservoir for them. Both oil and natural gas are compounds of carbon and hydrogen, derived from decayed living matter. In the earth's crust, oil and gas are protected from above by an impervious layer of rock, and in mining for them this impervious rock is drilled through and the oil or gas gushes out. Oil is usually found in sedimentary rocks of marine origin, and often a deposit of salt is present beneath the oil in the rock reservoir.

An *ore* is a mineral containing a considerable amount of a metal. The ores of a number of metals are commonly found in areas where there are igneous rocks, and seem to be of igneous origin. Metals are known to be prominently present in magmas. The minerals in the cooling intrusive magma or extrusive lava tend to separate out and form veins, due to differences in texture or other chemical or physical causes, and to the fact that certain minerals act upon one another chemically, producing an ore of the metal in a form in which it can be mined.

Metallic ores are also found in sedimentary rocks, however, and particularly large deposits of iron are often found in sedimentary formations. For practical use, iron is the most important of the metals, but gold, silver, copper, aluminum, and others are also greatly needed and greatly sought.

Deposits of *common salt* that are found in the earth's crust are usually part of the mineral residue accumulated at the time that the sea receded from an inland area which it had overflowed. Other *chemical salts* are sometimes found in similar formations, and many chemical compounds important as soil fertilization are derived by simple chemical action upon rock masses of appropriate composition.

Certain minerals are found to be of such exceptional brilliance or purity of color that they have, through the ages, come to be greatly prized. These are our *precious stones*—diamonds, emeralds, rubies, and sapphires —together with a number of semi-precious stones. Chemically they are very similar to other far more abundant minerals which are entirely undistinguished in appearance. But it is not their scarcity as much as their extraordinary beauty which sets precious stones apart. A beautiful gem is treasured for its personal associations and its fascination as a work of art, and is at the same time a constant reminder of the great geologic romance of the rocks.

THE EARTH'S HISTORY

THE ORIGIN OF THE EARTH

There are three principal theories of the earth's beginnings—the Laplacian or Nebular Hypothesis, the Planetesimal Hypothesis, and the Dust Cloud Hypothesis. The Nebular Hypothesis was developed by the French astronomer, Laplace, at the end of the eighteenth century, and was largely accepted until a few decades ago, when Professors Chamberlin and Moulton of the University of Chicago developed the Planetesimal Theory as accounting for certain phenomena not adequately explained under the Laplacian Theory. Laplace held that our solar system—the sun, its planets, and their satellites—was all a part of a revolving, very hot, gaseous nebula which included the whole part of the heavens now occupied by the solar system. It was assumed that as the nebula cooled it shrank and left outside an ellipitical ring of matter which collected to form a planet and then followed the elliptic ring as its orbit in revolving around the parent mass. Then further cooling and shrinking of the nebular mass produced another planet in the same way; and then another, and another, until the nine known planets and group of small planetoids or asteroids were all formed, leaving the sun as the residue of the nebula, at the center of the solar system.

The Planetesimal Theory starts from the fact that astronomic photography has revealed that in the heavens at the present time the most common form of nebula is spiral rather than elliptical. Also, Chamberlin and Moulton found the movement of matter in a spiral nebula better suited to explain the formation of the solar system. They considered that our sun, somewhat larger than at present, was the nucleus of such a nebula-like body, and that through the gravitational influence of a star which passed close to it, arm-like masses of material from the sun were drawn out on the two opposite sides—toward and away from the passing star. The arm-like extensions are believed to have taken up a spiral movement around the sun, thus presenting a formation similar to that of a spiral nebulae. It is assumed that these spiral arms consisted of molten or plastic solid particles—planetesimals—rather than of heated gas, and that the particles varied in size.

It is further assumed that at various points on the spiral extension there were large particles constituting knots of molten or plastic matter, such as are found by telescope and spectroscope in spiral nebulae today. The knots are believed to be the original form of the planets. The smaller particles are believed to have merged with neighboring larger particles when their orbits crossed and they came into contact with one another and the smaller became absorbed in the larger. Some of the smaller particles would not become absorbed, and would form orbits around the larger ones and constitute their satellites (the earth acquiring the moon as its satellite in this way), while the planets also formed orbits about the large central mass of the spiral which we know as the sun. At the present time this theory is the one most generally accepted by scientists, though it is likely to be modified in the future by new discoveries and knowledge.

The latest hypothesis, the Dust Cloud Theory, was suggested by Whipple and Spitzer. This theory ties in the fact that the age of the universe and the age of the solar system are of the same order of magnitude. According to this theory, matter was originally scattered more or less uniformly through space; but, under the influence of the radiation pressure of light, particles were driven together and their mutual gravitational attraction formed a cloud which began to contract. Those clouds which rotated broke apart under the increasing centrifugal force and gave rise to multiple stars. This accounts for the fact that most of the stars are multiple.

Clouds without angular momentum, such as the one from which our sun was derived, had smaller gravitational eddies set up within them. These smaller groupings formed the "proto-planets," while the main cloud collapsed to form the sun. The proto-planets condensed and became heated by this contraction. The sun's contraction caused sufficient heat to set off a thermonuclear reaction. Planet-clouds in rapid rotation flung off bits of matter, which became satellites. The earth-moon system may be considered to be a double planet. The Dust Cloud Theory, in addition to obviating some of the objections to previous theories, applies to galaxies as well as to the solar system, and thus describes the way in which the universe was formed. Estimates of the age of the universe, as obtained from astronomical data and from the decay of radioactive elements in meteorites, shows the universe to be approximately 5,000,-000,000 years old. We get a similar figure when we estimate the age of the earth from the amount of lead produced by the decay of uranium in the oldest rocks in the earth's surface.

EARLIEST STAGES OF THE EARTH

According to these theories, the gases present in the neighborhood of the earth's mass gathered about the planet to form its original atmosphere and were augmented by gases ejected from the earth itself. At this time, due either to gravitational pull toward its own center, or as a result of the impact of the planetesimals which merged with it, the primitive matter of the planet is believed to have become very hot and molten.

There is every indication that water vapor was present among the early gases of the atmosphere, and that when the atmosphere was saturated with the water vapor, and the earth's surface had cooled relatively, the water vapor condensed and fell to earth, settling in the most deeply depressed areas, forming the original oceans, and thus providing the earth with hydrosphere. The original land masses stood higher because they were composed principally of lighter rocks, as compared with the heavy rocks underlying the deep sea areas.

Geologists have carefully studied rock formations and rock strata in all parts of the world, and have been able to determine within certain limits which of the rocks go back to the earliest times and which were formed during the various later stages of the earth's history.

FOSSILS AND OTHER EVIDENCES OF ANCIENT LIFE

The greatest aids in identifying a rock formation as definitely of a certain period are the *fossils* found in it. Fossils are relics of living matter; they may be either shells or bones of animal life, or petrified wood or other preserved plant life, or merely an outline in the rock corresponding to some form of plant or animal life which has itself not been preserved.

Organic evolution, the study of the origin and rise of all the species of animals and plants, indicates a very definite progression from simpler to more complex forms of life, and this progression has taken place gradually through geologic ages. The very simple single-celled protozoa and bacteria are the most primitive forms of life known to us today, but the very earliest forms of life, which originated from non-living matter, must have been even simpler. At the present time we have no indication that life is being formed from non-living matter, but in the early period of the earth's history, when the seas were still comparatively new, conditions must have been favorable for the formation of the very elementary forms of life from which all others evolved gradually through the later ages.

Life presumably originated in shallow sea water, and developed in the sea until forms suited to the land were evolved. Even the land forms probably remained near the water area, as all forms of life are and presumably always have been dependent on water for sustenance. Consequently, it is not surprising that the great sedimentary rocks formed as strata in shallow sea water, which constitute our best record of the past history of the earth, contain fossils of the forms of life of the period when the rocks were deposited as sediment. Early forms of plants and animals were swept into the strata by tides or streams which brought the sediment, and in later ages remains of more complex forms of animal and plant life were also preserved in this way. Even though the perishable tissues naturally decayed, the bones of animals and the woody frame of plants, in most instances converted to stone by petrifaction, but still retaining their original outline, are in the rocks, and are a permanent guide to the forms of life which existed at the time of the sedimentation.

Thus far we have devoted very little space to animal and plant life because the study of all living matter is the province of biology rather than geology. Nevertheless, the history of life on earth, its origin and evolution, is such an important aspect of the earth's history that in surveying the stages of the earth's development, geologists indicate the forms of life which characterized the various geologic eras.

PERIODS OF GEOLOGIC TIME

There are many estimates of the age of the earth based on geologic and astronomic data. They vary greatly, and are at best very general indications. For reference, the following table with approximate durations of each era is convenient:

TABLE OF THE AGE OF THE EARTH

COSMIC ERA . . . . 400 million years
   Formation of the Planet from Planetesimals of Solar Nebula.

AZOIC ERA . . . . 600 million years
   Differentiation of the Earth into Lithosphere, Centrosphere, Atmosphere, and Hydrosphere before the existence of any forms of life.

ARCHEOZOIC ERA . . . . 500 million years
   The age of the very earliest forms of life, Protozoa and Protophyta, the one-celled animals and plants.

PROTEROZOIC ERA . . . . 500 million years
   The age of Primitive Life—the early marine invertebrates.

PALEOZOIC ERA . . . . 350 million years
   The age of Ancient Life—the higher (shelled) invertebrates, fishes, amphibians.

MESOZOIC ERA . . . . 125 million years
   Age of Reptiles—domination by the great reptilian forms such as the dinosaurs.

CENOZOIC ERA . . . . 59 million years
   Age of Mammals—domination by the great mammals such as the mastodons and other large forerunners of modern animals.

PSYCHOZOIC ERA . . . . 1 million years
   Age of Man—evolution of man, earliest men, primitive society, and finally modern civilization.

General Aspects of Earth History

Having considered the keys which aid us in deciphering the earth's history, we are now ready to turn to the history itself.

The great geologic phenomena which we have considered have been at work over almost countless ages, and have apparently acted in much the same way through all these ages. Although there have been continuous geologic changes, there have been only a few periods of such tremendous diastrophic activity as to constitute definite geologic revolutions. These periods of greatest change were very strikingly marked by mountain building on a vast scale, producing whole systems of ranges, and frequently accompanied by extensive volcanic activity, more often intrusively than extrusively. In the long periods between these revolutions, erosion proceeded steadily, minor folding produced lesser mountains, volcanic and earthquake disturbances occurred occasionally, and animals and plants evolved gradually. During each period of geologic revolution, the dominant form of animal life was largely extinguished by the upheaval, and in the following period a new form derived from some earlier but subordinate species came into special prominence. All these aspects of the earth's history will become clearer from the following brief account.

The Archeozoic Era

We have already summarized the theories of geologists with reference to the Cosmic and Azoic eras. Let us now consider the Archeozoic, the first era of which we have any record in the rocks. The Archean rocks, as the rocks of the Archeozoic Era are called, do not contain any fossils, which is not surprising, because the single-celled life of the period consisted of tissues all of which would certainly have decayed rather than fossilized. How then can we identify the Archean rocks? They are of special interest as they are the oldest known rocks. In areas such as the Grand Canyon in Arizona they are the lowest rocks, and are almost entirely igneous or metamorphic; they are separated from the rocks above by a marked unconformity. The rocks immediately above are largely sedimentary and contain some fossils of early marine invertebrates which are known to belong to the Proterozoic Era, which followed the Archeozoic. These Proterozoic formations are in turn separated by a marked unconformity from rocks above them which belong to the Paleozoic. These are clearly identified by abundant fossils characteristic of that period. The Grand Canyon shows us the sequence in an amazingly convincing manner. And the characteristics of these Archean rocks of the Grand Canyon are sufficiently like those of Archean rocks in other identifiable sequences in other parts of the world to make it possible for a geologist to recognize Archean rocks even when they are at the earth's surface and have no other formations above them to aid in the identification.

Although there are no recognized fossils in Archean rocks, these rocks do contain masses of graphite, which are believed to have formed from the decayed single-celled animal and plant life of the era.

Archean rocks are found exposed at the surface, or covered only by mantle and vegetation in large parts of central and eastern Canada. All indications from these rocks point to two great diastrophic periods during the Archeozoic Era; one along toward the middle of the era, which is known as the Laurentian Revolution (from the St. Lawrence River, in the neighborhood of which the uplift occurred). This was followed by a period of extensive erosion, and at the very end of the era another great uplift occurred, the Algomian Revolution.

THE PROTEROZOIC ERA

There are very few fossils in the Proterozoic rocks, but those which are found are sufficient for identification, and in addition there are masses of carbon compounds in the shales, slates, and schists of this era which are believed to be definitely derived from decayed organic matter. The nature of the unconformity between Archeozoic and Proterozoic rock reveals not only the fact that a geologic revolution separated the two eras but also that the great uplifts were largely eroded away, and that submergence took place, making it possible for the sea to flow over the land in large areas and to deposit sediments, forming the Proterozoic sedimentary rocks. There are several important subdivisions of the Proterozoic Era corresponding to successive major systems of rock formations which were formed in turn, and are termed respectively Huronian, Animikian, and Keweenawan. They are studied to best advantage in the region of Canada bordering on Lake Superior. Proterozoic rocks are rich in iron and copper, with lesser deposits of other metals. Glaciation is known to have occurred during the Proterozoic. The revolution which brought the era to a close is known as the Killarneyan (from the Killarney region north of Lake Huron, where there are evidences of the uplift).

THE PALEOZOIC ERA

In the Archeozoic and Proterozoic eras, life was just beginning to make a place for itself on the earth. But in the rocks of the Paleozoic Era we find abundant fossils of great variety which show that both animals and plants had advanced considerably over the forms in which they existed in the preceding era. With the transition to the Paleozoic, organic evolution seems to have speeded up, and as we follow the Paleozoic through its successive subdivisions we find the forms of life steadily increasing in complexity and in adaptability to new conditions. Animal and plant forms which had previously existed principally in shallow waters began to develop forms suitable for life upon land. At the beginning of the Paleozoic the animal life consisted principally of higher invertebrates such as early forms of snails, clams, crabs, and lobsters. Toward the middle of the Paleozoic, fishes became the dominant form of animal life, thus beginning the supremacy of vertebrate forms. And in the later Paleozoic the chief animals were amphibians, early representatives of frogs and toads, which are capable of living in the water and on land, thus bringing about transition to the land as the most important setting for animal life. The chief amphibians of the late Paleozoic were not small animals like our frogs, but ranged in size up to about eight feet in length, many of them being covered with heavy armor-like scales.

During the period when these large amphibians were the most important animal life, plants, which had developed gradually from early, very simple beginnings, reached a great tree-like development, though they were not like the principal trees of today; our palms suggest them in a very general way, but their leaves were more like those of their more lowly descendants, ferns and ground pine. The landscape must have been far more luxuriant than the landscapes in even the warmest tropical regions today. These plants of the late Paleozoic are of tremendous importance to us because they flourished and decayed in swampy land under conditions which turned them to a peaty substance which hardened into coal. The greatest coal deposits in the world today were formed then, and consequently this later part of the Paleozoic Era is known as the Carboniferous (coal-bearing) Age.

The variations in animal and plant life during the Paleozoic kept pace with changes in the earth's structure, and several successive rock formations were laid down. The formations represent quite distinct subdivisions of the Paleozoic, and each is important and contains characteristic fossils. The formations of the earlier Paleozoic arranged in sequence are called Cambrian, Ordovician, and Silurian. In North America there was apparently no important diastrophic activity between the earlier and later Paleozoic, but in Europe there was such extensive mountain building, especially in Scotland and Scandinavia, that it is customary to speak of a Caledonian revolution as bringing the earlier Paleozoic to a close.

The later Paleozoic, the great period of coal deposition and at the same time of oil and natural gas, is divided into four important subdivisions as shown in rock formations. Devonian, Mississippian, Pennsylvanian, and

Permian are the American names of the periods, though other names are used in Europe for certain of them.

During the Paleozoic the interior of North America was covered by shallow seas, the land areas being along the continental shores and including parts of the present continental shelves. Toward the end of the period the sea receded, leaving swamps in some parts and sedimentary rock strata in others.

The great Paleozoic Era ended in a great glacial period, followed by a series of vast earth movements, known as the Appalachian-Hercynian revolution, the term *Appalachian* especially describing the great mountain building in eastern North America, the term *Hercynian* describing important simultaneously formed ranges in Wales, France, Germany, and Central Europe.

THE MESOZOIC ERA

One of the most striking discoveries of geology is the fact that together with the diastrophic movements which accompany the changes from one geologic era to the next, there is an extremely important change in living organisms. With the ending of the Paleozoic, the large amphibians disappeared entirely, and the amphibians which continued into the Mesozoic were only small forms, like the frogs of today. Evidently the diastrophic activity and changes in the earth's climate were unfavorable for the larger forms, and, being unable to withstand the changing conditions, they died out. However, some relatively simple types of amphibians adapted themselves especially well to the new conditions, and from them the reptiles evolved. During the Mesozoic, the reptiles, represented today principally by snakes, turtles, and alligators, developed to great size, vastly exceeding the largest amphibians of the Paleozoic, becoming huge monsters having great legs, long bodies, often with long tails, but usually with comparatively small heads. Typical of these great reptiles are the dinosaurs, of which there were many species. The Mesozoic reptiles presented almost as varied a group of land animals as the mammals of today, and included also ichthyosaurs, capable of living in water, and pterosaurs, capable of flying; late in the Mesozoic, birds began to evolve from reptilian ancestors. The dinosaurs perhaps more than any other animals of early geologic times suggest to us the great changes which have taken place during the history of the earth.

During the Mesozoic the continent of North America was no longer covered by the great shallow seas which had covered it during such a large part of the Paleozoic. Some lakes remained, however, and along the shores the oceans submerged part of the land areas which had for a long period been exposed. Consequently the chief areas in which sedimentation could take place during the Mesozoic were along these submerged coasts and in the larger lakes. During the later Mesozoic, however, a great arm of what is now the Pacific swept into the continent, presumably in the neighborhood of what is now British Columbia, and reached across much of the area now occupied by the Rocky Mountains, which at that time was a trough or *geosyncline*.

The later part of the Mesozoic is known as the Cretaceous (from the Latin for "chalk") because of the abundant chalk deposits in the rocks of this period. The climate during the Cretaceous was warm throughout most of the globe, and Greenland at that time was free of ice and included in the temperate areas. It is not difficult to understand that the seas extended up onto the continental shelf and even onto the shores of the continental masses at that time, as the sea level was greatly raised by the presence of water which, in other eras, was often withdrawn from the sea by being held as ice. During the Cretaceous, plant life was very luxuriant, somewhat similar to that of the Carboniferous but more like modern tropical foliage. The decay of rich vegetation, like that of the earlier period, provided a great source of coal; sources of oil and gas were also formed at this time; there are important iron ores in Mesozoic rocks and some gold ores, and certain rocks of this period contain diamonds.

The rock formations of the Mesozoic reveal four major subdivisions, which are known respectively as the Triassic, the Jurassic, the Comanchean, and the final period, the Cretaceous, of which we have just spoken.

The transition from the Mesozoic to the Cenozoic was marked by great diastrophic activity, including the building of the Rocky Mountains and Andes in the Americas, and a large section of the Himalayas in Asia, and constituting the Laramide-Himalayan Revolution.

THE CENOZOIC ERA

With the Cenozoic or Recent Era, we seem to come almost in sight of our own age geologically, but as our summary of geologic time indicated, the Cenozoic must have continued for almost 60 million years before the evolution of man.

The chief sedimentary deposits laid down during the Cenozoic were on the floodplains of rivers, rather than in shallow seas as in earlier eras. These Cenozoic sedimentary formations are very extensive in America, being found especially in the Middle West. They are not as firmly consolidated as the sedimentary rocks of previous eras. Cenozoic rocks in America and elsewhere contain very important economic products: coal and oil are found, and deposits of many of the most valuable metals, including gold, silver, copper, and others.

The Cenozoic Era is the age in which mammals became the most important form of animal life. The great reptilian dinosaurs did not survive the transition to the new era, but from lesser reptilian stock the mammals evolved, developing during the Cenozoic into the forerunners of most of our modern animals. At the height of the Cenozoic, mammals of great size were common; they were considerably larger than the mammals of today. Among the giant mammals which have since disappeared are the titanothere, which must have been somewhat elephant-like but with a horn on the nose and no trunk; the uintathere, somewhat resembling a rhinoceros; the entelodont, a giant hog; and the megatherium, a giant ground sloth. Many other animals, forerunners of common species of today, were smaller than their present-day representatives. This is particularly true of the horse, which evolved from a very much smaller form.

The plant life of the Cenozoic was very like our own, most of the modern trees and many flowering plants having fully evolved at that time.

It is customary to recognize four divisions of the early Cenozoic: Eocene, Oligocene, Miocene, and Pliocene, corresponding to the chief rock formations. During the Pliocene the last great mountain-building

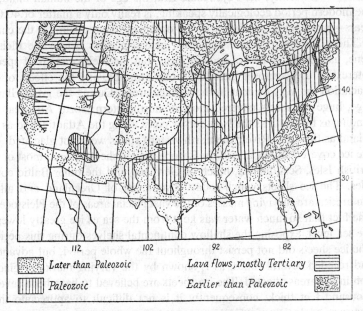

Later than Paleozoic   Lava flows, mostly Tertiary

Paleozoic   Earlier than Paleozoic

FIG. 5. Geological age of the United States.

period occurred. It is known as the Alpine-Cascadian Revolution, and it is the diastrophic activity that gave rise to the Alps, the Caucasus, later the ranges of the Himalayas, and in North America to the Cascade range in Washington and Oregon and the coast range in California. All of these mountains were, of course, modified by erosion subsequently, leading to their present form.

At this time, as at certain earlier times in geologic history, North America was connected with Europe by a land mass extending across Greenland and Iceland, and with Asia by a land mass from Alaska to Siberia. Consequently, animals roamed readily from one continent to another, and similar fossils are naturally found in various parts of the globe.

THE GREAT GLACIAL PERIOD

The Pleistocene or Glacial Period followed this last mighty diastrophic disturbance, and continued until the final retreat of the great ice sheets about 40,000 years ago. Primitive man existed during the Pleistocene, and the evolution of man goes back at least to the Pliocene. It is only after the end of the Pleistocene, however, that the human species began definitely to assume the characteristics which gradually gave rise to modern man. Consequently, the Psychozoic Era, the age of the human mind, or the modern period geologically speaking, is really only a matter of 40,000 years—since man's emergence as the dominant form of life on the earth.

There had been several important glacial periods before the Pleistocene, usually at the end of geologic eras, but the Pleistocene is of special interest to us because it introduced our own age, and the effects of the glaciation are very evident in the surface areas. During the great Glacial Age, huge ice sheets covered most of northeastern North America, extending as far south as the New Jersey coast along the Atlantic, and as far inland as the Ohio River; the northwestern states were not glaciated, but the ice covered all of Canada. In Europe the ice sheet covered most of the British Isles, Scandinavia, much of Germany and the other Baltic countries. The ice sheets which today cover most of Greenland and all of Antarctica are surviving masses of the vast glacial areas of the Pleistocene. The fact that so much water was kept from the sea as ice greatly lowered the sea level, exposing the shallow continental shelves during this period. The ice sheets did not persist throughout the whole period, but advanced and receded several times, as is shown by the varying marks of glaciation in the areas affected. The ice sheets are believed to have been several thousand feet thick; consequently it is not difficult to appreciate their power as geologic agents.

The sedimentation and other formations in the areas of the continents which were not covered by ice sheets during the Pleistocene do not vary greatly from those which we have already described for the earlier Cenozoic. Naturally all forms of animal life moved southward to escape the advancing ice, and remains of reindeer and other animals of northern climes are found in deposits south of the glaciated zone.

The areas which were covered by the ice have the characteristics of glaciated areas: reshaped valleys, remolded rock formations, and moraines. Most important of all the geologic results of the glaciation was the formation of a number of large lakes in areas where the ice had occupied great valleys. In melting and receding, the ice sheet left behind it the Great Lakes in North America and the Baltic Sea in Europe, and in addition, many small lakes in other areas, some of them in enclosed valleys high in the mountains.

THE AGE OF MAN

With the recession of the great ice sheets, the Pleistocene came to an end. Undoubtedly, during this period, the earth's surface had adjusted itself somewhat to the great load of ice and readjusted itself again afterward. But there was no great diastrophic activity. For us, however, the reappearance of a temperate climate following the Glacial Age constitutes a revolution of another sort. With the melting of the ice, man, almost unknown among the animals of the earth before, became the chief of living creatures, evolving through the years from most primitive beginnings to a mastery of the earth which is without any precedent in all the preceding ages.

Man quarries rocks for his buildings, enriches the soil for vegetation to serve him as food, breeds plants and animals, invents machines to simplify his work. Yet, with all his skill, man looks with uncertainty upon earthquakes, volcanic eruptions, and other geologic activity beyond his control. He views the future with hope, however. Geologically, man is still at the beginning of an era. With his power of adaptation to the most varied and constantly changing conditions, is it too much to believe that he will not only advance steadily through the great period ahead, but, adapting himself further, continue to move forward from geologic era to geologic era?

EXAMINATION QUESTIONS

1. What is geology?
2. What is the solid portion of the earth's surface called?
3. What is the centrosphere?
4. What are extrusive rocks?
5. How is limestone formed?
6. What is the relation between climate and weathering?

7. Name two agents of erosion.
8. What is talus?
9. What is a floodplain?
10. Do most tributaries meet the main stream at its own level?
11. Are all falls created by streams?
12. What is a delta?
13. How are artesian wells constructed?
14. Name three famous mineral springs.
15. How are underground caverns formed?
16. Do streams that flow into lakes always contribute water to the lakes?
17. What is peat?
18. What is a glacier?
19. What is an ice sheet?
20. What would happen if all the ice in the ice sheet of Greenland and Antarctica melted?
21. What is meteorology?
22. What part does wind play in erosion?
23. Describe a loess.
24. What is the proportion of sea area to land area?
25. What is the average ocean depth around the continents?
26. Characterize the coast of Maine geologically.
27. What is an atoll?
28. What are ocean tides due to?
29. What is a fold?
30. Give a famous example of jointing.

31. What are the causes of earthquakes?
32. What is the molten material in a volcano called?
33. How thick is the lithosphere estimated to be?
34. What instrument measures earthquake shocks?
35. Where are oil and natural gas formed?
36. Define an ore.
37. Is common table salt the same as sea salt?
38. Who was Laplace?
39. Who developed the Planetesimal Hypothesis?
40. What is a fossil?
41. What is the name given to the latest hypothesis on the origin of the earth?
42. Where is life presumed to have originated?
43. How are estimates of the age of the earth made?
44. What is the first era of the earth of which we have a record in rocks?
45. Were there many forms of life in the Paleozoic Era?
46. How did the Paleozoic Era end?
47. In what era did dinosaurs thrive?
48. In what era did mammals become the most important form of animal life?
49. To what era does the evolution of man go back?
50. What is the modern geologic era called?

For Further Study

Autobiography of Earth, by John H. Bradley. (Coward-McCann, New York.)

Earth Sciences, by J. Harlen Bretz. (John Wiley & Co., Philadelphia.)

Earth's Adventures, by Carroll L. Fenton. (John Day Co., New York.)

This Puzzling Planet, by Edwin T Brewster. (New Home Library Doubleday & Co., New York.)

XXIII

Physics Self Taught

WHAT IS PHYSICS?

PHYSICS IS the science which deals with energy and matter and with physical changes in matter. It is customary to group Physics and Chemistry together as the physical sciences; and the two subjects supplement one another. Together they are playing a leading role in shaping the character of our present-day civilization.

Physics is usually divided into seven parts: mechanics, heat, sound, light, magnetism, electricity, and nuclear physics.

The subject of mechanics is very broad. It is subdivided into three parts: *mechanics of solids, mechanics of liquids,* and *mechanics of gases.* The mechanics of solids involves mostly the study of force and motion, and from this study have developed the sciences of civil and mechanical engineering. All machinery is based on an applied knowledge of force and motion.

The mechanics of liquids is the study of the behavior of liquids and the behavior of solids in liquids. The principle of flotation which governs the construction of all ships, as well as the very important science of hydraulics (including sanitary engineering), is included in this branch of mechanics. Without a knowledge of hydraulics and sanitary engineering, we could have developed no adequate means of disposing of sewage, and there would be no proper water supply.

The mechanics of gases deals with properties of different gases under pressure. The principle of the gasoline engine (the automobile) comes under this heading.

Under the subject of heat we study, among other aspects of heat, the behavior of metals when heated. The entire science of thermodynamics, which gives us the steam engine and the automobile, is based on a knowledge of heat.

From our knowledge of sound we are able to construct musical instruments as well as such important inventions as the phonograph, the radio, television, and the talking motion pictures.

Under the subject of light comes the vitally important subject of optics, including research and development in the field of lenses. As you know, the lens is very useful—without it we would have no telescopes, no cameras, no eyeglasses, no movies.

Magnetism and electricity are closely related. The tremendous advantages to civilization of these two branches of physics are obvious. The coincidence of electricity and magnetism gives us the electromagnet—one of the most important scientific discoveries ever made. The electromagnet is a part of such instruments as the telephone, the telegraph, the wireless telegraph, and such important machines as the dynamo and the motor. Nearly all electrical appliances are run by electric motors, and electrified railroads are run by the combination of the dynamo and the motor. The subject of electricity also includes the study of electrical waves, such as the X-ray and radio waves.

Under the subject of nuclear physics comes the study of the atom and how we release energy from it. Other topics in nuclear physics are radioactivity, nuclear fission and fusion, and the applications of radioactive isotopes.

Until recently little was known about the nucleus or innermost portion of the atom. The rapid developments of the last decades, reaching a climax in the discovery of how to release nuclear energy on a large scale, have given rise to this new area of physics called nuclear physics. We have at our command today more energy than all of mankind has used up to this time. Modern atomic-power reactors can provide energy to drive ships, irrigate deserts, and perhaps even extend the average life span. Atomic energy has also put in our hands the most destructive force the world has ever known.

MEASUREMENT

The internationally used scientific system of measurement is called the *metric system*. It has decided advantages over the familiar so-called English system, for its divisions are decimal: that is, they are based on the multiple of 10. Whereas in the English system 12 inches equal one foot, in the metric system 10 millimeters equal one centimeter, and 100 (10 × 10) centimeters equal one meter. Every equivalent in the metric system is a multiple of 10, which makes computation very easy.

The common metric units for measuring length, with their English equivalents, are given in Table I. Notice that the meter is a little longer than the English yard—about 3⅓ inches longer.

Metric units of weight are also based on the multiple 10. The unit is the gram, which is the weight of one cubic centimeter of pure water at a temperature of 4° Centigrade. The common metric units for measuring weight, with their English equivalents, are given in Table II.

The measurement of area in the metric system involves square meters, square centimeters, and so on, just as in the English system it involves square yards and square inches. These units are given in Table III.

The measurement of volume is made clear in Table IV. The unit of liquid measure, a part of the measurement of volume, is the liter, which is almost exactly equal to the English quart, as you will observe.

TABLE I

UNITS OF LENGTH

ENGLISH.

1 foot (ft.) = 12 inches (in.)
1 yard (yd.) = 3 feet
1 mile (mi.) = 5280 feet

METRIC.

1 meter (m.) = 1000 millimeters (mm.)
1 meter = 100 centimeters (cm.)
1 kilometer (km.) = 1000 meters
1 inch = 2.540 centimeters
1 meter = 39.37 inches

TABLE II

UNITS OF WEIGHT

ENGLISH.

1 pound (lb.) = 16 ounces (oz.)
1 ton (T.) = 2000 pounds

METRIC.

1 gram (g.) = 1000 milligrams (mg.)
1 kilogram (kg.) = 1000 grams
1 kilogram = 2.20 pounds
1 cubic foot of water weighs 62.4 pounds
1 cubic centimeter of water weighs 1 gram

TABLE III

UNITS OF AREA

ENGLISH.

$$\begin{aligned}
1 \text{ square foot (sq. ft.)} &= 144 \text{ square inches (sq. in.)} \\
1 \text{ square yard (sq. yd.)} &= 9 \text{ square feet} \\
1 \text{ square rod (sq. rd.)} &= 30\tfrac{1}{4} \text{ square yards} \\
1 \text{ acre (A.)} &= 160 \text{ square rods}
\end{aligned}$$

METRIC.

$$\begin{aligned}
1 \text{ square centimeter (sq. cm.)} &= 100 \text{ square millimeters (sq. mm.)} \\
1 \text{ square meter (sq. m.)} &= 10,000 \text{ square centimeters} \\
1 \text{ square kilometer (sq. km.)} &= 1,000,000 \text{ square meters}
\end{aligned}$$

TABLE IV

UNITS OF VOLUME

ENGLISH.

$$\begin{aligned}
1 \text{ cubic foot (cu. ft.)} &= 1728 \text{ cubic inches (cu. in.)} \\
1 \text{ cubic yard (cu. yd.)} &= 27 \text{ cubic feet} \\
1 \text{ gallon (gal.)} &= 4 \text{ quarts (qt.)} = 231 \text{ cu. in.}
\end{aligned}$$

METRIC.

$$\begin{aligned}
1 \text{ liter (l.)} &= 1000 \text{ cubic centimeters (cm.}^3) \\
1 \text{ cubic meter (m.}^3) &= 1000 \text{ liters} \\
1 \text{ liter} &= 1.06 \text{ quarts}
\end{aligned}$$

MECHANICS OF SOLIDS

MACHINES

A machine is a device used to multiply force or speed or to change the direction of a force. There are three simple machines: (1) the lever, (2) the pulley, and (3) the inclined plane. Other machines are either modifications of one of these machines or combinations of two or more of them.

THE LEVER

A lever consists of a rigid bar which is pivoted at a fixed point called a *fulcrum*. If you lift a weight with a crowbar and use a stone as a fulcrum, you are employing a lever. The weight lifted by a lever is called the *resistance;* the force used at the end of the lever to lift the weight is called the *effort*.

There are only three main classes of levers. The lever of the first class is shown in Figure 1. It has the fulcrum between the effort and the resist-

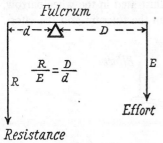

Fulcrum

$$\frac{R}{E} = \frac{D}{d}$$

R

E

Effort

Resistance

FIG. 1. Lever of the first class.

ance. The ordinary balance and the see-saw are examples of this. The longer the distance, or lever arm, between the fulcrum and the effort, the greater the weight that can be lifted. Archimedes once said, "Give me a lever large enough, and I can move the Earth." If he had had a fulcrum on which to rest his lever, he probably could have. By this principle you could lift a house if you had a long enough lever arm. (See Fig. 2.)

The principle briefly is this: In order to overcome a resistance you must do a certain amount of work. This work which you do is always

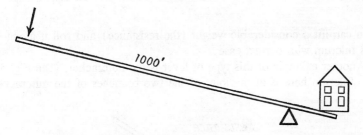

1000'

FIG. 2. An application of a lever of the first class.

the product of the force which you exert times the distance through which you move that force. What you lose in distance you gain in power, and

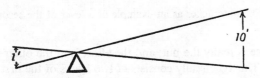

10'

1'

FIG. 3. Distances of effort and resistance in a first-class lever compared.

vice versa. Ten pounds, for example, moving through a distance of one foot is exactly equivalent to one pound moving through a distance of ten feet. So you could lift a ten-pound weight (resistance) one foot with a force (effort) of only one pound, but you would have to exert that force up or down ten feet. (See Fig. 3.)

Other examples of this type of lever, where the fulcrum is between the resistance and the effort, are crowbars, shears, glove stretchers, etc.

The lever of the second class is clearly illustrated in the wheelbarrow. (See Fig. 4.) Here the resistance is between the fulcrum and the effort.

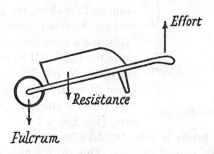

FIG. 4. The wheelbarrow as an example of a lever of the second class.

You can lift a considerable weight (the resistance) and roll it along on this fulcrum with perfect ease.

Another example of this type of lever is the nutcracker. (See Fig. 5.) The fulcrum here is at the joint of the two branches of the nutcracker.

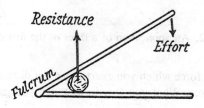

FIG. 5. The nutcracker as an example of a lever of the second class.

The resistance is really the nut, and the effort is at the other extremity at the handles. This type really consists of two levers of the first class joined together. If these two bars were not joined together, then the nut would be the fulcrum.

This second-class lever has the advantage of obtaining a tremendous force for very little effort. The nearer the nut is put to the fulcrum, and the longer the arm of the nutcracker, the greater will be the cracking force on the nut.

The lever of the third class has the fulcrum at one end and the weight at the other, the power being between them. This is shown in an ordinary

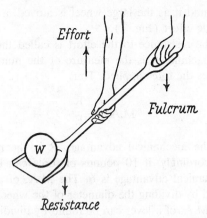

Fig. 6. The use of the shovel as an example of a lever of the third class.

shovel. (See Fig. 6.) Here the load on the shovel represents the resistance at one end, the effort is in the middle, and the handle is the fulcrum.

The slot-machine scales are a combination of levers carefully figured so that when you stand on the platform the platform moves down an exceedingly slight distance which is transmitted, with the aid of these levers, to a pointer which moves over the face of the machine. The typewriter and the piano contain scores of levers.

The law of the lever is: The resistance is to the effort as the effort arm is to the resistance arm, or

$$\frac{R}{E} = \frac{D}{d}$$

where R is the resistance, E the effort, D is the effort arm, and d the resistance arm.

THE WHEEL AND AXLE

The wheel and axle is really a development of the lever; it is a sort of lever revolving around a fulcrum. It consists of a wheel to which is attached a much smaller wheel.

If the large wheel is turned one revolution, the smaller wheel or axle, which also turns a revolution (because it is attached to the large wheel), will not turn so far; and consequently, by the principle of levers, it will have a definite lifting or pulling force greater than the force exerted to turn the large wheel.

If on a wheel six feet in diameter a small wheel one foot in diameter is mounted, and a rope is attached to the smaller wheel in such a way that it winds around it as the large wheel is moved, a great weight can be lifted with little effort (Fig. 7).

The ratio of the resistance to the effort is called the *mechanical advantage* of the machine. It is the measure of the number of times the machine multiplies the force applied. Thus

$$\text{M.A.} = \frac{R}{E}$$

where M.A. is the mechanical advantage, R is the resistance, and E is the effort. Accordingly, if 10 pounds of force can lift 60 pounds of weight, the mechanical advantage is 6. The M.A. of a wheel and axle can also be found by dividing the diameter of the wheel by the diameter of the axle. The M.A. of a lever can be found by dividing the effort arm (distance between the point of application of the effort to the fulcrum) by the resistance arm (distance between the fulcrum and the resistance).

Another important application of the wheel and axle—so important that nearly every machine you see is dependent upon it—is the gear wheel. You can easily see how power is produced by gearing (see Fig. 7) be-

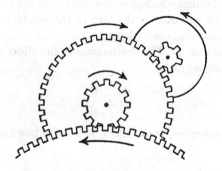

FIG. 7. An arrangement of gear wheels.

cause, by the principle of the wheel and axle, the axle turns more slowly than the rim of the large wheel but has correspondingly more power. This power can be transmitted to other gear wheels, which in turn transmit it to others—as with the familiar coal wagon, where you can watch a man lift a ton of coal by "winding up the wagon."

When you wind a watch it will go for a whole day because the big cogwheel which runs the hour hand, and is very powerful, is geared to the cogwheel which runs the minute hand, and is 1/60 as powerful. This cogwheel is attached to a large cogwheel, which in turn is geared to a smaller cogwheel. This cogwheel runs the second hand and is 1/3600 as powerful as the first cogwheel. What you lose in power you gain in distance, and consequently the second hand must move 3600 times as far as the hour hand, taking 3600 times as long.

THE PULLEY

If you ever visit a factory where heavy machinery is made, you will notice pulleys with numerous chains—perhaps four or six. If you pull on one of these you will observe that the pulley travels upward very, very slowly; but you also observe that you have no difficulty in pulling on it. It moves very easily. If a weight of 600 pounds were put on that end of this pulley, it would take a force of only 100 pounds to pull it up (Fig. 8).

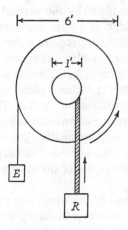

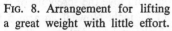

FIG. 8. Arrangement for lifting a great weight with little effort.

FIG. 9. Arrangement for lifting a great weight with application of little force.

There are two kinds of pulleys—the fixed and the movable. The fixed pulley is one with an immovable axis. You pull in one direction in order to make what you are pulling go in the opposite direction. There is no mechanical advantage in such a pulley. It is merely used to lift objects to places where you ordinarily could not lift them; such as, for example, a flag to the top of a flagpole, clothes on a line, etc.

The movable pulley (Fig. 9) is one with an axis free to move. The advantage of such a pulley is dependent on the number of ropes. By pulling with one-pound force, you can lift as many pounds of weight as there are ropes. If there were three pulleys in the system, the advantage would be 3. If there are ten pulleys, the advantage is 10.

Whenever you see a pulley, count the number of supporting chains or ropes which it contains, and you will instantly get the mechanical advantage of that pulley. If it contains six supporting ropes or chains, it means that one pound will lift six; if it contains ten, it means that one pound will lift ten. But naturally the more pounds it will lift per one-pound force, the slower it will move.

THE INCLINED PLANE

Any smooth surface that inclines or goes up is an inclined plane. A hill is an inclined plane. You will recognize that rolling a barrel up an inclined plane requires less force than carrying it up vertically through the same height. The mechanical advantage of an inclined plane can be determined by dividing the length of the plane by the vertical height. Thus an incline 20 feet long and 4 feet high at the summit would have a mechanical advantage of 5. It would therefore require a force of 40 pounds to move a 200-pound barrel up such a plane. It is well to note that in order to lift the barrel vertically up the 4 feet it would be necessary to exert a force of 200 pounds. With the inclined plane, however, a force of 40 pounds is exerted through a distance of 20 feet. The multiplication of the force is obtained at the expense of an increased distance.

Now imagine a road winding around a steep mountain. (See Fig. 10.) Think of this road up a mountain as being a thread of an ordinary screw, for that is exactly what it is like. The *screw* is one of the most powerful machines known.

Understanding the principle of levers and of the wheel and axle, you can readily see that if you have a screw with a pitch of ½ inch (Fig. 11), and you turn it one revolution, you will move the screw up or down (according to the direction you turn it) ½ inch. Now, if an arm 5 feet long is attached to this screw with ½-inch pitch, and the handle of the

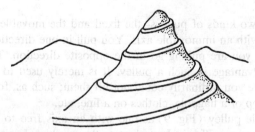

FIG. 10. A mountain road as an illustration of the principle of the screw.

arm is moved through one revolution (or 377 inches), the screw would move up or down (according to the direction of the handle) ½ inch, or

1/754 of the distance which the handle moved. This means that if you applied 10 pounds of force to the handle, you could lift a weight of more than 3½ tons. This principle is used in jacks, whereby automobiles

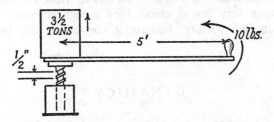

FIG. 11. A screw arrangement for lifting a great weight.

are lifted, houses are moved, and enormous resistances are overcome. The formula for the screw (S = pitch; l = radius turned through; π = 3.1416) is

$$\frac{R}{E} = \frac{2l\pi}{S}$$

The wedge is really a pair of inclined planes back to back. Wedges

FIG. 12. Wedge.

are used to tighten things. The ordinary knife and the chisel are examples of the wedge used as a tool.

To summarize: (1) In any lever the effort times its lever arm (distance from the effort to the fulcrum) always equals the resistance times its lever arm (the distance from the resistance to the fulcrum). For example, a force of 10 pounds over a lever arm of 5 feet is exactly equal to a force of 5 pounds over a lever arm of 10 feet; or a force of 25 pounds over a lever arm of 2 feet, etc. (2) In every machine what you gain in distance you lose in force, and vice versa. (3) Whatever you put into a machine in the way of work (force times distance) you must get out of that machine in the way of work (force times distance). Of course allowance must be made for loss of work due to friction in the machine. For this reason very few machines have a high efficiency. Perpetual motion is an impossibility, because it contradicts this fundamental principle.

DYNAMICS

NEWTON'S LAWS OF MOTION

First Law of Motion: *A body tends to remain in a state of rest or of uniform motion in a straight line unless acted upon by an outside force.* (This is sometimes referred to as the Law of Inertia.)

This means that if you start an object moving, it will keep on moving forever in a straight line until some force stops it. Of course we know that nothing will keep on moving forever, and this law may seem rather absurd. If you will stop to think that friction ultimately brings everything to rest, you will understand this law. A stone set in rapid motion over a frozen lake will come to rest in time, because it is stopped by the force of friction (rubbing of the stone on the ice). Similarly, every other moving object will come to rest in time because of friction. The first part of this law is quite obvious—no object can start of its own free will. Some force must start it.

Second Law of Motion: *A body acted upon by a constant force will move with a constant acceleration in the direction of the force; the amount of acceleration will be directly proportional to the acting force and inversely proportional to the mass of the body.*

This means that a body keeps on increasing in velocity under the influence of a constant force. An automobile to which a constant unbalanced force is applied will go faster and faster, it will gain in *velocity*. The rate of change of velocity is called *acceleration*. Thus an auto which starts from rest and achieves a velocity of 30 miles per hour in 5 seconds is said to have an acceleration of 5 miles per hour per second—usually written: 5 mi./hr./sec. The most common example of acceleration is that of falling bodies. When you drop an object it falls with ever-increasing speed because it is constantly acted upon by a force known as gravity. The acceleration due to gravity is 32 feet per second per second. This means that every second it increases in speed 32 feet per second. The general law of accelerated bodies is given in a simple algebraic formula:

Distance equals ½ the acceleration times the square of the time: or $S = \frac{1}{2}at^2$. The acceleration due to gravity is 32 feet per second per second, so that for falling bodies this formula becomes $S = 16t^2$. For example, in 5 seconds a body will fall 25×16 feet, or 400 feet; in 10 seconds it will fall 1,600 feet.

It is interesting to know that gravity acts independently of outside forces. If a cannon ball, for example, is shot horizontally from a tower 100 feet high at the same time that another cannon ball is merely dropped from the tower, both balls hit the ground at the same instant, even though the first ball traveled some 10 miles while the other ball traveled only 100 feet. The reason for this is simple. At the end of the first second the cannon ball which was shot horizontally is 16 feet nearer the ground re-

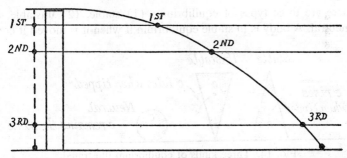

FIG. 13. Newton's Second Law of Motion illustrated by a dropping cannon ball.

gardless of its other position. At the end of the second second it is 48 feet nearer the ground regardless of its position, etc. This is also true of the cannon ball that was merely dropped. Figure 13 explains this more clearly.

Another interesting thing about the acceleration due to gravity is that all bodies fall *with exactly the same speed in vacuum.* A feather and a 10-pound shot, dropped from the same height, would reach the ground at the same time—if it were not for air resistance.

Third Law of Motion: *Action and reaction are equal and opposite.* This means that when you sit on a chair you are pressing down on it with a force equal to your own weight. The chair, on the other hand, is pressing up on you with exactly the same force. If it were not doing so, you would fall to the ground. If it pushed up on you with a force greater than your own weight, you would go up in the air.

When you say that a floor will sustain a weight of 150 pounds per square foot, it means every square foot of that floor is capable of meeting 150 pounds downward force with 150 pounds upward force.

Newton's Third Law gives us this principle of equilibrium: *For every force pulling one way on a body in equilibrium, there must be an equal and opposite force pulling in the opposite direction.*

Every object has weight or mass, and, while it may not be obvious, the weight of every body acts at a definite point. The weight of a bar, for example, acts at the center point. The weight of a flat disc acts at its center. The weight of an odd-shaped object acts at some point within that object, which can be determined. The point at which the entire weight of a body acts is called the center of gravity, or center of mass; and if an opposing force equal to this weight is applied to that point, the body will be balanced. For example, you can balance a yardstick on a knife edge by putting the knife edge exactly at the 18-inch point, or halfway.

There are three types of equilibrium: (1) stable, (2) unstable, and (3) neutral. A body is in stable equilibrium if when it is moved it comes

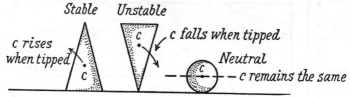

FIG. 14. Three kinds of equilibrium illustrated.

back to its original position. You will note (see Fig. 14) that a wide base, if tipped slightly, will come back to its original position. It can be seen from this that as long as the center of gravity rises when an object is tipped, that object will be in stable equilibrium. In the first figure, C (center of gravity) rises when tipped; in the second figure, C falls when tipped; in the third figure, C remains the same.

A body is in unstable equilibrium if when tipped it does not return to its original position. It falls. In this type of equilibrium the center of gravity is lowered when the object is tipped. Neutral equilibrium takes place only in rolling. The center of gravity is always the same—neither raised nor lowered.

The applications of the principles of equilibrium are numerous. They are the basis of all building and construction as well as mechanical engineering.

THE PENDULUM

The pendulum is a very interesting example of Newton's Laws. A pendulum is a weight hung from a string or stick. When the pendulum is a rest, the string is perpendicular to the ground: it really points to the center of the earth. Here we have action and reaction—equal and opposite in the same straight line (Fig. 15). When the weight is deflected, the action and reaction are not in the same straight line; and if the weight is let go, its tendency is to come back to equilibrium, where it was before it was deflected. Consequently it swings down toward its former position but, by Newton's First Law, continues to swing past its first position. (This is called Inertia.) When it has reached a point on the other side where the downward pull is greater than the swing, it starts back again. The pendulum thus swings from right to left and back again, each time losing a little bit of its inertia, until it finally comes to rest in its original position.

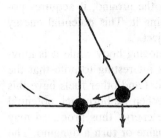

FIG. 15. A swinging pendulum.

The pendulum vibrates to a definite law discovered by Galileo. A pendulum approximately one meter long will swing once a second. This fact is frequently taken advantage of in the pendulum clock. The longer the pendulum the slower it will swing, and vice versa.

WORK

The definition of work in physics is not quite the same as the dictionary definition. Work always implies motion. It is the product of a definite force acting through a definite distance. The units of work are the *erg,* the *foot-poundal,* the *kilogram-meter,* and the *foot-pound.* The foot-pound is defined as the work done in raising vertically a weight of one pound through a distance of one foot. Thus an elevator lifting 10 people each weighing 150 pounds, from the bottom to the top of the Empire State Building (1200 ft.), does 1,800,000 foot-pounds of work (disregarding the weight of the elevator). Power is that which connects the important ideas of getting the job done with getting it done in time. The ratio of the work done to the time required to do it is called *power.* The most familiar unit of power is the *horsepower,* which represents 550 foot-pounds of work per second. The *watt* is also a familiar unit of power: it is 1/746 horsepower.

ENERGY

Energy has been defined as the ability to do work. There are two kinds of energy—*potential* and *kinetic.*

Potential energy is stored-up energy. When you wind a clock you are overcoming a certain resistance, and consequently you are doing work.

This work is stored up in the spring of the clock, and the clock is said to have potential energy—it will run for some time, a day or eight days, as the case may be. If you lift an object from the ground, it acquires potential energy because work is done in raising it. This potential energy will quickly be expended if you drop the object.

Kinetic energy is energy possessed by a moving body while it is moving. It is the result of potential energy. It is interesting to note that the sun is our primary source of heat energy. Coal and other fuels have this energy stored up in them in potential form. When we burn fuel, potential energy is liberated in the form of heat. The energy thus produced may be used to generate steam to run a steam engine or turn a dynamo. The dynamo in turn may run an electric railway or light a city, etc. We thus have a continual transformation of energy. Some energy transformations include chemical, mechanical, electrical, magnetic, heat, and light.

In recent years man has learned to unlock the energy in the nucleus of the atom. He is no longer primarily dependent on the sun for his energy. Nuclear energy comes from the conversion of a portion of the matter in the nucleus into energy. Science has discovered that the total amount of matter and energy in the universe is constant, and that one may be converted into the other. Thus we can consider matter as a sort of congealed energy.

MECHANICS OF LIQUIDS

LIQUID PRESSURE

If you fill a glass with water you naturally increase its weight—the water, of course, weighs something. The weight of this water acts on the bottom of the glass. Therefore, the higher the water in the glass, the greater will be the pressure exerted on the bottom of the glass. From

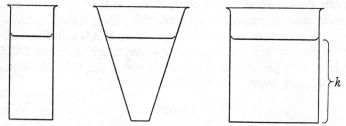

FIG. 16. Three vessels containing the same liquid at the same height.

this we can derive a very simple law: *The pressure of a liquid increases with its depth.*

Suppose a 10-pound weight is resting on a table. It exerts a force of 10 pounds against the table. If the area of the bottom side of the weight is 2 square inches, the force on any one square inch is 5 pounds. The pressure is therefore 5 pounds per square inch. Pressure is the force per unit of area. If two weights of 10 pounds each were standing side by side on the table, a force of 20 pounds would be acting on 4 square inches. The pressure under these weights would still be 5 pounds per square inch. Thus we see that pressure is independent of the area which the force acts upon, since pressure is always referred to a unit of area such as the square foot or square inch.

Liquid pressure therefore depends upon two factors: namely, the *height* and the *density* of the fluid. (Density is the weight per unit volume.) The pressure under any fluid can be found by multiplying the vertical height of the fluid by its density. For example, the pressure under 10 feet of fresh water (density = 62.5 lbs./cubic foot) would be 625 lbs. per sq. ft.

It is interesting to note that regardless of the shape of the vessels, if the height and the density of the liquid they contain is the same, the pressure at the bottom of each container is the same (see Fig. 16).

From what you have read you can understand why water always seeks its own level. Consider two tanks (A and B in Fig. 17) connected by a

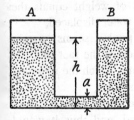

FIG. 17. Two connected tanks.

pipe at the bottom of each. If we pour water into tank A, it flows through the pipe into tank B. When we are through pouring the water we will find that the height of the fluid will be the same in both tanks. This is due to the fact that the pressure at the bottom of both tanks is the same. Adding water to tank A will raise its level, increase the pressure at the bottom, and destroy the balance. Immediately the greater pressure from A will cause a flow to raise the level in B until the two pressures are once again equal. When this happens, the level in both A and B will be the same.

Pascal's Law states that any external force exerted on a unit of area in a confined liquid is transmitted undiminished to every unit of area of the interior of the containing vessel. Thus, assuming we have a huge tank filled with water, at one end of which is an opening one square inch in area, and at the other end there is an opening 100 square inches in area, if we fit each opening with suitable pistons, a one-pound force acting on the one-square-inch piston would cause a pressure of one pound per square inch under the piston. According to Pascal's Law this pressure will be transmitted through the liquid to the bottom of the 100-square-inch piston. With one pound pressing against each square inch of the 100-square-inch piston, the total force against the piston will be 100 pounds. Thus we have a machine by means of which 1 pound can lift 100 pounds (see Fig. 18). This device is called a hydraulic press and, like any other machine, it gives us a gain in force at the expense of distance, or in this case actually surface.

ARCHIMEDES' PRINCIPLE

This is the principle of the hydraulic press. Archimedes' principle is unquestionably one of the most important laws in physics. Archimedes'

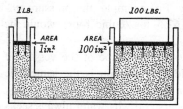

FIG. 18. The principle of the hydraulic press illustrated by a tank filled with water.

principle is that a body immersed in a fluid is buoyed up by a force equal to the weight of the liquid it displaces. When you get into a bathtub filled with water you notice that the water rises—it has to, to make room for your body. You will also notice that your body seems lighter. Its apparent loss of weight equals the weight of the water displaced.

When you lift a rock from the bottom of a pool it seems to gain weight as it breaks through the surface. This is due to the fact that the buoyant force (which equaled the weight of the water which the rock displaced) is no longer present when the rock is in the air.

For example, if the rock had a volume of one cubic foot, it would displace one cubic foot of water when submerged, and thus it would appear to lose 62.5 pounds of weight (the weight of one cubic foot of water). If the rock weighed 250 pounds in air, it would weigh 250 − 62.5 pounds, or 187.5 pounds, in water. A body which weighs in air more than the weight of the fluid it displaces will always sink to the bottom of the fluid. However, a body which weighs less than the volume of the fluid it displaces will float. If it is forcibly submerged and then released, the upward or buoyant force will exceed its weight, and it will move upward toward the surface of the fluid. As it breaks through the surface, the volume of fluid it displaces naturally decreases. It continues to rise through the surface until it displaces exactly its own weight in a fluid. A ship which weighs 1000 tons would, when floating, displace 1000 tons of water.

Specific Gravity

The *specific gravity* of a substance is the ratio of the weight of a given volume of that substance to the weight of the same volume of water at 4° C. When we say a substance has a specific gravity of 1, it means that a cubic foot of that substance weighs exactly the same as a cubic foot of water. If it has a specific gravity of ½, a cubic foot of it weighs half as much as a cubic foot of water.

Table of Specific Gravities

Platinum	21.5	Hard woods (seasoned)	0.7–1.1
Gold	19.3	Soft woods (seasoned)	0.4–0.7
Mercury	13.6	Ice	0.911
Lead	11.4	Human body	0.9–1.1
Silver	10.5	Cork	0.25
Copper	8.93	Sulphuric acid (conc.)	1.84
Brass	8.4	Sea water	1.03
Iron	7.1–7.9	Milk	1.03
Zinc	7.1	Fresh water	1.00
Glass	2.4–4.5	Kerosene	0.80
Granite, Marble, etc.	2.5–3.0	Gasoline	0.75
Aluminum	2.65	Air	0.0012

According to Archimedes' principle, substances whose specific gravity is less than 1 float in water. Substances whose specific gravity is greater than 1 sink in water. Ice, for example, has a specific gravity of 9/10 and, as a result, floats in water. But it floats in such a way that 9/10 of it is below the surface. This is the reason why only 1/10 of an iceberg is visible. Cork has a specific gravity of about 2/10. The result is that 8/10 of a piece of it in water is above the surface. The specific gravity of a floating substance can usually be determined by the percentage of volume of that substance which is submerged.

When we say that platinum is a very "heavy" metal, we mean that its specific gravity is high (21.5). A cubic foot of platinum weighs 21½ times as much as a cubic foot of water, which weighs 62½ pounds.

Surface Tension and Capillary Action

The best example of surface tension of a liquid is a soap bubble. Here you have an extremely thin film of water in the shape of a sphere enclosing air. This film is on the surface of all water and a similar film is on the surface of all other liquids. This is the result of *cohesion*—the tendency of molecules of the same substance to stick together.

This condition may be illustrated by carefully placing a dry needle or razor blade on the surface of a liquid such as water. The steel, though more dense than water, will rest on the surface and will not sink, because of the cohesion of the water molecules.

The next time you look at a glass of water, notice the rim. You will see that the liquid is drawn up slightly and all around the rim it is slightly concave (see Fig. 19, page 1108). This is the result of *adhesion*—the tendency of molecules of two separate substances to remain in contact. If the glass were a tube 1 inch in diameter, the liquid around the rim having a smaller area would be drawn up considerably higher, and there would be more concavity—because of the adhesion of water molecules to molecules of glass.

Now imagine a tube 1/100 inch in diameter filled with liquid. What would happen? There would be so much surface tension and so little surface that the liquid would actually run up the tube. This is called capillary action, and is familiar to everyone who has used blotting paper or has observed a kerosene lamp wick sucking up oil as the lamp burns. The liquid runs up the tiny fibers of the wick. In a candle the heat melts the paraffin and the melted wax runs up the wick by capillary action.

MECHANICS OF GASES

Suppose you look inside an empty tank in the form of a cylinder. You see that there is nothing in it. But if you were to fit a piston (which would *exactly* fit the tank) that would push down into it, you would soon find out that what you thought was an empty tank had something in it of considerable resistance. Air, when confined in a vessel and compressed, exerts terrific pressure on the sides of the vessel. If the quantity is unchanged and the temperature remains constant, the smaller the volume of air in the vessel, the greater will be the pressure on the sides of the vessel.

This principle is true of any gas, and is made use of in the steam engine, in which enormous quantities of steam are forced into a little box with a piston, the pressure being so great that the piston is pushed out and drives a wheel. The law of pressure is that when we decrease the volume we increase the pressure.

Let us look into this a little more thoroughly. The air in our original tank contains billions and billions of molecules, which are moving with great speed in all directions. These molecules in moving exert a certain amount of pressure on the walls of the tank in bumping against them.

There are a definite number of molecules which are moving in this way.

Now suppose we reduce the space by half. There are the same number of molecules in half the original space. Consequently, in traveling the same speed as before, they bump more often on the sides of the vessel, which gives us an increased pressure. If the volume (space) is reduced further, the pressure will be increased proportionately.

Air has weight. The reason you do not feel the weight of the air is because it acts on you equally from all sides. You can raise or lower your arm without the slightest difficulty, and when you put your hand over an empty glass you have no trouble removing it. The reason for this is that the air exerts equal pressure on all sides of your hand. If you place your hand flat on a table the same thing is true. The air under your hand, which seems negligible, is pressing up with just as much force as all the air above your hand.

If, however, you place your hand over the tube attached to a vacuum cleaner and turn on the vacuum cleaner, your hand will be sucked right up against the tube, and you will find it difficult to draw it away. The reason for this is that the air in the tube is pumped away and nothing remains but vacuum when one end of the tube is closed (by your hand). The air on the outside pushes against your hand with the full force of its own weight. There being no air in the vacuum tube, there is consequently no reverse pressure. Air exerts a pressure of 15 pounds on each square inch. The total force against your hand is considerable.

Of course this all refers to air at sea level. The higher up we go, the less the air weighs. That is why climbing a high mountain is so difficult; the pressure up there is only a few pounds per square inch, and human beings are constructed for a pressure of 15 pounds (exactly 14.7 pounds per square inch at sea level). Effects of high-altitude flying are well known. Nose bleeding, difficult breathing, and unconsciousness result from the exceedingly low air pressure. For this reason pressure cabins and oxygen helmets are required for high flying.

If a tube about a meter long is filled with mercury and inverted in a dish of mercury (Fig. 20), the mercury will drop until it is 76 centimeters (30 inches) high, and there it will remain. What keeps the mercury in the tube? Why does it not run out into the dish? The answer is that the atmosphere presses down with a weight of about 15 pounds per square inch all over the surface of the mercury in the dish, and this is enough to support the column of mercury in the tube 30 inches high. In other words, a tube of mercury 1 square inch in diameter and 30 inches high weighs about 15 pounds. The space in the tube above the mercury is almost a vacuum.

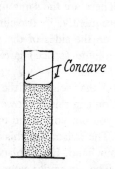

FIG. 19. Concavity of the
surface of water.

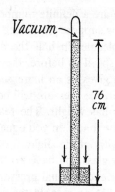

FIG. 20. Mercury in a tube
a meter long.

If this apparatus were taken to the top of a very high mountain, the mercury would be much lower in the tube, because of the reduction in atmospheric pressure. That is how aviators tell altitude. They have an instrument which records the decrease in atmospheric pressure as they go higher, and from this their altitude is determined. This instrument is an altimeter.

Inasmuch as mercury weighs about 13.6 times as much as water, it follows that the atmosphere will push water up a pipe 13.6 times as high as 30 inches, or about 34 feet. When we pump water in a well which is less than 34 feet below the surface, we are really making the atmosphere push the water up the pipe and out the spout, for that is exactly how a pump

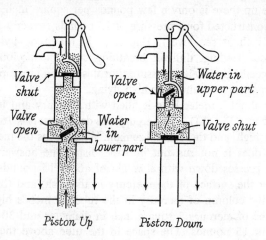

FIG. 21. The operation of a water pump.

works. The simplest kind of a pump consists of a cylinder into which fits a piston with a valve in it (Fig. 21). When the piston is pushed down the piston valve opens, and when it is pulled up the valve closes. There is also a spout in the upper portion of the cylinder, and from the bottom of the cylinder a pipe runs to the water. When the piston is pulled up it sucks the air out of the cylinder by way of the spout. This causes a vacuum, with a consequent rush of water up the pipe, because of atmospheric pressure on the water outside the lower end of the pipe. The water fills the cylinder under the piston.

When the piston is pushed down, the piston valve opens again and water pours into the upper part of the cylinder. When the piston is pulled up again, the valve closes and lifts this water to the spout through which it passes. This is briefly the principle of the pump.

The medicine dropper works on the same principle. You squeeze air out of it when you squeeze the bulb, and when you put it in the liquid, the liquid rushes up into it—pushed up by atmospheric pressure. The same is true when you drink anything through a straw. You first suck all the air out of the straw and up comes the liquid to take the place of the air.

EXPANSION OF LIQUIDS

Liquids, like solids, expand with almost irresistible force when they are heated. Water, like most substances, expands when heated, except near the freezing point. There is a point just slightly above the freezing point at which water will expand whether it is heated or whether it is cooled. Naturally, when water expands, it becomes lighter—steam is lighter than water and so is ice. It follows then that this point, which is 4° C., is the point at which water is the most dense. Thus one cubic centimeter of water weighs exactly one gram at 4° C. If it is cooled to zero degrees C. or below, it expands, and one cubic centimeter then weighs less than one gram (floats on water). If it is heated, it weighs less than a gram and keeps on getting lighter until the boiling point is reached, when it goes off in steam.

When the water in a lake freezes, a very curious phenomenon takes place. When the water at the surface reaches 4° C. it becomes heavier than the water beneath it, and consequently it goes to the bottom, and the water underneath comes up to the surface to be cooled in its turn to 4° C. This keeps up until the entire depth of the water in the lake has reached an even 4° C.; at that point the surface water becomes chilled further, with the result that ice is formed. Ice, being lighter than water, remains at the top.

HEAT

EXPANSION OF METALS

We all know that when brakes are applied to the wheels of a locomotive, or a knife is applied to the grindstone, numerous sparks result. Where do these sparks come from, and why do the locomotive brakes and the knife become hot? To understand this, we must know something about the nature of heat.

Heat is a form of energy. Heat arises from the rapid motion of molecules. When you rub your hands together the heat which results from the friction is due to the setting in rapid motion of molecules. When you light a candle, heat is produced by what is known as rapid oxidation, and it takes the form of rapid motion of the molecules making up the products of combustion. Let us imagine a hollow sphere about an inch in diameter. Inside this sphere there are millions of tiny molecules of air. All these molecules are moving about helter-skelter and bumping repeatedly against the sides of the sphere. If the air inside the sphere were heated, the molecules would move faster and consequently would bump against the sides of the sphere more frequently. The result would be a tendency to stretch or expand the sphere, because of this terrifically swift bombardment of molecules and the heat which it produces. Whenever you heat anything it expands for this reason. You heat a piece of iron and set its molecules into rapid vibration, causing the iron to expand in proportion to the amount you heat it.

The amount a metal will expand depends upon its nature and the intensity of the heat applied to it. For example, if we were to heat ten different metals to the same temperature, we would find that each one expands differently, some considerably more than others. The fact that mercury expands a great deal when heated is taken advantage of in the making of thermometers. On the other hand, the negligible expansion of invar (nickel steel) is made use of in the manufacture of precise and accurate instruments which can operate in almost any temperature.

The amount which a metal expands per degree of heat is called the *coefficient of linear expansion,* and is always figured as a percentage of its size. When we say that the coefficient of linear expansion of zinc is .000029 per degree of heat, we mean that a bar of zinc one foot long will expand 29/1,000,000 of a foot when heated one degree. The table following gives you the coefficient of expansion of a number of metals. Notice the extremely small coefficient of expansion of invar; zinc expands more than thirty times as much as invar.

Zinc	0.000029	Cast iron	0.000011
Lead	0.000029	Steel	0.000010
Aluminum	0.000023	Platinum	0.000009
Tin	0.000022	Glass	0.000009
Silver	0.000019	Pyrex glass	0.0000032
Brass	0.000019	Invar	0.0000009
Copper	0.000017		

What is the use of all this explanation about expansion? What practical value has it? If we did not know exactly how much different metals expand, all of our railroads, modern buildings, and machinery would be in a sad state.

For example, the cables in the huge George Washington Bridge over the Hudson River are capable of enormous expansion, and this must be allowed for in the design and construction. It may seem trivial to you that steel expands only 1/100,000 of its length for each degree of heat, but when you consider this mass of steel, thousands of feet long, and the variations of temperature which it is subjected to, from zero in the winter to between 90° and 100° in the summer, you will realize that this apparently trivial matter has assumed large proportions. This same principle must be taken into account in laying railroad tracks, and in making all kinds of machinery.

In any experiments in the physical or chemical laboratory which require accuracy, the temperature is nearly always considered, and every effort is made to maintain an even degree of heat.

You know that when you pour boiling water into a glass vessel, the vessel will break. This is because glass does not conduct heat rapidly, and the inside of the vessel expands while the outside does not, and something must give way to this irresistible force. If you have trouble opening a container fitted with a metal screw cap, the obvious thing to do is heat the cap and it will come off easily.

THERMOMETERS

There are three thermometer scales. One you are undoubtedly familiar with. It fixes the freezing point of water (or the melting point of ice) at 32 degrees, and the boiling point of water (or the condensing point of steam) at 212 degrees. This thermometer is called the Fahrenheit, after its inventor.

A scale with which you are perhaps less familiar is the Centigrade. The freezing point of water (or the melting point of ice) on the Centigrade thermometer is zero, and the boiling point of water (or condensing point of steam) is 100 degrees. Because of its extreme simplicity, this scale is always used in chemistry and physics.

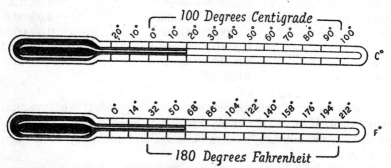

FIG. 22. Centigrade and Fahrenheit thermometer scales compared.

The third scale is used almost entirely for gases, and is called the Absolute thermometer. We have already learned that when you heat a gas it expands. As a matter of fact, it has been definitely proved that all gases expand 1/273 of their volume for every degree Centigrade that they are heated. It is also true that they shrink or contract 1/273 of their volume for every degree Centigrade that they are cooled. Thus if we had a volume of gas at a temperature of 0° C. and cooled it 10°, it would contract 10/273 of its volume. Theoretically, if we cooled it 273°, its volume would vanish. This hypothetical temperature, 273° below zero C., is known as the *absolute zero*. At this temperature all molecular motion would cease. So far, scientists, in their experiments, have not succeeded in reaching it, although some gases have been liquefied at temperatures as low as 272° below zero C.

Since 100 divisions of the Centigrade scale are equivalent to 180 divisions of the Fahrenheit scale (the interval between freezing point and boiling point of water on both scales), 1° Centigrade is equal to 180/100, or 9/5 of a degree Fahrenheit. To change Centigrade to Fahrenheit, we must therefore multiply each degree Centigrade by 9/5 and add 32 degrees.

For example, 20° C. is 20° above the freezing point on the Centigrade scale. Applying our formula, 20° C. is 20 × 9/5, or 36 degrees above the freezing point Fahrenheit. Therefore we see that 36 degrees above freezing is 68° (since the freezing point on the Fahrenheit scale is 32°).

To change Fahrenheit to Centigrade, we perform this computation in reverse—that is, we subtract 32 degrees and take 5/9 of the resulting number. For example, 212° F. equals 212° minus 32°, or 180° × 5/9, which equals 100° C.

CONVECTION

Hot-water heating systems operate on the basis that a given fluid is less dense when warm. As warm water rises to the top it is constantly replaced by cold water. Thus circulation of the water continues so long as heat is applied.

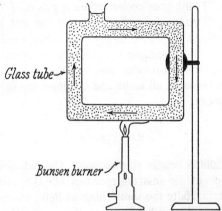

Glass tube

Bunsen burner

FIG. 23. The warm water rises and is replaced by cool water; thus there is constant circulation.

This principle can be illustrated by filling a glass ring with water, applying heat, and then dropping a few colored crystals of potassium permanganate through the opening at the top. The path taken by the colored water is indicated by the arrows.

The same principle is applied to ventilation and tells why windows are opened from top and bottom.

CONDUCTORS

Metals are good conductors of heat. This means that they become hot quickly when subjected to heat. If you put a silver teaspoon into a cup of boiling water, it is not long before the handle of the teaspoon becomes very hot. It would be very foolish indeed to attempt to use an old-fashioned flatiron after the bottom had been heated without putting an asbestos cloth over the handle. It is because metals are good conductors of heat that coffee percolators, electric irons, pokers, etc., usually have wooden handles, or handles made of some material that is a poor conductor of heat. Silver and copper are the best-known conductors of heat. Glass and wood, on the other hand, are poor conductors. A vacuum is an extremely poor conductor, and this fact is taken advantage of in the thermos bottle, which is so constructed that a liquid can be kept hot in a vessel which is insulated from the outside air by a vacuum. The vacuum prevents the heat from penetrating the outside wall of the bottle and escaping into the air. It also keeps the outside air, which is much cooler than the liquid within the bottle, from chilling the contents of the vessel.

Thermo-equilibrium occurs at the point where two substances of different temperatures become equal in temperature. How often have you heard people say, "Drink your coffee before it gets cold"? What is really meant by this is, "Drink your coffee before it has lost heat to the air, and the air has gained heat accordingly." In other words, "Drink your coffee before it becomes the same temperature as the air." The same is true, of course, of cold substances, and in summer we must hurry and eat our ice cream before it all melts and becomes the same temperature as the air in the room.

RADIATION

A hot object radiates heat in all directions. The radiation emitted from such a body travels at the amazing speed of 186,000 miles per second. This heat is fundamentally the same thing as light, except that you feel it instead of seeing it. If you heat a piece of iron slightly, it will give off heat which you can feel but cannot see. We speak of this as infrared radiation. When infrared strikes opaque objects, it sets the molecules of the object into motion, thus producing heat. If you heat the piece of iron long enough, the amount of radiation which comes from it becomes greater and greater, until it reaches the point where it is visible as a dull red, then as a lighter red, then yellow, and finally white (whence our expressions "red hot" and "white hot"). At white heat, of course, there is a considerable amount of light. As we continue to heat an object, it begins to radiate light to which our eyes are not sensitive. This is ultraviolet light. We shall also learn, under the subject of light, that radiation is a wave motion, and the number of vibrations per second determines whether we can see the radiation or merely feel it. Heat from the sun comes to us by radiation. Heat radiation is a wave process similar to light and radio waves but involves waves of different wave lengths.

Radiation can be reflected and transmitted in the same way that light can. The ordinary electric heater is an example of the reflection of radiation. The heater has a hot piece of metal in the center, and a reflecting surface. The metal glows with red heat set up by electricity running through it, and the rays are thrown out from the reflecting surface. If the reflecting surface were lacking, the radiation would be dissipated in all directions instead of in one direction.

A reading glass brings all the rays of the sun to one point. When the rays of the sun are concentrated in such a small area they are greatly increased in power, and it is possible to set fire to a paper or burn dry leaves merely by holding a reading glass in one place with the sun shining upon it.

HEAT ENGINES

Heat is a form of energy, and as such can do work. Man has devised several types of engines which transform heat energy into the energy of mechanical motion.

In the *steam engine,* steam under pressure is led into a cylinder where it pushes a piston back and forth as it expands. In the double-acting steam engine, steam is admitted alternately to opposite sides of the piston by means of a slide valve operated by the shaft of the engine itself. The spent steam is pushed out of the cylinder into the exhaust pipe.

In the *steam turbine,* expanding steam flows against the blades of a series of wheels, causing them to turn at high speed. After passing through the vanes of a movable wheel, the steam is redirected by vanes on a fixed wheel to strike the vanes of the next movable wheel.

The *gasoline engine* used in modern automobiles and airplanes is called an internal-combustion engine because the fuel is burned inside of the cylinder. (In the steam engine, the fuel is burned outside of the cylinder, and it is called an *external-combustion* engine.) In one gasoline engine, called the four-stroke-cycle internal-combustion engine, hot gases produced by the rapid burning of the fuel and air mixture drive a piston down the length of the cylinder. If intake and exhaust valves are placed in each cylinder, exhaust gases may be pushed out and a new charge sucked in.

The *diesel engine* is similar to the gasoline engine except that pure fuel is sprayed into the cylinder, where it ignites on contact with air, because the air has been previously heated by compression. Thus the diesel engine uses a fuel injector and it does not require a spark-plug ignition system.

The *rocket engine* operates according to Newton's Law of Action and Reaction. When a bullet is fired from a gun, the gun has a kick backward as the bullet fires forward. In the same manner, as gas streams from an opening at the rear of the rocket, the rocket itself is pushed forward. The thrust is produced by the constant burning of the fuel in an atmosphere of pure oxygen. The main difference between a rocket and a jet lies in the fact that a rocket carries its own supply of both fuel and oxygen, while the jet carries only the fuel and depends upon atmospheric oxygen for its burning.

The *turbo-jet,* which is the most common form of jet engine for aircraft, operates in this fashion: A compressor wheel (Fig. 24) is attached by shaft S to a turbine wheel. In starting, the shaft is rotated rapidly. The vanes on the rotating compressor force air at high speed into the combustion chamber beyond. Fuel is injected into this chamber, mixed with the air, and exploded. The explosion proceeds toward the rear faster than toward the front, since the wall of incoming air limits

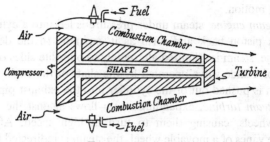

FIG. 24. Turbo-jet

the spread of the explosion in that direction. Gases passing over the turbine wheel on their way out of the exhaust pipe cause the compressor wheel to turn more rapidly and thus continue to feed air for the explosion and to act as a solid wall against the force of expansion. Thus considerable thrust backward is developed, and the engine is pushed forward. Once started, ignition of the fuel is sustained by the high temperature of the walls of the combustion chamber.

SOUND

Sound is caused by vibrating matter. If you strike a bell, it gives off a metallic sound. What you really do is to set the metal in very rapid vibration. This rapid vibration "moves" the air all around the bell in exact accordance with the way it vibrates. Waves of air set up which travel from the bell with a velocity of about 1,100 feet per second in all directions. These waves beating against our eardrums cause the sensation we know as sound.

Any vibrating object will produce a musical note provided it vibrates uniformly and fast enough. If you could take a metal bar and move it up and down in the air forty times per second, you would hear a very low note. If you could increase the motion and move it, say, one hundred times per second, the note would become clearer and higher. The more rapidly this metal bar is vibrated, the higher would be the resulting note. When we strike a tuning fork, we set the prongs in very rapid vibration.

with the result that a musical note is given off. The rate of vibration of most tuning forks is known, and when you have your piano tuned, you will notice that the first thing the tuner does is to take out his fork and test a certain note on the piano with the note of his fork. The violinist "tuning up" is adjusting the tension of his strings until the vibration of each strikes the required note.

If you put an electric bell in a jar and send a current through it, you will hear the bell ring through the jar. If you exhaust the air from that jar and send a current through the bell, you won't hear a sound. Without air there can be no sound, so that if it were possible to visit the moon, no such thing as conversation or music could take place there, because there is no atmosphere.

We find, on examination, that sound waves arise from the condensation and rarefaction of air. The air is normally "even." When a sound wave passes through it, we get a series of condensed areas and rare areas—that is, part of the air is compressed—followed by a part which is rarefied, just as in a water wave we have a "hill" and a "valley." Waves travel with great speed and there are as many of them per second as the musical note which sends them out; *e.g.,* if we strike middle C on the piano, the air around us is set in vibration 256 times per second—256 little waves of condensation and rarefaction reach our eardrums every second, setting them in motion and producing a tone which we recognize as middle C. If C an octave higher is struck, the air is set in vibration 512 times per second—that is, twice as many little waves reach our eardrums per second

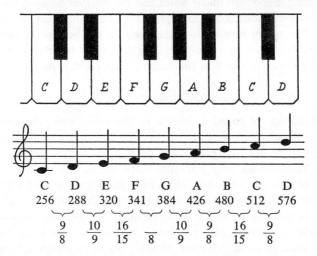

Fig. 25. The relationship between the notes that comprise an octave on the musical scale.

as before. If C an octave lower is struck, 128 or half as many vibrations are sent out. The whole musical scale is a series of vibrations in definite ratio to one another. This is given on page 1117: the first row of numerals gives the frequency per second of vibrations; the second row, the ratio of the frequency of vibrations of each note to the one following it.

These ratios determine the musical character of the intervals. When the ratio of two frequencies is 9/8 or 10/9 they are said to differ by a whole tone, while those whose ratio is 16/15 are said to be a half tone apart.

VELOCITY OF SOUND

The velocity of sound in air varies with the temperature. At 0° C. sound travels 1090 feet per second, increasing two feet per second for every degree rise in temperature. It is an interesting experiment to determine how far away a thunderstorm is by counting the number of seconds between the lightning and the resulting thunder. We know that they both take place simultaneously. We also know that the velocity of light is almost instantaneous for distances on the earth (186,000 miles per second). Therefore all we need to do is count the number of seconds and multiply by the velocity of sound and the approximate distance of the storm is instantly found.

Sound travels in water about four and one half times as fast as it does in air. Devices for testing the depth of the ocean are based on this fact. A huge gong is sounded under water and the interval between the sound and its echo is recorded and multiplied by 4820 (the speed of sound in water). The sound travels from the gong to the bottom of the ocean and is reflected back to the surface. The distance it travels is timed, and divided by two. The depth of the ocean at that point is readily obtained.

REFLECTION OF SOUND

The reflection of sound is known as the *echo,* which is familiar to everyone. As children we have all shouted in tunnels or against stone walls and heard our own echo come back at us.

Sound shadows are very common. They are very much like ordinary shadows of light. A cliff or a building will suddenly cut off a sharp sound. Sound, like light, is best reflected from hard, polished surfaces, and consequently, in gauging acoustics in building, it is obviously important to avoid such surfaces. A highly polished marble wall, or hard, bare expanse of wall, is undesirable for acoustic purposes unless it is so constructed as to focus the reflecting sound in the right direction.

Carnegie Hall, in New York, is one of the best examples of excellent acoustics in the world. High above the stage, in the ceiling, there is a huge hollowed spherical section, so gauged that sound coming from the stage is reflected to the audience throughout the entire hall. It is a remarkable thing that in the top gallery, some 200 feet from the stage, one can hear clearly the lightest notes of a pianist on the stage.

Draperies absorb sound. The more draperies in a room, the less the sound will be reflected. This is only natural when you stop to think that these tiny air waves which vibrate so rapidly are smothered as soon as they hit heavy cloth. They are absorbed, as it were, and all possible chance of reflection is eliminated. Long wave lengths have much more penetrating power than short ones. The low notes of a piano or violin can be heard more distinctly in the next room, with the door closed, than the high notes. The ticking of a watch, which sends out extremely high frequency waves, cannot be heard at all if you put a thin board between it and your ear.

Have you ever noticed how a grand piano or harp is constructed? If you have, you observed that the wires which produce the low notes in the bass are very long compared with the short wires in the high treble. That is what gives the piano and harp their characteristic shape. What is true for the piano is also true for the organ, in which there are pipes varying from several feet to several inches in length and with varying widths. Have you ever noticed a trombone player—how he is constantly changing the length of the trombone? If he wants a low note, he makes the instrument longer; if the note is high, the instrument is short. Cellos are really overgrown violins, and bass viols are even larger.

All this merely means one thing: namely, that the longer the wire in a string instrument, or the air column in a wind instrument, the lower will be the frequency of vibration, and the lower will be the note.

REPRODUCTION OF SOUND

Sound may be reproduced in various ways. The telephone, the radio, and the phonograph are examples. We shall discuss the first two later, under the subject of electricity; we describe phonographic reproduction of sound here briefly. In recording sound on a phonographic record, a microphone picks up the sound, electronic circuits amplify it and cause the needle to vibrate, which then impresses lines of varying characteristics on the wax record, according to the needle vibration. This original record is then treated by a process which enables thousands of copies to be made. In the playing of a copy—the regular phonograph disk used in homes—a needle passes over the grooves and picks up the vibrations.

These vibrations are transmitted to a crystal. This in turn changes them into electrical charges which activate a loud-speaker, thus reproducing the sound originally recorded on the disk.

MUSICAL SOUNDS

A musical sound is different from a noise. When we hear a musical note and compare it with the rattling of a motor truck or an elevated train, we realize that there is a tremendous difference. The difference lies in the fact that in a musical tone the frequency of vibration is uniform and regular. The vibrations pour out at the rate of exactly so many per second. In a noise the vibrations are irregular. They have no system, and they come from the source to your ear helter-skelter.

There are three fundamental characteristics of musical tones, as follows: (1) *Pitch* has to do entirely with the frequency of vibration—the higher the frequency, the higher the pitch. (2) *Intensity* has to do entirely with the volume of sound and the energy of vibration and varies with the amplitude of the sound wave. A loud note on the piano results when you hit the note hard. If you hit the same note gently, the tone will not be so loud. This is due entirely to the energy with which the string vibrates, and has nothing to do with the pitch. (3) *Quality* or *timbre,* a rather complex characteristic, enables us to distinguish one instrument from another. When you strike a note—for example, E—on the piano, and play the same E on the violin, both strings vibrate with the same frequency and their intensity may be exactly the same, yet the quality is entirely different, and you can easily tell which is the violin and which is the piano note. This difference is due to overtones which produce changes in wave shape.

Some definite laws of vibrating strings are:

(1) The frequency of vibration of a string is inversely proportional to its length. The longer the string, the less its vibration and the lower the note. The shorter the string, the more its vibration and the higher the note.

(2) The vibration frequency is directly proportional to the square root of the tension. This merely means that the greater the tension or pull on the string, the greater will be the frequency and the higher will be the note.

(3) The vibration frequency is inversely proportional to the square root of the density. In other words, the thinner the string, the greater the frequency and the higher the note.

All these laws can be easily demonstrated by examining the strings of a grand piano and noting the long, heavy coils in the base, the varying length of the strings through the middle part, and the short, thin, extremely tight strings in the high treble.

Almost the same laws apply to columns of air. In other words, the frequency of vibration of an air column, such as an organ or any other wind instrument, is inversely proportional to its length. The longer the pipe in an organ, the deeper the note. The shorter the pipe, the higher the note.

LIGHT

Light, like sound, is caused by wave motion. It differs from sound, however, in the nature of its motion and its velocity. Sound waves are a series of condensations and rarefactions—they are longitudinal vibrations. Sound waves can exist only in solids, liquids, or gases. Light, on the other hand, is a transverse wave motion and does not necessarily need a solid, liquid, or gas to conduct it. The light from the sun penetrates 93,000,000 miles of space which is practically a vacuum, for there is no atmosphere between the earth's atmosphere and the sun. It is thought that this wave motion is transmitted by what is known as the ether, which fills all the space in the universe not otherwise occupied. Sound travels about 1,100 *feet* per second. Light, on the other hand, travels at the amazing speed of 186,000 *miles* per second.

We see most things by reflected light—that is, some definite source of light shines upon them and the reflection penetrates the retina of the eye and causes the sensation of sight. We never see by direct light unless we happen to stare at the sun, or at a brilliant incandescent bulb or some other luminous object. Nearly all reflection that we see is diffused; that is, the light is scattered. The powerful light of the sun shines through the atmosphere, lighting it up in the soft, beautiful sky blue which we call daylight. On a cloudy day the sky is white and we see everything by this light. The white of the sky is merely diffused reflection.

When a beam of light strikes a highly polished surface, its direction is immediately changed—it is reflected. If the beam of light strikes the surface at an angle, it will be reflected from that surface at the same angle. The most familiar reflecting surface is a plane mirror. It may be proved very easily by plane geometry that an object is as far in front of a plane mirror as the image appears to be behind it; in other words, the mirror is halfway between object and image. Eye doctors with small offices frequently make use of this fact by placing the eye chart above the patient and making him look in a mirror at the other end of the room. The effect is as though the room were twice as long.

A spherical mirror is one in which the reflecting surface is a portion of a sphere. The amount of curvature of the mirror depends upon the radius of the sphere of which it is a section. When the reflecting surface is *outside* the sphere, the mirror is *convex*. When the reflecting surface is *inside* the sphere, the mirror is *concave*.

When parallel light rays strike a concave spherical mirror, the rays are brought down to a common point of intersection known as the principal focus. This is shown in Figure 26. Notice how the rays of light are all parallel to one another until they strike the concave surface of the mirror.

When a beam of parallel light strikes a plane mirror, the rays of light are all reflecting parallel to one another, both before and after the beam strikes the mirror. When a beam of light strikes a white surface such as snow, the reflected rays are not parallel—they are sent out in every direction. To make this a little clearer, imagine a small piece of ice whose highly polished surface reflects a beam of light to your eye. You see this by direct reflection because its rays commonly are reflected to your eye in the same parallel way that they struck the reflecting surface of the ice. If now you crush the ice into millions of tiny pieces, the reflected rays are sent out in all directions and the ice appears white. This is precisely the reason that snow appears white.

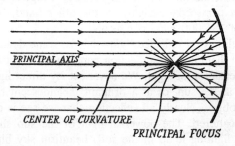

FIG. 26. A concave mirror focusing rays of light at a single point.

REFRACTION OF LIGHT

The velocity of light is diminished when it travels through a medium denser than air; *e.g.,* the velocity of light in glass, quartz, or water is less than the velocity of light in air. The light is, in a manner of speaking, retarded. It is very much like an army of soldiers marching eight abreast with a definite speed on a smooth pavement. As soon as they come to a rough pavement they slow up, and as you can see in Figure 27, the first man of the eight reaches the rough pavement first and starts traveling slower than the eighth man; then the second man reaches the rough pavement and keeps abreast of the first man while the other six are marching with the original speed on the smooth pavement. The result is a bending

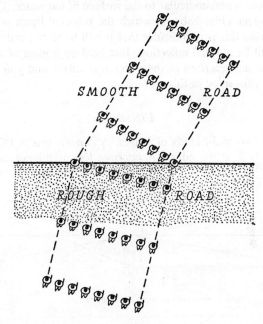

FIG. 27. The refraction of light compared to a line of marching soldiers.

of the line. This is exactly what happens when a beam of light penetrates water, glass, or other media denser than air. This phenomenon is known as refraction—the light is bent. That is why an oar will look bent when it is half out of water, or a spoon in a glass of water will appear bent. Some interesting illusions result from this.

Let a beam of light penetrate a glass jar of water from below (in Fig. 28a). According to the law of refraction it will emerge from the water

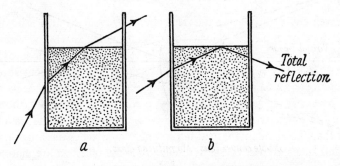

FIG. 28. A beam of light in a glass jar of water.

bent away from a perpendicular to the surface of the water. There will be a point, however (Fig. 28b), at which the reflected beam will be so far bent away from this perpendicular that it will be in the water itself, and the result will be internal reflection. Just hold up a glass of water above your eye: the undersurface of the water is a mirror and you will see the reflection of your hand in this surface.

LENSES

There are two main kinds of lenses. A *convex* lens is thicker in the middle than it is at the edges. A *concave* lens is thinner at the center

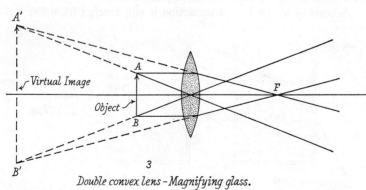

Double convex lens as used in a camera.

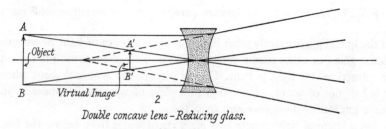

Double concave lens – Reducing glass.

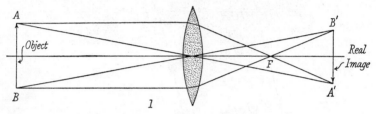

Double convex lens – Magnifying glass.

FIG. 29. Various kinds and uses of lenses.

than at the edges. Parallel rays of light passing through a convex lens are refracted in much the same way as they are reflected from the concave mirror. They all come to a point called the principal focus. There is, however, a point in the lens through which a ray of light passes without any refraction whatever. This is called the optical center. Bearing all this in mind, you can see with the aid of the diagrams in Figure 29 how images are formed by means of a lens. (F is the principle focus of the lens.)

THE TELESCOPE

The principle of the telescope is extremely simple. Light from a distant object passes through two convex lenses. The first lens produces a small inverted image which is then enlarged by the second lens. In the terrestrial telescope a lens is placed between the two to re-invert the image as shown in Figure 30.

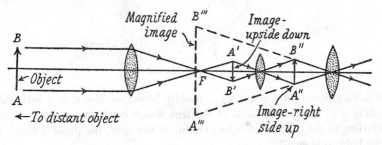

FIG. 30. The arrangement of lenses in a telescope.

THE CAMERA

The camera is a black box on the inside of which is a ground-glass screen. A movable lens is placed in such a way that the outside objects may be clearly pictured upon the ground-glass screen by adjusting to the proper focal length. By sliding a sensitized plate between the ground glass and the lens and exposing it, a permanent picture or negative results.

THE HUMAN EYE

The eye is essentially a camera in which the cornea (C in Fig. 31), a liquid known as the aqueous humor (A), and the crystalline lens (L) act as one single lens and form on the retina or back of the eye an image of whatever we look at. This retina is made up of thousands of little nerves connected with the optic nerve, which transmits the sensation to our brain.

Unlike the camera, in which the lens is moved back and forth in accordance with the varying focal length, the distance from the crystalline lens to the retina remains fixed. Nature takes care of the adjustment for distances by a muscular variation in this lens. Thus, for near-by objects the muscles automatically make the lens thicker; and for distant objects they automatically make it thinner. This variation in the thickness of this marvelous little lens (which is a gelatin composition and clearer than any manufactured lens) takes care of the varying focal length in exactly the same way as the moving back and forth of the lens of a camera. The

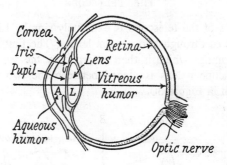

FIG. 31. The human eye.

iris, or colored part of the eye (usually brown or blue), is a little diaphragm of muscles in front of the lens which contracts or expands according to the amount of light present. In the dark, the pupil is large; in the light, it is small.

Sometimes it happens that the crystalline lens is slightly out of adjustment—that the image is formed either in front of or behind the retina; and when it strikes the retina, it is blurred. This may be remedied by placing before the retina a corrective pair of lenses, commonly known as eyeglasses.

COLOR

When a beam of white light is sent through a prism (Fig. 32), a rainbow or spectrum results. As the white light passes through the prism and is dispersed, it is broken into its component colors. The red light, which vibrates slowest and has the longest wave length, is bent the least, while the violet light, which has the highest frequency and consequently the shortest wave length, is bent the most. Other colors appear in between the red and the violet, depending on their frequency. The band of color composed of red, orange, yellow, green, blue, indigo, and violet light is called a spectrum.

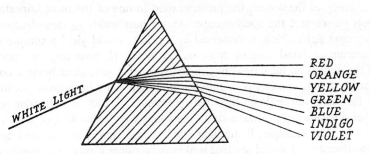

FIG. 32. White light as broken up by a prism.

The visible spectrum is only a small portion of the waves sent out by the light into which white light breaks up. There is a long extended portion beyond the violet, known as the ultraviolet, and a long portion beyond the red, known as the infra-red, neither of which the eye can see.

When we say that the spectrum is made up of seven colors we must remember that we do so merely for convenience. The spectrum consists of these colors and all the gradations (wave lengths) between them. White light is made up of all the colors. If we shine a beam of white light on a red tie, the tie appears red because the material absorbs all colors except red, and it reflects the red light to our eye. A purple tie (purple, you will note, is not a color in the spectrum) appears purple in white light because all colors except red and blue are absorbed. When the reflected red and blue light strikes our retina we get the sensation of seeing purple.

A blue tie in green light will appear black, since all the light which strikes the tie is absorbed and none reflected to our eye. Black is the absence of all light.

PIGMENTS

When we mix various colors of light, the color which results comes from the *addition* of the colors. When we mix paints or pigments, however, the resulting color comes from *subtracting* colors. For example, a blue paint generally reflects violet, blue, and green though it appears blue to the eye. A yellow paint generally reflects red, yellow, and green. Mixing the blue with the yellow paint results in green because green is the only color reflected by both pigments.

THE SPECTROSCOPE

Because a glass prism will arrange the light passing through it into a definite pattern which corresponds to the scale of increasing wave-length frequency of the colors, the prism is used in one of the most important tools of science, the spectroscope. As we heat solids to incandescence, they emit light which, if dispersed by a prism, would yield a continuous spectrum or band ranging from red to violet. If, however, the source of the light is an incandescent gas, the spectrum, instead of being a continuous band, consists of a number of bright lines in various portions of the spectrum with no light between them. In fact, a particular gas, when incandescent, always emits the same lines regardless of where it may be. For example, if the light from a neon sign were analyzed by a spectroscope we would see that it always produces a spectrum consisting of many lines in the red region, several in the orange and yellow, and a few in the blue and violet. This same combination of lines is found in the spectra of certain stars. We can thus be sure that they contain neon. By means of the spectroscope we can analyze the various components of gaseous materials and even determine the presence of minute amounts of impurity.

AIRPLANE FLIGHT

For purposes of our discussion we will consider only two phases of flight: namely, lift and horizontal motion.

When a body shaped like a wing shown in Figure 33 moves through the air, the air molecules stream over the wing surface and we find that the velocity of the air above the wing's surface is greater than the velocity of the air on the bottom of the wing.

According to Bernoulli's theorem, whenever a fluid is in motion, its head-on pressure increases at the expense of the sidewise pressure, which thus decreases. When air moves over the wing of an airplane (relative to the motion of the plane) the distance along the top of the wing is greater

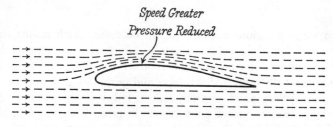

FIG. 33. Cross section of an airplane wing showing air flow.

than that along the bottom, because of the shape of the wing. Consequently, the air must move faster along the top than along the bottom. The rapid motion along the top surface causes a reduced pressure above the wing (compared with that below), and this produces the "lift" of the wing. The lift operating on a moving airplane wing depends on the shape of the wing, the air density, the area of the wing, and the velocity.

The forward motion of a plane is due to propeller action. The forward push exerted on the propeller is the result of the same principle that provides an upward lift on a moving wing and is due to the difference in velocity of the air on the front and back surface of the propeller. (See Fig. 34.)

As a plane takes off, the propeller action causes it to move forward. The forward motion, by causing air to flow over the wing, brings about

FIG. 34. An airplane propeller.

lift. As the horizontal motion increases, the wind velocity on top of the wing also increases, thereby reducing air pressure above the wing. This lifts the plane still higher until it leaves the ground.

Once in the air, the pilot maneuvers the plane by means of various controls. Ailerons, elevators, and rudder are used to steer the plane in the desired direction. Various instruments control speed and altitude. Automatic controls permit blind flying at night or through fog. Our discussion of the jet airplane motor came under the section "Heat Engines" (see page 1115).

MAGNETISM AND ELECTRICITY

Everyone is familiar with the old horseshoe magnet. We all played with it when we were children. We watched it pick up small bits of steel, needles, nails, etc., without really knowing the theory behind it. Here we shall study very briefly the theory of magnetism as an introduction to electricity.

MAGNETISM

Every magnet has two poles: a north pole and a south pole. In the case of a horseshoe magnet, one side is the north pole and the other side is the south pole. If you place two horseshoe magnets together, so that the north pole of one is in contact with the north pole of the other, and consequently their south poles are in contact—there will be absolutely no attraction. If, now, you place them so that the unlike poles are in contact with one another, there will be a great attraction. We thus have the law of magnetism that states: *Unlike poles attract; like poles repel.*

When you bring either pole of the magnet near a piece of steel, the steel is immediately magnetized with the opposite pole. Thus the north pole of the magnet near the end of a needle causes the appearance of a magnetic south pole at that end of the needle. The result is an attraction.

It is an interesting fact that if a bar magnet with a north and south pole is cut in half, the result is two bar magnets each with a north and a south pole. This can be done indefinitely—no matter how many times they are cut up, the resulting pieces will always be independent magnets with north and south poles. This leads us to believe that the atoms of all magnetic substances such as iron, cobalt, and nickel are themselves magnets, each with its north and south pole.

The earth is a huge magnet. It has a north magnetic pole in the northern part of North America (Latitude 70° 30′ North, Longitude 95° West) and a south magnetic pole at a point considerably south of Australia.

If a light needle is delicately pivoted so that it is free to swing, it will align itself with the two poles, one end pointing to the North Pole and the other to the South Pole. This fact is used in the compass. A compass does not give true north; it merely points to the north magnetic pole. The difference between the north magnetic pole and the North Pole is known and tabulated for all points in the northern hemisphere. The number of degrees by which at a given point on the earth the needle varies from the true north is called its declination at that point. Inasmuch as these declinations are all known, the compass proves a very useful guide to ships at sea, because the true north can easily be figured from it.

STATIC ELECTRICITY

There are two kinds of electricity: *static* electricity and *current* electricity. Static electricity is known to everyone who combs his hair with a hard rubber comb on a cold day. Almost every one of us has at some time surprised a friend with a "shock" by rubbing our feet on a carpet and touching that friend. This is static electricity. It exists in positive and negative charges. Bodies charged with the same kind of electricity repel each other; bodies charged with opposite kinds of electricity attract each other. Charges are produced whenever two unlike materials are rubbed together.

To understand the nature of charge, we must recall the structure of the atom. The atom consists of a nucleus containing positive charges (protons), around which electrons, which are negatively charged, move in orbits. There are usually the same number of positive as negative charges in each atom. By applying energy in such forms as friction, heat, or light, we can remove some of the electrons from an atom. The atom

PHYSICS SELF TAUGHT 1131

is thus left with a positive charge. When we rub a hard rubber rod with a piece of cat's fur, the fur loses electrons and becomes positively charged. The negatively charged electrons removed from the fur are now lodged on the rubber, thus giving it a negative charge.

During the summertime, when air becomes heated as it contacts the surface of the earth, the warm, moist air rises with considerable force, and as it cools in the upper atmosphere, a thunderhead cloud forms. When precipitation begins, the raindrops from the cloud pass through the violent updrafts of warm air and they become charged positively while the cloud accumulates a negative charge. The negatively charged cloud induces a positive charge in the ground below in very much the same manner that a south pole of a magnet induces a north pole in a near-by piece of iron. The result is a huge spark of electricity as electrons surge from cloud to ground and back to cloud several times. This discharge we call lightning. The heating effect of the huge current in the lightning creates a detonation known as thunder. Sometimes it happens that near-by clouds are charged oppositely, in which case lightning takes place between one cloud and another.

THE CONDENSER

A *condenser* is used to store electrical charge in much the same manner as charges of static electricity are stored in a cloud and on the earth. The condenser consists of two metallic plates separated by an insulator. As one plate is filled with charge it induces an opposite charge in the other. The charge in the first plate crowds toward the induced opposite charge in the other plate and allows us put additional charge on the first plate.

CONDUCTORS AND INSULATORS

Anything which transmits electricity is called a conductor. In other words, any substance through which electrons may move freely is a conductor. Anything which does not transmit electricity is called an insulator.

Metals are excellent conductors, particularly silver and copper. Rubber is an excellent insulator. So is glass.

CURRENT ELECTRICITY

The general accepted theory of electricity explains it as a rapid flow of billions and trillions of electrons, always flowing from where they are in excess to where they are lacking—from negative to positive. It should be kept in mind that the negative charge results from an excess of electrons, because an electron has a negative charge. A current in a wire is somewhat like the flow of water in a tube. Imagine two tanks of water, one high above the other. If we connect these two tanks with a rubber tube, the water will flow from the upper to the lower tank. The rate of flow depends upon the difference in elevation of the tanks, just as the rate of flow or current in an electric wire depends upon what is known as the difference of potential: that is, the difference of charge between two bodies.

To return to the analogy of the tanks: if we wish to keep a continual flow of water in the rubber tube, we must keep the upper tank always filled with water. In the same way, if we wish to maintain a continuous current, we must maintain a continual difference of potential. This is accomplished by the use of a voltaic cell, which consists of a strip of zinc which acts as a constant source of electrons and is thus negatively charged, and a strip of copper which becomes positively charged and is therefore a place to which electrons are attracted. The charges on the plates are produced when the plates are immersed in a solution of sulphuric acid. The function of the sulphuric acid is to transfer the electrons which arrive at the copper back to the zinc.

When the zinc and copper are connected, we have a continual flow of current, because of the chemical action of the sulphuric acid on the zinc and copper. This current will flow—that is, there will be a difference of potential between the zinc and copper—as long as the sulphuric acid acts upon the zinc and copper.

This principle is applied to all batteries, and there are a number of different types, such as the dry-cell battery, the storage battery, the Daniel Cell, the galvanic cell, etc.

In every electric current three factors are important:

(1) The number of electrons flowing past a given point in the circuit. If 6 billion billion electrons pass in one second, we say that the "current" is one *ampere*.

(2) The "electron-moving-force" (E.M.F.), or pressure behind each electron, which is measured in *volts*.

(3) The "resistance" which the conductor offers to the flow of electrons, which is measured in *ohms*.

The practical definitions of these three factors are as follows:

An *ampere* is 6 billion billion electrons flowing past a given point on a wire in one second.

The *volt* is the amount of force which will cause a current of one ampere to flow through a resistance of one ohm.

The *ohm* is that resistance which will allow one ampere to flow through it on a voltage of one volt. It is approximately the resistance offered to a steady current by a thread of mercury $106\frac{3}{10}$ centimeters long and one square millimeter in cross-sectional area.

There is one other factor which is important: the *watt*. It is defined as the amount of power required to keep a current of one ampere flowing under a potential difference of one volt. The watt, of course, is always a measure of power.

OHM'S LAW

Ohm's Law states that the current passing through a conductor is directly proportional to the electromotive force and inversely proportional to its resistance. Thus, if I is the current, E is the electromotive force, and R the resistance: $I = \frac{E}{R}$. This is a very important formula in electricity. To give one application: the average light bulb passes ½ ampere on a 120-volt circuit. What is its resistance? According to Ohm's Law it would be $\frac{120}{\frac{1}{2}}$ or 240 ohms. The applications of this law are very far-reaching.

MAGNETIC EFFECTS OF THE ELECTRIC CURRENT

When a wire is wound around a piece of soft iron a number of times and a current is sent through the wire, the iron immediately becomes a magnet. The magnetic field of the wire induces the iron to become magnetic.

When the current is stopped, the iron loses its magnetism. This is known as an electromagnet, and is unquestionably one of the most useful and valuable instruments in modern civilization. The electromagnet is basic to the construction and operation of electric motors and electric dynamos. A few other applications of the electromagnet will be studied here. These are: the telegraph, the electric bell, and the telephone.

THE TELEGRAPH

The telegraph consists essentially of a battery, a key, and a sounder (Fig. 35). The key is used for making and breaking the circuit. When the button is pushed down, a contact is made and the current flows through the wires. When the button is released, the circuit is broken and no current flows through the wire. At the other end of the line—it may be a mile or it may be a thousand miles away—is the sounder. This consists merely of an electromagnet over which a soft iron bar is placed. This iron bar is connected with a spring. On the iron bar is an iron crosspiece. When the button of the telegraph key is pushed down, a current flows through the circuit into the electromagnet of the sounder miles away.

The electromagnet attracts the iron crosspiece to it and this makes a click. When the button of the telegraph key is released, no current flows through the wire and the electromagnet loses its magnetism. The spring pulls the bar and crosspiece away from the magnet. It can readily be seen that every time you press the button of the telegraph key, the contact is formed, the electromagnet of the sounder becomes magnetized and the

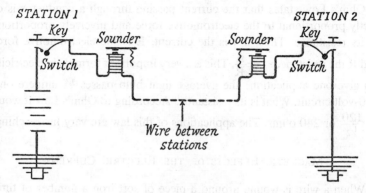

FIG. 35. Telegraph system.

crosspiece is drawn down to it with a click. When the button is released, the crosspiece is pulled up again. In this way a regular code (such as the Morse Code) of clicks—some long and some short—known as dots and dashes, can be tapped out on the button of the telegraph key in one place and the corresponding clicking will be heard in the sounder of another place thousands of miles away.

THE ELECTRIC BELL

The circuit of the electric bell (Fig. 36) consists of a battery, a push button, and the bell itself connected by wires. When the button is pushed, the current flows through the wire into the electromagnet of the bell. The magnet then attracts the little bar on which is attached the hammer. As soon as the bar strikes the magnet, the circuit is broken at the adjusting screw, with the result that the magnet loses its magnetism and the bar is pulled back to its original position by a spring. When the bar is back to its original position, it closes the circuit again and the magnet again becomes magnetic. The same thing takes place all over again. As long as the button is pushed, the bar will go back and forth between the electromagnet and the contact screw. The hammer which is attached to the bar will consequently hit the bell many times per second and we get a steady ringing of the bell.

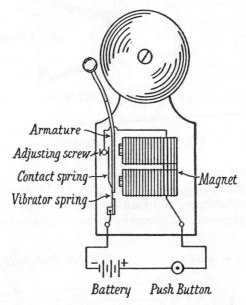

Armature

Adjusting screw

Contact spring

Vibrator spring

Magnet

Battery   Push Button

FIG. 36. Electric bell.

THE TELEPHONE

The transmitter of a telephone (Fig. 37) is essentially a carefully designed microphone. It contains a little box which is filled with tiny bits of carbon. The tiny bits of carbon form a contact between the front and back of the box in such a way that the current has to flow in through the front, through the carbon granules, and out through the back. It so happens that the resistance of carbon to an electric current is proportional to the pressure, so that when carbon is compressed, its resistance decreases and the current gets stronger. When someone talks into the mouthpiece of the transmitter, the diaphragm is vibrated, with the consequent compressing of the carbon granules. The result is that the current varies according to the sound waves of speech. Now let us follow these varying currents to the receiver (Fig. 38) at the other end of the line. The receiver consists of a permanent magnet at the end of which is a tiny electromagnet. In front of the electromagnet and very close to it is a soft iron diaphragm which is attracted to the electromagnet in exact accordance with the vary-

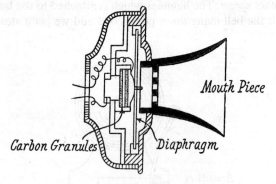

FIG. 37. Telephone transmitter.

ing currents sent up by the transmitter. If the resistance is great, the current will not be strong, the electromagnet will be weak, and the diaphragm will not be drawn in toward the magnet. If, on the other hand, the resistance is lessened, the current increases, the magnet is strengthened,

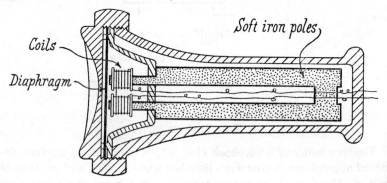

FIG. 38. Telephone receiver.

and the diaphragm will be drawn toward the magnet. In this way the diaphragm is made to vibrate the way the diaphragm of the transmitter vibrated when spoken into. The result is a reproduction of one's speech.

THE ELECTRIC MOTOR

The electric motor takes advantage of the fact that between two magnets there is an attraction between the unlike poles and a repulsion between the like poles. If we pivot a bar magnet freely on its center so that it may rotate in a horizontal plane and present the north pole of another magnet to the like pole of the pivoted magnet, there is immediately a repulsion between the two like poles. The north pole of the pivoted magnet swings away. Its south pole, attracted by the north pole of the stationary magnet, moves toward it—thus helping to complete a half-circle motion. Suppose, however, that just as the south pole of the pivoted magnet moves opposite the north pole of the stationary magnet, this magnet's position is reversed so as now to present a south pole to the moving magnet. The two south poles now repel and the pivoted magnet continues to swing another half-circle, returning to its original position. If the polarity of the stationary magnet is switched at the right moments, the pivoted magnet will rotate continuously. This is the principle of the electric motor. Instead of employing two permanent magnets, however, the motor uses two electromagnets. One electromagnet, called the field

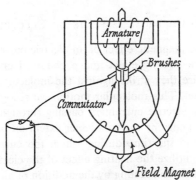

FIG. 39. A direct-current motor.

magnet, is stationary and has a constant polarity. Mounted between the poles of the field magnet is a moving, pivoted electromagnet, called the armature. By reversing the current through the armature at the right moments, the magnetic field of the armature constantly repels that of the field magnet and the armature rotates continuously. The device which switches the current in the armature is mounted directly on the shaft of the armature and consists of commutator segments and brushes. Figure 39 shows a diagram of a simple electric motor.

THE ELECTRIC GENERATOR

Michael Faraday, a nineteenth-century English scientist, discovered that whenever a wire moves across a magnetic field a current is induced to flow in the wire. We speak of this as electromagnetic induction.

If an armature similar to that of the electric motor is rotated in a magnetic field, a current is induced to flow in the armature coil. In order to get the current out of this generator without twisting the wires attached to the armature coil, we use a device similar to that used in the commutator of the motor. The design of this device determines whether the generator produces alternating (A.C.) or direct (D.C.) current.

A coil rotating in a magnetic field first cuts the field in one direction and then, as it turns, cuts the field in the other direction. This induces a current which first flows one way and then the other. This is an alternating current, and it is the type of current which an armature always produces. If we use a commutator consisting of two separate rings, alternating current flows from the brushes. If, however, we use a split-ring commutator similar to the one used in the motor described above, the split ring switches the brush connections at exactly the moment the alternating current switches direction, and the result is that direct current is sent out of the brushes.

HEATING AND CHEMICAL EFFECTS OF ELECTRIC CURRENT

In addition to the magnetic effect of an electric current, electricity has two other effects: a heating effect and a chemical effect. As electrons move through a wire they strike against the molecules of the wire and set them into motion. This molecular motion we recognize as heat. The heating effect of an electric current in passing through a conductor depends largely on the current and to a lesser extent on both the resistance of the conductor and the time during which the current flows. Fuses, toasters, irons, etc., utilize the heating effect of the electric current.

When water is made conducting by the addition of an acid, a base, or a salt, and a current of electricity is passed through the solution, we find that the water will break up into the elements of which it is composed, hydrogen and oxygen. This process is called *electrolysis*. If a metallic salt such as copper sulphate is used in the solution, and a sheet of copper is attached to the submerged positive terminal (anode) of a battery, copper will be transferred from this copper sheet into the solution and from there onto a metallic object attached to the negative terminal (cathode). The metal attached to the cathode will become completely coated with copper deposits if the current is allowed to flow for a sufficient time. This process is called electroplating and is used to coat objects with silver, gold, nickel, chromium, copper, etc.

ELECTROMAGNETIC RADIATION

ELECTROMAGNETIC WAVES

Whenever visible light is produced, radiant heat is also produced. This observation led physicists to the conclusion that radiant heat (infrared) and light have properties in common. They are both electromagnetic waves and, as we now know, they are only two of a number of varieties of this type of wave. Electromagnetic waves include radio waves, infrared, visible light, ultraviolet, X rays and gamma rays, all of which travel at 186,000 miles per second and differ from one another only in frequency of vibration.

RADIO WAVES

In any metallic conductor such as a wire there are always many unstable electrons—electrons which are held loosely by the nuclei of atoms. If we can make these electrons move rapidly back and forth through the wire, the wire becomes the center of a disturbance which moves out into space with the speed of light—186,000 miles per second. These waves which come from the agitation of the electrons are commonly called radio waves. If the back-and-forth motion of the electrons is relatively slow (let us say 60 vibrations or cycles per second), waves of very little energy result. If, however, we force the electrons to move back and forth 500,000 times in one second (500 kilocycles per second, a kilocycle being 1000 cycles), a radio wave is produced that can be detected within a 150-mile radius. Thus, in the antenna of a radio station broadcasting at 560 kilocycles per second, the electrons are made to surge up and down 560,000 times in one second. The standard broadcast band will have stations broadcasting from about 500 kilocycles to 1.6 megacycles (a megacycle is one million cycles).

As we go higher in frequency we enter the so-called short-wave band. Since the higher we go in frequency the more energetic are the waves, waves of short-wave frequency will cover great distances. Moreover, we

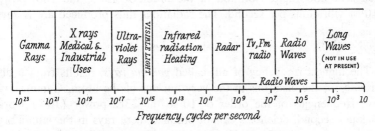

FIG. 40. The electromagnetic spectrum.

find that these waves bounce off of a layer of ionized air about 70 to 150 miles above the surface of the earth. This reflection of the waves greatly extends the distance of communication. The frequencies of short-wave transmitters range from about 2 megacycles to 30 megacycles.

If we employ waves of even higher frequency, we find that these waves behave very much like light in that they travel in straight lines. They are so energetic, however, that they travel through the ionosphere into the space beyond. Such waves, with a frequency of 30 megacycles to 1000 megacycles, have been reflected from the moon. These waves are used for commercial television broadcasts.

ULTRAVIOLET LIGHT

Heating an object makes the molecules move more rapidly; as the temperature rises and the energy of molecular collisions increases, the object first gives off invisible infrared radiation (see page 1114) and then visible light. Continued heating produces a frequency too high for us to see. This is ultraviolet light. The frequency of vibration of electrons which produces light is of the order of 10 to the 15th power (10^{15}) cycles per second.

X RAYS

Radio waves and ultraviolet light waves result from a disturbance of the outer electrons in the atom. If we disturb the electrons near the nucleus, we can produce even higher frequencies than ultraviolet. An extremely energetic radiation which can penetrate matter is produced by bombarding a metal target with high-speed electrons. In this manner, what we call X rays are produced. The electrons are given their great speed by the high voltage placed across the terminals of the X ray tube. The electrons crash through the outer electron layers of the atoms of the target and strike the electrons near the center of the atom. These are then sent into rapid vibration in the order of 10 to the 18th power (10^{18}) vibrations per second. The radiations thus produced are X rays.

GAMMA RAYS

The highest frequency of all, called *gamma rays,* results from a disturbance of the electrons in the very nucleus of the atom. Gamma rays have frequencies of the order of 10 to the 23rd power (10^{23}) vibrations per second. Scientists cannot produce these rays in the laboratory, but they are among the rays emitted by radioactive substances. Radium, uranium, thorium, etc., have been used for many years as sources of gamma rays. Today, however, by bombarding certain elements with neutrons (in an atomic pile), we can make a large number of artificially radioactive varieties of elements. One such, cobalt 60, produces gamma rays many times more powerful than those produced by radium.

ELECTRONICS

In the relatively short time since the discovery of electrons, man's ability to control these tiny bits of negative electricity has had a tremendous effect on the development of science, particularly in the field of communication. The story of electronics began in 1883 when Thomas Edison found that the filament of his newly invented electric lamp threw off negatively charged particles. It was not until several years later that these were identified as electrons.

It was established that a piece of metal which is heated within gives off electrons. A heated filament, however, cannot continue to throw off electrons indefinitely, unless the ones which leave are replaced. Furthermore, rather than allowing the electrons to escape at random into the space around the filament, scientists were looking for a way of attracting them to a single place. Sir Ambrose Fleming, an English physicist, solved both problems by the use of a high-voltage "B" battery. (The battery used to heat the filament is called the "A" battery.) By connecting the positive terminal of the "A" battery to a plate placed inside the tube with the filament, Fleming caused the released electrons to be attracted to this plate. The negative terminal of the "B" battery was attached to the filament to supply it with electrons. Thus there was a continuous flow of electrons from the negative filament to the positive plate, as though a conductor were placed between the two. Note, however, that if the terminals of the "B" battery were reversed so that the plate became negative and the filament positive, no such current could flow. Here, for the first time, we see a circuit in which electrons can flow in one direction but not in the other.

Such a vacuum tube containing a heated filament and a plate is called a *diode*. It can be used to rectify an alternating current; that is, change it to pulsating direct current, as it allows the electrons to flow from filament to plate but not the other way.

Shortly after 1900 the American scientist Lee De Forest added another feature, called the *grid,* to the diode, thus making it a *triode*. The grid is a meshwork or screen between the filament and the plate. With the negative filament and the positive plate, electrons pass through the grid and a flow of current appears in the plate circuit. If now the grid is made negative, electrons leaving the filament will be repelled and few if any will arrive at the plate. On the other hand, if the grid is made positive, it aids the positive plate and the current to the plate increases. Now the whole secret of the triode lies in the fact that a very small change in the charge on the grid will greatly vary the current to the plate. Thus even a weak signal placed on the grid will cause a strong signal to appear at the plate. This is amplification, and it is the prime function of the triode.

THE RADIO TRANSMITTER

A radio wave is produced, as we have said, whenever electrons surge rapidly back and forth in a wire. In the radio transmitter a triode is used to cause oscillation of electrons in the antenna. Oscillation having frequencies of about a million cycles per second is used. The frequency of the oscillation is determined by a coil and a condenser in the oscillating circuit. The oscillation produces radio waves which can travel great distances through space. They are, however, too rapid in vibration to be heard at the receiver. They are used only to *carry* the sound waves. We must impress on these radio waves the much slower frequencies of sound waves if we wish to transmit sound. Just as the horse carries the jockey, so the radio waves carry the sound waves. We may impress the sound waves on the radio waves in one of two ways. We can vary the strength or swing of the radio waves according to the pattern of the sound waves which are to be broadcast. This method of impressing or modulation is called *amplitude modulation*. In *frequency modulation* the radio or carrier wave keeps a constant amplitude but its frequency is changed according to the pattern of the sound waves. Frequency modulation has one advantage over amplitude modulation. In a receiver sensitive to charges on frequency rather than amplitude, static (which is an amplitude-modulated disturbance) is not picked up.

At the broadcasting station a microphone changes the pattern of the sounds to be broadcast into a corresponding electrical pattern, as in the telephone. This sound pattern is then impressed on the radio wave to produce the modulated wave which is then broadcast.

THE RADIO RECEIVER

As radio waves sweep past any metallic conductor they induce a surging of electrons in a rhythm corresponding to that of the electrons in the transmitting antenna. This surging is picked up by the receiving antenna and brought down into a coil and a condenser which has selected out the desired station. The high-frequency wave, having served its purpose in carrying the sound wave to the receiver, is stripped from the sound wave by a diode rectifier or a crystal detector which allows current to flow in only one direction. The weak sound signal is received as electrical impulses and then amplified in other vacuum tubes and appears in the headphones or a loud-speaker, which function exactly as the tele-

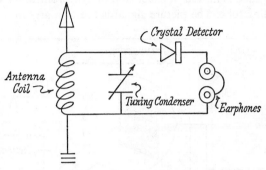

FIG. 41. A simple receiver

phone receiver in converting varying electrical currents into sound waves.

TELEVISION

The heart of the television transmitter is the *iconoscope* or *image orthicon.* It is a bottle-shaped tube which contains an *electron gun* in the neck. The electron gun is a heated filament from which a controlled stream of electrons is emitted. This stream of electrons can be directed to any spot on a *mosaic plate* within the tube. The direction of the beam is regulated by two pairs of plates on which charges are placed. One pair of the plates makes the beam move rapidly across the mosaic plate at regular intervals, while the other jerks it down a short distance after each sweep. The motion is like that of your eyes as you read a page of print. The mosaic plate consists of many tiny droplets of a material sensitive to light, usually the element cesium. Each droplet is actually a tiny photoelectric cell. The scene to be televised is focused on the mosaic plate by a lens, and the electron beam scans the images and converts them into a succession of electrical impulses. These impulses are then impressed on the carrier radio wave through amplitude modulation. Thus, line by line, the image is converted into a series of electrical waves. In American television there are 525 lines of scanning to each picture, and a full picture is scanned in 1/30 of a second. The sound wave is transmitted at a slightly different frequency and is frequency modulated so that the receiver can separate out the picture wave (video) from the sound wave (audio).

In the receiver the TV picture tube, or *kinescope,* converts the video signals back into light. The kinescope contains an electron gun whose stream of electrons is directed against a phosphorescent screen. Wherever the electrons strike the screen they cause a splash of light. The beam in the receiving tube is moved in exact step or *synchronization* with that in the transmitting tube. The picture signal is fed to a grid in the receiving

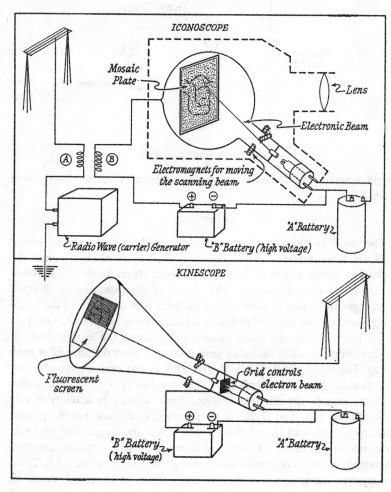

FIG. 42. Diagram of a television transmitter (above) and receiver (below).

tube which acts like a gate. When the transmitter is scanning a light image, the grid in the receiver is positive and the electrons go through to the screen and produce light. When a dark area is scanned, the grid is made negative by the signal and few or no electrons reach the screen, which remains dark. Thus a picture is painted out. As in viewing motion pictures, the rapid series of still pictures gives the illusion of continuous motion.

RADAR

Just before World War II it was discovered that objects, particularly metallic ones, reflect radio waves. Since we know that radio waves travel with the velocity of light (186,000 mi./sec.), by timing the interval between the sending and the return of radio waves, we may determine the distance to any object which reflects them back to the sender. This is the basic principle of radar, which gets its name from the first letters of its original title, "Radio Detection and Ranging."

The transmitter sends out regular, short pulses of very high frequency radio waves. During the intervals between pulses, a receiver near by listens for reflections of these pulses from various objects. The initial and the reflected waves are both fed to a picture tube in which an electron beam is moving across a screen. The distance between the two bumps or "pipe" can then be used to determine the distance of the object. By directing the beam downward from an airplane and varying the method of scanning used in the receiving tube, a rough, actual picture of the ground below appears on the face of the tube.

Radar can penetrate fog and rain. It can guide and locate airplanes and ships. It can even detect icebergs and show the position of storm centers. Recently, astronomers have used radar to track the paths of meteors and man-made earth satellites.

NUCLEAR PHYSICS

NUCLEAR ENERGY

Before December 2, 1942, practically all of the energy used by mankind was derived directly or indirectly from the energy of sunlight. On that day, however, man had accomplished the task of releasing the energy locked away in the atom, and thus a limitless amount of energy was made available to him to be used as he desired. This was the day that the first "atomic pile" went into operation.

ATOMIC STRUCTURE

The most important scientific event in the first half of the twentieth century was the release of atomic energy locked away in the nucleus of atoms. To understand the source of this energy, it is first necessary to understand something of atomic structure. It is suggested that the material in the section following on Chemistry be read and the following points kept in mind.

(1) There are 92 naturally occurring elements of which all things in the universe are made.

(2) Atoms consist of protons, neutrons, and electrons; and differences between atoms are differences in the number of these particles.

(3) Protons and neutrons clump together to form the nucleus of the atom, while a number of electrons equal to the number of protons circle the nucleus.

(4) The number of protons in the nucleus is the atomic number. The total number of protons plus neutrons is the atomic weight. For example, radium, atomic number 88, atomic weight 226 (written $_{88}Ra^{226}$) consists of a nucleus of 88 protons and 138 neutrons surrounded by 88 electrons.

ISOTOPES

Physicists have discovered that not all atoms of the same element have the same atomic weight. It has been found, for example, that at least two kinds of hydrogen atoms exist in nature. They are H^1 and H^2. The H^1 consists of 1 proton and 1 planetary electron. The H^2 consists of a nucleus made of 1 proton and 1 neutron surrounded by 1 planetary electron. Chemically, both hydrogens are identical, since the chemical properties

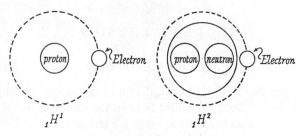

$_1H^1$ $_1H^2$

FIG. 43. Isotopes of hydrogen.

depend only on the outer electron shell. The H^2, however, weighs twice as much as the H^1. These atoms which have the same atomic number but different atomic weight are called isotopes. Almost all elements have one or more isotopes, and the figures given in most charts for the atomic weights of the various elements show an average atomic weight for all the naturally occurring isotopes.

NATURAL RADIOACTIVITY

In general, the atoms of elements with atomic numbers over 82 (the element with atomic number 82 is lead) seem to be too large to stay together. These heavy elements (radium, uranium, etc.) are unstable; their atoms have a strong tendency to expel fragments of their nuclei, thus being transformed into lighter, more stable elements. How these heavy atoms were ever formed in the first place has been the source of much speculation by scientists.

A heavy element becomes simplified into a lighter one through either of two processes. The atom may eject from its nucleus a unit of particles consisting of 2 protons and 2 neutrons. Such a unit is equivalent to the nucleus of a helium atom. The other process of simplification of a heavy atom is to convert a neutron in its nucleus into a proton by ejecting one electron. (This conversion results from the fact that a neutron is composed of a proton and an electron in close association.) Whenever an ejection of a helium nucleus or an electron from a heavy atom occurs, the process is usually accompanied by a radiation of gamma waves. From the earlier discussion of gamma waves, you will remember that they have a higher frequency than X rays and are consequently more penetrating. The emission of helium nuclei or electrons by heavy atoms and the resulting radiation is called *natural radioactivity*.

When Mme. Curie first discovered radioactivity, she identified three different things coming from the radioactive pitchblende. Not knowing anything about their nature, she called them rays and named them after the first three letters of the Greek alphabet—alpha, beta, and gamma rays. Today we know that the alpha and beta rays are not rays at all but streams of particles. The alphas are helium nuclei, the betas are electrons, but the gamma ray is a true ray.

Radioactive elements shoot off their rays and particles at different rates. As they do so, the elements are simplified until they are transformed usually into lead, with an atomic weight of 82. Lead is a stable element. Half of any sample of uranium will become lead in about four billion years. Radium, on the other hand, has a "half-life" of 1,650 years; that is, half of any sample is simplified into lead in 1,650 years. Some man-made elements like francium have a half-life of only about a millionth of a second.

ARTIFICIAL RADIOACTIVITY

Nitrogen has two naturally occurring isotopes. They are $_7N^{14}$ and $_7N^{15}$. Scientists wondered whether it could be possible to make $_7N^{16}$. By bombarding the $_7N^{15}$ with neutrons in a cyclotron, they were able to produce $_7N^{16}$. The $_7N^{16}$ was found to be radioactive. It emitted a beta particle (electron), becoming oxygen.

By bombarding elements with neutrons in an atomic pile or with charged particles from a cyclotron, scientists have produced isotopes which do not exist in nature. All such isotopes are radioactive and emit beta particles and gamma rays. These artificially made radio-isotopes or "labeled atoms" are useful in industry and medicine as "tracers." For example, if a plant is grown in an atmosphere containing carbon dioxide (CO_2) "labeled" with radioactive carbon atoms, we can track the carbon into the plant and learn more about how plants can manufacture starch from CO_2, water, and sunlight.

DETECTION OF RADIATION

The most convenient device for the detection of radiation is the Geiger counter. The heart of the counter is the Geiger tube, which consists of two conductors in a glass envelope containing gas under low pressure. A voltage is passed across the two conductors which are separated by the gas, and the voltage is adjusted to just below the sparking potential. If a particle or ray enters the tube, it makes the gas a conductor and there is a momentary spark. The sudden surge of electricity between the two wires may be used to produce a click in a pair of earphones or flash a light.

Photographic film is also sensitive to radiation; the radiation causes the film to darken on development. From the degree of darkening we can estimate the intensity of the radiation. The film badges worn by workers who are exposed to radiation are an application of this type of detection.

To record the path of individual particles in radiation, we employ the *cloud chamber*. If the moisture content, the pressure, and the temperature within a confined space are properly adjusted, the track of each particle passing through it becomes visible as a cloud, much as the vapor trails which define the path of high-altitude airplanes.

NUCLEAR FISSION

Uranium is the heaviest element which occurs naturally. By adding particles to uranium atoms, scientists have succeeded in creating artificial elements which are heavier than uranium and do not exist in nature. Bombarding uranium with neutrons has produced elements 93 and 94, neptunium and plutonium. In the process, scientists stumbled on a new and remarkable phenomenon. When the uranium isotope 235 was bombarded with neutrons, the final result was not a heavier, radioactive element, because the complex nucleus produced split into two fragments. These were nuclei of medium atomic weight. In addition, several independent neutrons were also ejected. This process of breaking down a large nucleus into two of comparable size is called *fission*. Two features of this process make it of great importance. First, the total weight of the two atoms and the neutrons which result from fission is less than the total weight of the original uranium atom plus that of the neutron which caused the fission. In other words, somehow in this process an infinitesimal amount of matter is completely annihilated or destroyed. Einstein had predicted, as long ago as 1905, that if matter could be annihilated, it would be transformed into energy. In fact, Einstein developed an exact formula for the transformation, which is:

$$E = mc^2$$

or, energy equals mass times the square of the speed of light. This is exactly what happens in fission. The two nuclei and the neutrons are ejected with an accompaniment of terrific energy and heat, light and gamma radiation resulting as by-products.

The second feature of fission which makes it of great interest is that fission is caused by neutron bombardment, and in the process neutrons are produced. This means that if a single atom of uranium 235 were struck by a neutron and underwent fission, it would produce other neutrons which in turn could cause fission in other atoms. Thus a *chain reaction* would be initiated. It is the application of these principles that has made possible the production of the atomic bomb—with its unprecedented destructive power.

NUCLEAR FUSION

Energy can also be released if we take the very light elements and fuse them to form heavier ones. If hydrogen gas is heated to a temperature of some 100 million degrees Centigrade, the molecules move so rapidly that their nuclei collide and are united. Four hydrogen atoms contain all the parts needed to unite into one helium atom, but one helium atom weighs slightly less than four hydrogen atoms. So, in the process of fusing hydrogen into helium, there is a loss in matter, and according to the Einstein mass-energy relation, energy is liberated. Since the process of *fusion* of light elements into heavier ones is initiated under high temperature, we speak of this type of reaction as a *thermonuclear reaction*. The thermonuclear reaction is the basis of the fusion bomb, sometimes called the H bomb.

We believe that the origin of the sun's energy lies in the thermonuclear reaction which fuses hydrogen into helium. Each second, 564 million tons of hydrogen are fused to form 560 million tons of helium. Even though the sun loses mass into energy at the rate of 4 million tons per second, the sun is so large that it would take 150 billion years for it to lose one per cent of its mass.

Nuclear fusion requires such a high temperature to start the reaction that at present the only way we can supply this temperature is by using an A bomb as a fuse. Thus we are not able to control the fusion, but in the very near future science is sure to solve the problem of controlling thermonuclear reactions and then mankind will have at its disposal an unlimited supply of energy which will be inexpensive and free from any problems of radioactive contamination. This energy can be used to transport water for irrigation, to provide industry with unlimited power, and for numerous other purposes which increase prosperity and raise the standard of living.

EXAMINATION QUESTIONS

1. What is physics?
2. What is the internationally used scientific system of measurement?
3. Name the three simple machines.
4. What statement by Archimedes showed complete confidence in the lever?
5. What principle of mechanics does a nutcracker illustrate?
6. What is a fixed pulley?
7. What governs the mechanical advantage of a movable pulley?
8. How can the mechanical advantage of an inclined plane be determined?
9. What is a wedge?
10. What does Newton's First Law of Motion mean?
11. What does Newton's Second Law of Motion mean?
12. What is the acceleration of a falling body?
13. If a cannon ball is shot horizontally from a tower 100 feet high at the same time that another cannon ball is dropped from the tower, which ball will hit the ground first?
14. How does a vacuum affect the speed of falling bodies?
15. What does it mean when you say that a floor will sustain a weight of 150 pounds per square foot?
16. What principle of equilibrium does Newton's Third Law give us?
17. What are the three types of equilibrium?
18. How does the length of a pendulum affect its swing?
19. Name the two kinds of energy.
20. On what two factors does liquid pressure depend?
21. What does Pascal's Law state?
22. What is Archimedes' principle?
23. What is specific gravity?
24. What principle in physics does the use of blotting paper illustrate?
25. If we reduce the volume of a given amount of gas, what is the effect on the pressure?
26. What is the weight of air?

27. What is heat?
28. Do all metals expand the same under the same heat?
29. Why does glass break when boiling water is poured into it?
30. What is the freezing point of water on the Centigrade thermometer?
31. What temperature is known as absolute zero and why?
32. Convert 59° Fahrenheit to Centigrade.
33. What are the best-known conductors of heat?
34. At what speed does heat radiate?
35. What is the most common form of jet engine for aircraft?
36. By what is sound caused?
37. What is the number of vibrations of middle C on the piano?
38. How fast does sound travel?
39. What is the reflection of sound called?

40. What phenomenon occurs when a beam of light penetrates water, glass, or other media denser than air?
41. Which color light vibrates slowest and has the longest wave length?
42. Name two kinds of electricity.
43. List some applications of the electromagnet.
44. List some kinds of electromagnetic waves.
45. When is a radio wave produced?
46. What is the basic principle of radar?
47. What is natural radioactivity?
48. How have scientists produced isotopes which do not exist in nature?
49. What is the heaviest element which occurs naturally?
50. What is Einstein's formula for the conversion of mass into energy?

For Further Study

ELEMENTS OF PHYSICS, by R. A. Millikan, H. G. Gale, and W. R. Pyle. (Ginn & Co., Boston.)

FROM GALILEO TO COSMIC RAYS, by H. B. Lemon. (University of Chicago Press, Chicago.)

FUNDAMENTALS OF PHYSICS, by Bowen C. Dees. (Barnes & Noble, New York.)

NEW PRACTICAL PHYSICS, by N. H. Black and H. N. Davis. (The Macmillan Co., New York.)

XXIV

Chemistry Self Taught

THE IMPORTANCE OF CHEMISTRY

CHEMISTRY IS the science which deals with the composition of matter. It is concerned with the properties of substances and the conditions under which they are transformed into other substances. As we mentioned at the beginning of the Physics section of this book, Chemistry and Physics supplement one another. Chemistry, in its applied form, studies the uses to which materials can be put and seeks to create new and formerly unavailable or nonexistent materials for specific uses.

Many of the applications of chemistry are extremely useful. It is no exaggeration to say that everything you see around you that is manufactured is produced with the aid of chemistry. The books you read are printed on paper made from wood pulp by means of a chemical process. The ink which prints the reading matter is produced by chemical means. The type could not be produced without the aid of the chemist. Photography is almost entirely chemical in nature. Artificial silk is a triumph of modern industry. So are aniline dyes, and cellophane, and quick-drying paints and enamels, and imitation leather, synthetic flavorings for use in cooking, and preserved foods of all kinds. The chemist not only improves and tests old products, but he is constantly developing new ones.

THE BASIS OF CHEMISTRY

Very likely it has not occurred to you that every second of the day almost everything you touch and see is undergoing a slow change. Iron rusts, fruit decays, wood rots. You yourself are continually undergoing chemical changes. You must, or you could not live. In breathing, you inhale a gas (air), allow it to pass into your body, and exhale a gas of different composition. And this you do continually, at the approximate rate of 18 times per minute.

Plant life also breathes. It takes in the very gas which we and other animals breathe *out,* while we breathe *in* the gas that plants give *out.* That is one of the reasons we find the air in the country so fresh and pure.

A chemical change like respiration, the rusting of iron, or the decaying of fruit takes place whenever a solid, liquid, or gas is transformed by a change of composition into something of an entirely different nature.

If you heat a piece of copper for a long time in a very hot flame, you will see that a fine powder forms on it. Scrape off this powder with a knife. Keep doing this for a long enough time, and the entire piece of copper will eventually be transformed into this powder. What has happened? The heat has made the copper combine with something in the air to form a new substance. In chemical terms, the copper has combined with oxygen in the air to form copper oxide. This is an example of a simple chemical change.

Consider the gases, oxygen and hydrogen. They are both invisible; they are both odorless. You cannot feel them; you cannot taste them. If these gases are mixed in a certain proportion, and a lighted match is applied to them, there is an explosion, and water is produced. Water is a liquid— two gases have been transformed into a liquid. This is another chemical change. Water does not resemble either oxygen or hydrogen, yet it is a combination of these two elements. Chemistry makes a study of the composition of the various substances found in the universe, and of the changes in their composition which are constantly taking place.

ELEMENTS

Oxygen and hydrogen are called elements, because, though they can be combined with each other and with other elements, neither in itself can be broken up into any substance simpler in composition. An *element* is a substance that cannot be separated into other substances by ordinary chemical means. The break-up of the atoms of an element produces particles—protons, neutrons, and electrons—which do not have the characteristics of the substance. There are 92 naturally occurring elements, many of which are very rare. The eight elements most abundant in the earth are oxygen, silicon, aluminium (commonly spelled "aluminum"), iron, calcium, magnesium, potassium, and sodium; these together make up nearly 98% of the earth's crust, mostly in chemical combination with other elements. The bodies of water, of course, contain large quantities of hydrogen; and the earth's atmosphere has very large amounts of nitrogen.

Some elements are more active than others. Oxygen readily combines with most metals to form *oxides.* If the metal mercury is heated in a test tube for any length of time, little red particles collect on the sides of the tube. If the heating is kept up long enough, all the mercury will change to this red powder. The red powder is a compound of mercury and oxygen, called mercuric oxide. If this red powder is heated to a higher temperature, it will ultimately break down into mercury and oxygen. Similarly, zinc oxide results if the metal zinc is heated in oxygen.

Everyone is familiar with burning. Every day we light matches to ignite cigarettes, we burn gas in cooking, or we start the furnace in late autumn. Burning, or combustion, is a common and very important chemical phenomenon. The light, or luminous quality, of the flame is due to inconceivably minute particles of a substance (usually carbon) heated to incandescence. Some flames, such as that of burning hydrogen, are almost invisible, due to a lack of such incandescent particles.

If a lighted match is applied to a piece of paper, the paper at once catches fire. But the same lighted match applied to a piece of wood or a piece of coal will not ignite it. Why? This is due to difference in *kindling temperature,* which is determined by the readiness with which a substance combines with the oxygen in the air. As soon as any substance is heated to a sufficiently high temperature, known as its kindling temperature, it bursts into flame. As a rule, the more intimately the substance is in contact with oxygen, the lower will be its kindling temperature.

A piece of paper has oxygen distributed loosely among its tiny fibers, and oxygen completely surrounding it, in the air. Hence its kindling temperature is very low: it is easily ignited when brought into contact with a flame. Wood requires a little more time than paper to catch fire; it must be heated longer because it is more compact than paper and oxygen is not so free among its fibers. Hence the kindling temperature of wood is higher than that of paper. Coal requires a still greater amount of heat because it is tremendously compact, and the oxygen inside of it (not in combination with it, of course) is very small in quantity. To start a coal fire it is necessary to begin with burning paper, which ignites wood, the burning wood finally igniting the coal. Each kind of fuel in turn heats the other to its respective higher kindling temperature.

Burning or combustion (in air or in oxygen) is very rapid *oxidation,* the combining of a substance with oxygen. This is clear because substances will burn, with the liberation of light and heat, only when oxygen is present. A fire may be smothered and put out by shutting off its supply of air. A candle will burn only briefly in a tightly closed jar.

Notice at this point that the *combining* of chemical elements or substances is quite different from a *mixing* of them. Carbon in the form of charcoal may be mixed with pure oxygen and remain unchanged as long as heat is not present; as soon as the mixture is heated, or the carbon is ignited, the carbon *combines* chemically with the oxygen, forming the *compound* known as carbon dioxide. The carbon dioxide is quite unlike either carbon or oxygen; it has its own form and properties.

OXYGEN

Oxygen is necessary for ordinary burning or combustion. Oxygen is necessary for all forms of life, too; it is the part of the air we utilize when we breathe air into our lungs, where the oxygen loosely combines with the red coloring matter (hemoglobin) of the blood and is carried thereby to the various parts of the body.

The earth's atmosphere, or "air," is made up of about 78% nitrogen, 21% oxygen, and 1% a mixture of other gases. If the air were entirely composed of nitrogen, burning would be impossible, for nitrogen does not support combustion. If the air were entirely oxygen, a fire would burn very fiercely and would be extremely difficult to extinguish. Even iron will burn in pure oxygen: if a rod of iron, preheated to a glowing red, is plunged into a container of pure oxygen, it will burn brightly, giving off brilliant sparks. Slow oxidation of iron takes place in the open air, forming what we call rust; non-rusting metal compounds, notably "stainless steel," are products of modern chemistry.

Oxygen is so much a part of the earth that everywhere man may dig he finds oxides, compounds of oxygen. Oxygen, as a matter of fact, is the most abundant element on the earth, forming nearly half of the total composition of the earth's crust.

Liquid air is a good source of oxygen when desired in quantity, but the apparatus required is too expensive for laboratory purposes.

The most common way of preparing oxygen in the laboratory is to heat potassium chlorate and manganese dioxide in a test tube. (A test tube is a glass tube closed at one end; it is used in scientific laboratories

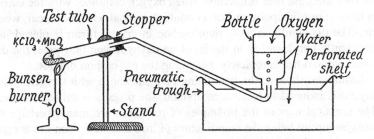

FIG. 1. Laboratory method of collecting oxygen.

as a convenient container for heating or otherwise treating substances experimentally.) Potassium chlorate requires only a slight amount of heat to liberate a large amount of oxygen. Potassium chlorate is a powder composed of three elements: potassium, chlorine, and oxygen, the latter forming an exceptionally large proportion. The presence of manganese dioxide helps the process of obtaining the oxygen from the potassium chlorate, but, curiously enough, the manganese dioxide remains unchanged; the part it plays is not yet clearly understood. Substances such as manganese dioxide, which facilitate a desired reaction but which are not themselves changed by the reaction, are referred to as *catalysts*.

Oxygen is an odorless, colorless, and tasteless gas, slightly heavier than air. In the pure state it has many uses. Doctors use it in the treatment of some diseases, particularly in severe cases of pneumonia, and during the administration of an anesthetic if the patient needs reviving suddenly. In the oxyhydrogen blowpipe, pure oxygen is mixed at the nozzle with pure hydrogen and ignited; the mixture burns with an intense heat, melting or vaporizing most metals; the flame of this blowpipe reaches a temperature as high as 5000° Fahrenheit. When this flame is projected against lime, the lime glows very brightly, a fact which is made use of in limelight or Drummond light.

The most striking property of oxygen is its tendency to support combustion. As a result of chemical combination with other elements, oxides are formed and energy is released. Indeed, oxygen combines with all the elements except fluorine, bromine, and five or six others (all very rare). Oxygen has a tremendous attraction or chemical affinity for two elements in particular: carbon and hydrogen. Oxygen will forsake many other compounds if heated in the presence of carbon or hydrogen, to combine with the carbon or hydrogen. The product of the combustion of hydrogen with oxygen is always water; that resulting from the combination of oxygen and carbon is carbon dioxide (sometimes carbon monoxide also, but this burns rapidly, in air, into carbon dioxide). Common substances used for fuel—because heat is liberated when oxygen combines with the carbon in them—are principally carbon in content, as coal, charcoal, peat, wood, etc. The diamond is almost pure carbon in crystal form; if placed in a sufficiently hot flame, as in the jet of an oxyhydrogen blowpipe, the diamond will oxidize completely, becoming the gas carbon dioxide.

Oxidation, then, is the combining of a substance with oxygen. When oxygen is induced to leave a compound, the process is called reduction. The practical uses of the principles of reduction are many, perhaps the most important being the manufacture of iron and steel. Iron ore is really iron oxide mixed with various impurities. The ore is heated in a huge furnace together with carbon (usually in the form of coke); the oxygen forsakes the iron oxide to unite with the carbon, leaving the iron, the impurities passing off as gases or remaining as slag. Iron, one of the metallic elements, is thus obtained, but it is not pure since much of the carbon remains in the iron. Cast iron contains much carbon and other substances (silicon, phosphorus, sulphur, etc.); wrought iron contains the least carbon of the commercial forms of iron. Steel is intermediate in carbon content between cast and wrought iron, and is made in various forms, depending on its composition.

Ozone is a curious form of concentrated oxygen. It has been humorously described as an "oxide of oxygen." Ozone is pure oxygen, for it always breaks down into nothing but oxygen; it seems to be made up of particles or molecules of oxygen more closely knit, in a manner of speaking, than the molecules of oxygen are. Electricity in the air causes the formation of ozone, as during thunderstorms or near electrical machines. The gas is colorless, but it has a peculiar odor (oxygen, it will be remembered, is odorless). Ozone is very unstable in composition, for it breaks down almost immediately into oxygen when it is liberated in the air. It is commonly thought that ozone is present in sea air and in the air of rural districts, but the presence of ozone in the air, to any large or permanent extent, has never been proved.

HYDROGEN

Hydrogen does not occur free in the air in any appreciable quantity, except near active volcanoes and natural gas wells, where it is present in the escaping fumes. Like oxygen, pure hydrogen is colorless (invisible), odorless, and tasteless; when somewhat impure, however, hydrogen has a distinct odor. Hydrogen is unique in being the lightest in weight of all the elements: 2,500 gallons of hydrogen weigh only a little over two pounds. Because of its lightness, the gas is used in balloons and dirigibles (illuminating gas, which contains hydrogen, has often been used in balloons). Hydrogen has one undesirable property for use in dirigibles: it is highly inflammable. (For this reason helium, a very light but non-inflammable gaseous element, is used where possible; helium is comparatively rare, and consequently very precious.) Hydrogen may be produced in the laboratory by placing some metal such as zinc in contact with hydrochloric or sulphuric acids and collecting the gas by displacement of water in a bottle.

Hydrogen burns in air or oxygen with a very pale, almost invisible blue flame. This flame is extremely hot, much hotter than an ordinary bright flame. Though pure hydrogen burns calmly in air, a mixture of hydrogen and air is highly explosive when ignited, the combustion being instantaneous; for this reason, hydrogen must be handled with extreme care in the laboratory and in commercial use. Hydrogen also "burns," in a special kind of combustion (oxygen not being present), in chlorine gas, with a bluish-white flame, forming hydrochloric acid gas. The product of hydrogen burning in oxygen is always water; the drops of water which sometimes gather on the bottom of pans over gas flames, in cooking, are formed from the combustion of hydrogen in the gas flame. The oxyacetylene torch, used to cut steel beams and other metals, works much like the oxyhydrogen blowpipe. Acetylene, a hydrocarbon gas, is burned in the presence of pure oxygen, giving a dazzling flame of tremendous heat.

Hydrogen is an essential component of all acids. It is combined with carbon in the great group of hydrocarbons, so called, which include kerosene, gasoline, naphtha, illuminating gas, etc. It is combined with carbon and oxygen in sugar, wood, paper, and other organic substances. It forms 1/9 (by weight) of water.

ACIDS, SALTS, AND BASES

An *acid* is a substance which in solution yields hydrogen ions. An *ion* is an atom or a group of atoms from which electrons have been removed or have been added. It is through the agency of atoms that most chemical combinations take place.

Because acids change the color of some substances, they can usually be identified by such a test. Litmus paper is used in the laboratory for this purpose. An acid turns blue litmus paper red. Acids contain hydrogen, which is liberated when an acid is placed in contact with a metal, leaving a salt. The salt is a combination of the metal and the other elements which the acid contains, excepting hydrogen, thus:

metal + acid = salt of the metal + hydrogen.

Hydrogen is usually prepared in the laboratory by the action of hydrochloric acid on zinc, giving hydrogen and the salt, zinc chloride.

Table salt is thought of when "salt" is mentioned. Chemical salts are of many kinds, though they usually occur in powdery form. A *salt* is produced when an acid and a metal interact chemically. Sodium chloride (table salt) is a salt of the metal sodium. Salts such as sodium chloride, formed by the union of strong acids and bases, have no effect on litmus paper. Other salts may turn blue litmus red, or vice versa, depending upon the relative strength of the acids and bases of which they are composed.

A *base* (or *alkali*) is chemically the antithesis of an acid; a base turns red litmus paper blue. Hydrogen and oxygen are combined with metals to form bases. Bases and acids neutralize one another; when an acid and a base interact, a salt is formed. For this reason, a base may be used as an antidote for the harmful effects of a powerful acid, though a base alone may be just as injurious as an acid alone. The words "injurious" and "harmful" are used relatively, for chemical action is objectionable only when it takes place in an undesired way and at an undesired moment.

The composition of acids, bases, and salts is often complex; that is, it is made up of two or more chemical elements. Hydrochloric acid, for example, is composed of hydrogen and chlorine in the proportion of one atom of hydrogen to one atom of chlorine. The base called sodium hydroxide contains one atom of sodium to each atom of oxygen and hydrogen (one of each). Curiously, the oxygen and hydrogen in bases unite, one atom of each, and act as a unit, as though together they formed a single element. Any group of atoms which acts as a unit in chemical combination is called a *radical*. The combination of an atom of oxygen and an atom of hydrogen (OH), which acts as a unit in bases, is known as the hydroxyl radical.

When an acid acts on a base, one neutralizes the other, and in the process a salt is formed *with the liberation of water* (usually) thus:

$$acid + base = salt + water$$

hydrochloric acid + sodium hydroxide = sodium chloride + water.

The water is formed from the hydroxyl radical of the base plus an extra atom of hydrogen from the acid, for water consists of hydrogen and oxygen in the proportion of two atoms of hydrogen to each atom of oxygen. The nonmetal of the acid then is left to combine with the metal of the base to form a salt, sometimes with the inclusion of oxygen.

The most common acids are sulphuric acid (hydrogen, oxygen, and sulphur), hydrochloric acid (hydrogen and chlorine), nitric acid (hydrogen, nitrogen, and oxygen), and acetic acid (carbon, hydrogen, and oxygen). Vinegar contains from 5% to 12% acetic acid. Usually acids are thought of as liquid in form; sulphuric and nitric acid are naturally liquid. Hydrogen chloride gas dissolved in water is known as hydrochloric acid. Citric acid is a solid; citrus fruits contain citric acid. Any solution of an acid in water is commonly called an "acid," in popular usage. Sulphuric acid is commercially known as "oil of vitriol," and hydrochloric acid as "muriatic acid."

Bases, particularly the stronger ones, are also known as alkalies. Most bases occur naturally as solids, but solutions of them (in water) are commonly called bases. Sodium hydroxide, a common base, is popularly called caustic soda, the word "caustic" referring to its corrosive property; potassium hydroxide is similarly called caustic potash. Slaked lime is the base calcium hydroxide. Ordinary ammonia is the base ammonium hydroxide in solution. Bases, or alkalies, are used in cleaning because they dissolve greases; they also interact with fats to form soaps—sodium hydroxide is largely employed in the manufacture of soap. Since bases contain hydrogen and oxygen as hydroxyl radicals, they are called hydroxides. In inorganic chemistry, bases are always hydroxides of metals.

Salts are compounds formed by the substitution of a metal for the hydrogen of an acid, or by the substitution of a nonmetal for the hydroxide radical of a base. The usual method of the formation of a salt is by the action of an acid on a base. A salt may also be formed by the action of an acid on an oxide (of certain metals), or by the action of an acid on a metal. Sulphuric acid acting on zinc gives zinc sulphate; sulphuric acid on magnesium gives magnesium sulphate; nitric acid on zinc gives zinc nitrate; carbonic acid on sodium gives sodium carbonate; etc.

Most nonmetals form oxides which, when united with water, form acids. Most metals form oxides which, when united with water, form hydroxides (bases). Thus, sulphur trioxide plus water forms sulphuric acid, and calcium oxide plus water forms calcium hydroxide.

WATER

Water is the most abundant liquid on the earth's surface. It occurs naturally as a gas (water vapor), a liquid, and a solid (ice). Water vapor is always present in the air, though in varying quantity; its presence causes the humidity which may be oppressive in hot weather. The phenomena of rain, hail, and snow concern the meteorologist; the geologist makes a study of the action of water in wearing away rocks and cutting valleys through hills; water power is of great importance to industry. The chemist is primarily concerned with the composition of water and its action in combining or mixing with various substances; the chemist is also called upon to purify public drinking water, just as the engineer is called upon to ensure its plentiful supply throughout the year.

Water does not exist pure in nature, but always contains a varying amount of dissolved substances. A substance is said to be dissolved in a liquid when it disappears and becomes apparently (so far as the eye can see) a part of that liquid, without having been altered chemically. Thousands of substances are varyingly soluble in water; many others may be held in suspension in fine particles in water. Pure water can be obtained by distillation, as follows: Water is heated in a closed vessel, the escaping water vapor being led by a tube to a cooling chamber, in which the hot vapor condenses to water again—the latter is distilled water, free of all nonvolatile impurities (provided that the container is clean). Water vapor should not be confused with what is popularly called steam; water vapor is invisible, but when suddenly cooled it condenses quickly into tiny drops of water which float in the air in clouds of steam. The mineral substances in solution in natural water are often beneficial to health, though the medicinal value of some mineral springs has been much exaggerated; good drinking water always contains some dissolved substances. Distilled water lacks these important minerals. The mineral matter dissolved in water, if in large quantities and if consisting principally of calcium and magnesium compounds, makes hard water.

The amount of a substance that water will dissolve varies with the temperature. A hundred pounds of water at 20° C. will hold in solution only about 42 pounds of copper sulphate; the same amount of water at 100° C. will hold in solution more than 200 pounds of copper sulphate. When a solution will dissolve no more of a dissolved substance, the solution is said to be *saturated*. A solution containing only a small amount of the dissolved substance is *dilute*. As a solution is cooled, it will hold less and less in solution, for solubility usually decreases with lower temperature. As a solid begins to separate from the solution, it often takes form in crystals. A solid can be separated by cooling the liquid; by evaporating the liquid, thus leaving the solid free; and by *precipitation,* a process which results when liquid in which the solid is not soluble (or is only slightly soluble) is added to the solution. A solid may also be brought out of solution by changing it chemically into an insoluble substance; this may be done by the addition of a substance which reacts with the solid in solution to form an insoluble compound.

Water is a compound of hydrogen and oxygen. This can be demonstrated in various ways; one proof is that when hydrogen is burned in oxygen, water is formed. A laboratory proof is called the *electrolysis of water*. Sulphuric acid is added to some water, to make it a conductor of electricity. The solution is placed in a special apparatus so that an electric current can be passed through the liquid. The electricity decomposes the water into two gases, one gathering in one tube, the other in another. It is found that one is oxygen, the other hydrogen, and that there is just twice as much hydrogen (by volume) as oxygen; it is also found that the weight of the two gases together is equal to the weight of the water decomposed. Several other chemical proofs of the composition of water are known, and all agree in this result.

THE STRUCTURE OF MATTER

MOLECULES AND ATOMS

Matter is composed of millions and millions of inconceivably small units called *molecules*. These are so small that an enormous number could fit on the head of a pin. Picture to yourself a marble an inch and a half in diameter. The marble is as many times larger than a molecule as the earth is larger than the marble, and the earth is about 8,000 *miles* (or more than 500,000,000 inches!) in diameter. Molecules are known to exist, and their existence is proved by complicated physical and chemical demonstrations, upon which all scientists are agreed. Certain large molecules have been seen through the electron microscope.

Yet a molecule is not the smallest particle of a substance. Each molecule is made up of one or more *atoms*. An atom is therefore a unit of a substance smaller than a molecule: "atom" comes from the Greek word meaning "indivisible." The molecule of an element is therefore composed of its own atoms, whereas compounds are composed of molecules containing atoms of two or more elements. As we shall see, atoms are made up of still smaller particles. But an atom may be considered "indivisible" in the sense that it is the smallest unit of any chemical substance which has the characteristics of the substance.

A molecule of water is composed of two atoms of hydrogen and one atom of oxygen—three atoms in all. You will recall that in the electrolysis of water a volume of hydrogen twice as great in volume as the volume of oxygen was derived from an equal weight of water. This proves that water contains twice as many atoms of hydrogen as of oxygen, for, according to a fundamental chemical hypothesis, equal volumes of all gases (at the same temperature and pressure) contain an equal number of molecules.

Chemical symbols are used to record and explain chemical action. Each element has a symbol, usually the initial letter or the first and another letter of its name (sometimes the English and sometimes the Latin name). The symbol of hydrogen is H, that of oxygen is O—the chemical *formula* of water is therefore H_2O, which means that a molecule of water contains two atoms of hydrogen to one of oxygen. The symbol of carbon is C. The composition of starch, an organic substance, may be represented by the formula $C_6H_{10}O_5$, which means that a molecule of starch contains six atoms of carbon and ten atoms of hydrogen to five atoms of oxygen.

THE CHEMICAL ELEMENTS

The factor in chemistry which makes elements combine in different ratios is called *valence*. The valence of an element is the power of its atoms, expressed by a number, to hold a certain number of atoms of other elements in combination. The valence of hydrogen is 1, and all elements which combine with hydrogen in the atomic proportion of one to one have the valence 1. Since oxygen combines with hydrogen in the proportion of one atom of oxygen to two of hydrogen, oxygen has a valence of 2. The following table lists all the known chemical elements, with the chemical symbol, atomic weight, valence, and atomic number of each, where known.

TABLE OF CHEMICAL ELEMENTS

Name	Symbol	Atomic Weight	Valence	Atomic Number
ACTINIUM	Ac	227	3	89
ALUMINIUM	Al	26.98	3	13
AMERICIUM	Am	243?	3, 4, 5 & 6	95
ANTIMONY	Sb	121.76	3 & 5	51
ARGON	A	39.944	0	18
ARSENIC	As	74.91	3 & 5	33
ASTATINE	At	211	?	85
BARIUM	Ba	137.36	2	56
BERKELIUM	Bk	245?	3 & 4	97
BERYLLIUM	Be	9.02	2	4
BISMUTH	Bi	209.0	3 & 5	83
BORON	B	10.82	3	5
BROMINE	Br	79.916	1 & 5	35
CADMIUM	Cd	112.41	2	48
CALCIUM	Ca	40.08	2	20
CALIFORNIUM	Cf	246?	3	98
CARBON	C	12.01	2 & 4	6
CERIUM	Ce	140.13	3 & 4	58
CESIUM	Cs	132.91	1	55
CHLORINE	Cl	35.457	1, 5 & 7	17
CHROMIUM	Cr	52.01	2, 3 & 6	24
COBALT	Co	58.94	2 & 3	27
COPPER	Cu	63.54	1 & 2	29
CURIUM	Cm	243?	3	96
DYSPROSIUM	Dy	162.5	3	66
EINSTEINIUM	E	253?	?	99
ERBIUM	Er	167.2	3	68
EUROPIUM	Eu	152.0	2 & 3	63
FERMIUM	Fm	255?	?	100
FLUORINE	F	19.0	1	9
FRANCIUM	Fr	223	1	87
GADOLINIUM	Gd	157.26	3	64
GALLIUM	Ga	69.72	3	31
GERMANIUM	Ge	72.6	4	32
GOLD	Au	197	1 & 3	79
HAFNIUM	Hf	178.50	4	72
HELIUM	He	4.003	0	2
HOLMIUM	Ho	164.94	3	67
HYDROGEN	H	1.0080	1	1

Name	Symbol	Atomic Weight	Valence	Atomic Number
INDIUM	In	114.82	3	49
IODINE	I	126.91	1, 5 & 7	53
IRIDIUM	Ir	193.1	3, 4 & 6	77
IRON	Fe	55.85	2 & 3	26
KRYPTON	Kr	83.80	0	36
LANTHANUM	La	138.92	3	57
LEAD	Pb	207.21	2 & 4	82
LITHIUM	Li	6.94	1	3
LUTETIUM	Lu	175.0	3	71
MAGNESIUM	Mg	24.32	2	12
MANGANESE	Mn	54.94	2, 3, 4, 6 & 7	25
MENDELEVIUM	Mv	256?	?	101
MERCURY	Hg	200.61	1 & 2	80
MOLYBDENUM	Mo	95.95	3, 5 & 6	42
NEODYMIUM	Nd	144.27	3	60
NEON	Ne	20.183	0	10
NEPTUNIUM	Np	237	3, 4, 5 & 6	93
NICKEL	Ni	58.71	2 & 3	28
NIOBIUM	Nb	92.91	3 & 5	41
NITROGEN	N	14.008	3 & 5	7
NOBELIUM	No	258	?	102
OSMIUM	Os	190.2	2, 3, 4 & 8	76
OXYGEN	O	16.0	2	8
PALLADIUM	Pd	106.4	2 & 4	46
PHOSPHORUS	P	30.975	3 & 5	15
PLATINUM	Pt	195.09	2 & 4	78
PLUTONIUM	Pu	242?	3, 4, 5 & 6	94
POLONIUM	Po	210.0	2, 4 & 6	84
POTASSIUM	K	39.100	1	19
PRASEODYMIUM	Pr	140.92	3	59
PROMETHIUM	Pm	145?	3	61
PROTACTINIUM	Pa	231	5	91
RADIUM	Ra	226.05	2	88
RADON	Rn	222.0	0	86
RHENIUM	Re	186.22	1, 4 & 7	75
RHODIUM	Rh	102.91	3 & 4	45
RUBIDIUM	Rb	85.48	1	37
RUTHENIUM	Ru	101.1	3, 4, 6 & 8	44
SAMARIUM	Sm	150.35	3	62
SCANDIUM	Sc	44.96	3	21
SELENIUM	Se	78.96	2, 4 & 6	34
SILICON	Si	28.06	4	14
SILVER	Ag	107.88	1	47

Name	Symbol	Atomic Weight	Valence	Atomic Number
SODIUM	Na	22.991	1	11
STRONTIUM	Sr	87.63	2	38
SULPHUR	S	32.06	2, 4 & 6	16
TANTALUM	Ta	180.95	5	73
TECHNETIUM	Tc	99	6 & 7	43
TELLURIUM	Te	127.61	2, 4 & 6	52
TERBIUM	Tb	159.2	3	65
THALLIUM	Tl	204.39	1 & 3	81
THORIUM	Th	232.05	4	90
THULIUM	Tm	168.94	3	69
TIN	Sn	118.7	2 & 4	50
TITANIUM	Ti	47.9	3 & 4	22
TUNGSTEN	W	183.86	6	74
URANIUM	U	238.07	3, 4 & 6	92
VANADIUM	V	50.95	2, 4 & 5	23
XENON	Xe	131.3	0	54
YTTERBIUM	Yb	173.04	2 & 3	70
YTTRIUM	Y	88.92	3	39
ZINC	Zn	65.38	2	30
ZIRCONIUM	Zr	91.22	4	40

Those elements with zero valence are *inert;* that is, they do not combine chemically with any other elements. The fact that helium is an inert gas is of importance in aeronautics (as we have already pointed out), for its lightness makes it desirable for use in dirigibles, and since it does not combine with any other element, it is not inflammable (as hydrogen is). The United States has the principal source of the world's supply of helium; the gas is commonly used in American dirigibles.

The ninety-two naturally occurring elements are roughly divided into *metals,* which form compounds known as bases, and *nonmetals,* which form compounds known as acids; some, however, form both basic and acid compounds. Only about twenty are nonmetals, but among these are such important elements as oxygen, hydrogen, nitrogen, sulphur, carbon, silicon, and chlorine. Mercury is the only metal which is not solid at ordinary temperatures; mercury occurs naturally as a liquid, commonly called quicksilver. Ten or so of the nonmetals are gases. Bromine is a liquid. The rest of the nonmetals are solids.

When the elements are arranged in the order of their ascending atomic weights, they group themselves in series conforming to the *periodic law.* (The order is more exactly indicated by the *atomic numbers* of the elements, which are derived independently of the atomic weights.) Each series consists of seven (sometimes nine) elements. The corresponding members in all the series form families of elements with similar valences and similar chemical properties.

Another factor in the description of an element is its density. The density of an element (or a compound) is generally given in *grams* per *cubic centimeter*. The gram and centimeter are units of measure in the so-called *metric system* of weights and measures, which is used in scientific work throughout the world. A cubic centimeter of water at 4° C. weighs one gram; therefore these density figures also indicate the ratio of the weight of each element to the weight of an equal volume of water; that is, zinc, with a density of 7.14, weighs 7.14 times as much as an equal volume of water at 4°. A gram is equal to 15.432 grains; there are 7000 grains in a pound avoirdupois. To convert density to pounds per cubic foot, it is only necessary to multiply the density of a given element in grams per cubic centimeter by 62½ (more exactly 62.4, the weight in pounds of a cubic foot of water).

THEORY OF ATOMIC STRUCTURE

Elements are substances which cannot be broken into anything simpler by ordinary chemical means. The physicist, however, using the cyclotron and atomic pile, is able to break down the atoms of elements; and when he does, all atoms seem to break down into the same basic particles—protons, electrons, and neutrons. The *proton* is a positive unit of electricity, while the *electron* has an equal but negative charge. The proton weighs about 1,847 times more than the electron. The *neutron* seems to be a proton and electron in such close association that their charges cancel each other, and thus the neutron shows no charge. A neutron weighs about the same as a proton, since the relative weight of the electron is negligible. The total number of protons in an atom is naturally the same as the total number of electrons, the atom therefore having a neutral charge.

Since the atoms of all elements apparently are made up of protons, neutrons, and electrons, the difference among the atoms of the various elements must consist of the relative number and structure of such particles. This first supposition is borne out by the fact that, since very ingenious and indirect methods have been devised to weigh atoms, scientists have found that the atoms of different elements have different weights.

The lightest and therefore the simplest of all atoms is the hydrogen atom. Experimentation has demonstrated that it is made of one proton and one electron. We picture the lighter particle, the electron (– charge), as circling around the proton (+ charge), the two particles being held in association by their electrical attraction—much as the moon is held in a circular orbit around the earth by gravitational attraction. In order to have a convenient unit for expressing the weights of atoms, physicists developed a scale based on the weight of the oxygen atom as 16 units. These units were called "atomic mass units" (a.m.u.). On this scale the weight of the hydrogen atom is approximately one atomic mass unit (1 a.m.u.), a proton and a neutron each weighing 1 a.m.u. The weight of an electron is, as we said earlier, negligible.

The atom just heavier than hydrogen is helium. It was presumed that helium contained 2 protons and therefore, to be electrically neutral, also 2 electrons. Measurements of its weight, however, indicate that it weighs 4 a.m.u. We reason that there must also be 2 neutrons in the atom. (A neutron is actually, as we said, an electron and a proton in very close association.) The helium atom, therefore, consists of 2 protons, 2 electrons, and 2 neutrons.

The protons and neutrons in any atom seem to clump together to form the *nucleus* of the atom, which contains almost the entire weight of the atom. The electrons (negligible weight) circle around the nucleus in orbits. Diagrams of the hydrogen and helium atoms are pictured in Figures 2 and 3.

The number of protons in an atom (or the number of electrons) is called the *atomic number* of the atom. The total number of protons and neutrons in the nucleus is called the *atomic weight*. If we arrange the

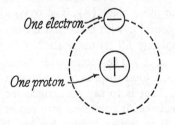

FIG. 2. Hydrogen atom, atomic weight 1.

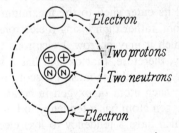

FIG. 3. Helium atom, atomic weight 4.

atoms in order of increasing atomic weight, we shall find that each element differs from the one preceding it in that it has one more proton in its nucleus (and therefore one more electron outside the nucleus). The number of neutrons also increases. For example, helium has 2 outer or planetary electrons and a nucleus consisting of 2 protons and 2 neutrons. Helium has an atomic number of 2 and an atomic weight of 4. The physicist usually writes it thus: $_2He^4$—putting the atomic number in the lower left and the atomic weight in the upper right.

Lithium ($_3Li^7$) has 3 electrons revolving about a nucleus consisting of 3 protons and 4 neutrons. Beryllium ($_4Be^9$) has 4 planetary electrons and a nucleus consisting of 4 protons and 5 neutrons. The atomic number tells us the number of protons (and, consequently, also the number of planetary electrons) while the atomic weight tells us the total number of particles in the nucleus (protons and neutrons). Thus uranium ($_{92}U^{238}$), the heaviest naturally occurring element, is composed of 92 planetary electrons and a nucleus of 92 protons and 146 neutrons ($92 + 146 = 238$).

In the picture of atomic structure which modern science proposes, the chemical properties of atoms (particularly valence) depend upon the number and arrangement of the electrons. The electrons circle about the nucleus of the atom in a number of orbits or rings. No more than two electrons can fit into the ring which is nearest the nucleus. The next two rings (farther from the nucleus) can each hold 8, then 18, and then 32— the maximum capacity of the rings increasing as they are farther from the nucleus, except that the *outermost shell,* which determines the valence, never can have more than 8. The oxygen atom ($_8O^{16}$), for example, has a nucleus consisting of 8 protons and 8 neutrons, which is surrounded by 8 electrons; the electrons are arranged in two shells, with 2 electrons in the ring nearest to the nucleus and 6 in the next. When an atom combines chemically with other atoms, it must either lose its outer shell completely or else borrow enough electrons from other atoms to fill its outer shell to the maximum for the outer shell (8). The oxygen atom, rather than losing 6 electrons, will combine with a substance from which it may borrow 2 electrons to completely fill its outer shell. (We say, therefore, that oxygen has a *valence* of 2.) The atoms with which oxygen combines must, consequently, have a total surplus of 2 electrons for each atom of oxygen in combination. That is to say that, since the oxygen atom has a tendency to borrow electrons, it combines with atoms which have a tendency to lose electrons. If hydrogen (which has but 1 electron in the outer shell) is to combine with oxygen, it would require 2 atoms of hydrogen to yield the 2 electrons necessary to fill the vacancies in the outer electron shell of the oxygen. This is why we write the formula for this compound of oxygen and hydrogen (which you will probably recognize as water) as H_2O, indicating that there are two atoms of hydrogen for each atom of oxygen.

It is interesting to note that those atoms whose outermost shells are entirely filled have an 0 valence and do not combine with any known element. They are stable in themselves. These include He, Ne, A, Kr, Xe, and Rn.

SOME IMPORTANT ELEMENTS AND THEIR COMPOUNDS

CHLORINE (Cl)

Chlorine is prepared in the laboratory by *oxidizing* hydrochloric acid. (You will recall that oxidation means adding oxygen to a substance.) If we oxidize hydrochloric acid, which is hydrogen chloride, we get water and chlorine; that is, the hydrogen of the hydrogen chloride is oxidized into water. To do this, we must add an oxidizing agent: manganese dioxide.

The equation for oxidizing HCl is as follows:

$$4HCl \quad + \quad MnO_2 \quad \rightarrow \quad 2H_2O \quad + \quad MnCl_2 \quad + \quad Cl_2$$

| hydrochloric acid | manganese dioxide | water | manganese chloride | chlorine (liberated as a gas) |

Each symbol in the equation represents an atom of an element. Thus H = 1 atom of hydrogen, Cl = 1 atom of chlorine. HCl = 1 molecule of hydrochloric acid. The coefficient 4 before the HCl means four molecules of hydrogen chloride (four atoms of hydrogen and four of chlorine). The small 2 below the O in MnO_2 means two atoms of O in the molecule of MnO_2. The 2 is used as a subscript rather than as coefficient because there is only one atom of Mn in MnO_2.

As you can see from the equation, the "4HCl," or four molecules of hydrochloric acid (hydrogen chloride), have been distributed among the three compounds on the right-hand side of the equation (the part to the right of the arrow). You will notice that here we have used up 2H in the water, Cl_2 in the manganese chloride, and Cl_2 in free chlorine. This is what happened to the 4HCl when it reacted with MnO_2.

MnO_2, the compound which reacted with the 4HCl, breaks up into 2O, which combines with the hydrogen to form the water, and Mn, which becomes part of the manganese chloride.

This *balancing of equations* will become more clear as you proceed. Here we were confronted with the problem of how to prepare chlorine. We knew that hydrochloric acid contains hydrogen and chlorine. We knew that if we could get the hydrogen out of hydrochloric acid, chlorine would be left. We knew that the best way to get hydrogen out of a compound was to oxidize it—that is, unite it with oxygen to form water. We did this with the aid of manganese dioxide—a compound which is rich in oxygen, having the formula MnO_2. As a result, we get a water solution of manganese chloride and free chlorine which is liberated and caught in a receptacle. The equation is *balanced* because there is exactly the same number of each kind of atom on each side of the equation—that is, before and after the chemical reaction—although they are arranged differently. If the equation did not balance, it would be false; it would describe an impossible reaction.

Chlorine is a greenish-yellow gas, heavier than air, with a heavy, noxious odor. It is used in small quantities as a disinfectant in swimming pools. However, in large quantities, the gas is highly poisonous.

Just as oxygen combines with carbon and hydrogen to form carbon dioxide and water, so chlorine combines with hydrogen to form hydrogen chloride. If hydrogen and chlorine are mixed and ignited we get hydrogen chloride (the gas of hydrochloric acid), thus:

$$H_2 \quad + \quad Cl_2 \quad \rightarrow \quad 2HCl$$

hydrogen   chlorine   hydrogen chloride

So great is the tendency of chlorine to combine with hydrogen that if a piece of paper is wet with turpentine (a compound of hydrogen and carbon) and put in a jar of chlorine, there is a violent action followed by a cloud of smoky soot. The chlorine combines instantly with the hydrogen in the turpentine, leaving soot (carbon) on the sides of the jar.

The molecules of hydrogen, nitrogen, oxygen, and chlorine contain two atoms each. Hence these molecules are written H_2, N_2, O_2, Cl_2. Before the atoms combine into molecules, the gas is nascent. A nascent gas is always very active, because its atoms must find the second atom to complete its molecules. Nascent oxygen is the most common nascent gas.

Nascent oxygen (O) is extremely active. It "runs around trying to find another atom of itself," so to speak. If it cannot find another atom of itself, it "takes hold of whatever it can." That is why hydrogen peroxide is a disinfectant. When you cut your finger and put hydrogen peroxide on the cut, the hydrogen peroxide breaks up into water and nascent oxygen, thus:

$$H_2O_2 \quad \rightarrow \quad H_2O \quad + \quad O$$

hydrogen peroxide   water   nascent oxygen

This nascent oxygen, for want of something else to combine with, takes hold of the poisonous matter in the wound. That is why we call it a disinfectant—no germs can remain near nascent oxygen. Nascent oxygen also combines with the color in hair or dye in cloth, and bleaches it. Hence peroxide is often used for bleaching.

When chlorine is dissolved in water, we get hydrochloric acid and nascent oxygen, thus:

$$Cl_2 \quad + \quad H_2O \quad \rightarrow \quad 2HCl \quad + \quad O$$

chlorine   water   hydrogen chloride   nascent
                                    (hydrochloric acid)   oxygen

This nascent oxygen is used commercially in bleaching. Raw cotton is bleached entirely by this very means. Laundries bleach or whiten washings with bleaching powder which contains chlorine. This powder, when put in the water, liberates nascent oxygen.

Hydrochloric acid is the water solution of hydrogen chloride. We have already learned that hydrogen chloride is produced by uniting hydrogen with chlorine, and consequently it would seem that this would be an easy way to prepare hydrochloric acid. Unfortunately, when hydrogen and chlorine combine, the action is very violent and difficult to control.

The most common way to prepare any acid is by the use of sulphuric acid. If you want to prepare hydrochloric acid, put sulphuric acid on a chloride. The most common chloride is table salt—sodium chloride. If sulphuric acid is put on sodium chloride, we immediately get sodium bisulphate and hydrochloric acid, thus:

$$NaCl + H_2SO_4 \rightarrow NaHSO_4 + HCl$$

sodium chloride   sulphuric acid   sodium bisulphate   hydrochloric acid

Before discussing the uses and properties of hydrochloric acid, let us summarize what we have learned about acids and apply it here. We learned that an acid and a metal when combined always give the metallic salt of that acid and hydrogen. We then learned that an acid and a metallic salt always give a new acid and a new salt.

Another acid and a nitrate give nitric acid plus a salt. Sulphuric acid and a chloride give hydrochloric acid plus a salt. Sulphuric acid and a carbonate give carbonic acid plus a salt.

Sulphuric acid, because of its high boiling point, is used to prepare other acids. Therefore the way to prepare hydrochloric acid would be to mix sulphuric acid with a chloride; the way to prepare nitric acid would be to mix sulphuric acid with a nitrate.

The most important use of hydrochloric acid is in the preparation of chlorides. There are only four common metals with which hydrochloric acid does not react to any great extent; these are mercury, silver, copper, and lead. Many other metals react to form chlorides and liberate hydrogen.

Hydrochloric acid and zinc give zinc chloride; hydrochloric acid and iron give iron chloride; hydrochloric acid and tin give tin chloride.

SODIUM (Na) AND POTASSIUM (K)

Sodium and potassium are usually grouped together because they are very similar. They both exhibit chemical properties such as those found in the more familiar metals. They are rarely seen in metallic form—you have never seen sodium or potassium kitchenware, because these metals are unsuitable for such use. You naturally think of a metal as something which is hard, shiny, or heavy. Actually, potassium and sodium are neither hard nor heavy. They are so soft that you can cut them with a knife, and so light that they float in water. Not only that, but both sodium and potassium react violently even to the point of minor explosion when put on water. When a small piece—the size of a pea—of either sodium or potassium is put in a pan of water, it goes hissing and sputtering over the surface, expending itself as it goes along, and eventually bursts into a flame. Both sodium and potassium conduct heat and electricity, and combine with acids in exactly the same way that other metals do. Because of their extreme activity, sodium and potassium must be stored in kerosene, with which they do not combine.

Sodium and potassium cannot be used as ordinary metals. However, the salts of sodium and potassium are so numerous and so useful that it is a question whether life could exist without them. A great many of them are used in medicine, the commercial names of the most common being soda and potash. All the salts of sodium and of potassium are soluble in water.

SULPHUR (S)

Sulphur is, of course, an essential element in sulphuric acid. This chemical has innumerable uses. It is necessary in the manufacture of fertilizers, explosives, kerosene, storage batteries, drugs, dyes, and many other commodities, and in the production of many other acids. These acids, in turn, or their salts, are necessary every minute of our lives.

Sulphur is found in nature either free or in combination with other elements. It is found in its natural state in great abundance in Louisiana and Texas, hundreds of feet below the surface of the earth. It is found also in volcanic regions. Few other elements have as many varieties of form as sulphur. There is, for example, rhombic sulphur—small crystals, yellowish in appearance and somewhat octagonal in shape. Then there is prismatic sulphur, which is more of a powder than rhombic and not quite so heavy. Then there is amorphous sulphur, which has the consistency of rubber and can be poured. There are a number of other varieties also. The commercial form of sulphur is roll sulphur, which consists almost entirely of the rhombic variety (small crystals).

Sulphur burns readily in oxygen, forming sulphur dioxide, thus:

$$S+O_2 \rightarrow SO_2$$

Sulphur also combines with metals to form what are known as sulphides. For example, copper plus sulphur gives copper sulphide; zinc plus sulphur gives zinc sulphide; hydrogen plus sulphur gives hydrogen sulphide. (This last-named compound is given off by rotten eggs; the bad odor is partly due to this gas.)

As we have seen, sulphur combines with oxygen to form sulphur dioxide (SO_2). This sulphur dioxide also combines with oxygen, forming sulphur trioxide (SO_3), thus:

$$S + O_2 \rightarrow SO_2$$
$$2SO_2 + O_2 \rightarrow 2SO_3$$

Sulphur trioxide (SO_3), when dissolved in water, instantly gives the heavy, oily liquid known as sulphuric acid, thus:

$$SO_3 + H_2O \rightarrow H_2SO_4$$
sulphuric acid

Sulphuric acid and a metal or a salt produce sulphates. Thus sulphuric acid and zinc produce zinc sulphate and hydrogen; sulphuric acid and iron produce iron sulphate and hydrogen; sulphuric acid and sodium produce sodium sulphate and hydrogen; etc. Sulphuric acid on copper has a slightly different reaction. Copper ordinarily does not react to cold sulphuric acid, but when the acid is heated, copper and sulphuric acid give copper sulphate, water, and sulphur dioxide.

Sulphuric acid and a base give water and a salt, as any acid and base do. For instance, sulphuric acid and potassium hydroxide produce water and potassium sulphate; sulphuric acid and sodium hydroxide produce water and sodium sulphate; sulphuric acid and calcium hydroxide produce water and calcium sulphate.

Sulphides result from the direct union of sulphur with a metal. The sulphides are salts of hydrosulphuric acid (H_2S), often called hydrogen sulphide. When we put sulphuric acid on metals, we get sulphates. The difference between a *sulphate* and a *sulphide* is that a sulphide never contains oxygen, whereas a sulphate always does. A *sulphite* contains oxygen in lesser quantity than a *sulphate*.

Thus we have three distinct groups: sulphides, identified by S; sulphites, identified by SO_3; and sulphates, identified by SO_4. Sulphites are usually produced by the action of sulphur*ous* acid, which has the formula H_2SO_3. It is extremely important to note these three groups carefully. Note, first, the sulph*ides*, and the lack of oxygen in that group. Note, secondly, the sulph*ites*, and the characteristic SO_3. And note, lastly, the sulph*ates*, with the ending SO_4. Whenever you see these endings in a formula you will recognize their identity instantly. Note a corresponding similarity in other groups of salts as shown in the table on pages 1178–79.

NITROGEN (N)

We have already seen that the air is about four-fifths nitrogen. This being so, you might naturally expect to find an abundance of nitrates in the earth, just as you find an abundance of oxides. Nitrates are indeed very plentiful, being essential to fertile soil, as every farmer knows.

Nitrogen is prepared in a number of ways. The simplest way is to get it from the air. This is done by passing air through a tube in which copper gauze is placed, and heating the tube. The air, in passing over the heated copper, loses its oxygen to the copper, forming copper oxide. The remaining gas is nitrogen. Of course it is not entirely pure nitrogen, because air contains traces of carbon dioxide and very slight amounts of some other gases. But for practical purposes air from which the oxygen has been removed may be regarded as pure nitrogen.

Nitrogen is slightly lighter than air. It is odorless, tasteless, and colorless, and does not support combustion. Nitrogen unites with oxygen, in various proportions, to form nitric oxide, nitrous oxide, and nitrogen peroxide, thus:

NO	N_2O	NO_2
nitric oxide	nitrous oxide	nitrogen peroxide

Nitrogen unites with hydrogen to form a very familiar gas known as ammonia, with the formula NH_3. The common household ammonia with which we are familiar is the water solution of this gas (NH_3+H_2O), known as ammonium hydroxide (NH_4OH).

There are five oxides of nitrogen, some of which have already been mentioned. The most common is nitrous oxide (N_2O), which has an anesthetic effect and is known as laughing gas.

Nitric acid (HNO_3) is prepared by mixing sulphuric acid with a nitrate. Either sodium nitrate (saltpeter) or potassium nitrate is ideal for the purpose.

The action of sulphuric acid on sodium nitrate is as follows:

$2NaNO_3$	$+$	H_2SO_4	$\rightarrow$	Na_2SO_4	$+$	$2HNO_3$
sodium nitrate		sulphuric acid		sodium sulphate		nitric acid

Nitric acid (HNO_3) is a very powerful acid. It is unique in one respect—namely, that whereas it reacts with a great many metals to form nitrates, hydrogen is *not* liberated.

Nitric acid is used extensively to make nitroglycerine, guncotton, and many drugs, dyes, etc.

All explosives contain nitrogen. Dynamite is pure nitroglycerine mixed with a certain kind of earth known as infusorial earth. Nitroglycerine, the main constituent of dynamite, is prepared by mixing nitric acid and glycerine. Nitroglycerine is a thick, heavy oil which burns slowly. When it is heated to a certain temperature it explodes with terrific violence. Nitroglycerine can also be exploded by sending an electric charge through it, or by percussion. By mixing this oil with infusorial earth to make dynamite, we have it in a form that is not so sensitive and can be handled with more ease and safety than in the pure form.

Gunpowder is a combination of potassium nitrate, sulphur, and charcoal. It burns with extreme rapidity. If a pile of gunpowder is spread out and lighted, it will flare up in a bright flame, and in a fraction of a second the whole pile will be burnt up. This is due to the fact that there is a quantity of oxygen present in the nitrate which is unstable—ready to leave the nitrogen. Compressed gunpowder burns as fast as when in open space and produces nearly 2,000 times its own volume of gases. Hence it explodes violently.

Air

Air is neither an element nor a chemical compound. Air is a mixture of gases; though they are thoroughly mixed, these gases are not in chemical combination. This explains why, when you send air through a tube containing hot copper gauze, the oxygen of the air remains behind to combine with the copper and lets the nitrogen pass through. The composition of air is as follows:

78.02%	nitrogen
21.00%	oxygen
.93%	argon
.04%	carbon dioxide
.01%	traces of other gases

Varying amounts of water vapor are also present in air.

Plants utilize carbon dioxide, which human beings eliminate in breathing. Carbon dioxide is always present in the air, though in very small quantities. Nevertheless, it is sufficient for the plant life, which takes it in and changes it to carbon and oxygen, using the carbon for food and giving off the oxygen into the air.

Ammonia (NH₃)

Ammonia is prepared by uniting nitrogen with hydrogen and is also obtained as a by-product of the destructive distillation of soft coal. Ammonia gas is easily produced, and its odor is well known to anyone who has used the household form of it.

Ammonia is readily soluble in water—it is one of the most soluble gases. Ammonia in solution forms a typical base, called ammonium hydroxide. It will react with acids to form water and an ammonium salt. If the acid is sulphuric, the result is water and ammonium sulphate; if the acid is hydrochloric, the result is water and ammonium chloride; and so on.

The chief use of ammonia is in the manufacture of ice. The principle is very simple. It is based on the fact that when a gas is liquefied, heat is set free; and when a liquid is made into a gas, heat is absorbed. You can see how true this is, because it is necessary for water to absorb an enormous amount of heat in order to become steam. Ammonia gas is pumped through a series of pipes. This gas is then condensed; that is, it is cooled and liquefied. The liquid ammonia is run through another series of pipes which are submerged in a solution of salt water. In this solution of salt water there are also a number of cans of pure water. The liquid ammonia circulating in the pipes has a marked tendency to go back to the gaseous state in which it was originally produced. It does this readily, but in order for it to do so, something must supply the heat, because to transform liquid into a gas, heat is needed. The salt-water solution in which the liquid-ammonia pipes are submerged has to supply the heat to turn this liquid back into ammonia gas. This it does with a decided and inevitable drop in temperature. In a short time the temperature of the salt solution drops to a point far below freezing. The cans of pure water submerged in this terrifically cold salt solution are naturally chilled below the freezing point, as is the pure water in them. In a short time the water in these cans is brought down to the freezing point and ice is formed.

PHOSPHORUS (P)

Phosphorus is found in the bones and teeth of animals in the form of calcium phosphate. To secure phosphorus, calcium phosphate is ground up into a fine powder and put in an electric furnace together with sand and coal. Phosphorus exists in two forms, white phosphorus and red phosphorus. White phosphorus is a waxy, translucent solid which must always be kept under water because the instant it is exposed to air it bursts into flame. The reason for this is that it has an extremely low kindling temperature and when it is exposed to air it begins to oxidize immediately. The heat which is generated in the process of oxidation raises the phosphorus to its kindling temperature almost immediately, and a brilliant flame results. The reaction is

$$4P + 5O_2 \rightarrow 2P_2O_5$$

White phosphorus is extremely poisonous: the slightest quantity taken internally causes instant death. Red phosphorus is the result of heating white phosphorus to about 250° C. in a vessel from which air has been extracted. Red phosphorus is a soft reddish powder, much less poisonous than white phosphorus, and does not burn until heated by friction or other means.

A common match consists of a stick of wood which has been dipped in melted wax. The head of the match is composed of phosphorus sesquisulphide, a high oxidizing agent such as potassium chlorate, and glue. (Sometimes other chemicals are used; the composition of patented matches is likely to be a trade secret.) The glue in the head of the match holds the potassium chlorate and the phosphorus together. When you strike the match, the heat generated by friction ignites the tip. The result is immediately a bright flame. This is helped along by the oxygen in the potassium chlorate. If the potassium chlorate were not present, the match would light and go out almost immediately. After the burst of flame which results upon first striking the match, you will notice a more gradual burning. This is the potassium chlorate, which helps to raise the stick to its kindling temperature, and in less than a second the stick has caught fire and burns slowly, owing to the wax in which it was dipped. When the match is burned out, it does not glow after the flame is gone. This is due to a certain chemical with which the wood has been treated in order to lessen the danger of fires from carelessly discarded matches that have merely been blown out.

THE HALOGENS

The halogens consist of four elements, as follows: fluorine, chlorine, bromine, and iodine. These four elements belong to the same group according to the periodic law. They react to acids in a similar way and are very much alike chemically in other respects.

The word *halogen* means salt-former. These four elements are so called because they all unite directly with a large number of metallic elements to form salts. The salts thus formed containing bromine are called bromides; those containing chlorine, chlorides (as we have already seen); those containing fluorine and iodine, fluorides and iodides, respectively.

Bromides occur in nature along with chlorides. Large deposits of crude salt (sodium chloride) also contain sodium and magnesium bromide. Bromine is easily prepared from magnesium bromide by replacing it with chlorine. Magnesium bromide and chlorine give magnesium chloride and bromine.

Bromine is a dark, brownish-red liquid, much denser than water. An interesting characteristic of bromine is that it is the only nonmetallic element which exists in a liquid form. It has an odor resembling chlorine, and vaporizes very quickly. It is poisonous, but not so destructive as chlorine. The chemical properties of bromine are similar to those of chlorine.

Just as we had hydrochloric acid from chlorine, so we have hydrobromic acid (HBr) from bromine, which is prepared by mixing sulphuric acid and potassium bromide, giving potassium sulphate and hydrobromic acid.

Iodine is obtained from seaweed: when seaweed (kelp) is burned, the remaining ashes contain potassium and sodium iodides. By heating a mixture of sulphuric acid, manganese dioxide, and potassium iodide, we obtain potassium sulphate, manganese sulphate, water, and iodine.

Iodine is a blackish-gray solid, slightly soluble in water and extremely soluble in alcohol. The alcohol solution, known as tincture of iodine, is what you paint your cuts and bruises with to prevent infection. Even a very small amount of pure iodine will turn common starch blue.

Iodine unites directly with a great many elements to form iodides, but these iodides are not particularly important.

Fluorine is the only member of the halogen group which does not closely resemble its brothers. It is obtained in a rather complicated way from potassium fluoride. It is a pale, greenish-yellow gas with an extremely poisonous odor, much more poisonous than chlorine. Fluorine has a greater tendency to form salts than any of the other halogens.

Hydrofluoric acid, which corresponds with hydrochloric, hydrobromic, and hydriodic acids (in chlorine, bromine, and iodine, respectively), is prepared by mixing sulphuric acid and calcium fluoride. The preparation is made in a lead dish, and hydrofluoric acid is kept in wax bottles, because it attacks glass and dissolves it. Nearly all etching that is done on glass is done with hydrofluoric acid. This acid is extremely dangerous, for it combines with almost anything with which it comes in contact.

TABLE OF COMMON SALTS

All chlorates and nitrates are soluble in water. All K (potassium), Na (sodium), and NH_4 (ammonium) salts are soluble in water. All carbonates, oxides, and hydroxides are insoluble in water except those of K, Na, and NH_4.

For symbols used in the following list, see the Table of Chemical Elements, page 1162.

BROMINE forms *bromides* (example: KBr, potassium bromide), all soluble in water except AgBr and HgBr salts.

CARBON forms *carbides* (example: CaC_2, calcium carbide); and *carbonates* (example: $CaCO_3$, calcium carbonate), latter insoluble in water except K, Na, and NH_4 salts.

CHLORINE forms *chlorides* (example: NaCl, sodium chloride), all soluble in water except AgCl and HgCl; and *chlorates* (example: $KClO_3$), all soluble in water.

IODINE forms *iodides* (example: HI, hydrogen iodide), all soluble in water except Pb, Hg, and Ag salts.

NITROGEN forms *nitrites* (example: KNO_2, potassium nitrite); and *nitrates* (example: $AgNO_3$, silver nitrate), latter all soluble in water.

OXYGEN forms *oxides* (example: CuO, copper oxide), all insoluble in water except K, Na, and Ba oxides.

SULPHUR forms *sulphides* (example: H_2S, hydrogen sulphide); *sulphites* (example: Na_2SO_3, sodium sulphite); and *sulphates* (example: Na_2SO_4, sodium sulphate), all the latter soluble in water except Ba and Pb salts.

HYDROXIDES (example: KOH, potassium hydroxide) are all insoluble in water except K, Na, Ba, and NH_4 hydroxides.

SOME COMMON ELEMENTS AND THEIR BEST-KNOWN SALTS

ALUMINIUM (Al), metal—*properties:* gray color, extremely light, reacts with HCl and H_2SO_4; used for kitchenware; forms aluminium oxide (Al_2O_3) and aluminium hydroxide (Al[OH]$_3$); salts used in welding and dyeing.

BROMINE (Br), liquid—*properties:* dark brown color, combines with metals; forms silver bromide (AgBr) and potassium bromide (KBr); salts used in photography and medicine.

CALCIUM (Ca), metal—*properties:* silver-white color, very light; forms calcium oxide (CaO), calcium hydroxide (Ca[OH]$_2$), and calcium carbonate ($CaCO_3$); salts used in making lime, mortar, and cement.

CHLORINE (Cl), gas—*properties:* greenish color, poisonous odor; used in bleaching and sterilizing, especially drinking water and swimming pools; forms sodium chloride or common salt (NaCl), chlorides of most of the metals, potassium chlorate ($KClO_3$); salts used in medicine, gunpowder, matches.

COPPER (Cu), metal—*properties:* yellow metal with reddish tinge, very good conductor of heat and electricity; used in wiring and photo-engraving; forms copper sulphate ($CuSO_4$), used in electroplating and in electric batteries.

FLUORINE (F), gas—*properties:* very poisonous; forms hydrofluoric acid (HF), used in etching on glass.

GOLD (Au), metal—*properties:* yellow color, heavy, slow in combining with other elements, good conductor of heat; used in coins and jewelry.

HYDROGEN (H), gas—*properties:* lightest gas known, highly inflammable; used in inflating balloons and dirigibles; compounds are mostly acids; used in preparations of other chemicals.

IODINE (I), solid—*properties:* gray color, crystalline in form, soluble in alcohol and in water; used in solution as an antiseptic; forms potassium iodide (KI); salts used in medicine, dyeing, and photography.

LEAD (Pb), metal—*properties:* gray color, dull luster, heavy and very soft; used for pipes and printers' type (in alloys); forms lead carbonate ($PbCO_3$); salts used in making paints.

MAGNESIUM (Mg), metal—*properties:* silvery white color, burns readily; used in flashlight photography; forms magnesium sulphate ($MgSO_4$) and magnesium carbonate ($MgCO_3$); salts used in medicine and in making talc and face powders.

MERCURY (Hg), liquid metal—*properties:* silvery color, bright luster, expands and contracts readily with variations of temperature; used in thermometers and barometers; forms mercury chloride (HgCl) and mercury bichloride ($HgCl_2$); salts used in medicine and as a disinfectant.

NICKEL (Ni), metal—*properties:* silvery white color, will not rust; used in plating iron.

NITROGEN (N), gas—*properties:* invisible, tasteless, odorless, forms about $4/5$ of the earth's atmosphere; forms nitrous (N_2O) and nitric (NO) oxides; the chief constituent of laughing gas; salts used in making fertilizers and explosives.

OXYGEN (O), gas—*properties:* invisible, odorless, tasteless, forms about $1/5$ of the earth's atmosphere; used in pure state in blowpipes and pulmotors (for resuscitation); has hundreds of useful compounds.

PHOSPHORUS (P), solid—*properties:* white and red (two kinds), burns (oxidizes) readily in air; used in making matches, and as fertilizer in the form of phosphates (phosphorus combined with oxygen and metal).

PLATINUM (Pt), metal—*properties:* silvery white color, very heavy, slow in combining with other elements; used in jewelry and electrical instruments.

SILICON (Si), nonmetal—forms silicon dioxide (sand, SiO_2), used in making glass.

SILVER (Ag), metal—*properties:* shiny, silvery color, best conductor of heat known; used for making jewelry, coins, mirrors; forms silver nitrate ($AgNO_3$) and silver bromide (AgBr); salts used in medicine and photography.

ZINC (Zn), metal—*properties:* bluish-white color; used for galvanizing iron and in photoengraving; forms zinc oxide (ZnO); salts used in white pigment and in medicine.

METALS AND THEIR COMPOUNDS

Two important *metals,* sodium and potassium, have been discussed under the preceding main heading "Some Important Elements and Their Compounds." This was particularly desirable not only because they are important, but the knowledge of sodium and potassium makes it easier to present the compounds of the other elements discussed. However, it should be noted that except for sodium and potassium, all the other elements which are topics under "Some Important Elements and Their Compounds" are *nonmetals.* We turn now to the other important metals.

CALCIUM (Ca)

Metallic calcium is an active metal which releases hydrogen from acids and forms salts.

Thus:

$$Ca + 2HCl \rightarrow CaCl_2 + H_2$$

Metallic calcium finds but few uses. Its compounds, however, are quite useful.

Calcium carbonate ($CaCO_3$), the most common salt of calcium, occurs in nature almost as frequently as sodium chloride—ordinary salt. We are all familiar with it as limestone or marble—sometimes a whole mountain range is made up of limestone and marble. Pure calcium carbonate is a white solid which is frequently transparent. The color of marble, with its various streaks of blacks and grays, is due entirely to the impurities in the calcium carbonate.

Quicklime is calcium oxide, which is obtained by heating calcium carbonate to a red heat, thus:

$$CaCO_3 \rightarrow CaO + CO_2$$

Calcium oxide is a white powdery substance which, when heated to very high temperatures, gives a dazzling light called limelight.

When calcium oxide is mixed with water, we get another compound, known as slaked lime, the chemical name of which is calcium hydroxide. This substance is perhaps one of the most useful that Nature has given us. Slaked lime mixed with sand gives us mortar, which is necessary in the construction of brick buildings.

The reaction of mortar is very interesting. It is a pasty white mass consisting of calcium hydroxide, sand, and water. When it is allowed to stand in the air for any length of time, it draws carbon dioxide from the air (you will remember that air is a mixture and not a compound) to form calcium carbonate and water.

$$Ca(OH)_2 \quad + \quad CO_2 \quad \rightarrow \quad CaCO_3 \quad + \quad H_2O$$

mortar	carbon dioxide	limestone	water

Calcium carbonate, or limestone, is always a hard, brittle substance. That is the reason mortar hardens when exposed to the air.

There are three other important compounds of calcium: namely, calcium sulphate, which is commonly known as plaster of Paris; chlorinated lime, a disinfectant, known as bleaching powder; and calcium phosphate, an important fertilizer.

MAGNESIUM (Mg)

Magnesium is a very light, silvery white metal. It burns with a brilliant white light to which photographic plates are extremely sensitive. Magnesium is sometimes used in flashlight photography. The most common salts of magnesium are magnesium carbonate, magnesium citrate, and magnesium sulphate. The magnesium carbonate and hydroxide are used in face powders. Talcum powder contains a considerable amount of talc, which is magnesium silicate. Magnesium citrate, or citrate of magnesia, and sulphate of magnesia (Epsom salts) are used as laxatives.

ZINC (Zn)

Zinc is found combined with other elements in ores. Zinc oxide, or zincite (ZnO), is used in the preparation of pure zinc. The process involves reduction. The zinc oxide is heated with coal dust (carbon), and the carbon reduces the zinc oxide to zinc and carbon monoxide (carbon monoxide is a deadly gas with the formula CO).

Zinc is a bluish-white metal which is used extensively in making alloys such as brass, German silver, and bronze, in galvanizing iron to prevent rust, and in photoengraving. The last-named use gives us nearly all line-drawing reproductions in books, newspapers, and magazines.

Zinc readily unites with acids, forming zinc salts and hydrogen. Zinc oxide (ZnO) is an extremely white powder which is used as the basis of white pigment for paints. It is used also in the preparation of rubber. Zinc chloride ($ZnCl_2$) is used for preserving wood; wood soaked in a solution of zinc chloride resists decay.

MERCURY (Hg)

Mercury is found in an ore known as cinnabar or mercuric sulphide. It is obtained very simply by heating mercuric sulphide with oxygen, giving us mercury and sulphur dioxide:

$$\underset{\text{mercuric sulphide}}{HgS} \quad + \quad \underset{\text{oxygen}}{O_2} \quad \rightarrow \quad \underset{\text{mercury}}{Hg} \quad + \quad \underset{\text{sulphur dioxide}}{SO_2}$$

At ordinary temperature, mercury is a liquid—the only liquid metal—with a brilliant luster. It is commonly known as quicksilver, and seems heavy for its bulk because it has a comparatively high specific gravity or density.

An interesting property of mercury is that it forms what are known as amalgams with gold and silver. If you dip a five-dollar gold piece into a vessel containing mercury, it is instantly turned to the color of mercury; the mercury has amalgamated with the gold—that is, the mercury dissolves the gold and forms an alloy on the surface of the coin. Silver amalgam is used by dentists in filling teeth.

Mercury combines readily with halogens and sulphur. It is not acted on by acids in general. Of course the most common use of mercury is in barometers and thermometers. The chloride $(HgCl)$ and the bichloride $(HgCl_2)$ are useful compounds; mercurous chloride $(HgCl)$ is a white powder known in medicine as calomel. Mercuric chloride (bichloride of mercury), or corrosive sublimate $(HgCl_2)$, is a splendid disinfectant and a violent poison.

IRON (Fe)

Iron occurs in great abundance as an ore in the form of iron oxide (Fe_2O_3). The Latin name for iron is *ferrum;* the symbol is Fe; and compounds of iron are called ferric or ferrous.

Iron has a number of forms commercially, including cast iron, wrought iron, and pig iron.

Cast iron is produced in a blast furnace by reducing ferric oxide with carbon, thus:

$$\underset{\text{ferric oxide}}{Fe_2O_3} \quad + \quad \underset{\text{carbon}}{3C} \quad \rightarrow \quad \underset{\text{iron}}{2Fe} \quad + \quad \underset{\text{carbon monoxide}}{3CO}$$

The terrific heat necessary for this melts the iron, which is drawn out minus the slag at the bottom of the furnace. This molten iron, if cooled suddenly, becomes brittle and is called cast iron. It is used in stoves, plates upon which building columns rest, and in other places where it is not subject to tension. Because of its brittleness, it is of little use for beams and the like. It is excellent under compression. A great many molds, forms, and pipes are cast iron. Because of the fact that carbon is used in the manufacture of cast iron, there is a little excess carbon in cast iron. This carbon helps to make the iron even more brittle. There are also other impurities in cast iron, such as sulphur, phosphorus, and silicon, which were present in the original iron ore and not separated in the refining process.

A much purer form of iron is called wrought iron. It contains usually less than .15% of carbon, 1% to 2% of slag, and is practically free from sulphur and phosphorus.

Steel is made by removing most of the carbon, silicon, and impurities from cast iron. In the process of manufacturing steel, samples are constantly tested to determine how much of the various impurities have been removed and how much carbon it contains. The percentage of carbon in steel varies from .2% in soft steel to 2% in hard steel. Steel can be tempered according to the amount of carbon it contains. Tempered steel is used in tools.

There are many compounds of iron, the most common, of course, being ferric oxide (Fe_2O_3). Ferric oxide is a bright red powder used in pigments like Venetian red, Indian red, and sometimes scarlet.

Iron forms two classes of salts, the ferric and the ferrous, the difference being in the number of atoms required for the combination. Thus while ferric chloride's formula is $FeCl_3$, ferrous chloride's formula is $FeCl_2$.

There is another group of iron salts called the ferric and ferrous cyanides. The salts containing the cyanide group (CN) consist of carbon and nitrogen, and are violently poisonous. (Potassium cyanide is one of the most deadly poisons in existence. All the cyanide salts are poisonous.)

Iron and potassium together unite with the cyanide group to form potassium ferricyanide, with the formula $K_3Fe(CN)_6$. This potassium ferricyanide acts on ferrous chloride to produce ferrous ferricyanide, an intensely blue compound, thus:

$$3FeCl_2 + 2K_3Fe(CN)_6 \rightarrow 6KCl + Fe_3[Fe(CN)_6]_2$$

This is made use of in blueprints. The paper is coated with ferric ammonium citrate and potassium ferricyanide. When exposed to light, the paper serves as a reducing agent and the ferric salt is reduced to a ferrous salt. If this exposed paper is covered with water, the parts of the paper which have been reduced to the ferrous salt will turn an intense blue. The potassium ferricyanide acts as a developer.

COPPER (Cu)

Copper is another extremely useful metal. It occurs free in nature. Because of its high conductivity of heat and electricity, it is used extensively in wire and cables. It is also used in boilers, kettles, vacuum pans, etc. Copper is used extensively in scientific instruments. One of the most important uses of copper is in photoengraving; if it were not for zinc and copper, the advertisements you see in magazines with their elaborate pictures, and the pictures in newspapers, books, display cards, etc., would not be possible.

The most important compound of copper is copper sulphate ($CuSO_4$), a blue substance (blue vitriol) which is used in electric batteries and in electroplating, and in Bordeaux mixture—a common fungicide made of copper sulphate, lime, and water.

SILVER (Ag)

Silver, gold, and platinum are the precious metals—precious because they are rare and useful. Silver, with its salts, is by far the most useful. However, the rarity of gold and platinum makes them much more valuable. The Latin name for silver is *argentum,* and its symbol is Ag. Silver is grayish white, and is the best conductor of heat and electricity known. It is capable of receiving and retaining a very high polish, and consequently is the best reflector of light known. The better-grade mirrors are glass with silvered backs.

Silver does not combine readily with air, but in the presence of sulphur it blackens. This explains why silver spoons become discolored when used continually for eating eggs, for the eggs contain a compound of sulphur.

Pure solid silver is not hard, and consequently cannot be used commercially. It is only when silver is alloyed with copper that it is hard enough to stand the wear and tear of constant use. The half dollar contains 90% silver and about 10% copper. The British coins are a little higher in silver content (92½% silver); this is the best possible combination and is known as sterling silver.

Silver is used in making mirrors and in silver-plating. A mirror is made by pouring silver nitrate on polished plate glass. Over this solution are poured some ammonia and a reducing agent, and the whole is warmed. Ammonia, together with the reducing agent, reacts with the nitrate in the silver nitrate, leaving a deposit of pure silver on the glass in a very thin film. This is then washed, dried, and varnished to protect it.

Silver-plating is done in an electric bath. This bath consists of a solution of potassium cyanide and silver cyanide, two intensely poisonous chemicals. A bar of sheet silver is used at the positive end of the bath, and the article to be plated is placed at the negative end. When the current is turned on, it flows through the solution from the silver to the object to be plated, carrying with it atoms of silver and depositing them on the object to be plated.

The most important salt of silver is the bromide. Silver bromide is extremely sensitive to light, a fact which is made use of in photography. A photographic plate is of plain glass coated with gelatine and silver bromide. When the plate is put in a camera and an image is thrown upon it (through a lens), the light spots affect the silver bromide, and the dark spots leave it unaffected. The change in the plate cannot be noticed until a developer is used, and then we can detect what has happened. A developer is really a weak reducing agent which affects the silver bromide only where the light has struck it. In the parts where the light has struck silver bromide, chemical action has already started, and when the developer touches these spots the silver bromide is immediately reduced and an extremely thin deposit of silver remains on the plate. Silver is an excellent reflector of light; this is because it is most opaque. These silver deposits are black, and wherever the light has struck the silver bromide plate there will be black deposits of silver, the blackness varying according to the intensity of the light. When the plate is developed and these black deposits are brought out, the unaffected bromide (in parts which were not struck by light) is washed away in a solution of sodium hyposulphite known as "hypo."

When the plate comes out of the hypo, it is a negative—that is, it is just the reverse of the original picture: all the whites are black, and all the blacks are white. By reversing this principle—that is, putting the negative over a highly sensitized paper—the true picture is obtained, because no light can come through the black parts of the negative and light does enter the light parts of the negative (often just clear glass). The paper used is treated in much the same way as the original plate.

The making of line cuts and halftones for reproduction in books, newspapers, and magazines is more complicated. The principle is this: A pen-and-ink drawing is photographed on a regular photographic plate. This negative is printed on another photographic plate to make a positive. The positive is stripped onto a sheet of zinc, and where the dark parts are there will be a deposit of gelatine and silver bromide, and where the light spots are there will be nothing. When the zinc is treated with acid, the plate is eaten into or etched. All exposed parts of the plate—the parts which the light struck in the original picture—will be eaten away, because they are not covered with the protective coating of gelatine; but all the unexposed parts will be unaffected, because they are covered with the protective gelatine. The result is that all the blacks will be raised and all the whites eaten away, and when ink is run over this plate, the raised surface, or the lines in the line drawing, will reproduce black just as they did in the original drawing.

GOLD (Au)

Gold occurs free as fine particles in stone or sand. In the amalgamation process, often used in refining gold, the solid ore is crushed, pounded into a fine powder, and placed in iron troughs. Water is allowed to circulate through it. In doing this, it carries the muddy substance over a bed of mercury. As we have mentioned, mercury immediately amalgamates with any gold present and leaves the rest of the ore alone, to be drawn out by the running water. This amalgam is distilled, and the mercury goes off in vapor, leaving pure gold.

Impure gold is frequently refined by electrolysis, in which a current of electricity is passed through a hot gold-chloride solution in a porcelain cell. Pure gold is thus deposited from the solution onto the cathode plates (bars of pure gold) suspended alternately between the anode plates (impure gold bars) above the cell.

Gold is a soft, heavy metal which is extremely valuable. (Only osmium and platinum exceed it in density.) It can be hammered out to about 1/200,000 inch in thickness. This thin foil is known as gold leaf and is used for gold letters on signs, windows, etc. The chief use of gold is in jewelry and coins.

Pure gold is too soft for commercial use, except as gold leaf. To harden it, various alloys are employed. The fineness of gold, which is to say the proportionate amount of pure gold a coin or other object contains, is expressed in "carats." A carat is a twenty-fourth part—in 14-carat gold there are 14 parts of pure gold and 10 parts of other metals. Gold does not react with any dilute acid. A mixture of concentrated hydrochloric and nitric acids known as aqua regia does act upon gold to produce gold chloride.

PLATINUM (Pt)

Platinum is one of the most valuable metals known. It is extremely scarce and is used chiefly in electrical instruments and jewelry. Because of its tremendously high boiling point and its resistance to acids, it is used in the preparation of sulphuric acid. Huge platinum pans costing about $25,000 each are used in the process of manufacture to hold the hot, boiling sulphuric acid. Platinum is the most indestructible metal known, and one of the heaviest.

ALUMINIUM (Al)

Aluminium—commonly called aluminum—is used because of its extreme lightness, extensively for kitchenware, and in the construction of airplanes and in various other places where a strong but extremely light metal is needed.

Aluminum is also used in a process for repairing heavy iron machinery, for welding rails, beams, crankshafts, etc. In the Second World War, the process called thermit reaction was used extensively in the repair of breaks in large steel casings. Aluminium powder is mixed with Fe_3O_4 and ignited with magnesium ribbon. The reaction is as follows:

$$8Al + 3Fe_3O_4 \rightarrow 4Al_2O_3 + 9Fe \; (+heat)$$

The molten iron becomes white hot and flows between cracks, thus joining broken ends together.

The compounds of aluminum are very useful, particularly aluminum hydroxide. This is used in the purification of water and in dyeing. Aluminum silicates form the basis of all porcelain, pottery, and chinaware.

LEAD (Pb)

Because of its softness and its ability to be molded, lead is used in lead pipes, lead molds, and in the making of type. Type metal contains mostly lead, with a little tin and antimony in it to harden it. Lead is used also in solder, which is especially valuable in plumbing. Of course a great quantity of lead is used in shot. Its most important uses, however, are in the manufacture of pipes and of type metal.

Contrary to what one may think, lead is not used in "lead" pencils. The material here is carbon or graphite (popularly called "black lead," or plumbago), an entirely different element.

Lead carbonate is the most useful salt of lead, being the basis of most paints.

TIN (Sn)

Tin is a lustrous white metal which will not rust. Pure tin is a comparatively expensive metal. The most important use of tin is to cover other metals. Tinware is sheet iron which is thoroughly cleaned and dipped in molten tin. What many call a tin can is not a tin can at all. It is a can of sheet iron dipped in molten tin to prevent rust. The coating of the tin can is very thin, and after a while the can rusts because the coating of tin wears off.

Tin foil is used in wrapping candy and confections. This is pure tin, hammered and rolled into thin sheets. Soda-water fountains use tin pipes, since the carbonic acid would react with lead pipes. Tin is also used to make bronze, solder, and other alloys.

NICKEL (Ni)

Nickel is a hard metal resembling silver in color. Air does not attack it, and consequently it is used for plating metals that air does attack. Being a rather expensive metal, it is not used so much as tin. Nickel-plating is more expensive than tin-plating, but it is more permanent.

ORGANIC CHEMISTRY

CARBON (C) AND ITS COMPOUNDS

Of all the elements, carbon is the most basic in living matter. The human body must have carbon. Everything that lives needs carbon to maintain life. Carbon combines with hydrogen and oxygen in thousands of different ways, forming hydrocarbons. Plants contain hydrocarbons. Coal deposits consist mainly of carbon from the bodies of plants which existed millions of years ago.

Carbon is the basic element in that branch of chemistry known as *organic chemistry,* the chemistry of carbon compounds. Through organic chemistry we have been able to produce synthetically or artificially many things which were previously found only in nature. The first instance of this occurred in 1828, when a German chemist, Friedrich Woehler, synthesized urea, a compound formed in the bodies of animals. Since then many important compounds have been synthesized. In addition, our knowledge of organic chemistry has enabled us to make entirely new materials which never existed before. Among these are synthetic textiles such as rayon and nylon, and the plastics which we see in such forms as fountain pens, telephones, airplane noses, and many others. The most common forms of carbon are coal and graphite, two very plentiful and cheap substances. We have also a form of carbon which goes to the other extreme, and which, instead of being soft, black, and cheap, like graphite, is the hardest substance known, sparkling, brilliant, and very expensive. This crystallized form of carbon, produced by great heat and pressure, is diamond, the hardest substance in existence and one of the most precious.

Almost a million compounds of carbon are known. This is more than the total number of compounds made by all the other 91 elements. The number of carbon compounds seems to be almost unlimited. This is due to the ability of carbon atoms to join other carbon atoms in numerous combinations, forming chains of various lengths. The only other element which can form chains in the way that carbon does, but to a lesser degree, is silicon, present in many minerals.

The same laws of chemistry apply to organic and inorganic chemistry. However, the behavior of organic compounds shows some general differences. Most organic compounds do not dissolve in water but will usually dissolve in organic liquids such as alcohol, ether, carbon tetrachloride, etc. Organic compounds decompose more readily in heat than do inorganic compounds. If sugar is heated, for instance, it breaks down into water and a black charred mass of carbon.

Hydrocarbons are, as the name implies, compounds of hydrogen and carbon. The simplest hydrocarbon is methane (CH_4). Since carbon atoms link readily to other carbon atoms, each of which in turn may be linked to hydrogen atoms, the formulae of the heavier hydrocarbons contain over 100 atoms.

If the four hydrogen atoms in methane (CH_4) are replaced with chlorine atoms, we have carbon tetrachloride (CCl_4). If only three are substituted, we have chloroform ($CHCl_3$). It is possible to form numerous substitution products from hydrocarbons and thus produce a wide variety of substances.

Alcohols are produced by substituting one or more hydroxide (OH) groups for the hydrogen atoms. If one of the hydrogen atoms in methane (CH_4) is replaced by an OH group, we have methyl alcohol (CH_3OH) (wood alcohol, a poison). Similar substitutions in other hydrocarbons produce a wide variety of alcohols, including ethyl alcohol (C_2H_5OH) (which is the alcohol of alcoholic beverages), propyl alcohol, and glycerin.

Just as the alcohols are a counterpart of the *inorganic bases* in that they contain the OH group, so we have the counterpart of *inorganic acids* in *organic acids,* which are characterized by the presence of carboxyl (COOH). Formic acid, the material found in the sting of bees and ants, has the formula HCOOH. Other hydrocarbons can be used to form acetic acid, tartaric acid, and salicylic acid, which is the base from which acetyl salicylic acid, or aspirin, is made.

FUELS

Crude petroleum as it flows from oil wells is a mixture of many hydrocarbons. Petroleum is believed to be a material resulting from the partial decomposition of marine animal and vegetable organisms.

The various hydrocarbons in petroleum are separated out by a process known as fractional distillation. This process is based on the fact that different hydrocarbons have different boiling points. As the petroleum is heated, the first vapor to appear and be distilled is that of a mixture of light hydrocarbons called gasoline. Gasoline is mostly a mixture of hexane (C_6H_{14}), heptane (C_7H_{16}), and octane (C_8H_{18}). As the temperature of the petroleum is raised, kerosene begins to boil out. This is followed by fuel oil, then lubricating oil, and finally by greases, paraffin, and petroleum coke.

The United States produces more than 25 billion gallons of gasoline each year, and to increase the yield several processes have been developed. Cracking is the process by which the heavier hydrocarbons are broken down under great heat to form the simpler gasolines. Polymerization is the opposite of cracking. In this process the simple molecules, such as methane CH_4 and ethane C_2H_6, are forced to join together to make heavier molecules which constitute gasoline.

RUBBER AND PLASTICS

Rubber is a plastic hydrocarbon that is obtained from the sap or latex of rubber trees. Rubber molecules consist of long chains of isoprene (C_5H_8) molecules bound together—such chains being called polymers. This concatenation is what accounts for the elasticity of rubber.

With the advent of World War II and the loss of our sources of latex, the chemist applied his knowledge of natural rubber to produce several varieties of synthetic rubber. The principle was essentially that of polymerizing (joining together) molecules of the monomer (single particle) of isoprene (C_5H_8). By starting with chloroprene, the rubber called neoprene was produced. Buna is made by polymerizing butadiene.

The techniques applied in making synthetic rubber soon began to be used in producing other organic materials. A class of materials to which we give the name plastics was created. The raw materials for synthetic plastics include phenal, formaldehyde, urea, etc. Plastics may be divided into two groups, thermoplastic and thermosetting. The thermoplastic materials may be softened and changed in shape by gentle heating. Those which permanently harden under heat are thermosetting.

The plastic which came as a direct result of the researches on synthetic rubber is polystyrene. Styrene (C_8H_8) is polymerized to form polystyrene. This plastic is chemically inert and is capable of resisting the action of water, acids, etc. It is used greatly in the manufacture of containers.

The methacrylate plastics are made with acetylene (C_2H_2) as their base. This plastic can be rolled into large, very transparent sheets and is strong and shatterproof. Methyl methacrylate is thermoplastic.

TEXTILES AND PAPER

Textile fabrics are produced by weaving threads of the material in a variety of ways. The threads are derived from plant, animal, mineral, or synthetic sources. Our most important natural fiber is cotton, derived from the cotton plant. This fiber consists of molecules of cellulose ($C_6H_{10}O_5$) hooked together in long chains. The yarn is made by combing the fibers parallel to one another and then twisting them together to form a long strand. Cotton absorbs moisture readily and is a poor conductor of heat. It burns readily and is affected by acids. Linen, also a vegetable product, is processed from the fibers in the plant stem of the flax plant. Linen can absorb large quantities of water and the thread is extremely strong.

Wool is an animal product, made from the fur of sheep, goats, llamas, etc. Wool is a protein which contains carbon, hydrogen, oxygen, nitrogen, and sulphur. Therefore it burns, but not readily, and it is affected by alkalies. It is an excellent heat insulator.

Silk comes from the cocoons of the silkworm. It is a remarkably strong fiber considering its thinness; it is essentially protein in its constitution. Silk is used largely for its beauty as a lustrous, smooth fabric, but it does not have the heat-insulating qualities of cotton or wool, nor is it as durable as they.

There are several fibers obtained from minerals, the two most important of which are asbestos and glass. Asbestos is obtained by shredding magnesium silicate rock and twisting the long, thin crystals together to form a strand. It is fireproof and resistant to chemical attack. It is also used for heat insulation. Glass wool, a fluffy mass of very fine glass fibers, has many of the characteristics of asbestos but can more readily be spun into yarn and woven into cloth.

In recent years synthetic fibers have been developed which rival the natural ones in beauty and durability. Most of the synthetic fibers are produced by squirting a solution through a fine hole in a metal plate and passing the fine stream through another solution in which it hardens. Rayon is made by dissolving cellulose or wood to form a solution and then squirting this into dilute sulphuric acid, which hardens it into a fiber.

Of all the synthetic fibers, nylon is the most versatile. Nylon is made by a series of complex reactions between coal, air, and water, which produce a powdery mass called nylon salt. The molecules of nylon salt are polymerized to form giant spirally elongated molecules. The polymerized salt is then melted and forced through a spinneret (a metal plate with tiny holes). This lines up the molecules parallel to each other and produces a strong, elastic fiber. Nylon is relatively unshrinkable, relatively unaffected by chemicals, and wears well.

Paper is a fibrous material made from cellulose. Wood, cotton, and linen are the chief sources of cellulose. In making paper, individual fibers are separated by shredding and are bleached. The fibers are then suspended in water, and the mixture is forced through a slit onto a moving wire screen. As the water drains off, the fibers remain tangled together; after being squeezed to remove the water, they are tested to give the surface a smooth finish. The best papers are made from cotton and linen rags. Rag paper is strong and durable. Other types of paper are made by varying the wood-pulp concentration.

FOODS AND MEDICINES

In any proper diet there are five essential groups of nutrients which must be present. They are carbohydrates, fats, proteins, minerals, and vitamins. Each performs a specific and necessary function.

Carbohydrates are compounds of hydrogen, carbon, and oxygen, usually with the hydrogen and oxygen present in the same proportion as in water, namely two to one. Cane sugar ($C_{12}H_{22}O_{11}$), for example, exhibits the typical formula of a carbohydrate. Starch and the various sugars are the two classes of foods that make up carbohydrates. Carbohydrates make up the bulk of our diet and are used in the body chiefly as a source of readily available energy. When burned in the body, carbohydrates yield carbon dioxide (CO_2) and water (H_2O).

Fats are related to the organic acids and are likewise energy-producers. Weight for weight, fat yields twice as much energy as carbohydrates.

Proteins are complex compounds of carbon, nitrogen, hydrogen, oxygen, and sulphur. Protein molecules are relatively huge and their structure is not yet clearly understood. Their primary work in the body is to build tissue and repair cells that have been broken down in the normal functioning of the organism. No other nutrients can take the place of proteins for this purpose.

Minerals, derived from the salts in food, supply the calcium and the phosphorus essential in the building of bones, the iron for forming blood, and the iodine needed by the thyroid. In addition they supply the minute quantities of other elements, such as chlorine, copper, zinc, sodium, magnesium, etc., which are necessary to keep the body functioning normally.

Vitamins must be present in the diet for normal health. These are organic substances which seem to be necessary for the proper assimilation of food. There are more than a dozen substances which have been recognized as having the properties of vitamins. Some of them have been analyzed to the point where they may be prepared synthetically.

RADIOCHEMISTRY

Chemistry and Physics have both developed in new directions as a result of the recent work in the field of nuclear energy and its use. In addition to generating power, a nuclear reactor has provided the means for converting such common elements as hydrogen, iodine, phosphorus, and carbon into radioactive elements. (For a fuller discussion of radioactivity and nuclear energy see the section on Nuclear Physics on page 1145.) These radioactive isotopes are chemically identical with their non-radioactive counterparts. There is, however, one significant difference. They are emitting particles and rays and can thus be followed or traced by a Geiger counter. Such "tagged atoms" can be used to form part of any compound.

When these compounds are fed to plants and animals the movement of the radioactive isotope can be followed with great accuracy. Studies using the "tracers" reveal a great deal about the complex process taking place in living things. Radioactive carbon, for example, has been traced in photosynthesis from the carbon dioxide taken in by the plant to the final production of starch and sugar. Some day in the very near future we shall learn, through our use of the radio-isotope, the secret of the plant, and be able to undertake photosynthesis outside the plant. It may even be possible for us to get more information concerning cancer by the same technique.

Tracer atoms have also been of great importance in agriculture and industry. They are used to study the effectiveness of fertilizers and to determine the nutritive value of cattle feed. Radioactive isotopes are used to trace leaks in pipes, to observe the results of friction and wear, and to give us an insight into increasing the efficiency of complex industrial chemical processes.

These new applications in radiochemistry are additional indications of the constantly increasing ways in which chemistry influences and assists us in our daily lives.

EXAMINATION QUESTIONS

1. What chemical changes take place daily in iron, in fruit, in wood?
2. What two elements combined produce water?
3. What is an element?
4. What are formed through the combination of oxygen with most metals?
5. To what is the luminous quality of a flame due?
6. What usually governs the kindling temperature of a substance?
7. What gas is necessary for burning or combustion?
8. Of what is the earth's atmosphere composed?
9. What is the most common way of preparing oxygen in the laboratory?
10. What substance is almost pure carbon in a crystal form?
11. What part of water, by weight, does hydrogen form?
12. What color does an acid turn blue litmus paper?
13. When is a salt produced?
14. Of what is hydrochloric acid composed?
15. What is a saturated solution?
16. Of what are molecules composed?
17. What does the chemical formula for starch ($C_6H_{10}O_5$) signify?
18. What elements are represented by the following symbols: Au, Ni, P, K, Ra, Na, Sn, and W?

19. Of what gas has the United States the principal source of the world's supply?

20. Are there more metal elements than nonmetal?

21. Into what basic particles do atoms break down?

22. How many electrons could an atom with five protons have?

23. What does the chemical property of an atom depend upon?

24. When is a chemical equation balanced?

25. What gas, used in small quantities as a disinfectant, is highly poisonous in large quantities?

26. What happens when a small piece of sodium or potassium is put into water?

27. What are some uses of sulphur?

28. What does a sulphate contain that a sulphide never does?

29. In what way is nitric acid unique?

30. How is ammonia prepared?

31. What are the four halogens?

32. Where is iodine obtained?

33. Why is hydrofluoric acid kept in wax bottles?

34. What is the lightest gas known?

35. What compound do we get when

calc. ter?

36. What is .

37. What is steed with wa-

38. Why do silver colored when ıtal? eggs?

39. With what is a photog. coated?

40. How pure is 14-carat gold.

41. What is the most indestruc metal known?

42. What is the chief component part of type metal?

43. Is a tin can made of tin?

44. What element is the most basic in living matter?

45. Why is the number of carbon compounds almost unlimited?

46. What is the simplest hydrocarbon?

47. What is the process known as "cracking"?

48. What two important fibers are obtained from minerals?

49. What is paper?

50. What is the chief source of ready available energy in the human body?

For Further Study

Chemistry of Common Things, by R. B. Brownlee and others. (Allyn & Bacon, Boston.)

Chemistry in Industry, edited by H. E. Howe. (Chemical Foundation, New York.)

Creative Chemistry, by E. E. Slosson. (Doubleday & Co., New York.)

Everyman's Chemistry, by Ellwood Hendrick. (Harper & Bros., New York.)

Fundamentals of Chemistry, by Monroe M. Offner. (Barnes & Noble, New York.)

New Practical Chemistry, by N. H. Black and J. B. Conant. (The Macmillan Co., New York.)

The Romance of Chemistry, by William Foster. (Century Co., New York.)

XXV

Biology for Beginners

WHAT IS BIOLOGY?

BIOLOGY IS the science of life, or the science of organisms. A single living thing—animal or plant—is called an *organism*. Living substances are described as *organic,* in contrast to non-living or *inorganic* substances.

Biology embraces botany (the science of plant life) and zoology (the science of animal life) and—somewhat intermediate between the two—the science of microorganisms (living things so small that they can be observed only under the microscope, and which are in a realm where plant and animal often are much alike). Physiology (the science of the functions and functioning of tissues and organs) and anatomy (the science of the structure of organisms) are other phases of biology.

PROTOPLASM, BASIS OF LIFE

In their fundamentals, all forms of life are essentially the same. Protoplasm enclosed in cells is the basis of all life, and all life processes are accompanied by chemical changes or metabolism. Organic evolution, or the gradual development of higher forms of life from pre-existing lower forms, is today an accepted principle of biology. Scientists do not believe that there was ever any separate, unique creation of the species of animals and plants existing on the earth.

Whatever the phenomenon of life may ultimately be scientifically proven to be, it is well known that living things—animal or plant—owe their basic characteristics to the substance called *protoplasm*. Protoplasm is contained in units of structure which are called cells. A *cell* is usually a microscopic body—which may be long, cubic, oval, or spherical, etc.—enclosing within its wall or membrane a spherical *nucleus,* which is surrounded by *cytoplasm*. The entire cell is enclosed in a membrane. Nucleus and cytoplasm and cell membrane different forms. The cell wall surroust of protoplasm in somewhat consists of cellulose, which is non-livi..the membrane in plant cells closed only in a membrane. The nucle..ereas animal cells are en-..tains a number of rod-

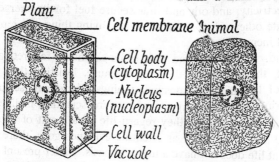

FIG. 1. Plant and animal cells.

shaped bodies called *chromosomes,* which are important in transmitting hereditary traits from parents to offspring.

Under the microscope, protoplasm appears to be granular; the granular appearance of the cytoplasm is finer than that of the nucleus. The "grains" appear to float in a fluid (cell sap). Whitish (colorless and "grainless") areas can sometimes be perceived; these are cell sap only, and are called *vacuoles.* Variations in the size and granulation of nucleus, cytoplasm, and vacuoles, together with the characteristic shape of the cell as a whole, give the different kinds of cells their different appearance. Plant cells often have additional bodies, called *chloroplasts,* which are colored green by a pigment known as *chlorophyll*—the coloring matter of all green plants.

The chemical composition of protoplasm is known; but protoplasm is no longer in the living state when chemical analysis can be made. Protoplasm consists principally of oxygen, hydrogen, carbon, and nitrogen —these four elements make up 97 per cent of its composition; the remainder consists of minute quantities of sulphur, phosphorus, chlorine, sodium, magnesium, calcium, iron, potassium, iodine, and occasionally (though rarely) other elements. The chemical composition and physical structure of protoplasm is extremely complex, and, in the living state, somewhat unstable, constantly involving complex chemical changes which make up the larger activities of the living organism as a whole.

Protoplasm is not a compound in the sense that ferrous oxide is a compound of iron and oxygen. Protoplasm can best be described as an organization or association of chemical substances. This organization ex-

r (properties). First of all, it
hibits consistent and dependable bdent motion: it generates energy
has the extraordinary power of is shows some power of movement.
within itself, and even in fixed responds to light, gravity, heat, con-
Secondly, protoplasm is irrita. Thirdly, it has the ability or power to
tact, electricity, and other d thus secure fuel for its energetic activi-
assimilate other substancourthly, every living thing can reproduce its
ties and increase its m
own kind.   In the past some scientists favored a vitalistic
    What, then, is regarded life as a cause, insisting that there is a
theory of life: hich activates living things. There is no scientific proof
"vital princinple. The majority of modern scientists incline toward a
of such a theory of life: they regard life as a result of chemical and
material activities. So far as scientific evidence goes, there is nothing
mechathat life does not have a material basis. Under present conditions
to s earth, life never appears spontaneously, but must be derived from
he pre-existing form of life—it must be passed on, that is, from parent
to offspring.

Spontaneous generation, or the sudden appearance of life from inorganic or lifeless matter, does not occur under any known conditions.
Whether it occurred in the remote geological past, when chemical and
physical conditions on the earth may have been different from anything
we know, is an open question. Certainly it has never occurred under
conditions that have so far been developed in the laboratory.

ONE-CELLED ORGANISMS

The number of cells in an organism may vary from only one cell up
to millions of highly differentiated cells. Organisms which consist of only
one cell are called *unicellular;* many-celled organisms are called *multicellular.* Man is a multicellular animal.

AMOEBA

The *amoeba* is the simplest unicellular animal. The single-celled body
contains a nucleus and *cytoplasm* and a whitish space called, because it
alternately contracts and expands, a *contractile vacuole,* and a *gastric
vacuole* in which digestion occurs. A common species of amoeba is as
large as 1/100 of an inch in diameter.

    Among many curious things about the amoeba is its method of loco-
motion, which can be observed under a microscope. It appears to stretch
out one side of its cell, whereupon the cytoplasm flows into it, and a

further projection is drawn in "from behind," and thus the animal seems to stretch out front "feet" and withdraw back "feet," and move along fairly steadily. These "feet" are called *pseudopodia* ("false feet"). As the amoeba moves through the water (in which it lives), it meets and surrounds (ingests) food particles, which become imbedded in its cytoplasm, until their nourishment is absorbed, when the indigestible matter is cast off from the surface of the amoeba as it moves and flows about.

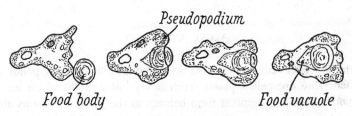

Pseudopodium

Food body   *Food vacuole*

FIG. 2. The feeding process of an amoeba.

The amoeba absorbs (by respiration) oxygen from its surroundings, and this oxygen combines with the protoplasm to liberate energy. The oxidation of living substance to liberate the energy with which the organism performs its activities is a phenomenon common to all living things. In the human being, respiration is a highly complex process, requiring the muscular co-ordination of the epiglottis, trachea, and chest, and the apparatus of nose and mouth, throat, windpipe (trachea), and lungs, with the elaborate system of lung capillaries containing the blood, sent there by pulmonary arteries and carried away by pulmonary veins, pumped by the beating of the heart. In human respiration, millions of cells take part, each group specially differentiated to perform its particular work, and dependent on the rest of the organism for other functions, as nourishment. In the amoeba, respiration is simplicity itself—it takes place directly between the cytoplasm and the surrounding medium (water).

The amoeba assimilates food: thus it grows. At a limit of size, it divides into two amoebae, by *fission*. Fission (reproduction) consists of the splitting of the full-grown single cell into two cells; the nucleus divides at the same time, one part going to each of the two new cells. The parent amoeba thus ceases to exist when its offspring are produced. If there is no moisture, the amoeba can dry up (become encysted) and live for an indefinite period without performing its usual functions. But as soon as it is in water again, it will go on as before.

Other one-celled animals move by means of *cilia,* which are tiny threads of protoplasm branching out from the cell wall, or by the lashing action of a long whip-like process, called the *flagellum.* Unicellular animals are collectively known as *protozoa* or *protozoans.* More than 10,000 different species are known and named. They are of varying complexity, though each organism contains only one cell, like the amoeba. The so-called flagellates exhibit both plant and animal characteristics. Indeed, in this microscopic realm many unicellular and even more complex organisms cannot be classed absolutely as either plant or animal.

ALGAE AND YEAST

The greenish scum which you sometimes see floating on ponds is a mass of tiny one-celled plants, each being but 1/2500 of an inch in diameter. This minute plant form belongs to the group known as *algae.* Most algae, however, consist of more than one cell. All algae contain a green coloring matter, by means of which they are able to make their own food.

This green coloring matter is the pigment *chlorophyll.* It is present not only in algae but in almost all higher plants. Chlorophyll takes part in a chemical process known as *photosynthesis,* by which, in the presence of carbon dioxide and under the action of sunlight, sugar is made by a chemical union of water with carbon dioxide. This unicellular plant, since it has chlorophyll in its single cell, can make its own food from the carbon dioxide in the air and the water present in its protoplasm or absorbed from its surroundings. All green plant cells, whether separate organisms or units of higher organisms, have this power to make their own food, provided that they have water, carbon dioxide, and sunlight.

A single-celled plant performs all the functions of a multicellular organism, including assimilation, respiration (breathing), and photosynthesis. It also reproduces itself by growing in size, then splitting into two new organisms. This is the method of reproduction known as *fission,* which we have already described. Cellular reproduction always takes place by fission or some modification of it.

Yeast is a familiar unicellular plant, but since it has no chlorophyll it is colorless. Nor can yeast make its own food. It is an example of a *saprophyte,* which must get its food outside itself, from non-living organic matter such as sugar. The sugar absorbed by yeast which it does not use is broken down, in the familiar process of fermentation, into alcohol, carbon dioxide, and small quantities of other substances.

BACTERIA

The tiniest and simplest plants are *bacteria*. They are found everywhere, some beneficial and some dangerous to man. Bacteria are unicellular plants, without chlorophyll, and are either saprophytes or parasites. *Parasites* live on other living organisms, from which they get nourishment.

A spherical bacterium is called a *coccus;* a rod-shaped bacterium is called a *bacillus;* a curved or spiral bacterium is called a *spirillum.* Some do not move; others move about by means of *cilia,* which are tiny threads, composed of protoplasm, branching out from the cell wall. The average length of bacilli is so small that it would take 800 of them, placed end to end, to reach across the head of a common pin; and it would take some 4,000 cocci (spherical bacteria), side by side, to reach the same

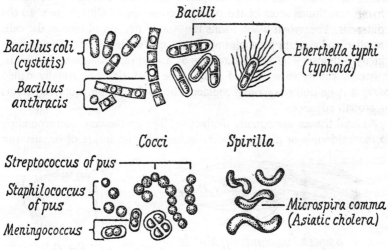

FIG. 3. Types of bacteria.

distance. Bacteria contain no clear nucleus; their structure is simple indeed. They reproduce very rapidly by fission; sometimes the divided cells remain together to form colonies or chains.

Many bacteria are present in the human body, especially in the alimentary tract, from the mouth down through the intestines. Most of these are harmless.

MANY-CELLED ORGANISMS

Some unicellular organisms remain together in colonies after multiplying by fission. These colonies sometimes approach the appearance and characteristics of the simplest many-celled organisms. For, somewhere in the process of evolution, such colonies of unicellular organisms began to develop special functions for groups of cells and to differentiate into multicellular organisms.

A multicellular organism consists of more than one cell, and these cells are of more than one kind. Division of labor results—some cells, all alike within a group, perform certain functions to the exclusion of others, and become dependent on the other cells for the functions which they do not themselves perform, and vice versa. A group of cells differentiated to perform a particular function is known as a tissue. The more complex the organism, the more kinds of tissue it has.

Plants have several characteristic tissues (see Fig. 5). The *epidermis* is the layer of cells which protects the surface of leaves, parts of flowers, stems, etc. There are few chloroplasts in epidermal cells. The *parenchyma* constitutes most of the plant; it comes just below or next to the epidermis. The *xylem* tissue forms the woody portion of plants; the cells are alive and contain protoplasm, but the cell walls are not alive and are chiefly cellulose. The xylem develops as a kind of passageway for fluids; it occurs chiefly in roots and stems. The *cork* tissue is usually called bark; it is an outer layer and replaces the epidermis on roots and stems as growth advances.

Animal tissues are equally distinctive. The *epithelium,* corresponding to the epidermis of plants, covers the outside and inside of organs (an

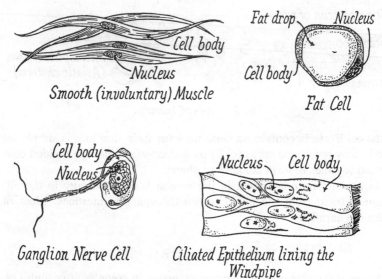

FIG. 4. Kinds of cells found in the human being.

organ is a specialized part, made up of several tissues). The outer skin of man is composed of epithelial tissue. *Muscle* tissue is specially adapted to contract; muscle cells, when stimulated, can shorten their length. There are three kinds of muscle tissue, usually called smooth, cardiac, and striped or *striated;* the voluntary muscles (under the control of the will) of man are striped; and among the smooth muscles (they act automatically or involuntarily) are those in the walls of the intestine. Cardiac muscle is a special type found only in the heart. *Nerve* tissue is very complex and highly specialized, being adapted to transmit impulses. A nerve is a bundle of nerve fibers, composed of protoplasm, extending from nerve cells, often for long distances. Various other tissues serve to connect parts of the body and support them; these include *bone, cartilage, tendon, ligament, blood,* and *fat.* The hardness of bone is due to accumulated mineral matter.

The tissues make up organs, which in plants are the roots, stem, leaf, flower, pistils, and stamens. In animals the organs vary, depending on the degree of development of the particular organism. In the higher animals the organs include the eyes, ears, brain, heart, lungs, kidneys, liver, ovaries, and stomach. Organs appear only in the higher plants and animals. Unicellular organisms have no organs, and many of the simpler multicellular organisms have no organs. Farther up the scale, organs are grouped into systems, as the nervous system, vascular system, and digestive system.

Let us summarize points which differentiate plants from animals, especially among the higher forms: (1) the cells of plants are enclosed in walls of cellulose, but animal cells usually are enclosed only in membranes; (2) plants usually possess a green-colored substance, chlorophyll; (3) plants usually either make their own food by photosynthesis or suck it up in liquid form, but animals take in solid food and have organs to digest it; (4) plants are usually fixed or stationary, but animals can usually move about from place to place.

THE PLANT KINGDOM

The plant kingdom includes a group of some 250,000 different species, subdivided into the following four great groups. The number of species given for each group is that now known and named.

The *thallophytes* (80,000 species) include all the algae, fungi, and lichens. The simpler forms are unicellular (as yeast), but multicellular forms are many. There are no distinct vegetative organs, such as root, stem, and leaf, although higher forms appear to have such organs (as some marine algae, commonly called seaweed). The scum on ponds is made up of tiny algae. Molds, bacteria, mildew, blight, and plant rust are fungi—they live on dead organic matter or on other organisms. Mushrooms are also fungi. Thallophytes have no seeds.

The *bryophytes* (16,000 species) include all the mosses and liverworts. They are not aquatic, but they seem to prefer moist places. There is some development of stem and leaf, but no root. They do not reproduce by seeds, but have a system of reproduction intermediary between the thallophytes and higher plants, called "alternation of generations."

The *pteridophytes* (5,000 species) include the ferns and allied forms. They are the highest type of flowerless plants, showing complete development of leaf, stem, and root. In reproduction, they exhibit very conspicuously the phenomenon of "alternation of generations," having no seeds. Horsetails and club mosses belong in this group.

The *spermatophytes* (135,000 species), the largest and most advanced group, are the seed-bearing plants. They have complex leaves, stems, and roots, and reproduce by flowering and developing seeds. Most familiar flowers, vegetables, and trees belong in this group. Spermatophytes are subdivided into *angiosperms* (the more numerous), those bearing seeds enclosed in a capsule (fruit); and *gymnosperms,* those bearing naked seeds (such as the evergreens, which bear naked seeds in cones).

THE PARTS OF PLANTS

THE ROOT

The root of a seed plant serves two purposes: it absorbs water and needed minerals (dissolved) and gases (also dissolved) from the soil, and it also anchors or fixes the plant to one spot, where it can grow. Roots are of various forms. One kind is a central taproot with branches; others are a cluster of many main shoots and branches. Root tips are ever growing and penetrating more deeply into the soil.

The growing part of a root is just back of the protecting cap which extends over its tip, protecting it as it pushes through the soil. The cells in the growing part divide and constantly increase in size. Farther back along the root is a region in which "root hairs" develop; these hairs are outgrowths from the root epidermis, and each is a single cell. Root hairs increase the absorbing surface of the root.

The fully developed (mature) root, if cut across and examined under the microscope, shows an outer layer, or *cortex,* and a central cylinder of cells, called the *vascular cylinder.* This part of the root is stiff and tough, the cortex having supporting parenchyma cells and a kind of cork tissue on the outside. The vascular cylinder is composed of a conducting system of specialized cells, differentiated into xylem and phloem tissues. Water passes upward through the xylem and dissolved food passes downward through the phloem.

Plants are popularly differentiated as annuals, biennials, and perennials. The annual plant lives for a year only; the biennial for two years; the perennial, year after year. In the autumn, the roots of all annuals die. But the roots of biennials accumulate food during the ensuing winter, so that the plant has a second season; in the second autumn, however, the roots of biennials die. The roots of perennials last through winter after winter, storing up food so that, though the part of the plant above ground may die, the root lives and sends up new stems and leaves year after year.

The Stem

The stem of the plant supports the leaves. It also has a conducting system, an extension of that in the root, acting as a go-between from leaves to root. Leaves are joined to the stem at nodes (points of attachment), according to a regular system or pattern which varies with the species of plant, and so arranged that one leaf does not come directly over another.

In the angle above the leaf, at the point where it joins the stem, there is usually a bud, which may, as the plant develops, shoot out to form a leaf-bearing branch of the main stem. Some buds, as those on most trees, last through the winter, even after the leaves have fallen off. The main stem extends itself or grows by means of a terminal bud at its upper end.

Most stems grow upright from the ground. Some, however, are specially differentiated for climbing or creeping. A few plants have stems running under the ground (not to be confused with true roots) which store up food. If the stem dies at the end of the growing season, the plant is classed as *herbaceous,* but if the stem survives (as in many perennials), the plant is *woody* (as are most trees). Some perennials are herbaceous.

The internal structure of the stem in most plants consists of an outer cortex, a hollow vascular cylinder, and a central core of pith. The vascular cylinder is mostly xylem, which helps to stiffen the stem. Between the phloem and xylem is a group of cells known as the *cambium;* it is this layer which grows and multiplies to form new xylem and new phloem. The successive layers of xylem (the rings in a cross section of tree trunk) indicate the number of years of growth. When the stem re-

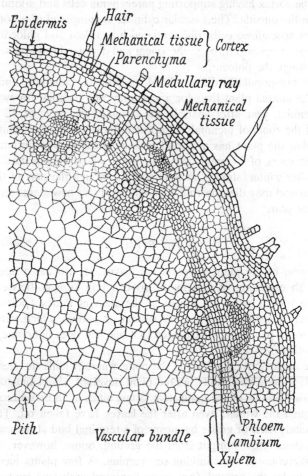

Fig. 5. Cross section of a sunflower stem.

mains above ground through the winter season, cork tissue develops year after year into the dead layer of cells forming the protective bark of trees. The living cells of a large tree are confined to a thin layer of inner bark.

THE LEAF

Most plants are conspicuous by their leaves. If deprived of their leaves in the growing season, they cannot live. For it is in the cells of the leaf, with their chloroplasts of green pigment (chlorophyll), that the photosynthesis of the plant takes place. The arrangement and development of the leaves provide for the greatest possible amount of sunlight over

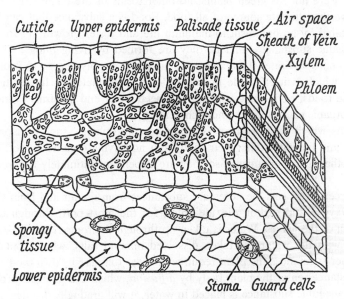

Fig. 6. Cross section of the blade of a leaf.

he largest possible surface. Inside the leaf, usually visible, are veins vhich extend from the vascular cylinder or bundles of the stem, carrying water to the leaf and taking away the nourishment produced by photosynthesis.

Leaves vary greatly in form and size. A pine needle is an extremely narrow leaf in contrast with the large and frond-like leaf of the banana tree. The edge of the leaf is sometimes smooth, sometimes serrate (sawtoothed), or otherwise modified. The pattern of the leaf is utilized by botanists as an aid to classification and identification. Leaves have a protective cuticle, which is waterproof and prevents evaporation of the fluids in the inner tissues. Gases pass in and out of the interior of the leaf through tiny openings called *stomata*.

PLANT PROCESSES

GROWTH

Plants require ten chemical elements for their growth; chief among these are carbon, hydrogen, and oxygen; the other seven are nitrogen, sulphur, phosphorus, potassium, calcium, magnesium, and iron. The process of securing these substances and utilizing them is *metabolism*.

If it were not for green plants, no other forms of life could exist, for they are the ultimate source of all food. Food is a substance that can be assimilated by an organism to maintain life and foster growth; all foods are organic substances—that is, they are formed by living things. They include carbohydrates, fats, and proteins, which supply energy to protoplasm, which is itself made up mostly of protein material. In addition to these foods, both plants and animals need water and minerals (which are inorganic) for complete nourishment.

Plants which are not green (not having chlorophyll), such as saprophytes and parasites, take their food from non-living organic matter, or from other living organisms, so they are dependent ultimately on green plants.

A green plant gets the necessary substances from the air and from the soil. Oxygen and carbon dioxide enter, for the most part, through the stomata of the leaves. Water is taken up through the roots from the soil. Along with the water are taken dissolved mineral salts, which contain the other substances the plant requires in order to make its own food.

Substances enter the plant body by *diffusion,* which is a physical process. If a soluble substance is placed in water, it will gradually disintegrate into molecules which pass evenly throughout the water, forming a solution. The molecules move steadily from higher to lower areas of concentration, until they are evenly distributed. This is diffusion, which explains *osmosis,* another physical process. If a solution is separated from pure water by a membrane, through which either water or the substance in solution can pass, osmosis takes place. That is, either the particles of dissolved substance diffuse into the pure water as though no membrane were present, or, if the membrane is not permeable to the dissolved substance, the water passes through the membrane into the solution, tending to reduce its concentration. Therefore, if a plant cell contains a fluid that is more concentrated than pure water and that cell is bathed by pure water, the water will pass through the membrane of the cytoplasm into the cytoplasm itself, that is, into the cell sap. (But the sugar inside the plant cell will not pass out into the water in the soil.) It is by this process of osmosis that the root cells of the plant absorb water from the soil, together with such dissolved mineral salts as may be needed (if the cell sap is low in them). In fact, all substances enter and leave living cells, in solution, by osmosis.

Soil water enters the root cells (in the root hairs) by osmosis, passes from cell to cell of the cortex, also by osmosis, finally reaching and passing up the xylem tissue through the vascular bundles to the stem and leaves.

In the leaves, water is being constantly evaporated during the process of photosynthesis. This evaporation cannot be avoided and must be compensated for by water sucked up from the root cells. Plant leaves constantly give off water vapor to the air during such evaporation. During drought, therefore, the plant is likely to wither and perhaps die.

In the green parts of the plant, in the stem and leaves, but especially in the latter, photosynthesis takes place. By this chemical process, which goes on only under the action of sunlight, from which energy is taken, and in the presence of chlorophyll (the green pigment of the chloroplasts), carbon dioxide and water are chemically combined to form grape sugar and oxygen, the oxygen being given off free into the air or partly utilized in respiration. The carbon dioxide enters the leaves through the stomata—carbon dioxide is always present in the air. At night, when sunlight is lacking, photosynthesis ceases, and the plant gives off no oxygen, but merely carbon dioxide (the product of respiration, which goes on all the time). The grape sugar formed is a carbohydrate, with stored energy, which can be utilized by the plant as food. A simple equation may be used to express photosynthesis:

$$\text{carbon dioxide} + \text{water} \xrightarrow[\text{chlorophyll}]{\text{sunlight}} \text{sugar} + \text{oxygen}$$

The grape sugar passes into the vascular bundles and is transmitted to all parts of the plant body, to be utilized immediately as food, or to be transformed into other forms of food and stored for later use. Any excess is changed to starch, which accumulates and at night may be reconverted into sugar and used as food. Water passes up to the leaves through the xylem tissue, but food (sugar) passes down to the other parts of the plant through the phloem tissue.

Fats and proteins are formed in the plant as derivative products of the carbohydrate, grape sugar, in combination with other substances. Plant fats take the form of vegetable oils; they are formed in all parts of the plant. Proteins are made from carbohydrates by the addition of nitrogen and some other elements. The free nitrogen which forms more than three-fourths of the air cannot be utilized by plants; therefore nitrogen salts (nitrates) in solution must be taken from the soil. Sulphur and phosphorus, also present in most proteins, are taken from the soil in the form of sulphates and phosphates. These essential substances are put into fertilizers to enrich soil intended for cultivation. Other elements—potassium, calcium, magnesium, and iron—are used by the plant in other ways.

Reserve supplies of food are usually stored as starch, although other forms of food also accumulate. Roots and underground stems are storage areas, especially the tubers (potatoes), bulbs, and rhizomes. Seeds also store up reserve food for the use of plant offspring.

Digestion, which is the chemical change of food into products the organism can use, occurs throughout the plant body—not in any special system of organs, as in most animals. When digested, or dissolved, food passes from cell to cell by osmosis, and ultimately replaces the protoplasm that is burned up in respiration (oxidation). Thus the food is assimilated.

The irritability of protoplasm enables the plant to adapt itself to its immediate environment. Plant protoplasm is stimulated by gravity, so the root always grows downward into the soil; and the protoplasm is also stimulated by moisture, and the stem grows upward through the soil, breaking through into the sunlight. Plant protoplasm is also stimulated by light; a house plant will "lean toward" a window.

REPRODUCTION

In green plants, the root, stem, and leaves, when such a system is present, are concerned with plant nutrition. In seed plants, the flower, fruit, and seed are concerned with carrying on the species—with reproduction.

Reproduction by fission (splitting in two) of the single cell occurs in unicellular algae. In a more complex plant, made up of many cells, the cells still reproduce by fission, but this contributes to the growth of the organism and not to the *reproduction of the organism*. A special group of tissues develops into organs which are concerned exclusively with reproducing the parent species.

One of the simplest forms of plant reproduction occurs by means of so-called spores. In the less complex algae the individual cells give off *spores,* which are cells without cell walls (and are therefore naked), having cilia, which enable them to swim through the water. These spores can develop directly into a new plant organism, exactly like the parent (the source of the spores). The spore develops into the new organism by cell fission; the process is called *germination.*

Some algae and most of the fungi have a specially adapted organ called the *sporangium,* in which spores are produced and set free. This is the beginning of the highly developed reproductive system in the higher plants. Also, in most fungi and in most higher plants, the spores are not the swimming type, but are given off into the air. Not naked, they are protected by a cell wall.

Yeast cells reproduce by a process called *budding*. In this process, instead of the parent cell dividing into two exactly equal cells, it divides unequally. At first the baby cell or bud remains attached to the parent cell until it reaches a size equal to that of the parent, after which the cells separate.

Every gardener knows that plants can be multiplied in other ways than by planting seeds. Strawberry plants send out runners, which take root at intervals, forming new plants. The tubers of the potato plant, which are specializations of the underground stem, also grow into new plants. Gardeners frequently plant "slips" (also called "cuttings") from growing plants, to increase the number of that species. Roots form on the lower end of the stem of a slip, and the new plant develops. These various methods of reproduction may be termed *vegetative propagation*.

Sexual reproduction, which occurs in many types of plants, requires sex cells, called *gametes;* two gametes (usually male and female, though in some organisms the gametes which fuse are alike) must unite, becoming one cell; the single cell resulting from the union of two gametes is called a *zygote*. In the lower algae, gametes are sometimes formed very much like the swimming spores. But the gametes cannot develop directly into a new plant—two unite, forming a zygote, which may have a rest period, later giving off spores which germinate, or itself developing into a new plant. Organisms reproducing sexually in one generation and reproducing asexually (without fertilization) in the next generation exhibit the phenomenon of *alternation of generations*.

In most plants above the lower algae, the gametes are differentiated into male and female; the male or sperm is small and active, and the female or egg is comparatively large and passive, waiting to be "fertilized" by union with the male gamete. Usually the zygote resulting from the union develops directly, soon after fertilization, into a new plant which grows and becomes like the parents which produced the gametes. In the higher algae, and on up the scale of plant life, gametes are produced in special sex organs, developed for that purpose exclusively—with the exception of the seed plants.

Plant reproduction in the spermatophytes (seed plants) requires the reproduction of seeds, enclosed in fruit (in the angiosperms) or naked (in the gymnosperms).

The process of reproduction in seed-bearing plants is familiar. First, a characteristic flower appears; the flower may be separated into a *calyx* (composed of sepals, or green leaf-like parts which cover the flower while it is a bud), a *corolla* (composed of the petals, white or colored), *stamens* (inside the corolla, producing a yellow powder called *pollen*), and *pistil* (one or more in the center of the corolla, each with an enlarged base called the *ovary*). The slender stalk of the pistil, projecting upward from the ovary, is the *style*. The tip of the style is developed into a *stigma,* specially adapted to receive pollen. The pollen grains are tiny cells, constituting the male element. In the ovary are larger cells, called *ovules* ("little eggs"), which may develop into seeds.

The ovules in the plant ovary must be fertilized. In the first step the pollen must pass from stamen to pistil. This is called *pollination.* The

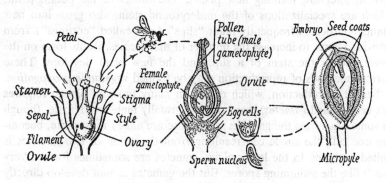

FIG. 7. The life cycle of a flowering plant.

pollen grains germinate *on the stigma,* each grain sending a tube-like extension down the inside of the style, called the pollen tube. After this happens, the petals and sepals of the flower usually wither and drop off, the pistil enlarges, and the style grows shorter as the ovary swells. The pollen tube, growing down inside the style, penetrates one of the ovules, forming a zygote (the pollen tube is not itself a gamete, but contains two nuclei, which correspond to the sperms or male gametes). The zygote germinates in the ovule, growing into a tiny plant called the *embryo.*

The embryo can be readily examined by splitting open a sunflower seed or a good-sized bean. It consists of a short stem (the *hypocotyl*), a kind of tiny bud (the *plumule*), and one or two leaf-like parts (the *cotyledons*). Beans, peas, and the like, in their seeds, consist of embryos only. But in many seeds, such as corn and wheat, there is a secondary development, a storage of nourishment, called the *endosperm,* which surrounds or is adjacent to the embryo. The embryo stops growing when it has reached the proper size of the seed, water is withdrawn from it, and it becomes comparatively dry and hard. Its development is stopped until it is deposited in a suitable spot, where it may germinate. Seeds can remain dormant for rather long periods of time (varying in different plants) and still germinate.

When the seed sprouts, if there is plenty of moisture, oxygen, and a suitable warm temperature, the embryo starts to grow. It develops into a mature plant, exactly like its parent, and goes through the same processes of making food, assimilating it, and blossoming into flowers which ultimately produce new seeds. The new plant is called a seedling as long as it derives nourishment from the endosperm (stored-up food).

The fruit is the enlarged ovary—a ripened ovary, containing ovules which are developing into seeds. The edible fruits are usually fleshy and juicy, such as plums, apples, and oranges. Nuts are dry fruits. The fruit contains the seeds by means of which the plant reproduces.

THE ANIMAL KINGDOM

There are something like 600,000 species, already named and catalogued, in the animal kingdom; most of these are insects. There are ten major groups or divisions of the animal kingdom, as follows:

The *protozoans* include 10,000 species of simple animals of one cell each, usually microscopic in size. All animals above the protozoans, which is to say all multicellular animals, are called *metazoans*.

The *sponges* (Porifera) are the simplest metazoans, numbering about 2,500 species. They live in water (usually salt water). They have simple tissues, but no organs; each cell receives and digests its own food. Sponges are fixed to objects in the water; they are radially symmetrical.

The *coelenterates* (animals with "hollow intestines"), 4,500 species, include corals, sea anemones, jellyfishes, and hydroids. They are mostly marine animals, and are found attached, free, or in colonies. The special characteristic of the coelenterates is the *coelenteron,* a kind of cavity into which there is only one opening—the mouth, often surrounded by tentacles. The body wall consists of only two cell layers (as in the sponges). There are organs, but the bodily processes are simple; the animals are radially symmetrical.

The *flatworms* (Platyhelminthes), about 5,000 species, include the tapeworms and other "flat" worms. They have soft bodies, are bilaterally (instead of radially) symmetrical, noticeably flat, and may or may not be segmented. There is no true body cavity, but there are various organs, with one opening to the outside. The flatworms exhibit increasing complexity, though still very simple as compared with higher animals.

The *roundworms* (Nemathelminthes), about 1,500 species, are cylindrical and unsegmented. The hookworm is perhaps the best-known example; the trichina also belongs to this group. They exhibit the characteristics of all higher animals in having both an alimentary tract (*enteron*) and a body cavity (*coelom*); the enteron has two openings, mouth and anus. Most of the roundworms are thread-like.

The *echinoderms,* about 4,000 species, are all marine animals, including the starfish, sea urchins, sea cucumbers, and brittle stars. They usually have both radial and bilateral symmetry; most of them are spiny on the surface, and many have star-like shapes of five prongs each. Somewhat more developed than the next nearest group below them, they are the surviving descendants of a very ancient type of animal.

The *annelids,* about 4,000 species, are the segmented worms, including earthworms, leeches, and sandworms. They are bilaterally symmetrical, having both coelom and enteron; they are increasingly complex, with a nervous system fairly well developed and a vascular system with red blood.

The *mollusks* number some 60,000 species, popularly called shellfish. They include oysters, clams, snails, mussels, and such "shell-less" forms as squids, cuttlefish, octopi, and slugs. All these animals have an organ which they use for locomotion, called the foot. Most of them have protecting shells covering their soft, bilaterally symmetrical bodies.

The *arthropods* (animals with "jointed feet"), some 500,000 species, are the largest single group of the animal kingdom. The body has appendages, such as *antennae* (feelers), legs, and mandibles. The segments of the body are grouped into distinct regions, as the head and the rest of the body. They have a hard outer shell or covering. Major divisions are the following: *crustaceans,* 16,000 species, including the crabs, lobsters, crayfish, shrimps, and barnacles, mostly marine; *myriapods* (many-footed), 1,000 species, including the centipedes and millipedes; *insects* (Hexapoda, "six-footed"), over 450,000 species, including butterflies, beetles, flies, mosquitoes, wasps, bees, ants, grasshoppers, moths, dragonflies, and locusts (the body has a distinct *head, thorax,* and *abdomen,* with six legs and two pairs of wings or rudimentary wings attached to the thorax); *arachnids,* 20,000 species, including the spiders, scorpions, mites, and ticks (the head and thorax are fused into the cephalothorax, and all have eight legs and no wings).

The nine preceding groups are referred to together as *invertebrates.*

The *chordates,* some 38,000 species, are the highest group of animals in development. It is to this great group that man belongs. They are bilaterally symmetrical animals, all having at some stage of life the distinctive feature of a rod of supporting tissue, called a *notochord,* developing into the *spinal cord* in higher forms, though the spinal cord does not correspond exactly to the notochord, being encased in the vertebral column which supplants the notochord in the adult. Chordates have a vertebral column and are classed together as *vertebrates,* distinguished from the *invertebrates,* which have no "backbone." All chordates exhibit gill slits (for breathing in water) at some stage of life, even man showing them in the embryonic stage. The nerve cord is hollow.

The major groups or subdivisions of the chordates are the following:

Fishes (15,000 species) are aquatic and cold-blooded vertebrates (that is, their temperature changes with their environment); they breathe through gills, lack limbs, move through water by means of fins, are scaled, and have a two-chambered heart.

Amphibians (15,000 species) are cold-blooded vertebrates, breathing with gills in early stages, and usually later breathing with lungs; amphibians live both in water and on land; most of them have four limbs,

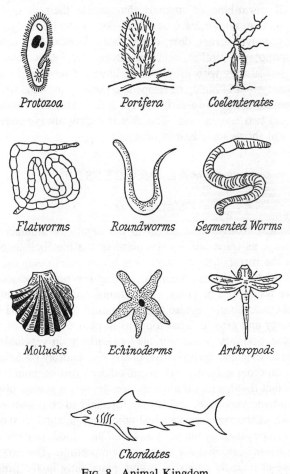

Protozoa   Porifera   Coelenterates

Flatworms   Roundworms   Segmented Worms

Mollusks   Echinoderms   Arthropods

Chordates

Fig. 8. Animal Kingdom.

with clawless toes, and a three-chambered heart; they include frogs, toads, salamanders, and newts.

Reptiles (3,500 species) are cold-blooded vertebrates, never breathing with gills but always with lungs; most of them have four limbs (snakes being exceptions), with clawed toes, plate- or scale-covered skin, and a three-chambered heart (four-chambered in crocodiles and alligators); they include lizards, snakes, turtles, tortoises, crocodiles, and alligators.

Birds (13,000 species) are warm-blooded, feathered vertebrates, never breathing with gills but always with lungs; they have four limbs (two feet and two wings); a four-chambered heart; scaled skin on the feet, with claws.

Mammals (about 3,500 species) are the highest class of vertebrates, including all warm-blooded animals that suckle their young, such as man, apes, monkeys, mice, rats, squirrels, dogs, cats, lions, tigers, moles, bats, whales, wolves, bears, deer, cows, sheep, horses, pigs, camels, elephants, hippopotami, giraffes, and kangaroos. Mammals never breathe with gills, but always with lungs. They have a four-chambered heart. The nervous system is highly developed, especially in man, where intelligence appears. There are nearly always four limbs, differentiated into two arms and two legs in man. The skin is nearly always covered with hair, and even shows some hair in man.

ANIMAL PROCESSES

METABOLISM

The chemical changes that go on in the organs of animals are very much the same as those which take place in the metabolism of plants, except that the metabolism of animals is much more complex, particularly in the higher animals. Animals, having the power of locomotion in all higher forms and in many lower forms, consume a great deal of energy, and consequently require a great amount of food. Food is necessary for energy and growth. That food, as in plants, consists of proteins, carbohydrates, and fats. Some animals live entirely on vegetable matter, and are therefore called *herbivorous;* others live entirely on animal matter, preying on other animals, and are called *carnivorous;* man is remarkable for the fact that his diet is all-inclusive—he eats a variety of different foods, animal and vegetable, and is therefore said to be *omnivorous*.

Only foods of the simplest chemical composition, such as simple sugars, can be directly used by the body as fuel. Other foods must be digested or "broken down" into simpler chemical composition. The processes of digestion are chemically complex, taking place only in the presence of substances called enzymes, which are secreted into the digestive cavity from adjacent body cells. Only in the very lowest animals (in protozoans and in sponges) is digestion distributed among the individual cells of the whole animal; in higher forms, digestion takes place in a special part of the body, usually in a hollow cavity or digestive tract, such as the human stomach and small intestine.

In the human body (which is a typical animal body) the first digestive juice is secreted in the mouth, during chewing; it is saliva (spit), which contains the enzyme *ptyalin,* which changes some of the starch in chewed food to sugar. Most of the digestion takes place in the stomach and small intestine. The gastric juice contains the various stomach secretions; gastric juice has in it the enzyme *pepsin* and some hydrochloric acid, which provides the acid medium needed for pepsin to act. Pepsin changes some proteins to peptones. The gastric juice also contains the enzyme *rennin,* which digests milk. In the small intestine, into which the food passes in a semi-liquid condition from the stomach, further foods are digested, especially the fats. The pancreatic juice is secreted by the pancreas (sweetbread) with three important enzymes: *amylopsin* (changes starch to sugar), *trypsin* (changes proteins to peptones), and *steapsin* (changes fats to glycerine and fatty acids). The pancreatic juice acts in the presence of bile from the gall bladder; the bile itself does not digest food, but its presence is chemically necessary for fat digestion. The small intestine secretes an intestinal juice containing the enzyme *erepsin,* which further aids the digestion of a protein called *casein.*

No digestion goes on in the large intestine, where the indigestible parts of the food, particularly the cellulose from vegetable food, is stored for a time until it can be evacuated from the body. Here colonies of beneficent bacteria partially decompose this waste matter before it leaves the body.

Dissolved foods, rendered soluble during digestion, pass through the walls of the small intestine by osmosis, reaching the blood, in which the food (fuel) is carried to all parts of the body, where it is assimilated by the cells. The blood also takes away from the body cells waste products, which are ultimately evaporated from the body through skin pores (as perspiration), in the lungs (in respiration), or are secreted from the kidneys (as urine). If there is an excess of food, it is stored in the body as adipose tissue (commonly called fat).

What happens in animal respiration is similar to the respiratory process in plants. For the transportation of nourishment through the body, animals (in higher groups) have a marvelous circulatory or vascular system (the blood stream and its vessels), with a pumping organ (the heart). This vascular system also takes part in animal respiration, sending venous blood (blood in the veins) to the lung capillaries (tiny blood vessels in the lungs) to be oxygenated (aërated). This process of oxidation is chemically much like burning—the oxygen of the air, breathed into the lungs, combines chemically with hemoglobin (the red coloring matter of the blood), and is taken to all parts of the body by the blood, where the oxygen is liberated, as needed, to oxidize the protoplasm in the cells during bodily activity. The liberation of oxygen is necessary to supply the energy required for the body to do its work, in which it acts like a great chemical machine.

In lower animals the system of lungs is not so well developed, or is lacking. Fish breathe through gills, utilizing the oxygen dissolved in the water. Some lower animals "breathe" through the outer cells of their skin; that is, the skin cells absorb oxygen directly. Insects have a complex system of tubes (tracheae), which open out of the body through many spiracles here and there about the surface; this system brings air directly to all parts of the body, instead of to specialized organs like the lungs in higher animals.

The most distinctive feature of higher animals, especially mammals, is a highly developed nervous system. The nerves, or, more exactly, the nerve cells, are specially developed to receive and transmit sensations and impulses. All protoplasm is irritable, but nerve cells have specialized protoplasm which is irritated only by specific stimuli. This elaborate nervous system enables animals to respond to their environment much more quickly than plants. An animal can hear a loud noise and flee from it, or see food and hurry toward it, with great rapidity, due to skillful coordination of muscles and other organs. The lowly earthworm has a relatively simple nervous system. In the frog the nervous system is quite well developed, and in mammals it is very complex. In man it reaches the apex of complexity in *intelligence*.

To summarize: animals secure food, take it into the body, usually through an opening (mouth) adapted to that purpose, digest it in a suitable tract (digestive tract), evacuate waste matter derived from the assimilation of digested food, breathe by taking oxygen into the body (usually in special organs, such as lungs), and, in general, go through the continuous round of replacing used-up protoplasm (utilized in bodily work) with new food (fuel). Animals have the power of locomotion, the better to get food of the right kind and in sufficient quantity for their needs. Bodily functions are performed by systems of highly specialized organs, especially in the higher animals, which also adapt themselves to their environment and escape danger because of a highly complex nervous system.

REPRODUCTION

In the protozoans, and in a few lower animals above the protozoans, reproduction takes place by simple fission; the one-celled animal divides into two. Occasionally fission is modified into a kind of budding, the

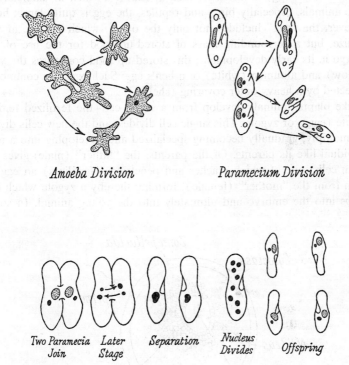

Amoeba Division   *Paramecium Division*

Two Paramecia Join   Later Stage   Separation   Nucleus Divides   Offspring

FIG. 9. Fission (above) and Conjugation (below).

bud growing into a new animal. In most animals reproduction is sexual, requiring the union of male and female to produce offspring.

Usually, in the animal kingdom, each species of animals has two kinds, male and female, differentiated from each other by special characteristics which may or may not contribute directly to the process of reproduction. The union (conjugation) of male and female is necessary, or at least the male gametes must meet and unite with the female gametes, in order that new animals may grow and carry on the species. The special cells, known as *sperm cells,* devoted to reproduction are distinct from the other cells of the body, which are concerned with metabolism. The latter are usually called *somatic.*

In general, the male gametes are called *sperms,* and are produced in male sex glands, called *testes;* the female gametes are called *ova* (eggs), and are produced in female sex glands, called *ovaries.* The sperms, or sperm cells, are active, often swimming; the ova are passive, awaiting the arrival of sperms. Both sperms and ova are very small; even the human ovum (egg) is no larger than 1/125 of an inch in diameter. In some animals, especially birds and reptiles, the egg is quite large; here, however, the "egg" includes not only the ovum, which the sperm will fertilize, but a surrounding mass of stored-up food for the use of the embryo in its early development; this stored-up food comprises the yolk (yellow) and albumen (white) of a hen's egg. Such eggs are commonly protected by a heavy outer covering (shell).

Like plants, animals develop from a single cell—the fertilized female gamete (egg), or zygote. This single cell divides, and the new cells divide and multiply, gradually becoming specialized and developing into a new individual like its parents. Of the parents, the "father" (male) gives off sperm cells, one of which reaches and penetrates (fertilizes) an egg or ovum from the "mother" (female), forming thereby a zygote which develops into the embryo and ultimately into the young animal. In some

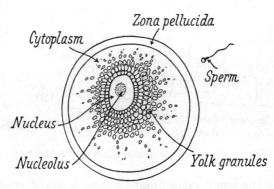

FIG. 10. Human egg cell and a sperm.

aquatic animals the female simply lays her eggs in the water, and the male ejects his sperms into the water; these are laid or ejected in great numbers, so that some of the sperms are almost sure to find and fertilize some of the eggs. This is external fertilization. But in most animals internal fertilization must take place. The male meets the female, conjugates with her, and, by means of a specially developed male organ, ejects the sperms into a specially developed cavity of the female, where they can swim to the eggs and fertilize one or more.

In a few animals (usually invertebrates) an egg may develop into a new individual without being fertilized. This process is called *parthenogenesis*. Bees exhibit this phenomenon to some degree. The female (queen) lays both fertilized and unfertilized eggs. The fertilized eggs develop into queens (females who can lay eggs) and workers (females who cannot lay eggs). Unfertilized eggs develop into drones (males), who do no work. The drones are born by parthenogenesis. Parthenogenesis occurs almost exclusively in certain insects, crustaceans, and worms. In the aphids or plant lice a number of generations produced by parthenogenesis, being females only, occur after the generation which is sexually produced. Finally males are produced, also by parthenogenesis, and sexual reproduction again occurs. Parthenogenesis is a modification of sexual reproduction which must not be confused with asexual (non-sexual) reproduction. In parthenogenesis the young develop from true eggs (unfertilized), not from buds or parts of the body as in asexual reproduction.

As the embryo develops from the zygote (fertilized egg), it goes through a series of changes which are outwardly similar in all metazoans. This phenomenon has greatly helped to demonstrate organic evolution.

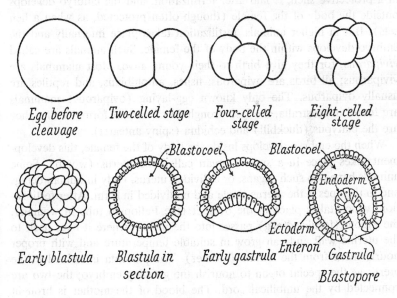

Egg before cleavage   Two-celled stage   Four-celled stage   Eight-celled stage

Blastocoel   Blastocoel   Endoderm

Ectoderm   Enteron

Early blastula   Blastula in section   Early gastrula   Gastrula   Blastopore

FIG. 11. Early stages in the development of a starfish.

For at a very early stage there is very little difference between the embryos of a fish, a salamander, a tortoise, a chick, a hog, a calf, a rabbit, and a man; they look nearly alike.

The embryo develops by cell fission. In general, starting from a single cell (zygote), it becomes a hollow ball or *blastula*. This ball then seems to have one side pushed in, which grows inward until it joins the outer side, forming a ball-shaped body with a hollow inside and an opening at one side (at this stage called the *gastrula*). A sponge is not developed beyond this stage; in general, the two lowest groups of metazoans remain in this stage.

In higher metazoans the embryo develops further, the cells dividing into millions, and the various organs and parts of the body forming slowly but surely into an image of the parents. There are three primary cell layers. From one of these (the *ectoderm*) develop the outer skin and scales, hair, nails, feathers (if present), and the nervous system. From another layer (the *endoderm*) develop the linings of digestive and respiratory cavities. From the third layer (the *mesoderm*) develop muscles, blood vessels, the blood, connecting and supporting tissues.

"Birth" takes place in two forms among animals where fertilization is internal. Animals which lay eggs are called *oviparous;* the egg, usually in a protective shell, is laid after fertilization, and the embryo develops outside the body of the female (though often protected, as when a hen sets). But in higher animals, fertilization takes place internally and the embryo develops within the body of the female. Such animals are called *viviparous,* for they give birth to their young alive. Most mammals are viviparous; all birds are oviparous; fishes, amphibians, and reptiles are usually oviparous. The only known egg-laying (oviparous) mammals are found in Australia, the last stronghold of ancient forms of life; they are the platypus (duckbill) and echidna (spiny anteater).

When the embryo develops inside the body of the female, this development takes place in a special organ called the uterus (womb). Some animals have two such organs, or a divided uterus. Only in human beings and in the apes is the uterus single and undivided in form. After fertilization, which takes place in the oviduct (the Fallopian tube in woman), the zygote (fertilized egg) passes into the uterus, where it fixes itself to the uterine wall and can grow in suitable temperature and with proper nourishment from the female (mother). The placenta is formed in the uterus as the special organ to nourish the growing embryo; the two are connected by the umbilical cord. The blood of the mother is brought into osmotic contact with the blood of the embryo; there is, however, neither direct blood nor direct nervous association between mother and embryo. Nourishment passes to the embryo, and waste products are taken away, entirely by osmosis. Mental or nervous excitement of the mother, contrary to popular notions, does not affect or "mark" her offspring.

In the process called birth, in viviparous animals, the fully developed embryo—often more than one among animals below the primates (man and the apes), but usually only one in human beings—is "born," which

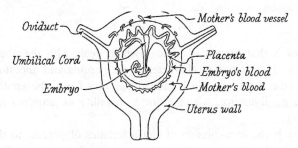

Fig. 12. Embryo of mammal in uterus.

is to say, it is passed out of the body of the mother during labor (parturition). The placenta follows as the "afterbirth." The newborn offspring is still attached to the mother by the umbilical cord, which is chewed apart by most animals, or severed by the attending physician in man. After birth, among mammals, the offspring is suckled at the female's mammary glands, which supply milk.

Insects exhibit a quite different process of development. With some exceptions, insects go through a series of changes called *metamorphosis*. The egg hatches into the *larva:* the caterpillar of butterflies and moths, the grub of beetles, and the maggot of flies, bees, wasps, and ants. The larva feeds and grows, and then passes into a semi-dormant state, called the *pupa*. The pupa does not usually feed, but it undergoes a series of changes, finally emerging as the *imago* or adult, like the parent. The butterfly pupa is sometimes called a *chrysalis*. The pupa of the mosquito, contrary to the general rule, is active, and is one of those "wrigglers" commonly present in stagnant pools, the other wrigglers being mosquito larvae.

As in the mosquito, the early stages of some other animals are aquatic. Amphibians, such as frogs and toads, also have larval stages. The eggs are laid and fertilized in water, and the young larvae, called tadpoles, grow and develop in water. There is no pupal stage among amphibians.

Some animals lay their eggs and promptly forget them. The parents give no attention to their young, which quite ably manage to shift for themselves. Among other animals, particularly among birds and mammals, the parents watch over their young in what seems to be paternal and maternal loving care, though it is wholly instinctive. With man's aid, even young chicks can do without their fussing mother hens, being hatched in an incubator and raised under mechanical "wings."

GENETICS

Genetics is that branch of biology which deals with the phenomena of heredity (inheritance of characters from parents and ancestors) and variation (the degree in which individuals vary from one another, and the points of difference, whether due to heredity or acquired from environment).

Heredity is the transmission of characteristics of parents to their offspring. Animals and plants strikingly resemble their "parents"; indeed, the resemblance is complete in all essential particulars. Heredity results from the actual connection existing between parents and offspring: the offspring grows from a single cell which has resulted from the union of two cells of the parents, one from the male and one from the female parent; or, in lower forms of life, from the simple division of one cell into two just like the original. Heredity is never altogether complete, for variation exists which makes the differences between individuals and which may give rise to new species.

The laws of heredity apply in general to all living things, whether plant or animal. When the organism multiplies by simple cell fission, the two resulting organisms are naturally like the one cell which gave rise to them. Some organisms are self-fertilized and exhibit a similar uniformity in offspring.

But in sexual reproduction, as we have seen, two parents give rise to the offspring, through the union of gametes (male and female). Since the offspring obviously resembles the parents, not only in belonging to the same species but in minor variations between individuals, these characters must be passed on to the offspring from the parents through the germ cells, since these cells are the only organic connection between parents and offspring. Also it appears that male and female are of equal influence in heredity.

Inherited characters must be distinguished from *acquired* characters. The latter are fostered by the individual's environment or surroundings. Inherited characters represent potential factors in development, such as musical inclination in human beings; or inherited characters are matters of physical appearance, as blue eyes. But the *ability to play* the piano is distinctly acquired (learned) and cannot be inherited.

MENDELISM

Gregor Mendel (1822–1884), an Austrian abbot, made an exhaustive study of variations in sweet peas grown by him, and discovered a law of heredity (Mendel's law of inheritance) which has since been found true of all organisms. If a red four-o'clock flower is crossed with a white flower of the same species (by taking pollen from one and placing it on the pistils of the other), the offspring will be a pink flower. The pink flower is called a *hybrid*. If two pink flowers (two hybrids) are cross-fertilized, the resulting offspring will include red, white, and pink flowers, and the offspring will vary approximately in the proportion of one red and one white flower to every two pink flowers. Further, if the red flowers born of pink parents are interbred, their offspring will all be red. The same is true of white flowers. But, in general, half the offspring of hybrids will always be hybrids. Suppose that a white flower is crossed with a pink flower—a pure flower with a hybrid. The offspring will occur in the ratio of half pink and half white; if there are one hundred, fifty will be white, fifty pink.

The variation is simple up to this point, but becomes more complicated, for there are what are known as *dominant* and *recessive* characters. In guinea pigs short hair is dominant over long hair; that is, if one of two parents is short-haired and the other is purebred long-haired, the offspring will be short-haired.

Tallness is a dominant character in a pea plant. If a purebred tall and a dwarf plant of the same species are crossed and the hybrid tall offspring crossed or interbred, according to the principle just formulated, the offspring should include one tall, one dwarf, and two intermediate. But tallness is dominant over dwarfness, and a somewhat different result follows. If the hybrid tall plants are interbred, they will produce offspring in the ratio of three tall plants to every dwarf. The dwarf plant (one in four) appears in the second generation, because a dwarf factor is taken from a hybrid tall parent and also from a dwarf. If organisms (of the same species) with various dominant and recessive characters are crossed, the resulting offspring will necessarily exhibit many variations.

Every flower possesses a pair of factors (genes) for each characteristic. The genes are located on corresponding *chromosomes* in the nucleus of each cell. As mentioned in the very beginning of our discussion of biology, on page 1197, the chromosomes are rod-shaped bodies located in the nucleus of each cell; these chromosomes are basic in the transmitting of hereditary traits from parents to offspring. Thus if we represent the tall

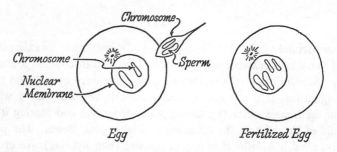

FIG. 13. Organism which has four chromosomes in each body cell.

factor by T (the dominant trait) and the dwarf factor by t (the recessive trait), then the genetic make-up of a purebred tall plant is TT, that of a dwarf plant is tt. When a TT plant is crossed with a tt plant, the result is a Tt or hybrid. When two Tt plants are crossed, the offspring are always in a ratio of $1TT: 2Tt: 1tt$. This is due to the phenomenon of segregation, in which the members of each pair of factors separate before going into the sex cells and recombining. Thus:

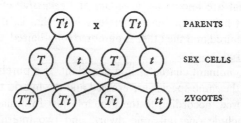

This explanation has been successfully applied to heredity in many other organisms, including man. Scientific plant and animal breeding depend upon correct understanding of the laws of heredity.

Color-blindness is a human recessive character that occurs mostly in males, but is inherited through the mother; thus, if a color-blind man mates with a woman who has normal vision, all his children will have normal vision and his son's children will have normal vision. But his daughters are carriers; though not color-blind themselves, they may transmit color-blindness to some of their children (males). A color-blind woman's sons will all be color-blind. But a color-blind woman must be the daughter of a color-blind father and a mother who is either color-blind or a descendant of a color-blind man or woman; the fact that this seldom happens explains the rarity of color-blindness in women.

BREEDING

Gardeners and animal breeders know the value of careful breeding. Luther Burbank won fame with his experiments on flowers and fruits. He showed that by carefully selecting the parents either plant or vegetable offspring can be developed along desired lines. Seedless oranges and grapefruit, white blackberries, large and juicy strawberries, hardy apple trees, and large nuts have all been scientifically developed by watching and observing the laws of heredity. The experimenter is limited to developing such variations as naturally occur in offspring by chance; acquired characters help him not at all, for they cannot be passed on to the succeeding generations by heredity.

A hit-or-miss process of breeding is known as mass culture. This consists in taking seed from only the tall plants and sowing it for a new crop. From the new crop seed is again taken only from the tall plants, and so on. Gradually a seed may be developed which will grow mostly into tall plants. But some of the tall plants are hybrids, and the hybrid tall plants, in succeeding generations, will produce a few dwarfs.

The more scientific system of breeding is according to pedigree, considering "relatives" in order to determine the purity of the parent stock. The pedigree system was used with animals long before it was applied to plant breeding, but it can also be used with plants. The system is especially successful with plants which naturally pollinate themselves with their own pollen, for this enables the breeder to keep the strain pure. Inbreeding is often necessary in order to secure offspring of a particular kind.

Hybrids among plants and animals sometimes are more desirable for human needs than the pure species. But hybrids are often sterile—that is, they cannot reproduce. A familiar example is the mule, a hybrid animal, offspring of a mare and a jackass. In animals, cross-breeding must always be resorted to in order to provide such hybrids. With plants, new individuals can be obtained by "vegetative reproduction"; that is, by taking slips or cutting from the hybrid.

Hybridization increases the hardiness or virility of the offspring. Continuous inbreeding is likely to result in a weakening of the native strength of the organism, especially its ability to resist disease or other adverse conditions. Cross-breeding restores vigor—most hybrids are hardier than either parent. Interbreeding among human beings is sometimes thought to result in a similar increase of vigor, and inbreeding to result in deterioration. However, human inbreeding (as the marriage of first cousins) is not likely to result in abnormal offspring unless undesirable recessive characters are in the family strain.

Eugenics

The science of eugenics is concerned with the influences that better the native or inborn qualities of a race or breed; it is especially concerned with the human race. Eugenics is scientific human breeding—the application of scientific principles to the birth of human offspring. Birth control and deliberate childbearing enter into the question.

Before eugenics can be applied, definite data must be collected as to what human beings inherit and what they acquire from their environment and training. Social barriers prevent the scientist from making the kind of experiments he would like to make with human beings. Man is more complex than any lower animal, and the possibilities of physical and mental variation in human offspring are therefore very great indeed, which makes the problem extremely difficult.

Some advocates of eugenics for human beings have argued for such extreme measures as state control of the conception and birth of offspring. Skeptical thinkers have said that eugenics for human beings, on anything like a scientific basis, is impossible, because of human nature. Between these two extremes of opinion, the talk about eugenics has given an impetus to choosing mates that are as highly endowed as the choosers. Two intelligent and talented parents are more likely to have intelligent and talented offspring than two dull and clumsy parents. Yet, unless the whole family tree of both parents is known, little can be predicted about the characters that the children will certainly inherit.

Experiments have been conducted to determine the relative effects of environment and heredity in determining human characteristics. Identical twins (presumably originating from a single fertilized egg which accidentally became divided into two parts at an early stage of development), when reared apart, show fewer differences in intelligence than in characteristics such as emotion, social qualities, and personality. Some experiments, however, do indicate marked differences in intelligence when identical twins are reared in different environments. It is difficult to draw any conclusions.

THE FITNESS OF NATURE

Every organism, plant or animal, lives in a definite relation to its environment, and it appears to be able so to live because of its inherited characters. A fish is adapted to life in sea water; it has gills for breathing in water, fins for swimming through water, and the like. The biological study of organisms in relation to their environment and to other organisms is called *ecology*.

ADAPTATION TO ENVIRONMENT

So happily adapted do many organisms appear that it is a great temptation to speak of them as having developed in that way because they desired or definitely tried to do so. To say that a polar bear has white fur to blend with his snowy surroundings in arctic wastes in order to protect himself is not scientific. The polar bear's white color is undoubtedly protective, but all that the scientist can ask is how it came about that the polar bear is so colored. Probably white bears survived in snowy regions, and their offspring tended to survive also, because of their greater protection from enemies, and the white color therefore became characteristic of the species. But the polar bear has no consciousness of his color, and does not choose to be white—nor could his ancestors have chosen to be white. A polar bear in a zoo in the temperate zone remains white; he would probably change his character, and become more adapted to zoo conditions, if he could, or if he had any consciousness that could control such adaptation. But in the zoo the polar bear is protected by man's aid, and even in thousands of years he would not change.

Instances of adaptation in nature are so remarkable that we are inclined to marvel at them. Cacti and other desert plants are particularly fitted to the dry sand and great heat of arid wastes. Many seeds are tufted to be borne by the wind, or barbed to be carried in the furry coats of animals or even on human trouser legs, thereby effecting wide dispersal of the offspring. We watch a bee invading a flower, to secure nectar or pollen, and wonder at the structure of the blossom which so effectively provides that the hairy bee shall brush off the pollen and carry it to other flowers, to bring about cross-pollination of the species. Some flowers attract bees, others attract butterflies and moths. The butterfly has a long tongue-like "mouth," called a proboscis, with which it can probe the sacs of certain flowers which contain a deposit of nectar, on which the insect feeds. Grasshoppers that live in grass are green; there is an insect called the walking stick, which looks almost exactly like a twig of the tree or bush on which it lives; there are moths which rest on the bark of trees in the daytime and are mottled to look exactly like that bark. The chameleon changes his hue, to match more nearly the surface on which he rests. The striped tiger blends with the foliage of his tropical jungle, and is not so much protected from enemies (chiefly man) as hidden from his prey.

Examples are plentiful. Walking and scratching birds have feet and claws developed seemingly for that purpose. Flying birds do not walk so well, and seldom, if ever, scratch. Hawks and eagles have claws for clutching and carrying prey. Ducks and other swimming birds are web-footed,

their feet serving as paddles. Even among higher mammals there is grea
adaptation, particularly in the teeth. Incisors, canines, and molars ar
variously developed to suit the eating of grass or other green vegetables
or to rend and chew meat. The giraffe's long neck enables him to ea
leaves from comparatively tall trees. The bat has his forelimbs adapted
to flying (it is the only mammal capable of true flight), and catches
insects on the wing or feeds on luscious fruits.

Such adaptations are always inherited; they are characteristic of genu
and species, and have so existed for hundreds of centuries. But most or
ganisms are capable of showing particular and incidental adaptation t
environment, in slight degrees. Plants develop differently if conditions c
light, moisture, and temperature are changed. Even human beings tak
on a coat of tan under prolonged exposure to the sunlight. Such tem
porary adaptations in the individual are not inherited. They must b
distinguished from the more permanent variations due to heredity.

THE CHEMICAL CYCLE OF LIFE

Specially adapted plants take their part in the great chemical cycle o
life: the compounding of inorganic elements into organic protoplasm
and the later breaking down of that protoplasm once more into inorgani
substances. Green plants make protoplasmic material out of carbo
dioxide and water, under the action of sunlight and chlorophyll, by th
process called photosynthesis. The living plant gives off some waste prod
ucts; and when the plant dies it wilts and "decays." What we call deca
is really the outward manifestation of the result of a living process—th
action of plants which live on dead organic matter.

When a stale piece of bread becomes "moldy," we regard it as spoiled
It has become the food of a saprophyte, a kind of tiny plant, which grow
on the bread and will consume some of it. Dead organic matter is fee
upon by a succession of organisms, mostly bacteria, which reduce it ulti
mately to inorganic compounds or elements, bringing about decomposi
tion or decay. These inorganic substances are returned to the air or the
soil, where they may again be utilized by green plants or by animals a:
oxygen, carbon dioxide, ammonia, or nitrates, phosphates, and the like
Meanwhile, living plant and animal organisms are eaten or consumed a
food by other organisms, which eliminate waste materials, or are de
composed when they in turn die and decay. So it is an endless cycle, from
inorganic to organic, and from organic to inorganic matter.

PARASITES AND SYMBIOSIS

Organisms which live on other organisms, taking their nourishment
from those organisms (called "hosts"), are called *parasites*, as we men-

tioned earlier. They are to be distinguished from animals which prey on other organisms—that is, herbivorous animals which eat living plants, or carnivorous animals which eat living animals or kill them and feed on the carcass. A parasite takes up its abode on the body of its host, and feeds on it without killing it, or without killing it immediately.

What we call disease is often the manifestation of the activities of parasites (usually bacteria or protozoans). Potato blight, a disease of potato plants, is caused by a parasitic fungus which feeds on the potato. Smuts, rusts, blights, mildews, and rots are caused by fungi, or sometimes by bacteria. Human diseases caused by bacteria include pneumonia, tetanus (lockjaw), tuberculosis, diphtheria, cholera, and typhoid fever. What we regard as the disease of typhoid is a sum of the symptoms of bacterial invasion of the human body by a particular microorganism.

Mistletoe is a familiar parasitic plant of a higher order of development. It takes as its host various kinds of trees, often the oak. Some mistletoe has chlorophyll (green leaves), and thus supplies some of its own food by photosynthesis, but it penetrates the stem of its host to get water and dissolved mineral substances, for the mistletoe has no roots in the soil.

Parasitic animals are particularly obnoxious to man, especially such insects as fleas, mites, ticks, and "cooties." They often live on furred animals; everyone knows how likely a dog is to have fleas. Some diseases are caused by animal organisms (protozoans) which invade the human body. Notable among them is malaria, caused by the malarial parasite, which requires both man and a particular kind of mosquito (Anopheles) for its development or life cycle. The female mosquito bites a person infected with malaria (or someone who has had malaria and is not completely cured), and takes some of the malarial organisms into its body. There the malarial parasite undergoes the sexual phase of its existence, and forms slender, pointed cells which are later injected into some other human being by the mosquito, shortly giving rise to "chills and fever" which characterize the disease. Malaria can be transmitted only by the female Anopheles mosquito. Other examples of human parasites are the trichina worm (which is obtained by eating infected uncooked or insufficiently cooked pork, and inhabits human muscle) and the tapeworm, which lodges inside the intestine.

A parasite is usually harmful to its host, if only in a small degree. The phenomenon of two organisms living together for mutual advantage is termed *symbiosis*. A lichen, which looks like a single plant, is an example of symbiosis—of an alga and a fungus living together, closely associated, seemingly one plant; the alga performs photosynthesis and provides extra food for the fungus, and the fungus secures moisture for the alga. Ants which tend aphids (plant lice) like "cattle" are another instance of sym-

biosis. The aphids are protected by the ants, and the ants take the swee
secretion or "milk" of the aphids.

Some bacteria are particularly adapted to utilizing free nitrogen of th
air, forming nitrates, which they leave in the soil. Such bacteria live in a
kind of union with legumes (beans, peas, clover, alfalfa, etc.). If a crop
of some legume is planted, it will have the effect, because of these bacteria
of restoring nitrates to the soil. This is one of the reasons for the "rota
tion of crops" in farming.

EVOLUTION

The evidence of the obvious relationships between different animal
and plants, their similarities as well as their differences, their adaptation to
their environment and to other organisms, their anatomical structure and
their physiology, the essential unity of all living things, all point to the fac
of evolution. The *theory of evolution,* given its most noted exposition b
Charles Darwin (1807–1882), accounts for the development over long
periods of time of higher, more complex organisms from lower, or sim
pler ones—a process of extremely slight modifications throughout many
generations. Embryology offers supporting evidence, for every multicel
lular organism begins as a single cell—just as originally multicellular or
ganisms evolved from unicellular ones.

Evolution does not mean that "man is descended from a monkey." I
may mean that man and monkey are different branches (apes and mon
keys forming lower branches) of the same main stem of the tree of life
No one can deny that man and the anthropoid (man-like) apes show re
markable similarities in anatomy: they are classed together in the anima
kingdom as *primates.* The "missing link," so called, often mentioned i
popular discussions of evolution, will not, if ever found and so designated
link man directly with any ape, but it may link man and the apes to a
common, though very remote, ancestor.

EVIDENCE FROM ANATOMY

A student of anatomy is impressed with the evolutionary evidence o
vestigial structures; they occur more commonly in animals than in plants
and are still inherited, generation after generation. The vermiform ap
pendix of the human body, which may be inflamed in the condition
called appendicitis, is probably such a vestigial structure—that is, may
have served some vital capacity in a remote human ancestor, although it is
dormant and useless in man today. It is actually used by certain lower
animals for digestive purposes. Another vestigial structure is the remnant
of the nictitating membrane in the eye. In the inner corner of the human
eye is the so-called semilunar fold (readily to be seen in a mirror); this

fold is the vestige of the nictitating membrane which, in birds, comes down over the eyeball in place of an eyelid.

The human animal has a vestigial tail. The coccyx, or the peculiarly shaped lower end of the vertebral column, is reminiscent of a movable tail. Indeed, it is strikingly similar to the vestigial tail bones of the gorilla or of any other tailless ape. Snakes have vestigial limbs in their skeletons. Horses, and other ungulates (hoofed animals), actually walk upon one

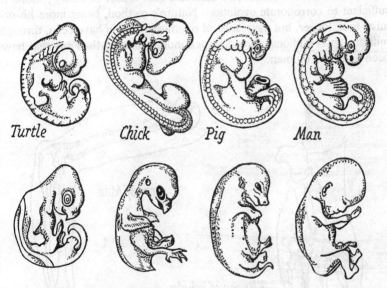

Turtle　　　　Chick　　　　Pig　　　　Man

Fig. 14. Early and later embryonic stages of various animals compared.

extended toe; the other digits are present higher up the leg as vestigial structures. All mammals exhibit signs of having descended from five-toed ancestors. Even the external human ear may be regarded as vestigial, for it serves no vital purpose in modern man, although in such animals as dogs and horses the outer ear may be slightly moved to catch sounds.

EVIDENCE FROM EMBRYOLOGY

The embryo, in its development, recapitulates the evolution of the race. In the first stages of development from the zygote (fertilized egg), animal embryos are remarkably alike. The very early stage of the embryo of a pig appears outwardly almost identical with the embryo of a human being at a comparable stage. As development proceeds, they become less and less alike, each embryo developing the peculiar characters of its parents.

All animal embryos exhibit, at some stage in their development, rudimentary gills or "gill slits." This indicates that all animals went through, in a more or less remote period of evolution, an aquatic existence. Land animals, therefore, are evolved from aquatic ancestors. Lungs, with which to breathe air, came comparatively late.

Breeding and the familiar practices of the cultivation of plants and the domestication of animals have resulted in the formation of practically new species of both plants and animals. This aspect of biology alone is sufficient to corroborate evolution. Nature's method, being more hit-or-miss, took longer, but the results of organic evolution have been, through millions upon millions of years, much more profound than any that have been achieved by man.

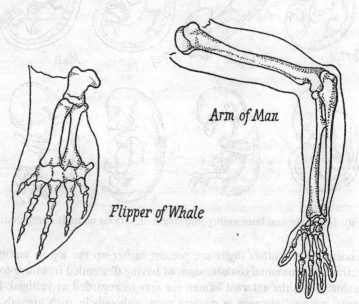

FIG. 15. Flipper of whale and arm of man compared.

The scientific classification of animals and plants points up the evidence for organic evolution, for organisms are classified strictly according to their similarities. All the animals of one species closely resemble one another; two domestic cats are noticeably alike. But the domestic cat differs markedly from a lion, though there are points of similarity—cats, lions, tigers, and leopards all belong to the cat family. Cats are like horses and cows and bears in that they suckle their young—a point of common likeness in all mammals.

Zoological (and usually also botanical) classification proceeds from higher to lower groups, from phylum to class, then, in descending (less inclusive) groups, through order, family, genus, species, and subspecies. Every organism is given a scientific name, usually Latin (so that it may be understood by all scientists, no matter what their native tongue), of two parts—first, the name of the genus to which the animal belongs, and, second, the name of the species. The giant kangaroo, the largest and best-known species, has the scientific name *Macropus giganteus*—species *giganteus* of the genus *Macropus*. Kangaroos, or most of the pouched mammals commonly known by that name, belong to the genus *Macropus*. Kangaroos of all genera belong to the family Macropodidae. This family belongs to the order Marsupialia, which includes not only the kangaroos, but also wombats and opossums. The Marsupialia is an order of the class Mammalia, which is the highest class of the vertebrates, including all animals which suckle their young and have mammary glands for that purpose. The vertebrates, scientifically designated as the Vertebrata, are a division of the phylum Chordata (chordates), which includes all organisms having a notochord at some stage of development.

THE EARTH'S BIOLOGICAL PAST

The study of the earth's crust or rocky envelope (called the lithosphere) reveals that in remote ages of the past there were other forms of plant and animal life, ancestors of the living organisms of today. Some of those former inhabitants of the earth's surface died and fell into water or sand in such a way that their bones became preserved or have left a clear impression in hardened rock. These remains of organisms are called *fossils*. The study of fossils is called *paleontology*. Fossils are prime exhibits as evidence of organic evolution.

The land surface of the earth is constantly being altered under weather conditions and as a result of erosion (wearing away) by rivers, ocean waves, rain, and the like, and by sediments laid down by standing bodies of water or by running streams. Geologists, who have studied the earth's rocks, know that the layers were put down, in past ages, in a definite order, the lowest layers (unless displaced by earthquakes) being the oldest. Physical and chemical changes in those layers (or strata) of rocks give a fair indication of their age, or of their age relative to other strata. The stratum in which a fossil is found is the key to the age of the fossil and to the time in which the animal or plant lived.

Fossils are of three kinds. The rarest, and the most desirable for study, are actual organic remains, marvelously preserved by some accident of nature. Most fossils, however, are really rocks; they are petrified forms of bones or hard parts of plants, in which mineral matter has supplanted the original organic matter. Many fossils are molds or casts, such as footprints in mud that later hardened into rock, or shapes of skeletons that decayed but left their form as a kind of mold for deposited sediment. Specimens of the various kinds of fossils can be seen in a museum of natural history.

The earliest forms of life on the earth were certainly unicellular, and probably were bacteria. Just how life began is still a mystery. Exceptionally favorable conditions probably existed at some time in the remote past, for the earth was warmer and more moist millions of years ago, and warmth and moisture are especially conducive to life, as is clear from the profuse life in the tropics today.

From these primitive unicellular organisms, higher organisms developed, becoming multicellular and specialized. Higher invertebrates appeared—giant "insects," huge scorpions, and the like, and many fishes that seem odd and strangely monstrous to us today. Ferns as large as trees grew in those remote warm and marshy ages. Amphibians appeared, and primitive reptiles. During the late Paleozoic Era the great plants died, became buried under layers of soil, and gradually solidified into the coal deposits, also forming adjacent petroleum and gas deposits so important to the machinery of our modern civilization.

In the Mesozoic Era, the Age of Reptiles, giant "monsters" stalked the earth. This was the time of the dinosaurs, pterosaurs, ichthyosaurs, plesiosaurs, and others. Reptiles swam in the sea, flew through the air, and roamed over the land. Brontosaurus was a herbivorous dinosaur 66 feet long and probably weighing something like 37 tons! Birds and mammals began to appear in the late Mesozoic Era. Birds are directly descended from reptiles; feathers are modified scales. The giant reptiles became extinct at the end of the Mesozoic Era, and made way for further development of birds, and for the Age of Mammals, which brings evolution down to our own time. We are living in the Psychozoic Age of Recent or Cenozoic time—in the age of human beings, so to speak. Meanwhile, plants had further developed, the seed-bearing plants taking the place of the early pteridophytes (ferns and such), and the angiosperms becoming the dominant type as they are today.

The trend of evolution has ever been from general types to more highly specialized and more specifically adapted forms of life. The highly adapted organism does not revert to the more general type, and cannot give rise to a new general type, but can evolve further in the direction of greater specialization.

Evolution has proceeded by descent, with the inheritance, in some way, of modifications. The process has been extremely gradual, operating

PSYCHOZOIC

CENOZOIC

MESOZOIC

PALEOZOIC

PROTEROZOIC

FIG. 16. Life in various stages of the history of the earth. Reading from bottom to top, we see the successive geological eras and the principal forms of life which are believed to have originated in each era.

through many millions of years and through countless millions of generations. Natural selection and the inheritance of acquired characters have both been advanced as theories to account for the fact of evolution. There is no scientific evidence to support the idea of inheritance of acquired characteristics. Much evidence supports a modified theory of natural selection, which is widely accepted by scientists today.

THE STORY OF MAN

That man is an animal cannot be disputed, in the light of anatomical, physiological, and psychological evidence. Further, evolutionary evidence, particularly fossils, indicates that man has descended from a remote animal ancestor. Man is classified as belonging to the primates, the highest order of the class Mammalia. The primates are divided into six main families: Lemuridae (lemurs), Hapalidae (marmosets), Cebidae (monkeys of South America), Cercopithecidae (monkeys of the eastern hemisphere), Simiidae (anthropoid or man-like apes), and Hominidae (human beings). Man is of the species *Homo sapiens,* of which there are several racial varieties or subspecies.

The anthropoid (man-like) apes include the chimpanzee, gibbon, orangutan, and gorilla. They are alike in having no tails, in having man-like teeth, in walking somewhat erect like man, in having short thumbs, and in having more brain development than the lower primates.

Man is unlike the anthropoid apes and other primates in that he has a truly highly developed brain and especially a large cerebrum; in having a vertically long face; in having a distinct chin; in having smaller teeth; in walking definitely erect, with an upright vertebral column or backbone; in having arms shorter than the legs; in having a highly opposable thumb (which can be brought against the forefinger), but without an opposable great toe; and in being able to speak. Man has reached his remarkable development as a civilized being because of two important characteristics: the opposable thumb, making him a tool-using animal, and high brain power, giving him the intelligence which has enabled him to dominate the earth.

The evolutionary family tree of man shows the following known ancestors in this order: primitive primates in the Eocene and Oligocene periods, a primitive anthropoid in the Miocene, the famous Ape Man (*Pithecanthropus erectus*) of Java in the Pliocene, the Heidelberg Man (*Homoheidelbergensis*) a little later in the Pleistocene, Neanderthal Man (*Homoneanderthalensis*) still later in the Pleistocene, and, about the same time, Cro-Magnon Man, the immediate ancestor of *Homo sapiens.* The modern races of man all developed from the Pleistocene ancestors just named. The bushmen of Australia are thought to be the most primitive living examples of the human race. Meanwhile, another link in the chain has been unearthed in China, the Peking Man.

How old is man? It is a difficult question, but probably man's ancestors have roamed the earth for a million years and perhaps longer. The Java Ape Man is sometimes placed at about 500,000 years ago, and the Cro-Magnon race at less than 100,000 years ago.

Paleontology and geology are still young sciences. Every year furthers our knowledge of the story of man, and a final word cannot yet be said about man's remote and fascinating past. The possibilities of finding further fossil human remains are by no means exhausted. "Diggers" are searching assiduously, and carefully correlating their findings.

BIOLOGY IN RELATION TO DAILY LIFE

Biology, and the science of life, includes within its scope the structure and functioning of the human body; and at various points in this section we have indicated how basic biological principles express themselves in the human body's activities. The subject of human anatomy and physiology is of such major concern to all of us that it is customary to devote a separate course to this very personal aspect of biology. The term Physiology is used to describe this division of biology, and we present it here as the next section of this book.

EXAMINATION QUESTIONS

1. What is biology?
2. What is the word used to describe living substances in contrast to non-living substances?
3. Name five sciences that biology embraces.
4. What is the basis of all life?
5. In what shape does protoplasm appear under the microscope?
6. As what do the majority of scientists regard life?
7. Describe the method of reproduction known as fission.
8. What is the amoeba?
9. What one-celled animals display both plant and animal characteristics?
10. What are the tiniest and simplest plants called?
11. What are the tiny threads by means of which some bacteria move called?
12. What forms the woody portion of plants?
13. What are the voluntary muscles?
14. How many different species are included in the plant kingdom?
15. What group of plants comprise those bearing seeds?
16. Tell the difference between annual, biennial, and perennial plants.
17. What ten chemical elements do plants require for their growth?
18. By what process does soil water enter the root cells of plants?
19. What form do plant fats take?

20. Why will a house plant "lean" toward a window?
21. Explain how yeast cells reproduce by budding.
22. What part of the flower of a seed-bearing plant produces the pollen?
23. What is pollination?
24. What contains the seeds that reproduce the plant?
25. How many species are there named and catalogued in the animal kingdom?
26. What constitutes the largest single group of the animal kingdom?
27. Do amphibians live in water or on land?
28. How are the highest class of vertebrates classified?
29. What is the classification of animals that live entirely on vegetable matter?
30. What enzyme does saliva contain?
31. How do fish breathe?
32. How do most animals reproduce?
33. What are the female gametes called?
34. How large is the human ovum?
35. What animals are called oviparous?

36. In what animals is the uterus single and undivided in form?
37. How is the offspring attached to the mother in viviparous animals?
38. What glands of the female supply the young with milk?
39. What is genetics?
40. What color will be the offspring if a red flower is crossed with a white flower of the same species?
41. How have seedless oranges and grapefruit been developed?
42. Of what animals is the mule the offspring?
43. With what is the science of eugenics concerned?
44. What is the name of the biological study of organisms in relation to their environment and to other organisms?
45. What is the butterfly's long tongue-like mouth called?
46. What brings about decay in organic matter?
47. What are parasites?
48. In what one way can malaria be transmitted?
49. What is evolution?
50. What evidence shows that man is an animal?

For Further Study

BIOLOGY FOR EVERYONE also called BASIC TEACHINGS OF THE GREAT BIOLOGISTS, by W. Gordon Whaley. (Doubleday & Co., New York.)

THE BIOTIC WORLD AND MAN, by Milne & Milne. (Prentice-Hall, New York.)

FOUNDATIONS OF BIOLOGY, by Lorande Loss Woodruff. (The Macmillan Co., New York.)

GENERAL BIOLOGY, by James Watt Mavor. (The Macmillan Co., New York.)

MICROBE HUNTERS, by Paul de Kruif. (Harcourt, Brace & Co., New York.)

OUR LIVING WORLD, by Elliot R. Downing. (Longmans, Green & Co., New York.)

THE SCIENCE OF LIFE, by H. G. Wells, J. S. Huxley, and G. P. Wells. (Doubleday & Co., New York.)

XXVI

Physiology Simplified

GENERAL DESCRIPTION OF THE BODY

THE HUMAN BODY IS made up of many parts, all working together in a unified whole. The study of the structure of the human body and of its parts is called *anatomy*. The study of the functions of the organs and parts of the body and how they work is called *physiology*. The study of the conditions favorable to normal growth and activity of the body, and of circumstances conducive to good health, is called *hygiene*. The study of the tissues and the microscopic inspection of the materials which make up both external and internal organs is called *histology*.

To understand descriptions of the parts of the body, a few fundamental terms must be defined. The end of the body toward the head is referred to as *anterior* (or *cephalic*); the end toward the "tail" as *posterior* (or *caudal*). The side of the body corresponding to the belly is called *ventral;* the opposite side corresponding to the back is called *dorsal*. These terms apply regardless of the position of the body—whether it is erect, reclining, or otherwise.

In the trunk of the human body, as in all vertebrates, there are two great cavities, one on the dorsal side (the spinal cord, culminating at the anterior end of the brain, protected by the vertebral column or spine), and one on the ventral side (the alimentary canal, stomach, and intestines, running from the mouth to the anus, together with the related organs, such as the liver, heart, lungs, and kidneys). In the dorsal cavity are the organs of control and feeling: the central nervous system. In the ventral cavity are the organs of digestion, respiration (breathing), and circulation of the blood.

The ventral cavity of the human body, as in all mammals, is again divided into two parts by a membrane called the diaphragm. Above this diaphragm (*i.e.*, toward the head) is the chest (or *thoracic*) cavity; below it is the abdominal cavity. In the chest cavity are the heart and lungs, and, behind them (dorsally), the anterior part of the alimentary canal (Fig. 1).

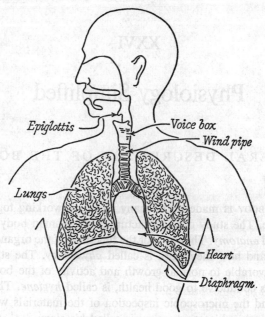

FIG. 1. Position of heart, lungs, etc.

In the abdominal cavity are the stomach (into which the alimentary canal empties), the small and large intestines, the liver, pancreas, spleen, kidneys, etc. What is usually called the stomach from the exterior appearance of the abdomen is the bulge of the massed coils of the intestines. The stomach itself is higher, under the lower ribs. The digestive system terminates in the anus and the genito-urinary organs. The latter are the organs for the elimination of waste liquids (urine) and the organs of reproduction.

Lining the walls of the ventral and dorsal cavities are membranes, moist and smooth, called the *serous* membranes. They have distinguishing names: the *arachnoid,* lining the dorsal cavity; the *pleura* (whence *pleurisy,* inflammation of this membrane), lining the chest; and the *peritoneum* (whence *peritonitis,* inflammation of the peritoneum), lining the abdominal cavity. The skin covers these cavities, on the outside, just as it does the rest of the body. The skin has two layers: the *epidermis,* or outer layer, and the *dermis,* which contains blood (you have perhaps noticed that a very light cut in the skin does not bleed, because the dermis has not been penetrated).

Beneath the skin, and sometimes between the skin and the serous membranes of the body cavities, are the bones (which give rigidity to the body) and the muscles, which move the parts of the body. The muscles of animals form the lean portion of meat, as in beef or pork. The chest cavity opens into the mouth, which is lined with mucous membranes (soft and moist, being kept wet by gland secretions); and it also opens into the nose, which is similarly lined. The *mucous membrane* is an extension of the skin, and has two layers also: corresponding to the epidermis is the *epithelium*, and corresponding to the dermis is the *corium*. The genito-urinary openings are also lined with mucous membranes (so called because their secretions contain *mucus*, the name given to the slippery fluid which moistens them). At the lips and nostrils, and at other points where the mucous membranes meet it, they are continuous with the outer skin.

The arms and legs are made up principally of bones, muscles, and protecting skin, with the necessary blood vessels and nerves. The brain controls the mechanisms of the body and is the center of intelligence. The posterior tapering of the brain leads into the spinal cord, which is a kind of switchboard controlling the telegraph system of nerves that reach to all parts of the body. Along the back, protecting the spinal cord, is the backbone or spine. Surrounding the brain is the heavy cranial bone or skull, which is further protected by an overgrowth of hair.

In animals that go on all fours, the vital parts of the body are protected. The ventral cavity, with its organs of respiration, digestion, and blood circulation, is fairly well hidden since it is toward the ground and between the legs. The back is protected by hair, and the spinal cord is protected by the backbone. The head is protected by the skull and hair. When man began to walk upright, he inevitably exposed the ventral and vital side of his body, and found it necessary to devise artificial protection in the form of clothing, or armor, or a shield to be held in front of him when fighting.

If any piece of the human body is carefully dissected and examined under the microscope, it will be found to be composed of cells. The *cell* is the smallest unit of composition of a living thing. A cell is made up of protoplasm (the basic substance of living organisms), with a nucleus (or center). The cells are massed into parts which make up the body as a whole. Any mass of similar cells is called a *tissue,* as a muscle or a gland.

Many scientists regard the human body as a kind of chemical machine. Many chemical elements enter into its composition; namely, carbon, hydrogen, oxygen, nitrogen, sulphur, phosphorus, chlorine, fluorine, iodine, silicon, sodium, lithium, calcium, potassium, magnesium, manganese, iron, zinc, and copper. Although these numerous elements are present, the body is more than two-thirds water. If you weigh 150 pounds, of that weight at least 100 pounds is water.

The elements named above do not exist in the body in an uncombined state (with a few exceptions), but in compounds, of which there are a large number. The body is known to contain such substances as sodium chloride (common salt), potassium chloride, calcium phosphate, hydrochloric acid (in the stomach), and such organic compounds as proteins, pigments (the coloring matter of hair, skin, blood, etc.), enzymes, fats, carbohydrates, acids, etc. The proteins include albumins, globulins, hemoglobins, proteoses, peptones. In general, the greater part of the material of protoplasm is *colloid,* which means that when evaporated the resultant mass will not form crystals but will be shapeless and gummy. A substance which becomes crystallized when the water has been evaporated from it is called *crystalloid.* Human body cells are made up of a small number of crystalloids and a large number of colloids.

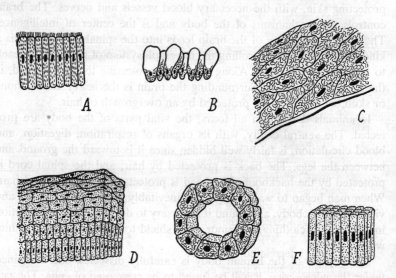

FIG. 2. Surface tissues. *A,* ciliated columnar cells; *B,* single-celled glands (the clear spaces are where the secretions are stored until discharged); *C,* squamous; *D,* stratified epithelium; *E,* cuboidal; *F,* columnar.

Each cell is enclosed in a cell membrane, which keeps it distinct and whole. Between the cells, which lie close together but not necessarily quite touching one another, are spaces filled with a watery fluid called *lymph.* Each cell must be fed, and food reaches it by way of the lymph in which it is bathed. As the cell feeds, it gives off waste products, which are passed into the lymph. The lymphatic fluid, therefore, is the medium in direct contact with the cells, which are the units of which the body is built. The lymph, in its turn, secures nourishment for the cells, from the circulating blood, and gives off its waste products to the blood. The blood is a great transportation system for bringing nourishment to all parts of the body and for carrying waste products from all parts to a central department for the elimination of that waste. The exchange of chemicals between blood and lymph, and lymph and cells, takes place *through* the intervening membranes. These processes of exchange are known as filtration, osmosis, and dialysis.

From the union of male and female cells in conception, through the stages of embryonic development, and from birth onward to adulthood, the cells of the body—of which there are many hundreds of different kinds, each with its special functions to perform—grow and multiply and divide, die and are replaced, in a marvelous and intricate process known as *mitosis*. Groups of cells form tissues and organs, which are teamed and grouped into systems, each with highly important functions. These systems are then co-ordinated into the whole body, which lives and acts as a unit made up of many separate and interacting parts.

Living organisms, of which the human being is the most highly specialized example, have the capacity to develop by growth, to assimilate nourishment or energy for that growth, to eliminate the waste products resulting from the use of that energy, and to reproduce themselves so that descendants may repeat the life cycle through countless generations. In order to maintain life in the face of various kinds of opposition, the living organism has senses which enable it to find food and secure it, or to perceive danger and escape it. Reduced to essentials, by far the majority of the activities of most living organisms are devoted to the finding and eating of food (as a source of energy), and the recovery (in sleep) from the fatigue engendered in the search for food. In man, between times, surplus energy is devoted to other pursuits which make up the great complexity of interrelated human lives in what we call civilization. For man has faculties which lower animals do not possess: intelligence, consciousness, and what they imply—the ability to understand his own activities, and, to some extent, to control them as he may wish.

THE SKELETON

The human body is soft to the touch: the skin is warm and resilient. Were it not for the supporting skeleton, made up of comparatively hard bones, the body would be an almost shapeless mass. The skeleton keeps the various parts in place and facilitates motion and increases the power of action. The skeleton, the framework on which the softer parts of the body are hung, is held together and jointed by the softer muscles, cartilages (supporting tissues), and tendons (the "wires" with which the muscles yank the movable parts about, in response to the impulses from the brain, sent along the nerves), and ligaments (tough elastic and fibrous tissues which connect the bones together at the joints).

THE BONES

The bones of the body are not exposed (except by injury or in a surgical operation), but are imbedded inside the skin, and, for the most part, are rather deeply hidden under muscles and the complex tissues of veins, arteries, etc. Some of the bones, nearer the surface, can be felt, as those beneath the scalp, in the face, at the elbows, knuckles, shins, ankles, and heels. These bones, and the others more deeply embedded, can be studied in a skeleton from which all the soft parts have been removed.

If the adult human skeleton is taken apart, bone from bone, more than 200 separate bones are found. In the growing child there are more, but as he reaches the adult state some multiple bones grow together into one. The *axial skeleton* is the main system of bones to which the limbs, and shoulder and pelvic arches, are attached. It consists of the skull, or head, the spine (vertebral column) or backbone, the breastbone (sternum), and the ribs.

The *skull* consists of 22 bones, eight of which form the upper part or cranium, which is a box holding the brain. The other 14 skull bones form the face. In the vertebral column, from which the whole skeleton may be said to hang, are 33 bones, called *vertebrae;* you can feel them with your finger as you bend your neck or back. They are so jointed that the neck can be turned, and the back can be bent backward and forward. The seven neck bones are called *cervical* vertebrae; the 12 *thoracic* bones come next below, and in the lower back are five *lumbar* bones (in the region where you may have lumbago), five *sacral* bones (united in the adult in the sacrum), and the four tail bones of the *coccyx*. The ribs are arranged in 12 pairs, which are linked to the 12 thoracic vertebrae. The *sternum* (breastbone) connects the upper ribs in front (ventrally). All are united and somewhat cushioned by gristles (cartilages) to prevent their scraping against each other. The cartilage pads of the spine are so flexible that in the morning, after a night's sleep, a man may be almost an inch taller than at night.

The *cranium* is formed of the forehead (*frontal*) bone, the crown (*parietal* bones, two), the base of the skull (*occipital* bone), two bones of the ear regions (*temporal*), and, just in front of the temporal bones,

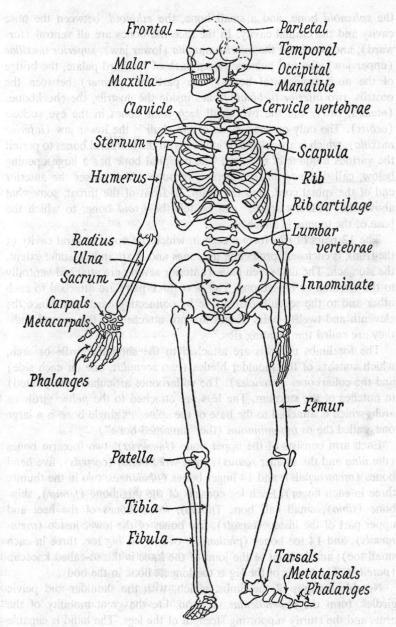

FIG. 3. The human skeleton.

the *sphenoid* bone, and a small bone, the *ethmoid,* between the nose cavity and the cranial cavity. In the face the bones are all ventral (forward), and consist of the *inferior maxilla* (lower jaw), *superior maxillae* (upper jaw), the two *palatine* bones back of the hard palate, the bridge of the nose (two nasal bones), the partition (*vomer*) between the nostrils, two *inferior turbinate* bones inside the nostrils, the cheekbones (*malars,* two), and the two small *lachrymal* bones in the eye sockets (*orbits*). The only movable bone of the skull is the lower jaw (*inferior maxilla*), which is articulated or jointed with the temporal bones to permit the various motions of chewing. The occipital bone has a large opening below, called the *foramen magnum,* through which passes the anterior end of the spinal cord, into the brain. In front of the throat, somewhat above the "Adam's apple," can be felt the *hyoid* bone, to which the base of the tongue is attached.

The 12 pairs of *ribs* form a cage in which the upper ventral cavity of the trunk is enclosed, protecting the lungs and heart and, to some extent, the stomach. The first seven pairs (anterior seven) are attached ventrally to the sternum or breastbone. The next three pairs are attached to each other and to the seventh pair above by connecting cartilages. Since the eleventh and twelfth pairs of ribs are not attached on the ventral ends, they are called the "floating ribs."

The forelimbs or arms are attached to the shoulder girdle or arch, which consists of the shoulder blades (two *scapulas,* one on each side) and the collarbones (*clavicles*). The collarbones articulate (are jointed) in notches of the sternum. The legs are attached to the *pelvic* girdle or arch, which is attached to the base of the spine; its single bone is a large one, called the *os innominatum* (the "unnamed bone").

Each arm consists of the upper bone (*humerus*), two forearm bones (the *ulna* and the smaller *radius*), eight wrist bones (*carpals*), five hand bones (*metacarpals*), and 14 finger bones (*phalanges:* two in the thumb, three in each finger). Each leg consists of the thighbone (*femur*), shinbone (*tibia*), small calf bone (*fibula*), seven bones of the heel and upper part of the instep (*tarsals*), five bones of the lower instep (*metatarsals*), and 14 toe bones (*phalanges:* two in the big toe, three in each small toe); and in front of the joint of the knee is the so-called kneecap (*patella*). The femur of the leg is the longest bone in the body.

Notable features of the limbs, which, with the shoulder and pelvic girdles, form the *appendicular* skeleton, are the great mobility of the arms and the sturdy supporting strength of the legs. The hand is capable of a wide variety of movements, largely because of the thumb, which is so articulated that it can be brought against any or all of the fingers. The foot, with its arch, is admirably adapted to walking and running, and is built to relieve as much as possible the consequent jar to the spinal column. If the arches of the feet are "fallen," the condition known as "flat feet" results, which increases the difficulty of walking and liability to fatigue.

The joinings of the bones are called articulations; there may or may not be the possibility of movement at the point where bones are united with one another. Where movement is possible, the articulation is called a joint; the most movable joints act according to the familiar mechanical principle of the ball-and-socket. Ligaments keep the bones united, and limit the possible movements. The joints permitting the least movement do not have the ball-and-socket arrangement of the upper arm and thigh bones, but are divided into hinge joints (as between the bones of the fingers), pivot joints (in the cervical or neck vertebrae), and gliding joints (which permit very slight movement, as in some of the bones of the feet). A dislocated bone is one that has been torn from its joint.

THE MUSCLES

The muscles are the chief organs of movement in the human body. The muscles, superimposed on the bony skeleton, give the body its characteristic shape, producing bulges and the roundness of limbs. The usual curves of the muscles may be increased or modified by layers of fat (adipose tissue). Some muscle tissue is differentiated to operate the contractions of the stomach, intestines, and other inner organs of the body. The muscles on the bony skeleton are distinguished by calling them *skeletal* muscles (also called, because of their microscopic structure, *striped* muscles); the muscles of the internal organs (*viscera*) are called *visceral* muscles (microscopically, they are unstriped or *smooth*). The skeletal muscles are controlled by voluntary impulses from the brain; the visceral muscles operate automatically, and are therefore described as *involuntary*. However, even the so-called *voluntary* muscles, which we regard as controlled by our wills, may be called into action involuntarily, as in the "start" of surprise or fear and in the blinking of the eye. Cardiac muscle is a special variety of involuntary, striped tissue which exists only in the heart.

A muscle consists of a bulging central portion or belly, tapering at the ends, which are attached by cords or tendons to the skeleton. A muscle easy to feel beneath the skin is the biceps muscle of the upper arm (humerus), which is connected to one end of the scapula and an adjacent muscle, and, at the other end, to the radius of the lower arm. The schoolboy who asks you to "feel" his "muscle," refers only to the biceps, and he bends his arm upward to flex the muscle, or contract it and "make it hard," so that you will be properly impressed.

The motive power of a muscle depends on its ability to contract under a nervous impulse. Thus, if you regard your bent arm as being like the capital letter L, the biceps is in the upright stroke and is attached to the lower stroke (corresponding to the radius of the lower arm) a little beyond the angle (elbow). If the L is straightened into an obtuse angle,

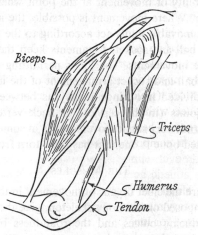

Fig. 4. Muscles of the upper arm.

the muscle is correspondingly extended or relaxed; the lower stroke of the L may now be brought upward into a right angle, or further into an acute angle, by the contraction of the muscle. In a similar way, all the skeletal muscles are suspended by tendons between two different bones or groups of bones. The variety of movements possible in the body shows the great variety of muscle structure and arrangement.

Between and within the muscles are nerves or nerve fibers, which carry impulses from the spinal cord, some of them having been sent down it

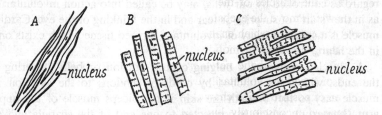

Fig. 5. Contractile tissue. *A*, smooth muscle fibers; *B*, skeletal muscle fibers; *C*, cardiac muscle.

from the brain, to the muscles, causing them to expand or contract. Also around and within the muscles is the intricate network of blood capillaries, which connect the system of veins and arteries, carrying energy (food) to the muscle cells and taking away the waste products of muscular activity.

The smooth or involuntary muscles enclose various viscera in muscular sacs which expand or contract to churn the food in digestion, or to pass the food or waste products along the great tubes of the intestines. These smooth muscles have no tendons. The heart or cardiac muscle is very similar; from before birth until death this muscle tissue (unless it is diseased) tirelessly keeps up its incessant work without our having to think about it. The heart muscle rests only between beats.

The activity of a muscle depends on complex chemical reactions. When the muscle does work (which means that it expands and contracts), it forms waste products within its cells, which are given off into the lymph and the blood stream. These waste products are chiefly carbon dioxide, water, and nitrogen compounds. Normally, the swiftly coursing blood keeps the waste products eliminated, so that there is no muscular fatigue. If, as in extreme athletic activity, the waste products are formed more rapidly than the blood can carry them away, muscular fatigue ensues. Smooth or involuntary muscles contract rhythmically, as in the intestines, or remain contracted for long periods at a time, as the sphincter muscles or openings into the stomach and bladder, without fatigue.

The skeletal muscles and their many duties may be classified as follows: (1) an arrangement of muscles to maintain the erect posture of man (or other "still" positions of the body), distributed chiefly in the front and back of the neck, down the back and over the abdomen, and in front of and behind the lower limbs; (2) an elaborate system of muscles of locomotion, used in walking, running, jumping, etc.; (3) a series of grasping or prehensile muscles, highly developed in the human hand, but almost atrophied in the human foot, and also present to some extent in the lips; (4) the muscles of the jaw (inferior maxilla), used in chewing (mastication), and the muscles of the throat, used in swallowing; (5) the tiny muscles which move the eyeballs and eyelids, enabling us to see all about us; (6) the muscles which enable us to speak and breathe. The muscles of breathing are kept in motion by an involuntary relationship to the autonomic or sympathetic nervous system. It is impossible to stop the motions of breathing voluntarily for more than a few minutes at a time.

The erect posture which characterizes the human body in its activities is maintained unconsciously, but is nevertheless controlled by the nervous system. Certain activities, such as standing upright, are learned with difficulty at first (in early childhood), and then become seemingly automatic, being taken over by a division of the brain called the cerebellum. That standing upright is controlled by nerves of consciousness which keep in proper position a large number of muscles, though we are not aware of it, is proved by the familiar fact that if a person is struck on the head into unconsciousness, or if he faints, the body immediately drops to the ground, even though no bone or muscle is injured.

Exercise keeps the muscles in good condition, and, moderately indulged in, keeps the body "feeling good." Muscles may be made to grow in size and strength by use, as is shown by the large biceps of men who engage in heavy manual work.

THE NERVOUS SYSTEM

The control of the many functions of the several parts of the human body depends on an intricate nervous system, which may be likened to a carefully co-ordinated telegraph organization, sometimes controlled by the brain and sometimes activated by automatic or semi-automatic "control boards." The impulses are usually due to some sensory reaction of sight, hearing, taste, smell, or touch. If someone says to you, "Look there!" your sense of hearing transmits the sound of the words to your brain, and in response, your brain sends the necessary (and highly complicated) messages along the proper nerves to the proper muscles to move your head and eyes as may be required in order to look as directed. The impulse may be involuntary, as when you jump for safety if an automobile horn sounds loudly almost in your ear.

THE CENTRAL NERVOUS SYSTEM

You do not stop to think about *what* messages to send along your nerves. The brain takes care of that for you. If you wish to wiggle your big toe, you merely *think the action* and your big toe wiggles! This process seems simple only because the body has become accustomed to it. The nerve channels along which the various impulses are sent, for various movements, were established, for the most part, in early childhood. The baby's experimental movements are the beginning of this process. The relations between things seen and heard and the objects themselves, and the following reactions, are soon learned, never to be forgotten.

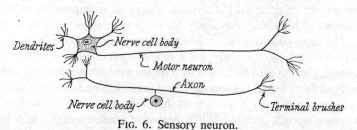

FIG. 6. Sensory neuron.

The brain and the spinal cord form the central nervous system of the body. They occupy the dorsal cavity of the trunk; the brain is enclosed in the skull and the spinal cord is protected by the vertebrae of the spine. Twelve pairs of nerve trunks (lines of nerves which branch farther at their extremities and into side lines along the way) lead out from the brain itself (the cranial nerves), and 31 pairs lead out from the spinal cord (spinal nerves). These 43 pairs of nerve trunks make up the peripheral nervous system. Part of this peripheral nervous system is specialized, forming the autonomic (sometimes called the *sympathetic*) system.

The spinal cord is almost cylindrical in shape, is about three-quarters of an inch in diameter (average), and is about 17 inches long. Its total weight is only an ounce and a half. At its anterior end the spinal cord passes almost imperceptibly into the brain; the division is made, for convenience in anatomy, at the outer margin of the opening (*foramen magnum*) in the occipital bone.

The brain normally weighs a trifle over three pounds in the male, and a trifle under three pounds in the female. The masses of the brain are commonly divided into forebrain, midbrain, and hindbrain, three in all.

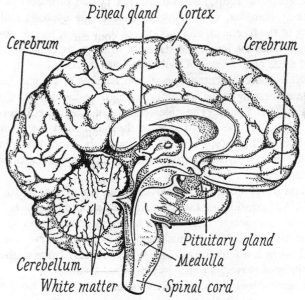

FIG. 7. Cross section of the human brain.

Of these three parts, the forebrain is by far the largest; it consists of two large convoluted masses, called the *cerebral hemispheres*. The midbrain connects the fore- to the hindbrain. The latter includes the *medulla oblongata,* which is continuous with the spinal cord, being a kind of expanded portion of it; the brain itself rests upon the spinal cord somewhat as though the cord were a stem. The deep folds or convolutions are characteristic of the human brain; it is believed that in these folds lie the cells in which are centered human intelligence. The so-called gray matter of the brain is the gray-colored material which characterizes all nerve-cell bodies in the brain; the surface of the convolutions, which is much increased in area by the deep folds, is gray on the surface and white on the inside of the lobes.

The spinal nerves branch variously to different parts of the body, some branches going to organs of sense, some to motor muscles, and so on. Wherever nerves branch into a neighboring trunk line, without making communication through the spinal cord, the network is called a *plexus.* The muscles and skin of the neck, the outer ears, and rear of the scalp are supplied by the *cervical* plexus; the upper limbs are reached from the *brachial* plexus; the *lumbar* plexus, in the lower back, supplies the lower trunks, buttocks, front of the thigh, and inner side of the leg.

The 12 pairs of cranial nerves include the *olfactory* (sense of smell), the *optic* (sense of sight), and others. The system of nerves in the head is extremely complex, controlling motions of the eyeballs and eyelids, wrinkling of the forehead, and motions of the tongue, larynx, soft palate, lips, etc., besides the important senses of hearing, sight, smell, taste, and the local areas of the sense of touch (feeling).

The sympathetic or autonomic system consists of *ganglia* (masses of nerve tissue forming nerve centers) running from the base of the skull to the *coccyx* (tail bone). The chief centers of these are known as the *cardiac plexus* on the dorsal side of the heart, and the *solar plexus,* in the abdominal cavity, "behind" the stomach. From the solar plexus branch the nerves which control, automatically, the stomach, liver, kidneys, intestines, etc.

Impulses travel along human nerves at the rate of 200 or 300 feet per second, which, considering the comparatively short distances in the body, is almost instantaneous. Nerve fibers apparently are not appreciably fatigued by the passage of nervous impulses along them. Nervous fatigue, so called, when it occurs, takes place in the "spaces" between the branching terminals of nerves, and not in the nerves themselves.

Some nervous reactions, called reflexes, take place without the intervention of the brain. Such reflexes, and their nerve paths or channels, are already present in the newborn infant—they do not have to be learned from experience or improved by training. Sneezing is a familiar reflex which is very hard to resist; sneezing cannot be duplicated voluntarily, although it can be imitated. Simple reflex actions are much more common in lower animals than in man.

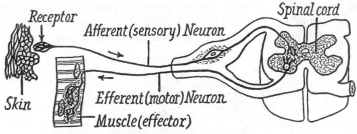

FIG. 8. The path of a simple reflex action.

More complicated reflexes take place in the *cerebellum,* part of the hindbrain. These are not born in us—we must learn them. Such highly complicated locomotor reflexes as walking, running, leaping, swimming, and riding a bicycle, once well learned, are taken over by the cerebellum, which co-ordinates the various stimuli coming from sensory nerves into the stimuli that cause the proper muscles to move the body as desired. For this reason it is only necessary for us to think of walking, and we walk; the cerebellum notes such visible sensory stimuli as the condition of the ground and the direction we are taking, and adjusts the co-ordination accordingly. The cerebellum, by taking over these complicated actions and making them almost automatic, releases the upper part of the brain, or forebrain, for the higher activities of thought which we term intellectual.

The forebrain is the center of human intelligence. The *cerebrum,* part of the forebrain, must acquire all its knowledge, for it is born with none. To acquire knowledge, the cerebrum has effective communication with the central nervous system. The spinal cord, in addition to its branches of nerve trunks, contains also the paths along which "information" is sent to the cerebrum of the brain.

The superficial gray matter of the cerebrum, a thin layer of its convoluted surface, is called the *cortex.* In this cortex are cells which take care of the complex activities we collectively call "thinking," memory, "will power," consciousness, and the like. Various areas of the cerebral cortex are confined to various sense impressions—as the body sense area, the visual area, the auditory (hearing) area, the olfactory (smelling) area, the gustatory (taste) area, and the motor area; in the last named are located the controlling centers of locomotion, when the movements are voluntarily directed from the cortex of the cerebrum instead of from the cerebellum. The consciousness, emotions, memory, and the like, which are believed to originate in the cerebrum, are studied in *psychology*.

The sympathetic nervous system was originally so called because it was believed to bring various organs into sympathy with one another. The better name is the *autonomic nervous system,* signifying an involuntary, practically automatic control of the beating of the heart, breathing, the secretion of sweat, the control of digestion, and so on. There is, however,

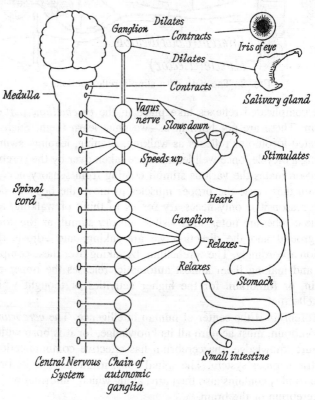

FIG. 9. The autonomic nervous system.

a connection with the sensory stimuli passing through the brainstem to the areas of consciousness, so that the autonomic nervous system is equipped to modify the activity of the "automatic" organs to accord with the immediate needs of the body. In an emergency, as when one is severely scared, the autonomic system can put the body in condition to meet danger: if sensory stimuli suggest impending peril, the autonomic system can dilate the eye pupils, inhibit the secretion of saliva in the mouth, make the hair seem to stand on end (a throwback to primeval times), reduce the blood in the skin's blood vessels (causing paleness), increase the speed of the heart, and hold up the digestive processes temporarily. All these actions, which are involuntary in the sense that they are not consciously controlled, tend to put the body in a state of resistance: the eyes can see more clearly, the stopping of secretions of saliva and digestive activity preserves energy for combat, taking the blood away from the skin reduces the chances of bleeding and also sends it to other parts of the body (as to the brain and muscles) where it may be needed more.

HORMONES

Hormones are the chemical messengers of the body. A *hormone* is a substance which is secreted by one organ (as a gland) and carried in the circulation of the blood to some other organ or organs, which it stimulates. Thus the adrenal bodies, each weighing about half an ounce, located on the kidneys, secrete a hormone called *adrenaline.* This substance keeps the body toned up, so to speak; in an emergency, it is released into the blood stream and causes the same reactions, during fear, as just described. When the symptoms of fear continue long after the cause of fear has been removed, adrenaline is still circulating in the blood.

Adrenaline also relieves fatigue, particularly during great exertion. Getting one's "second wind" and fighting with "the strength of despair" are familiar phenomena. What is regarded as reserve strength is brought to the body by the stimulation of adrenaline released under excitement or exertion. Adrenaline does not add strength to the body; it merely makes available, to the greatest possible extent, the strength already present, by causing the liver to release stored sugar into the blood stream.

The *thyroid,* a gland in the neck (its diseased enlargement is called *goiter*), also secretes a hormone. The thyroid controls the vital processes, collectively called *metabolism,* and is particularly influential in mental development. Lack of thyroid secretion in childhood produces cretinism or a bodily degeneration accompanied by mental deficiency. The condition can be remedied by feeding a medical preparation of animal thyroid. Indeed, the hormones are becoming important medical aids, being prepared from the corresponding glands of lower animals for the greater health and comfort of human beings.

The *pituitary* gland, located at the base of the brain, is known as the master gland, because it secretes hormones which regulate the flow of hormones from all other glands. It secretes a hormone which regulates growth of the long bones. Excess of this hormone produces giantism. Lack of it results in dwarfism. Another pituitary hormone regulates production of milk in mothers. Still another, known as ACTH (adreno-

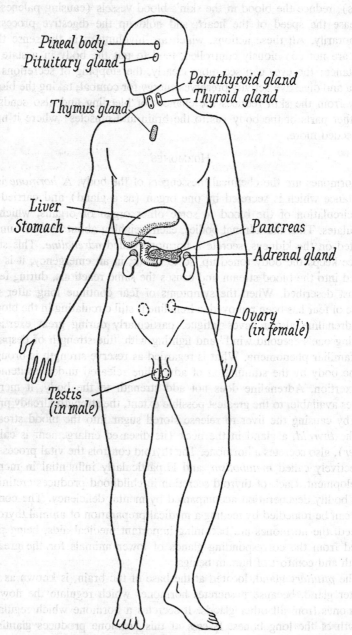

FIG. 10. Location of the endocrine glands in the human body and some which
may be endocrine.

corticotropic hormone), stimulates the production of *cortisone,* a hormone of the adrenal glands essential to mobilizing the defenses of the body when under stress.

The *pancreas* contains the *Islands of Langerhans,* which produce *insulin,* a hormone essential to metabolism of sugar. People suffering from diabetes lack insulin, and consequently their blood and urine contain much sugar which cannot be utilized by the body. Such individuals lack energy and by receiving daily injections of insulin may recover the ability to metabolize sugar and live normal lives.

The *thymus* gland secretes a hormone essential to development during adolescence. The *parathyroid,* four tiny glands located in the thyroids, regulate calcium metabolism. Proper formation of bones, teeth, and muscle action depend upon normal functioning of these glands.

The *sex* glands secrete hormones which determine secondary sex characteristics. The *androgenic* hormone, *testosterone,* produced by the testes, determines the hair, voice, and body characteristics of the male. The *estrogenic* hormones, produced by the ovaries, determine female body traits. Healthy men and women have some of both of these hormones, though males have a preponderance of androgens and females more of the estrogens.

Interaction occurs among the various glands and the nervous system through the stimulation of hormones, which go through the blood stream to all parts of the body.

THE SENSES

The average person thinks of himself as possessing five senses: touch, sight, taste, smell, and hearing. There are at least six other physiological senses: temperature (heat and cold), pain, hunger, thirst, balance or equilibrium, and the muscle sense. The stimuli causing these sensations are received and carried by the nervous system of the body.

The temperature sense is distributed over the whole skin of the body, and also in the mucous membranes of the mouth and the passage to the pharynx, in the pharynx itself, in the upper part of the alimentary canal, and in the openings of the nostrils. The centers which receive sensations of cold are different from those which receive sensations of heat. Such sensations of heat and cold are perceptible only when they represent sudden changes in the temperature stimuli of the body. This may be deceptive, as, when we touch a piece of iron, we have a sensation of cold, not because the iron is any colder than other objects with which we are then in contact, but because iron conducts heat rapidly away from the skin which touches it. Internal changes in the body may also cause heat or cold sensations—as when we have a chill or a fever—and sometimes we cannot tell whether the stimulus is from within or from without.

The brain associates the sensations it receives, not with the *areas of the brain* which are stimulated, but with the *ends of the nerves* which bring the stimuli to the brain. Every sensation is thus referred to the region of the body in which it arises, with the exception of the "external" senses of sight and sound, when the sensation is referred to the *object* which causes it, no matter how far away it may be from the body. If a nerve is stimulated midway of its length, the stimulus is still referred to its *ends;* it is for this reason that a man with an artificial leg appears to have sensations in the limb which has been amputated, for the stump of his leg contains the stumps of the nerve trunks which led to the leg, and if they are stimulated his brain refers to the stimuli to the ends of the nerves—even though they are not there.

The senses, wonderful as they are, are imperfect. We cannot always believe our senses (as we sometimes exclaim), for they are stimulated in ways which we cannot always judge accurately. A sensation of light may be caused by pressure on the eyes; that is why you see "stars" after a hard blow on the head. Optical illusions are familiar to everyone. Since there are corresponding illusions of the other senses, we can never be sure that what our senses tell us about the *sensations of our bodies* is completely indicative of conditions in the world outside of us.

THE EAR

You naturally think of the ear as that appendage on the side of your head. The ear, however, includes much more than that. The outside visible portion is a very small part of the complicated mechanism with which we hear an amazing variety of sounds.

If you could see one of your ears in cross section (that is, sliced through the middle of the parts, rendering visible the "insides"), you would notice that the opening of the external ear leads into a passage which goes to the tympanum, or eardrum. This drum membrane is so constructed that it will respond to a range of sound vibrations varying from 60 to 4,000 vibrations per second (and to an even wider range in people with exceptionally good hearing). These vibrations are transmitted to a series of interarticulated small bones, called (from their shape) by the quaint names of the hammer (*malleus*), the anvil (*incus*), and the stirrup (*stapes*). These bones are so arranged that, in turn, they transmit the sound vibrations (with diminished amplitude but increased power) to the internal ear, in which vibrations are set up in a fluid which affects the ends of auditory nerve fibers and causes in the brain the sensation we know as sound.

The human ear can detect not only noises, but musical sounds or notes, the quality of which depends on the regularity of their vibrations.

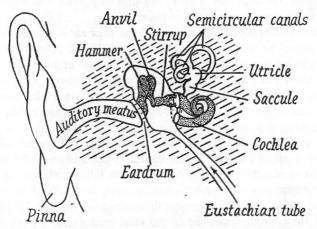

FIG. 11. The parts of the human ear.

The ear can also distinguish loudness (intensity of sound) in various degrees, pitch, and tone quality (the timbre, as, for example, the difference which exists between the note of a cornet and the note of a violin). Indeed, the range of the ear is truly marvelous, for it has been variously estimated that the normal ear can distinguish from 6,000 to 11,000 different tones. The art of music depends on the nice distinctions of which the human ear is capable.

The air pressure on both sides, inner as well as outer, of the eardrum (tympanum) is equalized by means of the *Eustachian tubes,* one from each ear, leading into the pharynx (back of the mouth). When a person swallows, he opens these tubes, and if the barometric pressure (of the atmosphere) has changed, the swallowing permits equalization on the inner side of the tympanum, in the cavity of the middle ear. The pain in the ears which sometimes accompanies ascending high mountains or going down into deep mines may be relieved by frequent swallowing.

Defects of hearing, in the normal ear, include the limitations of its range—some people cannot hear a cricket chirp, its pitch is so high—and the rather marked difficulty of judging the direction from which sounds come. Of course we naturally project sounds to their apparent source; that apparent source, however, is often wrong. It is extremely difficult to tell whether a sound comes from the front or from behind. We recognize best the direction and distance of the human voice, with which we are most familiar; yet we are easily fooled by the ventriloquist.

If the sound is prolonged, we can, by turning the head about, get a fairly accurate notion of its direction and distance. Animals whose outer ears are movable—as dogs and horses—can probably judge the direction of sounds much more readily than can man.

In the so-called *semicircular canals* of the inner ear is located the sense of equilibrium or balance, by which we maintain our poise when standing upright, or our balance when riding a bicycle, or by which we are able to know our position in the water when swimming. This sense of equilibrium is of great importance to aviators, who may often be driving their planes in the dark or in clouds; elaborate tests are given to prospective pilots to make sure that this sense is in no way impaired.

The sense of equilibrium depends, apparently, on the circulation set up in the fluids of the semicircular canals by the motion of the body. It is for this reason that a sensation of dizziness follows whirling or riding on revolving merry-go-rounds. After the body has whirled for a short time, the sense of direction ceases; then, when the body suddenly stops moving, the continued swirling in the semicircular canals gives the impression of movement even though the eyes inform the person that he has stopped. Objects continue to appear to revolve, so the person feels dizzy and totters drunkenly if he tries to walk.

THE EYE

The eye includes the eyeball and its appendages. The eyeball is very nearly the same size in all persons; apparent difference in the size of the eyes is due to a difference in the distance between the angles of the eyelids from end to end of the visible portion of the eyeball.

The eye socket (orbit) is a cavity filled with the muscles which move the eyeball, blood vessels to supply nourishment, nerves, and cushions of fat. The eyeball rotates or moves in the socket, pulled about by suitable muscles. It is protected in front by the eyelids, of which the upper lid is the more movable, being able to cover the entire eyeball in front. The eyes are said to be closed (as in sleep, to protect the eye and also to prevent distraction by visible phenomena) when the upper eyelid is shut down over the eyeball. The inner sides of the eyelids are covered with mucous membrane (the *conjunctiva*), which also covers the front of the eyeball. The edges of the eyelids are lined with hairs (eyelashes) which help to keep out flying particles of dust. Since wherever there are hairs there are sebaceous glands, which secrete a fatty substance to soften and lubricate the hair and skin, the edges of the eyelids are equipped with such glands. When their secretion is excessive the yellowish matter (hard and dried) occurs along the eyelids after a night's sleep, sometimes even being abundant enough to stick the lids together momentarily.

The *lachrymal* or tear-producing apparatus is in the eye. The lachrymal or tear glands supply the moisture which keeps the eyeball wet. Under

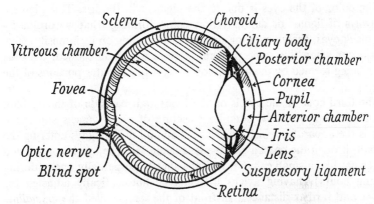

Fig. 12. The parts of the human eye, seen in cross section.

emotional stress, as when one cries, the tears are produced in abnormal quantity and sometimes overflow down the cheeks. Usually, however, the tears are carried off by the lachrymal canals, which open by a pore into the inner corner of each eye (this pore can be seen in a mirror, in either of your eyes, if you pull down the inner corner of the lower lid slightly). Tears carried off into the nose in this way run into the pharynx and are swallowed. This causes the gulping that accompanies prolonged weeping. The act of blinking keeps the moisture from the lachrymal glands evenly distributed over the eyeball, wiping off accumulated dust, washing it clean several times a minute.

The muscles of the eye, attached to the back of the eyeball in the orbit, are so arranged that they can move the eyes from side to side, or up and down, or obliquely, or rotate them, at will. These movements increase the range of vision, which is further amplified by turnings of the head. The two eyes are kept in alignment, moving simultaneously by a nice adjustment of muscles and nerves. If this adjustment is impaired, conditions known as squinting and "cross-eyes" ensue.

The eye itself is the shape of a globe, and is nearly spherical in its main part, being one inch from side to side and nine-tenths of an inch from front to back. The eyeball is protected by three coats of tissue: the outer is the *sclerotic,* of which the transparent part in front of the pupil and iris is the *cornea;* the sclerotic, where visible, is white, forming the "white" of the eye. The second coat includes the *iris,* which is the visible colored portion of the eye; in its center is the aperture through which we see, called the *pupil,* which looks black. A ring of muscle in the iris permits the contracting or narrowing of the pupil; the pupil is smaller in bright light than in diffused light.

The color of the eyes is due to the pigment in the iris. This pigment is always of lighter or darker yellow color, forming what we ordinarily call black eyes, brown eyes, or gray eyes, depending on its intensity. Blue eyes occur when this same pigment is more deeply imbedded, the blue color being formed by the absorption of light in the outer portions of the iris.

The third coat of the eye is on the inner and rear side of the eyeball; it is called the *retina.* Its complex structure of blood vessels and nerve cells is the apparatus which receives the stimuli of light rays entering the eyeball through the cornea and the lens behind it. The eye is constructed somewhat like a small camera, with the shutter perpetually open (during waking hours), having a lens that can be automatically adjusted for nearer and farther distances. In front of the lens (called the *crystalline lens*) is a space filled with transparent *aqueous humor* (water fluid); behind it is the great inner globe of the eye, which is filled with *vitreous* (jelly-like) *humor,* which is also transparent. The lens acts somewhat like an artificial glass lens (although not so perfectly as the finest lenses made by man) to focus on the sensitive retina the rays of light passing through the cornea and pupil.

The "blind spot," one of the defects of the eye, is at the point in the retina where the optic nerve enters the back of the eyeball—this spot is not sensitive to light stimuli. You can prove the existence of your own blind spot as follows: make a cross on a piece of paper and draw a circle about two inches to the right of it. Hold the paper in front of your eyes; close the left eye; with the right eye concentrated on the cross, move the paper away from your face. About ten inches away from the eye, the circle should disappear from your sight. It will reappear a little farther away.

The eye can detect only relative changes in the intensity of light. For example, stars cannot be seen in bright daylight; but from the bottom of a deep shaft, where the daylight does not enter to affect the vision, the stars can be seen at the upper opening of the shaft even though the sun is brightly shining elsewhere in the heavens. A cat's eyes seem to shine in the dark, although they are relatively less bright than in the light, because a cat's eyes reflect proportionately more light (what little light there may be) than other surrounding objects.

Very faint stimuli do not affect the center of vision, but may affect the fringes of the eye. Thus a very faint star may be seen out of the "tail" of the eye, and seem to disappear when one gazes directly at it. Faint impressions received by the fringes of the retina are sometimes not consciously noticed, but the eye acts upon them nevertheless, as when it blinks at a flying dust particle.

Light stimuli affect the retina for a short time after they have ceased; that is, the eye seems to see light for a brief moment after the light has vanished. Rockets and shooting stars thus appear to have luminous tails: the "memory" of the flash in the retina suggests a continuous streak. The stage magician's catchword that "the hand is quicker than the eye" is very true, for there is a limit to the quickness with which the eye can follow a movement.

Images on the retina are upside down, just as they are upside down on the plate of a camera. But we are not aware of this, and cannot possibly become aware of it, because from early childhood our other senses —touch, particularly—tell us how objects are arranged in the world. We quickly learn that an image in the lower retina is really, in the outside world, relatively *above* our eyes. The position of the image on the retina therefore helps us to locate its position in the picture before us at any given moment. The difference, slight though it is, in the images of our two eyes, enables us to judge the distance the object is away from us. However, optical judgments of distance are notoriously unreliable, and optical illusions of various kinds are extremely common. It is not always possible to believe what we see; the expression, "I could not believe my eyes," may sometimes be quite truthful.

Color vision is determined by special cells known as rods and cones, located in the retina. Normal eyes have a very good color sense. Some "color-blind" people do not distinguish between reds and greens. Difficulty with other colors is more rare. Distinguishing the finer tints and shades of color seems to depend somewhat on practice; women, being more familiar with colors, are usually more expert in picking them out than are men.

THE CIRCULATORY SYSTEM

THE BLOOD

The functions of the blood include not only carrying food and oxygen to the cells and carrying the waste products away, but also uniformly distributing heat over the body, properly dissipating excess heat, carrying the various hormones from organ to organ, and defending the body against dangerous organisms such as germs and bacteria, which, if unopposed, may cause death.

The blood—the familiar red fluid which oozes out when you cut yourself—reaches nearly all parts of the body, pumped through tubes (*veins* and *arteries,* with their tiny *capillaries*) by a pumping machine (the *heart*). The epidermis of the skin, the hard parts of the teeth, the hair, the nails, the cartilages, the lens and similar parts of the eye, do not have blood circulating through them. With these few exceptions, the blood travels swiftly to every part of the body, to feed and serve all the many thousands of cells.

Blood does not come directly into contact with the cells, except for the cells within itself and in the walls of the blood vessels. The veins, arteries, and tiny branchings of the hair-like tubes called capillaries form throughout a closed system of tubes. In the capillaries, where the blood is thinned out so that its cells can nearly all touch the intervening membrane, the lymph passes from the blood to bathe the tissue cells (the supply of lymph is replenished from the blood stream). The cells are constantly bathed in this watery fluid called lymph. Briefly, the process is this: if the capillaries containing blood are bathed by lymph, which is low in food content, the lymph takes food (energy or nourishment) from the blood, *through* the membranes (by osmosis); if the adjacent lymph is low in the waste products which the blood has picked up from lymph in other regions, it absorbs those from the blood; and so the process continues. The lymph near the muscles will need food and give off waste; the lymph of the kidneys (excretory organs), being kept free from waste by its adjacent cells, will be low in waste and take it from the blood as it flows through neighboring capillaries. The process of exchange, between blood and lymph, of food and waste, is aided by an additional system of lymphatic vessels.

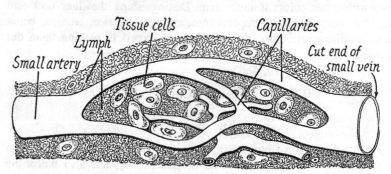

FIG. 13. Body cells surrounded by lymph.

The blood is made up of plasma or fluid (two-thirds) and corpuscles (one-third). The chief corpuscles are the red, which give the blood its characteristic color; when seen singly, or in diluted blood, these corpuscles are yellow. There are also present, in much smaller numbers, the white corpuscles, which are true cells; some of the white corpuscles, called *phagocytes,* literally eat dangerous microscopic organisms, broken-down tissue cells, etc., thereby removing them from the blood stream. The coloring matter of the red corpuscles is hemoglobin, a substance which readily and loosely unites with oxygen in the lung capillaries and carries it to the lymph, which bathes the tissue cells in other parts of the body, where it rapidly gives up the oxygen as needed. The average male has in his blood 75,000,000,000 red corpuscles to the cubic inch; the average female has somewhat fewer. All the hemoglobin in all the red corpuscles of a man weighing 140 pounds weighs only about 1½ pounds. Yet this hemoglobin, distributed in the circular red corpuscles as the blood stream passes through the lung capillaries, presents an effective area of more than 3,000 square yards exposed to the oxygen of breathed-in air every thirty seconds.

The red blood corpuscles are replaced from the red marrow of some of the bones of the body, where they are manufactured. Broken-down or worn-out corpuscles are picked out of the blood (so far as is known) by the spleen, one of the abdominal organs; the hemoglobin from these "old" corpuscles is passed on to the liver, where it is disintegrated.

The blood represents about a twentieth of the total weight of the body; in a man weighing 160 pounds, the blood constitutes about 8 pounds.

When foreign organisms (microscopic in size, being bacteria or germs, also called microbes) enter the body, they do so through abrasions of the skin, cuts, wounds, etc., and through the mucous membranes or the walls of the alimentary tract. Some infections are poisonous because of the substances they give off; others act upon the tissues, tending to destroy them. Various protective mechanisms known as *antibodies* are set up by the body, usually in the blood—first, to prevent the entry of such organisms into the body, and, second, to resist infection once it has set in. Many sicknesses are manifestations of the body's fight to resist infection. The physician aids the resistance of the body with medicines which do one or more of several things—aid the body's natural strength, counteract fatigue, help to kill the invading organisms, or help to offset the poisons or toxins produced by them. On the tendency of the blood to immunize itself against infection by foreign organisms is based the use of vaccinations, antitoxins, and serums as preventives of disease.

Another protective mechanism of the blood—or chemical reaction, as it should be called—is coagulation. You have noticed that when you bleed, the blood flows smoothly only at first. Almost at once—unless the cut is very large, or an artery has been severed (when a doctor should be summoned immediately)—the blood begins to harden and darken. A clot is formed which effectually stops the bleeding.

THE HEART

The heart is a kind of pump which keeps the blood in motion throughout the body during life. When the heart stops beating for any length of time, death occurs. Connected with the heart are the arteries and veins, which immediately branch into a complicated network of tubes, known collectively as the blood vessels. The arteries carry blood *from* the heart; in their narrowest branches the arteries become the tiny hair-like tubes called capillaries—it is these capillaries which are present in the dermis of the skin, and all the other parts of the body, tissues, muscles, membranes, walls, and so on. The capillaries branch finer and finer, until they connect with and expand into the smaller branches of the veins, which carry the blood—full of waste products, and having lost its oxygen—back *to* the heart. The heart pumps the blood into the arteries again, and they then carry it to the lungs, where it is refreshed with the oxygen of the air. This cycle of circulation is kept up endlessly while life lasts. The steady beat of the heart can be felt in arteries near the skin, particularly in the wrist, where the "pulse" may be counted to determine the rate of the heart beat. The normal beat of the heart is about 70 times each minute, though it varies with age, sex, and activity.

Although the heart is commonly thought of as being on the left side of the chest (because its beat can be more strongly felt to the left), it is actually situated almost in the center, just above the diaphragm. The "heart shape" used in Valentine symbols is a good approximation of the shape of the human heart, though the heart itself is less definitely outlined—it does not have the deep indention at the top nor the sharp point. The membrane surrounding the heart is called the *pericardium*. The internal membrane is the *endocardium*. The heart wall itself is mostly muscular tissue, mingled with blood vessels, nerve cells, etc.

The heart is divided into two chambers, and each chamber is divided into the *auricle,* into which the veins lead, and the *ventricle,* into which the arteries lead. Running into the heart at its "top" are a mass of arteries and veins, which lead, in various directions, to the greater branchings in the farther parts of the body, and to the lungs (pulmonary veins and arteries). The main artery is the *aorta,* at the back of the chest, which further branches to the head and brain, the arms, and other important parts. Various valves in the heart control the inflowing and outflowing blood.

A close study of the blood vessels shows us that a capillary blood vessel is about 1/1500 of an inch in diameter—so small that only two, or at most three, red blood corpuscles can race through it side by side. The work of the blood—its dispensation of nourishment and oxygen and its picking up of waste—is done in the capillaries.

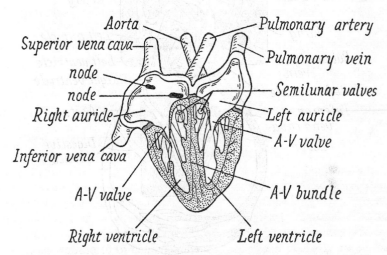

FIG. 14. The internal structure of the human heart. *A-V* stands for *auriculoventricular*.

As we have mentioned, the capillaries, at their "ends," branch into the veins, which lead back to the heart. Various valves throughout the system of blood vessels prevent the blood from flowing backward, as it might do between heart beats from the attraction of gravity or other causes if it were not prevented. The arteries are more deeply imbedded in the body and limbs than the veins, for they carry the fresh blood, full of oxygen from the lungs, and are more vital. The veins are frequently near the surface, and appear blue (or bluish red), because the blood they carry is loaded with carbon dioxide (formed when the tissue cells utilize oxygen); venous blood does not appear blue when a vein is cut, because the moment it touches the air it is immediately oxygenated.

The dark bluish-red blood which the arteries carry from the heart *to* the lungs has been brought back to the heart from other parts of the body. This impure blood is forced through the capillaries of the lungs, where it gives up its carbon dioxide (which is breathed out in exhalation) and takes up oxygen (by means of its hemoglobin), becoming bright scarlet in color. This oxygenated blood returns *from* the lungs to the heart by way of the pulmonary veins. Elsewhere in the body the veins always contain "stale" blood and the arteries always carry "fresh" blood.

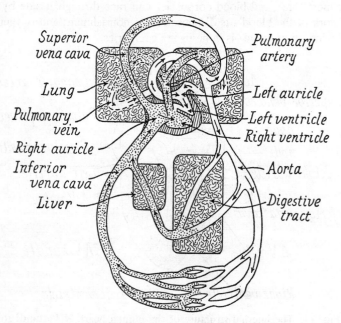

FIG. 15. The course of circulation of the blood in the human body. The stippled vessels contain blood that is poor in oxygen; the clear vessels contain blood that is rich in oxygen.

The beat of the heart is an alternating contraction and relaxation; the contraction is called the *systole,* and the relaxation the *diastole.* As it beats, the heart makes a characteristic sound which a physician recognizes when he listens through the stethoscope, the instrument he places against the chest to check up on the heart and lungs. The beat of a healthy heart is modified—made slower or swifter—by reflex control in the nervous system, which makes the heart beat faster during exertion than during rest, or more slowly during sleeping than during waking hours.

The blood pressure is the force exerted by the blood in the blood vessels, usually measured by physicians in the arteries; it depends on the condition of the body. The blood flows through the body with astonishing rapidity; it takes something like only 23 seconds for all the blood to make the complete round of the circulatory system. Arteriosclerosis, or hardening of the arteries, is a disease of the blood vessels often associated with the process of aging. However, some doctors believe there may be a relationship between arteriosclerosis and excessive fats in the diet. Atherosclerosis is a form of arteriosclerosis.

THE RESPIRATORY SYSTEM

The process of breathing goes on automatically throughout life, whether we will it or no. It is controlled by the autonomic nervous system; it is capable of modification, however, by the power of the will or voluntary nervous system, as when we take deep breaths deliberately, or when we hold our breath. We cannot hold our breath long enough to suffocate, for a nervous impulse set up by the increased carbon dioxide in the blood will shortly force us to breathe, unless we are prevented by some mechanical outside agency, as being strangled about the throat, or by being otherwise deprived of oxygen.

The action of respiration involves the movements of the diaphragm and chest which expand the chest cavity, causing an inflow of air through the nostrils or mouth, then through the pharynx into the windpipe (trachea), thence through the bronchi (branches of the windpipe) into the bronchial tubes, and finally into the ramifications of these tubes which spread in a fine array through the lungs. In the pulmonary (lung) capillaries of the circulatory system of the blood, oxygen is exchanged for carbon dioxide through membranes just as the reverse process (oxygen absorbed by the lymph and then by the tissue cells, and carbon dioxide given off to the lymph and then to the blood) takes place in the many tissues of the body and their adjacent capillaries. Oxidation takes place chemically in conjunction with the action of oxidases; oxygen aids in the burning of fats, carbohydrates, and some proteins. Heat is produced, as in all oxidation (burning is familiar oxidation), which helps to maintain the heat of the body at its normal temperature of about 98.6 degrees Fahrenheit. In addition, the energy required to do the work of the body results from oxidation.

When we inhale, the rib muscles contract, causing the ribs to move up and outward, and the diaphragm contracts, moving from its normal arched position to a flatter one. These movements increase the size of the chest cavity, causing air to rush into the expanded lungs. When we exhale, the rib muscles and diaphragm relax and return to their normal positions, thus decreasing the size of the chest cavity, causing the lungs to contract and expel the air. If the lungs cannot get the amount of oxygen required by the blood, asphyxia (as in exposure to poisonous gases) or suffocation (as in drowning) will ensue.

Everyday actions of the respiratory apparatus include what we call sighing (a long, deep inspiration, or breathing in, followed by a short, large expiration, or breathing out); yawning (the mouth is opened, and the air enters thereby instead of through the nose); hiccoughing (caused by contractions of the diaphragm); coughing (full inspiration followed by rapid expiration, often violent—the purpose is to remove from the windpipe or larynx any irritating matter, such as mucus or food swallowed "the wrong way"); sneezing (similar to coughing, except that the expelled air is sent through the nose, tending to remove irritating matter in the nasal passages); laughing and crying, which are physiologically much alike, and often pass into one another under emotional stress. These acts are primarily reflex; most of them cannot be induced voluntarily, although they can be very cleverly imitated. The tendency to yawn, cough, or sneeze can usually be successfully resisted. Hiccoughing is more difficult to resist, and has to be stopped by occupying the nervous system with some interfering action, as by deep breathing or swallowing water.

THE DIGESTIVE SYSTEM

Foods supply the body with the energy it requires to do its work—in the muscles, tissues, etc.—and with the nourishment necessary to maintain its structure and to repair the breaking down or wearing out of body cells. In children, foods do more: they contribute the nourishment necessary for growth. Normally, a person eats more than energy foods; he also takes into his stomach various accessory foods—water, of which the body requires a fairly large amount; salts; condiments (pepper, mustard, etc.); and the like. Some of these accessories contribute to bodily needs; others merely improve the taste or appearance of food and make it more palatable.

The body requires *vitamins,* which are present in various fruits, fresh vegetables, milk, butter, and, for growing children, in cod-liver oil; and also certain mineral salts, for the most part present in normal foods. A varied diet almost always provides the necessary substances.

TABLE SHOWING VITAMIN REQUIREMENTS OF THE HUMAN BODY

VITAMIN	CHIEF SOURCES	DEFICIENCY DISEASES RESULTING FROM LACK OF VITAMINS
A	butter, milk, yellow vegetables, cod-liver oil, escarole, spinach, beef liver	eye disease, lack of resistance to infection, colds

VITAMIN	CHIEF SOURCES	DEFICIENCY DISEASES RESULTING FROM LACK OF VITAMINS
B complex	whole-grain cereals (B_1, B_2), yeast, liver (B_1), eggs, enriched bread, oysters, turnips, prunes, green beans	nervous diseases, loss of appetite, skin eruptions, impaired growth (beriberi and pellagra)
C	citrus fruits, tomatoes, cabbage, horseradish, peppers, spinach	scurvy, loose teeth and swollen gums, general weakness and restlessness
D	fish-liver oils, sunshine, enriched milk, butter, eggs, oysters, sardines	soft bones and teeth, rickets
E	green leafy vegetables, wheat germ, milk, eggs, muscles of meat, fish	sterility, muscular atrophy (significance of Vitamin E in human nutrition not fully established)
K	green leafy vegetables, liver, cabbage, tomatoes	hemorrhages, inability of blood to clot

The strictly nutrient foods can be divided into three main constituents: proteins, carbohydrates, and fats. Few, if any, foods are made up of one of these alone—most carbohydrates are found in cereals and vegetables (including starch, dextrins, and sugars); fats are found in both meats and vegetables (including stearin, palmatin, and olein); proteins occur principally in animal foods, most of all in lean meats, but are also abundant in milk, eggs, cheese, and gluten of wheat, and much of the substance of beans and peas. Tea, coffee, cocoa, and chocolate, used as beverages, are valuable chiefly for their water content, and enjoyable for their pleasant taste; they are also mild stimulants to the nervous system and should be taken in moderation.

Opening at its anterior end in the mouth, the alimentary canal or food tract passes, in the form of a tube open at both ends, through the ventral body cavity, into the stomach, thence into the small intestine, and finally into the large intestine, which ends in the posterior opening called the anus. The canal is lined with mucous membranes at the two openings, where the membranes are continuous with the outer skin of the body.

The Mouth

The mouth cavity, or *buccal* cavity, opens between the lips and passes into the throat cavity (pharynx). The cheeks enclose the sides of the mouth, which has in its bottom the muscular tongue. In the roof of the mouth is the hard palate, which recedes into a soft portion, called the soft palate (the softening can be felt by moving the tip of your tongue backward across the roof of your mouth); from the back of the soft palate hangs that process called the *uvula,* which you can see at the back of your mouth if you examine the buccal cavity in a mirror. Inside the mouth is the apparatus with which you bite off, chew (masticate), and swallow your food. The biting and chewing mechanism consists of the teeth, set into the gums; they are activated by movements of the jaws. The teeth are of various shapes, *incisors, upper canines* (eyeteeth), *lower canines, bicuspids,* and *molars.* The 32 permanent teeth which grow into the mouth after the "milk teeth" of childhood are lost consist of eight incisors, four canines, eight bicuspids, and twelve molars, symmetrically arranged. The farthest back of the molars are popularly referred to as the "wisdom teeth," because they are the last to grow.

The tongue, being exceptionally mobile, plays its part in mastication; in it are embedded the nerve cells of the sense of taste. The tongue, too, plays a vital part in human speech. If your tongue has a "coat," or if you have a "bad taste" in your mouth, there is probably some digestive disorder causing it.

The moisture in the mouth is a secretion (called *saliva*) of several glands (salivary glands). Inflammation of the parotid salivary glands in front of each ear is called mumps (parotitis). The opening in the back of the mouth is technically called the *fauces;* at the sides of this opening are the tonsils, formed of lymphoid tissue and concerned with the lymph of the body. The normal person can easily do without tonsils: they are so frequently infected that they are often surgically removed.

The cavity in the back of the mouth is called the *pharynx.* Seven openings lead into it or away from it: the two *nares,* or openings to the nostrils; the two *Eustachian* tubes leading to the tympanic cavities of the ears; the *fauces,* from the front of the mouth; the opening to the larynx, or voice box, and windpipe; and the opening to the gullet (esophagus). The *epiglottis* is a plate-like formation of cartilage which acts as a lid to close the tube to the lungs when one is swallowing, keeping food from going down the windpipe. If anything swallowed goes down the windpipe, as sometimes happens, we speak of swallowing something "the wrong way." The gullet, or esophagus, is the tube which forms the upper end of the alimentary canal; it passes from the pharynx down through the neck and chest, through the diaphragm, ending in the stomach.

THE STOMACH AND THE INTESTINES

The stomach is a kind of bag into which the food passes almost directly from the mouth after being swallowed; food is carried down the gullet promptly, and literally dumped into the stomach. The stomach is located just under the lower ribs; what is commonly called the stomach, when referring to the exterior of the body, is properly called the abdomen. The size of the stomach varies to accommodate the amount of food deposited in it.

Through the *pylorus* or pyloric orifice the stomach opens into the

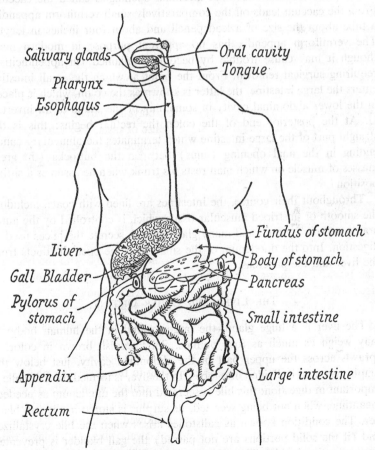

Salivary glands
Pharynx
Esophagus

Oral cavity
Tongue

Liver
Gall Bladder
Pylorus of stomach
Appendix
Rectum

Fundus of stomach
Body of stomach
Pancreas
Small intestine
Large intestine

FIG. 16. The human digestive system.

small intestine. The pylorus is kept closed by a ring of muscle, called a sphincter, which opens only when food in a certain stage of digestion is ready to be passed along to the small intestine. The average length of the small intestine is about 20 feet; it is coiled upon itself in the abdominal cavity, forming, with the large intestine, what are vulgarly called the "guts." The small intestine is divided anatomically into the *duodenum* (the first foot of its length), the *jejunum* (the next seven and a half feet, or thereabouts), and the *ileum* (the remaining eleven feet or so).

The large intestine forms the posterior part of the alimentary canal. It is about five feet long, consisting of the following divisions: the *caecum,* the *vermiform appendix,* the *colon,* and the *rectum.* The small intestine passes into the large intestine a little distance from its anterior end; the closed portion above the small intestinal opening is called the caecum. From the caecum leads off the comparatively small vermiform appendix, a tube about the size of a lead pencil and about four inches in length. The vermiform appendix has no apparent purpose in modern man, though it may cause trouble by becoming inflamed (in appendicitis), requiring surgical removal. From the point at which the small intestine enters the large intestine, the latter is known as the colon, which is placed in the lower abdominal cavity in something of the shape of an inverted U. At the posterior end of the colon the rectum begins: this is the straight part of the large intestine which terminates the alimentary canal, ending in the anal opening (anus) between the buttocks (the great masses of muscle on which man rests his trunk when he assumes a sitting position).

Throughout their course, the intestines are lined with coats, including the smooth or unstriped muscular tissue which is controlled by the autonomic nervous system, and many glands which secrete the juices used in digestion. Into the duodenum of the small intestine open the ducts from the liver and the pancreas.

THE LIVER AND OTHER ORGANS

The liver is a huge gland—the largest gland in the human body: it may weigh as much as four pounds. Soft, reddish brown in color, it sprawls across the upper part of the abdominal cavity, just below the diaphragm, and is divided into lobes. In the liver is formed the gall (bile), important in digestion; this bile is secreted into the duodenum as needed; meantime, when not being secreted, its surplus is stored in the gall bladder. The condition known as gallstones arises when the bile crystallizes and (if the solid portions are not passed) the gall bladder is prevented from secreting its bile. The pancreas is soft, pinkish yellow, and long. It lies along the stomach. Its function is to secrete an important digestive juice, and also the hormone *insulin,* which vitally affects the metabolism of the body.

THE PROCESS OF DIGESTION

The process of digestion is the splitting up by chemical action (chiefly the chemical action known as hydrolysis) of the compound molecules of nutritive foods into simple molecules, which are soluble, and which can pass through the intestinal membranes to the blood in the intestinal capillaries and be carried to the parts of the body which need and can absorb them. Inorganic salts and some other substances are not digested because the body can make use of them in the state in which they are swallowed. Indigestible substances (such as cellulose) are passed through the intestines and excreted unchanged.

The saliva, secreted in the mouth by the salivary glands, is the first of the digestive juices. Besides keeping the mouth moist and dissolving salts and similar substances so that we can taste them, the saliva, due to the action of its enzyme *ptyalin,* has a primary chemical action on starch, converting it into maltose.

When it reaches the stomach, the swallowed food comes in contact with the gastric (stomach) juice, which includes two-tenths of one per cent of hydrochloric acid. Also present are enzymes, including pepsin and rennin, which change proteins to peptones. After undergoing the chemical changes brought about in the stomach, the food is passed into the small intestine, where it is further changed by the juice from the pancreas (which contains more enzymes), and by the bile (which aids in the digestion of fats). The intestinal juice secreted by the walls of the intestines contains the enzymes which bring about the last stages of digestion in foods which have not already been taken care of. The end products of digestion are amino acids from protein, glucose from carbohydrates, and fatty acids from fats.

In both the small and large intestines are colonies of bacteria which are not harmful to the body. These bacteria ferment certain carbohydrates in the small intestine; diarrhea sometimes results when this fermentation is excessive. In the large intestine the bacteria act on certain undigested proteins, causing putrefaction, bringing about the condition of the contents which appears when they are expelled through the anus as excrement (*feces*).

The digestive juices are powerful chemical agents, yet they do not digest the stomach or intestinal walls. Ordinarily, such strong chemicals would harm the cells of the structures which contain them; but it seems that, during life, other chemical factors are present which keep the digestive juices from destroying their glandular sources.

You take the food into your mouth and proceed to chew or masticate it by combined motions of the lower jaw against the upper jaw, causing a grinding and cutting action of the teeth. The food is kept under the teeth by motions of the muscular tongue. A soft mass thoroughly mixed with saliva, the food is swallowed. Swallowing, technically called *deglutition,* involves pushing the mouthful backward to the pharynx or throat cavity. The opening into the windpipe or trachea is closed (you can feel the cartilage called the "Adam's apple" rise in your throat as you swallow, helping to close the epiglottis tightly), and the muscles of the throat contract, forcing the food down the only opening left for it—that into the alimentary canal, of which the gullet (esophagus) is the first section.

The food is propelled along the gullet, downward toward the stomach, by a series of muscular contractions called *peristalsis.* These contractions are set up by reflex nervous action. Reaching the sphincter muscle which closes the opening into the stomach, the food is let into the stomach bag. This sphincter muscle guarding the stomach is usually closed, to prevent the acid contents of the stomach from "backing up" the gullet into the mouth. (However, this sometimes happens, as when you belch severely.) The food, together with other mouthfuls which distend the stomach, is now thoroughly churned and mixed with the gastric juice by a series of contractions. This food mass, called *chyme,* now is in a fairly liquid state.

By a finely adjusted chemical arrangement the food is let into the small intestine through the pyloric sphincter, a small amount at a time, when it is ready for the action of a new mixture of juices. It takes from four to six hours to empty the stomach of an average meal. The pancreas and liver empty their ducts into the small intestine. The food (chyme) is further churned and mixed, and is slowly passed along the intestine (almost five feet an hour) by peristaltic waves.

While passing through the small intestine, the nutrition available in the digested food is absorbed by the blood capillaries, sometimes through the agency of the bathing lymph. Most of the water is retained, however, so that when the remnants of the food mass are given into the large intestine (through the *ileocolic valve,* as it is called), the contents of the intestine are quite watery. Here, under a kind of reserve churning, the last nutritive elements and most of the water are absorbed for use in the body. The solid matter remaining is passed on into the further bends of the colon, and finally into the rectum, where it awaits excretion from the body. The packing of the colon is aided, and helps normal bowel movements, by the presence in food of "roughage," which consists of indigestible matter. The normal meal of mixed foods usually includes enough roughage for good health.

EXCRETION

Excretion of waste products goes on in various ways in the human body. Carbon dioxide is given off in the lungs and breathed out in exhalation. Some water vapor is also given off in the lungs, as can be seen when the warm breath is blown against a cool glass, or on a cold day when the water vapor immediately condenses into small visible globules like steam. More water and occasionally small amounts of other substances are given off by the sweat glands of the skin. The liver plays a part as an excretory organ, for the bile is primarily a waste product, although it has some influence on the digestion of fats in the small intestine.

The principal organs for the excretion of waste fluids, containing waste substances in solution, are the kidneys and their accompanying apparatus. Ducts called *ureters* lead from the kidneys to the bladder. In the bladder the waste fluid, called *urine,* accumulates until it is expelled through a tube called the *urethra,* which has its exit adjacent to, or in conjunction with, the reproductive organs. The average daily excretion of urine varies from 40 to 60 fluid ounces, is usually amber in color, and, normally, is 96% water.

Variation in the chemical contents of the urine indicates temporary or chronic bodily disorders. For this reason, the urine is an important aid in diagnosis, and the physician finds it desirable to have an analysis made of one or more specimens of urine from the patient.

The skin as an excretory organ is of great importance in standardizing the temperature of the body. Evaporation of water from the skin cools it, which explains why one perspires in warm weather.

The sweat glands are the excretory apparatus of the skin. There are some 2,500,000 sweat glands scattered over all the skin surface of the body. The sweat itself is watery, being transparent and colorless, and varying in odor (according to its composition) in different individuals. Dietary differences probably account for most variations in perspiration odor. Perspiration, in some degree, is constantly secreted; it becomes apparent only when it is sufficient to cause small globules of water on the skin. Because the various skin glands are always secreting substances, which dry on the skin, frequent bathing is necessary in personal hygiene.

Characteristically embedded in the skin, more abundantly in some regions than in others (as on top of the head), are numerous hair follicles, with hairs growing out of them. The color of hair is due to pigment contained in it. Accompanying the hair follicles are the sebaceous glands, which secrete a kind of oily fluid in small quantities.

The bodily temperature is maintained at a fairly constant warmth by specially devised nervous reflex mechanisms. The consumption of fuel (energy) in the muscles produces heat, which is dissipated by the blood throughout the body; similar heat produced by the internal organs is dissipated in the same way. The body cools itself by the evaporation of moisture from the surfaces of the skin. Clothing aids bodily warmth by retarding the surface evaporation. The normal temperature of the body varies somewhat in its different parts, between 96.8 and 98.6 degrees Fahrenheit, externally; a clinical thermometer placed under the tongue registers around 98.6 degrees Fahrenheit as the normal temperature of the mouth. Rectal temperature is normally about one degree higher. Above normal temperature occurs in fevers, which usually indicate a pathological condition.

THE VOICE

The human voice originates in the larynx, or voice box, which is enclosed in a kind of receptacle of cartilage in the front part of the neck, visible as a hump under the skin, popularly called the "Adam's apple." This projection is much more prominent in some people than in others. The larynx itself is situated just above the windpipe (trachea), so that currents of air from the lungs readily pass through it, setting in vibration the stretched vocal cords, giving rise to the sounds we know as speech.

The vocal cords themselves are bands of elastic tissue, so placed that they can be variously stretched and set in vibration by currents of air from the lungs. The pitch of the tones used in ordinary speech varies little, although the loudness, which depends merely on the strength of the blast of air used, may vary considerably. Proper pitch is important in singing, and often requires training and practice to maintain. The range of the human voice is normally about three octaves; famous singers have occasionally exceeded this range to a surprising degree. The limitations of individual range cause the division of singers into groups, as soprano, alto, tenor, and bass. The voices of children are pitched much higher than those of adults; in youth, the boy's voice becomes the deeper voice of manhood, and during the period of change his voice may often "break."

The vowel sounds are formed back in the larynx; they are fundamentally musical tones. Singing depends for its effect largely on the stress of vowels. The consonant sounds are made with the voice plus different positions of the mouth, tongue, lips, etc. A few sounds, called gutturals, are made in the back of the throat with the aid of the soft palate and the root of the tongue. Whispering does not involve the true voice; it is a noise made by irregular vibrations, and many of the sounds are necessarily imperfect.

THE REPRODUCTIVE SYSTEM

Reproduction is the general name given to the capacity of a living organism to reproduce itself—to give rise to another organism which will grow into a living thing exactly similar, in all important aspects, to its parent. Parenthood is an important factor in the civilized life of human beings; except for emotional, temperamental, and intellectual differences, all children are physiologically and anatomically very much like one or both of their parents, and, of course, like all other human beings.

THE MALE REPRODUCTIVE SYSTEM

The male reproductive organs are chiefly external. The *scrotum* is a kind of pouch of skin, in which are the *testicles* or *testes,* a pair of glands in which is formed the male sexual fluid, called the *semen.* Inside each testicle are coiled tubules, only 1/180 of an inch in diameter but

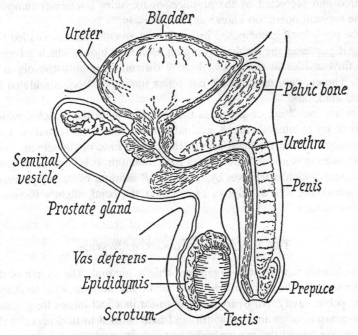

FIG. 17. The human male reproductive system.

about 27 inches long—about 800 in each testicle. These tubules connect with other coiled tubes, which finally empty into a common tube called the *vas deferens.* The vas deferens passes up the inner side of the skin of the groin, above the pelvis into the abdominal cavity, where it connects with the duct of the *seminal vesicle,* on the underside of the urinary bladder.

The seminal vesicles, two in number (one for each testicle), lie on each side of the bladder, and beneath it. Each is about two inches long and half an inch wide at its greatest dimensions. The duct from each seminal vesicle passes into the vas deferens, forming an ejaculatory duct, which one inch farther on joins the *urethra* (the tube leading from the bladder), through which urine passes when being excreted. The seminal vesicles serve as reservoirs in which the male semen is stored.

The point at which the ejaculatory duct enters the urethra is the region of the *prostate gland,* which sometimes gives considerable trouble in later life. It is about as large as a chestnut; through it pass both the urethra and the ducts from the seminal vesicles.

The urethra, which carries the male semen on occasion, leads from the bladder down through the *penis,* which is the male organ of copulation. The opening at the end of the penis is the *glans,* or tip, which is covered and protected by the *prepuce,* or foreskin, sometimes removed in the surgical operation known as circumcision.

The penis itself is composed principally of erectile tissue, so called because it possesses the faculty of gorging itself with blood, which is forced into tiny cavities in the penis, thereby distending it until the organ is rigid. The erection of the penis is a reflex nervous action, stimulated by sexual emotions.

The seminal fluid, or semen, is the secretion from the testicles, which is stored up at intervals in the seminal vesicles. The male sexual cells, or *spermatozoa,* form the main part of the composition of the semen. Each spermatozoon is about 1/500 of an inch in length; it is capable of great movement, which it achieves by "swimming" motions of its tail. In shape it is something like a tadpole, except that the head, slightly flattened, is more distinct.

THE FEMALE REPRODUCTIVE SYSTEM

The female reproductive organs are chiefly internal. The source of the female sexual cells is the *ovaries,* of which there are two, oval in shape, in the pelvic cavity. An ovary is about one and a half inches long, about three-quarters of an inch in width, and half an inch in thickness. In the ovaries are stored the ova or eggs; as they are ready for impregnation, the ova reach the surface of the ovaries, break through the enveloping fold of peritoneum in which the ovaries lie, and enter the *Fallopian tubes,* the ducts leading to the uterus or womb.

The *uterus* is hollow, formed of heavy walls of muscle. It is in the uterus that the impregnated female cell develops into the fetus and into the embryo, which, when fully developed, is born as an infant in the process of childbirth (parturition). Inside the pelvic cavity, the uterus lies between the urinary bladder and the rectum. At its anterior end the uterus has two "corners," so to speak, into each of which one Fallopian tube enters.

The lower or posterior end of the uterus is attached to and enters the anterior end of the vagina. During pregnancy, when the fetus is developing in the uterus, the walls of the womb (uterus) expand and bulge into the abdomen, forcing the abdominal organs more or less out of the usual positions.

The *vagina* is a passage entirely closed except for the almost microscopic opening in the posterior end of the uterus and the external open-

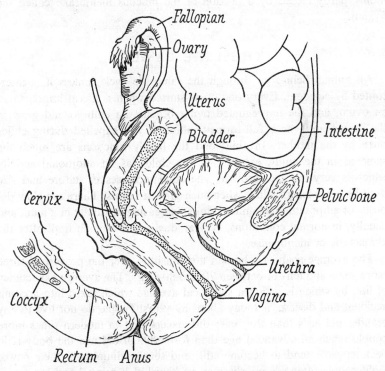

FIG. 18. The human female reproductive system.

ing between the anus and the small opening of the female *urethra*. It lies between the rectum and the bladder with its urethra. The lining of the vagina is a mucous membrane, continuous with the outer skin; the points at which the opening of the vagina reaches the outer skin are developed into folds, called the *labia majora* and *labia minora* (the large and small "lips"). The vagina receives the male organ during copulation. The semen is ejaculated into the vagina; the spermatozoa swim upward toward the uterus, and, if one of the spermatozoa finds an ovum or egg, the ovum may be penetrated by the spermatozoon, whereby conception takes place and pregnancy ensues.

The external female genital organs are collectively called the *vulva*. In front is an elevation of adipose tissue called the *mons Veneris*. Posterior to this is a small semi-erectile organ under the skin, called the *clitoris*. Between the labia are the inner lips, or labia minora, and between these is a kind of cavity, into which opens the female urethra, through which urine is excreted, and, somewhat more posterior in position, the vagina. In the virgin the external opening of the vagina is commonly partly closed by a portion of the mucous membrane called the *hymen*.

THE LIFE CYCLE

All human beings go through the same life cycle, unless it is interrupted by accident. Every one of us started when a sperm impregnated an ovum, and the impregnated ovum became an embryo and grew in the uterus until, as a full-formed infant, it was expelled during childbirth by the mother. In childhood the bodily functions are much the same as in the adult, except that the child has an additional activity which is very marked—growth. The child increases in stature and size until he becomes an adult, when such growth ceases. There are slow deposits of adipose tissue in most adults, increasing gradually in a man, and usually, in normal conditions, very gradually in a woman until after the climacteric or menopause.

The average span of a human life is a little over the proverbial three score years and ten—or between 70 and 80 years. The average expectancy of life, by which is meant a statistical average which takes into account accident and disease, is today about 69 years. People do not live to any grander old ages than they ever did, except that in modern times more people reach an advanced age than formerly. In old age the body is in decline; parts tend to become stiff, and senses diminish in their power —old people often see poorly, may be "hard of hearing," and are sometimes a little bent and walk slowly because of their stiffening joints. So old age gives way before the advancing younger generation, which is always more spry and more alert.

Death is the end of life. Unless it has been brought on prematurely by accident or fatal disease, death comes naturally when the decline of the body has reached a point where its co-ordinating parts can no longer sustain the complex activities of life. Sir Francis Bacon summed it up: "It is as natural to die as to be born." Certainly it is an inevitable physiological result of the living organism. Whether science can ever prolong the period of fully active life remains for the future to reveal.

HEALTH AND HYGIENE

As we have seen, the body is a highly complicated and intricately organized mechanism. Diseases and accidents are often unavoidable, and when they occur it is wise not to delay in consulting a doctor. Regular check-ups at the doctor's and dentist's offices, once every six months to a year, are recommended. There is much, however, which one can do in taking care of oneself and in preventing illness.

Every person should take daily exercise—walking, dancing, or a few minutes of calisthenics. This is necessary to keep all the organs and the muscles in proper function and to stimulate good circulation. It is necessary also to develop and maintain a good posture. Keeping oneself to the weight that is normal for one's height is most important. It is now believed that excessive overweight is unhealthy and may shorten one's life. If obesity is not glandular, it is usually caused by overeating and lack of exercise.

Proper nutrition is most important to health and the prevention of disease. We have already discussed the requirements of a well-balanced diet; a chart of the average vitamin requirements, their food sources, and the results of deficiency is on pages 1272–73. It is well known today that persons of normal weight may yet be undernourished; one must be careful to eat a variety of foods and to supplement with vitamins if necessary.

A number of minor accidents that occur around the home can be treated by oneself or may require attention before a doctor is available. One should know how to use a thermometer to determine whether fever is present, how to wash out cuts with antiseptic and bandage them, how to arrest serious bleeding, how to treat burns, etc. Often quick, simple, appropriate care of even a major accident will reduce the danger during the period before the doctor is able to come.

EXAMINATION QUESTIONS

1. How does physiology differ from anatomy?
2. What terms are used to distinguish the two ends of the body?
3. What are the names of the two layers of skin?
4. What is the center of intelligence?
5. What elements enter into the composition of the human body?
6. What proportion of the human body is composed of water?
7. What is the function of the blood?
8. Why do adults have fewer bones than growing children?
9. What is the sternum?
10. What are the seven neck bones called?
11. What is the inferior maxilla?
12. Why are the eleventh and twelfth pairs of ribs called floating ribs?
13. What is the upper bone of the arm called?
14. What are articulations?
15. How do the skeletal muscles differ from the visceral muscles?
16. What organ is the cardiac muscle?
17. What part of the body may be likened to a carefully co-ordinated telegraph organization?
18. What is the shape and size of the average spinal cord?
19. What is the normal weight of the human brain?
20. What sense do the olfactory nerves control?
21. What are ganglia?
22. How fast do impulses travel along human nerves?
23. Where are the cells which take care of complex activities such as "thinking," "memory," "will power," etc.?
24. What is a hormone?
25. What gland controls metabolism?

26. What physiological senses are there besides the commonly known five senses?
27. What is the usual range of vibrations to which the eardrum will respond?
28. What equalizes the air pressure on both sides of the eardrum?
29. To what is the apparent difference in the size of people's eyes due?
30. What is the lachrymal apparatus?
31. What are the chief colors which color-blind people have difficulty in distinguishing?
32. How many red corpuscles to the cubic inch has the average male in his blood?
33. What proportion of the weight of the body does blood represent?
34. What is the normal rate at which the heart beats?
35. What parts of the heart control the inflowing and outflowing blood?
36. In the beating of the heart, what are the terms used to designate the contraction and the relaxation?
37. What is the source of energy required to do the body's work?
38. What are the three main constituents of the strictly nutrient foods?
39. How many of each type of tooth are included in the thirty-two permanent teeth?
40. What is the duodenum?
41. What is the function of the vermiform appendix?
42. What is the largest gland in the human body?
43. What percentage of hydrochloric acid does the stomach juice contain?

44. What is the technical name of the act of swallowing?
45. What gas is breathed out in exhalation?
46. How many sweat glands are scattered over the skin surface of the body?
47. What is the normal temperature of the mouth?
48. What are the spermatozoa?
49. In what organ does the impregnated female cell develop into the fetus?
50. What is the process of childbirth called?

FOR FURTHER STUDY

FUNDAMENTALS OF PHYSIOLOGY, by Elbert Tokay. (Barnes & Noble, New York.)

THE HUMAN BODY, by Logan Clendening. (Alfred A. Knopf, New York.)

MAN: HIS STRUCTURE AND FUNC-TION, by Fritz Kahn. (Alfred A. Knopf, New York.)

TEXTBOOK OF ANATOMY AND PHYSIOLOGY, by Kimber, Gray, and Stackpole. (The Macmillan Co., New York.)

XXVII

Psychology for Beginners

WHAT IS PSYCHOLOGY?

THE SCIENCE of psychology endeavors to discover the roots of our behavior. It deals with aspects of behavior, as the basis of mental activity, habits and learning, intelligence and personality.

The word psychology comes from the Greek word *psyche,* meaning *soul,* and in ancient times psychology was the study of the soul. The soul included the whole personality. Later, "soul" was identified primarily with "mind," in the sense of mental processes; and this was the emphasis in nineteenth-century psychology. Today, psychology is concerned with human behavior as a whole, of which thinking, personality, and such physical factors as the brain and the nervous system are all aspects.

Psychology is thus seen to be closely linked with biology and physiology on the one hand and with philosophy (thought and its associations) on the other. Biology is the study of life and life processes, and physiology is the study of the structure and activity of the organism as a living thing. Life necessarily includes the brain and related parts, and their structure is necessarily a part of physiology. Psychology concentrates on behavior, and on human behavior in particular. Behavior, since we are more or less aware of it, and to some extent can control it (or so we think), is a manifestation of mental activity.

THE BASIS OF MENTAL ACTIVITY

The mind is dependent upon the body and its activities. Since the brain cells are of the same fundamental structure as other cells of the body, mental activity is basically as *physiological* as digestion.

In general, the *mind* is that which does our thinking, perceives our sensations, wills our actions, remembers our experiences. The mind is customarily associated with consciousness, with being aware of what is happening around us, and, to some extent, of what is going on inside us.

The highest manifestation of mind, and its associated attribute called *intelligence,* occurs in human beings. Intelligence as found in animals is less and less evident as we descend the scale of life. Yet, even in the simplest forms of life, something exists which is *akin* to intelligence. Under the microscope, unicellular (one-celled) organisms can be seen to live by meeting and ingesting (surrounding) food particles, and by eliminating or casting out waste particles; they maintain life by avoiding dangerous substances or dangerous spots. Since there is no "mind" as we know it, this activity is called irritability. As animals become more complex and composed of many cells, certain cells take on specialized irritabilities which serve the whole organism. In general, animals have developed their specialized irritabilities to a higher degree, for their food requirements have made it necessary for them to move around and to know what is going on about them in their environment. Plants have neither mind nor nervous system; plant cells, however, do have irritability, even in the lowest forms. The simplest plants are so nearly like the simplest animals that it is impossible to classify some microscopic organisms as strictly either plants or animals.

The degrees of specialization in irritability throughout the many forms of life are gradual. They grow slowly more complex in fishes, even more complex as one follows their variation among the animals immediately below man in the scale of life, and highly complex in man himself. Thus, in the human body, which is composed of millions of cells of many kinds, the nerve cells of the eye are irritated or stimulated by light rays, and those of the inner ear by sound waves.

As the organism grows more complex in the scale of animal life, it also develops a system of nerve fibers, ganglia, and centers of control and co-ordination. The greatest development of a center of control is the brain, which appears only in the higher animals, gradually becoming more complex, developing the cortex or complicated cellular structure forming the outer layer of the lobes, commonly called the "gray matter." What we know as intelligence is apparently an activity of the cortical cells.

METHODS OF PSYCHOLOGY

Psychology, following the procedure of all sciences, has developed by knowledge accumulated through observation and experiment. If you watch an animal or a person, you are using objective observation. You may notice that when a man touches a hot poker he jerks his hand away.

But suppose you observe yourself: when your own hand is touched by anything hot you have a sensation you call being burned—it is painful, you jerk your hand away, and perhaps suck the injured spot. Your examination of your own reactions, as nearly as you can make such an examination, is subjective observation. The self-examination of any conscious action, including how you think, how you notice things, and how you feel under the stress of emotion, is called *introspection* (looking within oneself). While analyzing thought, your mind is thinking—it can never dissociate itself from thinking long enough to perceive the thinking process as something apart. Here in this nebulous region true observation ceases and speculation begins.

By experiments on animals, children, and adults, psychology has discovered how they react to certain stimuli under certain conditions. In contrast with introspection, this is known as *objective observation of behavior*. After the rules for normal reaction have been laid down, various tests can be applied to individuals to determine how they may correspond with or be different from what is considered to be normal. Psychology may attempt to answer such questions as the following: Why does a baby look toward or reach for a bright object? What was the secret of Napoleon's power over his fellow men? Why does a person jump when he hears a sudden loud noise? What accounts for the mad actions of mobs?

Primitive man knew little of his actions and reactions—he could not guess, with any accuracy, why he did thus and so. There grew up, in his inherited traditions, notions of the supernatural—of something beyond the natural, beyond his understanding. Hand in hand with these notions went superstitions—things believed but not proved. Psychology is eliminating these blind gropings; from psychologists we hope to learn how to control ourselves, how to guide children in their best interests, how to find out what vocation we are best fitted for, and how to control or eradicate crime.

To illustrate the experimental method in psychology, the effect of verbal incentive on learning may be investigated. First, a large group of children may be given an associative learning test. Next, the group is divided into two equivalent groups of children matched for initial learning scores and in the same grades. After several weeks one group is praised for its initial performance and urged to do better and given the test again. The other (control) group is also given the test a second time, but without comment. Any increases in the scores of the experimental group as compared with the control are now taken as evidence of the effect of praise, since the other variable factors have been equalized.

In the case history of clinical method, the aim ordinarily is diagnosis and treatment of behavior problems. Here the procedure usually begins with an interview in which relevant biographical data is obtained, followed by aptitude, intelligence, and personality tests; reasons for past behavior are sought, and advice or treatment is offered.

RESPONSES TO STIMULI

The simplest response to a stimulus, a muscular action or "motor response," is called a *reflex*. The blinking of the eye as a particle of dust flies into it, or as an object swiftly approaches it, is a familiar reflex. Another example is the production of saliva upon the sight or smell of food. Such a stimulus-response action takes a fraction of a second. A reflex is an automatic, inborn response to a stimulus.

The speed of a reflex is accomplished by means of the arrangement of the nerve cells and nerve fibers which produce it. The sense stimulus is received by a sensory cell and conveyed almost instantaneously to an area in the spinal cord (or in the lower brain stem, depending on the part of the body involved); here the sense stimulus acts upon a motor nerve or nerves, sending impulses to the proper muscles, which move the part of the body concerned in the reflex. Such reflexes are elementary and do not have to be learned. Jerking the hand away from a hot object is another such reflex. (See Fig. 8, page 1255).

Next in complexity is the simple reaction. If you hear an automobile horn near you as you cross a street, you jump for the sidewalk; this is a simple reaction (response) to the motor horn. Your brain registers, through auditory nerves, the sound of the horn; your experience (memory) tells you that the horn means danger; your co-ordinating motor area (in your brain) sends down the spinal cord the required impulses, which act upon the proper motor nerves to produce the action which takes you out of danger. Such reactions are learned, though they may become almost automatic and approach the nature of reflexes.

Reflexes take place without the participation of the cells of the cortex of the brain. Simple reactions, as well as the more complex reactions, necessarily involve the brain cortex. Certain portions of that cortex comprise the motor area, for in that area occur the nervous activities which send out impulses causing muscular actions in the body. The cortex is further divided into centers: auditory, visual, motor, etc. In the motor area occurs the elaborate co-ordination necessary to bring about suitable actions of the body. The motor area can also control the body and prevent it from acting. It can even control reflex action, as when you persistently hang on to a hot dish that you do not wish to drop, even though the heat is painful.

Reactions that are not reflex derive from knowledge. The interpretation and use of knowledge takes place in the cortex. If you see a dog coming toward you, snapping and barking, you may run, lest you be bitten. Your brain cortex is utilizing the knowledge that you have acquired: that such an animal may bite if you let him get near you. But if, unnoticed by you, a dog nips your leg, you jump away and perhaps utter an exclamation of surprise or pain; the jumping is a reflex action, brought about by the pain of the dog's bite, no knowledge being required!

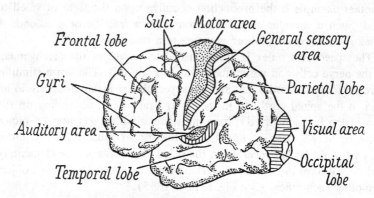

The localization of functions in the human brain.

Adjacent parts of the cortex, in conjunction with the motor area, determine the more skilled and complex muscular actions. Such actions, once learned, become less conscious or more automatic, as writing, throwing a ball, skating, or playing the piano. Simple movements do not require the attention of the cortex (apart from the motor area). Highly complex, indeed, is the center controlling speech, which is slowly trained in childhood; closely associated with it is the auditory center, for speech depends largely upon hearing, as is clearly evidenced by the imitative efforts of the child learning to talk. Visual centers control sight, and there is a small olfactory center which receives sensations of smell; the taste center has not been isolated.

Impairment of the motor area or of any of the cortical centers causes corresponding paralysis, either muscular or sensory. Impairment or lack of development of the higher co-ordinating cortex, adjacent to the various centers, deprives the individual of the more skilled reactions to stimuli. Variations in the cortex of the brain account for the differing abilities of various people in performing muscular acts, or in speaking or singing. An acrobat is necessarily equipped to perform highly skilled and closely co-ordinated muscular activity; his skill, of course, is due to practice, but the ability to profit by that practice must first be present. To this extent, an acrobat or a singer is born and not made.

Reflex action has no purpose or motive behind it. The reflex occurs in response to the stimulus, always the same, unless the higher brain centers inhibit it; in which case they may be said to exert a stronger stimulus than the stimulus which excites the reflex.

A stimulus acts either immediately, as in a reflex, or after a lapse of time when the person is prepared. A child may wait ten minutes after a signal before he starts to run, or may wait until he has counted to a certain number. The response can also be delayed by force, as when a child, anxious to follow some playmate, is delayed by his mother, but keeps in mind where his playmate went, so that he can follow in that direction the moment he is released.

The bloodhound following a scent follows that scent and that only, no matter how many other scents, perhaps stronger, may pass under his nose, and no matter what other stimuli may occur. A stimulus may therefore be continuous in its action: even if the bloodhound loses the scent, he runs around in circles in a strong effort to pick it up again. Though the stimulus is not present every moment, the response is continuous. It may almost be said that the bloodhound's behavior is motivated by that stimulus. There is something of a parallel between the bloodhound and the human being who is pursuing some particular object with absorbed attention. Anticipation of the goal is frequently the whole stimulus, or part of it, directing human reactions.

When a reaction to a stimulus is delayed, the person or animal is restless and dissatisfied, particularly if the stimulus is strong. Hunger or thirst is a strong stimulus, arousing the response to search for food or drink. If a person is hungry, he waits impatiently for lunch time, or for supper to be ready. The infant who is hungry is stimulated to cry in a complaining manner, and is prepared to begin sucking motions with his mouth as soon as he feels the nipple. Animals and savages seize food on sight if they are very hungry; but civilized people recognize, because of training, certain times for eating, and observe certain rules of etiquette in taking food and preparing it for the mouth with knife, fork, or spoon.

The sight of food not only stimulates the motor responses of the eating motions, but also stimulates the flow of saliva in the mouth—a glandular response. As the food is chewed, it further stimulates the secretion of saliva; when it reaches the stomach, it stimulates the flow of the gastric juices, which begin the work of digestion; in the intestines, it stimulates not only the needed secretions, but the rhythmical movements which pass it along from one part to another. Thus the body takes up energy and eliminates waste by an elaborate and co-ordinated system of stimuli followed by responses.

NATIVE AND ACQUIRED TRAITS

Traits of character and physical features are either native (inherited) or acquired. It is now generally believed that acquired characteristics cannot be inherited. Such things as stature, color of eyes and hair, the peculiar arrangement and size of features of the face, or the shape of the hands and fingers are native; they are determined to a large extent by inheritance. Scars, muscular development, and the like are acquired from the environment, by accident or by experience and training.

So it is with traits, many of which are so fundamentally native that we seldom think of them as such. The newborn baby breathes, cries, and makes muscular movements without being taught—such traits are native; they are common to all animals. The baby (according to the behaviorists, a particular school of psychologists) has three fundamental and native emotional reactions: fear, rage, and love. Fear is caused by two native or inborn tendencies to reaction, brought about by two stimuli: a loud noise or the sensation of loss of support (falling). Though we customarily speak of a child's learning to walk, a child would walk anyway when he reached the necessary degree of muscular and nervous development. Walking, like the flying of birds, is a native trait, and need not be learned. It may be retarded by barriers, or it may be encouraged by giving the child opportunity to try his legs.

The making of sounds is a native ability, but co-ordinated speech, in a particular language, is acquired by training. Children of all races and nationalities instinctively make the same sounds in infancy, but they learn whatever language they hear spoken around them. Vocal sounds are native, but speech is acquired. Native characters, such as the color of eyes, are not universal; but native traits, such as breathing, eating, making sounds, walking, and the like, are universal throughout the human race. Acquired traits are obviously developed in co-ordination with, and on the basis of, native traits.

Seeing, hearing, smelling, tasting, and the like, are native; but the interpretation of what we see or hear is an acquired trait. The baby naturally reaches for a bright object, but he gradually learns to tell one bright object from another, and that a burning flame or a red-hot ember should not be reached for. More succinctly, sensations are native, but the meaning of sensations is acquired.

MOTIVATION

In the early teaching of psychology strong *drives* with an inherited basis were described as instinct. This term is no longer generally used to describe human behavior. First, we find in man no such stereotyped pattern of behavior as is found in bees and ants. An insect can invariably be depended upon to do exactly thus and so when confronted with a particular set of conditions. In the higher animals instincts are more loosely followed. Human behavior varies greatly from person to person. The term instinct has been confused with learned behavior. For example, it has been said that some men play football instinctively.

A drive with some inherited basis, but whose expression is determined by environmental factors, is termed a *psychological motive*. Basic emotional drives and responses include anger→struggle; fear→escape; grief →weeping; love→affection.

Some psychologists assert that all drives are directly or indirectly concerned with either self-preservation or conservation and propagation of the species. Although some drives (psychological motives) can be readily so classified, others appear less associated with these fundamental impulses, and some appear to be altogether independent of them.

It must also be stressed that man is a social animal; he is gregarious, seeking the companionship of his kind. Some individuals enjoy a hermit's lonely existence, but man in general avoids solitude. For this reason many of man's activities have become social, as eating, drinking, and making a home. Most human recreations are social; to the majority of people a game of bridge is more enjoyable than a game of solitaire.

BASIC DRIVES

The sex drive is so basic that some psychologists (notably certain members of the Freudian school) explain mental illnesses as the result of inability to adjust the sex drive to other factors such as morality or unfortunate circumstances. A deep understanding of the various ramifications of sex attraction in all its stages is the basis of some psychoanalysis. *Psychoanalysis* is a branch of psychology which applies basic rules to a methodic analysis of a person's psychological make-up, called the *psyche,* in order to discover and prescribe cures for physical, nervous, or emotional disturbances whose causes are psychological. The Freudian school has been foremost in developing practical methodology, such as dream analysis.

Although many specific Freudian tenets have been disputed, there is no question about the soundness in pointing out the importance of sex in motivating human life: out of the gratification or repression of sex impulses, from childhood through youth to manhood and womanhood, come a great many of the acts, thoughts, and characteristics of human beings.

Some of man's love-making is native and some of it is learned or acquired. The ideals of romantic love are obviously acquired culturally. Assiduous attention to the loved one (courtship), strutting and display of physical charms and prowess, the whole game of pursuit-and-capture, are native in origin. Forceful capture, spurred on by the emotion of lust and followed by the unwilling submission of the pursued person, is primitive. Willing submission to an acceptable mate and consequent union by mutual consent (called marriage when the union is legalized) are more highly refined procedures; here the emotion is generally called love, or, when concentrated toward achieving sexual intercourse, passion.

The natural consequence of the mating drive and of sexual union is the conception and birth of offspring. The mother drive, so called, makes the mother care for her baby, feed it, cherish it, and protect it. The father drive is not often so strong. The force of the parental instinct varies in individuals, and in some seems to be almost totally absent. Frequently it takes some other form, as a fondness for pet animals, the care of plants, or social welfare and charity work. When a drive is satisfied in some learned or acquired way, it is said to be *sublimated*. Many desires which are not native, but are acquired from environment and training, can be sublimated.

In spite of the time-honored injunction that children should honor and obey their parents, there is no native tendency for children to do so. Their drive, on the contrary, is to take from their parents, as it is the parental drive to give to the children. A child may, however, acquire a respect for his parents and gratitude (usually) for what they have done for him, and may take a "mothering" attitude toward them as he grows older.

Many human drives tend toward play and recreation. The infant's purposeless movements and meaningless sounds are natural, arising from the sense of well-being, of just "feeling good," technically called *euphoria*. An active and noisy child is probably in the best of health. As the child develops he makes more purposeful movements, handling objects (toys), reaching for things, creeping and later walking toward things, exploring curiously here and there. Creeping, walking, and running are native; more skilled locomotion, as skating, skipping, and the like, is learned or acquired. The exploring drive often survives in adults, as witness the courageous explorers of the world's unknown regions, and the fun of touring in strange lands. The exploring tendency is counteracted or held in check by an almost native caution, which becomes more pronounced as the child grows older, and by an increasing satisfaction with things as they are. Children are naturally conservative, acquiring strong habits.

The impulse to laugh is fundamental, so much so that it is difficult to imitate genuine laughter. Yet what is the stimulus which produces laughter? An organic state, or emotion, called amusement or mirth, perhaps; yet this is not all. People laugh when they are tickled; children laugh for no reason at all, unless euphoria is a reason. Laughter is often a manifestation of cruelty, or at least an expression of superiority. The psychology of laughter and humor is not as yet fully understood.

Common social motives include: (1) *Self-assertion* and *the urge for mastery*. Pugnacity develops out of the attempt to defeat those people, institutions, etc., that may be restricting one's activity. In the case of the overanxious boy who reacts with hostility toward a stern father, severe punishment is likely to provoke even more anxiety and hostility based on fear. It is best to try to determine the cause of the boy's original anxiety and help to rid him of it. Self-assertion in childhood and adolescence often takes the form of rejecting adult aid and protesting against authority of parents and others whose domination is feared and resented. (2) *Achievement of prestige,* the desire to be praised and rewarded and given social approval, is a powerful social motive. The child seeks approval by performing and exhibiting, climbing, jumping, reciting, etc. If he does not receive attention he may try to obtain it through various anti-social or even criminal acts. (3) *Gregariousness* is the desire to be with one's kind, based on the need for security, sympathy, and understanding. (4) *Parental and filial drives* are strong urges to protect others in need, to take care of the helpless, or to be taken care of. (5) *Self-preservation* is a complex drive involving several emotions. For example, in face of danger, the need to escape is based on fear.

Man is a self-asserting, egotistic animal. He is the lord of the earth because of his native tendency to overcome all obstacles. This self-assertive drive reveals itself in games, whether physical or mental—the determination to win is just as strong in a tennis match as in a foot race or even in a game of chess. The determination to surpass one's fellows or to overcome a thing is the psychological explanation of the popularity of crossword and jigsaw puzzles, anagrams, quizzes, and similar tests of knowledge or mental ingenuity.

Ambition, zeal, determination, the will-to-power, enthusiasm, the desire to make money, all these are phases of native self-assertion. They are exhibited, in various forms, in most children and in all adults. Seldom is a state of discouragement and despair reached so hopeless that the individual cannot or will not assert his ego in some way. The disobedient child is asserting himself. To be sure, his self-assertion ought to be directed into useful channels, and child psychologists are seeking methods for accomplishing this. Hunting, driving a car, and using a camera are phases of self-assertion, for they give one a sense of power or achievement.

Next to striving to surpass is the striving to equal what someone else does, called emulation. If a boy performs a stunt, his playmates try to perform it also. The popular and neighborly pastime of "keeping up with the Joneses" is a pernicious form of this kind of self-assertion.

What happens when the self-assertive drive is thwarted? No doubt some persons are more easily discouraged than others, for individuals are variously endowed with nervous and physical energy, not to mention the capacity to become skillful in certain fields. When we do not succeed, in one way or another, we become sulky, resentful, ashamed, timid, bashful, stubborn, recalcitrant, gloomy, depressed. The "poor loser" exhibits such reactions when he is beaten, whether in a game or in the more earnest contest of business or politics. The child whose self-assertion is thwarted early in life may become shy, self-conscious, and in later years be completely baffled by life. On the other hand, he who has no real success to satisfy him may satisfy his ego by bragging and by bullying his inferiors.

EMOTIONS

Common emotions are hate, fear, anger, and love. The word *emotion* means a "stirred-up" state of being. It was once thought that each emotion had its particular organ or seat in the body; this idea explains the heart as a symbol of love. It is now known that the emotions are conditions of the individual as a whole, and not of any one organ or part.

Certain organic states are more or less localized: fatigue is localized in the muscles or nerves; hunger, in the alimentary tract; thirst, in the throat; drowsiness, in the eyes and muscles. These organic states modify responses to stimuli, but they do not come from the body as a whole, nor are they brought on by external stimuli. They are not, therefore, true emotions.

True emotions are brought about by something outside the body. The external stimulus may be a loud noise, someone's insulting voice, an overt act, or merely something which suggests cause for a particular emotion. Of course we do not perceive the cause for emotion and then proceed to "emote"! On the contrary, unless our feelings are very well controlled, the external stimulus sets up an emotional state in spite of us—and we are suddenly angry, afraid, or excited.

If you are very angry, you cannot benefit much from self-analysis by introspection. After the fit of anger has passed, you may perhaps think back to it and notice some aspects of it. But an observer can tell you things about yourself, when you were angry, that you were probably not aware of. You know that you have been angry, but do you know whether you clenched your fists, or breathed deeply, whether you spoke loudly, or whether your eyes bulged? These are common physical manifestations of anger. Also, the digestive processes may be arrested, and glandular responses take place of which one is not aware. It is unhealthful to become angry just after eating a hearty meal!

Glandular activity (secretion) commonly accompanies emotions. Tears are shed in grief or anger, and the skin exudes perspiration in anger or fear. Internal secretions are discharged into the blood, affecting various parts of the body. In particular, during fear or anger, the adrenal glands secrete adrenalin, which acts as a tonic throughout the body—giving the heart greater power, lessening the tendency of muscles to fatigue, liberating fuel for the muscles, increasing breathing and the consequent supply of oxygen, taking blood away from the skin and face to send it to the brain and muscles, dilating the eyes that they may see better, stopping digestive processes and secretions of the salivary glands (hence the "tightness" or thirstiness of the throat) so that energy may be conserved. The body is thus put into a state to undergo a struggle, to resist danger, or to overcome an enemy. Though we do not ordinarily need such reactions in civilized life, they are native, not acquired; we inherit them from the millions of years of man's evolutionary past.

An emotion is, in some degree, a preparatory reaction—preparatory to some act which will accomplish the safety or the satisfaction of the individual. Expressive of this preparation are some apparently useless movements, such as scowling, shaking the head, and exposing the teeth, which suggest displeasure or disgust or some similar feeling, and probably had some use in the remote past. Baring the teeth was preparatory to using the teeth in fighting. Clenching the fists is still part of getting ready for physical combat. Shouting is reminiscent of animal roars and snarls, designed to startle an adversary or astound him with the power of his antagonist.

Can you feel angry without exhibiting the visible signs of anger—or some of them at least? You can feel a dislike, perhaps, or you can remember that you were once angry with someone; but does not the anger cease as an emotion when the usual bodily signs disappear? An emotion may be the sensation produced by the combination of internal and external reactions which are taking place. Suppose someone tweaks your nose; if you feel that it is an affront to your dignity, or if it hurts, you are likely to try to tweak his nose in return or make some other physical retaliation. If he resists, or responds with some further indignity, you may become excited, a struggle may ensue, and as the struggle becomes more earnest you will exhibit all the signs of anger and *feel angry*.

What distinguishes a "cool" person in the face of danger? If anything, probably the fact that he is not afraid in the emotional sense; that is, he perceives danger intellectually, not emotionally, and meets it with rational effectiveness. A person who experiences the emotion of fear is likely to react in a more primitive and possibly less effective manner. The emotion of fear is frequently followed by panic, for there are many causes of fear in modern life which cannot be effectively met by spontaneous primitive reactions. For instance, flight is not an effective reaction to a fire in a theater.

The response to the stimuli of danger may be very swift—so swift, in fact, that the body has no time to reach the emotional state of fear. Immediately afterward, however, when the danger has passed, the person may tremble and exhibit all the signs of fear, and probably will feel afraid. "I wasn't afraid until it was all over," says the victim of an automobile accident, which may happen so suddenly that a passenger may not be aware of danger until he finds himself in the ditch. Here, also, the emotion is a result of the stirred-up state of the body, caused by awareness of danger even though it has passed.

Emotions can be rationally controlled to some extent. A person may feel an emotion without acting, for he can be angry and remain quite still. But an emotion usually is accompanied by an impulse to act, whether or not that impulse results in action. Such an impulse—for instance, to escape from danger when afraid, to injure an opponent when angry, or to caress and fondle the loved one when in love—is similar to an instinct. It is native and not acquired; the resistance to the impulse is acquired. But this emotional impulse differs from an instinct chiefly in that it is derived from a stirred-up condition of the body, and does not immediately follow an external stimulus, as does an uninterrupted instinctive reaction. Some drives are accompanied by emotion (as the mating instinct, accompanied by love).

FEELINGS AND SENSATIONS

You can always characterize your feelings by one of two adjectives, either *pleasant* or *unpleasant*. The two elementary feelings therefore appear to be pleasantness and unpleasantness.

The satisfaction of some drives is pleasant. You feel well pleased when you have made a difficult contract at bridge, or when you have made a profitable business deal. Such feelings, so called, should be distinguished from sensations, which are localized, coming from the "senses." What is pleasing to the senses contributes to the feeling of pleasantness, and vice versa. Sweet things are pleasing to the taste, and bitter things are unpleasant, even displeasing. Gratification of bodily needs (desires) helps to make us feel pleasant.

Associated with feelings are our likes and dislikes, some native, some acquired. The liking for sweets, fragrant odors, bright colors, and musical sounds is native. But persons sometimes have to learn to like certain foods or particular color combinations; and esthetic appreciation of colors (as in a painting) and sounds (as in a symphony) must often be learned. Natural likes and dislikes, together with those acquired from training or environment, are important factors to be considered in vocational psychology.

ELEMENTARY SENSATIONS

A sensation is a response to a stimulus, made by the sense organ stimulated, and recognized or interpreted in the associated brain centers. Thus the sensation of sight is caused by the stimulus of light acting upon the nerves of seeing in the retina of the eye, being registered in the visual center of the brain, and there interpreted or recognized. The five familiar senses are taste, smell, sight, sound (hearing), and touch; less commonly recognized are the senses of temperature, muscle, and pain. The "senses," so called, are native; they operate quite naturally, although what they report to the brain is interpreted and acted upon according to what the individual has learned.

The human skin is noticeably sensitive, having four kinds of "sense spots" on the surface, which receive the stimuli causing the sensations of touch, warmth, cold, and pain. These are the elementary skin sensations, of which other sensations are combinations. Moisture is a combination of smooth (touch) and cold (temperature) sensations. Extremes of heat and cold also stimulate the pain sense. The senses can be deceptive, for an extremely cold object will stimulate the warmth spots, giving a sensation of heat (warmth-pain combination). This deception is not serious when we see the object causing the sensation, for its appearance usually tells us whether it should feel hot or cold. The pain sense gives warning of danger—probable injury if the stimulus is not removed.

The sensation of taste seems simple, but is highly complex. It is compounded not only of taste proper, but of senses of touch, warmth, cold, and pain, for since the tongue has skin, sense spots are present in it. The "feel" of a morsel of food has a great deal to do with its taste: the taste is a combination of all the sensations the stimulus (food) causes. The muscle sense may also contribute, if the morsel is hard or gummy. Most tastes are partly smells, the odor reaching the olfactory cells of the nose through the back of the mouth. It is for this reason that you seem to lose much of your sense of taste when you have a bad cold in your nose.

The elementary tastes are sweet, sour, bitter, and salty. The taste of a cool glass of orangeade is a compound of sweetness, sourness, coldness, and the odor of the orange "flavor." Most tastes are *blends*. Their effect is total: it seems to be single, although it is really multiple.

The elementary odors are spicy, fragrant, flowery, fruity, resinous, foul, and scorched. As compared with that of animals, the human sense of smell is remarkably inefficient. But the human nose can detect surprisingly small quantities of odorous substances diffused in the air. Most odors, like tastes, are blends.

Sounds and sights may be blends, but they may also be *patterns*. A pattern, unlike a blend, depends on space or time. A musical composition, when played, is a time pattern of sound. A view of a crowded street is a complex pattern both in space and time, for many of the objects are in motion.

Some senses are more adaptable than others. The sense of smell fatigues rapidly, and a pronounced odor becomes less keen the longer it persists. Some tastes exhibit a similar fading. The senses become adapted to such prolonged stimuli, no longer responding to them. This adaptation is less noticeable in the sense of sight, though if you are in a room illuminated with yellow light, you are likely to suffer the illusion, after a time, of being in white light.

Sometimes sensations persist after the stimuli cease. This is especially true of sight. If you stare at an electric bulb, and suddenly shut it off, you will continue to see it for a moment afterward; this is the *after-image*. There may be a negative or opposite after-image, such as the black spots you see after gazing at a bright light like the sun. The persistence of sight sensation after the stimulus ceases is utilized in the familiar mechanism of the motion pictures, which of course do not move but appear to move because the eye carries over the impression of one picture to the impression of the next, which is projected on the screen too swiftly for the eye to perceive the jerk which actually accompanies the change.

Adaptation and after-images, together with contrast, help to make our eyes deceive us. A light color will appear lighter if placed in contrast with a darker, or with black; and the same color will appear darker if placed in contrast with a lighter, or with white.

Ordinary sounds which lack rhythm and regularity are noises. Music makes use of sound blends, together with pitch and the quality or timbre of the notes produced by different musical instruments. The human ear is limited in its capacity to perceive sounds, and the limitations vary with individuals and at different ages. Some persons can hear the squeak of a bat (they have exceptionally "good ears"); others cannot. The vowels of human speech are blends of sound tones, and, in most languages, the pitch of the sound does not change them (except in singing); the sounded consonants which are prolonged are also blends (like *m, n, r, f*), the other consonants being noises (like *p, k, g*). A noise is a blend of simple tones, but there is seldom anything like a tonal effect, and pitch is vague or lacking.

Though the eye can judge with fair accuracy the source of its stimuli (light rays), the ear can judge only slightly the direction or source of the sound waves which stimulate it, unless, as usually happens, it is aided by the eye.

There are also the senses of organic state, as hunger, thirst, and fatigue and the bodily senses. The bodily senses tell us whether we are moving and in what direction (when the eyes are closed), and the position of invisible parts of the body (which can be ascertained with fair accuracy by the muscle sense, especially if the part is moved slightly). The semi-circular canals of the inner ear are not concerned with hearing, but have a great deal to do with maintaining our equilibrium (balance) and the efficiency of our motor mechanism, and they also tell us of movements of the head or of the body as a whole. In these canals the sensations of dizziness and falling are located, although they seem to come from the body as a whole. The muscle sense helps us to judge how much we move an arm in the dark, or, in conjunction with the sense of touch, enables us to judge the weight of an object by "hefting" it.

ATTENTION

Man has a noticeable capacity for attention, or concentration, which is an adjustment of the mental faculties, in co-operation with physical faculties, to the reception of certain stimuli in preference to all others. A student concentrating on his textbook is giving attention to his reading, and to his consideration of that reading, above everything else for the moment. His stimulus to such attention is perhaps interest in the subject, or the desire to profit by its study and mastery.

When we attend to what we are doing, we concentrate our faculties upon it. This means that we shut out, so far as we can, all distracting stimuli and adjust our muscles as well as our minds to the matter in hand. The muscular adjustment is particularly important in physical activity, but it is also a factor in mental work, for good light and a comfortable position are necessary.

The attention constantly shifts, in spite of all we can do. Our thoughts leap momentarily from one thing to another, or from one aspect of a subject to another. If you look at a pattern of wallpaper, you will seem to perceive one arrangement for a moment, and then the arrangement will change. If you look at a group of dots, your eye will arrange them first in one pattern or grouping, and then in another. If you separate your two eyes by holding a red glass in front of one and a blue glass in front of the other, you will seem to see blue for a moment and then red, and vice versa. It is impossible to look at any object steadily, for any length of time, without the attention fluctuating.

Strictly speaking, it is impossible to give attention to more than one thing at a time. When a person seems to do so, he is really shifting his attention rapidly from one thing to another and back again. The performer who juggles and recites poetry at the same time is partly letting learned actions take their own course while he gives attention to others. Juggling can become practically automatic. Similarly, the writer who rattles off his ideas on a typewriter is not paying attention to the mechanics of typewriting, for since he has those well learned, he can give his mind to the ideas which he wishes to express. We are limited in how much we can attend to at a moment; in a single glance we can notice only four or five objects, and then only cursorily. The taking in of a person from head to foot, including the pattern of necktie, the color of socks, number of buttons on the coat, and so on, is impossible in a fraction of a second. Some extended attention must be given if such details are to be noted. It is just as impossible to sweep the glance, for the eye does not sweep—it jumps in short, quick jerks from one focus to another. The eye can follow a moving object, but it cannot sweep steadily over a room.

HABITS AND LEARNING

The Learning Process

A fundamental principle of learning is exercise, or practice. Anything repeated tends to become easier to remember and more familiar. This is equally true of learning to ride a bicycle or to recite the multiplication tables. When a response follows a stimulus again and again, learning is the result. Since a recent response to a particular stimulus has more force than more remote responses, you may "become rusty" or "get out of practice." Since vigorous exercise is more helpful than indifferent exercise, the intensity with which you practice, or the amount of attention you give, modifies the value of the practice. Exercise may be voluntary, as it usually is when you set out to learn to skate or to memorize your lessons in school, or it may come about as a consequence of necessity, as when a hunter learns to walk quietly in the woods. Here the *effect* of responses to stimuli modifies the repetition of the responses, until only those are made which accomplish the desired result. As you learn by practice, you tend to eliminate waste motions, being guided by the desired effect.

Exercise does not completely explain learning. We learn by association, by noting similarity or contrast, or by noting things that are close together in space or time. A collection of several stimuli may arouse one response, so that later, by association, one of the stimuli alone may arouse that response. Thus there may be what are called substitute stimuli and substitute responses.

A stimulus may, after a process of learning or conditioning, arouse a response which naturally should follow a quite different stimulus. Suppose a baby is shown a toy rabbit just as a loud noise is made. The baby is frightened by the noise when he sees the rabbit. He is thus led to associate the fright with the rabbit. After a few times he may exhibit fright at the sight of the rabbit, without hearing a noise. The rabbit becomes a *substitute* stimulus for the noise (technically called a *sign*), arousing the response of fright. The child learns the names of things in a similar way: he hears the word spoken when he sees the object, and ultimately will repeat the word when he sees the object, substituting the *visual* stimulus for the original *auditory* stimulus.

We learn by observation. This means that a group of stimuli arouses a certain response, and that later one of those stimuli alone may arouse that response. Thus, as you become acquainted with a person, you learn how he looks. You may later be reminded of him by hearing his voice over the telephone, by seeing him from the rear as he walks down the street, or by seeing someone who resembles him slightly. Children often respond wholeheartedly to a partial stimulus by calling all furry animals "kitties"—making the kitten response to the single stimulus of fur. Irrational likes and dislikes of foods, of people of different backgrounds than our own may be due to a response to one or a few stimuli out of many originally presented.

It is thus seen that learning is combination; it derives from stimuli received at first as a group, and later singly, with the responses acquired by experience and exercise (practice). Emotions follow certain stimuli, but, as the child grows older, the stimuli which arouse his emotions change. What makes a child angry may not necessarily make an adult angry; what amuses a child does not always amuse an adult. Our emotions and their expression (response to the stimulus of emotion) become modified in socially acceptable ways. When necessary, we make substitute responses: we respond to an insult with sarcasm instead of with fisticuffs.

Everyone is greatly influenced by his early environment and childhood associations. Are you afraid of snakes or mice? Those fears have been built into you by substitute responses which you have probably been unaware of. It is wise to fear some snakes, but not all. It is absurd to fear mice. But you will find it extremely difficult to reason yourself out of fears which seem to you instinctive, although you may readily admit that they are foolish.

To a certain extent, early and often accidental associations also explain likes and dislikes.

Human beings, unlike animals, can perceive a problem at the start and formulate a plan of attack. Their movements, though they may follow the trial-and-error method, are directed more surely to the goal. But, like animals, human beings learn by doing. A man can learn to use a hammer without any instruction whatever, although instruction may speed up his progress toward skill. Human superiority depends on observing as well as doing; few if any animals are capable of true observation prior to performing an act. An animal cannot benefit by watching another animal perform a trick, but a human being readily profits by example.

Human beings have the further ability to note and remember: the child may imitate something he has seen his father do, but some time after his father acted. This ability is exclusively a human characteristic. When a man ponders a problem in his study, and works out a solution, he *thinks*. In thinking, imagination and association of ideas are involved. So far as psychological evidence goes, animals other than man do not think, though chimpanzees and gorillas have some power of association.

With learning come our habits, good or bad. We sometimes acquire absurd reactions, or "bad habits." A habit is rather difficult to break, but it can be done with proper determination—usually by setting up, through practice, a counter-habit, or substitute response to the stimulus which brought on the habitual reaction. Habits, obviously, are acquired and not native.

MEMORY

Remembering is a part of learning. Some things we remember consciously, as when we think or "reason out" a problem; other facts are remembered almost automatically, as when we make a response to a stimulus by habit. Some persons have better memories than others; a few are blessed with exceptionally good memories. A poor memory may be improved to some degree.

The most familiar exercise of memory is "memorizing" something—the multiplication tables, a poem, or a speech. The most obvious way to memorize is to repeat the thing to be learned, over and over, until it is learned. The process can be speeded up by noting similarities between units; memorizing a poem, for example, is easier than memorizing prose, for rhythm and rhyme aid the memory. Recitation aloud is a sound aid to memory.

A principle in memorizing is that of spaced repetition: if you are learning something by rote, it saves time and effort to go over it twice each day for twelve days rather than to go over it twenty-four times in one day or six times daily for four days. In studying, it is wise to read over your assignment, and then, when you take up the next assignment the next day, to read over the previous assignment before proceeding to the new lesson. Thinking back over what you have read, verifying from the text any doubtful points, is very helpful. Experiment has shown, also, that going completely through what is to be learned, taking it as a whole each time, is more efficient than learning it part by part and then putting the parts together.

The will to learn includes conscious observation combined with reciting (practice). Unless you train yourself to observe carefully, you will seldom remember anything that you see, hear, or feel, except what naturally arouses your interest. (A costume designer might remember that a fleeing criminal wore a necktie that did not go well with his hat, shirt, and coat, but the average person would not be likely to note that fact.)

We are likely to forget what we learn if we have no occasion to bring it to mind over a long interval of time. The degree to which we forget a fact depends on how well it is memorized or noted in the first place and on how frequently it is brought to mind or used meanwhile. Some psychologists assert that we never forget anything the nerve cells of our cortex have ever "recorded." Streaming through our consciousness at any moment are dozens and hundreds of impressions or responses out of the past, some dim, some vivid, some weak, some strong—all helping us to "think," as we say, and influencing what we are and how we act.

You remember, or are "reminded" of something in your memory, by a stimulus which arouses that response; it may be a substitute stimulus or a substitute response. You see a friend's face and remember his name, what he talked about when you saw him last, whom he married. You are continually being reminded of facts in your memory, of what you have read, seen, heard, smelled, or felt. The more recent impressions are usually the most vivid, though not always. Very recent impressions may obtrude themselves into the memory almost unconsciously, as when a tune keeps running in your head; this perseveration seems to act without a stimulus, though there may be a stimulus so vague that you are unaware of it.

Everyone experiences occasional difficulties in recalling a name or a fact which he knows very well. Fear, anxiety, doubt, embarrassment, surprise, or some distraction may inhibit recall. The best way is to think of all the similar or related facts, quite calmly, and the desired and elusive name or number, or whatever it is, may "pop into your mind." If you do not recall at once, abandon the mental search and return to it a little later, when the "interference" may have faded and you can remember without difficulty.

Recognition is a curious aspect of memory, for you may recognize a person or place without immediately recalling the attendant facts. You know your intimate friends spontaneously, without any effort at recall. In terms of stimulus and response, recognition is a learned response to a certain stimulus or group of stimuli.

MENTAL IMAGERY AND ASSOCIATION

We can call to mind, in varying degree, sensations we have experienced. These recalled sensations constitute *mental images*—the more vivid mental images are usually visual. A person capable of recalling visual mental images has in his mind's eye a picture of what he has seen. To a lesser degree, he can recall things heard, felt, smelled, or tasted.

Usually mental images are aroused unconsciously—that is, without conscious effort. But a person can often bring to mind a picture of a past experience at will. He can re-experience to some extent both the visual aspect and the action of the event. In general, we have mental images that are complete only in so far as we have observed and noted; it is impossible to bring to mind consciously portions of a scene which we have not definitely observed.

However, images come to mind, quite often, which we *do not remember* having observed. These may be free associations of details which were observed separately, or they may be images which we have entirely forgotten with respect to place and time, but which upon a certain stimulus are aroused. Such images, of course, are primary to what we call *imagination;* because of the tendency of mental images to simplify, elaborate, associate, etc., imagination differs from memory. You recall sensations which are sensory images. But you can also call to mind facts, which were perhaps noted originally in connection with sensations, and yet you recall them without the accompanying sensations. You know, for instance, that water is wet, and you can recall this fact without any mental image of water.

Association plays a great part in mental imagery. You may permit yourself to daydream, or you may fall into a reverie. Images rapidly follow one another in your mind, without any conscious effort on your part, following outside stimuli in some degree, perhaps, but following more closely your mental attitude at the moment. Controlled associations help us in most of our mental acts. In performing the operations of arithmetic, we control our associations of numbers so that we add, multiply, subtract, or divide, as we wish. In reading, we control our associations of words according to the context: we do not associate speed with the word *fast* if we read, "He was tied fast to the pillar." In speaking, we similarly control our word associations.

PERCEPTION

Every moment of your life you are perceiving facts and deducing from them. You hear a cat's meow, and you say, "I hear a cat." You do not—you hear the sound the cat is making. But you perceive that the sound is typically that which a cat makes, and you interpret it accordingly. You may say that a lemon smells sour—this is perception, for the sensation of sour is a taste, but you associate the smell of the lemon with the taste you have experienced, and you perceive that such a smell indicates a sour taste. The smell of the lemon is a sensation, followed by the perception that it suggests sourness; perception, then, is a *secondary* response to a stimulus.

Perception takes place in the brain, in the cortical areas adjacent to the corresponding sensory centers. If you feel a pencil in the dark, you perceive that it is a pencil, and perhaps you can "guess" or picture to yourself how it looks, except that you have no means of perceiving its color. Your sensory center of touch, linked somewhat with your muscle sense, gives you the sensations of feeling and weight. The adjacent parts of the cortex enable you to perceive that the object is a pencil.

A person does not always perceive correctly. As a joke, someone may give him a skinned grape in the dark, and tell him that it is an animal's eye. Helped by the suggestion that it is an eye, the victim is likely to perceive that it is an eye, for it feels about as he thinks an eye would feel if handled. You often make momentary mistakes in perception. How often have you gone to the window, thinking you heard rain, and discovered that the noise was something else?

Mistakes in perception create many of our illusions, ephemeral though most of them are. "Oh, I thought I heard you speak," you say in apology to someone walking with you down the street. Or you are thinking of dogs, and you mistake a piece of burlap lying in the road for a sleeping dog, until you look more closely. "Ghosts" are often seen in this way. Thus you perceive things, true or false, without any definite recall of an image formerly experienced when confronted with the same stimuli. You can hear thunder and perceive that it is thunder without picturing a storm in your mind.

To perceive, you must combine various stimuli and isolate them from their surroundings. What you perceive may therefore depend upon what you are looking for. You certainly would never find a needle in a haystack if you were not looking for it; but if you searched methodically you might find it. To see it, you would isolate it from the hay and perceive that it was a needle by combining the visual and other sensory stimuli which confirmed your perception.

What are objects of perception? You perceive things, happenings (events), qualities, characteristics (colors), abstracts (such as straightness and truthfulness), and other facts. But you can also perceive indirectly. For instance, you can examine the bottom of a muddy stream with a long rod and get an idea of whether it is rough or smooth. You seem to perceive through the rod; really, you perceive (or interpret) the sensations produced by the end of the rod, in your hand. Such perception is aided by deduction, a power of reason. Then you can perceive the passage of time, not always accurately, but you can usually judge fairly well the difference between one hour and two hours, or between one second and three seconds. Perception of time is most important in playing a musical instrument or in singing.

Sounds tell us little of the direction from which they come, or of the distance from which they come; a ventriloquist, suggesting where the sounds he makes come from, takes advantage of the fact that we customarily assume a faint sound to come from a greater distance than a loud sound, or from a more enclosed place.

Perception of space is largely visual, except as it may be referred to the position of the body or its parts. Our binocular (two-eyed) vision helps us in estimating distances and the relative size of objects; also, the fact that distant objects seem smaller than nearer ones (the principle of perspective used by the artist), and the familiar phenomenon of nearer objects seeming to rush by while more distant objects stand still or move slowly in the opposite direction, experienced while looking out of a train window (and also to a lesser degree when the eye is moved while one is quite still), both help us to judge distance. The perception of space is by no means perfect, for we may be entirely deceived by apparent distances.

Artistic perception may usually be developed, or acquired. It involves a capacity to feel emotions, to sympathize (to feel other people's emotions), or to have one's feelings aroused by substitute stimuli (as by a painting or a drama). Some esthetic perceptions, as those of symmetry and natural fittingness, seem to be native. Most persons have an inborn sense of balance and proportion in visual matters, and some persons have an inborn sense of rhythm in auditory matters.

ILLUSIONS

Some illusions are very familiar. A piece of marble feels colder than a piece of wood. If you come into a moderately warm room from the cold outside air, it may appear very warm indeed. An hour interestingly spent seems much shorter than an hour passed in boredom. Some of these errors are constant—we are always at their mercy, and cannot help making them. Other errors depend on circumstances or conditions which are temporary.

Generally speaking, a person makes more errors in perceiving small differences than he does in perceiving greater ones. This holds true of all relative or similar differences. If the room is lighted by one candle, and you light a second, the fact that the room is twice as bright is readily noticeable; the addition of a third candle is less noticeable, and finally, the addition of a hundredth candle to ninety-nine already lighted in a room is hardly discernible at all.

Preoccupation or mental attitude can cause illusions, such as hallucinations. If you are looking for a friend in a crowd, your mental attitude may cause you momentarily to mistake someone else for him, until your error is corrected by some additional stimulus. "Hearing burglars" in the house after reading of a midnight robbery in the paper is a familiar auditory illusion, due to preoccupation with a specific idea. "Seeing ghosts" is nearly always due to a mental attitude, which brings about mistaken perceptions.

Many optical illusions are utilized in puzzles and tricks with the pencil. The ancient Greeks recognized an optical illusion in modeling temple columns; they appear straight to the eye, but they are not straight; if they were straight, they would not appear straight!

INTELLIGENCE AND INTELLIGENCE TESTS

The student who learns his lessons easily, the mechanic who is handy with tools, and the salesman who sizes up customers quickly are all considered intelligent in different ways. Efficiency in the solution of everyday problems is a good working definition of intelligence. It demands both power and speed. For convenience, the psychologist distinguishes three areas of intelligent activity:

(1) Abstract—capacity for dealing with numbers, symbols, diagrams, ideas.

(2) Mechanical—ability to handle mechanical devices.

(3) Social—the knack of getting along well with people.

Psychologists have found that abilities are positively related. People tend to be more often above average in all of their achievements or below average in all their achievements than far above average in some and far below in others. A student is rarely very good in one subject and poor in all the rest, though he is likely to be better in some subjects than in others.

INTELLIGENCE TESTS

General intelligence tests widely used today are primarily measures of abstract intelligence. *Special tests* applying to mechanical intelligence, involving perceptual ability, motor skill, and ingenuity, have also been developed. Social intelligence is sometimes measured by tests, but frequently by rating scales and questionnaires and other methods.

I.Q., or intelligence quotient, is the ratio of a child's mental age to his chronological age. Thus a child of ten whose mental age is that of a fifteen-year-old has an I.Q. of 150. I.Q. is a measure of brightness or dullness.

It seems probable that intelligence is located in the brain and has something to do with the degree of complexity of the cortex, especially of that part of the cortex just behind the forehead. The exact relationship of intelligence to the brain is as yet unknown. Some men with rather small brains have been highly intelligent. Though some animals have large brains, they are not nearly so intelligent as human beings. But the frontal part of the cortex and the areas of cortex immediately adjacent to the motor and sensory centers of the brain seem to be the source of intelligence and skill.

REASONING

Reasoning power sharply separates man from other animals. In reasoning, you perceive facts and draw inferences from them. You perceive that a spark-plug wire has come loose, and you infer that that is the cause of the engine stopping dead. Your bank informs you that your account is overdrawn, and you infer at once that one of three things must be true: (1) the bank has made a mistake, (2) you have made a mistake, or (3) a check has been raised or forged. By examination of your figures and of the canceled vouchers, you can arrive at the correct explanation. But if, while thinking it over, before you examine any figures, you suddenly remember that you wrote a check a week ago without putting it down in your checkbook, you infer immediately that your neglect caused the error.

Reasoning is subject to false inferences, or fallacies. The loose thinker is more prone to become a victim of fallacies than the careful reasoner. Deliberate misleading of unwary thinkers is called sophistry. The analysis of reasoning and its fallacies is called *logic*.

Reasoning answers such questions as why? how? what? by whom? We are in a difficulty—how are we going to get out of it? We need money—how are we going to get it? My friend avoids me—why? Given enough relevant facts, the answer can be "reasoned out."

Rationalization is not reasoning, but rather a form of self-justification. If a husband is unkind to his wife because of what has happened at the office, he may justify himself by seeking some other "reason" for, or cause of, his behavior. Children are often particularly expert at rationalizing their conduct—not always from a wish to deceive, for they may not know the real reason themselves.

IMAGING AND DREAMS

Man is undoubtedly an imagining animal: he is continually bringing images to mind, and drawing conclusions from them, or acting upon what they suggest to him.

The child manipulates his toys and, by imagination, is able to build his blocks into towers, to arrange dolls like real people, to construct machines from his building outfits. Curiosity and exploration, memory and reasoning, perception, all enter into it. Ultimately, imagination tends to create something new out of what one has already learned. Play and recreation depend a great deal on imagination. Games may be looked upon as fantasies acted out—they satisfy self-assertive or other instincts, because we imagine them to be real. We make substitute responses, or we are reacting to substitute stimuli, but our mental life during the process is imagination.

A particular aspect of imagination is called *empathy*. If you watch a bird flying, and enjoy the sight because you seem to imagine yourself smoothly flying through the air, that imaginative self-projection is an instance of empathy. Empathy partially explains our enjoyment of such things as art, literature, and contests of skill (when we watch them). Self-projection into the personality of another person, to feel how he feels, is much like empathy, but it is called by the familiar name of sympathy.

Daydreaming is a form of imagination which enables us to enjoy something that is not happening at the moment or is impossible to us in real life. We may imagine ourselves to be conquering heroes, or masters of industry, or Don Juans in love. The daydream is a mild form of mental dissipation; usually it has no practical result.

Worry and anxiety are brought on by imagining what one does not want to have happen, but what one thinks might happen. In extreme instances of worry, the imagination is given full rein and allowed to bring to mind all sorts of terrors.

Freud held that when a person sleeps, his unconsciousness obtrudes into his consciousness, giving his dreams a basically sexual coloring, to be found in symbolic substitutions which are explained in psychoanalysis and "dream interpretation." Psychoanalysts consider dreams to be disguised wish fantasies. Interpretation of dreams is an important part of modern psychotherapy.

When you dream, you are probably not deeply asleep. Dreams seem to take place when you sleep lightly, or just before you fully awaken. That is, those dreams which you remember after you wake up take place in light sleep. Some authorities believe that you always dream, but that you forget the greater part of your dreams—that is, that they make no impression on the waking mind.

Dreams are not prophetic. They are born of the past, and may be prophetic only in so far as they may indicate tendencies or wishes that may sometime be fulfilled. Apparent contradictions of this truth can usually be explained if all the attendant facts are known.

Controlled imagination, directed toward some result in reality, has practical value. The inventor who produces some new machine or chemical process does so by means of controlled imagination. His inventive imagination is constantly subjected to the criticism of what he already knows to be true or false. He continually tests his idea by asking such questions as the following: Will it work? Will the public find a use for it? Can it be manufactured cheaply enough to be commercially profitable?

Art is a product of the imagination. The artist makes use of his imagination (as well as his intellect and learning) as he composes a symphony, paints a picture, writes a novel, or models a piece of sculpture. He gives expression to a conception which he has in his imagination. That conception is new to him—it is some novel expression of a life-truth which he feels should be given form, and which, in the degree in which it is art, will be admired and appreciated.

To enjoy art, the individual must be imaginative along lines similar to those which produced the work of art, though not necessarily in the same degree. Appreciation of art, involving both empathy and sympathy to its parts and a detached comprehension of the whole, is not vicarious living.

No matter how far your imagination reaches, it can never conceive anything which is not made up of what you have perceived, what you have experienced, what you have learned. The products of the imagination are new combinations of old facts.

PERSONALITY

Personality is derived from inherited physical factors as well as environment. Physical factors influence personality in a number of ways. First, psychologists have made classifications of physical "types," based either on physique or on glandular activity. A person of a particular type shows a propensity toward a certain type of emotional reaction.

Less direct though perhaps more understandable physical influences on personality are those produced by physical handicaps. These often produce a sense of inferiority.

The theory of personality arrived at by Sigmund Freud in his research on psychoanalysis is as follows: the fundamental energy in a person is called the *libido*. The libido is basically a sex urge, or, more broadly, a love urge. A person's mental health and balance depend in great part on how the libido is released, to what "objects" it attaches itself, etc. The *Id,* referring in large part to the unconscious life of the individual, strives to satisfy the libido. The Id is primitive, non-moral in nature. The *Ego* is the rational, civilized part of the individual. It acts as a control on the Id, often "repressing" (either consciously or unconsciously) its urges. These repressed desires become unconscious. A further factor in personality, according to Freud, is the *Super-ego,* which corresponds closely to what we call conscience. This factor acts as a control over both Ego and Id, imposing on them moral ideas. Basically we may see that the Super-ego (conscience) and the Id (primitive nature) are in constant conflict, which the Ego (reason) tries to resolve. This basic outline of personality is accepted by many psychologists today.

There are numerous social influences on personality. The first influence on anyone's personality comes from parents and other persons in the home. How the adults behave and how they behave toward the child have a strong influence on his later development. This is particularly so because of the child's ability to imitate others, even identify himself with others. It is rare that an unharmonious home with an atmosphere of conflict and animosity will produce a well-balanced child. A child who has not known tenderness and affection may grow up with neurotic problems or even delinquent traits. Overaffection is likely to be less harmful, although it "spoils" the child and retards maturity. Parents should seek a happy medium in this matter. Likewise, between rigorous discipline and overprotection on the one hand and neglectful submission to the child's whims on the other hand—a happy medium must be sought.

Relationships among brothers and sisters in a family and with other children and teachers at school have also a strong influence on the growing child's personality. Many problems are involved in this area, among them: feelings of inadequacy on the part of the duller child or the less popular child; individual conflicts; struggles for superiority; etc.

Finally, the individual's position in the community as well as his social and economic standing may be major determinants of personality—not so much in themselves as in the way that the individual responds to these situations.

WILL

Is there such a thing as "free will"? The issue is sharply divided, and there are about as many authorities on one side as on the other. The more mechanistically minded authorities dispute the exercise of anything like free will; the more spiritually minded defend the faculty.

Certainly all of us experience the feeling that we can do as we wish. If that is what we mean by free will, it undoubtedly exists. But are we self-deceived? Is what we wish determined by stimuli which we cannot control? When we seem to weigh two courses of action, are we not merely examining two sets of stimuli, finally yielding to the stronger? Those stimuli, whether from the outside or set up within ourselves, are ultimately beyond our control, viewed psychologically, for they come either from our present or past environment, or from the equipment, mental and physical, with which we were born.

For practical purposes, we speak of voluntary and involuntary actions. We distinguish them by saying that voluntary actions can be initiated by the higher brain centers, or controlled by them. Involuntary actions—such as the breathing, beating of the heart, and some reflexes—cannot be so initiated or so controlled. But is that higher control in itself voluntary, or does it arise as a response to stimuli beyond the individual's ultimate control? That is the timeworn insoluble problem.

The most familiar exercise of our will, which is the name we give to the voluntary and cumulative action of our "mind," occurs when we are faced with conflicting stimuli or the impulses brought about by them, and must make a decision or choice. We weigh the issue, and usually choose one way or another, or else decide to choose none. Some individuals have difficulty in deciding—they vacillate between two courses of action. This may be caused by vague rather than clear-cut desires, and by a consequent failure to receive the full benefit of the conflicting stimuli. A well-defined personality, with a definite purpose in every action, seldom vacillates.

You exercise your will when you meet obstacles and overcome them. "Where there's a will, there's a way," says the old proverb. Not always; but it is a worthy motto, if it does not make one foolishly stubborn in the face of contrary facts. When an obstruction appears, you exert effort to overcome it. You are thereby responding to your self-assertive instinct, bringing all your knowledge and skill to the struggle.

People vary greatly in their determination and in the manner in which they go about their activities. It is a common practice to divide men loosely into those who think and those who act—but men who act wisely must necessarily think, and men who think well must necessarily act. Purpose, ambition, interest, and the like, all tend to bring about definite and concerted action toward the attaining of some goal.

MODERN SCHOOLS OF PSYCHOLOGY

All modern schools of psychology, and particularly psychotherapy, have been influenced by Sigmund Freud (1856–1939), founder of psychoanalysis. Freud was the first to theorize on and practice the analysis of dreams as an access to the subconscious mind, and to use this method and that of free association, in which the subject is allowed to associate automatically objects and ideas and recollections which are related in his mind. These techniques have replaced the older method of investigation under hypnosis. Freud concentrated his theories at first primarily on the sex urge. Repressions due to social mores or parental instruction cause substitute desires, or might lead to a rejection of reality, which when critical is called *schizophrenia*.

Alfred Adler (1870–1937) was a student of Freud. His experiments are characterized by the conclusion that the primary drive of all individuals is not the sex urge but the will to power. Both Freudian and Adlerian psychology are considered valid in therapy today.

The third important psychological school stems from Carl Jung (born 1875). He is often considered the most spiritual of the three. He has devoted much of his life to a study of mythology and religions, in an effort to account for man's persistent search for concrete images of spiritual power. His studies are dominated by the theory of archetypes, such as the father image, the mother image, the hero image, etc., which have recurred throughout the beliefs of mankind ever since history. They are for him expressions of the subconscious spiritual complex, just as the respectable man, the virtuous man, the man of social prestige, are expressions of the complex of surface personality. Among these generalized forms of expression, the individual seeks to find himself, as a personality and as a spiritual being. He is in danger always of surrendering to one of the superficial types of convention. He is also in danger of being swallowed up by an obsession with one of the cultural archetypes, as in the case of the fanatic. Thus Jung has attempted to salvage psychology from the single-minded materialistic views of his predecessors and place an emphasis on the expression of the whole individual. From the point of view of practical psychotherapy, however, the theories of single dominant drives may be most useful.

Much new work is being done in the field of psychology. Recently the discovery of a relationship between mental disturbance and blood composition has reaffirmed the importance of viewing mind and body as one unified complex.

The interaction of mental states and bodily states becomes increasingly apparent to many people, particularly to physicians who practice in fields in which psychology and medicine come into close contact. The important work of Adolf Meyer (1866–1950) in Baltimore has been developed further in this area, which may be referred to as psychosomatic medicine.

APPLICATIONS OF PSYCHOLOGY IN DAILY LIFE

Psychology and its findings can be of great help to us in many areas of everyday life. Vocational guidance, personnel work, individual adjustment, family relationships, mental health are only a few of the fields in which trained psychologists are equipped to provide valuable assistance to both young people and adults.

In the vocational field, those who are seeking the sort of employment for which they are best qualified often find that their decision is made easier if they avail themselves of the services of an organization which specializes in giving vocational tests. Such organizations are to be found in the larger cities, and in most communities individual specialists in vocational counseling may be consulted. Vocational tests would usually include I.Q. (intelligence quotient) tests and aptitude tests of various sorts.

Without doubt one of the primary factors in everyone's life is his vocation. A steady job occupies most of one's time, and it is of the first importance that it be appropriate to one's interests, intelligence, and aptitude. Apart from the tests which we have mentioned, there are certain suggestions which can be made here as a general guide.

The broad fields in which one may choose an occupation are:

> Agriculture
> Forestry, Mining, and Fishing
> Business and Commerce
> The Professions
> Literature and the Arts
> Skilled Mechanical and Industrial Occupations
> Transportation
> Communication
> Civil Service
> Personal and Domestic Service

In evaluating one's interests and aptitudes, one must judge in terms of one's past experience, both in schoolwork and in hobbies and leisure activities. Thus, for example, anyone who always did badly in mathematics will not be inclined to work as a bank teller, accountant, bookkeeper, cashier, or other occupation consisting primarily of work with numbers. In such a case, as almost always, one's inclinations and one's aptitudes go together.

In making a choice, one must also take into consideration such factors as one's ability to get along well with others (of prime importance in sales, public relations, etc.), one's capacity to work under supervision, and the type of life one wants to lead. Work as a newspaperman or in the theater, for instance, generally requires a certain physical endurance, a capacity for a very active life, a readiness to travel, etc.

The degree and type of one's intelligence will greatly influence choice of a career. Many careers, especially the professions (law, medicine, etc.), require extensive postgraduate training. A capacity and inclination for studies is necessarily involved. Certain fields call for an ability to deal with ideas and abstractions (science, engineering, etc.); whereas in others a stress is upon creative imagination (advertising, art, etc.); and in many the important qualification is practical knowledge (business, industry, etc.). It is in deciding where one's particular talents lie that aptitude tests are often useful.

Guidance and counseling are available not only in the vocational field but also in areas of personal adjustment. Problems which arise in marriage and family life may often be resolved more easily through conferences with professionally trained psychologists, who practice guidance work in many communities.

Apart from its usefulness to the individual, psychology also has many applications in the business world. Advertising, for example, relies largely on analyses of psychological reactions to the manner in which it presents products and services through various media. And in large industrial organizations such questions as qualifications of applicants, effectiveness of work, and suitability of working conditions are studied by a special personnel staff, which constantly makes use of the findings of psychology.

Examination Questions

1. What does psychology deal with?
2. With what other sciences is psychology closely linked?
3. Why do we say that mental activity is basically physiological?
4. What function akin to intelligence exists in even the simplest form of life?
5. What is subjective observation called?
6. What are we learning from psychologists?
7. What is the simplest response to a stimulus called?
8. What is the name of the response when you jump out of the way on hearing an automobile horn?
9. What is the center of the brain that receives sensations of smell?
10. Has the taste center of the brain been isolated?
11. Is the reflex occurring in response to the stimulus always the same?
12. When the flow of saliva in the mouth is stimulated by the sight of food, what is the response called?
13. What three fundamental and native emotional reactions do the behaviorists say that babies have?
14. Is walking a native or an acquired trait?
15. Differentiate between the ability to make sounds and to use coordinated speech.
16. What is a psychological motive?
17. Is the father drive usually as strong as the mother drive?
18. When is a drive said to be sublimated?
19. Is there a native tendency for children to honor and obey their parents?
20. What is euphoria?
21. What is gregariousness and on what is it based?
22. What are four common emotions?
23. Are emotions conditions of any one part of the body?
24. When is it particularly unhealthful to become angry?
25. What secretion is made by the adrenal glands during fear or anger, and what is its use?
26. What emotions are suggested by scowling, shaking the head, and exposing the teeth?
27. What distinguishes a "cool" person in the face of danger?
28. Name a drive that is accompanied by emotion.
29. What are the two elementary feelings?
30. What is a sensation?
31. By what is the exploring tendency held in check?
32. What is the psychological explanation of the popularity of crossword puzzles?
33. What are the five familiar senses?
34. What are the elementary tastes?
35. What are the elementary odors?

36. Give an ordinary example of a sensation that persists after the stimulus has ceased.
37. How may habits be broken?
38. What is the principle of spaced repetition in memorizing something?
39. What factors may inhibit remembering?
40. Explain the statement that a lemon smells sour.
41. What is the mistake if you think a piece of burlap lying in the road is a sleeping dog?
42. Explain "hearing burglars" in the house after reading of a midnight robbery in the paper.
43. What three areas of intelligent

activity are distinguished by psychologists?
44. Does the size of the brain have anything to do with intelligence?
45. What is the analysis of reasoning and its fallacies called?
46. What is rationalization?
47. What aspect of imagination is called empathy?
48. What is libido, according to Sigmund Freud?
49. What is the primary drive of all individuals according to Alfred Adler?
50. What discovery has reaffirmed the importance of viewing mind and body as one unified complex?

FOR FURTHER STUDY

BASIC TEACHINGS OF THE GREAT PSYCHOLOGISTS, by S. Stansfeld Sargent. (Barnes & Noble, New York.)

GENERAL INTRODUCTION TO PSYCHOANALYSIS, by Sigmund Freud. (Liveright Publishing Corp., New York.)

THE HUMAN MIND, by Karl A. Menninger. (Alfred A. Knopf, New York.)

PSYCHOLOGY, by Robert S. Woodworth. (Henry Holt & Co., New York.)

THE PSYCHOLOGY OF ADJUSTMENT, by Laurance F. Shaffer. (Houghton Mifflin Co., Boston.)

THE WHOLESOME PERSONALITY, by W. H. Burnham. (Appleton-Century, New York.)

XXVIII

Sociology Simplified

WHAT IS SOCIOLOGY?

IN THESE DAYS of world-wide political, economic, and social change, we are aware as never before that the evolution of mankind is not the story of single nations or states but of society as a whole. We may contrast one country with another, one race with another; we may note different customs and different traits; we may stress the special characteristics of Western civilization as compared with the Orient. But underlying all these variations we find an essential similarity. Men and women, no matter where or how they live, are concerned about a few major matters: about their families, their work, their government, their religion. Their conceptions of love, their marriage customs, their attitude toward the home, may be widely unlike, as may also their versatility and skill in industry, agriculture, and commerce, their standards of living, their interests in culture, in education, art, science, and literature, their sense of justice, their observance of law, their convictions concerning war and peace, their creeds and faiths.

Yet, despite striking differences in attitude and method, human life and human nature in all parts of the world are faced with the solution of the universal, elemental problems of mankind: the problems of home and family, of work and wealth, of education and culture, of law and order, of right living, and of religious beliefs. And it is these fundamental interests and activities and problems which constitute the subject matter of the science which deals with society (using the word "society" to mean "mankind as a whole"), the science of Sociology.

The sociologist examines the conditions of human life as they are today in civilized communities and in more primitive groups, and contrasts modern society with the life of ancient times. The sociologist is concerned with the things men do in groups, large or small groups, but in groups rather than as individuals. Psychology studies the individual mind and the behavior of individuals. Sociology does not deal directly with the mind or with behavior; it studies the institutions which man has evolved in the process of meeting the major problems of life, and it observes the variations in custom and practice associated with these institutions in all parts of the world and through the ages.

Sociology and psychology supplement each other in their approach to the ways of men. If a man rises to great power in his country and reveals a genius for statesmanship, psychology is interested in his intellectual and emotional make-up, sociology is interested in the changes in social institutions, in the methods of handling the problems of industry, trade, finance, in the methods of insuring justice, which characterize his administration. If a man commits a serious crime, psychology is concerned with his mentality, sociology is concerned with the effect of the crime upon the community and the means devised to prevent repetition of the crime. If a man becomes destitute and dependent on charity for his support, psychology seeks to discover the traits in the man himself which have handicapped him, sociology seeks to discover the conditions in the community which have made progress difficult for him and looks for plans for providing improved opportunities.

Thus far we have considered only the social groups, the social institutions, which constitute what may be called the structure of society. But sociology is concerned equally with the dynamic aspects of society, with the way in which society evolves and changes, with the social forces constantly at work, social forces which are far greater, far more irresistible than the power of any of the countless men and women whose lives they influence, forces which make for war, for revolution, for crime, for economic depression and poverty, forces which make for peace, for stability, for security, for prosperity and progress.

To a certain extent we plan what we do on a given day or any day, to a certain extent our activities are planned by others, to a certain extent things merely happen. If a man could plan his life with a view to making it well-ordered, secure, and happy, what would he do? In order to answer this question, it is necessary to have a knowledge not only of man's psychological nature but also of the effect upon him of traditions and social institutions.

CIVILIZED AND PRIMITIVE PEOPLES

At first sight the life of our modern civilized communities seems wholly unlike the life of primitive peoples. The tribes which inhabit more remote parts of Asia, Africa, and Australia, and some of the islands of the

Pacific, the Eskimos and such of our American Indian groups as still preserve their native traditions, live in accordance with customs which are strikingly different from our own. Yet, if we think in terms of the fundamental problems of society, our civilization differs from the life of primitive peoples principally in its degree of complexity. Most of the daily duties of a primitive man or woman can be carried out without moving very far from home, whereas most of the daily duties of civilized communities involve the use of one or several of our modern mechanical means of transportation. Primitive peoples use only the simplest utensils for tilling the soil and caring for their crops, for hunting, for cooking, for the preparation of their garments and the construction of their shelters. Men and women in modern civilized communities are for the most part dependent on a complex system for supplying them with food, clothing, and housing. Although the life of the farm in its direct contact with nature corresponds more nearly than the life of the city with the simpler ways of primitive groups, the increasing use of intricate mechanical instruments in agriculture and the ease of modern communication and transportation are greatly increasing the complexity of rural life. Nevertheless life in the country is much simpler than it is in a modern city.

It is not only in its relative simplicity, however, that the life of primitive tribes differs from civilized life; primitive life is essentially cruder. Most primitive tribes know little about sanitation or medicine, are more hampered by fears and superstitions, and not infrequently resort to violence. Formerly primitive peoples were always thought of and spoken of as savages, and were pictured as war-like and given to uncontrolled violence. This conception has been much modified in recent years by the work of anthropologists who have lived long among primitive peoples. To be sure, there is much that is brutal in primitive life, and there may well have been much more brutality in earlier times. However, most primitive peoples nowadays live according to laws of their own devising, which are often entirely just, even according to our standards, and are enforced by methods which when understood are seen to be reasonable and fair.

THE ORIGIN AND EVOLUTION OF SOCIETY

The culture of civilized nations today consists of an aggregation of traits that originated in peoples of all races, living in all parts of the world. Archaeological investigations have enabled us to trace the development of culture in Europe for the last one hundred thousand years, a development which began slowly and which proceeded at an ever-increasing tempo. Until modern times the most important factor in this development has been the acquisition of traits from neighboring cultures by the process of *diffusion:* in modern times, with European civilization spreading over the greater part of the globe, the greater number of additions to our culture come from inventions which occur within the civilization itself. The investigations of anthropologists into the lives of contemporary primitive peoples enable us to appreciate both the widely varying customs under which man may live and the underlying principles which remain the same even under differing circumstances, thereby giving us a more vivid insight into life in simpler circumstances than our own, life such as our own ancestors must have lived.

Associated with the evolution of culture is the question of the origin of society. Did men live alone as individuals before they lived semi-organized in groups? We have no definite evidence with which to answer conclusively, but the psychological nature of primitive and civilized man and the social organization of allied forms of life are such as to indicate that an elementary form of society must be older than the human race.

Perhaps the strongest clue to the origin of society is found in the two fundamental human urges, self-preservation and self-perpetuation, which determine the basic outline of human life and create the basic structure of human society. Of these two needs, the need for food and the need for sexual satisfaction (perpetuating the race), the sexual need is very definitely social. Man may seek food alone, but in his need of a mate we find one of the beginnings of society. Of course these motives take many forms, some of them not obviously related to the basic urges; as, for example, the desire for prestige, which is the predominant desire of man in his social organization. As the group in which man lives advances in degree of civilization, other interests take their place beside these most fundamental desires. With increasing civilization, man's approach to all his activities becomes increasingly complex, his interests more and more specialized; yet beneath the changing surface of human life, the two elemental needs remain unchanged in their importance.

THE CLASSIFICATION OF HUMAN GROUPS

Fundamentally, there are two radically different ways in which human groups can be classified: according to their race or according to their customs. But as there are many different customs that may serve for classificatory purposes, there actually seems to be an unlimited number of ways in which classification may be performed. Besides race, the commonest methods are classification by language, by nationality, by religion, and by cultural origin. Each method is important in its own field, but it is indeed unfortunate that there should be a great deal of popular misconception whereby classifications which are really linguistic are confused with those that are racial, and so on.

There are three obvious divisions of the human race: the Caucasians, Mongoloids, and Negroids; to which anthropologists usually add a fourth, Australoids. These divisions correspond roughly to the popular classification by color, Caucasians being "white," Mongoloids "yellow," and Negroids and Australoids "black" or "brown." Actually, other biological characteristics, particularly the cross section of the hair, are much more revealing than color, and play a more important role in racial classification. Within each major group there are a number of subdivisions, more or less important according to the amount of divergence found in that group. Within the classification of Negroids there is one highly differentiated group known as the African Bushmen, or Pygmies. The Mongoloids include the Eskimo and the American Indians, as well as the "yellow" races of Asia, the peoples of North and South China, Mongolia, Tibet, Japan, and Indo-China, and the Malayan peninsula. The subdivisions of the Caucasian race are not as distinct from one another. They are the Nordics, Alpines, and Mediterranean. The Armenoids are sometimes distinguished from the Alpines, the Hindus from the Mediterraneans. Besides these main races and principal subdivisions there are several racial groups that are apparently mixtures of the principal races; thus the Polynesians of the northern Pacific area are a mixture of Mongoloid, Caucasian, and Negroid; while the Melanesians further south are probably a similar mixture with Negroid predominating. Race is in itself unimportant to the sociologist. Differences in the skills of the major races are so slight that they cannot be demonstrated beyond question.

That man may be classified by nationality or religion is obvious to everyone. The linguistic classification is not so clear. French, Spanish, and Italian are all "Latin" tongues, so that speakers of those languages are sometimes known as Latins. The Latin languages, together with the Teutonic, Slavic, and Greek, are derived from a language once spoken in northern India and known from the region of origin as "Aryan." The Aryan group of languages is the largest in Europe; the Semitic and Hamitic groups are of much less importance. In other parts of the world there are other linguistic groups. Thus, in North America, Algonquian was the most important linguistic stock of the Indians, while Siouan, Athapascan, Shoshonean, and many other stocks also existed.

THE PRINCIPAL SOCIAL INSTITUTIONS

The chief divisions of sociology correspond to the fundamental interests and activities of mankind, and more specifically to the social institutions which are the expression of these interests and activities. Let us see more precisely than we have thus far what these institutions are and how they are related to one another; and, after defining the range of each institution and our approach to it, we shall study each in turn in some detail. In naming these major institutions we find a lack of adequate terminology. The institutions are more definite than the phrases by which we designate them:

(1) *The Family* as a social institution includes the intimate family group (husband, wife, and children), the larger family group (the relatives of either husband or wife or both), and the customs and practices associated with the family and with marriage and divorce.

(2) *Classes* and *Social Associations,* such as clubs and secret societies, are other important personal groups which, despite their differences in inclusiveness, may be considered together.

(3) *Work,* in the sociological sense, is man's daily means of earning a living, including all branches of industry, the professions, and wealth and property—all of man's economic activities.

(4) *The State,* as a sociological institution, includes the national and local administration of justice, preservation of law and order, all government regulation of domestic and foreign affairs, all political activities.

(5) *Education* consists of the processes by which men and women seek to fit themselves and their children for the various activities of life, including their knowledge about health and their ethical conceptions, their standards of right living.

(6) *Culture* is perhaps the best word we have for the various avocational or leisure interests of men and women—art, music, literature, and drama, recreation and sports, all phases of knowledge as a background for living.

(7) *Religion* includes the faith of men and women in the spiritual things of life, their convictions concerning Divinity, fate, and immortality, and the role of the church and other religious organizations in human life.

The social groups corresponding to these seven great social institutions are obviously not mutually exclusive. Men and women may be and usually are identified with most or all of these groups, but identified with each in a different way. A man is likely to be the father of a family, a worker in industry, a citizen of the state, a graduate of a school or college, a theater-goer, concert-goer, or sport enthusiast, and he will belong to a certain class, be associated with a certain club or social circle, and be a member of a religious organization. Consequently each of the major social institutions touch his life very closely, and all of the institutions taken together constitute a full range of his activities and interests.

Sociology gives us a very inclusive survey of the aspects of society. Sociology presents the larger, more universal, more human view of each of the social institutions. There are, however, individual social sciences which deal with the detailed workings and practical applications of the individual institutions. The most fully and systematically developed of these are *economics* and *political science*. *Anthropology* deals especially with primitive man. *History* views the sequence of human events chronologically, whereas sociology views not individual events, but movements and changes in their larger, more fundamental aspects.

THE FAMILY

The family is the most universal, most fundamental of all social groups; based as it is upon man's simplest social needs, it is the earliest social institution; and to this day the family, as a group, is the child's first social contact, his introduction to society.

Has the nature of the family changed since its primitive beginnings? If so, how? Is the family changing at the present time? If so, why? The family has changed and is still changing, and it has existed simultaneously in different forms in different parts of the world. We shall want to see how these forms differ and to compare them with the family as we know it and as we feel that it ought to be.

Whether man in early times took a mate for life or not, it is impossible for us to know definitely. But there is every reason to believe that he did. For a partnership of male and female for the protection and education of the young is a common enough trait of mammals generally, and with the increased dependence of human offspring upon their parents, partnership would doubtless be intensified rather than diminished. Even with the lower mammals and with birds there is a tendency for the same couples to mate year after year; when the period during which the offspring are dependent upon their parents overlaps the birth of further offspring, a semi-permanent marriage relationship would be almost necessary. Thus there is good reason to believe that marriage, or the relatively permanent union of man and woman, is older than the human race. In fact, the apes and some other animals have a family life not altogether unlike our own.

MARRIAGE AMONG PRIMITIVE PEOPLES

Marriage as we think of it today is a life partnership between a man and a woman, based on the love and admiration of each for the other, and including the establishment of a home and family, and the joint responsibility of the parents for the care of the children.

What other conceptions of marriage are there? As contrasted with *monogamy*—the marriage of one man and one woman—which is the only legally recognized form of marriage in most civilized countries, there is today, and there has been in the past, the practice of *polygamy*. The more common type of *polygamy,* one man having several wives, is specifically known as *polygyny,* and the less common type, one woman having several husbands, is known as *polyandry*. Polygamy of one or the other type is most likely to occur in communities where there is a wide difference in the number of men and women. In the natural course of events, approximately the same number of boys and girls are born and grow to adulthood in any given community. Among primitive peoples, however, as, for instance, among African tribes and certain groups of American Indians, numerous groups are or were dependent for their sustenance on the skill of the men of the tribe in capturing wild animals, and for their protection on the strength and bravery of the men in their encounters with hostile tribes. Clearly where many men are lost in the perils of daily life, there will be more women than men in the community. In order that the women may all realize motherhood, it becomes necessary for such a group to recognize the right of one man to have several wives.

Polygyny exists also among peoples where there is great inequality of wealth or property, or great inequality of power. In certain Asiatic countries a man of wealth or power is likely to have many wives because he can afford or demand them, whereas one wife is all that a poor man can obtain!

Polyandry, on the other hand, usually occurs in communities where the environment is itself unfavorable; for example, among the Eskimos of the frozen Arctic it is sometimes considered necessary to permit some of the female infants to die of exposure in order to avoid a greater population than the region can sustain. In these communities there are more men than women, and several men therefore share one wife. The wife in many instances lives part of the year with each husband, though among some groups the home is shared by all.

The investigations of sociologists and anthropologists definitely indicate that, despite numerous exceptions, the tendency among even the most primitive people is toward monogamy, and that the alternative practices are found principally where economic and environmental conditions are such as to make monogamy difficult. Tradition plays an important part, however, and communities which in early times or under unfavorable conditions recognized polygamy may continue to practice it long after it is really necessary.

There is another important aspect and explanation of polygyny; namely, that in communities (as in parts of the Orient) where all the household work is done by the women of the family, the first wife herself may welcome additional wives as aids. Ordinarily the first wife takes precedence over the others and has a certain amount of authority over them.

One other form of marriage is sometimes found among primitive peoples—group marriage. Group marriage is not, however, precisely what the name implies. It consists of the marriage of more than one man and more than one woman, any man being a recognized husband of any woman. But this group does not live together in a sort of limitedly promiscuous relationship. Group marriage usually occurs when men are forced to travel a great deal, and therefore share wives in several localities. In fact, the situation is not unlike the traditional situation of a sailor's having a wife in every port, it being understood, however, that the group wives, in turn, have a husband on every ship.

MARRIAGE RESTRICTIONS

There are certain degrees of blood relationship which are considered too close for marriage. The most primitive as well as the most civilized people forbid marriage between brother and sister, father and daughter, son and mother, and look upon sexual relations between men and women bound by these closest ties of blood as *incestuous*. Among some peoples marriage between first cousins or even more distant cousins is forbidden, although the marriage of cousins is more often permitted than forbidden; and even brother-sister marriage is accepted in some primitive groups. Just why the rules against incest should be so nearly universal is not at all clear. Because of our own traditions in the matter, we are apt to believe that the reason is an attempt to avoid certain dangers of inbreeding. But these dangers have never been proven. The real biological objection is that inbreeding standardizes human nature, and thus prevents rapid evolutionary development; but this point can hardly be the motive in the case of primitive societies. Two possibilities remain: the occasional appearance of undesirable recessive traits in the progeny may lead to the view that all intercourse of close relatives is bad; or the real objection may lie in the social injustices that would occur if a man were permitted to marry women who were under his control because of other relationships than those of marriage.

The degree of kinship which is considered too close for marriage varies greatly among different peoples. Usually the determination of whether two persons may marry or not depends upon the groups to which they belong. Certain groups are known as *exogamous;* that is to say, a person belonging to the group may not marry another member of the same group. Family groups, both in the limited sense and in the larger conceptions of the unilateral family, such as the gens and clan, are usually exogamous. So also are certain other groups found among primitives, such as the moiety and marriage class. Other groups are commonly *endogamous;* that is, one member of the group marries another member of the same group. The tribe itself is endogamous, and where classes are distinct each class is usually endogamous. The local group is sometimes endogamous, sometimes exogamous, sometimes neither. Consequently we see that in many instances a man belongs to groups of both types, and the possible ways in which he may marry are limited by his obligations as a member of a group.

Thus, whether two relatives may marry depends more upon their group affiliations than upon their biological closeness. The family group is regularly exogamous, and brother and sister belong to the same group whether relationships are bilateral, matrilinear, or patrilinear. Therefore brother and sister are regularly forbidden to marry each other. But certain exceptions occur. In a class system the members of the highest classes are frequently so limited in number that brother and sister are the only members of the highest endogamous class. In such cases the rule of endogamy has often superseded that of exogamy. Thus the Egyptian Pharaoh married his own sister, and the Incas of Peru also followed this custom. Frequently Polynesians of the highest rank are reduced to brother-sister marriage for the same reason.

When we come to the marriage of cousins, the situation is more complex. The children of a brother and a sister belong necessarily to different groups, whether the groups be matrilinear or patrilinear. Consequently there is ordinarily no objection to their marriage, and it is even encouraged in a large number of tribes. This relationship is known as that of cross-cousin. But children of two brothers in a patrilinear group belong to the same group, and children of two sisters in a matrilinear society belong to the same group: two parallel cousins often may not marry.

MARRIAGE CUSTOMS

Several other marriage practices of primitive peoples are of great interest in indicating the extent to which the institution of marriage varies from place to place and from one type or degree of civilization to another. Thus the rule known as the *sororate* requires a man to marry the eldest of a group of sisters, and the younger sisters to become his subordinate wives. The term *levirate* is applied to the inheritance of a man's wife or wives by his younger brother or nearest male relative upon his death.

The custom of *marriage by purchase,* found among the majority of primitive peoples, is an example of the conception of marriage as an act of the group rather than of the individual. In order to marry a certain girl, a man or his family must pay the family of the girl a sum, known as the bride price, in terms of produce, cattle, or other valuables, and when complete payment has been made, the girl becomes to some extent a member of the man's group. Among the most primitive tribes the young wife loses all connection with her own family, but this does not happen among more advanced tribes. Among other tribes we find that payment is made by an exchange of women, so that each of two families or other groups receives a woman in exchange for the one it gives away. Sometimes the payment is made by the husband's working for the bride's family, or performing some ceremonies in their behalf. Very commonly the payment for the bride is purely nominal, and is made only as a ceremonial token of marriage. Another common custom is *dowry,* where the bride's family makes the gift to the husband. The custom of dowry is not intrinsically different from that of bride price.

Marriage by capture is and always has been an uncommon event. It occurs when the more powerful individual or group seizes women by virtue of their power. Its importance is limited, but its hold on the imagination is so great that it is frequently used as a symbolical gesture in the ceremonies of marriage that are not at all marriages by force. The term "marriage by capture" is thus applied to the practice whereby the prospective bridegroom must engage in wrestling and other feats of skill with the bride's relatives prior to the consummation of the marriage.

Our survey of the most important marriage customs and practices among primitive peoples would be incomplete if we did not mention a custom practiced at times among all primitive peoples and among all civilized peoples as well—the custom of *elopement.* In all times and places some young men and women are unwilling to accept the traditions of their group with regard to marriage. A marriage in defiance of group traditions involves much the same problems among primitive as among civilized peoples.

MARRIAGE IN MODERN LIFE

We speak of a "love match" as the finest and truest marriage, a marriage in which a man and woman feel drawn to one another by personal attraction and look forward to the establishment of a jointly directed home in which the children will grow up under the guidance of parental love. Nevertheless, in some parts of the western world, marriages which appear desirable from the economic or social point of view are arranged.

In countries where marriage is by arrangement, the ideals of marriage may be just as high as in those countries in which marriage is based on mutual attraction, and if the husband and wife prove congenial, their home may be just as happy, and the devotion between them and between them and their children just as great as in marriages founded on falling in love.

Actully, marriage of mutual attraction and marriage by arrangement are not as different in practice as their designations would indicate. Thus most young Americans grow up with the intention of marrying when they reach marriageable age, and with the expectation of marrying someone whose social and economic status and background are approximately the same as their own. The specific choice of a marriage partner is ordinarily determined by attraction, but for the most part the range of choice is limited by various other factors. On the other hand, where young men and women reach marriageable age after having grown up with the thought that a suitable marriage will be arranged for them and that they can find their happiness within the institution of marriage and the family, they are ready to call forth the best qualities in their partners in marriage. The principal difference between these two approaches to marriage is that one emphasizes the importance of individual choice and action, the other stresses the importance of marriage as an institution. The arranged marriage, called a "marriage of convenience," is becoming less frequent, particularly as class barriers and class traditions are becoming less marked.

DIVORCE

There have been divorces since the earliest times, but statistics show that voluntary or legal termination of marriage is far more common today than ever before in the history of modern civilization. Does this indicate that the institution of marriage is not as well suited to the conditions of modern life as it was to the life of earlier times? Or does it indicate that it is our modern life and not the institution of marriage which is out of gear?

Two factors, essentially opposed to one another, combine in accounting very largely for the increase in divorce: they are the greater frankness and the greater selfishness of our modern life. Greater frankness, as compared with former times, is in itself a great gain. For happy marriages do not have to conceal their strong foundations, and wholly unhappy marriages only sink into deeper misery as a result of secrecy and unwillingness to face the facts. Divorces resulting from an honest recognition of the complete lack of any true basis for the continuation of a marriage are socially and personally beneficial and desirable.

Society, after all, has no interest in continuing a marriage between two persons when they are unable to live happily together. When there is a third party to the situation, a child, then society has a right to demand that the parents stay together, even if it is a sacrifice for them, for the sake of the child. But it is not at all certain that society would be wise to insist upon this right: a child is usually handicapped by the divorce of his parents and by being deprived of a normal home environment with two parents; but it might easily be worse for the child to be brought up in a home where its parents were maladjusted and unhappy.

But the other explanation of increased divorce, greater selfishness, works differently. For willingness to see the point of view of one's partner in marriage, eagerness to harmonize one's own point of view with that of one's marriage partner wherever possible, and readiness to respect the other point of view where the two are at variance, are essentials to a happy marriage; and, more than that, they are essentials which marriage as an institution has a right to expect, for they are not merely essentials of marriage, but essentials of right living generally. If they are lacking in a marriage, the fault lies not in the institution of marriage but in the parties to the marriage. The institution would not be worth continuing if it were not now proving to be, as it always has been, on the whole, the best basis for individual contentment. If it is true that the strains and stresses of modern living wear one ragged, make one irritable, and if society expects one to bear up reasonably well in public, it is nevertheless far from sensible to concentrate in the privacy of one's home the accumulation of dissatisfaction which is the result of lack of headway in the other daily problems and contacts of life. Under such conditions marriage is called upon to bear more than its rightful burden.

A third factor, purely economic, may have contributed to the increasing number of divorces. Women in the past few decades have achieved a degree of economic and political independence which rivals that of men. Women are no longer obliged to be married and to remain so to enjoy a comfortable existence.

THE LARGER FAMILY GROUP

When a man and woman marry, their marriage is the starting point of their own intimate family. But at the same time each of them remains a member of a larger family group. The parents and brothers and sisters of the husband and his more distant relatives and more remote ancestors are all part of his family; and, likewise, the corresponding immediate and more remote relatives of the wife are all part of her family. In this larger sense the family is the whole group of blood, collateral, and adopted relatives.

In modern society the paternal and maternal branches of the family are equally important, and the modern family is consequently said to be *bilateral*. Nevertheless, in modern communities the family name is always that of the male line. (In Spain this custom is modified; the family name of the father and mother are used jointly.)

Among primitive peoples the paternal and maternal branches are commonly not looked upon as equal in importance. Some groups give precedence to one, some to the other. Where the male line determines relationship, the family is said to be *patrilinear;* where descent is traced primarily through the mother's family, the family is said to be *matrilinear*. Early sociologists, drawing their conclusions from the history of modern civilized groups, assumed that the patrilinear family was almost universal, but later students, making extensive researches among the existing primitive peoples, found the matrilinear family exceedingly common. Where the family is reckoned on one line of descent only, it is known as a *sib*. Where the sib is matrilinear, it is known technically as the *clan;* where patrilinear, as the *gens*. Whether a tribe is organized into clans or gentes or into bilateral families, the general rule is that the men have the power and control over the group. In this case, and particularly when the ruler is the oldest man of the family group, the group or tribe is called *patriarchal,* and the system a *patriarchate*. In the very unusual cases where women have the major power, as among the Iroquois Indians, the group is called *matriarchal,* and the system a *matriarchate*. With the matrilinear clan system there is no tendency for women to rule, but sometimes authority over a family is vested in the mother's eldest brother or other male relative, rather than in the father. Such a system is known as an *avunculate*. In most matrilinear communities men live with their wives' families: such residence is *matrilocal*. Where men bring their wives to live in the vicinity of the men's families, the residence is *patrilocal*. It is possible, though uncommon, for a community to be at once matrilinear and patrilocal.

The word *taboo,* or *tabu,* which came originally from the Pacific regions, means the prohibition of an act or object. There are tabus on all subjects, but some important ones deal with the relationships of relatives to each other. The prohibition of incestuous marriages is a tabu, and so are many prohibitions of sexual and non-sexual intimacies between brother and sister. The parent-in-law tabu is one of the most common, prohibiting a person sometimes from even looking at his parent-in-law. Of the four possible types of parent-in-law tabu, the most common is that between a man and his mother-in-law. The reason for the prevalence of this tabu is undoubtedly to prevent a conflict of authority between the husband and parents of a young woman.

The Family Unit Today

In modern society the larger family group does not function as a unit to any great extent. Members of the same larger family group often live far from one another, and are closely associated with the customs, practices, and interests of their own locality rather than with those of the more scattered family group. Most of the responsibilities assumed by the larger family group among primitives are functions of the state in modern society.

Among primitive peoples the traditions of the family, traced back to remote ancestors, are of great importance in determining the practices of the family group. Until very recently the ancestral tradition was the guiding influence in the life of the Chinese people. Yet, in modern society, family tradition does not carry the weight which it once did, and ordinarily it does not extend back very far.

The influence of the larger family group has lessened, and with increasing divorce and with occasional experimentation in the rearing of children away from the home, the family in the narrower sense—the small, immediate family group—is having to prove its right to existence. Nevertheless, the indications are that the intimate family group has a unique function to perform which no other group can manage, and that, buffeted though it is by the rigors of social change, it will remain the basic social institution, the cornerstone of human society.

CLASSES AND SOCIAL ASSOCIATIONS

Next to the family, the most personal of the social institutions are the groups of people not necessarily related by birth yet connected through belonging to the same class of society, or through the closer bond of membership in the same circle of friends, or in the same club or other social association (using the word "social" in its narrower sense, referring to companionship in recreational activities).

Society in practically all parts of the world is divided into classes representing different social levels, although usually there are no clear lines of demarcation between classes. In feudal times the social classes were very sharply differentiated into the nobility, the clergy, the middle-class small landholders, and the serfs or laborers. In India, class distinction until recently existed in extreme form, constituting what is known as a caste system. A man was born into a certain caste; and, with certain exceptions, changes in wealth or accomplishment could not change his caste, and he was expected to marry within his own caste. There were various gradations in the caste system, from the highest Brahmans to the Pariahs (the outcasts beneath any of the classes of the caste system), each caste having its own work to perform and its own manner of living.

Among more democratic peoples, class distinctions are also clearly recognized. Where the government is monarchial, royalty and nobility constitute social classes, and there are upper and lower classes among the commoners, wealth and achievement being the basis for inclusion in the upper classes. In a republic, although titled classes do not exist, social leaders constitute an upper class into which their children are born, and which may ordinarily be entered by others only through the acquisition of great wealth or by outstanding accomplishment of some sort. Nevertheless, in countries of relatively recent traditions, people advance from one class to another with comparative ease or are permitted to drop to a lower class if they are unable to maintain their position.

Under socialistic and communistic doctrines, the distinction between the bourgeoisie or capitalistic middle classes and the proletariat or laboring classes is emphatically stressed, and the differences between the bourgeois property owners and the proletarian workers are held to be so fundamental as to make class conflict inevitable. In putting Marxist doctrines into practice, Soviet Russia has abolished class distinctions by recognizing the existence only of a working class; yet power is actually in the hands of a small minority. Even a legally established equality is difficult to maintain, since differences in individual ability exist in all groups, and greater ability almost inevitably leads to greater recognition, greater authority, and, in time, ordinarily to higher social standing.

From the sociological point of view all class distinctions which separate people into higher and lower ranks are undesirable. Social groupings based on common interests are natural and desirable; classes based upon rank divide society into antagonistic levels. Social groupings based on common interests enrich the interests by the encouragement which the group gives to its individual members; and each enriched social group contributes its share to the enrichment of the life of society as a whole.

CLUBS AND "SECRET SOCIETIES"

The typical secret society of primitive culture is very different from the type of organization among us that bears the same name. The most common primitive secret society is the group that consists of all adult men in the community. Such a group is usually politically important, governing the whole community and managing religious affairs. The group is not exclusive; every boy joins the society as a matter of course when he reaches the age of puberty. At that time the society functions to teach him many things: about sex and marriage, about the tribal religion, about ways of curing the sick, about governmental functions. A frequent function is to initiate the boys into the society in such a way as to impress upon the boy the tribal morality and its importance, emphasizing courage in war-like communities, the financial virtues in trading communities, and many other virtues in communities where they are especially important. Occasionally there are similar societies for women.

Frequently there are other societies among primitives, whose membership is less than the whole group of men and which function for particular purposes. Such are the medicine societies and war societies among American Indians, and religious societies in parts of Africa. But anyone who wants to may join these groups.

A third type of society among primitive peoples is the age group. The oldest men, or the young warriors, or the unmarried men may belong to separate groups that play important parts in communal life. The group of unmarried men is very common; sometimes they live together in a *men's house* which frequently becomes an important center for the community.

In our modern society, organizations such as the churches, political parties, YMCA, Boy Scouts, and many other organizations correspond in certain respects to the secret society of primitive cultures. They may have elements of secrecy, but membership is essentially open to anyone of the proper sex and age, and with an interest in the particular functioning of that organization. Most of our clubs are of this pattern; a few, such as our Greek letter fraternities, are genuinely secret, and membership is not available to everyone. This type, which is infrequently met with among primitives, is of much less social importance than the other varieties.

OTHER ORGANIZATIONS

Mankind sometimes divides itself into groups of types other than those we have already discussed. Sometimes a community is divided into two parts, called *moieties,* which take opposite sides in games and contests, and may also assume differing functions in ceremonies and dances. Sometimes a community is divided into more than two such divisions, which are then called *phratries*.

In Australia, *marriage classes* are common. A man belonging to one marriage class must marry a woman from a particular marriage class, not his own. The marriage classes are not family groups.

Commonly, human groups of any sort are symbolized, frequently by animals. Sometimes the belief is held that the group is descended from the animal used to symbolize them. This use of symbolism, known as *totemism,* is found in our own society as well as in primitive ones. When we symbolize a nation by a flag or bird, political parties by animals, colleges by various devices, professions by barber poles and similar signs, and so forth, we are practicing the same sort of totemism found in more primitive cultures.

The Circle of Friends

The most intimate personal group apart from the family is the circle of friends and close acquaintances. Friendship, among primitive peoples, among ancient civilized peoples, and in our own society, is one of the strongest of social bonds. A circle of friends is a social group of the utmost importance for society as a whole, for the co-operative spirit which may develop in small, intimate gatherings carries over into the larger groupings. Friendship is not necessarily based upon similarity of views, but it is based upon mutual respect and consideration. Without agreeing about specific problems, friends are nevertheless ordinarily in harmony about major matters. It is often remarked that the rush and confusion of modern life interfere with the full development of friendships, and undoubtedly this is true; yet it is a condition which society as it advances must rectify. For the friendship of a group of men and women is the surest indication that understanding, sympathy, and co-operation can increasingly become the determining factors in the evolution of society.

WORK AND WEALTH

Why do men work? Primarily to earn a living, undoubtedly; and earning a living means acquiring the wherewithal to supply oneself and one's family with the necessities of life and a reasonable share of the luxuries, conveniences, and pleasures of life. Nevertheless, men do not work only to earn a living. Some men work because they want to express the abilities which are in them, because they have natural or acquired skill which will not remain unused, because working is not merely a means of earning a living, but is in itself a manner of living. Welcome as leisure, idleness, and rest may be at times, few human beings can devote themselves entirely to play. Human nature is made for work, for the experiences, the attempts, the achievements which come in the course of working.

Work among Primitive Peoples

The instinct of self-preservation, the need for sustenance and shelter, compel primitive men and women to work. They undertake the tasks which are necessary in order to provide themselves with food, clothing, and housing of some sort. In very primitive societies each group of families is ordinarily an independent economic unit, its members working together to supply the needs of the community without joining with the economic activities of other communities.

The division of work between men and women was rather clearly defined even in the early stages in the development of society. At first men were principally hunters, women doing such simple agricultural work as necessary and preparing the food; men constructed the shelters, and women made the clothing.

There are various typical ways in which communities obtain food. The simplest and perhaps the most primitive type is that in which men live upon whatever their environment has to offer, *collecting* such objects as seem useful for nourishment—gathering eggs, insects, wild plants, fruits, and berries for food. Besides this method of subsistence, *hunting* and *fishing* may be the main sources of food. Hunting communities are extremely common; fishing communities are rather rare. When man learns to plant crops he comes soon to depend largely upon agricultural products, and we have *agricultural* communities. Sometimes a community will rely largely upon domestic animals for their food, and we have *pastoral* communities.

With more advanced cultures, the major occupation need not be the provision of food, so we have *commercial* and *industrial* communities.

Of course these types are not mutually exclusive. A hunting community may do some gathering and fishing on the side, as well as a certain amount of trading and perhaps some agriculture; and the modern industrial community gets its food from agriculture, the keeping of animals, and fishing.

In tracing the development of culture in Europe, we find that European man was first a hunter. Then he learned both agriculture and the domestication of animals at about the same time, becoming primarily agricultural about eight thousand years ago. In fairly modern times European man became commercial, and finally industrial. At no time, as far as we know, were Europeans chiefly a gathering, fishing, or pastoral community.

PROPERTY AMONG PRIMITIVE PEOPLES

Men work primarily in order to provide themselves and their families with the necessities of life. Some of these necessities, among them the most indispensable, such as food, are perishable and must be used promptly; others have permanence and may be kept almost indefinitely, such as materials from which a man constructs his shelter, and especially the land upon which he builds. Very early man had a sense of ownership, a feeling that what he had acquired belonged to him, was his property. At first his property was the product of his own work or his wife's, or of his neighbor's and acquired by exchange; or the land which he had cleared and settled upon. Later property of all sorts began to have a definite value placed upon it, to be reckoned in terms of exchange, to represent wealth—thus the conception of money as tokens of value developed. Capital as we know it today has evolved from the concrete types of property of primitive peoples.

Most peoples of ancient times and most primitive tribes of today recognize private ownership; all men recognize the semi-exclusive right of an individual to his tools, his clothing, and the other products of his industry; commonly property rights are recognized in names, dances, and other intangible objects; even land is frequently looked upon as the personal possession of the individual or the family who develop it. Not only do primitive peoples recognize a man's claim to his own property, but, in many groups, inheritance of property is an accepted custom. Besides individual property, primitive communities often recognize the ownership of property by families, sibs, societies, and by the community as a whole.

LABOR IN EARLIER TIMES

Fairly early in his evolution man must have discovered that he could compel other men to do his bidding, for indications are that slavery is a very ancient practice; but in very simple cultures the life of a slave is hardly to be distinguished from that of his master. In fact, in a very simple community master and slave of necessity engage in the same activities in order to support life, and the existence of a slave or so does not free others in the community from the search for the major part of their own necessities. Even in the early days of Greece and Rome a slave more often than not was practically a personal friend of his master. But advancing civilizations often demanded a large number of slaves, and their condition became much worse, as it did in Egypt, North Africa, later Greece and Rome, Europe, and America.

Through long periods the custom of enslaving men as a result of superior strength or conquest prevailed in many parts of the world and, in our own history, persisted beyond the middle of the nineteenth century. In Europe, slavery as a widespread practice gave way to serfdom during the Middle Ages. Under the feudal system a serf held his own small piece of land, subject, however, to the authority of his overlord, who in turn was a vassal or subordinate of a still more powerful noble, and so on in stages up to the king. The serf was obliged to give his overlord half of the produce of his land and to devote half of his time to his overlord's interests, including warfare.

Work in Modern Life

The modern system of wage earning is based upon the assumption that each man can earn according to his ability. Under an economic order affording equal opportunities to all, this system might very well work out fairly. Yet the relation of an employer and an employee constitutes a distinction equivalent to that between classes, and men who live on an income from stocks and bonds and mortages set themselves apart from those who are dependent entirely on their daily earnings.

Modern industry produces more than modern man can possibly use, yet modern society fails to distribute its industrial and agricultural products so that all men can benefit by the increased facilities for production. Modern machinery constantly changes the qualifications expected of workers and reduces the number of workers required to meet the needs of industry. Consequently there are many men and women to whom little opportunity for advancement is offered, and even little opportunity for work.

The difference between primitive and civilized society is very evident in the evolution of work. Primitive peoples work to provide themselves with the necessities of life; their own abilities determine their success, for, allowing for differences in climate, each man has the same factors to contend with, the same assistance and the same opposition on the part of Nature.

Think of the life of the farmer in the days when sun and rain and his own endurance and that of his animals were the determining factors in the progress of his work. Think of a modern city, where food, clothing, and all the supplies needed for living can be bought in stores; some food, to be sure, sold in the natural state in which it came from the soil, but much in packages, in cans, in boxes, in bottles, in containers of one sort or another. Are the packaged, bottled, frozen, processed, canned foods as good as, less good than, or better than the natural foods? And does the housewife find her tasks simplified, her labor lessened, her home improved by the use of mechanically prepared foods in place of natural foods? There is clearly no simple, single answer to these questions. Modern methods have brought gains and losses with them.

Types of Work

Men choose work for which they are qualified, and in so far as they can, they qualify themselves for work which is to their liking. Whether a man shall be a mechanic, an electrician, a carpenter, a mason, a farmer, a printer, a salesman, a merchant, an engineer, an architect, an author, an artist, a musician, an actor, a financier, a lawyer, a doctor, a teacher, a minister, or devote himself to any of the other vocational or professional occupations, is often decided, however, by circumstances rather than by choice. A man may be trained for the trade or profession which his father has followed, or one which is the principal activity of the community in which he lives, or he may be headed toward a career determined for him by the ambition of his parents or friends.

As society adjusts itself it should provide all men and women with ample opportunity to acquaint themselves early with the various trades and professions, to try out their abilities and skills while they are quite young, so that they can decide for themselves the vocation which suits them best, which makes most use of their equipment for work, and which affords them the greatest satisfaction.

LABOR ORGANIZATIONS AND LABOR UNREST

Yet it is not enough for men to be able to choose the work for which they are fitted. Men must have conditions for work which are conducive to good work. The tendency toward the organization of workers in unions has become marked in many fields in recent years, partly because the workers have found that only by joint action can they make their voices heard and bring their needs forcefully before their employers, partly because many of the workers have no interest in their work other than as a means of livelihood, or gain no personal satisfaction from their labor. With conditions such as they are, it is readily understandable that labor unions should be organized solely for the protection of the workers' rights. Yet under a more equitable opportunity for work, labor unions might well become groups for the advancement of the workers' interest in the field of their activity.

Strikes, lockouts, bargaining for adjustment of wages, and other manifestations of labor unrest are symptoms of social change, indications of an age of social instability, an age which has not succeeded in adjusting itself to the needs of human life. Clearly, the Industrial Revolution, the introduction of machinery into industry, brought about changes so far-reaching that its effects have increased and multiplied down to the present day. Economically, socially, and psychologically, the advent of the machine has complicated man's life, and as yet man has been unable to find a new equilibrium within this new complexity.

WEALTH, POVERTY, AND UNEMPLOYMENT

Men must work and must benefit from their work in the satisfaction of their needs. The acquisition of wealth is often looked upon as an indication of success in life. To a certain extent it may be an indication of success in work, but it is far from being an indication of success in living. Even with regard to work it indicates little, for, where opportunities are unequal, accomplishment cannot be measured in terms of the amassing of wealth.

There can be no justification for great wealth for some, where there is poverty for others. If equality is impossible and undesirable, surely a minimum of comfort and security is the social right of everyone. Throughout the ages there have always been people dependent upon the charity of others. But society itself must be to blame for the existence of poverty. Poverty may be due to inability to work, to unwillingness to work, or to the lack of opportunity for work. If the inability is caused by illness or by lack of training, if the unwillingness is caused by shiftlessness, the problems must be solved by society through its handling of matters of health and education, by its better care for the individual. But if there is lack of opportunity for work, if there is unemployment because of overproduction resulting from the needlessly vast capacity of machines, then the problem involved cannot be solved by caring more adequately for individual health and education. Unemployment on any considerable scale is an unmistakable sign of social maladjustment, a clear-cut call for a readjustment of economic life. In a stable, ordered society, work must be expected of all, there must be opportunity for all to work, and work must bring a full measure of satisfaction to all.

THE STATE

Why does man feel the need for a state, for some form of government? Governments provide men with the necessary setting for life, giving them a sense of security, a sense that justice and personal safety are assured. The state is man's own creation, to which he surrenders many powers of regulation and control, feeling that the good of the whole is more important than the advantage of the individual. The state, at its best, expresses the will of the majority and yet gives full opportunity for the expression of the individual will as well.

GOVERNMENT AMONG PRIMITIVE PEOPLES

The instinct of self-preservation which compels primitive men and women to work for the necessities of life also compels them to band together for protection from common natural dangers and for protection from strangers who are potential enemies. From joint activity for purposes of protection and economic activity, primitive peoples progress in time to formal organization of the community, the better to achieve the advantages to be gained by co-operation in joint endeavor.

Among many primitive peoples the older men are the leaders of the group; they are recognized as having the right to make rules which the others in the group must follow, and in their authority and their deliberations we find the beginnings of the state. Among other groups the men as a whole rule the community, or sometimes the young warriors. More frequently there is a chief, who owes his position to his outstanding personality, his wealth, or his supposed magical powers. Some tribes have several chiefs, each one ruling the community in those activities that he knows much about. Later the chieftainship sometimes becomes formalized, a man inheriting the right to rule, and thus becoming a king.

As we have seen, the larger family group is in effect a political unit among many primitive peoples. But most communities include several family groups, and in time the need for some recognized controlling power superior to that of the family becomes evident. One of the earliest powers of the state is undoubtedly the regulation of the use of force. The political organization which governs a community determines to what extent force may be used by individual members of the group, eliminates conflicts within the group in so far as that is possible, and organizes the use of force against hostile communities when that becomes necessary.

JUSTICE AND LAW AMONG PRIMITIVE PEOPLES

The state is for the most part not highly organized among primitive peoples; nevertheless there is a very definite sense of right and wrong. Primitive standards differ from our own standards in many respects, but the accepted customs and standards are more fundamentally just than would be generally assumed. Among many tribes a definite system of fines, payable in animals or other produce, is in use in place of violence for the settlement of disputes.

Tribes in which group sentiment is not highly developed permit individuals to obtain justice for themselves in their own way. On the other hand, tribes which recognize the importance of the community assign the responsibility to the leaders. Among the peoples who are conscious of the unity of the group, there are two very different conceptions of leadership. The tribes of Africa are strongly monarchial, the authority resting in a powerful king, whereas among the American Indians we find an essentially democratic sentiment, the chief sharing his power with others.

FORMS OF GOVERNMENT

The state has taken on increasing authority in its evolution through the ages, coming in time to be thought of as having something of an existence of its own apart from that of the individuals who compose it.

With more frequent and more rapid communication, travel, and contact between neighboring or widely separated nations, each state has necessarily thought of itself as the representative of its people in dealing with other states. States have developed a conception of sovereignty, of state authority and power, to be respected by other states. In some parts of the world and in some generations, the state, which was developed to exist as an aid to men, has insisted that its citizens existed for it, that the state or nation is greater than the sum of its individual members.

The specific form which government takes among a given people is determined by many factors, including the traditions and temperament of the people themselves, the tendency of the age in which they live, the extent to which they are influenced by the convictions of individual leaders. Democracy, monarchy, fascism, nazism, socialism, communism are all modern conceptions; in earlier times there were autocracy, despotism, feudalism, the city-states, and leagues of free cities. Some nations have been content to remain within their own boundaries, while others have embarked on expansion into far corners of the globe, following the way of imperialism. Some nations have magnified their own importance at the expense of others, have stressed the claims of individual statehood, of nationalism; others have recognized clearly the need for constant active co-operation between nations, paving the way for internationalism. The United Nations (UN) is the furthest step which has yet been taken toward bringing the nations of the world into harmony with one another.

THE STATE AND THE INDIVIDUAL

The state is ordinarily evident in daily life chiefly in the protection which it offers to the individual; and as his expression of citizenship a man pays taxes, votes, and recognizes the right of the state to call him to arms in the national defense. In recent years the state has been authorized to intervene to a greater extent than ever before in the economic life of its inhabitants; man's status as a worker, as a producer, as an owner, has become so uncertain that the state has had to extend its authority to the economic sphere, to legislate about matters of industry, agriculture, and commerce, about investment and property.

Many who believe that individual initiative is the basis for work feel that the government should not intervene; others who believe that the state must provide a sure means of livelihood for all would like the state to go further, to take over the ownership of industry itself. There can be no doubt that in times of stress and change, individuals and the state must co-operate at all points and to the fullest extent, and that the assistance which the state can render in the economic field must be welcomed whole-heartedly. On the other hand, when society finds itself in a condition of relative equilibrium, of comparative stability, the functions of the state and the functions of industry may well be clearly distinguished from one another; the tendency will be to separate the economic and political aspects of life while still keeping them closely correlated and in harmony with one another.

CRIME

The state in its administration of justice finds itself called upon to handle the problems of crime. The criminal is an offender against society —a danger to society and a maladjusted member of society. Those guilty of corruption in the conduct of industry or government are criminals as truly as those guilty of individual crime. It is the function of the state to punish offenders, protect individuals, and make all its members well-adjusted citizens. Until recently the principal problems in handling crime were the establishment of guilt and the meting out of punishment. To these have now been added the important task of aiding the offenders to gain full control of themselves and to become useful and dependable members of society, and even more fundamental, the prevention of crime by the sympathetic study of individuals and their adjustments to society.

Heredity and environment are both important factors in laying the foundation for crime. Many criminals are found to have grown up in an environment of low moral standards, where instances and examples of crime were common.

Heredity and environment may afford explanations, but they cannot remove the responsibility from the individual. For those whose development is stunted so that they have no true sense of right and wrong, the problem is one which must be treated as an illness. For those who deliberately plan and carry out a crime knowing fully its significance, the community reserves its most severe punishments.

Some form of confinement and supervision of those guilty of crimes is absolutely essential for the protection of society, but sociologists are convinced that the life of a confined person must have the essential elements of living if there is to be any progress toward permanent improvement in the confined person's attitude toward and qualifications for life. Solitary imprisonment may produce remorse, but it does not increase a man's capacity for leading a life which will be a benefit to society. More and more those who have committed crimes are being permitted to work and study during their confinement, and they are also being aided to see life rightly. Even those who are imprisoned for life are being given opportunities for work and study, so that within their prison walls they may benefit others and themselves.

When a mob in its fury seizes a man guilty of a crime and sets about obtaining justice in its own way, to punish by lynching, the authority of the state is challenged. The mob in its passion for revenge may inflict punishment, but in defying the state the mob itself is committing a crime. The state exists to preserve law and order, and must be made to administer justice promptly, but an angry mob only endangers justice, only invites more widespread indulgence in crime.

The state must act promptly and firmly. It must keep under constant supervision anyone who has shown inability to live in accordance with the just standards of society. It must make certain that a man can be so confined as to make escape impossible, so that society's protection will be complete. If the state can demand that a man offer his life on the battlefield, it can certainly demand that a man who deliberately has taken the life of another should forfeit his life in atonement; but a world which is seeking to eliminate war altogether may well consider whether the state, in administering justice, should inflict capital punishment by putting an end to a human life.

War and Peace

War is the most destructive force with which society has to contend. Disease, accidents, disasters due to earthquake and volcanic eruption, claim heavy tolls, but man is learning steadily how better to combat disease, he is working steadily to make accidents less likely, he is even learning to build for greater security against the vast natural catastrophes which at times shake part of the earth and in the presence of which he is largely helpless. But war is a man-made disaster, a catastrophe of society itself, to which man must put a final stop. There are several types of wars, each presenting its own problems.

First there is warfare between neighboring nations, intended to solve some disagreement between them. It has often been pointed out that just as men once tried to settle their personal grievances by duels and in time recognized that personal justice could never be obtained by the use of sword or firearms, that the law courts must be the place for obtaining justice, that so, too, nations must in time recognize that their differences must be settled before a justly constituted and justly organized international court.

Civil war is the second type of warfare. Here the conflict is ordinarily a spontaneous, sudden uprising, a clash between temporary opponents belonging to the same group. Some deep emotional dissatisfaction causes part of a nation to band together to overthrow the existing order, and the supporters of the existing order fight back. The causes of civil war lie far deeper in human nature than do the traditional causes of war between neighboring nations, but as society adjusts itself increasingly well to human needs, the possibility of revolutions and civil wars will inevitably grow less.

World wars, wars involving many widely separated nations, constitute the third type. Superficially, they may seem to be merely wars between neighboring nations on a larger scale. But actually their significance is quite different. For distant nations are not readily drawn into wars unless "the time is ripe" for war. And the time ripens not because of any specific conflict of sovereignty, but because of some deep-seated condition in the world's population. It is not personal emotion, like the cause of civil wars, but an actual pressure of overcrowding populations against one another, which causes world wars. Not that there is insufficient room in the world for its populations, as the English economist Malthus predicted there would be, but that from time to time populations in the more crowded parts of the world seem to have growing pains, to feel the need for expansion, to be restless, ready to endanger the long, hard-won civilization of the years of peace. When this mood is upon great groups of men, war is difficult to avert.

Some sociologists have called war a crude safety valve, a way in which society restores equilibrium in a world in which population is out of balance. This conception of war as a blind force in society seems to remove it from the realms of human control. But even sociologists who recognize how elemental this stirring of population may be would hardly conclude that society is powerless to devise some method by which these strains can be released without recourse to war. Woodrow Wilson, Franklin D. Roosevelt, and other world leaders felt that a great world forum where nations could present their cases, make known their urgent needs, would provide a means of ending the possibility of war. At the end of the First World War the League of Nations was formed to accomplish this purpose, yet it failed to prevent another conflict. At the close of the Second World War the United Nations was established to provide a new and more effective instrumentality for the preservation of peace.

The preparation of atomic and hydrogen bombs and long-range missiles of various types has revealed man's terrifying capacity for unlimited destruction. The horror which the use of these weapons would produce acts as a powerful deterrent.

More fundamental is the realization that when human nature matures to the point where war is recognized as the denial of all that society aims to be, then war will be permanently eliminated from the ways of men. Then the deep stirrings of population will direct themselves toward peaceful solutions of their problems and will turn their powerful energies to the upbuilding of society in all parts of the world on a firm foundation of uninterrupted peace.

EDUCATION

From the point of view of society, education is not limited to schooling; it includes all of man's means for equipping himself for life. We hear much nowadays about adult education, courses and books designed to carry a man or woman's education through life; about health education, aiming to aid men and women in the treatment of and preventing of disease and accidents; about moral education, seeking to develop in all men and women a clear, strong, permanent sense of right and wrong. The acquisition of knowledge and the preparation for a vocation are fundamental, but in addition to these sociology is concerned with the other aspects of education.

FORMAL AND INFORMAL EDUCATION

Primitive peoples learn more by doing than by hearing about things; there is work which must be done, and means must be found to do it. In primitive groups, boys and girls are expected to lend a hand; they work in the fields or in the house; they help in so far as they can in all the daily tasks. With increasing practice and experience they acquire notable skill. They have no formal education; they learn while working, while playing. They hear tales of prowess, stories of the earliest adventures of their tribes; they listen to the recollections of their elders, and they learn from what they hear, but only as a supplement to what they have learned by doing.

In modern civilized communities, education is largely *formal,* administered by schools and universities. The fields of knowledge have been organized for systematic presentation; and for students who are academically minded, formal education has an endless wealth of material to offer. But many students are essentially practical in their approach to life, do not learn as well from books as from experience. Those who do learn well from books need the steadying, the stabilizing, which comes from learning in the midst of working and playing, and from learning to do things when knowing how to do them is essential for progress in the task at hand. From this concrete approach to knowledge most boys and girls, young men and young women, will in time want to reach out to the learning which is found principally in books.

It is only very recently that educators and teachers have begun to realize that in coming as far as we have from the ways in which primitive peoples learned, we have lost as well as gained. It is not only in the long jump from primitive to modern society that we have lost fundamental physical endurance essential for ease in doing the things which need to be done all about us; it is true that in the transition from the country to the city we have lost many indispensable abilities and that in moving from individual homes to apartments with central heating, cooling, lighting, and other services, we have been spared still more tasks and lost still more qualifications for daily living.

It is for this reason that many educators feel that what was once learned in the course of actual daily duties—was learned, that is to say, *informally*—must now be made part of our schooling so that these fundamental abilities will not be lost altogether.

SCHOOLS

There is no question that society has benefited greatly by the emphasis laid in recent years upon the necessities of formal schooling for all. Many who would have lived lives of drudgery have been fitted for better work by their schooling; many who would have few interests apart from their work have become interested in cultural aspects of life and have rounded out their lives by deriving tremendous enjoyment from their new interests.

The schools offer to children, and indirectly to their parents, the great treasures of human knowledge; and they provide them with a background for earning a living. These two functions raise schooling to great importance. Yet there is a weakness in our school system, a tendency for it to become stereotyped, rigid, and inflexible, to repeat itself rather than to adapt itself to changed conditions, to expect all students to fit into a common mold rather than to recognize the qualifications, background, needs, and future plans of the individual student. Clearly it would be a great deal to ask of our schools that they meet the special requirements of each student, but this must come in time. Meanwhile it is important for parents to see education in this newer light and to supplement the work of the schools, in so far as possible, toward this newer goal.

HEALTH

Knowledge about matters of health and hygiene is an exceedingly important part of education. The great advances of medicine in recent years in the control and cure of disease have been due in considerable part to the greater alertness of the public, the greater readiness of the public to co-operate with physicians in matters of vaccination and inoculation against diseases, recognition of symptoms, quarantine during illness, and scientific care during convalescence. Clearly the guarding and improving of health is in the very forefront of the needs of society.

ETHICS

Do men and women instinctively distinguish between right and wrong? Or have our moral standards evolved through the ages? There was a widespread sense of justice and fairness among primitive peoples. We cannot say that this was the expression of a moral instinct, but human beings must have recognized early the necessity of standards for behavior, the necessity of encouraging certain types of conduct and prohibiting others. These standards, enforced by universal support, have become the guiding ethical principles of society.

In times of social change, moral standards are frequently challenged or disregarded by individuals, and are often upheld less strictly by society as a whole. In such times there may be less restraint in speech and dress; but such symptoms are likely to be temporary. Unless they are accompanied by a deeper disregard for moral standards, society need not concern itself greatly with minor habits, but it must at all times preserve the fundamental standards of right and wrong—it must make right living the guiding principle of every human life.

CULTURE

Culture is a general term which brings together all the leisure interests of men and women, all the activities which enrich life by giving it variety. Although the cultural interests are less concretely practical than the activities called for in earning a living or governing a community, they are no less essential to life. For a life which is lived from day to day with no thought other than the necessity of providing sustenance and protection is wholly meaningless; and furthermore, industry and government themselves are handled more successfully, more effectively, more efficiently, by men who have the ability to see beyond their immediate tasks, to recognize and to adopt improved methods as a result of their more varied background.

For most people the cultural interests—literature, drama, art, architecture, music, the outdoors (nature, gardening, sports), scientific knowledge, and philosophic thought—are definitely leisure interests, activities to be pursued when time permits and inclination prompts. For some, however, they are of the utmost practical concern; they constitute the means by which the author, painter, sculptor, composer, and scientist earn their livelihood. For those whose daily work is within the cultural activities, as well as for those who turn to cultural interests only at times, culture is something added to life.

CULTURE AMONG PRIMITIVE PEOPLES

The beginnings of culture are clearly present in the lives of primitive peoples. Language and handicrafts are among the most fundamental cultural expressions, and the origins of language and crafts go back to the very beginnings of human life. Among animals there are, of course, very definitely developed and recognized cries, calls, songs, and other means of communication, so that human beings must always have communicated with one another and must very early have elaborated their system of communication and set in motion the evolution of language. Writing, the recording of language, came later, first in the form of drawings of the objects referred to—writing and painting have a common origin. Dancing, also, must have been a very early trait, and song scarcely less so. In their crafts, the making of clothing and cooking utensils, primitive peoples showed early an interest in adornment, in decoration; many arts go back to the primitive use of color and design. The necessary task of providing shelter is the forerunner of architecture and of branches of engineering. The primitive uses of tools, of fire, of water, are the simple forerunners of physics and chemistry.

CULTURE IN MODERN LIFE

Culture, in its beginnings so intimately bound up with the daily tasks of primitive life, so deeply cherished at many high points in the history of civilization, tends to be set aside amid the confused duties which characterize our complex modern age. Yet, if it is true, as it very apparently is, that with the aid of machines all the work required to meet the needs of the community as a whole can be done in a comparatively few hours a day, provided some work is done by everyone; and if work is distributed wisely and fairly, so that all can work, and can work at tasks for which they are qualified, then everyone will have more leisure than heretofore, as well as more energy to devote to leisure interests. Where for a long time cultural activities have been thought of as at best diversion, amusement, recreation, they are already taking their rightful place as true and valuable interests for all. Men and women are discovering once more how indispensable the expression of individual effort in some form of artistic and scientific endeavor is in the rounding of every life.

RELIGION

Religion is man's faith in his own highest spiritual nature and in the spiritual power which transcends human life—the power called God. Religion is man's approach to the whole of life and to the great unsolved problems of life; problems which lie beyond the realm of science—problems of life after death, of the nature of Deity.

PRIMITIVE RELIGIOUS BELIEFS AND CUSTOMS

Among primitive peoples, Nature, inanimate Nature, was strange, unknown. Sun, moon, and stars—darkness and wind and rain—thunder and lightning—fire, streams, rivers, and the sea—the tops of mountains and the depths of caves—were filled with mystery. Primitive man found Nature uncertain, now helpful, now hostile, and beyond his power to control. He sought to understand Nature, but its meaning lay far beyond his knowledge. He felt that the unknown powers of Nature must be beings greater than himself; he looked upon natural objects as powers in themselves; the forces of Nature he believed to be controlled by deities which did not reveal themselves but merely revealed their power. Among some primitive peoples these mysterious powers are all thought to be manifestations of one great vast spirit pervading the whole universe. When peoples held individual objects in Nature to be powerful in themselves, such objects were treated with awe and reverence and became fetishes of the tribe. Yet whether they attribute superhuman powers to one or to many spirits or objects, all primitive peoples believe that there is some unrevealed explanation for happenings which they cannot understand, and it is in this belief that we find the beginnings of religion.

Primitive peoples dread things which they do not understand; consequently fear and superstition are closely bound up with the earliest religious feelings, and many primitive religious practices were for the purpose of winning favor and protection of the mysterious Spirit or the lesser deities, or atoning for some act which was believed to have aroused the anger of the higher powers. Storms, floods, gales, plagues were looked upon as signs of the displeasure of the great forces of Nature, and such a rare phenomenon as an eclipse of the sun, with its awe-inspiring fascination for us today, has at all times been looked upon by primitive peoples as an indication of the might of the unknown powers.

Primitive man must have discovered very early that his views about Nature, his beliefs and his fears, were shared by the others in his tribe, discovered also that one or more men in the group had confidence in their ability to approach the mysterious spirits and to seek their help or forgiveness. Such men would be looked upon as leaders in dealing with all that was not easily understood—with the calming of fears, the healing of wounds, the curing of sickness, the recognition of death, with the hopes of men for increased fertility of the soil, with all questions concerning the hidden spirit or soul in man himself, with the fate of the soul after death, and the nature of the great spirit or spirits which guided the universe. Such an early religious leader, medicine man or shaman, was at once priest, doctor, and magician. Skilled beyond others in his group in many ways, and helpful according to his skill, he oftentimes claimed for himself powers far beyond his abilities, magical powers which called for elaborate rituals for worship, fasting, punishment, sacrifice, gradually making him a mysterious figure, partaking somewhat of the mystery of the unknown in life, which it was his task to explain. Mystery has combined with ecstasy in the religious celebrations of many times and places: in the spring revels of the ancient Celts and Slavs, the Bacchic orgies of the Greeks, the mystical exaltation of the medieval saints, and the revivalism of later days.

THE CHURCH AND OTHER RELIGIOUS ORGANIZATIONS

A man's religion may be the creed of the religious organization to which he belongs and whose views he accepts. How closely he associates himself, if he does, to an established creed depends partly on his own individual conclusions concerning life and the unsolved problems of his relation to the universe. Men whose beliefs are identical naturally group together, naturally turn for guidance to leaders whose views represent their own. Faith is heightened when it is shared with others, and joint faith can offer its benefits to many who would not be reached or touched by individual convictions. The followers of the primitive medicine men constituted the first religious groups; and as society advanced in complexity, churches and other religious organizations came into being in simple form and evolved into the great religious institutions of our own day.

The history of religion is a story of contrasting beliefs in different parts of the world, of beliefs taking precedence one over another, of beliefs modified, re-enforced, reconsidered, changing to meet new conditions. And the history of the churches and other religious organizations through which man has expressed his views and his aspirations is also a story of great variety, a story of the upholding of faith in periods of doubt, and of the personal courage of many religious leaders.

We cannot attempt here to indicate the difference between the various great religions, between Christianity, Judaism, Mohammedanism, Buddhism, Brahmanism, Confucianism, Zoroastrianism, the polytheism of the ancient Greeks and Romans, and other cults. Each has its elements of greatness in satisfying human religious needs, each has made vast contributions to the welfare and progress of mankind. Yet each has at times revealed weaknesses—limitations in adapting itself to changed conditions. Religious churches have risen to great heights of temporal power, have fallen again, have sometimes gained, sometimes lost in eminence.

It is important to recognize that many of the great benefits of the religious organizations to mankind have been in such fields as education, welfare and health, morality and standards of conduct. Sociologically these fields are the concern of social institutions other than religion. Consequently the churches are more than religious organizations. They perform great social services of varied nature. In many communities the church is the meeting place of many interests and many activities. In periods of political uncertainty and instability, the churches are often the strongholds of sane thinking in political matters, though at times they are found on the side of reaction. This wider role of the churches must be differentiated from their function as the expression of the strictly religious aspects of the lives of men and women.

RELIGION IN MODERN LIFE

One hears fairly often nowadays that religion is losing its hold, that the churches are not satisfying individual needs as fully as they formerly did. Is this true, and if so, to what extent, and why?

In a time of great social unrest and social change, man is hard put to meet the demands of daily life. Most of his efforts, his energy, his attention, is devoted to the mere business of living. Reflection and contemplation have little place in a world in ferment. Some people, to be sure, seek to escape from the uncertain realities about them, to lose themselves in the great eternal problems which are untouched by material changes. Yet true religion is not an escape from the realities of daily living. It has a most important place in a well-rounded life, lived in full acceptance of all the demands of living. Yet when daily life becomes too demanding, requiring all of a man's time, religion may be crowded out.

Again, approached from another angle, religion recedes at certain points before the advance of science. Some of the tenets of established religion are challenged by geology in its study of the evolution of the earth, others are challenged by biology in its study of the evolution of life, still others by psychology in its study of the evolution of the mind. Often it is held that science and religion are diametrically opposed to one another; but there may be problems which science can never solve, problems which must always rest for their solution on human faith. There can be no question that there are problems which lie beyond the realms of science, problems which men can approach only through reflection, through philosophy, and possibly through sensing the spiritual quality in each other which is the essence of religion.

TEMPORARY SOCIAL GROUPS

We have now considered the chief divisions of society, the permanent social institutions. There are, however, certain temporary social groupings which are of extraordinary interest to sociology; they are mobs, crowds, audiences, rallies—brought together largely by chance. In studying them we are concerned with behavior rather than with institutions. We are in reality in a field which lies between sociology and psychology and is known as social psychology.

People in certain group gatherings, such as audiences at theaters and concerts and sports events, remain essentially themselves, though their reactions are heightened by the presence of others, their pleasure intensified or their disappointment increased.

Individuals who become a part of a mob behave differently; they lose their own personality in the drive of the group; they are motivated by a herd instinct, derived from the instinct of gregariousness in animals. More often than not they are moved by an unreasoning urge to carry out the momentary will of the mob. Mobs are more easily swayed emotionally than individuals are; inhibitions are removed, repressions released; and in action, mobs inflamed by revolutionary spirit or by desire for vengeance are destructive, having no respect for property or life.

Crowds, on the other hand, driven to action by common danger, by fire or explosion, behave differently from herd-like mobs. In panic and fright they may cause destruction, but it is the disorder and not a released herd emotion which is the cause.

Group feeling has its influence upon people brought together in a common setting: at a hotel, on a ship or train; in a hospital; and there are the worshipers at a religious service; there are officers and men in war, in the midst of battle; and there are workers banded together in mines and plants in the industries of peace.

SOCIAL FORCES AND SOCIAL CHANGE

In discussing the principal social institutions we have noted many forces at work, many changes during the evolution of society. Sociologists define social forces in many ways. For our purposes we shall use the term *social forces* to apply to those great movements within society which bring about social change. Some of these build up society, others tear it down.

The need for sustenance and the need for sexual satisfaction, increases in population, cycles of prosperity and depression, revolutions in methods of industry or in forms of government, tendencies toward nationalism or imperialism, war, movements for international solidarity and peace, are all forces working in harmony or in conflict with one another within the framework of society. These social forces are of such magnitude that individuals seem powerless before them. Great wars, great depressions, apparently run their courses despite the efforts of men to limit them or to end them; great periods of prosperity and progress seem to advance to their zenith unhampered by the mistakes of men. Yet men are not wholly helpless before social forces; very slowly, but cumulatively over long years, men can modify these forces, can turn them more nearly in the direction that they want them to go.

Less vast than the social forces in their irresistible power, yet more continuous in their influence, are the *social habits,* the *folkways* and *mores* of society, to use the terms of one of the most penetrating and original of American sociologists, William Graham Sumner. *Folkways* are the customary ways of doing things within a given group, the usual practices with regard to marriage and the family, work, property, government, and the other social institutions. When they develop into firmly established local customs and conventions enhanced by local tradition, they become *mores.*

Social forces and social habits between them determine *social selection.* To a certain extent social forces resemble natural forces; yet because of the modifying influence of social habits, social selection does not proceed as natural selection would toward the "survival of the fittest" in the physical sense. Society aims to provide the weak and the strong equally with opportunities for life. In its care of those who are sick in body or mind, or guilty of crime, society in its humanity aids those whom Nature would not aid; yet for its own protection it necessarily prevents them from endangering the health, welfare, and security of mankind. Social selection aims at social fitness, and in testing for this fitness it considers intellectual and emotional as well as physical qualifications. Survival in society calls for a balance between strength and ability.

Social evolution is the general movement of social change. We have studied the evolution of various social institutions, but as yet we have scarcely noted their relation to one another. We have stressed the fact that in the development of society, when changes take place, economic changes occur first, political changes after them, educational and cultural changes later still, and religious changes last of all. Let us see how this works in actual life today. Social forces are clearly at work bringing about social changes. The changes are apparent first as disturbances in our daily work, as upsets in wealth, property, and employment. Without as yet having arrived at a new stability in the economic world, these social forces are now reaching out to the sphere of political activity and calling upon governments to adapt themselves to changing economic conditions. Education and culture and religion have hardly been able to keep pace with these changes, and are only now beginning to sense the new roles which they will play when society is once more in comparative equilibrium.

These stages of social change mark every period of social evolution and, omitting the immediate family because it is a personal rather than a general institution, the economic needs are, at all times, the groundwork for the whole social structure. This conception is basic in Karl Marx's economic (or materialistic) interpretation of history. According to this view, it is not kings, not parliaments, not ideas that are the basic determinants of the course of history, but the need of each group of people for the simplest things of life, for food and shelter, for an opportunity to work in order to provide for oneself and one's family, that on a larger scale it is commercial, agricultural, or industrial rivalry between nations, which makes the succession of events in history what they are. Such a view is, of course, very incomplete. Fundamental as the economic factors may be, they are no more than the foundations. It is the political, social, cultural, and personal superstructures which are the richer and fuller expressions of human living.

SOCIETY TODAY

We are living in an age of such rapid, such thoroughgoing, such universal social change that sociology is, as never before, the science of the moment. There have been earlier periods of tremendous social change: the transition from the autocracy of the late Roman Empire on one hand and the tribal government of the Teutons on the other to the feudalism of the Middle Ages; then the transition to monarchy during the commercial revolution which accompanied the Renaissance; then to democracy during the industrial revolution, commencing toward the end of the eighteenth century.

Whether the changes which are now taking place all about us are as momentous as these earlier great transitions, it is still too early to say. The likelihood is that we are indeed on the threshold of a new era, economically, politically, and socially. Seldom have people been so aware of being in the midst of great social changes as we are today. Society, having evolved to its present complexity, is at last beginning to submit itself to study. While men are learning to understand something about the nature and structure and forces of society, its structure is rapidly changing, its forces are rapidly at work. Life today, with all its hardships and uncertainties, is more thrilling than ever before; for man, with his first glimpse at the nature of society, has his first opportunity to set himself to modifying the forces of social change, his first opportunity to assist at the birth of a new social order, his first opportunity to be himself the founder and designer of a new and more human society.

EXAMINATION QUESTIONS

1. How does sociology differ from psychology?
2. What is the principal difference between primitive cultures and our own?
3. What, until recent times, has been the most important factor in the development of our civilization?
4. What are the four principal races of mankind?
5. What differences are there between human races?
6. What is marriage, actually and ideally?
7. What is the most common form of marriage?
8. What is polyandry?
9. What reasons can be given for the occurrence of polyandry?
10. What reasons can be given for the occurrence of polygyny?
11. What is group marriage?
12. Is there a biological objection to inbreeding?
13. What groups are usually endogamous?
14. What groups are usually exogamous?
15. What is meant by the term "cross-cousin"?
16. Show that cross-cousins belong to different groups.
17. What is sororate?
18. What is the significance of the method of marriage which is most common among primitives?
19. What is "marriage by arrangement"?
20. Has divorce always existed?
21. Are divorces socially desirable?
22. Why do we call our family system bilateral?
23. What is a gens?
24. What is the distinction between these three terms: patrilinear, patrilocal, patriarchal?
25. What is a tabu?
26. Between what sets of relatives are social tabus frequently found?
27. What is the reason for the commonest of tabus?
28. What was the caste system of India?
29. Why is it difficult to maintain a classless society?
30. Are class distinctions necessary and desirable?
31. Among primitive societies, what is the commonest form of "secret society"?
32. How does it differ from what we know as secret societies in our own culture?
33. What are the functions of the primitive secret society?
34. What are a moiety's functions?
35. What is the social importance of friendships?

36. Could it ever be possible for the average working time to be reduced to a few hours a year?
37. Is the conception of property a modern development?
38. When was the state first organized?
39. Should the state interfere with the conduct of business?
40. What principles should govern the treatment of confined criminals?
41. What is meant by "informal" education?
42. What are the two functions of education?
43. What are two fundamental cultural expressions?
44. What was the earliest form of writing?
45. What is the commonest form of religious belief among primitive communities?
46. What is fetishism?
47. Do religions change and develop?
48. How does a mob differ from a crowd?
49. What are "social forces"?
50. What was the basic doctrine of Karl Marx?

FOR FURTHER STUDY

AMERICAN WAY OF LIFE, by Harry Elmer Barnes and Oreen M. Ruedi. (Prentice Hall, New York.)

THE BASIC TEACHINGS OF SOCIOLOGY, by Samuel Koenig. (Barnes & Noble, New York.)

MAN'S ROUGH ROAD, by Albert G. Keller. (Yale University Press, New York.)

MIDDLETOWN and MIDDLETOWN IN TRANSITION, by Robert S. and Helen M. Lynd. (Harcourt, Brace & Co., New York.)

SOCIAL INSTITUTIONS IN AN ERA OF WORLD UPHEAVAL, by Harry Elmer Barnes. (Prentice Hall, New York.)

SOCIETY, by Robert M. MacIver. (Rinehart & Co., New York.)

SOCIOLOGY, by Emory S. Bogardus. (The Macmillan Co., New York.)

Answers to Examination Questions

(For instructions see page xviii)

I. ANCIENT HISTORY

1. Until he began to record his activities. (page 1)
2. The period in history before men learned to work in metals. (page 1)
3. Messenger. (page 2)
4. 5000 B.C. (page 3)
5. The Pharaohs built them for tombs. (page 3)
6. Cleopatra was an Egyptian queen who was the last of the line of the Greek Ptolemies. (page 5)
7. The Sumerians impressed their records on clay tiles, while the Egyptians wrote on papyrus. (page 5)
8. Hammurabi. (page 6)
9. In Arabia. (page 7)
10. For their activity as navigators and traders. (page 8)
11. Monarchies (ruled by one man), oligarchies (ruled by a select group of a few men), and democracies (ruled by all the citizens). (page 12)
12. 776 B.C., the year of the first Olympic games. (page 13)
13. Periods of four years between the Olympic games. (page 13)
14. The Assyrian empire. (page 6)
15. An enslaved class of farmers and soldiers. (page 14)
16. Solon. (page 15)
17. In the island of Lesbos. (page 15)
18. Heavily armed infantry. (page 17)
19. A messenger who ran 150 miles to get reinforcements for the battle of Marathon, and later, mortally wounded, ran ahead 22 miles to Athens to announce the victory. (page 17)
20. The pass of Thermopylae. (page 17)
21. Pericles was an Athenian leader of the fifth century B.C. who consolidated the empire. (page 18)
22. Phidias. (page 19)
23. Socrates, an Athenian philosopher of the fifth century B.C. It was a method of asking pertinent questions which would lead those who answered them to discover the truth of the matter under discussion. (page 20)
24. The Peloponnesian War. (page 20)
25. Philip II of Macedon. (page 22)
26. Alexander the Great. (page 22)
27. Alexandria. (page 23)

28. To the Punjab region of northern India. (page 23)
29. Ptolemy, one of Alexander the Great's generals. (page 24)
30. From Greece. (page 28)
31. Twenty-three years. (page 29)
32. Rome was the only power, imperial or military, in the Mediterranean world. (page 33)
33. All Spain, northern Africa, Italy and adjacent islands, Macedonia and Greece. Western Asia, including Syria, was a Roman dependency. (page 33)
34. Rome sold the right to collect taxes (from dependencies) to the highest bidder, who made what profit he could for himself in the transaction. (page 34)
35. Pompey. (page 35)
36. In 59 B.C. (page 35)
37. At the battle of Pharsalus, in Thessaly. (page 36)
38. By assassination. (page 36)
39. Officers of his guard slew him. (page 37)
40. Nero. (page 40)
41. Flavius Vespasianus (Vespasian). (page 37)
42. In 79–81 A.D., during the reign of Titus. (page 37)
43. Because they would not honor the Roman gods. (page 38)
44. The barrel vault, which permitted the construction of arched edifices. (page 38)
45. Theodosius. (page 40)
46. Constantine. (page 40)
47. Alaric and his Gothic hosts. (page 41)
48. From the steppes of Asia. (page 41)
49. Siddhartha Gautama, who was born in India around the middle of the sixth century B.C. (page 42)

50. Shi Hwang-ti. (page 43)

II. MEDIEVAL HISTORY

1. In 476 A.D. with the deposition of the last Roman emperor. (page 46)
2. The period commencing in the fifth century (fall of Rome) and ending in the fifteenth century, or somewhat earlier in parts of Europe. (page 46)
3. In the reign of Justinian, 527–565 A.D. (page 49)
4. The Franks were Germanic tribes from the lower Rhine. (page 49)
5. Clovis, who was a Salian Frank. (page 49)
6. Forty-six years, from 768 to 814 A.D. (page 50)
7. He was a Christian. (page 51)
8. Between the ninth and eleventh centuries. (page 56)
9. In the fifth century A.D. (page 53)
10. The Christian missionary who came to England in the sixth century. (page 53)
11. Until 1453 when the Turks captured Constantinople. (page 55)
12. Constantine. (page 54)
13. From the early Greek city Byzantium on the site of which Constantinople was built. (page 55)
14. Out of Arabia. (page 56)
15. They developed agriculture to a science, effected many improvements in manufacturing, and made great advances in chemistry, mathematics, and medicine. (page 57)
16. Scandinavia, comprising Norway, Sweden, and Denmark. (page 58)

17. The sea-going warriors of Scandinavia. (page 58)
18. Normandy. (page 59)
19. Canute. (page 59)
20. In 1066. (page 59)
21. The Kingdom of the Two Sicilies. (page 60)
22. From the ninth to the fourteenth century. (page 60)
23. The feudal system was based on land. (page 60)
24. A trial in which the accused and the accuser fought with each other, and the winner was recognized as the choice of God. (page 61)
25. The privilege of clergymen to be tried in an ecclesiastical court. (page 62)
26. The clergy. (page 63)
27. Innocent III (1198–1216). (page 64)
28. A period of nineteen years (1254–1273) during which Germany was without a ruler. (page 64)
29. 1095–1291 A.D. (page 66)
30. Saladin was a famous Moslem monarch and the first sultan of Egypt. (page 66)
31. The reign of William the Conqueror in the eleventh century. (pages 67–68)
32. The Magna Carta, or Great Charter. (page 68)
33. The House of Lords and the House of Commons. (page 69)
34. The power to grant funds to the king. (page 69)
35. The nobles, the clergy, and the commons. (pages 69–70)
36. The longbow. (page 70)
37. France and England, 1337 to 1453. (page 70)
38. She was only seventeen. (page 70)
39. Rodrigo Diaz. (page 71)
40. The Hapsburgs. (page 72)
41. To the Slavs. (page 73)
42. A chieftain who became the builder of the Mongol Empire. (page 73)
43. A famous Venetian traveler who visited the Mongol realms during the reign of Kublai Khan. (page 73)
44. The empire of the Mongols, or Tatars, in Russia. (page 74)
45. The Janizaries were a specially trained body of Turkish troops, led against Constantinople in 1453 by the sultan Mohammed II. (page 75)
46. Apprentice, journeyman, master. (page 76)
47. A trade protectorate formed by northern German cities. (page 77)
48. Dante (1265–1321) and Chaucer (1340–1400). (pages 78–79)
49. Architecture. (page 78)
50. It revolutionized warfare and rendered obsolete the existing methods of offense and defense. (page 80)

III. MODERN HISTORY

1. In the fifteenth century. (page 82)
2. The invention of nautical instruments. (page 83)
3. He believed that he would reach the Indies. (page 83)
4. The invention of printing and the use of paper. (page 85)
5. By the end of the Middle Ages. (page 86)
6. An English heretical preacher who advocated belief in the Bible

apart from its interpretation by the church. (page 88)

7. Martin Luther. (page 88)

8. Cardinal Wolsey, who became the British Chancellor. (page 90)

9. This was held chiefly in Spain and Portugal in the thirteenth century, and again in the fifteenth and sixteenth centuries. (page 91)

10. Forty-five years. (page 91)

11. The defeat by the English of the Spanish Armada. (page 93)

12. Cardinal Richelieu was adviser to King Louis XIII of France. (pages 93–94)

13. The Dutch Republic. (page 94)

14. Charles II, with whom the Stuart line of monarchs was restored to the throne. (page 97)

15. William and Mary. (page 98)

16. Louis XIV. (page 99)

17. An edict which granted freedom of worship and full political rights. (page 100)

18. George I, who was a German by birth. (page 103)

19. The wife of Louis XVI of France. (page 105)

20. The storming of the Bastille on July 14, 1789. (page 105)

21. From 1792 to 1804. (page 107)

22. Marat, a French radical leader. (page 108)

23. Napoleon was born in 1769 on the island of Corsica, a French dependency. (page 108)

24. On December 2, 1804. (page 109)

25. The Russians retreated, luring Napoleon farther and farther away from his base of supplies—at the same time laying waste the surrounding country so that it could not support Napoleon's men. (page 110)

26. Some 300 independent governments were reduced to less than 40. (page 112)

27. In 1807. (page 115)

28. With the scientific advance in knowledge and invention. (page 115)

29. In the early nineteenth century. (page 116)

30. The standard of living rose. (page 116)

31. In British dominions, in 1833. (page 119)

32. In 1837, at the age of eighteen. (page 127)

33. In February, 1848. (page 121)

34. Louis Napoleon, a nephew of the Emperor Napoleon. (page 121)

35. Cavour, Mazzini, and Garibaldi. (page 122)

36. The Prussians under Bismarck's leadership. (page 124)

37. To keep France powerless against Prussia, Bismarck engineered, in 1879, an alliance between the German Empire and Austria-Hungary, later to be joined by Italy. (page 126)

38. Benjamin Disraeli. (page 127)

39. About 12,000,000 square miles of land surface. (page 128)

40. Nicholas II. (page 128)

41. A secret society formed to annihilate western invaders. (page 133)

42. Japan surprised the world with her fighting prowess, and defeated Russia. (page 134)

43. France, Russia, and Great Britain. (page 140)

44. November 11, 1918. (page 142)

45. Poland. (page 147)

46. December 7, 1941. (page 148)

47. United Nations. (page 153)

48. General Dwight D. Eisenhower. (page 156)

49. Poland, Czechoslovakia, Hungary, Rumania, Bulgaria, Albania, and East Germany. (page 157)
50. On June 25, 1950, the North Korean Army made a sudden attack on South Korea. (page 160)

IV. UNITED STATES HISTORY

1. He believed he had reached the Indies by a western route. (page 168)
2. Amerigo Vespucci, an explorer. (page 168)
3. They were predominantly English, with some other nationalities, notably Dutch and Swedish. (page 169)
4. Queen Elizabeth, the "Virgin Queen" of England. (page 170)
5. They landed at Plymouth, Massachusetts, in 1620. (page 170)
6. Henry Hudson was an English explorer, working for Holland. (page 170)
7. New York was settled by the Dutch, who called it New Amsterdam. (page 170)
8. In 1755. (page 172)
9. Agriculture. (page 173)
10. Harvard. (page 174)
11. The Stamp Act. (page 175)
12. A protest against the duty on tea staged by a group of Bostonians disguised as Indians who boarded a British vessel and dumped its tea cargo into the harbor. (page 176)
13. The American Declaration of Independence. (page 177)
14. Lafayette. (page 178)
15. Vessels fitted out by private enterprise, which cruised about much like pirates, although licensed in their activities by the exigencies of war. (page 179)
16. October 19, 1781. (page 179)
17. Benjamin Franklin. (page 180)
18. George Washington. (page 181)
19. To put an end to the piracy of Tripoli and the other Barbary states in the Mediterranean. (pages 182–183)
20. $15,000,000. (page 183)
21. The battle of New Orleans, in January, 1815, which was a victory for the American forces. (page 185)
22. Great Britain. (page 186)
23. Removing from government positions all office holders who were of the opposing party and "rewarding" adherents and friends with those same positions. (page 188)
24. Texas. (page 190)
25. In April, 1846. (page 190)
26. In the North a protective tariff was desirable, while the Southerners much preferred to have free trade with foreign countries. (page 192)
27. *Uncle Tom's Cabin,* by Harriet Beecher Stowe. (page 194)
28. About 4,000,000 people. (page 191)
29. In April, 1861. (page 195)
30. The North had twenty-three states, while the South had eleven. (page 196)
31. The *Monitor* and the *Merrimac.* (page 196)
32. 23,000 Union soldiers and 20,000 Confederate soldiers. (page 198)
33. About 800,000. (page 199)
34. Because he dismissed Secretary of War Stanton in defiance of an Act of Congress forbidding the dismissal of a cabinet officer

without the consent of the Senate. (page 201)

35. The Sioux War in 1876. (page 202)

36. In 1883 Congress created the Civil Service Commission provided for in the Pendleton Act. (pages 202–203)

37. A law prohibiting the amalgamation of great corporations into huge trusts for "cornering" the market in a particular commodity. (pages 203–204)

38. The blowing up of the U.S. battleship *Maine* in the harbor of Havana, Cuba. (page 204)

39. Theodore Roosevelt's. (page 205)

40. During William H. Taft's administration. (page 206)

41. Woodrow Wilson. (page 207)

42. In April, 1917. (page 207)

43. General John J. Pershing. (page 207)

44. Charles A. Lindbergh. (pages 208–209)

45. New Deal. (page 210)

46. United States, Great Britain, and the Soviet Union. (page 212)

47. The establishment of the United Nations. (page 215)

48. To stimulate prosperity in the countries of Western Europe and ensure their remaining outside the Soviet orbit. (page 218)

49. In 1953. (page 219)

50. The U.S. would not lag behind the Soviet Union in research and production of necessary defensive equipment, and that no opening to a renewal of disarmament talks would be neglected. (pages 221–222)

V. CIVICS AND THE UNITED STATES GOVERNMENT

1. Civics is the science of civil government. (page 224)

2. By naturalization. (page 224)

3. By returning to his country of origin and residing there for two years or more, or by becoming a resident of some other country and residing there for five years or more. (page 224)

4. The majority of the people. (page 225)

5. Three-fourths. (pages 225–226)

6. The central or federal government. (page 226)

7. "To form a more perfect Union, establish justice, insure domestic tranquillity, provide for the common defense, promote the general welfare, and secure the blessings of liberty to ourselves and our posterity." (page 227)

8. It is generally accepted that the one most recently passed or made shall be binding. However, a treaty always takes precedence over a state law. (page 228)

9. The legislative, executive, and judicial. (page 229)

10. The House of Representatives is apportioned according to the population; while the Senate is made up of two members from each of the states. (page 229)

11. Six years each. (page 230)

12. Income taxes, customs duties, and excise taxes. (page 231)

13. The Federal Trade Commission. (page 232)

14. The carrying of first-class mail. (page 232)

15. The Democratic and Republican. (page 233)

16. With a reading of the President's message suggesting desirable legislation. (page 234)

17. When the President fails to take action on it within ten days after he receives it from Congress. (page 235)

18. A person must be a native-born citizen of the United States, at least 35 years of age, and must have been a resident of the United States at least 14 years. (page 236)

19. By national convention of the various political parties. (page 237)

20. On the 20th of January following the November elections. (page 237)

21. The President chooses the members of his cabinet, and the Senate customarily approves the appointments. (page 240)

22. No. Nor is he subject to the mandates of any court, high or low, while he is in office. (page 239)

23. The Secretary of State, Secretary of the Treasury, Secretary of Defense, Attorney-General, Postmaster-General, Secretary of the Interior, Secretary of Agriculture, Secretary of Commerce, Secretary of Labor, Secretary of Health, Education, and Welfare. (page 240)

24. Under the Department of State. (page 240)

25. The diplomatic service, which is an arm of the Department of State. (page 240)

26. The President. (page 241)

27. It looks after the welfare and improvement of conditions of wage-earners and supervises aspects of immigration related to labor statistics and employment. (pages 241–242)

28. The Civil Service Commission. (page 242)

29. The Supreme Court of the United States. (page 242)

30. For life, unless they resign, retire, or are impeached and tried by Congress. (page 243)

31. By impeachment. (page 244)

32. A writ compelling the civil authorities to give any person an immediate preliminary hearing before a court, in order that he may know why he is being held. (page 244)

33. The legal rights of a citizen. (page 245)

34. The first ten amendments to the Constitution. (page 245)

35. To the states, or to the people. (page 247)

VI. GEOGRAPHY

1. Writing about or description of the earth. (page 249)

2. The rocky envelope of the earth. (page 249)

3. Triangular. (page 250)

4. About 25,000 miles. (page 250)

5. About 13,000 feet. (page 251)

6. Because they ebb and flow twice in every 24 hours and 51 minutes. (page 251)

7. An imaginary line drawn around the earth, equally distant from both poles. (page 251)

8. The distance of a point north or south from the equator. (pages 251–252)

9. The animals which inhabit a particular region. (page 254)

10. The emu and the cassowary. (page 256)

11. North America. (page 257)
12. Europe, Asia, North America, North America, South America, Australia. (pages 258–259)
13. 3,026,789 square miles. (page 259)
14. Superior, Michigan, Huron, Erie, and Ontario. (page 259)
15. The Upper Mississippi, the Missouri, and the Ohio. (page 260)
16. Cotton and tobacco. (page 265)
17. Chicago. (page 266)
18. The Central states. (page 266)
19. Chicago, Detroit, Cleveland, St. Louis, and Milwaukee. (page 266)
20. Nevada. (page 268)
21. Alaska. (page 268)
22. San Juan and Ponce. (page 269)
23. In the Caribbean region, east of Puerto Rico. (page 270)
24. Over 600,000,000. (page 270)
25. Ottawa. (page 271)
26. Nicaragua. (page 274)
27. Sugar. (page 275)
28. Guadeloupe and Martinique. (page 276)
29. Venezuela. (page 277)
30. Coffee. (page 279)
31. Argentina. (page 280)
32. Santiago. (page 281)
33. Between England and Ireland. (page 282)
34. France. (page 285)
35. The Netherlands. (page 285)
36. Sulphur. (page 286)
37. Vatican City. (page 287)
38. The Rhine, the Elbe, and the Oder. (page 288)
39. Sweden is a kingdom. (page 289)
40. The Union of Soviet Socialist Republics. (page 292)
41. Over 200,000,000. (page 292)
42. Jerusalem. (page 296)

43. In southwestern Asia. (page 296)
44. Iran. (page 296)
45. It is over 601 million. (page 300)
46. Production of silk. (page 301)
47. Over three thousand islands. (page 301)
48. On the southern side of West Africa. (page 305)
49. Canberra. (page 307)
50. Great Britain. (page 309)

VII. Economics

1. Economic wealth consists of those things that man uses either in production or in consumption, and which are not freely found in the environment in the form in which man uses them. (page 311)
2. Ownership was originally determined by creation, discovery, and use. (page 312)
3. Exchange and inheritance are two additional factors of ownership found in modern society. (pages 312–313)
4. Capital consists of all goods required to assist in the production of wealth. (page 313)
5. Workers are paid in wages out of the original capital before the joint product of labor and capital is sold and money received. (page 314)
6. Those elements of wealth used in production but not consumed by the production are known as capital investment; such elements are land, factories, machines, patent rights, etc. (page 315)
7. The loss of value of capital investment as it wears out or be-

comes outmoded must be passed on to the customer by being added to the price of the articles produced by that capital investment. (pages 315–316)

8. There must be a greater risk that the "B" stock will not be paid than exists in the case of the "A" stock; therefore the "A" stock must have preference over the "B" stock as to assets or dividends or both. (page 316)

9. Yes. (page 317)

10. It is not subject to deterioration or great seasonal fluctuations, and its use is not important to the community. (page 318)

11. Because it is only valuable when and if someone else is willing to accept it in exchange for commodities; and its real value fluctuates according to the quantities of commodities that it will buy. (page 318)

12. The amount and quality of necessities and luxuries consumed by the average person. (pages 320–321)

13. In 1946 a dollar bought less of some simple foods, less labor, and less of most commodities where hand-work plays a large part of the manufacture. In many respects, however, the dollar bought more in 1946 than in 1846 due to decreased costs of manufacturing. (pages 320–321)

14. As the total amount of monetary wealth in the world is but a fraction of the amount involved in commercial transactions, these transactions must be completed in terms of bank credit. (pages 321–322)

15. Because in the great majority of cases the bank merely establishes a credit which is never converted into cash. In addition, a bank can operate upon the capital of other banks by rediscounting its own loans. (pages 323–325)

16. In both cases, the value of the currency depends upon the habitual willingness of people to accept the currency in exchange for commodities. (page 325)

17. Monetary inflation is the decrease of the value of currency. (page 326)

18. By devaluing currency in terms of gold or by increasing the supply of currency without a corresponding increase in gold reserves. (page 326)

19. Credit inflation occurs normally with periodic prosperity. Its effects are not as severe or dangerous as those of currency inflation. (pages 326–327)

20. No. (page 329)

21. The law of supply and demand is the fundamental one. (page 329)

22. The marginal cost is the cost of producing a further unit quantity of any product beyond the quantity already produced. (page 328)

23. In the long run they are equal. (page 328)

24. The two laws are actually one, since marginal cost is the measure of supply and marginal utility is the measure of demand. (page 328)

25. Profiteering takes place in the interval between an upset in the equilibrium of prices and the time when economic forces establish a new equilibrium. Such an upset occurs when demand

suddenly increases, as for certain products in wartime, or when supply is suddenly curtailed, as in crop failure. (page 329)

26. Because the supply of labor is inelastic: the number of laborers available is practically a constant. The supply of trained labor within a special field, and the supply of professional men in the professions, is inelastic in that it takes a long time to prepare other men to enter the field. (page 330)

27. For two principal reasons: because the high price might attract competition, and because demand at the higher price might be so low that total profits would be less. (page 331)

28. When an individual company or group of companies constitute the whole market for a given product. (page 331)

29. By a bargaining process. (page 332)

30. Because the depression is apt to continue until reduced consumption overtakes reduced production and consumes the inventories on hand. (page 333)

31. Yes. (pages 333–334)

32. Division of labor has brought it about that many persons are engaged in the production of luxuries, and their living is consequently dependent upon the continuance of trade. (pages 333–334)

33. Yes, because unemployed workers in an undeveloped country can usually find agricultural employment or make new homesteads for themselves on previously unoccupied land. (page 333)

34. Socialism is the view that wealth should be distributed to each individual in proportion to the amount he contributes to society by his productive efforts. (page 335)

35. Socialism would prohibit the inheritance of any large quantity of wealth. (page 336)

36. The economic creed of communism is that wealth should be distributed according to need. (page 337)

37. No. (page 337)

38. Karl Marx. (page 338)

39. The glorification of the state, the abolition of democracy, militarism, and economic isolation. (page 338)

40. If the population should continue to grow at an increasing rate a time might come when there would not be enough food, but there is no danger of this for several centuries. (pages 338–339)

41. A greater amount of leisure time is made possible by increased efficiency in production. It is necessary to have a greater amount of leisure time as luxuries are produced which must be consumed at leisure. (page 339)

42. If the number of hours in the working week are more than the number which should exist to accord with the efficiency of production, chronic unemployment will result. (pages 339–340)

43. Production of goods is increased. (page 340)

44. Reduction of working hours, as in the case of women entering industry. (page 340)

45. Since the industries of different regions are in competition, employers of a given region cannot

pay their employees much more than employees are paid in other regions. Hence the existence of poorly paid workers in any region constitutes a drag upon the workers of all other regions. (page 340)

46. By withholding half the supply from the market, Brazil hoped to raise the price sufficiently so that the value of half the crop would be greater than the value of the whole crop. (page 341)

47. The keen competition for markets that are not unlimited. (page 342)

48. Governmental control of production based on anticipated consumption. (page 343)

49. The law of diminishing returns states that after a certain optimum size of a business has been reached, any further increase in size is attended by a reduction in the rate of returns. (pages 343–344)

50. By the use of new methods, materials, and processes in industry and agriculture. (page 344)

VIII. GOOD ENGLISH

1. We visited my two *sisters-in-law* last night. (page 355)

2. Two *calves* occupy the rear stalls in the barn. (page 356)

3. Some bacteria *are* helpful to man. (page 356)

4. *Charles'* (or *Charles's*) books arrived. (page 357)

5. Someone has lost *his* coat. (page 358)

6. Everyone had better hold on to *his* tickets. (page 358)

7. The rain got into our very bones, *causing us great annoyance.* (page 359)

8. *We* girls were the first ones here. (page 360)

9. It is *he* I like most. (page 360)

10. We greeted Ed, the lawyer's son, and *her.* (page 360)

11. Between you and *me,* he is completely wrong. (page 360)

12. Do you know *who* she was? (page 361)

13. *Whom* did you give it to? (page 361)

14. Choose *whoever* wants to go. (page 361)

15. The book is losing *its* interest for me. (page 361)

16. *Who's* going to the party? (page 362)

17. Fresh coffee tastes very *good* to me in the morning. (pages 363, 364)

18. Running at full speed, *he tripped over the chair.* (page 365)

19. My brother and cousin, whom I haven't seen in several months, *are* coming for dinner. (page 366)

20. Mathematics *is* one subject that I find uninteresting. (page 366)

21. The committee *were* in violent disagreement. (pages 365–366)

22. There *are* a chair with a straw seat and a day bed in my room. (page 366)

23. He *has been* in this country for two years now. (page 367)

24. Norman *laid* the book on the table. (page 370)

25. I *lay* in bed all day because I had a sore throat. (page 370)

26. He has *lain* there since early afternoon. (page 370)

27. Won't you *sit* down? (page 371)

28. The water main has *burst.* (page 372)

29. The prisoner *fled* from the jail in the confusion. (page 372)

30. The picture was *hung* in the living room. (page 372)

31. Have you ever *trod* the light fantastic? (page 374)

32. I'll take two of *this* kind. (page 375)

33. Did you sleep *well* last night? (page 376)

34. Which pair do you like *better*—the black or the brown? (page 378)

35. I think that my typewriter is better *than* his. (page 379)

36. You should read Anthony Trollope's *Barchester Towers*. (page 381)

37. Theodore Dreiser is, I believe, a powerful writer. (page 382)

38. We are coming home tonight; we will leave tomorrow. (page 384)

39. "I'm so tired," Ellen cried, "that I think I shall be very bad company." (page 384)

40. Do you feel *all right?* (pages 385, 394)

41. His remarks were *sacrilegious*. (page 387)

42. Don't *lose* your temper now. (page 386)

43. Keep a steady *rhythm* while dancing. (page 387)

44. A mirage is an optical *illusion*. (page 394)

45. You will have to choose *between* him and me. (page 394)

46. What makes you so *angry with* him? (page 394)

47. *Besides,* I have nothing to do now anyway. (page 394)

48. Blood from a person of one color or religion is no different *from* blood from a person of another color or religion. (page 395)

49. *Almost* all of us ski in winter. (page 396)

50. The accident *happened* on the busiest street in town. (page 396)

IX. EFFECTIVE SPEAKING

1. A pleasing personality and presence, the ability to cultivate friendships and improve his acquaintanceships, and to make the most of his social contacts. (page 399)

2. Your mental equipment—being well read and having a command of good English. (page 400)

3. Self-consciousness. (page 400)

4. Seize eagerly all opportunities for speaking that may come your way. Force yourself to ignore your own fear. Cultivate self-confidence. (pages 400–401)

5. The sense which enables a speaker to know whether his audience is interested or bored, sympathetic or antagonistic. It enables a speaker to know when he has spoken long enough. (page 401)

6. Introduction, body, and conclusion. (page 402)

7. To open with a funny story if it is appropriate to the occasion and the subject. Sometimes praise of the audience's intelligence is a good opening. (page 402)

8. The *body* of the speech is its main substance. (page 402)

9. Your own life and experiences, and your reading. (pages 403–404)

10. Particularly in the daily press, magazines, and in special speakers' anthologies. (page 405)

11. It may be used as a textbook to illustrate the elements of different

sorts of speeches that may be followed in planning his own speeches. (page 405)

12. The relations between men and women—love, romance, courtship, marriage, etc.; self-improvement—in education, health, business, and sports; money—how to get it and invest it. (page 406)

13. On a broad human level. (page 406)

14. By meeting the audience on a common ground. (page 407)

15. By the vocabulary of your audience. You must avoid words that they are not likely to understand. (page 409)

16. Because long sentences are more difficult for the audience to follow. (page 409)

17. By learning it as a whole instead of sentence by sentence. (page 410)

18. It helps the speaker to develop appropriate gestures. (page 411)

19. By restating it in different language. (page 412)

20. Specific instances or definite, concrete examples are more convincing. (page 412)

21. The quotation of authorities or of experts in their fields. (page 413)

22. In the rebuttal, each debater attacks the arguments previously advanced by his opponents and attempts to destroy them by bringing forward arguments against them. (page 413)

23. It should seldom take longer than thirty minutes. A safe rule is: the shorter the better. (page 414)

24. The toast should be short, witty, and should have a definite application to the moment or occasion. (page 414)

25. The knowledge that a large un-

seen audience is listening in. (page 415)

26. He must be brief. He must keep exactly within his allotted time. He must submit a written copy of his speech in advance. (page 416)

27. Articulation is sometimes synonymous with pronunciation, but it refers more exactly to the position of the tongue in making sounds. (page 416)

28. Enunciation consists in giving fullness and clearness to every sound in pronunciation or articulation. (page 417)

29. Inflection should be varied to suit the sense of the statements you are making. (page 417)

30. It is excellent training in voice culture. (page 417)

31. The important words, those that carry the meaning. (page 418)

32. Distinctly, but lightly. (page 418)

33. A change in the pitch or tone of the voice. (page 419)

34. It may be either rising or falling. (page 419)

35. By practice and by listening to good speakers. (page 419)

36. For emphasis, to lend expression and drama, to let a thought sink in, to arouse suspense and interest. (page 419)

37. Between 150 and 200 words a minute. (page 419)

38. The good standing posture of everyday life—upright, feet firmly on the floor, head up, shoulders back. (page 420)

39. A forceful downward gesture, pounding on the table with the fist, or pounding one fist into the other hand. (page 421)

40. Solemnity when required—a

pleasant smile at proper moments. (page 421)

41. It gives convincing weight to a speech. (page 421)

42. The actor may be called upon to give in to powerful emotions that prevent his speaking, but the speaker must never allow himself to become so worked up that he cannot speak. (page 422)

43. Positive feelings are those which are directed toward healthful, progressive, forward-looking action. (page 422)

44. Negative feelings include fear, grief, pain, mistrust, jealousy, envy, hate, melancholy, and disrespect. (page 422)

45. A well-developed voice, one that can give fullness and clearness to the language sounds, and one that does not fatigue easily. (page 422)

46. Good speaking requires deep breathing and wide opening of the mouth; wide enough to give a full round tone to the vowels. (page 423)

47. Because of an improper conception of the physiology of speaking. (page 423)

48. "Ladies and gentlemen" or "Fellow townspeople" or "Friends." (page 423)

49. It should end sharply with the climax. (page 424)

50. No. It is out of date. (page 424)

X. LITERATURE

1. *Beowulf.* (page 438)
2. In Wales. (page 439)
3. Geoffrey Chaucer. (page 440)
4. They were in manuscript form, copied largely by monks in the monasteries. (page 441)
5. Sir Thomas More. (page 441)
6. Miracle plays. (page 442)
7. William Shakespeare. (page 442)
8. Edmund Spenser. (page 443)
9. He was born in 1564 and died in 1616. (page 443)
10. In both prose and poetry. (page 444)
11. *Hamlet* is a tragedy. (page 444)
12. Ben Jonson. (page 444)
13. John Donne. (page 447)
14. *Paradise Lost.* (page 447)
15. John Bunyan. (page 448)
16. *Robinson Crusoe.* (page 449)
17. An imaginary country gentleman appearing in the *Spectator*. (page 449)
18. As satire. (page 449)
19. With his English Dictionary, and with the biography of him written by James Boswell. (page 450)
20. *The Vicar of Wakefield.* (page 450)
21. William Wordsworth. (page 452)
22. He wrote a pamphlet on atheism. (pages 452–453)
23. Mary Wollstonecraft Shelley, second wife of the poet Shelley. (page 453)
24. Charles Lamb. (page 453)
25. The death of his friend, Arthur Hallam. (page 454)
26. A poet, the wife of Robert Browning. (page 455)
27. *A Tale of Two Cities.* (page 456)
28. William Makepeace Thackeray. (page 456)
29. Charles L. Dodgson. (page 457)
30. W. S. Gilbert. (page 458)
31. India. (page 459)

32. The drama, especially comedy. (page 460)
33. John Galsworthy. (page 460)
34. A. E. Housman. (page 461)
35. James Joyce. (page 462)
36. Dylan Thomas. (page 463)
37. William Butler Yeats. (page 464)
38. Thomas Jefferson. (page 466)
39. Romantic and adventurous. (page 467)
40. Ralph Waldo Emerson, Henry David Thoreau, Nathaniel Hawthorne, Amos Bronson Alcott, Margaret Fuller. (page 468)
41. Oliver Wendell Holmes, to save the frigate *Constitution* from destruction. (page 469)
42. Their eerie scenes, their impressions of gloom, their somber tragedy. (page 469)
43. Nathaniel Hawthorne. (page 469)
44. *Tom Sawyer* and *Huckleberry Finn*. (page 471)
45. William James, a philosopher. (page 471)
46. An almost photographic study of life in a typical small town. (page 473)
47. Upton Sinclair, *The Jungle*. (page 474)
48. Ezra Pound. (page 474)
49. A Negro who reverts to savagery. (page 475)
50. E. E. Cummings. (pages 475–476)
51. William Faulkner. (page 476)
52. John Steinbeck. (page 476)
53. In the Orient. (page 478)
54. A Babylonian legendary account of the hero Gilgamesh. (page 478)
55. *The Rubaiyat of Omar Khayyam*. (page 478)
56. The Egyptian classic, which gives the instructions thought necessary to the soul on its last journey. (page 478)
57. *The Thousand and One Nights* or *Arabian Nights' Entertainment*. (pages 478–479)
58. The Koran. (page 478)
59. In Sanskrit. (page 479)
60. 551–478 B.C. (page 479)
61. Homer's epic of the Greek expedition against Troy, or Ilium. (page 480)
62. Mythical beautiful maidens described in the *Odyssey* as seeking to lure mariners on dangerous rocks. (pages 480–481)
63. The first of the lyric Greek poets. She lived about 600 B.C. (page 481)
64. Aeschylus. (page 481)
65. Euripides. (page 482)
66. Herodotus. (page 482)
67. Socrates. (page 483)
68. Plutarch. (page 483)
69. In Latin. (page 483)
70. As "the tenderest of Roman poets." (page 484)
71. By its plaintive tone and mournfulness. (page 485)
72. A Greek slave credited with the invention of many fables. (pages 485–486)
73. St. Thomas Aquinas. (page 486)
74. *The Divine Comedy*. (page 486)
75. A collection of 100 tales told by ten people to while away the time while they were isolated to escape the plague raging in Florence. (page 487)
76. Machiavelli's *The Prince*. (page 488)
77. Luigi Pirandello. (page 489)
78. "The best novel in the world beyond all comparison." (page 489)
79. Some 1800. (page 490)

80. They recapture the simplicity and force of classical tragedy. (pages 490–491)
81. A poet, vagabond, thief, and rogue. (page 492)
82. From *Gargantua*, by François Rabelais. (page 492)
83. Jean Racine. (page 492)
84. *Candide*. (page 493)
85. *Les Miserables, The Hunchback of Notre Dame, Toilers of the Sea, Ninety-Three*. (page 494)
86. Charles Baudelaire. (page 495)
87. The short story. (page 497)
88. *The Remembrance of Things Past*. (page 498)
89. Jean Paul Sartre. (page 499)
90. Belgian. (page 500)
91. A philosopher. (page 501)
92. A medieval doctor of magic, who sold his soul to the devil. (page 502)
93. The doctrine of a superman and the will-to-power as the salvation of the race. (page 503)
94. *The Trial, The Castle, The Penal Colony*. (page 504)
95. For his fairy tales. (page 506)
96. Feminism. (page 507)
97. His earlier plays deal with realistically sordid, oppressive themes; later he expressed himself in symbolic and often morbid fantasy. (pages 507–508)
98. Turgenev, Dostoevski, and Tolstoy. (page 509)
99. Leo Tolstoy. (page 509)
100. Chekhov or Gorki. (page 509)

XI. THE ARTS

1. The desire to ornament his dwellings and to record facts in a more or less permanent form. (page 518)
2. Egypt. (page 518)
3. The human figure. (page 519)
4. Pompeii. (page 520)
5. The fact that the political personalities became more important than religious subjects. (page 521)
6. Cimabue. (page 522)
7. Leonardo da Vinci. (page 523)
8. 1475–1564. (page 523)
9. Caravaggio. (page 524)
10. Shepherds in satin, immaculate sheep nibbling Arcadian foliage, and romancing court lovers. (page 525)
11. Courbet. (page 526)
12. Claude Monet's studies of the Rouen Cathedral. (page 527)
13. His lithograph posters, particularly those of the Moulin Rouge. (page 527)
14. Picasso and Georges Braque. (page 528)
15. A style of pure design—consisting of only lines and blocks of color. (page 530)
16. Spanish. (page 530)
17. Hubert van Eyck and Jan van Eyck. (page 531)
18. Rembrandt. (page 532)
19. Illuminated manuscripts and inferior wall paintings. (page 533)
20. The fashions and vices of his time. (page 534)
21. In England. (page 535)
22. Alexander Calder. (page 536)
23. The obelisk. (page 537)
24. The temples. (page 537)
25. 80,000. (page 539)
26. The tomb of an Indian ruler's favorite wife. (page 540)
27. The style of Christian architecture founded on the Roman. (page 541)
28. Gothic. (page 542)
29. In Italy. (page 543)

30. Baroque. (page 545)
31. Fontainebleau and Versailles. (page 545)
32. Neo-Roman. (page 545)
33. Huge size and indestructibility. (page 546)
34. Phidias. (page 547)
35. Because it could not be used to teach Bible stories without suggesting heathen idols. (page 549)
36. A Florentine craftsman who worked in metals and enamels. (page 551)
37. Rodin. (page 552)
38. The song. (page 553)
39. From the church. (page 554)
40. Many-toned. (page 554)
41. *Pizzicato.* (page 554)
42. Wagner's. (page 555)
43. A dramatic poem in musical setting. (page 556)
44. Handel's *Messiah.* (page 556)
45. The harpsichord and the clavichord. (pages 556–557)
46. As program music. (page 562)
47. As classical. (page 561)
48. Beethoven. (page 561)
49. Four. (page 561)
50. Stravinsky. (page 562)

XII. French

1. Dans la cour à la maison.
2. Au mur de ma chambre au deuxième étage, au-delà de la fenêtre.
3. Au-dessus de la bibliothèque près de son lit.
4. Je suis fâché que vous avez peur.
5. Il a une chambre au-delà du salon.
6. Ce monsieur est mon professeur et l'ami de mon père.
7. J'ai tant d'argent; je suis très content.
8. J'ai mangé de la viande.
9. Avant de manger un poulet, on le rôtit.
10. Vous rappelez-vous du peu d'espace dont nous disposions?
11. Bientôt les officiers du port viendront à bord, et demain nous nous trouverons dans la ville du Havre.
12. Nous avons quitté la maison dans le petit village où nous demeurions, il y a huit jours.
13. Il était évident que tout le monde nous a pris pour américains; autrement on n'aurait jamais osé nous demander un tel prix pour deux chambres.
14. Il y avait même un telephone sur une petite table dans un coin.
15. Après avoir quitté le vaisseau, nous avons monté dans un taxi qui se trouvait près du quai.
16. Messieurs désirent?
17. Combien faut-il payer par semaine?
18. Malgré les trois cent francs par semaine, nous sommes bien contents de nos chambres.
19. Nous venons de nous asseoir, il y a deux minutes au plus.
20. Il faut nous tenir sur nos gardes; ils coûtent cher.
21. Mon ami m'épargne la peine de choisir, et j'en suis bien content.
22. Les ris de veau, les soufflés, et une infinité de mets rares et délicats nous attendent dans tous les restaurants de la France; mais à présent un diner simple et bien préparé nous va mieux.
23. Il est inutile de vous souhaiter un bon appétit.
24. J'aurai des fraises avec de la crème, des petits gâteaux, et naturellement du café noir avec un petit verre de cognac.

25. A la vôtre (A votre santé)! Moi, je préfère en gouter d'avance.
26. We are glad; they are hungry.
27. I am glad that they are not in the street.
28. My room is on the ground floor.
29. I have something to say to you, Mr. Lebon.
30. My (lady) friends are all beautiful, and their children are all fine-looking.
31. You have sugar and cream.
32. I have so many peaches that I have no desire to eat.
33. Is your father a friend of my professor?
34. The mothers are all beautiful.
35. I am not your father, but I am your friend.
36. She has a beautiful rug on the wall, from the ceiling to the floor.
37. I have peaches and cream to eat today.
38. That very evening, we found ourselves late.
39. That's enough! I am dying of hunger.
40. In short, you are eating a better dinner than I.
41. Here we are, old fellow, and I am very glad.
42. They are waiting for us, and, myself, I don't know what to do.
43. It is a dessert which goes with this white wine.
44. Furthermore, they are expensive.
45. Finally I found the station and climbed into the coach just as the train was stopping.
46. He doesn't want to wait on board the vessel.
47. No, I do not wish to go up.
48. Perhaps she is ready to sit down at the table.
49. He followed me to my bedroom.

50. The waiter seized the tip and preceded us to Number 40.

XIII. SPANISH

1. La mujer habla español; usted lo escribe.
2. Él escribe su lección; usted no hace nada.
3. Nosotros tenemos calor; ella tiene sed; la madre tiene un resfriado.
4. La madre tiene razón; el perro tiene ganas de dormir.
5. San Francisco es una ciudad lejos de aquí.
6. Por contra, nosotros trabajamos.
7. Si no me equivoco, está enfermo.
8. Tengo que comprar muchas cosas para la cocina.
9. Cerca de la plaza están una buena fonda y dos o tres pequeños restaurantes.
10. ¿Cuánto valen estas naranjas?
11. Está bien. No me gustan manzanas; yo tomaré una docena de naranjas y media docena de limones.
12. Necesito también doce huevos, una libra de café, cinco libras de azúcar, y dos panes.
13. ¡Tengo mucho gusto en conocerle, señor!
14. ¡Que duerma usted bien la noche!
15. Al almuerzo se come una sopa, fideos o arroz con tomate y carne, la ensalada y frutas.
16. El almuerzo se sirve a la una de la tarde.
17. ¿Y qué lleva la mujer cuando sale de la casa?
18. Cuando hay una lluvia fuerte y se moja el traje, hay que mudar la ropa.

19. Algunas veces lleva un par de guantes y un bastón.
20. Los trajes de mujer se pasan de moda con tan frecuencia que yo no me atrevo a describirlos.
21. Por lo común, hace calor.
22. Mi querido amigo, ¿que le va a usted?
23. Desearía una mesita para máquina de escribir, modelo número 8 (ocho).
24. Tenemos el gusto de enviarle todos los artículos citados en su carta.
25. Llame usted al mozo; desearía pagar la cuenta.
26. The dog eats, but he does not work.
27. He is not writing anything now.
28. You are sleepy, but I am ashamed.
29. John is ill; he has a terrible cold.
30. On the other hand, he is here with us.
31. Mother is right.
32. I have water; I am not thirsty.
33. She has a dog; he is not afraid.
34. You are hot; you have no cold (you have not a cold).
35. John is ashamed.
36. Yes, if they are sold in those stores, and they are not dear.
37. Have the goodness to say thank you!
38. Before going to bed, he goes for a walk in the park.
39. We do not wear overcoats in summer.
40. I do not like a man who carries gloves and a cane.
41. After bathing, I found that I had one sock.
42. When it is cold I wear a felt hat; in summer I wear a straw (panama) hat.
43. I do not dare to go for a walk in the park (through the park).
44. Dinner is on the table (ready), isn't it?
45. It isn't worth the trouble to stay in bed.
46. We have received your letter of the current month.
47. Is there anything you would like? Yes. Bring me the salad.
48. Look out! What's the matter? What's wrong with you?
49. Pardon me (excuse me)! I am very sorry!
50. Give a tip? I should say so!

XIV. LATIN

1. Agricolae terram amant.
2. Nuntii Gallia litteras portantne?
3. Legati urbis sumus.
4. Amici puellae non sunt.
5. Viri muros altos aedificabant.
6. Agricolae in oppido multum frumentum celabunt.
7. Periculum nautae magnum erit.
8. Multi viri pilis pugnaverunt.
9. Multae provinciae in Gallia sunt.
10. Caesar in nomine populi Romani senatum convocavit.
11. Quis est dux militum Romanorum?
12. Rex circum hostem milites movit.
13. Equus niger tela militum timet.
14. Nunc Gallia pars Romae est.
15. Iulia equum pulchrumque parvum habet.
16. Secunda hora milites ex navibus in urbem libenter tela portaverunt.
17. Pulchrum animal parvum a malis pueris lapidibus vulnerabatur.
18. Novi vici a militibus defessis post proelium aedificati sunt.

19. In mente semper crescere poterisne?

20. Prima luce dux ab urbe trans pontem pedites eduxit.

21. Rex facto obses cohortum erat.

22. Carolus miserior est quam Iulia.

23. Equites Romani fortiter pugnaverunt sed Helvetios superare non poterant.

24. Prima aetate Caesar terras Germanorum vastare voluit.

25. Roma urbs aeterna saepe vocatur.

26. The girl sounds the trumpet.

27. Are you telling the girls' story to the farmer?

28. No, I'm not telling the girls' story to the farmer.

29. The man shows the farmer's fields to the boys.

30. We were building the little town's new walls.

31. The horse will carry the farmer's grain.

32. Will the ambassadors spend the winter in their beloved native land?

33. The danger of war in Gaul was great.

34. The messenger praised the beautiful girls to the stars.

35. The farmer gave his dear son, Charles, a basket full of apples, both good and bad.

36. Where, in Rome, have the messengers concealed the general's weapons?

37. Who wounded the merchant with the broad sword?

38. The Roman soldiers attacked the people of Gaul with javelins and swords.

39. The king and his soldiers laid waste that part of the city on the river embankment around the great gate.

40. At night, the Roman emperor sees the enemy's camp in the high mountains and warns his men to destroy it by fire.

41. With great shouts the little children showed the pretty little horse to their father.

42. Where is the city of the Roman people?

43. It is in Italy on the banks of a river.

44. Cincinnatus was summoned from the fields to Rome by messengers.

45. In time of danger, a great man can save his country.

46. The journey led across high mountains and through great swamps.

47. It is good to be able to write Latin.

48. At dawn, Caesar will lead the legions out of the camp.

49. After the death of Caesar, Mark Antony made a great speech to the Roman people in the name of the state.

50. After Julius Caesar, the Roman emperors always bore the name of Caesar in his honor.

XV. MATHEMATICS
Exercise 1 (page 729)

a. Fifty-five million, six hundred forty-six thousand, eight hundred eight.

b. Four million, nine hundred thousand, nine.

c. One hundred six million, four hundred fifty-six thousand, eight hundred thirty-seven.

d. Ten billion, four hundred fifty-eight thousand, nine hundred seventy-five.

e. Eight hundred eight million, nine thousand, six hundred six.

f. Seventy-seven billion, fifty million, seven hundred thirty-one thousand, three hundred ten.

g. Four hundred sixty-five million, six hundred seventy-two thousand, four hundred eight.

h. Eighty million, seven hundred sixty-three thousand, twenty-nine.

i. Five billion, six hundred seventy-nine million, five thousand, fifty.

l. Forty thousand and four, and four ten thousandths.

m. Seven hundred twenty-nine, and eighty-six ten thousandths.

n. Seven thousand seven, and seven hundred seven ten thousandths.

o. Three thousand thirty-three, and thirty-three thousandths.

Exercise 2 (page 730)

a. 80,763,029
b. 10,000,458,975
c. 4,900,009
d. 55,646,808

Exercise 4 (page 731)

a. 600.06
b. 1212.012
c. 50,000.050
d. 1,600,054.054
e. 1404.1404

Exercise 3 (pages 730–731)

a. Fifty-five thousand, fifty-five, and five-tenths.

b. Six thousand, nine sixty-seven, and sixty-seven hundredths.

c. One hundred thousand, six, and six hundred seventy-six thousandths.

d. Fourteen thousand, five hundred eighty, and eight thousand eight fifty-six ten thousandths.

e. Seven hundred three thousand, seven hundred three, and seven hundred three thousandths.

f. One thousand, five hundred five, and sixty-nine thousandths.

g. Two thousand, nine hundred sixty, and eight ten thousandths.

h. Twenty-two thousand, twenty-two, and twenty-two ten thousandths.

i. Four thousand, six hundred seventy-eight, and nine thousandths.

j. Five thousand and five thousandths.

k. Nine thousand and nine, and nine thousandths.

Exercise 7a (page 733)

Totals by goods:
Millinery	$ 34,788.32
Clothing	122,849.62
Shoes	28,401.78
Handbags	14,729.73

Totals by months:
Jan.	$ 15,163.09
Feb.	11,262.06
Mar.	21,412.04
April	22,328.70
May	14,582.60
June	16,263.09
July	11,299.39
Aug.	11,807.20
Sept.	22,258.07
Oct.	20,726.07
Nov.	18,119.72
Dec.	15,547.42
Grand total	200,769.45

Exercise 7b (page 734)

Payroll totals for year:
Millinery	$ 9,076.90
Clothing	17,792.40
Shoes	5,236.10
Handbags	2,777.00

Monthly totals:

Jan.	$ 2,541.20
Feb.	2,714.95
Mar.	3,573.25
April	2,675.60
May	2,349.85
June	3,047.60
July	1,983.60
Aug.	2,224.65
Sept.	3,910.40
Oct.	3,592.15
Nov.	3,169.65
Dec.	3,099.50
Total	34,882.40

Exercise 7c (page 734)

Expenses:

Millinery	$ 3,218.68
Clothing	12,834.69
Shoes	3,313.47
Handbags	1,500.49
Total	20,867.33

Monthly totals:

Jan.	$ 1,550.90
Feb.	1,623.64
Mar.	1,932.03
April	1,987.89
May	1,574.34
June	1,617.48
July	1,378.74
Aug.	1,792.96
Sept.	2,068.05
Oct.	1,718.21
Nov.	1,999.82
Dec.	1,623.27
Total	20,867.33

Exercise 7d (page 735)

1,094.6535   1,393.527   9,953.4333

Exercise 7e (page 735)

1. 67.91   3. 32.88   5. 66.504
2. 71.1   4. 28.105

Exercise 9 (pages 736–737)

a. $530.74   e. $796.67   i. $524.08
b. 267.39   f. 1,359.38   j. 835.89
c. 894.98   g. 409.24   k. 637.99
d. 923.73   h. 562.73

Exercise 10 (page 737)

a. $231.74   e. $333.52   i. $61.03
b. 92.39   f. 558.12   j. 126.42
c. 757.84   g. 817.81
d. 948.54   h. 170.27

Total invoice amount, $4,187.81
Total net amount, $4,097.68
Total discount, $90.13

Exercise 12a (page 739)

	$1777.50
	90.00
	610.50
	166.25
	85.80
	495.00
	462.00
	69.30
	368.50
	26.10
	101.25
Total	$4252.20

Exercise 12b (page 739)

	$ 45.75
	38.22
	36.75
	87.04
	60.84
	223.74
Total	$492.34

Exercise 12c (page 739)

$29.60
29.48
17.16
30.24
20.16
30.60
18.85
33.00
23.60
45.50
33.06

Total $311.25

Exercise 14 (page 742)

$728.75

Exercise 15 (page 742)

a. ⅝	g. ¼	m. ⅞
b. ¼	h. ¾	n. ⅙
c. ⅛	i. ⅔	o. ⅙
d. ¾	j. ⅛	p. ⅚
e. ⅓	k. ⅔	q. ⅜
f. ⅝	l. ⅔	r. ⅝

Exercise 17 (page 743)

a. 155.	e. 27.	i. 33.57
b. 45.	f. 463.	j. 53.
c. 67.	g. 470.22	
d. 345.	h. 831.	

Exercise 19 (page 746)

a.	544.34	h.	450.
b.	136.59	i.	4500.
c.	30,399.30	j.	45,000.
d.	.20152	k.	45.
e.	8.62424	l.	45.
f.	.153054	m.	3600.
g.	3.7577	n.	150.

Exercise 21 (page 747)

a. $1247.50	e. $112.50	i. $18.70
b. 172.86	f. 177.63	j. 28.50
c. 78.20	g. 10.25	
d. 7.56	h. 32.29	

Problems (page 755)

1. $.50   5. 20 pages   (b) ½
2. 4,005.00 6. $15.00 9. $93.75
3. ¾   7. $1755 10. C. owns
4. $20.00   8. (a) ⅓   ¼

Exercise 30 (page 759)

1. 40%   5. 37½%   9. 70%
2. 16⅔%   6. 20%   10. 50%
3. 12½%   7. 20%
4. 40%   8. 30%

Exercise 31 (pages 759–760)

1. $600.   8. $1800.   15. $30.
2. 2,320.   9.   48.   16. 40.
3. 720.   10.   15.   17. 400.
4. 840.   11. 9,000.   18. 90.
5. 256.   12. 12,000. 19. 50.
6. 1,536. 13. 88,800. 20. 179.20
7.   40.   14. 12,000.

Exercise 32 (page 760)

1. 240   5. 18   9. 700
2. 220   6. 40   10. 300
3. 73.5   7. 480
4. 7000   8. 1000

Exercise 33 (page 761)

1. 12   5. 90   9. 800
2. 100   6. 800   10. 64
3. 180   7. 112
4. 200   8. 2000

Problems (pages 762–763)

1.	$75	10.	60%
2.	5%	11.	$451.13
3.	$1.75	12.	$48,000
4.	$17,000	13.	3.14% profit
5.	$364	14.	A's profit $750
6.	$60		B's profit 900
7.	$6320		Difference 150
8.	$28,636	15.	$223.50 profit
9.	37½%		

Exercise 34 (page 764)

a.	$5.40	e.	$8.50	i.	$4.74
b.	25.65	f.	2.74	j.	9.00
c.	8.40	g.	13.09		
d.	1.60	h.	29.07		

Exercise 35 (page 765)

a.	32½%	f.	37.66%
b.	43%	g.	56.35%
c.	47½%	h.	27.325%
d.	33⅓%	i.	16⅞%
e.	43.3%	j.	50%

Problems (page 765)

1.	$25.14	6.	$4.50
2.	134.66	7.	105.00
3.	53.98	8.	.87⅓ (decrease)
4.	80.00	9.	.95
5.	50.67	10.	30.00

Exercise 36 (page 766)

	Gross Profit	% of Gross Profit on Sales
1.	$1.20	50%
2.	5.00	25%
3.	1.80	33⅓%
4.	2.50	25%
5.	.49	28%
6.	.30	40%

7.	.50	40%
8.	2.00	36⁴⁄₁₁%
9.	2.50	28⁴⁄₇%

Exercise 38 (page 768)

	Equivalent Rate on Cost	Profit	Selling Price
1.	25%	$1.00	$5.00
2.	66⅔%	.50	1.25
3.	14²⁄₇%	.30	2.40
4.	50%	2.50	7.50
5.	60%	.39	1.04
6.	100%	.85	1.70
7.	42⁶⁄₇%	3.00	10.00
8.	11⅑%	.12	1.20
9.	20%	.30	1.80
10.	81⁹⁄₁₁%	.54	1.20
11.	60%	.27	.72
12.	16⅔%	.29	2.03
13.	40%	1.20	4.20

Exercise 39 (page 769)

1.	$30.00	5.	$2.00	9.	$41.00
2.	3.00	6.	10.00	10.	142.89
3.	1.50	7.	200.00		
4.	1.90	8.	3000.00		

Exercise 40 (page 770)

1.	$3.00	5.	$50.00	9.	$6.00
2.	7.50	6.	70.00	10.	6.00
3.	28.00	7.	36.00		
4.	6.00	8.	6.24		

Problems (page 770)

1.	$2.75	6.	A sells it for 45¢ less
2.	33⅓%		
3.	25%	7.	$4.22
4.	$2.00	8.	$1.33⅓
5.	$687.27		

Exercise 41 (page 772)

1.	$1144.22	6.	$3275.20
2.	2980.83	7.	518.29
3.	456.32	8.	990.48
4.	2289.08	9.	759.54
5.	1657.25	10.	1379.41

Problems (pages 772–773)

1.	$4565.45	5.	$2095.05
2.	$6404.81	6.	3873.55
3.	27.01%	7.	2821.87
4.	$900.00	8.	102.00

Exercise 42 (page 774)

	2%	3%	4%	5%	6%
1.	$10.00	$15.00	$20.00	$25.00	$30.00
2.	4.00	6.00	8.00	10.00	12.00
3.	2.00	3.00	4.00	5.00	6.00
4.	4.00	6.00	8.00	10.00	12.00
5.	1.00	1.50	2.00	2.50	3.00
6.	50.00	75.00	100.00	125.00	150.00
7.	4.00	6.00	8.00	10.00	12.00
8.	4.00	6.00	8.00	10.00	12.00
9.	.40	.60	.80	1.00	1.20
10.	.40	.60	.80	1.00	1.20

Exercise 44 (page 777)

	6%	5%	7%	4%	2%
1.	$9.00	$7.50	$10.50	$6.00	$3.00
2.	18.00	15.00	21.00	12.00	6.00
3.	48.00	40.00	56.00	32.00	16.00
4.	1.80	1.50	2.10	1.20	.60
5.	8.80	7.33	10.27	5.86	2.93
6.	9.00	7.50	10.50	6.00	3.00
7.	12.00	10.00	14.00	8.00	4.00
8.	30.00	25.00	35.00	20.00	10.00
9.	60.00	50.00	70.00	40.00	20.00
10.	120.00	100.00	140.00	80.00	40.00

Exercise 45 (page 779)

1.	59 days	5.	46 days	9.	66 days
2.	89 days	6.	92 days	10.	60 days
3.	30 days	7.	30 days		
4.	60 days	8.	90 days		

Exercise 46 (page 780)

1.	March 6	6.	September 7
2.	May 11	7.	August 26
3.	April 9	8.	September 24
4.	June 1	9.	December 29
5.	August 23	10.	December 20

Exercise 47 (page 782)

1.	$1522.50	6.	$4422.00
2.	4567.50	7.	282.80
3.	505.00	8.	447.62
4.	5050.00	9.	741.60
5.	3618.00	10.	816.00

Exercise 48 (page 782)

1.	50 days	6.	49 days
2.	48 days	7.	33 days
3.	20 days	8.	117 days
4.	25 days	9.	41 days
5.	80 days	10.	85 days

Exercise 49 (page 782)

	Discount	Net Proceeds
1.	$10.10	$999.90
2.	6.19	602.81
3.	14.98	1233.47
4.	6.97	902.03
5.	4.17	450.33
6.	8.46	1483.59
7.	3.83	761.98
8.	20.30	2009.70

Exercise 50 (page 784)

	Rate per $1	Rate per $100	Rate per $1000
1.	$.015	$1.50	$15.00
2.	.05	5.00	50.00
3.	.0175	1.75	7.50
4.	.0125	1.25	12.50
5.	.03	3.00	30.00

Exercise 51 (page 784)

	Rate per $100	Rate per $1000
1.	$3.50	$35.00
2.	3.50	35.00
3.	2.00	20.00
4.	2.75	27.50
5.	2.75	27.50
6.	1.864	18.64
7.	8.225	82.25
8.	7.50	75.00
9.	7.50	75.00
10.	1.864	18.64

Exercise 52 (page 785)

1. $178.75 5. $204.96 9. $215.20
2. 210.96 6. 377.43 10. 85.56
3. 206.35 7. 78.62
4. 365.00 8. 105.59

Exercise 53 (page 786)

1. .0175   3. $2353.13 5. $850,000
2. $32,000 4. 1.25 mills

Exercise 54 (page 790)

1. 825 yds.
2. 9600 acres
3. 160 pts.
4. 240 drachms
5. 200 pwt.
6. 384 qts.
10. 9.504 gr.
11. 364 pts.
12. 2239 gr.
13. 359 drachms
14. 13 pts.
15. 221,184 cu. in.

7. 160 drams
8. 900 lbs.
9. 990 lbs.
16. 20,434 sq. in.
17. 34,130 ft.
18. 391 days

Exercise 55 (pages 790–791)

1. 25 rds. 5 yds. 2 ft. 8 in.
2. 1 sq. rd. 14 sq. yds. 4 sq. ft.
3. 22 A. 80 sq. rds.
4. 58 gals. 1 pt.
5. 10 bu.
6. 1 oz. 3 pwt. 8 gr.
7. 3 gal. 2 pts. 9 oz.
8. 11 cu. yds. 3 cu. ft.
9. 2 mi. 135 rds.
10. 7 T. 16 cwt. 25 lbs.

Exercise 56 (page 792)

1. 100 yds. 1 ft. 2 in.
2. 39 cwt. 24 lbs.
3. 85 gals. 2 qts.
4. 151 A. 135 sq. rds.
5. 116 bu. 2 pks. 5 qts. 1 pt.
6. 19 T. 19 cwt. 20 lbs.
7. 32 cu. yds. 3 cu. ft.
8. 2 lbs. 1 oz. 6 pwt. 22 gr.
9. 2 lbs. 7 oz. 4 dr.
10. 44 hrs. 35 min.
11. 10 yds. 2 ft. 1 in.
12. 3 cwt. 67 lbs. 13 oz.
13. 12 gals. 2 qts. 1 pt.
14. 4 A. 130 sq. rds.
15. 25 bu. 1 pk. 1 pt.
16. 11 T. 8 cwt. 85 lbs.
17. 2 cu. yds. 25 cu. ft.
18. 4 oz. 16 pwt. 16 gr.
19. 3 oz. 6 dr.
20. 4 hrs. 44 min. 20 sec.

Problems (page 795)

1. $66.00
2. 8 rolls
3. 2648.37 ft.
4. 231 ft. 8 in.
5. 9424.8 ft.

Problems (page 799)

1. 88 sq. yds., 4 sq. ft.
2. 38 bundles
3. $15.71
4. $70.00
5. $15.71
6. $81.67
7. $333.65

Exercise 57 (page 802)

1. 1 ft. 3.65 in.
2. 32.01 ft.
3. 13.41 ft.
4. 14.42 ft.
5. 1764
6. 11,025
7. 5625
8. 15,625
9. 2.62
10. 19.38
11. 6.5
12. 3.22

Exercise 58 (pages 805–806)

1. 1914.88 gals.
2. 2244 gals.
3. 1436.16 gals.
4. 1649.34 gals.
5. 244.34 gals.
6. 2992 gals.
7. 3007.89 gals.
8. 4699.83 gals.
9. 563.98 gals.
10. 187.99 gals.
11. 2537.91 gals.
12. 79.31 gals.
13. 1.3 pt.
14. 313.32 gals.
15. 657.97 gals.
16. 281.99 gals.
17. 211.98 gals.
18. 1152.04 gals.
19. 2½ cds.
20. 3 cds.
21. 6 cds.
22. 6 cds.
23. 2¼ cds.
24. 8⁷⁄₁₆ cds.
25. 80 bd. ft.
26. 277⅓ bd. ft.
27. 750 bd. ft.
28. 384 bd. ft.
29. 48 bd. ft.
30. 400 bd. ft.

Problems (page 806)

1. 10 ft.
2. $6.14
3. $84.50
4. 3 ft. 4 in.
5. 1 cord
6. $257.60
7. 16 T.
8. $1913.34
9. 140 cu. ft.
10. $29.68

XVI. ALGEBRA

Exercise I (page 811)

1. $\dfrac{bc}{a}$

2. $de + \sqrt[3]{a}$

3. $\dfrac{4bc}{b^2}$

4. $\dfrac{a + 3b - b^3}{10}$

5. $\dfrac{-b + \sqrt{b^2}}{2a}$

6. $\sqrt[3]{abc}$
7. 100
8. 72
9. 16
10. 58
11. 86.485
12. 5

Exercise II (page 812)

1. 10
2. 25
3. 5
4. 6
5. 10
6. 12
7. 10
8. 2

Exercise III (page 813)

1. -3
2. -14
3. $+5$
4. $+5$
5. $+1$
6. -23

Exercise IV (page 815)

1. $+12$
2. -15
3. -14
4. -25
5. $+4$
6. $+9$
7. -8
8. -6
9. $+121$
10. -6
11. 62
12. 36
13. -18
14. 1
15. 10
16. -64
17. 2
18. 6
19. -24
20. -72
21. 27
22. -8
23. -1
24. -48
25. -15
26. -54
27. -120
28. -750
29. -6
30. 6

Exercise V (page 817)

1. $+15a$
2. $+5b$
3. $+8bc$
4. $5a - 3b$
5. $2b + 3c$
6. $a + 3b - c$

Exercise VI (page 818)

1. $18x+14y-7z$ 3. $7x-y+6z$
2. $8d^2+12d-3$ 4. $10x-3y-6z$

Exercise VII (page 820)

1. $x+5y-12$ 4. $x-y-z$
2. $x^2+11x-9$ 5. $-10x^2-21y^2+5z$
3. $-a+5c+6$

Exercise VIII (page 821)

1. $x=3$ 3. $x=25$ 5. $x=10$
2. $x=4$ 4. $y=16$ 6. $y=-1$

Exercise IX (page 822)

1. $x=5$ 3. $x=9$ 5. $x=11$
2. $x=12$ 4. $x=9$ 6. $x=3$

Exercise X (page 822)

1. $x=17$ 3. $x=\frac{2}{3}$ 5. $x=-5$
2. $x=\frac{5}{3}$ 4. $x=-5$ 6. $x=6$

Exercise XI (page 823)

1. $x=42$ 3. $x=238$ 5. $x=310$
2. $x=60$ 4. $x=300$ 6. $x=36$

Exercise XII (page 825)

1. $x=4$ 3. $x=8$ 5. $x=1$
2. $x=-9$ 4. $x=8$ 6. $x=4$

Exercise XIII (page 825)

1. $3x-25=2x-15$
   $x=10$
2. $2x+10=14$
   $x=2$
3. $2x+30=90-3x$
   $x=12$

Exercise XIV (page 827)

1. Uncle = 24 yrs. old
   Nephew = 12 yrs. old
2. 3, 6
3. Son = 9
   Mother = 27
   Father = 28

Exercise XV (page 828)

1. 10   4. $3x+3y-z$
2. 2   5. $x-2a+b-3c+d$
3. 8   6. $x+2a-2$

Exercise XVI (page 830)

1. b^{12} 3. x^6 5. a^5b^4
2. a^{10} 4. a^5b^3 6. b^4d^5

Exercise XVII (page 831)

1. $12b^6$ 6. $30a^3b^3c^5$
2. $30a^6$ 7. $-24a^5b^2$
3. $28a^3b$ 8. $12a^3d^4$
4. $24b^4c^6$ 9. $-50x^8y^3$
5. $24x^6y^5z^7$ 10. x^9y^3

Exercise XVIII (page 832)

1. $2bx+4b^2-2bcd$
2. $2xy+6xy^2+4y^2$
3. $4x^4-5x^3+2x^2$
4. $40a^3bc+12a^2b^2c-16a^3bc^2$
5. $12a^3b^2-18ab^2c+9abc$
6. $8ab^4+4a^2b^3+4a^4b^2$

Exercise XIX (page 833)

1. 30   4. 48   7. 45
2. 77   5. 30   8. 26
3. 15   6. 52   9. -13

4. $3a - a^2x + 6a^3x^2$

Exercise XX (page 833)

1. $x^2 - xy$
2. $2x^2 + 6xy$
3. $3a^3 + 9a^2b^2$
4. $4a^5 + 12a^3b + 4a^3c$
5. $a^3b + 2a^2b^2$
6. $2a^5 + 4a^6$
7. $5a^2b^4 - 15a^3b^5$
8. $10a^4b^5 - 40a^5b^4$

Exercise XXI (page 835)

1. $2x^4 - 4x^3 - 16x^2$
2. $a^5 + 3a^4b + 2a^3b + 6a^2b^2$
3. $4x^3 - 14x^2 - 4x + 32$
4. $6m^4 - 13m^3 + 20m^2 - 21m$
5. $9x^4 + 9x^3 - 16x^2 + 4x$
6. $x^4 - 2x^3 - 7x^2 - 4x$

Exercise XXII (page 839)

1. 196
2. 484
3. 2304
4. $x^2 + 2xy + y^2$
5. $4x^2 - 12xy + 9y^2$
6. $25 - 20y + 4y^2$
7. $9a^2 - 6ay + y^2$

Exercise XXIII (page 840)

1. $(18+3)(18-3) = 324 - 9 = 315$
2. $(22+5)(22-5) = 484 - 25 = 459$
3. $(25+5)(25-5) = 625 - 25 = 600$
4. $a^2 - 4b^2$
5. $9x^2 - 4y^2$

Exercise XXIV (page 841)

1. $2x^2$
2. $3a$
3. $2a^2bc^2$
4. $3a^3b^3$

Exercise XXV (page 842)

1. $2p - 4np^2$
2. $2a^2b^2 - 3a^3b^3 - 4a^4b^4$
3. $7 - 9xy^2 + y$

Exercise XXVI (page 844)

1. $a - 2$
2. $2p - n$
3. $n^2 - 4n + 3$
4. $3a(1 + 2a)$

Exercise XXVII (page 845)

1. $3ax(1 - 5a)$
2. $4by(3b^2 + 2by - 1)$
3. $a(y - bc - by)$
4. $3c(c - 4 - 6c^3)$
5. $5ad(1 + 2ad - 3a^2)$

Exercise XXVIII (page 846)

1. $(4+a)(x+2y)$
2. $(a+b)(x^2+2)$
3. $(a+b)(x+y)$
4. $11(ax+by)$

Exercise XXIX (page 848)

1. $(x+2)^2$
2. $(a+3)^2$
3. $(y-5)^2$
4. $(b-7)^2$

XVII. Plane Geometry

Exercise II (page 891)

1. $x = 10$
2. $x = 21$
3. $x = 4$
4. $x = 2$
5. $x = 24$
6. $x = 12$
7. $x = 3$
8. $x = 1$
9. $x = 10$

Exercise III (page 893)

1. 6
2. 10.8
3. $10\frac{2}{7}$
4. 12
5. 20

Exercise IV (pages 900–901)

1. 10″
2. 7′
3. 5″
4. 29 yds.
5. 7.211″

6. 13′
7. 11.62″
8. 9.899″

Exercise V (page 913)

1. 120°
2. 360° (see Prop. XXII, cor. 1)
3. 18°
4. 9
5. 200 in.
6. 196π sq. ft.

Exercise VI (page 920)

1. 50°   2. 40°   3. 45°

XVIII. Solid Geometry

Exercise I (page 934)

1. 27 cu. ft.   3. 160 sq. ft.
2. 4 yds.   4. 72π sq. ft.

Exercise II (page 936)

1. 120 sq. ft.   4. 125 cu. yds.
2. 40π sq. in.   5. 108π cu. ft.
3. 120 cu. ft.

XIX. Trigonometry

Exercise I (page 943)

1. 1.0000   5. .7265
2. .5774   6. 20°
3. .5095   7. 35°
4. 3.0777   8. 53°

Exercise II (page 945)

1. 808 ft.   3. 110.1 ft.
2. 376.2 ft.   4. 37°

Exercise III (page 947)

1. $\dfrac{5}{13}, \dfrac{12}{13}, \dfrac{5}{12}, \dfrac{12}{5}, \dfrac{13}{12}, \dfrac{13}{5}$

$\dfrac{12}{13}, \dfrac{5}{13}, \dfrac{12}{5}, \dfrac{5}{12}, \dfrac{13}{5}, \dfrac{13}{12}$

2. $\dfrac{2}{\sqrt{29}}, \dfrac{5}{\sqrt{29}}, \dfrac{2}{5}, \dfrac{5}{2}, \dfrac{\sqrt{29}}{5}, \dfrac{\sqrt{29}}{2}$

$\dfrac{5}{\sqrt{29}}, \dfrac{2}{\sqrt{29}}, \dfrac{5}{2}, \dfrac{2}{5}, \dfrac{\sqrt{29}}{2}, \dfrac{\sqrt{29}}{5}$

3. $\dfrac{5}{13}, \dfrac{12}{13}, \dfrac{5}{12}, \dfrac{12}{5}, \dfrac{13}{12}, \dfrac{13}{5}$

Exercise IV (pages 948–949)

1. a. $\dfrac{3}{7}$
   b. $\dfrac{3}{11}$
   c. $\dfrac{8}{3}$
   d. $\dfrac{2}{3}$
2. a. cos
   b. cot
   c. sec
   d. sin
   e. tan
   f. csc
3. a. cos 20°
   b. cot 35°
   c. csc 18°
4. a. $\dfrac{3}{2}$
   b. $\dfrac{4}{3}$
   c. $\dfrac{8}{3}$

Exercise V (page 951)

1. 1
2. 0
3. $6\sqrt{3}$
4. 6
5. $48\sqrt{3}$
6. 11
7. 7
8. $\dfrac{\sqrt{3}+\sqrt{2}}{2}$
9. $\dfrac{3+8\sqrt{3}}{6}$
10. $\dfrac{1}{2}$

Exercise VI (page 953)

1. a.	.9397	2. a.	65°
b.	5.6713	b.	80°
c.	.3584	c.	52°
d.	1.6243	d.	76°
e.	1.3456	e.	51°
f.	.8693	f.	77°

Exercise VII (page 956)

1. a.	.5324	2. a.	26°22'
b.	.3773	b.	15°7'
c.	.8158	c.	38°44'
d.	.7674	d.	19°40'

Exercise VIII (page 961)

1. 268 ft.
2. 659 ft.
3. 13 ft.
4. 82 ft.
5. 23°35'
6. 137 ft.
7. 423 ft.
8. 36°52'
9. 64 ft.
10. 13 ft.
11. 619 ft.

XX. GENERAL SCIENCE

1. Louis Pasteur and Robert Koch. (page 967)
2. The Wright brothers flew from Kitty Hawk, North Carolina, in 1903. (page 967)
3. The germ-killing power of penicillin. (page 969)
4. Substances actually gain weight when burned, due to addition of oxygen. (page 970)
5. A check or comparison with the rest of the experiment. (page 971)
6. The point at which planes reach the speed of sound, about 750 miles per hour. (page 971)
7. Weightlessness, human endurance, lack of air, meteorites striking the plane's surface, effects of change of speed. (page 972)
8. The pilot blacks out and loses control of the plane for a number of seconds. (page 972)
9. Objects in motion tend to stay in motion in the same direction unless acted upon by outside force. (page 973)
10. Temperature, moisture content of air, air pressure, direction and speed of wind, cloud formation, precipitation. (page 976)
11. Warm air escapes through the top; cool air comes in through the bottom to replace it. (page 976)
12. Changes of temperature caused by the effect of the sun's rays. (page 976)
13. Bad weather or storms ahead. (page 978)
14. The amount of water vapor in the air compared with the amount of water vapor the air can hold at that temperature. (page 979)
15. The most violent of all large storms—occurring at sea. (page 980)
16. The discharge of electricity from one cloud to another causes lightning. The rapid expansion and contraction of air masses produces thunder. (pages 980–981)
17. The *Clermont*. (page 982)
18. Because they vaporize easily and have a low kindling temperature, thus producing an explosion. (page 982)

19. Intake, compression, ignition, and exhaust. (page 983)
20. Because of greater compression developed. (page 983)
21. The counterforce of the air against the plane. (page 985)
22. An electromagnet which attracts a pliable strip of metal when the current is on and releases it when the current is off. (page 987)
23. The microphone. (page 987)
24. Radioactive rays coming from outer space. (page 988)
25. To measure amount and kind of radiation emanating from a source of radioactive matter. (page 988)
26. Henri Becquerel, in 1896. (page 989)
27. The cyclotron. (page 989)
28. Equivalent of five million pounds of coal or nine thousand tons of TNT. (page 989)
29. By fusion of hydrogen atoms. (page 990)
30. Radioactive isotopes as tracers, radioactive cobalt and iodine in treatment of cancer, heating as fuel, atomic submarines, possible powering of ships and aircraft. (pages 990–991)
31. Green leaves of plants. (page 991)
32. They have no chlorophyl. (page 992)
33. Ammonia. (page 992)
34. Flavoring cheeses, souring milk, making sauerkraut, softening and flavoring meats, netting flax, curing tobacco, tanning leather. (page 993)
35. He introduced the idea of vaccinating against smallpox with cowpox germs. (page 996)

XXI. ASTRONOMY

1. The science of the heavenly bodies—the sun, the planets, the moons, the comets, the meteors, the stars. (page 999)
2. Astrology, not now regarded as a science. (page 999)
3. 25 trillion miles. (page 999)
4. The distance traveled by light in one year. (page 1000)
5. Once. (page 1001)
6. Approximately 365¼ days. (page 1001)
7. In the west after sunset, or in the east before sunrise. (page 1002)
8. About 93 million miles. (page 1002)
9. About eight minutes. (page 1002)
10. About eight minutes. (page 1002)
11. Mercury, Venus, Earth, Mars, Jupiter, Saturn, Uranus, Neptune, and Pluto. (page 1004)
12. Saturn. (page 1004)
13. An ellipse. (page 1006)
14. 332,000 times as much. (pages 1006–1007)
15. About 11,000 degrees. (page 1008)
16. One part in 120 million. (page 1008)
17. 28 days. (page 1009)
18. An oblate spheroid. (page 1011)
19. 8,000 miles. (page 1011)
20. 23 hours, 56 minutes, and 4.095 seconds. (page 1012)
21. Polaris; Vega. (page 1012)
22. The force of gravity. (page 1013)
23. Its period of rotation so nearly coincides with its period of revolution around the earth. (page 1015)

24. The sun. (page 1018)
25. Mercury's is about 1/27 that of Earth. (page 1019)
26. Venus. (page 1019)
27. That there is very little chance of life anything like ours. (page 1020)
28. To an observer on earth, Mars appears a reddish hue, while Venus appears almost white. (page 1021)
29. Ceres; 500 miles in diameter. (page 1021)
30. Eros, which comes within 14,-000,000 miles of the earth. (page 1022)
31. The first four discovered satellites of Jupiter. (page 1023)
32. Almost thirty years. (page 1023)
33. Sir William Herschel. (page 1024)
34. About seventeen times as large. (page 1025)
35. About 75 years. (page 1025)
36. As many as 120,000. (page 1027)
37. Sometimes parts of comets' tails, but more often just isolated tiny bodies roaming through space. (page 1028)
38. Chiefly iron and nickel. (page 1029)
39. That all the starry universe is essentially of the same chemical composition. (page 1029)
40. About 6,000. (page 1030)
41. About six trillion miles. (page 1029)
42. Betelgeuse. (page 1031)
43. Nearly 100 times as great. (page 1033)
44. Stars which do not emit the same amount of light steadily. (page 1033)
45. The spectroscope. (page 1033)

46. About one and one-half billion years. (page 1035)
47. About as one to eighty. (page 1035)
48. Independent aggregates of stars. (page 1035)
49. The ecliptic. (page 1036)
50. Seven. (pages 1037–1038)

XXII. GEOLOGY

1. Geology is the study of the earth in all its aspects. (page 1043)
2. The lithosphere. (page 1044)
3. The earth's interior. (page 1044)
4. Igneous rocks which have been brought to the surface and which are exposed while hardening. (page 1047)
5. It is composed almost entirely of calcium carbonate derived from shells and other animal products. (page 1048)
6. Climate determines the rate of weathering. (page 1049)
7. Streams and rivers, ocean waves, glaciers, and wind. (page 1050)
8. Debris which accumulates at the base of a cliff or in a valley. (page 1050)
9. Sediment deposited by a stream, forming new land along the side of the stream opposite a bend. (page 1051)
10. Ordinarily tributaries meet the main stream at its own level. (page 1051)
11. Some falls result from a variation in rock levels which existed before the stream made its way. (page 1051)
12. Sediment deposited by a river at its mouth. (page 1051)
13. By blasting through impervious rock to water. (page 1053)

14. Saratoga, Carlsbad, Vichy. (page 1053)

15. Water brings soluble matter in the rocks into solution, then carries away the solution, leaving a chamber. (page 1053)

16. Sometimes a stream which flows into a lake deposits sediment which may form a delta, thus reducing area of lake. (page 1054)

17. Peat is composed of decomposed carbonaceous material. (page 1055)

18. A moving mass of ice. (page 1055)

19. A great glacier which blankets a large area with ice. (page 1055)

20. The level of the oceans would be raised 150 feet, thus submerging large areas now above sea level. (page 1057)

21. Meteorology is the science of the atmosphere. (page 1057)

22. Sand and other sharp rock particles blown by the wind against rocky surfaces aid in disintegrating the softer surfaces and in polishing the harder stones. (page 1061)

23. Loess consists of finely grained particles which are carried by the wind and deposited in compact masses. (page 1061)

24. There is twice as much sea area as land area. (page 1061)

25. 600 feet. (page 1061)

26. The coast of Maine is a shoreline of submergence. (page 1062)

27. An atoll is a circle of reef which remains after a coral island has disappeared. (page 1063)

28. Ocean tides are due to the gravitational pull on the earth by the sun and the moon. (page 1063)

29. A stratum of rock bent into rather regular curves. (page 1064)

30. The Giant's Causeway in northern Ireland. (page 1065)

31. Disturbances within the earth's interior. (page 1066)

32. Molten material in a volcano is called magma. (page 1067)

33. The lithosphere is probably 30 or 40 miles thick. (page 1071)

34. A seismograph measures earthquake shocks. (page 1071)

35. Oil and natural gas are formed in rock sufficiently porous to make a reservoir for them. (page 1073)

36. An ore is a mineral which contains metal. (page 1073)

37. Common salt is usually part of the residue accumulated when the sea receded from an inland area, and so has the same source as sea salt. (page 1073)

38. Laplace was a French astronomer who developed the Nebular Hypothesis. (page 1074)

39. Chamberlin and Moulton developed the Planetesimal Hypothesis. (page 1074)

40. A fossil is animal or plant matter that has been preserved through the ages or which forms an outline in a rock. (page 1076)

41. The Dust Cloud Theory. (page 1075)

42. In shallow sea water. (page 1076)

43. By studying rock formations and rock strata in all parts of the world. (page 1076)

44. The Archeozoic Era. (page 1078)

45. The abundant fossils belonging to this era indicate a variety of plant and animal life. (page 1079)

46. The Paleozoic Era ended in a great glacial period. (page 1081)

47. In the Mesozoic Era. (page 1081)

48. Mammals became the most important form of animal life in the Cenozoic Era. (page 1083)

49. To the Pliocene Period. (page 1084)

50. The Psychozoic Era. (page 1084)

XXIII. PHYSICS

1. Physics is the science which deals with energy and matter and with physical changes in matter. (page 1087)

2. The metric system. (page 1088)

3. The lever, the pulley, and the inclined plane. (page 1090)

4. "Give me a lever large enough, and I can move the Earth." (page 1091)

5. The lever of the second class. (page 1092)

6. A fixed pulley is one with an immovable axis. (page 1095)

7. The number of chains or ropes which it contains. (page 1096)

8. By dividing the length of the plane by the vertical height. (page 1096)

9. A pair of inclined planes back to back. (page 1097)

10. It means that if you start an object moving, it will keep on moving forever in a straight line until some force stops it. (page 1098)

11. It means that a body keeps on increasing in velocity under the influence of a constant force. (page 1098)

12. Thirty-two feet per second per second. (page 1098)

13. Both balls will hit the ground at the same instant. (page 1099)

14. In a vacuum, all bodies fall with exactly the same speed. (page 1099)

15. That every square foot of that floor is capable of meeting 150 pounds downward force with 150 pounds upward force. (page 1099)

16. For every force pulling one way on a body in equilibrium, there must be an equal and opposite force pulling in the opposite direction. (page 1100)

17. Stable, unstable, and neutral. (page 1100)

18. The longer the pendulum, the slower it will swing, and vice versa. (page 1101)

19. Potential and kinetic. (page 1101)

20. The height and the density of the fluid. (page 1103)

21. That any external force exerted on a unit of area in a confined liquid is transmitted undiminished to every unit of area of the interior of the containing vessel. (page 1103)

22. A body immersed in a fluid is buoyed up by a force equal to the weight of the liquid it displaces. (page 1104)

23. The ratio of the weight of a given volume of that substance to the weight of the same volume of water at 4° C. (page 1105)

24. Capillary action. (page 1106)

25. It is increased proportionately. (page 1106)

26. At sea level, about 15 pounds to the square inch. (page 1107)

27. Primarily a form of energy, due to extra-rapid motion of molecules. (page 1110)

28. No. (page 1110)

29. Because glass does not conduct heat rapidly, and the inside of the

ANSWERS TO EXAMINATION QUESTIONS

vessel expands while the outside does not. (page 1111)

30. Zero. (pages 1111–1112)

31. 273° below zero Centigrade; because at this temperature all molecular motion would cease. (page 1112)

32. 15° C. (page 1112)

33. Silver and copper. (page 1113)

34. 186,000 miles per second. (page 1114)

35. The turbojet. (page 1116)

36. By vibrating matter. (page 1116)

37. 256 per second. (page 1117)

38. At zero Centigrade, approximately 1090 feet per second, increasing two feet per second for every degree rise in temperature. (page 1118)

39. The echo. (page 1118)

40. Refraction. (page 1123)

41. Red color. (page 1126)

42. Static electricity and current electricity. (page 1130)

43. Electric motors, electric dynamos, telegraph, electric bells, telephone. (page 1133)

44. Radio waves, infrared, visible light, ultraviolet, X rays, and gamma rays. (page 1139)

45. Whenever electrons surge rapidly back and forth in a wire. (page 1139)

46. By timing the interval between the sending and the return of radio waves, the distance to any object which reflects them back to the sender may be determined. (page 1145)

47. The emission of helium nuclei or electrons by heavy atoms and the resulting radiation. (page 1147)

48. By bombarding elements with neutrons in an atomic pile or with charged particles from a cyclotron. (page 1148)

49. Uranium. (page 1148)

50. $E = mc^2$. (page 1149)

XXIV. CHEMISTRY

1. Iron rusts, fruit decays, wood rots. (page 1152)

2. Oxygen and hydrogen. (page 1153)

3. An element is a substance which cannot be separated into other substances. (page 1153)

4. Oxides. (page 1153)

5. To inconceivably minute particles of a substance (usually carbon) heated to incandescence. (page 1154)

6. As a rule, the more intimately the substance is in contact with oxygen, the lower is its kindling temperature. (page 1154)

7. Oxygen. (page 1155)

8. About 78% nitrogen, 21% oxygen, and 1% a mixture of other gases. (page 1155)

9. By heating potassium chlorate and manganese dioxide in a test tube. (page 1155)

10. The diamond. (page 1156)

11. One-ninth. (page 1158)

12. Red. (page 1158)

13. When an acid and a metal interact chemically. (page 1158)

14. Hydrogen and chlorine in the proportion of one atom of hydrogen to one atom of chlorine. (page 1159)

15. A solution that will dissolve no more of a dissolved substance. (page 1161)

16. Atoms. (page 1162)

17. That a molecule of starch contains six atoms of carbon and ten atoms of hydrogen to five atoms of oxygen. (page 1162)

18. Gold, nickel, phosphorus, potassium, radium, sodium, tin, and tungsten. (pages 1163–1165)
19. Helium. (page 1165)
20. Yes. Only about twenty of the naturally occurring elements are nonmetals. (page 1165)
21. Protons, electrons, and neutrons. (page 1166)
22. Five electrons, because the total number of protons in an atom is the same as the total number of electrons. (page 1166)
23. The number and arrangement of the electrons. (page 1168)
24. When there is the same number of each kind of atom on each side of the equation—that is, before and after the chemical reaction. (pages 1169–1170)
25. Chlorine gas. (page 1170)
26. It eventually bursts into flame. (page 1172)
27. In sulphuric acid, fertilizers, explosives, kerosene, storage batteries, drugs, dyes. (page 1172)
28. Oxygen. (page 1173)
29. Whereas it reacts with a great many metals to form nitrates, hydrogen is not liberated. (page 1174)
30. By uniting nitrogen with hydrogen. (page 1175)
31. Bromine, chlorine, fluorine, and iodine. (page 1177)
32. From seaweed. (page 1178)
33. Because it dissolves glass. (page 1178)
34. Hydrogen. (page 1179)
35. Slaked lime. (page 1181)
36. Mercury. (page 1183)
37. Steel is cast iron with a great percentage of the carbon eliminated. (page 1184)
38. Eggs contain hydrogen sulphide,

a compound of sulphur, which blackens silver. (page 1185)
39. Gelatine and silver bromide. (page 1185)
40. It has 14 parts of pure gold and 10 parts of other metals. (page 1187)
41. Platinum. (page 1187)
42. Lead. (page 1188)
43. No. It is a can of sheet iron dipped in molten tin to prevent rust. (page 1188)
44. Carbon. (page 1189)
45. Because of the ability of carbon atoms to join other carbon atoms in numerous combustions. (page 1189)
46. Methane. (page 1190)
47. The process by which heavy hydrocarbons are broken down under great heat to form the simpler gasolines. (page 1190)
48. Asbestos and glass. (page 1192)
49. A fibrous material made from cellulose. (page 1192)
50. Carbohydrates. (page 1193)

XXV. BIOLOGY

1. The science of life, or of organisms. (page 1196)
2. Organic. (page 1196)
3. Botany, zoology, the science of microorganisms, physiology, and anatomy. (page 1196)
4. Protoplasm. (page 1196)
5. Granular. (page 1197)
6. As a result of chemical and mechanical activities. (page 1198)
7. The single plant cell grows in size and splits into two new organisms; the nucleus also divides, one part going to each of the two cells formed by the division of the original cell. (page 1199)

8. The simplest unicellular animal. (page 1198)

9. The so-called flagellates. (page 1200)

10. Bacteria. (page 1201)

11. Cilia. (page 1201)

12. The xylem tissue. (page 1202)

13. The muscles under the control of the will. (page 1203)

14. Some 250,000. (page 1203)

15. The spermatophytes. (page 1204)

16. Annuals live for a year, biennials for two years, and perennials year after year. (page 1205)

17. Carbon, hydrogen, oxygen, nitrogen, sulphur, phosphorus, potassium, calcium, magnesium, and iron. (pages 1207–1208)

18. Osmosis. (page 1208)

19. Vegetable oils. (page 1209)

20. Because plant protoplasm is stimulated by light. (page 1210)

21. The parent cell divides unequally and at first the baby cell or bud remains attached to the parent cell. (page 1211)

22. The stamens. (page 1211)

23. The passing of the pollen from stamen to pistil. (page 1212)

24. The fruit. (page 1213)

25. Something like 600,000. (page 1213)

26. The arthropods. (page 1214)

27. Amphibians live both in water and on land. (page 1215)

28. As mammals. (page 1216)

29. Herbivorous. (page 1216)

30. Ptyalin. (page 1217)

31. Through gills, utilizing the oxygen dissolved in the water. (page 1218)

32. By the union of the male and the female. (page 1219)

33. Ova (eggs). (page 1220)

34. No more than 1/125 of an inch in diameter. (page 1220)

35. Those which lay eggs. (page 1222)

36. Only in human beings and in the apes. (page 1222)

37. By the umbilical cord. (page 1222)

38. The mammary glands. (page 1223)

39. The branch of biology which deals with the phenomena of heredity. (page 1224)

40. A pink flower. (page 1225)

41. By watching and observing the laws of heredity. (page 1227)

42. A mare and a jackass. (page 1227)

43. With the influences that better the native or inborn qualities of a race or breed. (page 1228)

44. Ecology. (page 1228)

45. The proboscis. (page 1229)

46. Bacteria and other organisms act upon dead organic matter, causing decomposition. (page 1230)

47. Organisms which live on other organisms, taking their nourishment from them. (page 1230)

48. Only by the Anopheles mosquito. (page 1231)

49. The process of development of higher organisms from lower. (page 1232)

50. Anatomical, physiological, and psychological evidence. (page 1238)

XXVI. PHYSIOLOGY

1. Anatomy is the study of the structure of the body, of its parts and how they grow; while physiology is the study of the functions of the organs and parts of the body

and how they work. (page 1241)

2. The end toward the head is referred to as anterior (or cephalic); the end toward the "tail" as posterior (or caudal). (page 1241)

3. The epidermis, or outer layer, and the dermis beneath. (page 1242)

4. The brain. (page 1243)

5. Carbon, hydrogen, oxygen, nitrogen, sulphur, phosphorus, chlorine, fluorine, iodine, silicon, sodium, lithium, calcium, potassium, magnesium, manganese, iron, zinc, and copper. (page 1243)

6. More than two-thirds. (page 1244)

7. The blood is a great transportation system for bringing nourishment to all parts of the body and for carrying waste products from all parts to a central department for the elimination of that waste. (page 1245)

8. Because in the adult some multiple bones grow together. (page 1246)

9. The breastbone. (page 1246)

10. The cervical vertebrae. (page 1246)

11. The lower jaw. (page 1248)

12. Because they are not attached on the ventral ends. (page 1248)

13. The humerus. (page 1248)

14. The joinings of the bones. (page 1248)

15. The skeletal muscles are controlled by voluntary impulses from the brain, while the visceral muscles operate automatically. (page 1249)

16. The heart. (page 1249)

17. The nervous system. (page 1252)

18. Almost cylindrical, and about three-quarters of an inch in diameter and about 17 inches long. (page 1253)

19. A trifle over three pounds in the male and a trifle under three pounds in the female. (page 1253)

20. The sense of smell. (page 1254)

21. Masses of nerve tissue forming nerve centers. (page 1254)

22. From 200 to 300 feet per second. (page 1254)

23. In the cortex, the superficial gray matter of the cerebrum. (page 1255)

24. A hormone is a substance which is secreted by one organ (as a gland) and carried in the circulation of the blood to some other organ or organs which it stimulates. (page 1257)

25. The thyroid gland. (page 1257)

26. Temperature (heat and cold), pain, hunger, thirst, balance or equilibrium, and the muscle sense. (page 1259)

27. From 60 to 4,000 vibrations per second. (page 1260)

28. The Eustachian tubes. (page 1261)

29. To a difference in the distance between the angles of the eyelids from end to end of the visible portion of the eyeball. (page 1262)

30. That which produces tears. (page 1263)

31. Red and green. (page 1265)

32. 75 billion. (page 1267)

33. About one-twentieth. (page 1267)

34. About 70 times each minute. (page 1268)

35. The various valves. (page 1268)

36. The contraction is called the sys-

tole, and the relaxation the diastole. (page 1270)

37. Oxidation in the respiratory system. (page 1271)

38. Proteins, carbohydrates, and fats. (page 1273)

39. Eight incisors, four canines, eight bicuspids, and twelve molars. (page 1274)

40. The first foot of the length of the small intestine. (page 1276)

41. It has no apparent purpose. (page 1276)

42. The liver. (page 1276)

43. Two-tenths of one per cent. (page 1277)

44. Deglutition. (page 1278)

45. Carbon dioxide. (page 1279)

46. About 2,500,000. (page 1279)

47. Around 98.6 degrees Fahrenheit. (page 1280)

48. The male sexual cells. (page 1282)

49. In the uterus. (page 1283)

50. Parturition. (page 1283)

XXVII. Psychology

1. Such aspects of behavior as the basis of mental activity, habits and learning, intelligence and personality. (page 1288)

2. Biology, physiology, and philosophy. (page 1288)

3. Because the brain cells are of the same fundamental structure as other cells of the body. (page 1288)

4. Irritability. (page 1289)

5. Introspection. (page 1290)

6. How to control ourselves, how to guide children in their best interests, how to find out what vocation we are best fitted for, and how to control or eradicate crime. (page 1290)

7. A reflex. (page 1291)

8. A simple reaction. (page 1291)

9. The olfactory center. (page 1292)

10. No. (page 1292)

11. Yes, unless the higher brain centers inhibit it. (page 1293)

12. A glandular response. (page 1293)

13. Fear, rage, and love. (page 1294)

14. Native. (page 1294)

15. Vocal sounds are native, but speech is acquired. (page 1294)

16. A drive with some inherited basis but whose expression is determined by environmental factors. (page 1295)

17. No. (page 1296)

18. When it is satisfied in some learned or acquired way. (page 1296)

19. No. (page 1296)

20. The sense of well-being, or just "feeling good." (page 1296)

21. It is the desire to be with one's kind, based on the need for security, sympathy, and understanding. (page 1297)

22. Hate, fear, anger, and love. (page 1298)

23. They are conditions of the individual as a whole, and not of any one organ or part. (page 1298)

24. Just after eating a hearty meal. (page 1299)

25. Adrenalin, which acts as a tonic throughout the body. (page 1299)

26. Displeasure, disgust, or some similar feeling. (page 1299)

27. The fact that he is not afraid in the emotional sense. (page 1300)

28. The mating drive, accompanied by love. (page 1300)

29. Pleasantness and unpleasantness. (page 1300)

30. A response to a stimulus, made by the sense organ stimulated, and recognized or interpreted in the associated brain centers. (page 1301)

31. By an almost instinctive caution. (pages 1296–1297)

32. The determination to surpass one's fellows, or to overcome the thing itself. (page 1297)

33. Taste, smell, sight, hearing, and touch. (page 1301)

34. Sweet, sour, bitter, and salty. (page 1302)

35. Spicy, fragrant, fruity, flowery, foul, resinous, and scorched. (page 1302)

36. If you stare at an electric light, and suddenly shut it off, you will continue to see it for a moment afterward. (page 1302)

37. Usually by setting up, through practice, a counter-habit, or substitute response to the stimulus which brought on the habitual reaction. (page 1306)

38. That it saves time and effort to go over it twice each day for twelve days rather than to go over it twenty-four times in one day or six times daily for four days. (page 1307)

39. Fear, anxiety, doubt, embarrassment, surprise, or some distraction. (page 1308)

40. The smell of the lemon is associated with the taste that has been experienced. (page 1309)

41. An error in perception. (pages 1309–1310)

42. It is an auditory illusion, due to preoccupation with a specific idea. (page 1311)

43. Abstract, mechanical, and social. (page 1312)

44. The exact relationship of intelligence to the size of the brain is as yet unknown. Some men with rather small brains have been highly intelligent. (page 1312)

45. Logic. (page 1313)

46. A form of self-justification, which is not reasoning. (page 1313)

47. Imaginative self-projection. (page 1313)

48. It is the fundamental energy in a person, basically a sex urge, or, more broadly, a love urge. (page 1315)

49. The will to power. (page 1317)

50. The discovery of a relationship between mental disturbance and blood composition. (page 1318)

XXVIII. Sociology

1. Sociology is concerned with man's behavior in groups; psychology is concerned with the behavior of the individual. Sociology is concerned with the effect of institutions upon human beings; psychology does not concern itself with institutions. (pages 1322–1323)

2. Primitive cultures are much simpler than our own. (page 1324)

3. Until European culture occupied the greater part of the world, diffusion was the principal factor in its development. (pages 1324–1325)

4. Caucasian, Mongoloid, Negroid, and Australoid. (page 1326)

5. Human races differ in the struc-

ture of the hair, the color of the skin, and in other physical traits. (page 1326)

6. Marriage is actually the relatively permanent association of a man with a woman. Marriage is ideally a life partnership of a man and a woman based on mutual love and admiration. (page 1328)

7. Monogamy. (page 1329)

8. Polyandry is the association in marriage of one woman with several men. (page 1329)

9. Polyandry usually exists where there is a considerable surplus of men over women, produced by the practice of infanticide where male children are preferred to female. It is usually associated with unfavorable climatic conditions. (page 1329)

10. Polygyny, the condition where a man has more than one wife, may be produced by the existence of an excess of females, due to infanticide, war, or the difficulties of economic existence. It may also be produced by inequalities of wealth and power among men. (page 1329)

11. Group marriage is the marriage of several men to several women, usually where the men travel about and visit the women. (page 1330)

12. Yes. Inbreeding stabilizes the type and prevents the rapid progress of evolution. But this objection only holds if the practice is made common. Otherwise there is a fairly even balance between the advantages and disadvantages. (page 1330)

13. The tribe, caste, or class, and sometimes the local group, tend

to be endogamous. (page 1331)

14. The family, sib, marriage class, moiety, and sometimes the local group, tend to be exogamous. (pages 1330–1331)

15. Cross-cousins are the children of brother and sister. (page 1331)

16. If the group is patrilinear, the child of the brother will belong to the same group as the brother and sister, while the child of the sister will belong to the group of the sister's husband, necessarily a different group. If the group is matrilinear, the sister's child will belong to her group and her brother's child to a different one. (page 1331)

17. When a man marries the eldest of a group of unmarried sisters, and then may take the younger sisters as subordinate wives, the practice is known as sororate. (page 1331)

18. Marriage by purchase, the commonest form, is significant of the interfamily or intergroup nature of marriage, rather than the purely personal significance to the husband and wife. (page 1332)

19. Marriage by arrangement is the type of marriage where the families decide upon the choice of mate, largely from social, economic, or political motives. (page 1333)

20. Yes. (page 1333)

21. This depends upon two factors. First, whether divorce should occur depends upon whether any children by the marriage would be harmed or benefited thereby. Second, even in the absence of children, divorce should only take place if there is a genuine

incompatibility between the marital partners. When selfishness leads to divorce, there is no reason to suppose that any other marriage would be more successful. (page 1334)

22. Because we count the relatives of both father and mother equally (father's brother and mother's brother are both uncles). (page 1335)

23. A gens is a patrilinear sib. (page 1335)

24. Patrilinear means descent in the male line, children belonging to their fathers' groups. Patrilocal means residence of the wife with or near the husband's family. Patriarchal means the authority of the man, usually the oldest man of the group. (page 1335)

25. A tabu is the prohibition of an act or a thing. (page 1335)

26. Tabus are frequently found between a person and his or her parents-in-law; also between brother and sister. (page 1335)

27. The mother-in-law–husband tabu is the commonest, undoubtedly to prevent a conflict of authority and subsequent ill-will. (page 1335)

28. The caste system of India was the division of the populace into classes according to their occupation, each person assuming the occupation of his parents, and normally remaining in that caste forever. Each caste had its own customs and social status, and the castes were endogamous. (pages 1336–1337)

29. Differences in individual ability inevitably lead to greater recognition, authority, and higher social standing. (page 1337)

30. No. Rigid distinctions are neither necessary nor desirable. (page 1337)

31. The commonest form of secret society is the association of adult men. (page 1337)

32. The primitive society is not exclusive. (page 1337)

33. It exercises the functions of government and religion, and has often an important educational function at the time of the initiation of boys into membership. (pages 1337–1338)

34. The moiety functions in games and social activities. (page 1338)

35. Friendships develop understanding, sympathy, and co-operation. (page 1339)

36. It might be theoretically possible, but it could never be practicable, because work is not merely a means to live but also a manner of living, which man could not do without. (page 1339)

37. No. It is found among all primitives. (pages 1340–1341)

38. The state had no specific beginning, but grew gradually out of the control which one man or a group of men had over the community generally. (page 1345)

39. Such intervention is necessary at times, and obviously should occur when it is. (pages 1346–1347)

40. Confined criminals should be permitted to work and study, to enable them to be re-educated to the point where they can adapt themselves to society. (page 1348)

41. Informal education is education derived from work and play and from the experiences of everyday living. (page 1350)

42. Education should enable a person to work and to accept his other responsibilities toward society. In addition, education should broaden a person's outlook and enable him to have a fuller, a more meaningful, existence. (page 1351)

43. Language and handicrafts, the origins of which go back to the very beginnings of human life. (page 1353)

44. The earliest form of writing was by the use of pictures. (page 1353)

45. The most common primitive religious belief is in the existence of nature deities, or personal spirits that control the sun and moon and other natural phenomena. (page 1354)

46. Fetishism is the belief that certain objects have mysterious and magical powers, such as a horseshoe to bring luck. (page 1354)

47. Yes. (page 1356)

48. A mob consists of individuals in such an emotional state that their inhibitions are released and their reasoning powers suspended. (page 1357)

49. Social forces are those elements within society that bring about social change. (pages 1357–1358)

50. The fundamental doctrine of Marx was the doctrine of economic determination, that economic factors were the basic ones to produce changes, that social forces were at bottom economic. (page 1359)

Index